VIRAL AND RICKETTSIAL
INFECTIONS OF MAN

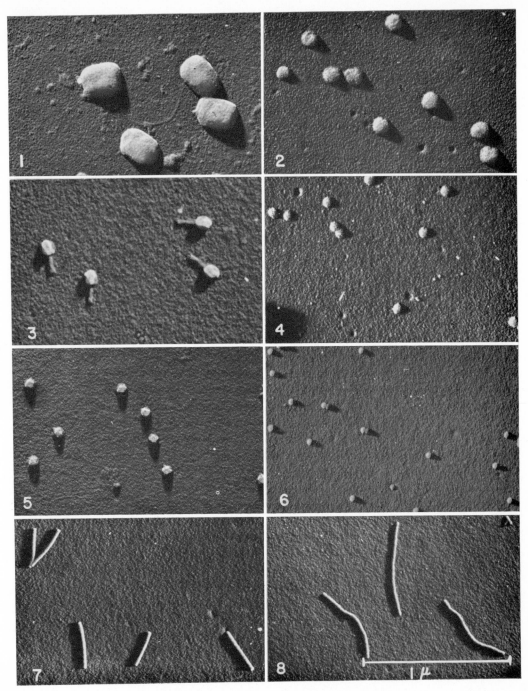

Electron micrographs of eight viruses shown at the same magnification (x 40,000):
(1) Vaccine virus; (2) PR8 influenza virus; (3) T$_2$ bacteriophage; (4) Shope papilloma
virus; (5) T$_3$ bacteriophage; (6) Bushy-stunt virus; (7) Tobacco-mosaic virus; (8)
Cymbidium (orchid) mosaic virus, Gold, A. H., and Jensen, D.D., 1951. (Micrographs by
Williams, R. C., unpublished; virus preparations by staff members, Virus Laboratory,
University of California, Berkeley.)

VIRAL AND RICKETTSIAL
INFECTIONS OF MAN

Edited by

THOMAS M. RIVERS, M.D.

Director of the Hospital

The Rockefeller Institute for Medical Research

SECOND EDITION

90 Illustrations

Including 7 Plates in Color

PHILADELPHIA • LONDON • MONTREAL

J. B. LIPPINCOTT COMPANY

Aided by a grant from The National
Foundation for Infantile Paralysis, Inc.

Contributors

J. BRONFENBRENNER, Ph.D.

Wake Forest College, The Bowman Gray School of Medicine

G. JOHN BUDDINGH, M.D.

Louisiana State University School of Medicine, New Orleans

J. CASALS, M.D.

The Rockefeller Institute for Medical Research

HERALD R. COX, Sc.D.

Lederle Laboratories Division, American Cyanamid Company

EDWARD C. CURNEN, M.D.

Yale University, School of Medicine

JOHN F. ENDERS, Ph.D.

The Children's Hospital, Boston

W. PAUL HAVENS, JR., M.D.

Jefferson Medical College

A. D. HERSHEY, Ph.D.

Carnegie Institution of Washington

FRANK L. HORSFALL, JR., M.D.

The Rockefeller Institute for Medical Research

GEORGE K. HIRST, M.D.

The Public Health Research Institute of The City of New York, Inc.

HOWARD A. HOWE, M.D.

Poliomyelitis Laboratory, The Johns Hopkins University

HARALD N. JOHNSON, M.D.,

Laboratories of the Division of Medicine and Public Health, The Rockefeller Foundation

MAX A. LAUFFER, Ph.D.

University of Pittsburgh

KENNETH F. MAXCY, M.D.

The Johns Hopkins University, School of Hygiene and Public Health

JOSEPH L. MELNICK, Ph.D.

Yale University, School of Medicine

KARL F. MEYER, M.D.

George Williams Hooper Foundation for Medical Research, University of California

PETER K. OLITSKY, M.D.

The Rockefeller Institute for Medical Research

JOHN R. PAUL, M.D.

Yale University, School of Medicine

GEOFFREY W. RAKE, M.B., B.S.

The Squibb Institute for Medical Research

THOMAS M. RIVERS, M.D.

Director of the Hospital, The Rockefeller Institute for Medical Research

ALBERT B. SABIN, M.D.

The Children's Hospital Research Foundation, University of Cincinnati College of Medicine

(Continued on next page)

R. WALTER SCHLESINGER, M.D.

The Public Health Research Institute of The City of New York, Inc.

THOMAS F. McNAIR SCOTT, M.D.

University of Pennsylvania, School of Medicine

JOSEPH E. SMADEL, M.D.

Scientific Director, Department of Virus and Rickettsial Diseases, Army Medical Service Graduate School

JOHN C. SNYDER, M.D.

Harvard University, School of Public Health

WENDELL M. STANLEY, Ph.D.

University of California

JOSEPH STOKES, JR., M.D.

University of Pennsylvania, School of Medicine

MAX THEILER, M.R.C.S. (Eng.), L.R.C.P. (Lond.)

Laboratories of the Division of Medicine and Public Health, The Rockefeller Foundation

PHILLIPS THYGESON, M.D.

University of California Medical School

JOEL WARREN, Ph.D.

Army Medical Service Graduate School

Preface

There is need for a book on viral and rickettsial infections of man to which medical students and practicing physicians may turn for information. Knowledge concerning these infections has developed so rapidly during the past two decades that any book written during that time would have been out of date before publication. Furthermore, ideas about infectious agents responsible for these diseases were in such a state of flux that any book written by a number of authors would have confused those not actively working with them. Within the past few years there has been considerable stabilization of knowledge and ideas, and it is now time that these be brought together in such a way that interested people not actively engaged in the study of viral and rickettsial infections may have easy access to them. Bacterial and mycotic infections of man are discussed in a companion volume edited by Dr. René J. Dubos.

It would be impossible for one person to write authoritatively about all of the diseases and their causal agents discussed in this book. Consequently, experts in the different fields have been chosen to participate in a co-operative venture. At first, it seemed not unlikely that there might be many different opinions recorded by the various authors, but this has not occurred, indicating that much of the information presented is basic and will not have to be altered.

Viruses and rickettsiae are obligate parasites and multiply only in susceptible cells of a living host or in living cells in tissue cultures. In view of this, much of the book naturally has to deal with clinical and pathologic pictures induced by these active agents in natural and experimental hosts.

To give a complete picture of viral and rickettsial infections for medical students and physicians, sections on epidemiology and control measures are included in each chapter.

To publish a book of this nature costs a great deal, and without subsidy it would be available to only a limited number of people. The National Foundation for Infantile Paralysis has provided financial aid for the preparation and the publication of the volume so that its price should not be a factor limiting the number of people who read it.

The editor has had splendid co-operation from all of the contributors and from The National Foundation for Infantile Paralysis, for which he expresses deepest appreciation.

Above is the Preface that appeared four years ago in the first edition. Since then, so much has happened that a thorough revision of old material and addition of new matter have become obligatory if students and physicians, through it, hope to keep abreast of knowledge recently acquired in the viral and rickettsial fields. Descriptions of swineherd's disease and pretibial fever, which are now known to be caused by leptospiral organisms instead of viruses, have been omitted from this edition and appear in the companion volume on Bacterial and Mycotic Infections of Man. A new chapter has been devoted to discussion of human infections produced by the recently discovered Coxsackie viruses. Viral hemagglutination and interference between animal viruses are interesting and important phenomena and to each a new chapter has been allotted. Valuable information for the practice of medicine is scattered throughout the book in different chapters, and, at times, a

PREFACE

student or physician may have difficulty in finding it in usable form. Consequently, in an effort to overcome some of this difficulty, an integration of knowledge about viral and rickettsial infections of man has been attempted in a special chapter on diagnosis.

This revision, as well as the first edition, would have been impossible without the cooperation of the contributors and The National Foundation for Infantile Paralysis; to them the editor again expresses his deep gratitude.

Hospital of The Rockefeller Institute
for Medical Research
New York

THOMAS M. RIVERS, M.D.

Contents

CONTENTS

THOMAS M. RIVERS, M.D.

Hospital of The Rockefeller Institute for Medical Research

1

General Aspects of Viral and Rickettsial Infections

For many centuries contagious diseases have been recognized, and infection was long an obvious phenomenon before the causes of contagion or infection were known. Then came the discovery of protozoa and bacteria, although considerable work had to be done over a period of many years with these tiny animals and plants before it was realized that they had anything to do with contagion and infection. The flowering of such works ushered in the microbiologic era in infectious diseases—when it was firmly established that these maladies are caused by bacteria, fungi, and protozoa.

Long before the microbiologic era in infectious diseases, a method of preventing one infectious malady had been devised and its usefulness thoroughly established, namely, vaccination against smallpox. When it was shown that micro-organisms cause disease, investigators attempted to find a bacterium or a protozoan parasite responsible for smallpox. In fact, many different kinds of micro-organism were described as the etiologic agent of this malady, but no agreement was reached regarding any of them. In 1898, the filterable-virus era was vigorously initiated by the rediscovery that tobacco mosaic is caused by an agent capable of passing through earthenware filters impervious to ordinary bacteria. Shortly following this, numerous etiologic agents, including those of smallpox and vaccinia, were shown to pass such filters and to be so small that it was impossible or very difficult to see them by means of ordinary microscopes. Some years later, rickettsiae were discovered, which along with viruses constitute the two groups of agents discussed in this book. Most rickettsiae do not pass through bacteria-tight filters, and they have been generally accepted as living micro-organisms capable of multiplication only in susceptible host cells; in view of this, relatively little will be said about them in this chapter.

NATURE OF VIRUSES AND RICKETTSIAE

Thus, in addition to protozoa, bacteria, and fungi, two groups of infectious agents now known and spoken of as rickettsiae and viruses were recognized. As soon as the latter group was discovered, lengthy discussions arose regarding the nature of its members and the character of diseases produced by them. These discussions are still in progress, but fortunately much of the mystery and misunderstanding about viruses is gradually being dissipated, because within recent years a great deal of information has been obtained concerning these peculiar incitants of disease. This information has to do with their size, shape, density, autonomous existence, origin, reproduction, metabolic activity, reaction to chemical and physical agents, chemical constitution, antigenic qualities, transmission from host to host, and so forth.

The size of a virus may be determined by filtration, centrifugation, diffusion, and direct mensuration under a light microscope provided the virus is sufficiently large, or, if the virus is smaller, by means of an electron microscope. Of the methods mentioned, diffusion is the least and microscopy the most accurate. The size of practically every virus has been estimated in one or more ways, and, from available evidence, it is obvious that among viruses there is no uniformity in so far as size is concerned (Frontispiece). Some, e.g., the virus of foot-and-mouth disease which has a diameter of 12 mμ, are exceedingly small, indeed smaller than the largest protein molecules; while others, e.g., the virus of lymphogranuloma venereum which has a diameter of from 300 to 400 mμ, are relatively large, in fact larger than the smallest bacteria. In between these two limits, other viruses form an almost continuous spectrum with respect to size. Size alone indicates that some viruses can be complex entities, while others must of necessity lack such complexity.

Among viruses there is also no uniformity whatsoever regarding shape (Frontispiece). Some are spherical; others are ovoid; others are cubes or minute parallelepipeds; still others are tadpole-shaped; and, finally, some are rod-shaped.

The density of water is 1.0, while that of protein molecules is approximately 1.33. The density of tissue cells and bacteria lies between these figures, that of the latter being in the neighborhood of 1.10. The density of only a few viruses has been estimated. Stanley (1938a) reported that the density of tobacco-mosaic virus is 1.3; according to Elford and Andrewes (1936),

the density of vaccine virus is 1.18; according to Wyckoff (1937-38), the density of staphylococcus bacteriophage is approximately 1.20; according to Lauffer and Stanley (1944), the density of influenza virus is 1.1; and, finally, the results of work by Tang et al. (1937) and Schlesinger and Galloway (1937) indicate that some viruses, in addition to tobacco-mosaic virus, may have a density similar to that of protein molecules. There is need for additional data and confirmation of those already obtained, because, in order to determine the size of virus particles by means of centrifugation, it is essential to know their density as well as their shape. Consequently, some of the figures already obtained by centrifugation for the size of viruses may have to be changed to comply with new information regarding the density and shape of the active agents.

In order to learn more about the nature of viruses, their composition and certain of their activities, they must be obtained in a pure or relatively pure state. Unfortunately, this has not been accomplished in many instances. The outstanding exception is the work of Stanley and his associates on plant viruses. In 1935, from the sap of infected plants, Stanley (1935) isolated a crystalline protein with the properties of tobacco-mosaic virus. Stanley's observation that a specific, disease-producing, crystalline protein can be obtained from infected plants has been abundantly confirmed by Bawden and Pirie (1937a, b) and others. Improved technics for the isolation and purification of this virus have been devised, the best being differential centrifugation. Following Stanley's discovery of tobacco-mosaic-virus protein, Bawden and Pirie pointed out that the active material is not an ordinary protein but a nucleoprotein, and other active, plant-virus proteins have been isolated and studied.

Since Stanley's original work many investigators have attempted to purify all sorts of virus and study their chemical composition. These efforts resulted in a number of papers appearing in the literature concerning the chemical properties of purified viruses, and the idea got abroad that all viruses are nothing more than macromolecules of nucleoprotein; unfortunately, such an idea is still held by many. In most instances, the so-called purified virus preparations were not shown to consist of viruses alone; in fact, because of inherent difficulties in making accurate titrations, at least 50 and up to 90 per cent of some of them may have consisted of impurities. This being the case, statements concerning the chemical composition of many viruses are inaccurate and misleading.

The work of Knight (1946a, b) on influenza virus indicated that part of purified virus preparations consisted of material derived from the host. For instance, if the purified virus was obtained from mouse lungs or from embryonated hens' eggs, a substantial part of it, as determined by serologic and chemical tests, was of mouse or chick-embryo origin, respectively. Some workers interpret these results to mean that part of the virus particle itself is serologically active host material, while others are inclined to consider them as evidence of impurities in the viral preparations. The latter viewpoint becomes more likely in the light of recent work of Curnen, Pickels and Horsfall (1947) and Curnen and Horsfall (1947) on pneumonia virus of mice (PVM) in which it was shown that the original figure of 140 mμ for the diameter of the virus was grossly wrong, because it represented only the minimal diameter of a combination consisting of virus bound to particles of mouse-lung tissues. They were able to liberate the virus from mouse-lung particles; in the free state it had a diameter of 40 mμ. From these findings it is obvious how easily one might be mistaken when one speaks of working with a purified virus.

In addition to the plant viruses that have been crystallized, only a few others have been obtained in a sufficiently pure state for accurate chemical analysis. One of the best examples of a highly purified animal virus is that of vaccinia. Workers in Rivers' laboratory (see chapter on Vaccinia) have been able to secure quantities of elementary bodies of vaccinia sufficiently pure to make results of their studies reasonably accurate. These results indicate that the bodies are cuboidal structures with several areas of condensation within them; they have a limiting membrane; they are composed of lipids, carbohydrate, thymonucleic acid, several serologically distinct proteins, copper, biotin, and riboflavin; and they possess no respiratory, metabolic or reproductive activities in the absence of living, susceptible host cells. This is good evidence that at least one animal virus is a complex structure quite different in composition from certain plant viruses, e.g., tobacco-mosaic virus, which consist only of nucleoprotein.

In spite of occasional statements to the contrary, no virus has been cultivated or induced to increase in amount in the absence of living, susceptible cells. Whatever the nature of reproduction of viruses may be, it is now generally believed that it goes on within infected cells. Why are living cells essential for the multiplication of viruses? When one is asked such a question, one gets the impression that the interrogator believes that intracellular multiplication of infectious agents is something peculiar. However, obligate, intracellular parasitism is a well-known phenomenon, even though its mechanism or reasons for its existence may not be fully understood. In any event, it is assumed that the host cell is the only place where an obligate parasite finds conditions suitable for growth or multiplication. Many workers are of the opinion that viruses do not possess enzyme systems and metabolic processes essential for growth or multiplication and that host cells supply all or part of them. The word parasite to some investigators implies that the agent is alive; there is no reason except usage for this limitation. If some of the viruses are not living agents but fabrications of their host cells, these cells are still essential for their multiplication, even though the process by which the fabrication is brought about is not known.

When one thinks of reproduction, one usually has in mind an increase in size which is followed by division. Yet, according to Luria (1950), "all growth and reproduction should ultimately be traceable to *replication of specific chemical configurations by an essentially discontinuous appearance of discrete replicas."* Many now believe that the bacteriophages and certain other viruses, upon entering host cells, do not reproduce themselves by growth and division, but that they disintegrate into component parts of specific chemical configurations which, after being replicated, are recombined in some unknown way into complete, infectious virus particles. This very interesting hypothesis was set forth by Luria (1950, 1951), and in support of it there is a considerable amount of data (see chapter on Bacteriophages). There is at the present time, however, a trend away from this hypothesis to more conventional ideas of reproduction (Delbrück, personal communication).

It has become fashionable to speak of the mutation of viruses. Whether or not it is correct to speak of changes arising in a nucleoprotein molecule as mutations, remains for geneticists to determine. In any event, it is known that certain things happen to tobacco-mosaic-virus particles which give rise to changes in the picture of disease in plants. Moreover, once a modified disease appears, it persists indefinitely. Of considerable significance is the fact that strains of tobacco-mosaic virus have been found to differ in protein composition (Chap. 2). Workers interested in bacteriophage (see chapter on Bacteriophages) have no hesitancy in speaking of genetics in relation to these active agents. In fact, it is thought that some of the large bacterial viruses have at least 50 genes. Regardless of what name is applied to the phenomenon, many interesting alterations of viruses have been observed to occur under natural and experimental conditions. For example, the 17D strain of yellow fever virus is quite different in many respects from its parent strain, and after many years still breeds true (see chapter on Yellow Fever). Passing dengue virus through mice has resulted in an agent which can be used for vaccination of human beings (see chapter on Dengue). Outstanding experiments along these lines are those of Berry and Dedrick (1936) in which fibroma virus was transformed into myxoma virus by a procedure similar to that employed by Griffith in transforming one type of pneumococcus into another. Many investigators consider the phenomena just mentioned as evidence prejudicial to the idea that viruses are inanimate. Whether or not this is the correct attitude to assume remains to be determined.

Some viruses, such as that causing smallpox, are relatively stable in respect to antigenic structure as well as to other characteristics. This is not true of all viruses as exemplified by the great variability of the active agents responsible for influenza. The stability of certain viruses and the variability of others, respectively, influence the diseases caused by them and the effectiveness of methods used in their control. For further consideration of this important matter in regard to one virus disease, see chapter on Influenza.

When one looks at the evidence concerning rickettsiae, one cannot avoid the conclusion that they are minute, highly parasitic micro-organisms. On the other hand, when one reviews the evidence concerning viruses, one immediately is impressed by their striking heterogeneity. Elementary bodies of the psittacosis-lymphogranuloma-trachoma group are almost as large as rickettsiae and are probably as complex; most workers think they are living agents. Then come the elementary bodies of the pock diseases. They are slightly smaller than the group of agents just mentioned and are very complex; many workers look upon them as living agents. At the other end of the spectrum, crystalline plant viruses consisting of nucleoproteins are found. Between the elementary bodies and crystalline plant-virus proteins there are many viruses varying widely in size and complexity. Many arguments have occurred concerning whether or not the small viruses, particularly the crystalline ones, are living. Some contend that they are not and only represent fabrications of their host cells through processes of autocatalysis. Others look upon them as entities in the twilight zone between the living and nonliving. The answer to this question is not available at the moment and is not essential for the purposes of this book. In view of what has been said, it is difficult, if not impossible, to give a concise definition of a virus. Nevertheless, those who work with viruses concede that they differ in certain respects from rickettsiae and bacteria. Perhaps the best short definition of viruses is that they constitute a hetrogeneous group of infectious agents which are smaller than ordinary bacteria and require susceptible host cells for multiplication and activity.

Facts are essential for scientific purposes, but even scientists at times wish to go beyond facts and delve into metaphysics. Metaphysics in relation to viruses has to do with their origin and nature. Immediately it can be said that proof of the origin of any virus is lacking, but there has been abundant speculation about the matter. No attempt will be made to set forth all views; only the two most popular ones will be mentioned.

Green (1935), speaking of the nature of filterable viruses, stated that "they are the smallest units showing the reproductive property considered typical of life." In regard to their origin he discussed the following possibilities:

First, they may be surviving parasitic forms developing from free-living ultramicrobes formerly inhabiting the earth and now extinct. Secondly, they may be parasitic forms of life developing by retrograde evolution from visible microbes similar to the visible forms now existent. The assumption of a present or past world of free-living ultramicrobes is pure conjecture, with no single fact to substantiate the assumption. A theory of microbic origin of

filterable viruses by retrograde evolution from visible microbes naturally follows our knowledge of evolution in the visible world.

Sir Patrick Laidlaw (1938), in his Rede Lecture, set forth his conception of the nature and origin of viruses, which in all respects is similar to that of Green, and stated that viruses "live a borrowed life, truly the supreme summit of parasitism."

Stanley (1935), in his first paper on crystalline tobacco-mosaic virus, stated that the agent "is regarded as an autocatalytic protein which, for the present, may be assumed to require the presence of living cells for multiplication." Later, Stanley (1938a), in speaking of having called it an autocatalyst, said:

Although this is technically incorrect in that the reaction is very probably not that of true autocatalysis, the term was used because the net result is somewhat similar to that of an autocatalytic reaction. However, the mechanism by means of which a molecule in a specific living cell is able to cause the production of identical or similar molecules is unknown. It may be similar to the mechanism which the geneticists postulate for the production of genes.

Again, Stanley (1938b) remarked:

We are forced to conclude, therefore, that, although tobacco mosaic virus protein has the ordinary properties of molecules, it also has the ability to reproduce and to mutate, properties not ordinarily ascribed to molecules, and hence that tobacco mosaic virus protein represents an entity unfamiliar to us.

From the practical standpoint of infectious diseases and their spread in a population, it is not absolutely essential to be fully aware of the origin and nature of viruses, for in many respects they operate in a manner similar to that of other infectious agents, e.g., bacteria and protozoa.

PATHOLOGY

Since it is now generally believed that all viruses multiply or are reduplicated within susceptible cells instead of in the fluids surrounding them, it is not surprising that certain pathologic pictures are more or less characteristic of viral diseases. Intracellular changes, e.g., inclusion bodies and ballooning degeneration, resulting from an intimate virus-cell relationship, were among the first to be noticed. Although they were the first to be emphasized, they are not necessarily the only or the most important ones.

Many, but by no means all, viruses induce inclusions in their host cells. Some viral inclusions are found only in the cytoplasm and others only in the nucleus, while a few occur in both the nucleus and cytoplasm. For example, Guarnieri bodies of vaccinia, Bollinger bodies of fowl-pox, and Negri bodies of rabies are found only in the cytoplasm; the inclusion bodies of herpes simplex and chickenpox occur only in nuclei; and the inclusions of smallpox and paravaccinia are situated in both the nucleus and cytoplasm. Not only does the location of inclusion bodies vary, but their composition and staining reactions may be quite diverse. A Bollinger body consists of a lipoid membrane derived from the host cell and filled with elementary or Borrel bodies embedded in a matrix. Guarnieri bodies consist of altered host-cell material in which are embedded many but not all the elementary or Paschen bodies within the cell. An intranuclear inclusion is usually an acidophilic mass occupying most of the nuclear area and is surrounded by a clear zone or halo; the basophilic chromatin of the nucleus marginates on the nuclear membrane. The nature of intranuclear inclusions is not well known, nor is there evidence that virus is present in nuclei so affected. However, there is no reason why a virus cannot invade a nucleus and multiply there, because rickettsiae of Rocky Mountain spotted fever have a predilection for nuclei of host cells, while those of typhus fever are found only in the cytoplasm.

At one time, inclusion bodies were of great importance in viral work and were used for diagnostic purposes. Negri bodies are still important for this reason, but most of the others have become less significant, because more accurate methods of making diagnoses and identifying viruses have been developed. Although the interest of pathologists has largely centered around the study of inclusions, some workers have either ignored the existence of such structures or held that they are of no special significance. Moreover, these workers have contended that the pathology of viral diseases is not essentially different from that observed in inflammatory processes produced by bacteria. The fact that inflammation occurs in many viral diseases cannot be denied, and, despite the acute nature of some of them, if secondary bacterial infections do not intervene, the inflammatory process is usually characterized by the infiltration of mononuclear cells. The question whether inflammation is a primary or a secondary phenomenon has in many instances led to lengthy discussions. For example, some pathologists have looked upon the primary changes caused by the virus of smallpox as noninflammatory and considered them necrobiotic or diphtheroid. According to them, the inflammatory reaction appears as a secondary phenomenon. On the contrary, other workers have regarded the variolous changes in the skin from their inception as the expression only of an acute inflammatory process.

It is often impossible, because of the complexity of tissues involved, to ascertain the nature of primary changes induced by the activity of viruses. On the other hand, in some diseases and under certain conditions in others, information concerning this question may be obtained. For instance, in vaccinal lesions of a rabbit's cornea, definite and characteristic changes are observed in the epithelial cells before any evidence of inflammation in the form of cellular exudate is seen. Moreover, lesions of molluscum contagiosum are confined to the epidermis and little or no inflammatory reaction is observed in the corium. Kligler et al. (1929) observed that young fowl-pox lesions induced by the bite of infected mosquitoes showed only hyperplasia of epithelial cells, many of which contained

Bollinger bodies; in other words, there was no evidence of an inflammatory reaction in young lesions. Furthermore, Goodpasture (1925) found that the first evidence of injury caused by rabies virus is observed "within ganglion cells, not in surrounding tissues," and that "the cells may undergo complete necrosis without cellular or other exudate about them." Finally, Rivers (1933-34) demonstrated that Purkinje cells in monkeys with louping-ill are lysed or completely destroyed before definite evidence of inflammation appears.

If inflammation is a secondary phenomenon in viral diseases, what then are the primary changes produced in cells by the active agents? They are either proliferative or degenerative; both types of changes are usually seen and it is difficult at times to determine definitely which appears first. The relation of degeneration to proliferation in tissues infected with vaccine virus can be observed in the cornea of a rabbit. Within 3 to 6 hours after the cornea is inoculated, changes are seen in the immediate vicinity of the area infected; the epithelial cells are larger and stain less intensely than usual, and mitotic figures and amitotic giant cells begin to appear. Within 6 to 24 hours after infection, Guarnieri bodies are found in affected cells. Small nodules are observed on the surface of the cornea 24 to 48 hours after inoculation, and examination of the nodules reveals, in addition to hypertrophy of individual cells, a definite hyperplasia or increase in the number of cells. Evidences of degeneration and inflammation do not appear until about 48 hours after inoculation. The picture just described illustrates the sequence of pathologic changes which occur in a number of viral diseases. However, in certain viral maladies not all of the phenomena mentioned are observed, or some of them play a negligible role. For instance, in Rous' sarcoma and in Shope's papilloma, hyperplasia or overgrowth of tissue is the predominant change noted; multiplication or activity of the viruses in some manner stimulates the host cells to such an extent that formation of tumors results. As the cells divide, virus goes along with each daughter cell. Thus, the stimulation is not interrupted, and the tumors continue to grow more or less indefinitely. This takes place even in the presence of development of immunity in the animals, for it has been shown by several investigators (Rivers et al., 1929; Andrewes, 1928; Rivers and Pearce, 1925) that virus situated within cells is not affected by humoral antibodies. In other viral diseases, infected cells are incapable of multiplication, e.g., nerve cells or neurons. Consequently, in rabies, poliomyelitis, and louping-ill, hyperplasia is absent; the first evidence of infection is necrobiosis or lysis of infected cells. In still other viral maladies, e.g., Rift Valley fever, yellow fever, and foot-and-mouth disease, the active agents produce their effects so rapidly that there is insufficient time for hyperplasia to occur, or, if it does, it plays a minor role in the picture.

For a long time, it has been recognized that degeneration and hyperplasia occur in viral diseases. Indeed, Philibert (1924) divided some of these diseases into cytolytic and cytokinetic groups. Rivers (1928) pointed out that hyperplasia alone, hyperplasia followed by necrosis, and necrosis alone are the primary pathologic changes in all viral maladies. Since then, several workers have arranged viral diseases according to the amount of hyperplasia and necrosis present in each. In such an arrangement Shope's papilloma and Rous' sarcoma are at one end of a spectrum, while at the other end appear louping-ill, foot-and-mouth disease, and Rift Valley fever.

Observations concerning hyperplasia and necrosis as they occur in virus diseases may be summarized briefly as follows. If action of a virus is not extremely rapid and explosive, and if susceptible cells are capable of multiplication, the primary effect of the active agent is stimulation leading to cellular hyperplasia. Following the hyperplasia there is usually destruction or necrosis of the cells, which in turn is attended or followed by a secondary inflammation representing a reaction of the neighboring tissues and of the host. The balance between the stimulative and destructive tendencies of a virus determines whether hyperplasia or necrosis is the predominant part of the pathologic picture. If the action of a virus is explosive or rapid, or if the susceptible cells are incapable of division and multiplication, then the primary pathologic changes are necrobiosis and lysis of cells.

Rous' sarcoma occurs in chickens. Shope's papilloma is a disease of rabbits. Consequently, none of the above remarks should be taken as acceptable evidence that viruses cause sarcomas, cancers or other malignant growths in human beings.

Many years ago workers attempted to find evidence that viruses produce toxins. At that time quantities of viruses could not be obtained in a sufficiently pure state to determine whether or not toxins are associated with them. Then came a period when most workers believed that all effects of viruses and rickettsiae result from their multiplication and activity within infected cells. Recently, however, it has been shown that large quantities of purified influenza virus, certain viruses of the psittacosis-lymphogranuloma group and some rickettsiae, when injected into experimental animals, produce illness and death so rapidly that one can hardly escape the conclusion that these effects are due to toxic properties; all evidence points to the fact that the toxicity cannot be separated from the viral particles. As yet, the role that these toxic properties play in the clinical and pathologic pictures of naturally acquired viral and rickettsial diseases is not known (see chapters on Influenza, Psittacosis-Lymphogranuloma Group, and Rickettsiae).

IMMUNITY

The basic principles of immunology and serology are operative in all fields of biology. Consequently, one should not be surprised to find familiar immunologic and serologic phenomena associated with viral and rickettsial diseases as well as with other infectious maladies. From a historical point of view it is interesting to call attention to the fact that one attack of a disease frequently results in protection against other attacks of the same disease, a fact probably first noted in connection with smallpox and measles. Immunity is relative, and the term indicates either complete resistance or different grades of partial resistance to infection or to the effects of infection in case it is established. As with other infectious diseases, there are recognized in connection with viral and rickettsial maladies three kinds of immunity, namely, natural, actively acquired and passively acquired.

Natural immunity is the state of resistance to infection not dependent upon a previous, spontaneous or experimental contact with infectious agents or their antibodies. It is known that this type of immunity to viral diseases, as well as to other kinds of infectious maladies, is in some manner not infrequently dependent upon the species, age, sex, state of nutrition, and genetic background of the host as well as upon climatic conditions.

Some viral maladies, e.g., rabies and vaccinia, attack many kinds of host; others are highly species specific, for instance, Virus III infection of rabbits, infectious papilloma (Shope) of rabbits, and salivary-gland disease of guinea pigs. In addition to species specificity, there is in certain instances a marked cellular specificity. Some viruses, e.g., those of herpes simplex and vaccinia, attack cells arising from all three embryonal layers. Others are more specific, e.g., rabies virus and poliomyelitis virus are highly neurotropic, and molluscum contagiosum virus attacks only epidermal cells. Others are still more specific, requiring certain kinds of epithelial cells, e.g., the virus of Shope's papilloma produces lesions in epidermal cells but not in epithelial cells of the buccal mucosa, while another wart virus of rabbits will produce lesions in epithelial cells of the buccal mucosa but not in epidermal cells.

Age, sex, climate and genetic background undoubtedly in many instances influence susceptibility to infection. However, it is not always easy to assess the importance of these factors. For example, females and young people may seem to escape certain diseases because of fundamental differences due to age and sex; yet they are fully susceptible and escape for lack of exposure to infection. The same is true of climate; certain diseases are prevalent in the tropics merely because their vectors are found only there. Genetics play a role in viral infections, but it is not always possible to detect it in diseases so highly infectious as measles and smallpox. On the other hand, it may be possible to detect it in maladies such as paralytic poliomyelitis (Aycock, 1934), which is seen in relatively few people, and in certain experimental diseases (Webster, 1933a, b; Webster and Clow, 1936a; Holmes, 1937). From the results of Webster's experimental work in mice, it was not possible to relate susceptibility and resistance to viral infections with one or more specific genes, even though through selective inbreeding virus-susceptible and virus-resistant animals were obtained. Holmes, however, in his work on tobacco mosaic in pepper plants was more fortunate, for he found a correlation.

It is well known that excellent health is no protection against measles, influenza, chickenpox and smallpox. Furthermore, it is a definite impression of many people working with viruses that unhealthy animals are either more resistant or react less severely to certain viral maladies than do perfectly normal animals. Indeed, as long ago as the time of Jenner and Willan there was talk of and reports regarding certain individuals being less susceptible to vaccinia because of the presence in them of other diseases. These observations were taken to indicate that as a result of some previous or concomitant disease individuals were not so highly susceptible to other kinds of disease as they would have been had they been perfectly healthy. In Rivers' (1939) laboratory it has been a common observation that unhealthy or malnourished rabbits show less reaction to vaccine virus and exhibit a lower titer with the active agent than do perfectly healthy animals. Moreover, in recent years several groups of workers have shown that undernourished or malnourished mice are less susceptible than normal animals to certain encephalitis viruses. Observations of such a nature further emphasize the intimate type of parasitism observed in viral diseases, which has evolved from long association of the active agents with host cells, resulting in their use, for ecologic reasons, of entirely normal cells for their multiplication and activity.

For a number of years, it has been known that the inoculation of plants with some viruses created within them resistance to infection with certain other viruses. More recently, observations of a similar character have been made with viral diseases of bacteria and animals. Neurotropic yellow fever virus inoculated intramuscularly in monkeys produces little or no obvious disease, while certain strains of viscerotropic yellow fever virus are usually 100 per cent fatal. Hoskins (1935) showed that an injection of neurotropic virus protects a monkey against infection with a viscerotropic strain; the inoculations of the neurotropic virus may be made shortly prior to, simultaneously with, or 20 hours subsequent to the injections of a viscerotropic strain. It is agreed that this phenomenon is not dependent upon the immunizing effect of the neurotropic virus. Somewhat similar observations have been made when different strains of herpes-simplex virus were used to infect rabbits. In the examples just cited, exception might be taken to the fact that the two strains of each virus used were immunologically identical or similar. However, from the results of the experiments of Findlay and MacCallum (1937) with Rift Valley fever and yellow fever, it is evident that a specifically acquired immunity was not responsible for the protection noted and that the protection lasted only a short time. The happenings just described are spoken of as examples of the "interference phenomenon." A number of examples are now known (see chapters on Influenza, Bacteriophages and Interference). Horsfall and McCarty (1947) have shown that various bacteria or polysaccharides derived from these bacteria interfere with the multiplication of pneumonia virus of mice (PVM). Here the interference takes place not between two viruses but between a bacterium or its polysaccharide and a virus. Although the interference phenomenon is now well known, it clearly does not occur with all combinations of viruses and its mechanism is not fully understood. Several explanations have been offered but need not be gone into in detail at this time other than to state that the phenomenon is perhaps just another expression of the "supreme summit" of parasitism so beautifully exhibited in the intimate association of viruses with their host cells.

Active immunity is the state of resistance to infection engendered by a spontaneous attack of an infectious disease, by the experimental or intentional production of the disease or a modified form of it, or by the injection of a vaccine. At present there is no reason to believe that the definition of active immunity should be modified to meet observations in the viral field. It is a well-known fact that recovery from a viral infection is usually followed by an enduring immunity. In many instances, the immunity is operative during the remainder of a person's life. There are exceptions to the rule: common colds and herpes, for example, recur frequently in the same individual, and it is usual for a person to have more than one attack of influenza. The persistence of immunity in hosts recovered from some viral diseases is so striking that it is not surprising that an explanation of the phenomenon has been sought. Furthermore, if it is a rule to encounter lasting immunity following viral diseases, one would like to know the reason for exceptions.

In the case of poliomyelitis and measles, the viruses of which are encountered frequently throughout life, one might explain the persistent immunity and the continuous presence of humoral antibodies on the basis of repeated contacts with the active agents. On the other hand, it is impossible to explain in such a manner the enduring immunity to yellow fever which is accompanied by the presence of humoral antibodies in persons who, following an attack of the disease, have not for periods of 50 or even 75 years been in areas where the malady is endemic or epidemic. In view of the facts just mentioned and since it is known that a refractory state to some bacterial and spirochetal diseases is associated with the persistence of these agents in hosts, it has been suggested by a number of workers that, at least in certain instances, the protracted immunity following viral diseases is due to a prolonged or persistent sojourn of viruses in hosts. Such persistence of viruses in hosts would not necessarily lead to numerous persons capable of spreading disease, because the active agents might well be situated in parts of the body not readily in communication with the outside world. Sufficient instances in which viruses have been recovered from immune hosts have been recorded to show that it is not an unusual occurrence. For example, it has been noted in the salivary-gland disease of guinea pigs, psittacosis, infectious anemia of horses, lymphocytic choriomeningitis of mice, and certain viral diseases of plants. It is not unlikely that in some instances there is a causal relation between the persistence of a virus and enduring immunity. Moreover, it must be remembered that failure to recover a virus from an immune host is not positive evidence that it is not present. These agents are intracellularly located, and as long as they remain so situated are in no danger of being eliminated from the body. If they do not kill host cells, they can multiply and pass into daughter host cells whenever cellular division takes place without coming in contact with or being subjected to the activities of humoral antibodies. In this manner it is possible for them to remain indefinitely in an immune host, and such is undoubtedly what happens in a number of viral diseases, e.g., virus tumors of chickens and rabbits.

It is not known why permanent immunity is not developed to common colds, influenza, herpes simplex, and certain other viral diseases. It is interesting to speculate, however. Such viruses may be unable to establish themselves permanently in a host; if they do, they may periodically, for unknown reasons, become active as is the case with the virus of herpes simplex, or the superficial nature of the infections caused by them may have something to do with the poor development of immunity.

Active immunity can be obtained by the introduction of fully virulent viruses through unnatural portals of entry; variolation is an example. The use of fully virulent viruses for immunization has not been popular, however, because of the attendant dangers to persons receiving them and in view of the fact that in certain instances intentional inoculation of a virus for protection of an individual might result in widespread epidemics. Consequently, attempts have been made to find or produce modified viruses without the objectionable features just mentioned but still possessing properties essential for the production of immunity against naturally acquired diseases. Success has attended some of these attempts, e.g., those directed toward the production of attenuated viruses for protection against rabies, yellow fever, dengue fever and cattle plague.

For a long time, it was considered difficult or impossible to produce an effective immunity against viral diseases by means of completely inactivated viruses. This view is still correct about certain maladies, e.g., yellow fever, smallpox, and dengue fever. On the other hand, it has been shown that an effective immunity against some diseases can be obtained by properly inactivated viruses or rickettsiae given in sufficient quantities, e.g., western equine encephalitis, rabies, influenza, Rocky Mountain spotted fever, and typhus fever. It must be remembered that immunity obtained in this manner is not lasting. In most cases, vaccination with inactive viruses must be repeated relatively frequently, at approximately yearly intervals, if serviceable immunity needs to be maintained. The reason for this is not known. On the other hand, one can speculate. If the natural disease, e.g., influenza, does not produce persistent immunity, one would not expect enduring protection from a vaccine consisting of inactive virus. If enduring immunity when it occurs results from persistent, latent infection, such an infection could not be established by a vaccine consisting of inactive virus, and immunity obtained in this way might be expected to be evanescent.

Associated in most instances, but not all, with the development of active immunity against viruses is the appearance of humoral antibodies in the sera of immune persons. Sternberg (1896) in 1892 demonstrated that the serum of an animal recovered from vaccinia possesses the property of neutralizing the activity of the causative virus. Freyer (1904) was the first definitely to demonstrate that flocculation occurs in a mixture of vaccinia-immune serum and vaccine virus. Jobling (1906) demonstrated that complement is fixed in the presence of a mixture of vaccine virus and sera from calves convalescent from vaccinia. Paschen (1913) reported that elementary bodies of vaccinia are specifically agglutinated by vaccinia-immune serum. Thus, very early in the viral era, neutralizing antibodies, precipitins, agglutinins, and complement-fixing antibodies were demonstrated in the sera of animals convalescent from at least one viral disease. Later, when several serologically different proteins were found in vaccine virus, it was shown that there are precipitating and complement-fixing antibodies specific for them. Over the years, serologic tests for the identification of viruses and diagnosis of diseases caused by them have been developed so that now such tests have replaced the old cumbersome ones involving animal inoculation and cross-immunity reactions (see chapter on Serologic Reactions). Antibodies that fix complement and are active in the precipitin and agglutination reactions are likely to be the same, merely exhibiting their activity in different ways when they cause agglutination, complement fixation, and precipitation. There is reason to believe that neutralizing antibodies, at least in certain instances, are different from the others. In cases that this is true, they are responsible for protection.

Neutralization is a striking phenomenon and has long been known, but there is still considerable discussion about how it is accomplished. At one time, it was believed that the immune serum in the mixtures "killed" the virus, hence the antibodies were spoken of as being virucidal. But the results of the work of several investigators have revealed that some viruses in so-called neutral mixtures can be induced to become active again under certain conditions, e.g. after dilution or centrifugation of the mixtures. In other words, if a neutral mixture of vaccine virus and vaccinia-immune serum is diluted 100 to 1,000 times, active virus can be demonstrated upon inoculation of small amounts of the diluted material into susceptible animals; or if, after a neutral mixture is centrifuged and the supernatant fluid is discarded, the sediment is resuspended in physiologic salt solution, active virus is demonstrable. In most instances, while no firm union takes place immediately upon preparing the mixtures mentioned, one does occur eventually and at this time active virus cannot be recovered by dilution or centrifugation.

At the moment most workers agree that what has just been said is true; but, granting that it is, one is still left without a satisfactory explanation of why mixtures of virus and immune serum immediately after preparation are neutral or incapable of pro-

ducing lesions. Indeed, certain virus-serum mixtures are neutral when injected into the skin but are not inactive when inoculated into the brain or testicles. In other words, the neutrality or inactivity of a virus-serum mixture is conditioned by the organ in which it is tested. Various explanations of the phenomenon mentioned have been offered. One is that the serum in neutral mixtures acts upon the cells of the host rather than upon the virus and thus prevents the development of lesions. Another is that certain parts of an animal's body are less susceptible to slight amounts of residual active virus in the neutral mixtures than are others. None of these explanations, however, is quite adequate.

What relation do humoral antibodies have to immunity against virus diseases? Animals may possess agglutinins, precipitins and complement-fixing antibodies against certain viruses without being resistant to infection. In most instances, but not all, the presence of neutralizing antibodies in an animal's serum against a virus indicates that such an animal is resistant to the active agent. However, some animals recovered from a virus infection are resistant to reinfection without possessing demonstrable neutralizing antibodies. One school of thought holds that humoral antibodies are of no great significance in actively acquired immunity and contends that a cellular or tissue immunity is the important factor. Another school is of the opinion that humoral antibodies are the important factor. Furthermore, according to these workers, the fact that such antibodies are not demonstrable by methods now used cannot be accepted as evidence of their absence, because they may be present in amounts too small for demonstration or they may be sessile, i.e., attached to cells instead of being free in the circulating blood. There are arguments for both points of view, but whether or not one is correct to the exclusion of the other remains to be determined.

Passive immunity is a state of resistance to infection produced in a normal person by the parenteral administration of serum from an actively immunized person or animal containing circulating antibodies. So far as is known, this state of resistance to virus diseases can be brought about only by the injection of serum containing neutralizing antibodies. In passive immunity it is quite obvious that humoral antibodies are the important factors rather than tissue immunity. Whether the antibodies introduced into people protect susceptible cells against the entry of virus, whether they act directly on the virus in such a manner as to prevent the production of disease, or, finally, whether they enhance the destruction of virus by certain phagocytic cells, is not known. Passive immunity is of great practical interest because of its use in connection with prophylaxis and treatment of virus diseases, a matter discussed later in the chapter.

TRANSMISSION

The way by which viruses are disseminated in a population varies. Some diseases, e.g., smallpox, chickenpox and measles, are extremely contagious and are spread by contact or by droplet nuclei in the air. At least one virus disease, rabies, is transmitted only through a wound, usually one induced by the bite of a rabid animal. Many viral and rickettsial diseases are transmitted in nature by arthropod vectors; mosquitoes, mites, fleas, and ticks are the ones usually involved. In most instances, the arthropods that act as vectors are infected by the viruses and rickettsiae and remain infected as long as they live. Indeed, the rickettsiae of epidemic typhus not only make a louse sick but cause its death. In some instances, viruses and rickettsiae are transmitted to an insect's offspring through eggs. In this way, some rickettsiae can be perpetuated in nature. There are other hosts, in addition to man, for many viral and rickettsial diseases. Indeed, in some cases, the appearance of certain diseases in man is only accidental or an ecologic by-product of the infectious agents. For example, yellow fever probably has always been a disease of mosquitoes and monkeys with man becoming infected only incidentally. The same is probably true of western equine encephalitis; small mammals, birds, and mosquitoes usually keep the disease going in nature, while infection of man and horses is relatively infrequent. As one reads the different chapters in this book, many examples of what has been stated will be found and one cannot avoid being impressed with the ecologic phenomena of disease. In understanding and controlling human infections that require insect vectors and animal reservoirs, one must be equally familiar with the ecology of vectors, reservoirs, and human beings. Very few viral diseases are water-borne, infectious hepatitis being an outstanding exception (and even this disease is not usually spread by water but by contact). Only a few viruses are spread by food; three milk-borne epidemics of poliomyelitis, which is usually considered a contact disease, have been reported, and at least one outbreak of infectious hepatitis has been caused by contaminated milk. In summary, viral and rickettsial diseases are usually spread by contact, droplet nuclei in the air, or arthropod vectors. Occasionally, a few can be disseminated by means of contaminated water or milk, and some can be spread in more than one way.

The usual methods by which viruses are spread and maintained in nature have just been described. There are, however, instances in which these occur in an unusual manner. Two examples will be given, one from the work of Shope (1939) and the other from the investigations of Syverton et al. (1947). According to Shope, embryonated lung-worm ova, passing to the outside world either by way of the feces or of bronchial exudate from a hog that has had influenza, are ingested by earthworms. The lung-worm larvae pass through three stages of development in the earthworm. After reaching the third stage, in which they are capable of infecting swine, the larvae remain in the earthworm host until the worm is eaten by a hog; they are then liberated, penetrate the swine's intestinal mucosa, and migrate to the respiratory tract by way of the lymphatics and blood stream. This cycle may require several years for its completion, but under ideal conditions it is accomplished in about a month. After the lung-worm larvae carrying the influenza virus finally reach the lungs of a susceptible hog, nothing happens unless the proper stimulus materializes. In the absence of such stimuli the influenza virus lies dormant and is not detectable by ordinary means. But when the proper stimulus occurs, for instance, several injections of certain kinds of bacilli or an infestation with round worms at the proper time of year, the virus becomes active and the hog develops a typical attack of swine influenza. Syverton et al. (1947) showed that, when guinea pigs were simultaneously infected with the virus of lymphocytic choriomeningitis and *Trichinella spiralis,* the nematode larvae picked up the virus and after maturation were able to transmit it to susceptible hosts. According to them, the transmission under these conditions was not due to adherence of the virus to the outer surface of the larvae but to its presence within them.

PREVENTION AND TREATMENT

In approaching prevention and treatment of viral and rickettsial diseases, the questions of quarantine and control of vectors and reservoirs immediately come to mind. At this time, nothing will be said of these matters, because the latter will be handled in chapters on specific diseases, and quarantine as conducted in relation to human diseases is of very doubtful value. Vaccines have been discussed earlier in the chapter. Consequently, remarks will be limited to prevention and treatment by means of drugs and immune sera. At this point, it should be mentioned that misunderstanding in regard to the use of the word "treatment" frequently occurs: some physicians insist that all measures instigated after exposure to an infectious agent, even though the exposed person is still well, constitute treatment, while others employ the word to designate those measures initiated only after the onset of signs and symptoms of disease. Therefore, in order to avoid confusion, the time of administration of drugs and convalescent sera in relation to exposure and onset of signs of disease should be indicated when possible.

Two sets of experiments that throw considerable light on prevention and treatment of viral and rickettsial diseases by means of immune sera will be described. Rivers et al. (1929) removed corneas from normal rabbits, inoculated them with vaccine virus, and then embedded them in clots of plasma containing abundant antivaccinal antibodies. Upon incubation, typical vaccinal lesions with Guarnieri bodies and an abundant amount of active virus developed in such tissues, in spite of the fact that, in the plasma surrounding them, sufficient antibodies to neutralize the virus were present. Andrewes (1929) showed that antivaccinal serum infiltrated into the shaved skin of a rabbit prevented the development of a vaccinal lesion in the treated skin even though the virus was inoculated immediately afterward. However, if the virus was injected into the skin five minutes prior to the time that the infiltration of immune serum was made, no amount of serum sufficed to prevent a lesion; and, if eight hours were allowed to elapse after inoculation, not even the size of the lesion was influenced. Furthermore, it was demonstrated that large amounts of immune serum, administered intravenously shortly after the virus was inoculated intradermally, would prevent a generalized eruption but would exert no influence upon the lesion at the site of inoculation. In this connection, it should be remembered that no gross evidence of infection is seen during the first 48 hours after vaccine virus is injected into the skin of a rabbit.

In certain viral diseases, the administration of immune sera after exposure and before appearance of clinical signs and symptoms is efficacious, but, as a rule, once signs and symptoms of a viral or rickettsial disease have manifested themselves, the administration even of large quantities of immune sera is not very effective. Some workers disagree with this statement to a certain extent, but they have been unable to bring convincing evidence against the soundness of the view. In contesting the view, investigators admit that viruses or rickettsiae already in cells are not affected by immune substances but stress the fact that immune sera will prevent other cells in the body from becoming infected. The fallacy in the argument lies in the fact that, by the time patients have signs and symptoms sufficient to warrant the attendance of a physician, practically all cells in their bodies that are going to be infected have already been invaded by the viruses. This may be hard to comprehend, but there is sufficient experimental evidence in lower animals to substantiate the statement. Galloway and Perdrau (1935) found that after instillation of louping-ill virus in the nose of a monkey, the active agent was well distributed throughout the central nervous system several days before the animal showed signs of sickness. Hurst (1936) instilled equine encephalomyelitis virus into the noses of monkeys, sacrificed them at different times after inoculation, tested various parts of their central nervous systems for the presence of virus, and correlated the findings with clinical observations made on the animals before they were killed. According to him, all parts of the central nervous system except the cord contained virus within 30 hours after onset of fever, and several hours later, at the time of onset of nervous signs, even the lumbar cord was infectious. Webster and Clow (1936b) dropped virus of the St. Louis type of encephalitis into the noses of mice, sacrificed some at different times in order to test for the presence of virus in various parts of the brain and cord, killed others to determine the time of appearance and progression of lesions, and allowed others to sicken and die in order to determine the time of onset

of clinical signs. The data obtained in this manner clearly showed that virus was present in tissues 24 to 48 hours before the appearance of lesions detectable under the microscope, and that all parts of the brain and cord contained large amounts of virus before the animals became ill. Faber and Gebhardt (1933) conducted similar experiments with monkeys that had been infected by means of intranasal instillation of poliomyelitis virus. Their findings indicated that by the fifth, sixth or seventh day after inoculation, at which time only an occasional rise of temperature or tremor and hyperesthesia were present and before paralysis had occurred, virus was distributed throughout the central nervous system. Thus, it seems logical to assume that the viruses of a number of diseases by the time signs and symptoms of disease become obvious have already reached practically all the cells that are likely to be attacked. If such be the case, one would expect convalescent or immune sera given after the onset of signs of disease to be valueless in most instances.

Although the brilliant results obtained in the therapy of certain bacterial and protozoan diseases by the use of chemical agents and antibiotics emphasize the absence of similar successes in the treatment of viral and rickettsial diseases, sufficient evidence has been obtained to warrant the hope that eventually chemotherapeutic agents and antibiotics will be found effective against maladies in the latter group. When one reads the different chapters in this book, one will find that sulfonamides and penicillin are somewhat efficacious against the action of certain viruses of the psittacosis-lymphogranuloma-trachoma group, and that Chloromycetin and aureomycin are very effective in the treatment of psittacosis and the rickettsial diseases of man. At the present time, however, indiscriminate use of known chemotherapeutic agents and antibiotics in the treatment of all viral diseases of man is fruitless and inexcusable.

The difference between the response of bacterial diseases on the one hand and viral and rickettsial diseases on the other to chemotherapy is probably due to fundamental differences in the nature and metabolic activities of the two groups of disease-producing agents. A striking feature about the results of work on chemotherapy of experimental viral and rickettsial diseases is that the viruses and rickettsiae themselves are not inactivated or injured by the substances used: all that happens is that further multiplication of the disease-producing agents ceases. This is quite different from what takes place when bacteria come in contact with chemotherapeutic agents and antibiotics. In most instances, these microorganisms are killed by adequate concentrations of the therapeutic substances, and their death is believed to be brought about by an interference with certain of their enzyme systems or metabolic processes. On the other hand, viruses and rickettsiae are intracellular parasites and are believed not to possess complete enzyme systems essential for multiplication. If this is true, then such systems are supplied wholly or in part by their host cells and therapeutic agents can have no direct, deleterious effect on them through disruption of such systems. Nevertheless, their activities can be interfered with and their multiplication inhibited indirectly through the action of therapeutic agents which disturb enzyme systems and metabolic processes of their host cells. What has just been said offers a logical explanation of why known chemotherapeutic agents and antibiotics yield different results in different kinds of infectious disease and indicates a practicable approach to therapeutic problems in the viral and rickettsial field.

REFERENCES

Andrewes, C. H., 1928, The action of immune serum on vaccinia and Virus III *in vitro*. J. Path. and Bact., *31*, 671-698.

Andrewes, C. H., 1929, Anti-vaccinial serum. J. Path. and Bact., *32*, 265-274.

Aycock, W. L., 1934, Autarceology of poliomyelitis. A study of the recurrence of the disease in the same family. West Virginia Med. J., *30*, 481-489.

Bawden, F. C., and Pirie, N. W., 1937a, The isolation and some properties of liquid crystalline substances from solanaceous plants infected with three strains of tobacco mosaic virus. Proc. Roy. Soc. London, Series B, *123*, 274-320.

Bawden, F. C., and Pirie, N. W., 1937b, The relationships between liquid crystalline preparations of cucumber viruses 3 and 4 and strains of tobacco mosaic virus. Brit. J. Exp. Path., *18*, 275-291.

Berry, G. P., and Dedrick, H. M., 1936, A method for changing the virus of rabbit fibroma (Shope) into that of infectious myxomatosis (Sanarelli). J. Bact., *31*, 50-51.

Curnen, E. C., and Horsfall, F. L., Jr., 1947, Properties of pneumonia virus of mice (PVM) in relation to its state. J. Exp. Med., *85*, 39-53.

Curnen, E. C., Pickels, E. G., and Horsfall, F. L., Jr., 1947, Centrifugation studies on pneumonia virus of mice (PVM). The relative sizes of free and combined virus. J. Exp. Med., *85*, 23-38.

Elford, W. J., and Andrewes, C. H., 1936, Centrifugation studies. II. The viruses of vaccinia, influenza and Rous sarcoma. Brit. J. Exp. Path., *17*, 422-430.

Faber, H. K., and Gebhardt, L. P., 1933, Localizations of the virus of poliomyelitis in the central nervous system during the preparalytic period, after intranasal instillation. J. Exp. Med., *57*, 933-954.

Findlay, G. M., and MacCallum, F. O., 1937, An interference phenomenon in relation to yellow fever and other viruses. J. Path. and Bact., *44*, 405-424.

Freyer, M., 1904, Das Immunserum der Kuhpockenlymphe. Zentr. Bakt., Abt. 1, Orig., *36*, 272-282.

Galloway, I. A., and Perdrau, J. R., 1935, Louping-ill in monkeys. Infection by the nose. J. Hyg., *35*, 339-346.

Goodpasture, E. W., 1925, A study of rabies, with reference to a neural transmission of the virus in rabbits, and the structure and significance of Negri bodies. Am. J. Path., *1*, 547-582.

Green, R. G., 1935, On the nature of filterable viruses. Science, *82*, 443-445.

Holmes, F. O., 1937, Inheritance of resistance to tobacco-mosaic disease in the pepper. Phytopathology, *27*, 637-642.

Horsfall, F. L., Jr., and McCarty, M., 1947, The modifying effects of certain substances of bacterial origin on the course of infection with pneumonia virus of mice (PVM). J. Exp. Med., *85*, 623-646.

Hoskins, M., 1935, A protective action of neurotropic against viscerotropic yellow fever virus in *Macacus rhesus*. Am. J. Trop. Med., *15*, 675-680.

Hurst, E. W., 1936, Infections of the *rhesus* monkey (*Macaca mulatta*) and the guinea-pig with the virus of equine encephalomyelitis. J. Path. and Bact., *42*, 271-302.

Jobling, J. W., 1906, The occurrence of specific immunity principles in the blood of vaccinated calves. J. Exp. Med., *8*, 707-712.

Kligler, I. J., Muckenfuss, R. S., and Rivers, T. M., 1929, Transmission of fowl-pox by mosquitoes. J. Exp. Med., *49*, 649-660.

Knight, C. A., 1946a, The preparation of highly purified PR8 influenza virus from infected mouse lungs. J. Exp. Med., *83*, 11-24.

Knight, C. A., 1946b, Precipitin reactions of highly purified influenza viruses and related materials. J. Exp. Med., *83*, 281-294.

Laidlaw, Sir P. P., 1938, Virus Diseases and Viruses. Cambridge University Press.

Lauffer, M. A., and Stanley, W. M., 1944, Biophysical properties of preparations of PR8 influenza virus. J. Exp. Med., *80*, 531-548.

Luria, S. E., 1950, Bacteriophage. An essay on virus reproduction, *in* Viruses 1950, Pasadena, California Institute of Technology, pp. 7-16.

Luria, S. E., 1951, Mechanism of bacteriophage reproduction, Federation Proceedings, *10*, 582-584.

Paschen, E., 1913, Zur Aetiologie der Variola und Vakzine. Deutsch. med. Wchnschr., *39*, 2132-2136.

Philibert, A., 1924, Virus cytotropes. Ann. Med., *16*, 283-308.

Rivers, T. M., 1928, Some general aspects of pathological conditions caused by filterable viruses. Am. J. Path., *4*, 91-124.

Rivers, T. M., 1933-34, Filterable viruses with particular reference to psittacosis. The Harvey Lectures, Series XXIX, 220-244.

Rivers, T. M., 1939, Lane Medical Lectures: Viruses and Virus Diseases. Stanford University Press.

Rivers, T. M., Haagen, E., and Muckenfuss, R. S., 1929, A study of vaccinal immunity in tissue cultures. J. Exp. Med., *50*, 673-685.

Rivers, T. M., and Pearce, L., 1925, Growth and persistence of filterable viruses in a transplantable rabbit neoplasm. J. Exp. Med., *42*, 523-537.

Schlesinger, M., and Galloway, I. A., 1937, Sedimentation of the virus of foot-and-mouth disease in the Sharples-Super Centrifuge. J. Hyg., *37*, 445-462.

Shope, R. E., 1939, An intermediate host for the swine influenza virus. Science, *89*, 441-442.

Stanley, W. M., 1935, Isolation of a crystalline protein possessing the properties of tobacco-mosaic virus. Science, *81*, 644-645.

Stanley, W. M., 1938a, Virus proteins—a new group of macromolecules. J. Phys. Chem., *42*, 55-70.

Stanley, W. M., 1938b, The reproduction of virus proteins. Am. Naturalist, *72*, 110-123.

Sternberg, G. M., 1896, Wissenschaftliche Untersuchungen über das spezifische Infektionsagens der Blattern und die Erzeugung künstlicher Immunität gegen diese Krankheit. Zentr. Bakt., Abt. 1, *19*, 857-869.

Syverton, J. T., McCoy, O. R., and Koomen, J., Jr., 1947, The transmission of the virus of lymphocytic choriomeningitis by *Trichinella spiralis*. J. Exp. Med., *85*, 759-769.

Tang, F. F., Elford, W. J., and Galloway, I. A., 1937, Centrifugation studies. IV. The megatherium bacteriophage and the viruses of equine encephalomyelitis and louping ill. Brit. J. Exp. Path., *18*, 269-275.

Webster, L. T., 1933a, Inherited and acquired factors in resistance to infection. I. Development of resistant and susceptible lines of mice through selective breeding. J. Exp. Med., *57*, 793-818.

Webster, L. T., 1933b, Inherited and acquired factors in resistance to infection. II. A comparison of mice inherently resistant or susceptible to *Bacillus enteritidis* infection with respect to fertility, weight, and susceptibility to various routes and types of infection. J. Exp. Med., *57*, 819-844.

Webster, L. T., and Clow, A. D., 1936a, Experimental encephalitis (St. Louis type) in mice with high inborn resistance. A chronic subclinical infection. J. Exp. Med., *63*, 827-846.

Webster, L. T., and Clow, A. D., 1936b, The limited neurotropic character of the encephalitis virus (St. Louis type) in susceptible mice. J. Exp. Med., *63*, 433-448.

Wyckoff, R. W. G., 1937-38, An ultracentrifugal analysis of concentrated staphylococcus bacteriophage preparations. J. Gen. Physiol., *21*, 367-374.

W. M. STANLEY, PH.D., AND MAX A. LAUFFER, PH.D.

*The University of California, Berkeley,
and the University of Pittsburgh*

2

Chemical and Physical Procedures

HISTORICAL INTRODUCTION

Viruses were discovered by means of a physical technic, namely, filtration, and since 1892, when Iwanowski (1892) reported the results of his filtration experiments with the agent responsible for the tobacco-mosaic disease, physical and chemical technics have played an increasingly important role in studies on viruses. The filtration experiments were repeated, independently, by Beijerinck (1898), who extended the work to include studies on the serial passage of the tobacco-mosaic disease by means of filtrates, on the inactivation of the infectious agent by heat and on the diffusion of the agent into agar blocks. Beijerinck also showed that the causative agent of the disease could be dried at low temperature or precipitated with alcohol with retention of its infectious nature. Beijerinck recognized the significance of his experiments, and realized that a new type of infectious agent, which he referred to as a *contagium vivum fluidum*, had been discovered.

The discovery of tobacco-mosaic virus was followed by the finding of the virus of foot-and-mouth disease of cattle in 1898 (Loeffler and Frosch, 1898), and the virus of yellow fever of man in 1901 (Reed et al., 1911); subsequently a host of viruses affecting plants, lower animals and man were discovered. In most cases, the existence of these viruses was demonstrated by means of filtration. However, early filtration experiments did little except to establish the very important fact that most viruses were smaller than most bacteria. The ordinary light microscope, and even the ultraviolet light microscope, yielded practically no information except in the cases of a few large viruses. For several years little was known concerning the nature or the absolute sizes of the viruses. Then, about 1930 several approaches began to bear fruit. There had been a growing suspicion that the elementary bodies of vaccinia, fowl-pox and psittacosis were, in fact, the viruses themselves. This suspicion appeared to be substantiated in 1930, when Woodruff and Goodpasture (1929, 1930) isolated inclusions of fowl-pox, showed that a single inclusion could be broken up to yield many infective units, and that it contained as many as 20,000 elementary bodies. Although MacCallum and Oppenheimer (1922) found that vaccinia virus could be concentrated by centrifugation, it was not until about 1930 that renewed interest in this approach became evident. About this time Bland (1928), Ledingham (1931) and Craigie (1932) also showed that the elementary bodies of vaccinia could be sedimented and concentrated by centrifugation. This work was extended by Rivers and his associates (Hughes et al., 1935; Parker and Rivers, 1935, 1936a, b,

18

1937; Parker and Smythe, 1937) who prepared appreciable amounts of purified elementary bodies of vaccina, analyzed them chemically, demonstrated a correlation between number of bodies and virus activity and found no measurable metabolism even with concentrated suspensions of bodies. Unfortunately, this work had little influence on the trend of investigations on other viruses, probably because the elementary bodies were as large as certain bacteria and hence were regarded as small living organisms. Then Elford (1931) began his important work on the filtration of virus preparations through graded collodion membranes of known porosity. He soon established the fact that different viruses possessed different and characteristic sizes and that some viruses possessed diameters of about 10 mμ, while others had diameters of about 300 mμ.

A chart showing the approximate sizes of several viruses and some reference materials, prepared largely from data obtained with the electron microscope, is provided in Chart 1.

The use of chemical technics in the study of viruses also began to assume importance around 1930. Vinson and Petre (1929, 1931) showed that tobacco-mosaic virus could be subjected to numerous chemical manipulations with retention of virus activity. Many investigators working with different viruses conducted studies on the effect of different chemicals on virus activity. Chemical investigations directed toward the concentration and purification of certain viruses were started. One of these led to the isolation, in 1935, of tobacco-mosaic virus in the form of a crystalline material of unusually high molecular weight (Stanley, 1935). This material was subsequently shown to be a nucleoprotein with a particle size of 15 by 300 mμ and a molecular weight of about 40,000,000 (Bawden and Pirie, 1937a; Stanley, 1937a; Loring, 1939; Stanley and Anderson, 1941; Lauffer, 1944). This discovery was followed by the isolation of over a dozen viruses in highly purified, and in some

instances, crystalline form. All these purified viruses have been found to be at least as complex as a nucleoprotein. The chemical and physical technics which have been used in the study of these materials will be described in the present chapter.

PURIFICATION

CHEMICAL METHODS OF PURIFICATION

The purification of a virus by chemical technics involves the use of a procedure or, usually, of a series of different procedures which results in a relative enrichment of virus. Obviously a means of following virus activity with fair accuracy must be available so that it will be possible to determine whether or not a given treatment results in a relative enrichment of virus. It is also advisable to determine the pH stability range of the virus under investigation, for chemical treatments involving hydrogen ion concentrations outside of the range of stability of the virus cannot be employed. Another factor of considerable importance is the selection of the starting material. Thus, for example, other factors, such as approximate amount of virus, etc., being equal, it would be better to use the extraembryonic fluids of the infected chicken embryo rather than an extract of emulsified whole chicken embryo as starting material, for the former contains far less extraneous material than does the latter. Every effort should be made to secure a starting material containing the highest possible concentration of virus and the lowest possible concentration of nonviral materials having properties similar to those of the virus. Because viruses differ in their chemical properties, and because the impurities associated with any given virus also differ, it is not possible to outline a definite procedure for the purification of viruses. However, because all purified viruses now known are at least as complex as a nucleoprotein, the general methods which have been employed in work with proteins have been found of value in work with viruses. Some degree of

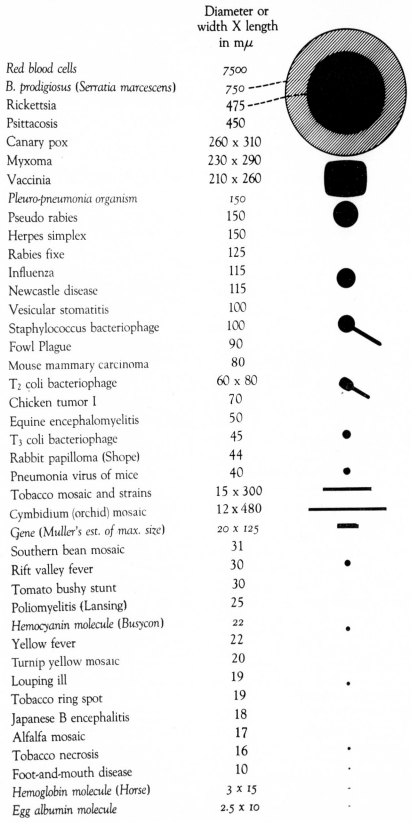

	Diameter or width X length in mμ	
Red blood cells	7500	
B. prodigiosus (Serratia marcescens)	750	
Rickettsia	475	
Psittacosis	450	
Canary pox	260 x 310	
Myxoma	230 x 290	
Vaccinia	210 x 260	
Pleuro-pneumonia organism	150	
Pseudo rabies	150	
Herpes simplex	150	
Rabies fixe	125	
Influenza	115	
Newcastle disease	115	
Vesicular stomatitis	100	
Staphylococcus bacteriophage	100	
Fowl Plague	90	
Mouse mammary carcinoma	80	
T₂ coli bacteriophage	60 x 80	
Chicken tumor I	70	
Equine encephalomyelitis	50	
T₃ coli bacteriophage	45	
Rabbit papilloma (Shope)	44	
Pneumonia virus of mice	40	
Tobacco mosaic and strains	15 x 300	
Cymbidium (orchid) mosaic	12 x 480	
Gene (Muller's est. of max. size)	20 X 125	
Southern bean mosaic	31	
Rift valley fever	30	
Tomato bushy stunt	30	
Poliomyelitis (Lansing)	25	
Hemocyanin molecule (Busycon)	22	
Yellow fever	22	
Turnip yellow mosaic	20	
Louping ill	19	
Tobacco ring spot	19	
Japanese B encephalitis	18	
Alfalfa mosaic	17	
Tobacco necrosis	16	
Foot-and-mouth disease	10	
Hemoglobin molecule (Horse)	3 X 15	
Egg albumin molecule	2.5 X 10	

* Revised in 1952 by W. M. Stanley from Stanley, W. M., 1947, Chemical studies on viruses, Chemical and Engineering News, *25*, 3786-3791.

purification can usually be achieved by treatment with salts such as ammonium or magnesium sulfate. Generally, increasing amounts of salt are added to aliquots of a virus preparation buffered to a definite hydrogen ion concentration and the amount of salt necessary to precipitate all of the virus activity is determined. Any impurities remaining in the supernatant liquid can then be separated from the virus. Another general procedure of value involves the adsorption of virus on some material at a given pH or temperature and the separation of this material plus adsorbed virus from the bulk of the liquid and accompanying impurities, followed by the elution of the virus from the adsorbent at another pH or temperature. The adsorption of tobacco-mosaic virus on celite at pH 4.5 followed by elution at pH 7 (Stanley, 1935), or the adsorption of influenza virus on chicken red blood cells at 4° C. followed by elution at 37° C. (Hirst, 1941; McClelland and Hare, 1941) are examples of the use of this procedure.

Different enzymes have been used to digest protein impurities present in virus preparations. It is, of course, necessary to demonstrate that the enzyme used does not cause inactivation of the virus. It is also necessary to develop a method for separating the enzyme, as well as the products of proteolysis, from the virus. In some cases it has been possible to purify a virus by precipitation with agents such as lead acetate, acetone or alcohol. Usually certain other proteins are carried down and must be separated from the virus by various means. Occasionally, isoelectric precipitation, either of the virus or of protein impurities, can be used to good advantage. In recent years, certain viruses have been purified by use of immunochemical methods. An antiserum to a crude virus preparation is made and then absorbed with extracts of normal materials from the same kind of host used for production of the virus. The residual antibodies presumably are for the virus, and, from the virus-antibody precipitate, the virus can be obtained by dissociation or in some cases by removal of the antibody portion by means of enzymatic digestion.

Since several of the chemical procedures described in the preceding paragraphs were actually employed in the original isolation of purified tobacco-mosaic virus, a short description of the purification of this virus will be given (Stanley, 1936b). Young Turkish tobacco plants were infected with tobacco-mosaic virus, and after about three weeks the plants were harvested and placed in a room held at about −12° C. Freezing is useful not only because it appears to cause a more complete rupture of the plant cells and hence a more complete release of virus, but also because it appears to result in the denaturation of some of the normal proteins of the plant. The frozen plant material was then put through a meat grinder and about 4 per cent by weight of disodium phosphate in the form of a concentrated solution was stirred into the frozen macerated plant material. After the plant material had thawed, the juice was pressed out and clarified by centrifugation or by means of filtration on a Buchner funnel through a thin layer of coarse celite. The clarified juice, which was at about pH 7 because of the addition of the alkaline phosphate, was brought to 0.4 saturation with ammonium sulfate. The precipitate, containing essentially all of the virus plus some normal protein and pigmented impurities, was separated from the supernatant liquid by centrifugation or by means of filtration on paper or on a thin layer of celite. The precipitate was dissolved in water and the virus fraction again precipitated with ammonium sulfate. This precipitation was repeated until the liquid, which was separated from the precipitate, was almost colorless. The precipitated virus fraction was then dissolved in 0.1 M phosphate buffer at pH 7 and treated with a small volume of a solution of lead subacetate. The precipitate which formed contained little virus and a large amount of pigmented material. The supernatant liquid containing most of the virus was almost colorless and possessed a characteristic opalescent appearance. This liquid was adjusted to pH 4.5, and 2 per cent by weight of celite was added. The mixture was then filtered on a Buchner funnel with suction and the yellow-colored filtrate was found to contain an inactive protein fraction. The filter cake containing the virus was suspended in 0.1 M phosphate buffer at pH 7 and filtered on a Buchner funnel with suction. The filter cake was washed with small volumes of the phosphate buffer, and the washings were added to the main filtrate containing most of the virus.

Fig. 1. Crystals of tobacco-mosaic virus. $\times$ 675. (Stanley, W. M., 1937, Crystalline tobacco-mosaic virus protein. American Journal of Botany, 24, 59-68.)

This procedure, which in essence consisted of the isoelectric precipitation of the virus, was repeated twice in order to remove practically all the inactive protein fraction. Finally the filtrate from the suspension of celite and virus at pH 7 was treated with sufficient ammonium sulfate to cause a faint turbidity. Then a solution consisting of one part of glacial acetic acid in 20 parts of 0.5 saturated ammonium sulfate was added slowly with stirring. A characteristic sheen-like appearance resulted, and the liquid contained crystals, such as those shown in Figure 1, consisting of highly purified tobacco-mosaic virus. The characterization of

this and similar purified materials and the correlation of such materials with virus activity will be described in subsequent paragraphs.

PHYSICAL METHODS OF PURIFICATION

When chemical methods were used in attempts to purify certain viruses which were less stable than tobacco-mosaic virus, the viruses were largely inactivated. It became obvious that some new and less drastic purification procedures would have to be developed for such viruses. As a result, a physical method of purification involving high-speed centrifugation in a vacuum-type angle centrifuge has come into prominence. Many of the objectives formerly accomplished by filtration are now accomplished by means of high-speed centrifugation.

Vacuum-Type Angle Centrifuge. Although differential centrifugation was used by MacCallum and Oppenheimer (1922) to purify vaccinia virus and by Ledingham (1931) to purify vaccinia and fowl-pox viruses, it did not gain immediate favor as a means of purification of other viruses. This was probably due to the lack of adequate centrifuges and the meager knowledge concerning the sizes of various viruses. However, when the sizes of several viruses became known through data obtained by filtration, it became obvious that they could be sedimented readily, provided centrifugal fields of from 50,000 to 100,000 times gravity could be made available. The air-driven, spinning top of Henriot and Huguenard (1925) was one type of apparatus capable of delivering fields of this magnitude. However, this apparatus was not entirely suitable because of the small volume of liquid which it could hold at one time. The principle of the air-driven rotor was utilized by Beams and Pickels (1935) to provide a driving mechanism for a rotor of large capacity suspended in a vacuum. This apparatus was developed further by Bauer and Pickels (1936), and again by Pickels (1938). A vertical cross-sectional drawing of the driving mechanism as used by Pickels is given in Figure 2. The entire centrifuge is shown in Figure 3.

Within the past few years, high-speed electric drives capable of operating at 50,000 r.p.m. or more have been developed. Suitable bearings for the connection between drive and rotor and for the support of large rotors operated in a vacuum chamber have also been developed so that these high-speed drives are replacing the air turbine in the high-speed centrifuges. Certain of these centrifuges possess the added advantages provided by magnetically supported rotors. These centrifuges are quite compact, are capable of holding 200 cc. of liquid and can be operated in an ordinary laboratory (Beams, 1942).

One type of motor-driven vacuum centrifuge, available commercially, is illustrated in Figures 4A and 4B. Rotors for the machine are shown in Figure 5 and on the left corner of the cabinet in Figure 4A. They are machined from solid blocks of duraluminum alloy and contain holes for inserting 10 or more celluloid composition containers holding 6 or more cc. each. The head of the rotor fits snugly and is made airtight by means of a rubber gasket. The rotor is so designed that, while rotating in a high vacuum, its contents are at atmospheric pressure. Since the rotor spins in a vacuum, there is little friction, and very little heat is generated. For use with unstable viruses, the rotor may be cooled to about 0° C. During a three-hour run, it warms up less than 5°; hence, the material may be kept cold during the entire centrifugation process. Much of the temperature rise observed is probably due to radiation of heat from the walls; mechanical refrigeration available on commercial models should make better control possible.

Fortunately, in the cases of several viruses, starting materials have been found in which the impurities have rates of sedimentation quite different from that of the virus. In these special cases, it is a simple task to secure relatively pure virus preparations. The starting material is first centri-

fuged at a speed and for a length of time sufficient to sediment practically all materials which migrate more rapidly than the

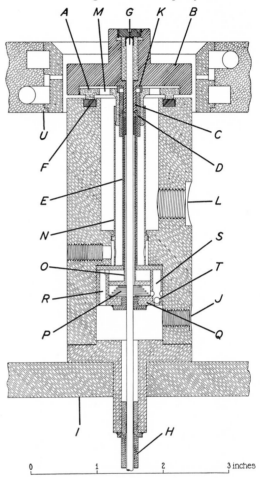

Fig. 2. Vertical cross-sectional drawing of driving mechanism of vacuum-type centrifuge. (A) Air bearing disk; (B) Steel turbine; (C) Stem of steel turbine; (D,E) Bronze bushing of turbine; (F) Neoprene rest for air bearing disk; (G) Drive shaft; (H) Bronze bushing for drive shaft; (I) Brass support plate; (J) Oil inlet; (K) Bronze rest for turbine; (L,M) Air inlet; (N) Oil outlet; (O to T) Damping arrangement; (O) Metal tube; (P) Steel spring; (Q) Brass cylinder; (R) Oil outlet; (S) Oil inlet; (T) Steel ball oil valve; (U) Cross arm mounting. (Pickels, E. G., 1938, A new type of air bearing for air-driven high-speed centrifuges. Review of Scientific Instruments, 9, 358-364.)

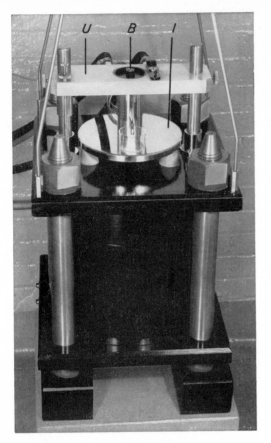

virus. Following the removal of heavy impurities, the supernatant liquid is removed and then centrifuged at a speed and for a length of time necessary to sediment all or most of the virus. The supernatant liquid is discarded and the pellets of virus, which are usually small and opalescent, are suspended in a liquid known to provide a favorable environment. This virus preparation is then subjected to another cycle of differential centrifugation and this is repeated until tests indicate that practically all light and heavy impurities have been removed. One or two such cycles of differential centrifugation are sufficient to convert the infectious juice from mosaic-diseased Turkish tobacco plants into a preparation which will yield directly the crystals shown in Figure 1.

In the case of tomato-bushy-stunt virus,

Fig. 3. Concentration centrifuge utilizing drive mechanism illustrated in Figure 2. (Pickels, E. G., 1938, A new type of air bearing for air-driven high-speed centrifuges. Review of Scientific Instruments, 9, 358-364.)

Fig. 4. (A, *left*) Commercially available motor-driven vacuum centrifuge. (B, *right*) Schematic drawing showing details of centrifuge: (1) indicators and controls; (2) rotor in vacuum chamber; (3) refrigeration unit; (4) electronic control unit; (5) electrical drive; (6) vacuum pump.

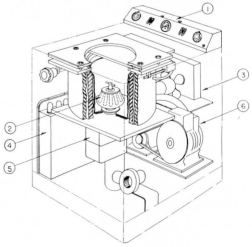

four cycles of differential centrifugation yielded a preparation which gave the crystals of bushy-stunt virus shown in Figure 6. The method has also been used to purify the viruses of equine encephalomyelitis (Taylor et al., 1943a), rabbit papilloma (Beard et al., 1939), influenza (Taylor et al., 1943b; Stanley, 1944a; Sharp et al., 1944c), Lansing poliomyelitis (Loring and

was encountered, for the extracts of the normal hosts were found to contain material which sedimented at a rate near that of the viruses. If it is assumed that these materials of the normal hosts will also be present in the extracts from the diseased hosts, it is obvious that such impurities could never be separated from the viruses by means of differential centrifugation. Other means, such

FIG. 5. Details of rotor used in centrifuge presented in Figures 4 A and B.

Schwerdt, 1946), Newcastle disease of chickens (Bang, 1946; Cunha et al., 1947), polyhedral disease of silkworm (Bergold, 1947), tobacco ring spot (Stanley, 1939), potato latent mosaic (Loring, 1938), tobacco necrosis (Pirie et al., 1938) and southern bean mosaic (Price, 1946), as well as T_2 coli bacteriophage (Hook et al., 1946; Anderson, 1946). In the cases of the viruses of Japanese B encephalitis in mouse brains (Duffy and Stanley, 1945) and potato yellow dwarf (Black et al., 1948), considerable difficulty

as immunochemical procedures, must be employed to separate impurities of this type.

It should be emphasized that purification by means of differential centrifugation is especially suitable for unstable viruses, since the operations can be conducted quickly and in the cold (Stanley and Wyckoff, 1937). The procedure is quite mild and has been found to cause little or no change in the characteristics of the viruses studied. It seems likely that this method will continue to be used extensively in virus research, and, when used in conjunction with analyzing devices such as the Svedberg ultracentrifuge, the electrophoresis apparatus and the separation cell, it is very powerful. The only difficulty encountered has been a certain amount of stirring within the centrifuge tubes due to thermal convection currents. In the cases of viruses

gradients with materials such as sucrose or serum albumin, but this expedient is unnecessary for the routine purification of viruses (Pickels, 1943; Stanley, 1944b).

Continuous-Flow Centrifuge. The success of differential centrifugation in high-speed, vacuum-type angle centrifuges as a means of virus purification naturally led to

FIG. 6. Crystals of tomato-bushy-stunt virus. $\times$ 224. (Stanley, W. M., 1940, Purification of tomato-bushy-stunt virus by differential centrifugation. Journal of Biological Chemistry, *135*, 437-454.)

which are not sufficiently homogeneous to provide a sharp sedimenting boundary, this stirring has resulted in a small proportion of the virus remaining in the supernatant liquid when subjected to conditions which should have caused all of the virus to sediment. This difficulty is not serious in connection with purification procedures, since only a small percentage of the virus remains in the supernatant liquid. It can, of course, be eliminated by providing artificial density

experimentation with continuous-flow types of centrifuge, since these have a considerably larger capacity. McKinney (1927) attempted to use the commercially available Sharples Laboratory Supercentrifuge for the concentration of tobacco-mosaic virus, but, because of the large volumes of liquid required, it was soon discarded in favor of a small, specially constructed centrifuge with a closed bowl holding about 10 cc. Schlesinger (1933) showed that a coli-bacteriophage could be concentrated and purified by means of a similar, specially constructed centrifuge having a closed hollow cylinder. The first successful attempt to purify viruses by means of the Sharples Supercentrifuge equipped with a bowl for continuous flow, but modified considerably in other respects, appears to have been made by McIntosh and Selbie (1940). These workers demonstrated that the virus activity of large volumes of liquid containing vaccinia virus or either of two bacteriophages could be reduced at least 100 times by passage through the centrifuge. The infective particles that were removed from the effluent liquid were recovered in the sediment contained in the centrifuge bowl. Later, Stanley (1942a) reported that large amounts of purified tobacco-mosaic virus could be prepared by means of the commercially available Sharples Laboratory Supercentrifuge equipped with the regular clarifier bowl operated at a speed of 50,000 r.p.m. by means of compressed air. The only modification of the centrifuge consisted of the use of a cooling coil and the replacement of the original delivery jet with a short piece of tubing from a No. 22 hypodermic needle. The juice from mosaic-diseased Turkish tobacco plants was first clarified by means of filtration through a layer of celite or by passage through the Sharples centrifuge at a high rate of flow. The clarified juice was then passed through the centrifuge at a rate of about 15 cc. per minute. The effluent liquid was found to contain only about 10 per cent of the virus, while about 90 per cent was obtained in the sediment contained within the centrifuge bowl. The sedimented material was dissolved in 0.1 M phosphate buffer at pH 7, diluted to about 10 mg. of protein per cc., centrifuged in a bucket-type centrifuge at about 2,000 r.p.m. to remove insoluble material and again passed through the Sharples centrifuge at a rate of about 15 cc. per minute. This process was repeated once or twice to yield the final preparation of purified virus. It was possible to prepare from 10 to 15 Gm.

of tobacco-mosaic virus, sufficiently pure for most purposes, during the course of ten hours by means of a single centrifuge. The factor having the greatest influence on the yield of virus was the rate of flow of liquid through the centrifuge; rates of 30 cc. or greater per minute resulted in yields of 50 per cent or less, whereas rates of 20 to 25 cc. per minute gave yields of 60 to 75 per cent. In a later study of the efficiency of Sharples centrifuge bowls carrying liquid layers 0.5, 0.25 and 0.125 inches thick, Stanley (1946) found that the type of bowl, the concentration of virus and the use of a 3-way vane in the bowl had little or no effect on the yield of virus. As in the earlier study, the rate of flow of liquid through the centrifuge was found to be the dominant factor.

Stanley (1944a) and later Taylor and coworkers (1945) demonstrated that influenza virus in the extraembryonic fluids of infected chick embryos could be purified by means of the Sharples centrifuge. In the cases of the PR8 and Lee strains, about 85 to 90 per cent of the virus could be recovered in the sediment in the bowl at rates of flow around 50 cc. per minute. During the course of an 8-hour day it is possible to process about 24 liters of infectious extraembryonic fluid and secure about 2.4 Gm. of purified influenza virus by means of a single centrifuge. Because of the efficiency and ease of this process, and because of the purity of the product, this method has been adopted for the commercial production of purified influenza virus for use in vaccines (Stanley, 1945), and was accepted by the Army in April of 1945 as a suitable alternative to the adsorption and elution method used during the preceding years. Recently, Cox and co-workers (1947) stated that alcohol precipitation followed by continuous-flow centrifugation provides an efficient method for working with very large volumes of extraembryonic fluid in the production of influenza vaccine.

The method involving the use of the Sharples centrifuge has recently been employed by Randall and associates (1947) for the purification of Japanese B encephalitis virus and it seems probable that the method will find extensive use in the future for the purification of other viruses. The large volumes of fluid which can be processed in this type of centrifuge provides a distinct advantage over the closed or angle centrifuges. In work with potentially dangerous viruses it is necessary to operate the centrifuge in a closed space which can be sterilized by chemical sprays or by the use of ultraviolet light. Recently, a new model called the Sharples Laboratory Presurtite Centrifuge was introduced, which provides for centrifugation in a closed system that can be sterilized before and after use. In cases in which active virus is not required and the virus can be characterized by other than activity tests, it is possible to inactivate the virus by formaldehyde or ultraviolet light prior to centrifugation and thus eliminate dangers accompanying work with active virus.

IDENTIFICATION OF VIRUS WITH PURIFIED PRODUCTS

CHEMICAL FRACTIONATION

When a supposedly purified product has been obtained, it is, of course, necessary to prove that the material in question actually consists of virus and not of a mixture of virus and extraneous materials. One way of doing this is to subject the purified product to a series of chemical procedures which result in the separation of the material into two or more fractions. These fractions can then be tested for their specific virus activity, that is, activity per unit weight, and if the specific virus activity of one fraction is greater than that of other fractions, the results provide definite evidence that the purified material actually consists of a mixture of virus and impurities. However, if all fractions are found to possess the same specific virus activity, the results can be regarded as providing evidence that the purified product is actually the virus. It

should be emphasized that a series of different types of chemical fractionation procedure should be used, for although a virus and impurity might be fractionated in the same proportion by one procedure, it is highly unlikely that they would always be fractionated in the same proportion by a wide variety of procedures. However, failure to secure fractionation of a purified product is, at best, negative evidence for inhomogeneity, and such tests gain weight only as they are increased in number and in variety (Stanley, 1938a).

One simple method of securing the separation of a purified virus product into two fractions consists of the addition of sufficient ammonium sulfate or magnesium sulfate to cause the precipitation of part of the purified product. The precipitated material can be separated from the liquid portion by centrifugation or filtration. Protein nitrogen determinations can be made on the two fractions, and, the results being used as a basis for making dilutions, the specific virus activity of the two fractions per mg. of protein nitrogen can be determined. This procedure was used in connection with early tests on tobacco-mosaic virus and it was found that the specific virus activity of the two fractions was the same. It may be of interest to note that when purified preparations of two strains of tobacco-mosaic virus were mixed and subjected to fractionation with salt, it was possible to secure a fraction, essentially all of which consisted of one strain, and another fraction, essentially all of which consisted of the other strain.

It is obvious that other methods of fractionation such as the use of alcohol, acetone, lead acetate or specific antisera, as well as isoelectric precipitation, can be used. Another procedure of importance consists of treating the purified product with an adsorbent, such as charcoal, celite or aluminum hydroxide, followed by tests on the adsorbed and unadsorbed portions of the preparation. In all cases, it is necessary to prove that the chemical used to achieve fractionation does not cause inactivation of the virus. However, another important method of testing for homogeneity consists in the actual destruction or inactivation of a portion of the purified product, followed by tests for specific virus activity of the remainder. Reagents such as acids, alkalis, urea, enzymes and various detergents, as well as heat or high pressures, can be used for this purpose. If the specific virus activity of the remaining portion is the same as that of the starting material, the results can be regarded as providing evidence of homogeneity. If the specific virus activity of the remaining portion is decreased, this might be due to the partial inactivation of the virus or to the preferential destruction of virus in a mixture of virus and impurity.

Advantage should be taken of special situations which provide opportunities for fractionation. Thus, in the case of influenza virus, adsorption of virus on washed chicken red blood cells provides a means of fractionation. With impure preparations of influenza virus, adsorption on chicken red blood cells followed by elution yields a product of higher virus activity. However, with highly purified influenza virus preparations the virus activity is unchanged following adsorption on and elution from chicken red blood cells.

Physical Fractionation

Since physical methods are, in general, somewhat milder than chemical methods, they have been used widely in attempts to fractionate virus preparations. The general approach has been similar to that described above for chemical methods. The purified virus preparation is subjected to one or more physical processes which result in the separation of the material into two or more fractions, and the specific virus activities of these are then determined. Fractionation has been achieved by means of centrifugation, electrophoresis, and filtration through collodion membranes. In early work with purified tobacco-mosaic virus,

Stanley (1937c) centrifuged solutions of the virus at pH 2.4, 6.7 and 9.4, so that about 85 to 95 per cent of the protein was removed from the upper portions of the supernatant liquids, and found that the virus activity of the separated upper and lower portions of the solutions was exactly proportional to the amount of protein present. Since the isoelectric point of this virus is about pH 3.5, the virus was sedimented on both sides of the isoelectric point, that is, as negatively charged particles and as positively charged particles. The results provided a powerful argument against the idea that virus activity is due to an entity adsorbed on the protein or to a dissociable active group attached to the protein. In experiments in which a supposedly pure preparation of influenza virus was separated into two fractions by centrifugation (Lauffer and Stanley, 1944), it was found that, although the two fractions appeared about the same in the electron microscope, the material in the upper portion proved to have a considerably higher viscosity than the material in the lower portion. Eventually, a highly viscous impurity was found to be present. Although it proved difficult to separate this impurity from the virus by means of centrifugation, it was possible to remove it from the virus by means of electrophoresis or by adsorption on and elution from chicken red blood cells (Knight, 1944; Miller, Lauffer and Stanley, 1944).

In contrast to centrifugation, which permits fractionation by virtue of movement of the virus in a centrifugal field, electrophoresis achieves the same result through movement of the virus in an electrical field. If the pH range of stability of a given virus is sufficiently broad, the virus can be caused to migrate as either negatively or positively charged particles. If, following movement over appreciable distances and under different conditions of pH, the specific virus activity per mg. of nitrogen or of protein nitrogen of different portions of the liquid remains unchanged, it may be concluded that the preparation is homogeneous with respect to electrophoretic mobility. Since it is highly unlikely that the virus and an impurity would migrate at exactly the same rate at different hydrogen ion concentrations, such results can be regarded as strong evidence that the virus preparation is pure. The argument is strengthened if similar results are obtained by centrifugation. Tests of this nature have been made with several virus preparations, including those of tobacco mosaic (Eriksson-Quensel and Svedberg, 1936), rabbit papilloma (Sharp et al., 1942) and influenza (Miller et al., 1944).

Although the sizes of practically all viruses for which there are suitable biologic tests have been determined by means of ultrafiltration, this technic has not been used extensively for the fractionation of purified virus preparations. Whenever the technic has been used, however, it has generally proved satisfactory. Collodion filters which will just permit the virus to pass, or which will just retain the virus, are used to determine whether or not the preparation contains impurities possessing filtration characteristics different from that of the virus. As in the cases of centrifugation and electrophoresis, virus preparations at different hydrogen ion concentrations can be tested. If the material passes through or is retained by filters under the same conditions under which the virus passes through or is retained, the results provide evidence that the material in question is actually the virus. It should be emphasized again that as many tests as possible involving chemical, as well as physical, methods of fractionation should be made, for a single negative result indicates only that the material is homogeneous under a given set of conditions. However, when attempts to fractionate the material by a variety of methods yield no evidence for the existence of an impurity, the burden of proof for the existence of an impurity can be regarded as resting upon those who wish to postulate its presence.

OPERATIONAL IDENTIFICATION

A somewhat more general approach to the problem of identification, exemplified by the study of Epstein and Lauffer (1952) on southern-bean-mosaic virus, can be derived from the operational philosophy so useful in modern physics. It is consistent with operational philosophy to recognize that when a virus is studied by biologic means the infectious entity is characterized, and that when it is studied by optical or by other physical means the characteristic particle is described. Thus, when virus material is subjected to physical or chemical treatment and the result is observed by means of infectivity measurements, a property of the infectious entity is determined. When the effect is followed by some physical means, a property of the characteristic particle is evaluated. If the infectious entity and the characteristic particle are identical, then the results obtained in these two experiments should be the same. In fact, identical results should be obtained every time the effect of a given treatment is followed by both biologic and physical methods. Ultracentrifugation and electrophoresis experiments, to be described in detail later, and even the physical and chemical fractionation experiments described above can be interpreted in terms of this operational point of view.

CHARACTERIZATION OF VIRUS MATERIALS

ULTRAFILTRATION

The oldest physical procedure employed in the study of viruses is filtration. Bacteriologists had learned early that bacteria could be retained by certain types of filters. Iwanowski (1892) observed that the etiologic agent of tobacco mosaic was not retained by a filter which would hold back all pathogenic bacteria then known. Later in the study of virus diseases, it was found that filters could be produced which would retain viruses. Allard (1916) found that, even though tobacco-mosaic virus would pass through a Berkefeld filter, it was held back by a Livingstone atometer porous cup. Since that time, filters graded for pore size have been made available, and these can be used for the determination of the approximate sizes of viruses (Elford, 1931; Ferry, 1936).

The physical principles involved in ultrafiltration can be understood by comparing the process to the grading of sand. An easy way to estimate the size of sand grains is to find a sieve through which the grains of sand will just pass and then measure the size of the pores in the sieve. The process of determining the size of a virus by ultrafiltration is more complex than this, but the basic idea is essentially the same.

Ultrafilters with various pore sizes can be made from collodion by varying the composition of the solvent used. The average pore size for each filter can be determined. It was shown by Poiseuille that it is possible to measure the size of a capillary tube by determining the rate of flow of a liquid through it. The following equation shows the relationship between the volume of liquid, V, which will flow through a capillary tube in time, t, and the pressure, P, applied across the tube, the radius, r, and the length, l, of the tube, and the viscosity, η. of the liquid: $\dfrac{V}{t} = \dfrac{\pi P r^4}{8\, l\eta}$.

Obviously, if the length of the tube and the rate of flow through it under known pressure of a liquid of known viscosity are determined, one can calculate the radius of the tube. One can visualize a filter as being made up of a great many pores of cylindrical nature. If all of the pores have the same radius, the volume of flow per unit time through the filter will be equal to that through a single capillary multiplied by the number of capillary pores. In order to determine the radius from such measurements, some method must be found for eliminating the uncertainty occasioned by lack of knowledge of the number of pores. This can be done by estimating the total pore space in the filter through a measurement of the volume of liquid, S, which the filter can absorb. The volume of liquid is equal to the number of pores, n, times the volume of each pore, or n π r²l. When this relationship is combined with the relationship for the flow of liquid through the membrane, one can see that the volume of liquid which should flow through a membrane in time, t, is given by the following equation:

$$\frac{V}{t} = \frac{S P r^2}{8\, l^2 \eta}.$$

The length of the pores can be taken as the thickness of the filter. By determining all of the other quantities in this relationship, the radius of the pores can be calculated. The value obtained is simply the radius that the pores in the filter would have if they were all cylinders of uniform circular cross section. None of these conditions can be expected to obtain in a filter made of a material like collodion, and therefore the value of the radius obtained is nothing more than a kind of average. At best, it merely gives an estimate of the order of magnitude of the average pore size.

In order to determine the size of a virus particle by means of ultrafiltration, one attempts to pass it through a series of filters, graded with respect to pore size. The size of the virus is then related to the size of the pores in the finest filter through which the particles will pass. Several complications are encountered in filtration. It has been found necessary to use surface tension active substances, such as sodium oleate or nutrient broth in order to prevent clogging of the filters. Even when this is done, some materials known to be smaller than the pores will not pass. This is thought to be due, at least in part, to the surface electric charges of the filter and the particles. Elford has shown experimentally that there is no exact correspondence between the average pore size determined as indicated in the preceding paragraph and the size of the particles. Particularly is this true in the case of filters with very small average pore diameters. By passing colloidal particles with dimensions determined by other means through a graded series of filters, Elford (1933) obtained the data presented in Table 1 showing the approximate relationship between pore size and particle size. It can be seen that, for fine filters, the average pore size must be from two to three times the particle diameter in order for the particles to pass. For filters with large pores there is more nearly exact correspondence between average pore size and the size of the particles which will pass.

Filtration has been applied to the determination of the particle size of many viruses. Many of the sizes indicated in Chart 1 were estimated by this method. The precision of the method can be evaluated by comparing sizes calculated from results

ugation studies have shown that it is about 115 mμ (Lauffer and Stanley, 1944; Sharp et al., 1944b, c). Ultrafiltration studies of Thornberry (1935) showed that tobacco-mosaic virus will just pass through a filter with an average pore diameter of 45 mμ. It is now known that tobacco-mosaic virus is a rod-shaped body; therefore, these filtration results should indicate the diameter of the particle and they show it to be between 15 and 22 mμ. X-ray diffraction studies have shown that the rod has a diameter of 15.2 mμ (Bernal and Fankuchen, 1941). These data are sufficient to indicate that the method of ultrafiltration can be used for an approximation of the size of a virus. However, it is apparent that no

TABLE 1. THE RELATIONSHIP BETWEEN THE AVERAGE MEMBRANE PORE DIAMETER AND THE RATIO $\dfrac{\text{Particle Diameter}}{\text{Pore Diameter}}$

AVERAGE MEMBRANE PORE DIAMETER IN mμ	$\dfrac{\text{PARTICLE DIAMETER}}{\text{PORE DIAMETER}}$
10- 100	1/3- 1/2
100- 500	1/2- 3/4
500-1,000	3/4-1

of filtration with those obtained by other means. Elford and Andrewes (1932) filtered vaccinia virus and showed that it would just pass through a filter with an average pore diameter of 250 millimicrons. One can estimate, by using the correction factor shown in Table 1, that the diameter of the virus is between 125 and 175 mμ. It has since been shown by means of the ultracentrifuge (Elford and Andrewes, 1936; Smadel et al., 1938) that the diameter of vaccinia virus is between 236 and 252 mμ. Recent electron micrographs indicate that vaccinia virus is a brick-shaped particle about 210 by 260 mμ in size (Green, Anderson and Smadel, 1942). The diameter of influenza virus was determined by filtration (Elford, Andrewes and Tang, 1936) to be between 80 and 120 mμ, and electron microscope and ultracentrif-

high degree of precision can be expected from this procedure.

DIFFUSION, ULTRACENTRIFUGATION, VISCOSITY, AND DOUBLE REFRACTION

One of the important problems confronting those who study viruses is the determination of the size and shape of the virus particles. It has already been shown how ultrafiltration can be used to obtain some idea of size. It is obvious that the electron microscope is admirably adapted to this end. However, until the electron microscope was developed, it was necessary to rely upon indirect methods of physics and physical chemistry to gain knowledge of the physical nature of virus particles. Some of these are capable of providing information which cannot be obtained with the electron microscope. The methods involving ultra-centrifugation, diffusion, viscosity, and stream double refraction stand out for their utility. All of these involve the movement of a particle with respect to the medium in which it is suspended. The branch of physics known as hydrodynamics covers this field. From the way in which particles move in their surrounding medium, it is possible to determine something of the size and shape. It is the purpose of the following paragraphs to indicate how this is done. Both sedimentation and diffusion are processes which involve the linear displacement of a particle in a medium. The particle meets resistance in such movement, and this resistance is proportional to its friction coefficient. Thus, in order to interpret diffusion and sedimentation results, it is necessary to understand something about this coefficient.

Friction Coefficient. When a particle such as a protein molecule, a virus, or a bacterium moves through a medium such as water, its motion is opposed by frictional resistance. The frictional force, F, acting on the particle is directly proportional to its velocity, v. The proportionality constant is called the friction coefficient and is usually symbolized by the letter, f. Therefore $F = fv$. The magnitude of the friction coefficient depends upon the viscosity of the liquid and upon the size and shape of the moving particle. According to Stokes' law, the friction coefficient, f, of a spherical particle is equal to $6\pi r\eta$ where r is the radius and η is the viscosity of the liquid. The viscosity of the liquid can be measured directly. Thus, one can calculate the radius of a particle from its coefficient of friction.

If the particle is not spherical, it is more difficult to interpret the meaning of the friction coefficient. In this case, the coefficient is an intricate function of the various dimensions of the particle and of the viscosity of the liquid. The situation, however, is not entirely hopeless, for several simplifications can be made. It is possible to consider that most nonspherical particles are approximated in shape by ellipsoids of revolution, either rodlike or platelike. The relations between the coefficient of friction and the dimensions for both flattened and elongated ellipsoids are fairly complex, but a simplification can be achieved by a mathematical manipulation. The ratio of the actual friction coefficient of an ellipsoid of

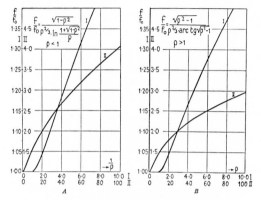

CHART 2. Relationship between friction ratio (f/f_o) and axial ratio (P) for elongated (*left*) and flattened (*right*) ellipsoids of revolution. (Svedberg, T., and Pedersen, K. O., 1940, The Ultracentrifuge. Oxford, Clarendon Press.)

revolution to the friction coefficient the particle would have if it were a sphere of the same volume, commonly called the friction ratio, is related only to the ratio of the long to the short dimension. It is possible to evaluate the friction ratio in some cases, and when this is done, it can be interpreted in terms of the ratio of the long dimension to the short dimension of the particle. The relationships between friction ratio and axial ratio for both elongated and flattened ellipsoids of revolution are presented graphically in Chart 2. Since these relationships were derived by Herzog and his associates and by Perrin, the equations are known as the Herzog-Perrin equations. The actual measurement of friction coefficients and friction ratios and their interpretation will be discussed in the following paragraphs.

Diffusion. It is commonly known that

if a layer of water is placed very carefully over a concentrated solution of a salt, such as copper sulfate, initially a very sharp line of demarcation between the copper sulfate solution and the water can be observed. However, the copper sulfate will gradually intermingle with the water and eventually will be completely dispersed. This movement of the copper sulfate molecules is brought about by the process of

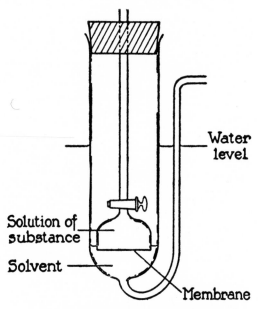

Fig. 7. Porous-membrane type of diffusion cell. (Scherp, H. W., 1933, The diffusion coefficient of crystalline trypsin. Journal of General Physiology, *16*, 795-800.)

diffusion. Materials tend to diffuse from a region in which they exist at a high concentration into a region in which they exist at low concentration. The rate at which a particle diffuses is proportional to the concentration gradient and to a characteristic of the particle known as the diffusion constant, D. According to Fick's law, $dS = - DQ \frac{dc}{dx} dt$, where dS is the amount of material which will diffuse across an imaginary plane of area, Q, in time, dt, when the concentration gradient is dc/dx. Independently, Einstein and Sutherland came to the conclusion that the diffusion constant of a particle is inversely proportional to its friction coefficient. $D = \frac{RT}{Nf}$. R is the gas constant, T is the absolute temperature, and N is Avogadro's number. Thus, if the diffusion constant of a material can be measured, the friction coefficient can be calculated directly.

There are two generally used methods for measuring the diffusion constant. The simpler involves placing a solution of the material in a vessel to which a thin, porous membrane has been sealed. A diagrammatic representation of such a diffusion cup is shown in Figure 7. This filled cell is then placed into contact with pure solvent. Through the process of diffusion, the particles on the inside of the cup gradually pass out through the porous membrane into the solvent. The diffusion constant can be evaluated by measuring the ratio of the concentrations of diffusible material inside the porous cup and outside after a given period of time. This particular method has been described in detail by Northrop and Anson (1929) and was used by them to determine the diffusion constants of certain enzymes (Anson and Northrop, 1937). It has also been used by Hills and Vinson (1938) for the study of the diffusion of tobacco-mosaic virus.

A second commonly used method is to place a solution of diffusible material in direct contact with the solvent. This must be done with great care in order to ensure a sharp boundary between the solution and the solvent. Several sorts of apparatus have been designed to accomplish this (Lamm, 1937; Neurath, 1942). An alternative is to establish a boundary by any convenient method in a cell with windows of good optical quality and then sharpen the boundary by slowly withdrawing liquid through a capillary tube whose end is placed in the plane of the boundary or through a narrow slit in the wall of the vessel at the level of the boundary (Kahn and Polson, 1947). After the initial boundary between the diffusing material and the solvent has been established, it will gradually become broad because of the diffusion of particles from the solution into the solvent. Thus, there will be a gradual change in concentration between the solution and the solvent. This gradual change in concentration can be determined by various optical methods, and from the exact nature of the change in concentration after a fixed period of time, it is possible to calculate the diffusion constant of the material. This method has been applied to the study of several viruses. Neurath and Saum (1938) first attempted the measurement of the diffusion constant of tobacco-mosaic virus. Later, Neurath and Cooper (1940) used it to measure the diffusion constant of tomato-bushy-stunt virus. Lauffer (1944) and Schramm and Bergold (1947) studied the diffusion of tobacco-mosaic virus and finally Miller and Price (1946a) used the method to obtain the diffusion constant for southern-bean-mosaic virus.

Interpretation of the diffusion constant of tomato-bushy-stunt virus and of southern-bean-mosaic virus is fairly direct and straightforward. It is known from electron microscope data and from other types of information that these two viruses are essentially spherical (Stanley and Anderson, 1941; Price et al., 1945). The diffusion constant of bushy-stunt virus was found to have a value of 1.15×10^{-7} cm^2/sec. in a solvent which has a viscosity equal to that of water at 20° C. (Neurath and Cooper, 1940). From this, a value of 3.49×10^{-7} g/sec. can be calculated for the friction coefficient by using the Einstein-Sutherland equation. By making use of this value and the value for the viscosity of water at 20° C., the radius of bushy-stunt virus can be calculated directly according to Stokes' law. A value of 18.5×10^{-7} cm. was obtained. The diffusion constant of southern-bean-mosaic virus was found to have a value of 1.39×10^{-7} in a solvent having the viscosity of water at 20° C. (Miller and Price, 1946a). In a like manner, the friction

coefficient and then the radius of this particle can be evaluated. It has a radius of 15.3×10^{-7} cm. In the case of tobacco-mosaic virus, the diffusion constant obtained by Lauffer (1944) is 5.3×10^{-8} and the friction coefficient is 7.64×10^{-7}. However, it is known that tobacco-mosaic virus is not spherical, and, therefore, it is not possible to interpret the friction coefficient directly in terms of the size of the particle.

Sedimentation. Another method of getting at the value for the friction coefficient of a particle is through the study of its sedimentation rate. However, unlike diffusion rate, sedimentation rate does not depend solely upon the friction coefficient. When a particle moves through a viscous medium under the influence of a centrifugal or gravitational field, it is subjected to two forces, an accelerating force equal to the product of the effective mass and the acceleration of the field, and a force of resistance which, as was shown previously, is equal to the product of the velocity of the particle and its friction coefficient. When these two forces are exactly equal, the particle sediments with a uniform velocity. Under such conditions one can write the

equation $s = \dfrac{v}{g} = \dfrac{m_p \left(1 - \dfrac{d_o}{d}\right)}{f}$, in which v

is the velocity of the particle, f is its friction coefficient, g is the acceleration of the field, s is the sedimentation constant defined as the rate of sedimentation in a field with unit acceleration, m_p is the mass of the particle, and d_o and d are the densities of the particle and of the liquid, respectively. This equation states that the sedimentation constant of a particle is directly proportional to the mass of the particle corrected for the buoyancy of the liquid and inversely proportional to the coefficient of friction.

It is possible to measure the sedimentation constant by observing the rate at which the particle moves in a field of known acceleration. One merely divides the observed velocity by the acceleration to determine

Fig. 8 A. Commercially available ultracentrifuge.

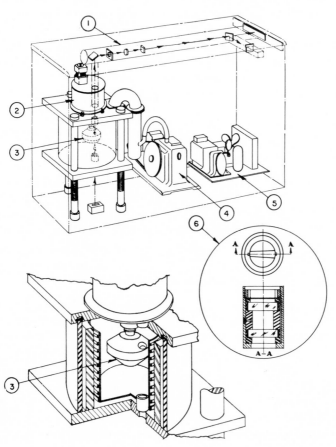

Fig. 8 B. Schematic drawing of ultracentrifuge showing (1) optical system; (2) electrical drive; (3) rotor in vacuum chamber; (4) evacuating system; (5) refrigeration unit; (6) analytical rotor cell.

the sedimentation constant. The magnitude of the field in a centrifuge, expressed in dynes per gram, is equal to $(2\pi n)^2 x$, where n is the number of revolutions per second and x is the distance in centimeters from the particle to the axis of rotation.

In an ultracentrifugation experiment, the virus preparation to be studied, usually at a concentration of from 0.1 to 1 per cent, is placed in a small cell with optically perfect quartz windows, and this cell is placed in the rotor of the centrifuge. The rotor is then spun at a known high speed. Figure 8 A is a picture of an electrically driven ultracentrifuge. Figure 8 B shows sketches of the assembly of this ultracentrifuge and of the

The boundary between solvent and solution migrates toward the periphery at the rate of each particle. If the material in the preparation consists of two kinds of homogeneous particles with different sedimentation rates, two boundaries will appear as shown in Figure 9. If a large number of types of particles with slightly different sedimentation rates are present, a single boundary, which gets very foggy as sedimentation progresses, will appear. Thus, the centrifuge can be used to determine homogeneity.

There are special optical methods which make it possible to detect a boundary between a solution and its solvent, most of

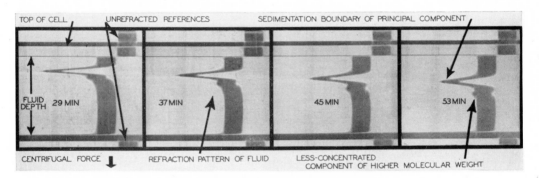

Fig. 9. Ultracentrifuge diagram of a two-component system obtained with centrifuge shown in Figure 8 A and B.

ultracentrifuge cell. When the centrifuge is rotated, the particles generally sediment toward the periphery. If all the particles have exactly the same size, shape, and density, they will all sediment at exactly the same rate. Thus, the particles which were initially at the position nearest the axis of rotation will sediment toward the periphery at the same rate as all the other particles in the solution, but there will be no other particles to follow them. Thus, they will constitute a boundary between a position where there are particles and a position where there is nothing but solvent. This is true in exactly the same sense as the last car in a train constitutes a boundary between the positions where there are cars and where there is none.

which depend upon the fact that there is a refractive index gradient at such a boundary. The centrifuge is arranged in such a way that the cell in which sedimentation is taking place passes over the optical path once during each revolution. Thus, in a single second one obtains n exposures of the cell. Pictures can be made at various time intervals. Each picture will show the position of the boundary at the time of the exposure. By measuring the distance between the boundary positions for two successive exposures with a known time interval, it is possible to determine how far the boundary moved in a known time. From this, one can calculate the velocity of migration of the boundary and hence the velocity of migration of each particle. When this is divided by the centrifugal acceleration, one obtains the value for the sedimentation constant.

It is relatively simple to interpret the sedimentation constant of a spherical particle, because both the mass of the particle and the friction coefficient are directly dependent upon the radius. Hence, one can determine the radius of a spherical particle directly from its sedimentation constant. The only additional data needed are the

ciation of water with these particles when in solution. Thus, the density in a liquid medium is intermediate between the dry density and the density of water, and its exact value will depend upon the amount of water associated with the particle.

The ultracentrifuge can be used to determine the density of a virus particle in solution. The equation $s = \dfrac{m_p\left(1 - \dfrac{d_o}{d}\right)}{f}$ shows that the sedimentation constant de-

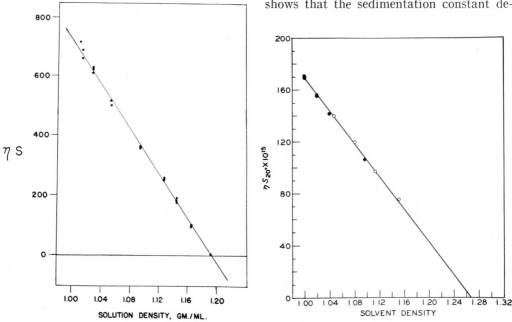

CHART 3. The sedimentation rates of influenza (*left*) and tobacco-mosaic (*right*) viruses in sucrose solutions of different densities (Lauffer, M. A., and Taylor, N. W., Unpublished results of work on influenza A virus; Schachman, H. K., and Lauffer, M. A., 1949. The hydration size and shape of tobacco-mosaic virus, J. Am. Chem. Soc., *71*, 536).

density of the solvent and the density of the particle. The density of the solvent can be determined by weighing a known volume. The density of the dissolved material can be determined in several ways. The simplest method is to calculate it from the weight and the volume of a dry preparation. However, it is quite probable that the density of a biologic particle, such as a protein molecule or a virus particle, is not the same in solution as in the dry state. This is probably due principally to the asso-

pends upon the density of the solvent. If a particle is suspended in a medium which has exactly the same density as the particle itself, it will not sediment, no matter how great the magnitude of the centrifugal field. Therefore, if one measured the sedimentation rate of a virus in solvents of different densities, one might expect to find a solvent of such density that the virus will not sediment. In this solvent, the virus has the same density as has the solvent itself. Numerous investigators have attempted to determine the density of viruses in solution by sedimenting them in solvents composed of sucrose solutions of different densities. The method was first used by MacCallum and Oppenheimer (1922) to estimate the density of vaccinia virus. Elford and Andrewes (1936) found that influenza virus has a sedimentation constant of zero in a sugar solution with a density of about 1.2. The same method of approach was used by Smadel, Pickels and Shedlovsky (1938) on vaccinia virus, by Lauffer and Stanley (1944), Sharp and associates (1944a; 1945) and Lauffer and Taylor (1951) on influenza virus, by Schachman and Lauffer (1949) on tobacco-mosaic virus and by Miller and Price (1946a) and Lauffer, Taylor and Wunder (1952) on southern-bean-mosaic virus. The data obtained with tobacco-mosaic virus and the most recent data obtained on influenza virus are shown in Chart 3.

The interpretation of data of this sort is not quite as simple as a straight-forward application of the obvious principle would imply. Of this much, however, one can be reasonably sure; the effective density of a virus particle in a sucrose solution of the same density can be measured with reasonable precision, for this is equal to the density at which the sedimentation rate is zero. As can be observed by inspection of Chart 3, this value in some cases can be obtained without resorting to extrapolation. Therefore, the value obtained can be as reliable as the measurements of the density of the sucrose solutions.

The simplest assumption that one can make in interpreting this density is that the sedimenting unit consists of virus material plus water of hydration and nothing else. If the dry density of the virus material and the density of water are known, it is possible to calculate the hydration of the virus on the basis of this assumption. However, if the virus particle also binds sucrose, then the calculation just described will not give the correct value of the actual water bound. It can be shown by rigorous algebraic rea-

soning that, if the virus particle actually binds sucrose, the water of hydration calculated on the assumption that it does not bind sucrose will be less than the actual amount of water bound. In other words, the degree of hydration calculated on the basis of the assumption that the particle does not bind sucrose is a minimum value. It is also the value which pertains to the virus surrounded by a sucrose medium. The hydration in pure water might not be the same.

The mechanism by which water is associated with the virus cannot be specified on the basis of experiments of this sort. What the method actually detects is the excess of water in the immediate region of a virus particle, i.e., the excess of water over the amount in the sucrose solution. This could arise through selective permeability of a membrane, through stronger forces of attraction between water and virus than between sucrose and virus, or even through actual repulsion of sucrose particles without any effect on water molecules. This uncertainty in the interpretation of the nature of hydration, particularly in a sucrose solution, defeats in some measure one of the purposes of studies of this sort, namely, the determination of the density of the sedimenting unit. Nevertheless, at the present time, the only solution to the problem is to assume that the value of the density of the sedimenting unit in a concentrated sucrose solution is the same as that in pure water.

The characteristic particles of influenza virus and southern-bean-mosaic virus are essentially spherical. When the value for the density of influenza virus particles in solution, 1.193 (Lauffer and Taylor, 1952), and the value of the sedimentation constant, 722×10^{-13} (Lauffer and Stanley, 1944), are substituted into the equation for the sedimentation of spherical particles, the diameter of the influenza particle in solution can be calculated to be 82×10^{-7} cm. Values for the sedimentation constant and for the density in solution of southern-bean-mosaic virus characteristic particles (Lauffer, Taylor and Wunder, 1952) are 114.7×10^{-13}

and 1.26, respectively. When these values are substituted into the sedimentation formula for spherical particles, a value of 28 mμ is obtained for the diameter.

When one attempts to measure and to interpret the sedimentation constant of non-spherical particles considerable difficulty is encountered. The measurement is complicated by the fact that the sedimentation constant depends upon the concentration. Lauffer (1944) showed that the reciprocal of the sedimentation constant of tobacco-mosaic virus is related, by the equation of a straight line, to the concentration of virus. In interpretation, it is necessary to obtain the sedimentation constant at infinite dilution. Lauffer showed that this can be done by extrapolation of the data or by applying a correction for the viscosity of the virus solution.

The interpretation is difficult because both the coefficient of friction and the mass of a nonspherical particle are complex functions of the dimensions of the particle. However, a method has been evolved which makes it possible to determine the size of such particles even though the shape is not known. It will be recalled that both the sedimentation constant and the diffusion constant of particles are inversely proportional to the friction coefficient. Therefore, the ratio of the sedimentation constant to the diffusion constant must be independent of the friction coefficient. This ratio is, therefore, proportional only to the mass of the particle corrected for buoyancy. These ideas can be summarized by the Svedberg equation: $M = \dfrac{RTs}{D(1 - d_o/d)}$. Thus, from measurements of the sedimentation constant, the diffusion constant, and the density of a particle in solution, it is possible to calculate its molecular weight regardless of its shape.

It is even possible to determine the shape of a particle from sedimentation and diffusion data. If the molecular weight of the particle in solution is determined accurately from sedimentation, diffusion, and density data, then it is a simple problem in solid geometry to calculate the volume of such a hydrated particle. Next, one can calculate the radius that this hydrated particle would have if it were a sphere, and then, using Stokes' law, one can determine the friction coefficient the particle would have if it were a sphere. The actual friction coefficient of the particle can be determined from its diffusion constant. Thus, the friction ratio of the particle can be evaluated. The friction ratio has already been shown to be dependent upon the ratio of the dimensions of the ellipsoid of revolution which approximates the particle, and, therefore, one can evaluate this ratio. If one knows the total volume of a particle and also the ratio of length to thickness, it is a simple matter to calculate the actual dimensions of the particle. This sort of approach was used to determine the dimensions of to-bacco-mosaic virus (Lauffer, 1944). The molecular weight was first determined from sedimentation and diffusion data, and then the shape was determined in the manner just indicated. Values were obtained which are in reasonable agreement with those indicated by the electron microscope. One precaution must be observed in utilizing this method of approach. The actual density of the particle in solution must be used in these considerations; otherwise, an incorrect estimate of the shape of the particle is obtained. Until recently, such density values were not available, and thus some of the early calculations of shapes from sedimentation and diffusion data were somewhat in error. Studies of Schachman and Lauffer (1949) indicate that the density of tobacco-mosaic virus particles in a sucrose solution is 1.27 Gm. per cc. When size, shape and hydration are calculated on the basis of this density value from viscosity and sedimentation results, values are obtained in excellent agreement with direct measurements with the electron microscope.

The ultracentrifuge can also be used to help establish the relationship between particles in a purified preparation and the virus. In the manner just described, the sedimentation constant of a physical entity can be measured. The determination is purely physical in its nature, and it characterizes only the physical particles which one has obtained. However, there is available a device known as the separation cell, designed by Tiselius, Pederson and Svedberg (1937), of which a diagrammatic representation is shown in Figure 10. By means of this cell measurements of the sedimentation rate of the entity bearing virus activity can be made; the material to be studied is placed in the cell and is then spun at high speed. As the particles bearing virus activity sediment toward the periphery, they pass through the barrier located in the center of the cell. After a certain period of sedimentation, it is possible to stop the centrifuge and to withdraw the contents from the two sides of the barrier for biologic analysis. From the relative amounts of biologic activity in the upper and lower compartments, it is possible to calculate the sedimentation rate of the entity bearing virus activity. This figure can be compared with the value obtained by wholly physical means for the sedimentation constant of the particles. If the two coincide, one has strong evidence that the virus activity is actually a property of the isolated particles, and that the particle, therefore, is the virus. Evidence of this nature has been obtained for tobacco-mosaic virus (Lauffer, 1943a) and influenza virus (Lauffer and Miller, 1944). In the case of tobacco-mosaic virus, it was found that the infectious agent sedimented at a rate which was indistinguishable from that of the particle, 15 by 300 mμ in size. In the case of influenza virus, it was found that both the ability to infect and the ability to agglutinate red blood cells sedimented at a rate indistinguishable from that of the particle, 115 mμ in diameter, commonly regarded as influenza virus. In both cases, therefore, a reasonably strong case can be made for the assumption that virus activity is an integral characteristic of the particle involved.

Viscosity. It is possible to learn something about the shape and the state of hydration of particles, such as viruses, through the study of the viscosity of their solutions. Viscosity can be defined in general terms as the amounts of energy that must be expended in order to maintain a certain rate of flow in a liquid, and is generally measured by determining the time required for a certain volume of a liquid to flow through a capillary tube. It is also sometimes measured by determining the rate at which a spherical ball settles

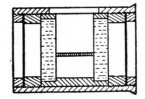 

FIG. 10. Longitudinal and cross-sectional views of separation cell.

through the liquid, or by determining the drag on one of two concentric cylinders when the space between them is filled with the liquid and the other cylinder is rotated at constant velocity. If η_0 is the viscosity of a solvent, and η the viscosity of a solution of particles, such as those of a virus, in that solvent, then η/η_0 is the relative viscosity of the solution. The quantity, $\eta/\eta_0 - 1$ is defined as the specific viscosity. Both relative and specific viscosities depend upon the volume concentration of the dissolved or suspended material. Specific viscosity divided by volume concentration is, therefore, a characteristic of the dissolved or suspended material. When this quantity is evaluated for an extremely dilute solution, it is given the name, intrinsic viscosity, [η]. The intrinsic viscosity of a material, such as a virus, can be interpreted in terms of its hydration and shape. Einstein showed that the intrinsic viscosity of a solution or suspension of spherical particles should be equal to 2.5, or stated slightly differently, the specific viscosity of a very dilute solution of spheres should be equal to 2.5 times the volume concentration. Thus, if one measures the specific viscosity of a suspension of spheres, one can evaluate the total volume occupied by these spheres in the solution. From the weight and the density of the dry matter in the solution, one can calculate what the total volume of the material would be if there were no hydration. From the difference between the volume obtained by viscosity and that obtained

depends upon the shape of the particle. Simha (1940) derived equations which show how the ratio of length to thickness of a rod-shaped particle and the ratio of diameter to thickness of a plate-shaped particle can be calculated from intrinsic viscosity. These relationships are presented graphically in Chart 4. Lauffer (1944) studied the intrinsic viscosity of tobacco-mosaic virus and, from the data, calculated the ratio of

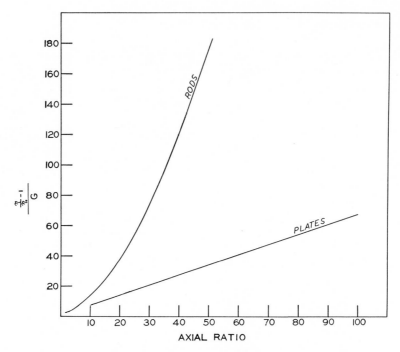

CHART 4. Intrinsic viscosity as a function of axial ratio for rodlike and platelike ellipsoids of revolution.

from the dry weight of the dissolved or suspended material, one can determine how much water is associated with each unit weight of the dry material. This method has been used to determine the hydration of influenza virus (Lauffer and Stanley, 1944) and southern-bean-mosaic virus (Miller and Price, 1946a). In both cases, values were found which were in reasonable agreement with those obtained by other studies.

When the dissolved or suspended particles are not spherical but rod-shaped or plate-shaped, then the intrinsic viscosity

length to thickness of the virus on the assumption that it was not hydrated. Values were obtained which were in fair agreement with those found with the electron microscope. Better agreement was obtained when the calculations were based on a hydrated particle containing 15 per cent water by volume (Schachman and Lauffer, 1949). A similar equation can be used to calculate the ratio of diameter to thickness of a flattened particle from the intrinsic viscosity. Thus, it is necessary to know whether a particle is elongated or flattened in shape in order to interpret its intrinsic viscosity. It is also necessary to know the extent of hydration, for, otherwise, the calculations can be in error.

Stream Double Refraction. Double refraction is a property of many crystalline bodies, best illustrated by the familiar calcite or Iceland spar crystal. When a spot of light is viewed through such a crystal, it appears as two spots separated by a certain distance. This occurs because the light coming from the spot to the eye is broken into two beams which are refracted or bent to different degrees. The property of double refraction can be detected most readily by examining the object between crossed Polaroid plates or crossed Nicol prisms. When it is oriented in certain ways, it appears to be illuminated against a dark background. It has long been known that when certain colloidal solutions, such as a vanadium pentoxide sol, are caused to flow through a capillary tube, they become double refracting. This double refraction of flow can be caused by internal strains in the liquid, commonly referred to as the photoelastic effect, or by the orientation of rod-shaped or plate-shaped particles in the flowing stream. If the double refraction of the flowing liquid persists after the liquid leaves the capillary tube, it provides evidence that the double refraction of flow is not due to the photoelastic effect. If the entire path of the flowing stream is double-refracting, it provides evidence that the stream double refraction is due to the orientation of rod-shaped particles, for, in the case of plate-shaped particles, only the edges of the flowing stream are double-refracting.

Takahashi and Rawlins (1932, 1937) noted that the juice of tobacco-mosaic-diseased plants exhibited stream double refraction and that the entire path of the juice was double-refracting. They concluded that the infective agent of the tobacco-mosaic disease was composed of or associated with rod-shaped particles. Following the isolation of purified tobacco-mosaic virus, Lauffer and Stanley (1938) demonstrated that solutions of the purified virus, as well as solutions of several other strains of tobacco-mosaic virus, exhibited stream double refraction. Purified preparations of the virus of latent-mosaic of potato also showed double refraction of flow. The double refraction of flow was shown to be due to the orientation of rod-shaped particles and not to the photoelastic effect. Figure 11 shows a stream of tobacco-mosaic-virus solution flowing from a pipette photographed between crossed and parallel Polaroid plates. The stream photographed between crossed Polaroid plates appears to be illuminated against a dark background. The interpretation of this phenomenon is that the rod-shaped, tobacco-mosaic-virus particles are lined up more or less parallel to each other by the stream lines in the flowing liquid. When these particles are oriented in this manner they resemble a crystal to a certain extent. This pseudocrystalline nature of the virus solution during flow is responsible for the double refraction of flow.

ELECTRON MICROSCOPE

One of the most useful physical tools that can be brought to bear upon the study of viruses is the electron microscope (Zworykin et al., 1945; Wyckoff, 1949). With this instrument it has been possible to obtain micrographs of many viruses. In order to understand the electron microscope, it is necessary to consider the limitations of the optical microscope and also to examine some of the fundamental properties of electrons.

There is no theoretical upper limit to the magnification which can be achieved by lenses using ordinary light. However, there is a theoretical lower limit to the size of an object which can be distinguished by optical means. When light is converged by a lens, a certain amount of diffraction occurs at the edge of the lens surface and results in phase differences in the light forming the image. The effect is that when an image of a point light source is produced, one does not obtain a point image but rather a circle surrounded by several fainter rings. The circular disk is called the circle of confusion. If two point sources of light are very close together, their circles of confusion will overlap. If they overlap too much, the two point sources will appear as a single source. In general, unless the two points are far enough apart so that the center of one circle of confusion lies outside the other, the two points cannot be resolved.

is approximately equal to $\dfrac{5}{8}\dfrac{\lambda}{\text{N.A.}}$. It is impossible to construct a lens with a numerical aperture very much greater than 1.5. Therefore, the minimum resolvable distance between two points on the object must be about $\dfrac{5}{12}$ the wave length of light. Since ordinary light has a wave length of around

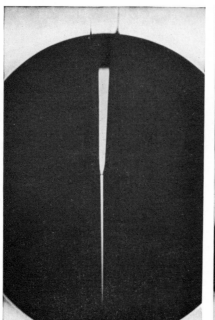 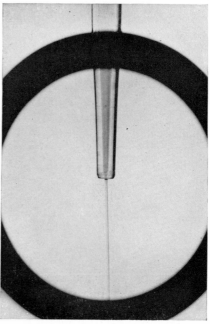

FIG. 11 (*Left*). Double refracting stream of tobacco-mosaic-virus solution photographed between crossed Polaroid plates arranged so that the vibration direction of each plate makes an angle of 45° with the direction of flow. (*Right*) Same system photographed between parallel Polaroid plates (Lauffer, M. A., and Stanley, W. M., 1938, Stream double refraction of virus proteins. Journal of Biological Chemistry, *123*, 507-525.)

Whether or not the two circles of confusion in the image can be distinguished depends upon the distance between the point sources, the wave length, λ, of the light, and a property of the lens called the numerical aperature, N.A. The N.A. is defined approximately as the product of the index of refraction of the space between object and lens, times the ratio of the lens radius to its focal length. The distance between two points which are just resolvable

5,000 Å, the smallest distance that can be resolved is about 2,000 Å or 200 mμ. Most viruses have diameters shorter than this figure, hence they cannot be seen with the ordinary microscope. However, they can be seen with the electron microscope.

The electron microscope depends for its operation upon the facts that a stream of electrons moving at high velocity behaves like a beam of light of very short wave length, that matter scatters electrons, and that an electron stream can be focused by magnetic or electrostatic fields. The electron microscope is in many ways analogous to the light microscope. It differs principally in that an electron gun replaces the light source, a stream of electrons replaces electron gun is an electromagnet which is analogous to the condensing lens in a microscope. It focuses the stream of electrons upon the object. The object in this case is placed upon a very thin film of collodion or some similar material supported by a fine

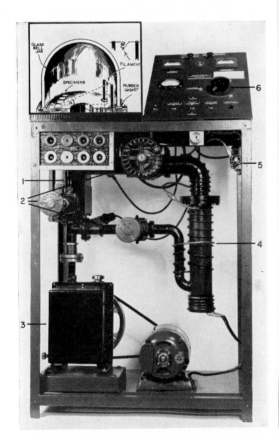

FIG. 12. Commercially available shadowing unit. (*Left*) The unit with panels removed to show details: (1) exhaust manifold, (2) vacuum valves, (3) fore pump, (4) diffusion pump, (5) air-inlet valve, (6) electrical control panel. The insert drawing shows details of vacuum bell-jar, filament position and specimen position. (*Right*) The completely assembled shadowing unit.

the beam of light, electromagnets take the place of the lenses, and either a fluorescent screen or a photographic plate replaces the retina of the eye for the formation of the final image. In the most commonly used form, the electron gun is at the top of the instrument. It operates at a potential usually around 60,000 volts. Just beneath the wire mesh. Just beyond the position of the specimen is a second electromagnet which corresponds to the objective lens in a microscope. It forms a real image of the object just in front of the third electromagnet. This electromagnet corresponds to the projecting lens in a microscope arranged for making photomicrographs. Its function is to focus the final image upon the photographic plate or upon the fluorescent screen. The fluorescent screen enables the electron image to be viewed directly. Focusing with the electron microscope differs slightly from focusing with the optical microscope. The penetrate air, the whole electron path must be in a vacuum. Devices must be available for introducing the photographic plate and also the object into the system from which air has been removed. This imposes a limitation on the usefulness of the electron

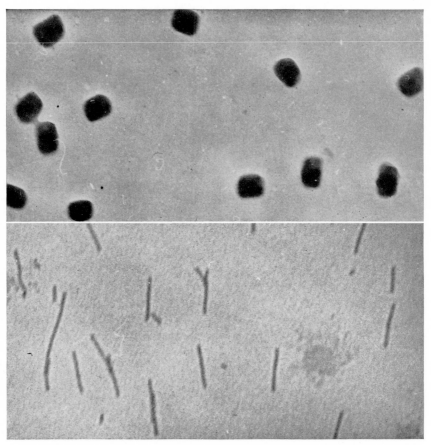

Fig. 13 (*Upper*). Purified preparations of elementary bodies of vaccinia. × 26,800. (Green et al., 1942, Journal of Experimental Medicine, *75*, 651-656.) (*Lower*) Purified preparation of tobacco-mosaic virus. × 41,600. (Stanley, W. M., and Anderson, T. F., 1941, Journal of Biological Chemistry, *139*, 325-338.)

focal length of the electromagnetic lens depends upon the current flowing through the coils. Hence, the focusing is accomplished by adjusting the focal length through control of the current in the magnets.

In the back part of the microscope complicated electric circuits provide steady currents for the lenses and a high potential for the electron gun. Since electrons cannot microscope, for it is very difficult to obtain images of anything other than thoroughly dried material.

The theoretical lower limit of resolution with the electron microscope is a small fraction of an Angstrom unit. However, in practice, it is difficult to obtain resolution better than 10 to 100 Å. The reason for this is that no method has yet been discovered for producing a magnetic lens with a high numerical aperture. Electron microscopes, however, do have resolutions which make possible the micrographing of particles with sizes in the range in which all known viruses fall. Therefore, it has been of tremendous value in advancing knowledge of the nature of viruses.

Electrons are scattered by matter, hence when a stream of electrons impinges upon an object, the electrons will be scattered and will not be able to enter the field of the objective magnetic lens. Therefore, the position on the image corresponding to the position of the particle on the specimen will appear dark. Thus, the electron image is essentially a shadow. The extent to which matter scatters electrons depends upon its density. A material with high density, such as gold, scatters electrons much more readily than does a material with low density, such as protein. In the electron microscope the specimen is supported by a very thin film of collodion or similar material. Since this film tends to scatter electrons to a certain extent, the background illumination appears gray instead of white. When a virus particle is placed on such a film, it scatters electrons only a little bit more effectively than does the film itself. Hence, an electron micrograph of a virus shows dark gray shadows on a light gray background. In general, the contrast is not very good.

A technic has been developed which increases greatly the contrast exhibited by small objects, such as virus particles, and provides a three-dimensional impression in the electron micrographs. The method was first reported (Müller, 1942) for the measurement of heights of specimen objects, but was later shown in an independent development (Williams and Wyckoff, 1944, 1945a) to be of great value also in delineating detail in micrographs of small objects and in showing surface contours of larger objects. In this technic, called shadowing or shadow-casting, a very thin film of some dense metal, such as uranium, is evaporated at an oblique angle onto the specimen mounted

on its supporting membrane. The filming is carried out in a vacuum chamber, with the material to be evaporated placed upon a tungsten filament. When the tungsten filament is heated with an electric current, the metal is evaporated, and the particles of the metal shoot off in straight lines. If the speci-

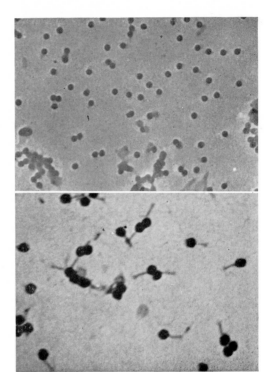

FIG. 14 (*Upper*). Purified preparation of eastern strain of equine encephalomyelitis virus treated with 0.023 molar calcium chloride. $\times$ 30,600. (Sharp, et al., 1943, Archives of Pathology, *36*, 167-176.) (*Lower*) Purified preparation of T_2 bacteriophage treated with phosphotungstic acid. $\times$ 30,600. (Sigurgeirsson, T., and Stanley, W. M., unpublished.)

men is held at an angle to the direction in which the molecules of the metal are shooting, it will be coated with a very thin film of the metal. However, the film of metal will not be entirely uniform. Since the virus particles have thickness, the part of the collodion film lying just behind the virus particle will be protected from the molecules of the metal. That is, the particle will, in effect, cast a shadow. When such a specimen is examined in the electron microscope, these shadows show up in very strong contrast. The appearance of the specimen under these circumstances is analogous to that which is obtained when a landscape is photographed in the early morning or the late afternoon;

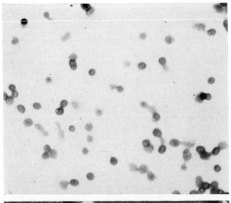

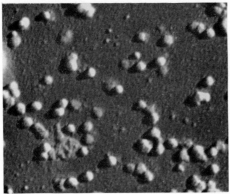

FIG. 15. Electron micrographs of identical fields containing partially purified influenza virus (PR8). (*Upper*) Unshadowed micrograph of a preparation previously treated with calcium chloride to enhance contrast. (*Lower*) The same area of the preparation after being shadowed with chromium. $\times$ 25,000. (Williams, R. C., unpublished.)

a strong impression of a third-dimensional effect is produced. Most of the more recent electron micrographs of viruses have been made by the metal-shadowing technic. Figure 12 shows a commercially available shadowing unit.

Another, less-used method of improving contrast is to allow the virus to react with a compound of some heavy element before micrographing. This is essentially a staining technic.

Results Obtained with Electron Microscope. The improvement in the pictures of viruses taken by means of the electron microscope during the past nine years provides striking testimony to the advances that have been made in the microscope itself and in the technics involved in its use. Contrast in early pictures was poor, providing only a general idea of the size and shape of virus particles. With the improvement of the microscope better pictures were obtained. Figure 13 shows pictures of vaccinia and tobacco-mosaic viruses taken with the RCA electron microscope in 1942 and 1941, upper and lower respectively. Treatment of viruses or of the electron-microscope mounts of viruses with materials such as calcium chloride or phosphotungstic acid was found useful as a means of increasing contrast. Figure 14 shows pictures of the eastern strain of equine encephalomyelitis virus and the T_2 bacteriophage following treatment with dilute calcium chloride and phosphotungstic acid, upper and lower respectively.

The electron microscope has been used to secure pictures of protein molecules (Stanley and Anderson, 1942; Williams and Wyckoff, 1945b; Hall, 1950) and to study the reaction between viruses and their antisera (Anderson and Stanley, 1941; Black, Price and Wyckoff, 1946). When a mixture of the rod-shaped tobacco-mosaic and the spherically shaped tomato-bushy-stunt viruses are treated with an antiserum to the latter virus, electron micrographs show it to be clumped, whereas the tobacco-mosaic virus appears unaffected.

The application of the metal-shadowing technic to problems of electron microscopy was a notable advance, for it provided better contrast, better definition of the structure of virus particles, and a three-dimensional effect. The 8 pictures in the frontispiece were obtained by means of this technic in which the shadowing metal was uranium. Figure 15 shows identical fields from a preparation of influenza virus before and after shadowing. The unshadowed preparation had been treated previously with calcium chloride. Figure 16 shows the degree of detail which is rendered visible by shadowing with uranium.

Striking photographs have been obtained of two-dimensional and three-dimensional crystalline arrays of the spherical viruses and of some larger protein molecules (Price, Williams and Wyckoff, 1946; Wyckoff, 1948; Hall, 1950). These show highly regular two-dimensional and three-dimensional arrays and go far to indicate that the particles in the crystals are highly uniform in patterns (Fig. 17 B), which can be photographed in their entirety. It is absolutely essential that an entire pattern be photographed in order to make sure that a representative sample of the mixture is under consideration. A simple determination of the ratio of the number of virus particles to the number of indicator particles yields directly the number of virus particles present in the suspension which was sprayed. This method supplements completely relative assays obtained by infectivity and serologic titrations. If the virus suspension is known

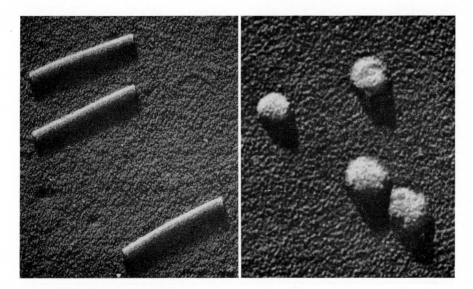

FIG. 16. Purified preparations of tobacco-mosaic virus (*left*) and influenza virus (*right*) shadowed with uranium. $\times$ 100,000. (Williams, R. C., unpublished.)

size and shape. Figure 17 A shows a two-dimensional array of partially purified bushy-stunt virus.

An advance of considerable importance in the electron microscopy of viruses is the development of a technic for counting the number of virus particles present in a suspension (Backus and Williams, 1949). In this method the virus preparation is mixed with a suspension of indicator particles, polystyrene latex spheres, whose absolute numerical concentration is known. The mixture is then sprayed upon the specimen films for subsequent microscopy. The minute drops, upon drying, form very small to be pure, the particle (or molecular) weight of the virus can also be obtained by drying and weighing a known volume of the virus suspension (Williams and Backus, 1949).

Tissue-culture technics have been applied to electron microscopy of some of the larger virus particles (Claude and Porter, 1947; Porter and Thompson, 1948). It is necessary to grow the tissue cells in a manner which will cause them to become very thin toward their peripheries. In infected cells, bodies resembling virus particles have been seen in the thinner regions. It has also been demonstrated that ultrathin tissue sections can be examined in the electron micro-scope, and the largest viruses, such as that of vaccinia (Wyckoff, 1951) can be photo-graphed in sectioned material.

It is obvious that means are now at hand for detailed studies of a wide variety on virus preparations (Luria et al., 1943; Lor-ing et al., 1946). Studies should be made on both purified and unpurified virus prepa-rations under different conditions and fol-

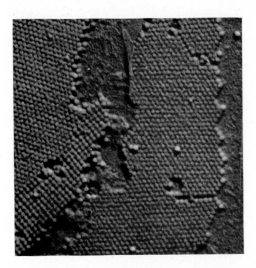

FIG. 17 A. A two-dimensional crys-talline array of the particles of bushy-stunt virus obtained from a partially purified preparation. Both a hexagonal and a square array are shown. × 29,000. (Steere, R. L., and Williams, R. C., 1948, A simplified method of preparing tomato bushy-stunt virus for electron microscopy. Phytopathology, 38, 948-954.)

lowing various chemical and physical treat-ments. Many viruses which have not yet been examined by means of the electron microscope should be studied, especially those which are not readily transmitted mechanically or which are transmitted by a specific insect vector. The possibility of using the electron microscope as a diag-nostic aid should be explored thoroughly, since means are available for securing very thin tissue slices suitable for direct exami-nation in the electron microscope (Rich-

ards, Anderson and Hance, 1942; Fullam and Gessler, 1946).

X-RAY DIFFRACTION

When a flattened beam of light coming from a narrow slit is passed through a dif-fraction grating, which consists of a glass plate containing a series of fine scratches very close together, and is then focused upon a screen, the image of the light source is found to consist of a series of lines. The central line will be the brightest and will be the principal image of the slit-light source. Above and below it will be other images of lower intensity. The distance be-tween the successive images depends upon the distance between the diffraction grating and the screen, upon the distance between the lines on the diffraction grating, and upon the wave length of the light. If one knows the wave length of the light and the distance between the grating and the screen, one can calculate the distance between the lines on the grating.

In a somewhat analogous way, when an x-ray beam is passed through a crystal, the beam is diffracted. The crystal can be con-sidered as a three-dimensional diffraction grating, because the individual molecules are arranged in a regular three-dimensional network. The type of diffraction pattern produced with such a three-dimensional dif-fraction grating is far more complex than that produced by a two-dimensional grating consisting of ruled lines on a glass plate. A great number of spots will be obtained on the photographic plate in the three-dimensional case. However, the distance between the principal image of the light source and these spots is related to the dis-tance between molecules in the crystal in much the same way as the distance between the lines on a simple diffraction grating is related to the scratches on the plate. Thus, from an x-ray diffraction pattern of a crys-tal, one can measure the distance between molecules in that crystal. If it is assumed that the molecules are tightly packed in the crystal, then one can assume that the diam-

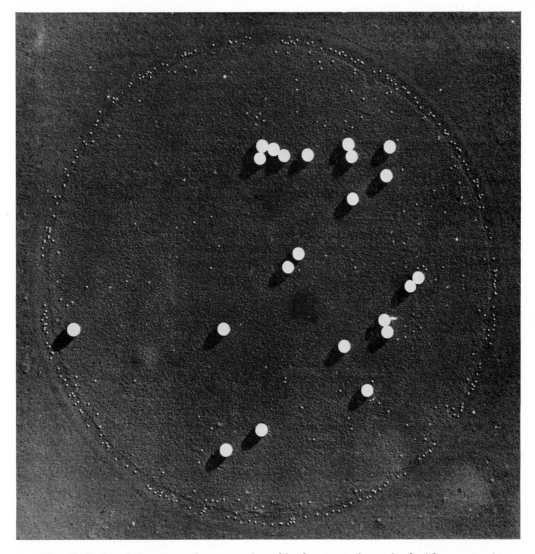

Fig. 17 B. Droplet pattern of a suspension of bushy-stunt virus mixed with a suspension of polystyrene latex indicator particles at a concentration of 3.20 x 10^{10} particles/ml. The large, opaque spheres are the polystyrene particles. $\times$ 13,500. (Williams, R. C., and Backus, R. C., unpublished.)

eter of the molecule is equal to the shortest distance between molecules. Hence from x-ray diffraction patterns obtained on crystals, one can calculate molecular sizes. Many proteins and some viruses have been obtained in crystalline form. X-ray diffraction patterns can be obtained with protein crystals and also with virus crystals, and from these it is possible to determine the maximum size of the particle. The x-ray method has been used by Bernal and Fan-

kuchen (1941) to assess the size of the tomato-bushy-stunt virus and also to determine the diameter of the tobacco-mosaic-virus rods. Figure 18 represents diagrammatically the view of Bernal and Fankuchen relative to the arrangement of rod-shaped tobacco-mosaic-virus particles in the rod-like crystals of the virus. The particles are arranged with perfect hexagonal symmetry with respect to cross section, but with no regularity with respect to length. The distance of closest approach between parallel rods, 15.2 mμ, represents an estimate of the diameter of a tobacco-mosaic-virus rod.

FIG. 18. Longitudinal and cross-sectional representations of arrangement of rod-shaped tobacco-mosaic virus in rodlike crystals. (Lauffer, M. A., and Stanley, W. M., 1939, The physical chemistry of tobacco-mosaic virus protein. Chemical Reviews, *24*, 303-321.)

IRRADIATION

It is well known that viruses can be inactivated or changed in other ways as a result of the effects of various kinds of radiations. To understand these effects, it is necessary to differentiate between those radiations which excite atoms and those which ionize atoms. Visible and ultraviolet light produce their effect by excitation; alpha, beta, gamma and x-rays, accelerated neutrons, protons and deuterons, etc., are ionizing radiations.

The effect of nonionizing or exciting radiations on viruses and other biologic materials has been reviewed by McLaren (1949). The effects produced by radiations of this sort, e.g., ultraviolet light, represent a special aspect of photochemistry. Experience with photochemical reactions extending over more than a century has led to the formulation of two laws: (1) only light adsorbed can cause a reaction; (2) in the primary process one quantum of light is adsorbed by each molecule which reacts. A molecule which has adsorbed a quantum of radiation has a higher energy level than its neighbors. In this high energy state, it and the group of molecules of which it is a part are likely to undergo chemical change. If the chemical configuration which changes is one of those essential to some vital function, then a biologic change results.

Ultraviolet-irradiation studies have been carried out on many viruses and bacteriophages, e.g., equine encephalomyelitis, herpes, influenza, poliomyelitis, vaccinia, rabies, tobacco-mosaic and tomato-bushy-stunt viruses, and *Staphylococcus aureus* and *E. coli* bacteriophages. Quantitative studies on the inactivation of tobacco-mosaic virus by ultraviolet light have been carried out in many investigations, the most recent of which were done by Oster and McLaren (1950). When the virus was irradiated with ultraviolet light of wave length 2537 Å, it was found that the logarithm of the relative infectivity remaining was inversely proportional to the radiation dose, i.e., to the time of irradiation with a beam of constant intensity. This is the kind of result that one gets whenever the rate of the change being measured is directly proportional to the number of individuals remaining unchanged. If the absorption of a single photon of radiation is sufficient to cause a virus particle to become inactivated, then the probability of a particular virus particle's being hit in a short time interval will be a constant when the radiation intensity is maintained constant. The number of virus particles changing in that time will depend only upon the number of unchanged particles remaining. This would lead to the kind of result which was actually obtained. Hence, a result of this sort is conventionally ascribed to a one-hit process.

In spite of the fact that this inactivation is a one-hit phenomenon, the quantum yield was found to be only 4 x 10^{-5}. This was obtained by comparing the total amount of ultraviolet light absorbed by the virus protein at wave length 2537 Å with the number of particles inactivated. It means that something like 25,000 photons are absorbed on the average by each particle which becomes inactivated. Yet, it has been seen that only one of these photons is effective in inactivating the particle.

The action of ionizing radiations on biologic materials, including viruses, has been reviewed in great detail by Lea (1947). The energy from ionizing radiations is absorbed by the irradiated material by the mechanism of ionization. When a tissue is irradiated with x-rays or with gamma rays, the photons of radiation collide with atoms and cause ionization by knocking out electrons with very high energies. These electrons or elementary particles of negative electricity speed through the tissue and cause secondary ionizations along their path. Secondary ionization results when an electron is moved out of the orbit of one atom, leaving a positive ion behind, and is captured by another atom, producing a negative ion. The production of each ion pair results in the dissipation of some of the energy of the primary electron, and ultimately all of the energy is dissipated, and the primary electron stops. These ion pairs are produced along tracks, i.e., along the path of the primary ionizing particle. The density of ion production is inversely related to the energy of the primary ionizing electron, i.e., low energy resulting from low-energy x-rays produce short electron paths with dense ionization, while fast electrons produced originally from high-energy x-rays or gamma rays result in long paths with sparse ionization. Beta rays from radioactive decay or cathode rays are high-speed electrons. These behave in exactly the same manner as the ionizing electrons which result from absorption of x-rays or gamma rays. Alpha particles, which are helium nuclei and are produced as a result of radioactive decay, directly induce ion pairs in the tissue. However, alpha particles are very efficient ionizers and therefore produce very dense ionization along a relatively short path. High-speed protons, which can be obtained from a cyclotron, behave somewhat like alpha particles but produce ionization densities intermediate between those of alpha particles and electrons. Neutrons, which can be obtained from the cyclotron, collide with an atom and knock out a proton. This proton in turn behaves in the same way as a proton coming originally from the cyclotron.

It takes energy to produce an ion pair.

Ultimately, the excess electrons on the negative members of the ion pairs will find their way back to the electron-deficient orbits of the positive members of the pair, and, when this happens, energy is made available at that spot. This energy leaves the molecule or chemical grouping which contained the ionized atom in a high-energy or excited state, capable of undergoing reaction. If the chemical reaction is in a configuration essential for biologic function, the particle loses its biologic activity.

Irradiation studies on biologic materials, including viruses, are sometimes carried out with the material in solution. In such a case the effect of the radiation can be either direct or indirect; i.e., an ion pair can be produced in the biologic particle itself and directly cause an effect, or it can be produced in the solvent, leading to the formation of some substance in the solvent which is detrimental to the biologically active material. It is thought by some that peroxides are formed in water and that these produce an indirect effect on viruses or other biologic materials. This indirect effect of radiation can, in principle, be suppressed by irradiating only highly concentrated suspensions or by adding substances like gelatin to the solution for the purpose of absorbing the bulk of the detrimental substances produced.

When a sample of virus is irradiated in the dry state or when adequate precautions are exercised during the irradiation of solutions, it is usually assumed that the effects observed are the result of direct ionizations within the virus particle. It is customary to interpret the direct action of radiations in terms of the so-called target theory. When a virus is irradiated with a particle, which produces dense ion tracks, i.e., tracks along which the ion pairs are so dense that the distance between them is small compared with the size of a virus particle, then the probability that an ionization will be produced within a particular virus particle depends only upon the cross-sectional area of the virus particle and upon the number of ion tracks per unit of cross-sectional area in the irradiated material. This situation would obtain when viruses are irradiated with alpha particles. The fraction of the number of viable virus particles which become inactivated in a given small unit of time then would depend solely upon the dose rate of irradiation and upon the effective cross-sectional area of the virus particle. When the dose rate is known, then it is possible in principle to calculate the cross-sectional area from the observed rate of inactivation.

When a virus is irradiated with some radiation which results in ion tracks in which the ion pairs are located far apart compared with the size of a virus particle, as would be the case if gamma rays were used, then the probability that a particular virus particle will have an ionization produced within it depends upon the volume of the particle and upon the number of ion pairs produced per unit volume of the irradiated system. In this case, if the dose rate of the irradiation is known, the volume of the target can be calculated from the observed rate of inactivation. If the ionizations are produced at distances intermediate between these two limiting cases, then the relationship between the rate of inactivation and the dose is more complex than in these two sample cases. Lea has described a detailed theory which takes into account all possible situations. The essential feature of the target theory is that some functions of the effective size of a virus particle can be evaluated from the inactivation-dose response.

If inactivation is the result of a single event, i.e., either the production of a single ionization within the volume of a single virus particle or the intersection of a particle with one ion track, then the dose-response curve should be a straight line when the logarithm of response is plotted against the dose. Many viruses have been irradiated with various kinds of ionizing radiations. Representative studies are described by Lea (1947) and by Pollard (1951). In general, the dose-response curves obtained are of the single-hit type. Also in many cases the effective particle sizes calculated from such studies are about the same as the sizes of the characteristic particles of the virus as determined by means of electron microscopy and other physical methods discussed previously in this chapter. When this is observed, it can be interpreted to mean that the entire substance of the characteristic virus particle is vulnerable to inactivation by ionization, i.e., an ion pair produced anywhere within the particle will result in loss of ability to infect. In cases where the target size obtained from radiation studies is considerably smaller than the size of the characteristic particle, it can mean either that the infectious entity is something much smaller than the suspected characteristic particle or that only some portions of it are vulnerable.

OSMOTIC PRESSURE AND RELATED PHENOMENA

There are certain indirect physicochemical methods which can be used to count the number of particles in a given volume. The mass of particulate matter can be determined readily if the preparation happens to be pure. Therefore, with a measure of the amount of material per unit volume and the number of particles per unit volume, one can determine the mass of a single particle. It is well known that the osmotic pressure, the freezing point depression and the vapor pressure lowering of a solution depend only upon the number of particles dissolved or dispersed in the solvent. One virus particle will have exactly the same effect as one molecule of sugar or one ion of a salt. The osmotic pressure method is the only one which is applicable to large particles, such as protein molecules. The earliest estimate of the size of purified tobacco-mosaic virus was derived from the observation that it had an extremely low osmotic pressure (Stanley, 1935). The method is not particularly well adapted to the study of viruses, however, because of the fact that the osmotic pressures of virus suspensions are extremely low, and are, therefore, difficult to measure with reasonable precision.

LIGHT-SCATTERING METHODS

The sizes of the characteristic particles of influenza virus, tomato-bushy-stunt virus and tobacco-mosaic virus have been determined by the method of light scattering (Oster, 1946; Oster, Doty and Zimm, 1947). The method and its biophysical and biochemical applications have been reviewed by Edsall and Dandliker (1951). Particles too small to resolve light might nevertheless scatter it. The extent of scattering (therefore, the turbidity) depends upon several factors, among which are the concentration and the molecular weight of the dissolved particles, the refractive indices of solvent and solution and the wave length of light. Thus, from turbidity measurements and measurements of the concentration of the material it is possible to determine the molecular weight. For the study of particles much smaller than the wave length of light, the experimental arrangements can be very simple. Most of the scattered light will not be transmitted through the solution in its original direction. Thus, the ratio of the intensity of light transmitted by the solvent to that of light transmitted by suspension of virus particles is related directly to the turbidity. Transmitted light can be measured in an ordinary laboratory colorimeter. Thus, the method of light scattering may involve only apparatus which is commonly available in clinical laboratories, and it does give satisfactory results for the size of spherical viruses. With an apparatus which permits observation of scattering at different angles it is possible to investigate particles having at least one dimension as great as or greater than the wave length of light. Oster, Doty and Zimm (1947) determined both the molecular weight and the lengths of tobacco-mosaic-virus particles and obtained values in agreement with those determined by other methods. The theory of light scattering parallels that of osmotic pressure. For this reason it is possible to

investigate the interaction between virus particles or other particles in solution by measuring light scattering at various concentrations.

ELECTROPHORESIS

Viruses, because of their chemical composition, possess carboxyl and amino groups

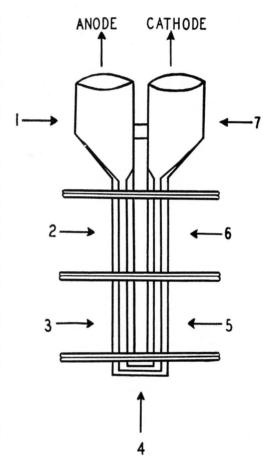

FIG. 19. The Tiselius electrophoresis cell. (Lauffer, M. A., and Price, W. C., 1947, Electrophoretic purification of southern-bean-mosaic virus. Archives of Biochemistry, *15*, 115-124.)

on their surfaces and possibly other groups capable of ionizing as acids or as bases. The dissociation of carboxyl and other acidic groups is suppressed by the addition of strong acids to the medium. The addition of strong bases causes the suppression of the ionization of the amino and other basic groups. Thus, it can be seen that the relative degree of dissociation of the acidic and the basic groups on the surface of a virus particle depends upon the pH of the medium. If a surface has many more dissociated acidic groups than basic groups, it will possess an overall negative electric charge, and it will behave like a giant polyvalent negative ion. On the other hand, if the particle contains an excess of ionized basic groups, it will have a net positive charge and will behave like a large polyvalent basic ion. When the protein contains an equal number of dissociated acidic and basic groups, it will have a net electric charge of zero and will be in the isoelectric state. The pH value of the medium in which the protein is in the isoelectric state is called the isoelectric point.

An electric current is carried through a solution of ions by the migration of the ions. Charged macromolecules also migrate in an electric field and thereby help to transport current. The velocity of migration of the macromolecules per unit of field strength, generally called the electrophoretic mobility, depends upon the net charge which is a function of pH, upon the electrolyte concentration and viscosity of the medium, and upon the size and shape of the charged particles. Since the surface chemical composition and the size and shape of various proteins and viruses differ widely, it is only natural that individual proteins and viruses have distinctive mobilities in the same solvent. Thus, electrophoretic mobility can be used as a means of identifying a protein or a virus and also as a means of separating it from other proteins.

Electrophoresis experiments are usually carried out in the Tiselius apparatus (Tiselius, 1937; Longsworth, 1942), the essential features of which are shown in Figure 19. It consists of a U-shaped channel of rectangular cross section connected at each end to a nonpolarizable electrode. The U-shaped channel is made in sections, each mounted on ground glass plates. These can be moved mechanically in such a way as to divide the U channel into several isolated compartments. When a protein or virus solution is to be studied, it is poured into the U channel until the lower two side sections are completely filled and the top sections are partly filled. Then the lower side sections are displaced with respect to the top sections in order to isolate them. The virus or the protein solution is then removed from the two top-side sections and is replaced with a medium identical with that in which the protein or virus is dissolved. The electrodes are connected with the top portion of the U channel and the whole system is closed in order to prevent movement due to the effect of gravity. Finally, the lower side sections of the U tube are moved back to their position directly under the top sections. This causes the establishment of two very sharp boundaries between the virus solution and the solvent medium. The electrodes are connected to a source of electric potential and current is sent through the U tube. If the protein or virus particles have a net negative charge, they will migrate toward the positive electrode. If all of the virus or protein particles are identical, all will migrate at the same rate. Thus, the sharp boundary between protein and solvent will be maintained, because all of the protein particles in the region will move toward the positive electrode at the same rate. The boundary will rise in the positive side of the U tube and descend in the negative side. The U tube is placed in a thermostatically controlled water bath equipped with a specialized optical system which enables the boundary to be seen. Thus, the rate of migration of the boundary can be determined by merely noting its displacement in a fixed period of time. If more than one type of protein is present, the initial boundary between protein and medium will separate into two or more boundaries, each of which will migrate at a different rate.

Electrophoresis has been used to purify viruses. Price (1946) observed that some preparations of southern-bean-mosaic virus contained a dark brown pigment which could not be removed readily. It was found by Lauffer and Price (1947) that in a 0.02 M phosphate buffer at pH 7, this pigment migrated more rapidly in the Tiselius electrophoresis apparatus than did the southern-bean-mosaic virus. By making use of this principle, it was possible to separate the pigment from the virus and to obtain a virus preparation which was essentially free from colored material.

The electrophoresis apparatus can also be used for determining the homogeneity of a virus preparation. If the virus preparation contains appreciable amounts of other proteinlike components, more than one boundary will be observed. Therefore, if

point can be determined by measuring the electrophoretic mobility in buffers with different pH values. The isoelectric point will be the pH value of that buffer in which the protein or virus does not migrate in an electric field. Tobacco-mosaic virus, PR8 influenza A virus, tomato-bushy-stunt virus, southern-bean-mosaic virus, and rabbit-papilloma virus are electrochemically homogeneous. Their isoelectric points have the values indicated in Table 2.

Electrophoresis can also be used to help establish the identity between a particle and the infectious entity. As was shown previously, it is possible to determine, by optical means, the rate at which particles migrate in an electric field. It is possible to carry out the experiment in such a way that frac-

TABLE 2

Virus	Isoelectric Point pH	Reference
Tobacco mosaic	3.49	Eriksson-Quensel and Svedberg (1936)
PR8 influenza A	5.30	Miller, Lauffer and Stanley (1944)
Tomato bushy stunt	4.11	McFarlane and Kekwick (1938)
Rabbit papilloma	5.0	Sharp et al. (1942)
Southern-bean mosaic	5.9	MacDonald, Price and Lauffer (1949)

only one boundary is observed, this constitutes evidence that the virus preparation is essentially pure. If all of the migrating particles are absolutely identical with respect to size, shape, and electric constitution, the boundary will remain relatively sharp as it migrates. However, if the preparation consists of a distribution of particles with a distribution of electrophoretic mobilities, the boundary will tend to become foggy or diffuse as it migrates. Thus, from the character of the observed boundary one can infer something of the nature of the protein or virus particles.

One of the characteristic physical constants by which a protein or virus can be identified is its isoelectric point. Since the material has zero net charge at the isoelectric point, it will not migrate either to the positive or the negative electrode in an electrophoresis apparatus. The isoelectric

tions can be obtained for biologic analysis. From such analyses, it is possible to determine the rate of migration of the biologic activity in an electric field. If this turns out to be the same, within experimental error, as the rate of migration of the physical entity, then one has strong evidence that virus activity is an integral property of that entity, and that, therefore, the physical unit may be the virus itself. Evidence of this sort was obtained in the case of the red blood cell precipitating activity of influenza virus. It was found that this activity migrated in an electric field with the same rate as the particles commonly regarded as the influenza virus particle (Miller et al., 1944).

CHEMISTRY

Chemical Analysis. Elementary chemical analyses have been made on purified preparations of several viruses and several strains of the same virus, but the results cannot be regarded as highly significant, since, in many cases, the analyses for different viruses were very similar, due apparently to the fact that many viruses are nucleoproteins. The plant viruses appear to and Loring, 1939; Ross and Stanley, 1939). The Shope rabbit-papilloma virus appears to contain about 1.5 per cent of lipid in addition to nucleoprotein (Taylor et al., 1942). Influenza virus has been found to contain in addition to nucleoprotein, a

TABLE 3. ANALYSES FOR THE ELEMENTS AND FOR CERTAIN COMPONENTS OF PURIFIED VIRUS PREPARATIONS

VIRUS	C	H	N	P	S	PROTEIN	NUCLEIC ACID	LIPID	
Alfalfa mosaic .	53.8	6.7	16.2	1.4	0.65	85	15		(Ross, 1941a)
Cucumber virus 4	50-51	7.0-7.6	15.3-15.8	0.54-0.6	0.0-0.84	94	6		(Bawden and Pirie, 1937b; Knight and Stanley, 1941)
Potato latent mosaic	47.8	7.3-7.6	14.6-16.1	0.53-0.69	1.1	92	6		(Loring, 1938)
Ribgrass	50.3	7.0	15.7	0.6	0.64	94	6		(Knight, 1942a)
Southern-bean mosaic	45.6	6.5	17	1.9	1.3	79	21		(Miller and Price, 1946a)
Tobacco ring spot	50.5	7.6	14.6	3.6	0.39	60	40		(Stanley, 1939)
Tobacco mosaic	51	7.6	16.6	0.6	0.2	94	6		(Stanley and Loring, 1939)
Tobacco necrosis	45	6.5	16.3	1.6	1.6	82	18		(Pirie et al., 1938)
Tomato bushy stunt	47-50	7.2-8.2	15.8-16.4	1.3-1.5	0.4-0.8	83	17		(Bawden and Pirie, 1938; Stanley, 1940)
Rabbit papilloma	49.6	7.2	14.5-15	0.9	2.2	89.5	9	1.5	(Beard et al., 1939; Taylor et al., 1942)
Equine encepholomyelitis ..	62.2	9.2	7.7	2.2		45	4.4	48	(Taylor et al., 1943a)
Influenza	53		10	0.9		67	5	23	(Taylor, 1944; Knight, 1947a, b)
Newcastle disease	51.8		9.9	0.85		67	6	27	(Cunha et al., 1947)
Vaccinia	33.7		15.3	0.57		83	5.6	4	(Hughes et al., 1935; Hoagland et al., 1940)
T$_2$ bacteriophage	42		13.5	4.8-5.2		ca50	45	ca2	(Taylor, 1946)

be the least complex chemically, for all which have been purified have been found to be simple nucleoproteins. The amount of nucleic acid has been found to vary from about 6 per cent in the case of tobaccomosaic virus to about 40 per cent in the case of tobacco-ring-spot virus (Bawden and Pirie, 1937a; Stanley, 1939; Stanley polysaccharide composed of mannose, galactose and glucosamine units, and lipid (Knight, 1947a). Equine encephalomyelitis virus was found to contain large amounts of lipid in the form of phospholipid, cholesterol and neutral fat (Beard, 1945). The results of elementary analyses and analyses for special components are given in Table 3.

It can be seen that the viruses which have been purified and studied have been found to consist of various combinations of nucleic acid and protein with lipid, extranucleic acid carbohydrate or certain other components which are present in some instances. Thus far, only pentose nucleic acid has been found in the plant viruses, while either pentose nucleic acid, or desoxypentose nucleic acid, or both have been reported to be present in animal viruses. The role which nucleic acid plays in virus activity is obscure, but the fact that nucleic acid has been found in all viruses so far examined cannot be ignored.

Because of the rather drastic methods that have been employed to secure the nucleic acid components of viruses, it is probable that most of these preparations have been altered considerably. For example, in the case of tobacco-mosaic virus, the nucleic acid obtained by alkali treatment was found to be only slightly viscous and to possess a molecular weight of about 15,000, while the nucleic acid obtained by heat treatment was found to be very viscous, spontaneously birefringent and to possess a molecular weight of about 300,000 (Cohen and Stanley, 1942). The nucleic acid component of tobacco-mosaic virus has been studied in some detail (Loring, 1939; Schwerdt and Loring, 1947). It was concluded that at least three of the component nucleotides were identical with those of yeast nucleic acid. However, much more work on the structure of virus nucleic acids is needed, for nucleic acid structure may eventually prove of the greatest importance in connection with virus activity. Since the transforming agent of pneumococcus can be regarded as possessing viruslike activity, the fact that this agent appears to be a desoxyribonucleic acid has provided additional impetus to studies of nucleic acid structure (Avery, MacLeod and McCarty, 1944).

A finding of considerable significance was that, although all strains of tobacco-mosaic virus contained the same amount of nucleic acid, as indicated by phosphorus analyses, they possessed different chemical properties (Stanley, 1937a; 1943). Furthermore, the properties of different preparations of tobacco-mosaic virus obtained at different times of the year and even from different kinds of hosts were found to be identical by all tests applied (Stanley and Loring, 1936; Stanley, 1938b; Gaw and Stanley, 1947). It seemed possible, therefore, that the chemical differences between the strains might reside in differences in the protein components. Accordingly, studies were inaugurated on the amino acid composition of different strains of tobacco-mosaic virus. The first studies, made by isolation and colorimetric methods, were later supplemented by microbiologic methods of analysis (Ross and Stanley, 1939; Ross, 1941b, 1942; Knight, 1942b, 1947c). The results which have been obtained are presented in Table 4. It can be seen that the differences in the composition of the eight strains involved sixteen of the nineteen amino acids that were determined. In some cases, a strain is characterized by changes in the amount of one or more amino acids, in other cases by the presence of an entirely new amino acid, and in still other cases by the absence of an amino acid that is present in tobacco-mosaic virus. The results indicate that the mutation of a virus can be accompanied by changes in the amount of one or more amino acids, by the introduction of a new amino acid or by the elimination of an amino acid. The results also suggest that there is a correlation between the number of demonstrable chemical changes and the degree of relationship of the virus strains. Thus, the HR strain, which was found to differ chemically in many respects from tobacco-mosaic virus, is almost certainly a distant relative of the latter in view of the fact that representatives of its type have not been observed among the many mutants of tobacco-mosaic virus. On the other hand, the J14D1 strain was presumably obtained directly from tobacco-mosaic virus as a result of only two successive mutations; and it may be highly significant that only two differences in composition were found. Since the J14D1 strain always kills young Turkish tobacco or tomato plants whereas tobacco-mosaic virus usually does not, it is obvious that small changes in chemical structure can be accompanied by marked changes in virulence. Despite the profound differences in compo-

strain of influenza A virus and of the Lee strain of influenza B virus (Knight, 1947b). Although purified tobacco-mosaic virus and its strains were found to be immunochemically unrelated to the proteins of the normal hosts used to produce the viruses, the influenza viruses were found to be immunochemically related to materials present in the hosts (Chester, 1935; Knight, 1946a, b;

TABLE 4. AMINO ACID CONTENTS OF HIGHLY PURIFIED PREPARATIONS OF SOME STRAINS OF TOBACCO-MOSAIC VIRUS*

AMINO ACID	TMV†	M	J14D1	GA	YA	HR	CV3	CV4	MD‡
Alanine	5.1	5.2	4.8	5.1	5.1	*6.4*		*6.1*	0.2
Arginine	9.8	9.9	10.0	*11.1*	*11.2*	9.9	9.3	*9.3*	0.2
Aspartic Acid	13.5	13.5	13.4	13.7	13.8	*12.6*		13.1	0.2
Cysteine	0.69	0.67	0.64	0.60	0.60	0.70	*0*	*0*	
Cystine	0		0	0	0			0	
Glutamic Acid	11.3	11.5	*10.4*	11.5	11.3	*15.5*	6.4	*6.5*	0.2
Glycine	1.9	1.7	1.9	1.9	1.8	*1.3*	1.2	*1.5*	0.1
Histidine	0	0	0	0	0	*0.72*	0	0	0.01
Isoleucine	6.6	6.7	6.6	*5.7*	*5.7*	*5.9*	5.4	*4.6*	0.2
Leucine	9.3	9.3	9.4	9.2	9.4	9.0	9.3	9.4	0.2
Lysine	1.47	1.49	*1.95*	1.45	1.47	1.51	*2.55*	*2.43*	0.04
Methionine	0	0	0	0	0	2.2	0	0	0.1
Phenylalanine	8.4	8.4	8.4	8.3	8.4	*5.4*	*9.9*	*9.8*	0.2
Proline	5.8	5.9	5.5	5.8	5.7	5.5		5.7	0.2
Serine	7.2	7.0	6.8	7.0	7.1	*5.7*	9.3	9.4	0.3
Threonine	9.9	10.1	10.0	10.4	10.1	*8.2*	6.9	*7.0*	0.1
Tryptophane	2.1	2.2	2.2	2.1	2.1	*1.4*	*0.5*	*0.5*	0.1
Tyrosine	3.8	3.8	3.9	3.7	3.7	*6.8*	3.8	3.7	0.1
Valine	9.2	9.0	8.9	8.8	9.1	*6.2*	8.8	8.9	0.2

* The values given in the table represent percentages of the indicated amino acids. In order to facilitate comparison, the values which are considered to differ significantly from those of TMV are set in italics.
† TMV, tobacco-mosaic virus; M, Holmes' masked strain; GA, green aucuba; YA, yellow aucuba; HR, Holmes' ribgrass; CV3, cucumber virus 3; CV4, cucumber virus 4.
‡ Mean deviation of the values of single determinations from the averages given in the table. Three to 5 preparations of each strain were analyzed for each amino acid, with the exception of cysteine, and the results were averaged to give the figures presented in the table.
(Knight, C. A., 1947, The nature of some of the chemical differences among strains of tobacco-mosaic virus. Journal of Biological Chemistry, *171*, 297-308.)

sition that have been found in strains of tobacco-mosaic virus, the particles of these strains appear to have the same size and shape. Figure 20 is an electron micrograph which shows the particles of eight strains of tobacco-mosaic virus. It would appear that despite the differences in composition some general directive force is effective during the construction of these virus particles.

Amino acid analyses have also been made on highly purified preparations of the PR8

Gaw and Stanley, 1947; Malkiel, 1947). Nevertheless, the compositions of the PR8 and Lee influenza viruses were so characteristic that they could undoubtedly be used for purposes of identification. These two strains were found to contain approximately the same amounts of alanine, aspartic acid, glycine, histidine, isoleucine, leucine, methionine, phenylalanine, proline, serine, threonine and valine. However, significant and characteristic differences were found in the amounts of arginine, glutamic acid, lysine,

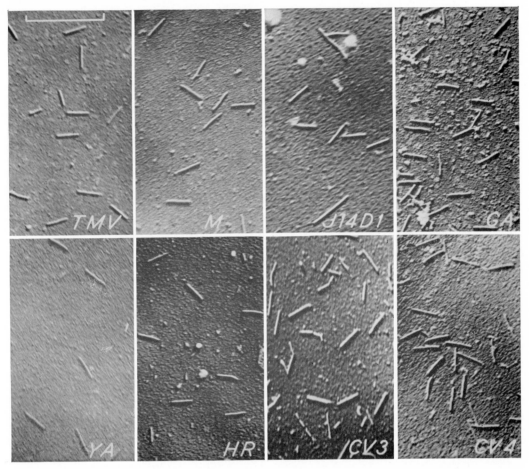

Fig. 20. Gold-shadow-cast electron micrographs of eight strains of tobacco-mosaic virus. × 20,800. (Knight, C. A., and Oster, G., 1947, The size of the particles of some strains of tobacco-mosaic virus as shown by the electron microscope. Archives of Biochemistry, *15*, 289-294.)

tryptophane and tyrosine. These differences might well be responsible, at least in part, for the lack of immunologic relationship between the strains, for their different pH stability ranges (Miller, 1944), for their different red cell agglutinating capacities (Knight, 1946a), and for their widely divergent heat stabilities (Salk, 1946). As a whole, the preliminary results that have been obtained in the amino acid analyses of strains of tobacco-mosaic virus provide information of great potential significance. The mutation of a virus to form a new virus strain is not so mysterious as it was a few years ago. However, much remains to be investigated, but the importance of the general problem of virus mutation, as well as mutation in higher organisms, is so great that research work in this direction will undoubtedly be pushed forward with the greatest vigor.

Chemical Modification. As purified virus materials of definite chemical composition became available, the possibility of changing the chemical structure of these materials by means of known chemical reactants became apparent. For example, tobacco-mosaic virus was found to possess certain functional groups, such as carboxyl, amino, sulfhydryl, phenolic and indolic groups, which in ordinary molecules are susceptible to different kinds of chemical reactions. It appeared of prime importance to determine the nature of chemical changes which resulted in a loss of virus activity, to determine whether or not these changes could be reversed, and especially to determine whether or not a change in chemical structure could be made which would be accompanied, not by a loss, but by a change in the nature of the biologic activity. The latter approach appeared especially attractive because of the possibility of securing heritable chemical changes in the structure of a virus. If the infecting particles of a chemically modified virus serve as exact models for reproduction, one would expect to isolate chemically modified virus from the infected host. The accomplishment of such a feat would, of course, correspond to the directed mutation of a virus in vitro. If, on the other hand, infection with chemically modified virus resulted in the production of ordinary virus, it might be concluded that the structural changes were reversed within the cells of the host, or that the portion of the virus structure involved in the chemical modification was unimportant in the reactions involved in virus reproduction.

In early studies on the inactivation of tobacco-mosaic virus, it was found that treatment with hydrogen peroxide, formaldehyde or nitrous acid yielded inactive virus which still retained certain characteristic chemical and serologic properties (Stanley, 1936a). The reaction with formaldehyde was studied in some detail by Ross and Stanley (1938) who found that the inactivation was accompanied by a decrease in amino groups and in groups which react with Folin's reagent at pH 7.7. Of considerable importance was the finding that when virus, which was partially inactivated by formaldehyde, was dialyzed at pH 3, a greater number of lesions was obtained than in the case of the material not subjected to this treatment. This was interpreted to mean that the virus was reactivated by

dialysis. The activity of pH 3 dialyzed virus was generally about tenfold greater than that of the virus not subjected to this treatment. This difference was also found to be accompanied by differences in amino nitrogen and in the groups that react with Folin's reagent. Kassanis and Kleczkowski (1944) also studied the reaction between tobacco-mosaic virus and formaldehyde, and after carrying out experiments similar to, but not identical with, those of Ross and Stanley, reported that they were unable to secure reactivation of formolized virus. However, the experiments of Ross and Stanley have been repeated and the results confirmed in another laboratory (Fischer and Lauffer, 1949).

Anson and Stanley (1941) reported that the sulfhydryl groups of tobacco-mosaic virus could be oxidized with iodine without changing the specific virus activity, but that the inoculation of this oxidized virus in Turkish tobacco plants resulted in the production of ordinary tobacco-mosaic virus. Miller and Stanley (1941, 1942) found that chemical derivatives of tobacco-mosaic virus could be obtained by treatment with ketene, phenyl isocyanate, carbobenzoxy chloride, p-chlorobenzoyl chloride and benzenesulfonyl chloride. About 70 per cent of the amino groups and about 20 per cent of the phenol plus indole groups of the virus could be covered without significant inactivation of the virus. Further coverage was accompanied by considerable loss of virus activity. It is of interest that the coverage of functional groups which can be accomplished without change in specific virus activity, as measured on leaves of *Nicotiana glutinosa,* corresponds to about 3,000 amino groups and 2,000 to 4,000 phenolic groups per molecule of tobacco-mosaic virus. It is of further interest that the disease caused by these chemical derivatives in Turkish tobacco plants was indistinguishable from the ordinary tobacco-mosaic disease, and that the virus isolated from such plants was indistinguishable from ordinary tobacco-mosaic virus. It was concluded that the chemical derivatives were converted into ordinary virus within the cells of the host or that the infecting molecules may not necessarily serve as exact patterns for reproduction. In view of the chemical stability and unusual nature of some of the chemical changes, the second possibility appears to be the more probable one. One finding of potential importance was obtained when the specific virus activity of the chemical derivatives was tested on different kinds of host plants. It was found that, when tested on leaves of the bean, *Phaseolus vulgaris*, the derivatives showed a significantly lower specific activity than when tested on leaves of *Nicotiana glutinosa*. The results provided the first indication that, upon the formation of a chemical derivative of the virus, a property of the virus, which perhaps can best be described as virulence, can remain unchanged for one host, but be modified with respect to another. It is obvious that attempts should be made to secure other types of chemically modified viruses, possibly some similar to naturally occurring strains, for such changes might have a profound effect on virus activity and yield virus derivatives which might prove very useful. Eventually it may prove possible to secure definite chemical changes in the structure of a virus in the test tube which will be heritable (Stanley, 1941b).

The use of stable and radioactive isotopes in research work on viruses will doubtless yield important results. Stanley (1942b) and Schramm, Born and Lang (1942) have already prepared tobacco-mosaic virus containing radioactive phosphorus. Although the phosphorus of the virus was stable in vitro, it was found to be dissociable within plant cells, hence the virus containing radioactive phosphorus did not prove useful in connection with experiments designed to yield information concerning the mode of virus reproduction. However, it does appear likely that the use of tracer technics will eventually provide an answer to the important question as to whether or not the substance of virus used as inoculum appears in the progeny or newly formed virus particles. Stimulating advances have already been reported by Cohen (1948), by Kozloff and associates (1950, 1951), by Putman and Kozloff (1950) and by Hershey and associates (1951) with radioactive phosphorus and heavy nitrogen in studies on the reproduction of bacteriophages. Although these investigators have found that about 80 per cent of the viral phosphorus and nitrogen come from the medium and only about 20 per cent from the bacterial cell and that phage preparations can be obtained with a sufficiently high specific radioactivity to cause a progressive inactivation of phage due solely to the effects of radioactive decay of the phosphorus, the work has not progressed sufficiently to permit a definite answer concerning the mode of virus reproduction. Several investigators are now studying the consequences of using virus possessing a high specific radioactivity as inoculum, and very informative results may be expected in the near future.

Carpenter and associates (1948) treated tobacco-mosaic virus with benzyl or n-butyl β-chloroethyl sulfide and found that the vesicant residues were attached to both the nucleic acid and the protein moieties of the virus and that the vesicant-protein linkage was more labile to alkali than was the vesicant-nucleic acid linkage.

KINETICS OF DISINTEGRATION

When tobacco-mosaic virus is subjected to the action of high temperatures, extremely high pressures, and chemical agents such as urea, acids, and bases, it is broken up, with the loss of nucleic acid, into small noninfectious fragments which are no longer soluble in dilute salt solutions. The kinetics of these disintegration reactions has been studied in some detail. The study of the kinetics of a reaction is the study of the rate at which the reaction takes place and of the manner in which that rate can be changed. The process of disintegrating tobacco-mosaic-virus protein at high temperatures proceeds in an orderly manner as is shown in Chart 5 (Lauffer and Price, 1940). When the logarithm of the amount of unchanged virus is plotted against the time of heating, a straight line is obtained.

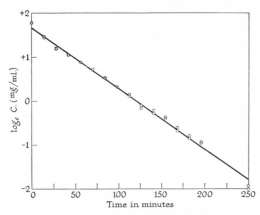

CHART 5. The manner in which the amount of undenatured tobacco-mosaic virus varies with time of heating. (Lauffer, M. A., and Price, W. C., 1940, Thermal denaturation of tobacco-mosaic virus. Journal of Biological Chemistry, *113*, 1-15.)

This means that in equal time intervals equal fractions of the residual unchanged virus protein will be changed into the disintegrated form. A process which takes place in this manner is called a first order reaction. The slope of the straight line obtained when the natural logarithm of amount remaining is plotted against time is called the specific reaction rate for the reaction under the particular conditions studied. It was found that the specific reaction rate for the disintegration of tobacco-mosaic virus varies with the temperature when all other conditions are maintained constant. When the logarithm of the specific reaction rate of most chemical reactions is plotted against the reciprocal of the absolute temperature, a straight time is obtained. The results shown in Chart 6 indicate that the same is true of tobacco-mosaic virus.

Present-day theories of reaction kinetics are in essential agreement in that most of them include the assumption that in order for a molecule to react, it must first pass into a highly activated state. When it is in this highly activated state, it then has the option of either reacting or passing back into the normal state. Molecules in this activated or high-energy state are thought to be in equilibrium with the molecules in the normal state, and a simple mass action equation with a characteristic equilibrium constant can be written for this equilibrium. It is believed that when the temperature is raised, the equilibrium is shifted so that at a given time a higher proportion will be in the activated state. Thus, a higher proportion will be able to change over into the reacted form in a given time. Hence, the reaction is speeded up. This represents a possible explanation of the influence of temperature upon reaction rates.

It has been found that tobacco-mosaic virus is disintegrated very much more rapidly at extremely high pressures than at ordinary pressures (Lauffer and Dow, 1941). That is, even though the virus is

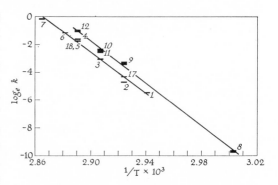

CHART 6. The manner in which the rate of denaturation of tobacco-mosaic virus varies with temperature for two different concentrations. (Lauffer, M. A., and Price, W. C., 1940, Thermal denaturation of tobacco-mosaic virus. Journal of Biological Chemistry, *113*, 1-15.)

perfectly stable at 30° C. at atmospheric pressure, it will disintegrate if it is subjected to a pressure of from 5,000 to 10,000 atmospheres at 30° C. The course of the disintegration at high pressures has been shown to be of the first order. The effect of high pressures on the disintegration of to-bacco-mosaic virus can be understood on the basis of the assumption that the activated virus particles occupy slightly less volume than the normal virus particles. If this is so, then one would expect the application of high pressures to shift the equilibrium between normal virus and activated virus in such a way as to increase the proportion of particles in the activated state. Thus, the reaction rate would be speeded up. More recently, Johnson et al. (1948) showed that at pressures around 500 atmospheres denaturation of tobacco-mosaic-virus protein was less rapid than at atmospheric pressure. This result demonstrated conclusively that denaturation processes at 500 and at 7,500 atmospheres are not the same.

The disintegration of tobacco-mosaic virus by urea presents some very interesting features (Stanley and Lauffer, 1939; Lauffer, 1943b; Lauffer and Stanley, 1943). When the virus is placed in a strong urea solution, it gradually disintegrates. This reaction has been shown to be of the first order. The specific reaction rate was found to vary with the temperature in the very unexpected and unusual manner illustrated in Chart 7, namely, the urea disintegration of tobacco-mosaic virus proceeded slowly at room temperature, but the rate increased when the temperature was increased above room temperature and also when the temperature was decreased below room temperature. Other viruses have been shown to behave in the same manner (Bawden and Pirie, 1940). It is even possible that the urea denaturation of egg albumen behaves in the same manner. This very unexpected behavior was explained on the basis of the assumption that the virus reacts with urea to form a complex compound which then undergoes disintegration. By making the postulate that at least two different kinds of complexes can be formed with urea, one can explain the unusual dependence of reaction rate upon temperature.

Rather extensive studies on the kinetics of the destruction of infectivity of tobacco-mosaic virus and of other plant viruses were carried out by Price (1940). In general, it was found that these inactivations follow the course of a first order reaction. The kinetics of the loss of red blood cell agglutinating activity and of infectivity of

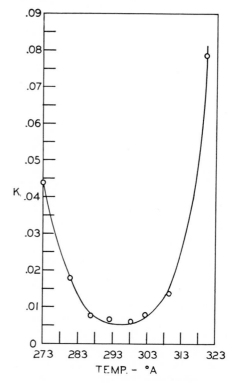

CHART 7. The effect of temperature upon the rate of denaturation of tobacco-mosaic virus in urea. (Lauffer, M. A., 1943, Denaturation of tobacco-mosaic virus by urea. II. Kinetic aspects. Journal of the American Chemical Society, *65*, 1793-1802.)

the PR8 strain of influenza A virus has been studied by Lauffer and associates (Lauffer and Carnelly, 1945; Lauffer and Wheatley, 1951; Lauffer et al., 1948; Scott and Lauffer, 1946a, b). Studies of this sort are of importance to virologists because they shed a certain amount of light upon the inactivation of viruses at high temperatures. During much of the early work, a given virus was characterized by its inactivation temperature or its thermal death point. This was defined as the temperature at which a virus would be inactivated in some arbitrary time. It is now realized that the thermal inactivation of a virus is merely one aspect of the broader problem of the denaturation or disintegration of virus proteins. Inactivation is a reaction which takes place over a wide range of temperatures. However, the reaction has the property of changing velocity greatly for small temperature changes. Thus, a change of temperature of only a few degrees can cause the reaction velocity to change from an imperceptibly low value to one so high that virtually all of the activity is destroyed in a short period of time. Hence, one can obtain an apparent inactivation temperature. These inactivation temperatures or thermal death points were used as characteristics to describe the nature of a particular virus. Much more useful information can be obtained from data describing the way in which the rate of the inactivation varies with temperature and with other conditions.

REFERENCES

Allard, H. A., 1916, Some properties of the virus of the mosaic disease of tobacco. J. Ag. Res., 6, 649-674.

Anderson, T. F., 1946, Morphological and chemical relations in viruses and bacteriophages. Cold Spring Harbor Symp. on Quant. Biol., 11, 1-13.

Anderson, T. F., and Stanley, W. M., 1941, A study by means of the electron microscope of the reaction between tobacco mosaic virus and its antiserum. J. Biol. Chem., 139, 339-344.

Anson, M. L., and Northrop, J. H., 1937, The calibration of diffusion membranes and the calculation of molecular volumes from diffusion coefficients. J. Gen. Physiol., 20, 575-588.

Anson, M. L., and Stanley, W. M., 1941, Some effects of iodine and other reagents on the structure and activity of tobacco mosaic virus. J. Gen. Physiol., 24, 679-690.

Avery, O. T., MacLeod, C. M., and McCarty, M., 1944, Studies on the chemical nature of the substance inducing transformation of pneumococcal types. Induction of transformation by a desoxyribonucleic acid fraction isolated from pneumococcus type III. J. Exp. Med., 79, 137-158.

Backus, R. C., and Williams, R. C., 1950, The use of spraying methods and of volatile suspending media in the preparation of specimens for electron microscopy. J. Appl. Physics, 21, 11-15.

Bang, F. B., 1946, Filamentous forms of Newcastle virus. Proc. Soc. Exp. Biol. and Med., 63, 5-7.

Bauer, J. H., and Pickels, E. G., 1936, A high speed vacuum centrifuge suitable for the study of filterable viruses. J. Exp. Med., 64, 503-528.

Bawden, F. C., and Pirie, N. W., 1937a, The isolation and some properties of liquid crystalline substances from solanaceous plants infected with three strains of tobacco mosaic virus. Proc. Roy. Soc. London, Ser. B., 123, 274-320.

Bawden, F. C., and Pirie, N. W., 1937b, The relationships between liquid crystalline preparations of cucumber viruses 3 and 4 and strains of tobacco mosaic virus. Brit. J. Exp. Path., 18, 275-291.

Bawden, F. C., and Pirie, N. W., 1938, Crystalline preparations of tomato bushy stunt virus. Brit. J. Exp. Path., 19, 251-263.

Bawden, F. C., and Pirie, N. W., 1940, The inactivation of some plant viruses by urea. Biochem. J., 34, 1258-1277.

Beams, J. W., 1942, The production and maintenance of high centrifugal fields for use in biology and medicine. Annals N. Y. Acad. Sci., 43, 177-193.

Beams, J. W., and Pickels, E. G., 1935, Production of high rotational speeds. Rev. Sci. Inst., 6, 299-308.

Beard, J. W., 1945, The ultracentrifugal, chemical and electron micrographic characters of purified animal viruses. Proc. Inst. Med. Chicago, 15, 294-313.

Beard, J. W., Bryan, W. R., and Wyckoff, R. W. G., 1939, The isolation of the rabbit papilloma virus protein. J. Infect. Dis., 65, 45-52.

Beijerinck, M. W., 1898, Ueber ein Contagium vivum fluidum als Ursache der Fleckenkrankheit der Tabaksblätter. Verh. Akad. Wetensch. Amsterdam, II, 6, no. 5, 1-21.

Bergold, G., 1947, Die Isolierung des Polyeder-Virus und die Natur der Polyeder. Ztschr. f. Naturforsch., 2b, 122-143.

Bernal, J. D., and Fankuchen, I., 1941, X-ray and crystallographic studies of plant virus preparations. I. Introduction and preparation of specimens. II. Modes of aggregation of the virus particles. III. J. Gen. Physiol., 25, 111-165.

Black, L. M., Mosley, V. M., and Wyckoff, R. W. G., 1948, Electron microscopy of potato yellow-dwarf virus. Biochimica et Biophysica Acta, 2, 121-123.

Black, L. M., Price, W. C., and Wyckoff, R. W. G., 1946, The electron micrography of plant virus-antibody mixtures. Proc. Soc. Exp. Biol. and Med., 61, 9-12.

Bland, J. O. W., 1928, Filter and centrifuge experiments with guinea-pig vaccinia virus. Brit. J. Exp. Path., 9, 283-290.

von Borries, B., Ruska, E., and Ruska, H., 1938, Bakterien und Virus in übermikroskopscher Aufnahme. Klin. Wchnschr., 17, 921-925.

Carpenter, F. H., Wood, J. L., Stevens, C. M., and

du Vigneaud, V., 1948, Chemical studies on vesicant-treated proteins. J. Am. Chem. Soc., 70, 2551.

Chester, K. S., 1935, The antigenicity of the plant viruses. Phytopathology, 25, 702-714.

Claude, A., Porter, K. R., and Pickels, E. G., 1947, Electron microscope study of chicken tumor cells. Cancer Research, 7, 421-430.

Cohen, S. S., 1948, The synthesis of bacterial viruses. II. The origin of the phosphorus found in the desoxyribonucleic acids of the T_2 and T_4 bacteriophages. J. Biol. Chem., 174, 295-303.

Cohen, S. S., and Stanley, W. M., 1942, The molecular size and shape of the nucleic acid of tobacco mosaic virus. J. Biol. Chem., 144, 589-598.

Cox, H. R., van der Scheer, J., Aiston, S., and Bohnel, E., 1947, The purification and concentration of influenza virus by means of alcohol precipitation. J. Immunol., 56, 149-166.

Craigie, J., 1932, The nature of the vaccinia flocculation reaction, and observations on the elementary bodies of vaccinia. Brit. J. Exp. Path., 13, 259-268.

Cunha, R., Weil, M. L., Beard, D., Taylor, A. R., Sharp, D. G., and Beard, J. W., 1947, Purification and characters of the Newcastle disease virus (Calif. strain). J. Immunol., 55, 69-89.

Duffy, C. E., and Stanley, W. M., 1945, Studies on the biochemical, biophysical, and immunogenic properties of Japanese B type encephalitis virus and vaccines. J. Exp. Med., 82, 385-410.

Edsall, J. T., and Dandliker, W. B., 1951, Light scattering in solutions of proteins and other large molecules. Its relation to molecular size and shape and molecular interactions. Fortsch. d. Chem. Forsch., 2, 1-56.

Elford, W. J., 1931, A new series of graded collodion membranes suitable for general bacteriological use, especially in filterable virus studies. J. Path and Bact., 34, 505-521.

Elford, W. J., 1933, Principles of ultrafiltration as applied in biological studies. Proc. Roy. Soc. London, Ser. B., 112, 384-406.

Elford, W. J., and Andrewes, C. H., 1932, Filtration of vaccinia virus through gradocol membranes. Brit. J. Exp. Path., 13, 36-42.

Elford, W. J., and Andrewes, C. H., 1936, Centrifugation studies. II. The viruses of vaccinia, influenza, and Rous sarcoma. Brit. J. Exp. Path., 17, 422-430.

Elford, W. J., Andrewes, C. H., and Tang, F. F., 1936, The sizes of the viruses of human and swine influenza as determined by ultrafiltration. Brit. J. Exp. Path., 17, 51-53.

Epstein, H. T., and Lauffer, M. A., 1952, Ultracentrifugal identification of infectious entities with characteristic particles. Arch. Biochem. and Biophys., 36, 371-382.

Eriksson-Quensel, I. B., and Svedberg, T., 1936, Sedimentation and electrophoresis of the tobacco mosaic virus protein. J. Am. Chem. Soc., 58, 1863-1867.

Ferry, J. D., 1936, Ultrafilter membranes and ultrafiltration. Chem. Rev., 18, 373-455.

Fischer, M. A., and Lauffer, M. A., 1949, The reaction of tobacco mosaic virus with formaldehyde. I. Electrophoretic studies. Arch. Biochem., 23, 291-296.

Fullam, E. F., and Gessler, A. E., 1946, The high-speed microtome for the electron microscope. Rev. Sci. Inst., 17, 23-35.

Gaw, H. Z., and Stanley, W. M., 1947, Comparative properties of purified preparations of two distinctive strains of tobacco mosaic virus obtained from diseased Turkish tobacco and phlox plants. J. Biol. Chem., 167, 765-772.

Gold, A. H., and Jensen, D. D., 1951, An electron microscope study of Cymbidium mosaic virus. Am. J. Bot., 38, 577-578.

Green, R. H., Anderson, T. F., and Smadel, J. E., 1942, Morphological structure of the virus of vaccinia. J. Exp. Med., 75, 651-656.

Hall, C. E., 1950, Electron microscopy of crystalline edestin. J. Biol. Chem., 185, 45-51.

Henriot, E., and Huguenard, E., 1925, Sur la réalisation de très grandes vitesses de rotation. Compt. rend. Acad. sci., 180, 1389-1392.

Hershey, A. D., Kamen, M. D., Kennedy, J. W., and Gest, H., 1951, The mortality of bacteriophage containing assimilated radioactive phosphorus. J. Gen. Physiol., 34, 305-319.

Hills, C. H., and Vinson, C. G., 1938, Particle size of tobacco mosaic virus. Missouri Ag. Exp. Stat. Res. Bull., no. 286.

Hirst, G. K., 1941, The agglutination of red cells by allantoic fluid of chick embryos infected with influenza virus. Science, 94, 22-23.

Hoagland, C. L., Lavin, G. I., Smadel, J. E., and Rivers, T. M., 1940, Constituents of elementary bodies of vaccinia. II. Properties of nucleic acid obtained from vaccine virus. J. Exp. Med., 72, 139-147.

Hook, A. E., Beard, D., Taylor, A. R., Sharp, D. G., and Beard, J. W., 1946, Isolation and characterization of the T_2 bacteriophage of Escherichia coli. J. Biol. Chem., 165, 241-258.

Hughes, T. P., Parker, R. F., and Rivers, T. M., 1935, Immunological and chemical investigations of vaccine virus. II. Chemical analysis of elementary bodies of vaccinia. J. Exp. Med., 62, 349-352.

Iwanowski, D., 1892, Über die Mosaikkrankheit der Tabakspflanze. Bull. Acad. imp. sci., St. Petersburg, 3, 67-70.

Johnson, F. H., Baylor, M. B., and Fraser, D., 1948, The thermal denaturation of tobacco mosaic virus in relation to hydrostatic pressure. Arch. Biochem., 19, 237-245.

Kahn, D. S., and Polson, A., 1947, A new method for forming sharp boundaries in diffusion experiments. J. Phys. and Colloid Chem., 51, 816-825.

Kassanis, B., and Kleczkowski, A., 1944, The effect of formaldehyde and mercuric chloride on tobacco mosaic virus. Biochem. J., 38, 20-24.

Knight, C. A., 1942a, The physical and chemical properties of a distinctive strain of tobacco mosaic virus. J. Biol. Chem., 145, 11-18.

Knight, C. A., 1942b, Basic amino acids in strains of tobacco mosaic virus. J. Am. Chem. Soc., 64, 2734-2736.

Knight, C. A., 1944, A sedimentable component of allantoic fluid and its relationship to influenza viruses. J. Exp. Med., 80, 83-100.

Knight, C. A., 1946a, Precipitin reactions of highly

purified influenza viruses and related materials. J. Exp. Med., *83*, 281-294.

Knight, C. A., 1946b, The preparation of highly purified PR8 influenza virus from infected mouse lungs. J. Exp. Med., *83*, 11-24.

Knight, C. A., 1947a, The nucleic acid and carbohydrate of influenza virus. J. Exp. Med., *85*, 99-116.

Knight, C. A., 1947b, Amino acid composition of highly purified viral particles of influenza A and B. J. Exp. Med., *86*, 125-129.

Knight, C. A., 1947c, The nature of some of the chemical differences among strains of tobacco mosaic virus. J. Biol. Chem., *171*, 297-308.

Knight, C. A., 1947d, Nucleoproteins and virus activity. Cold Spring Harbor Symp. on Quant. Biol., *12*, 115-121.

Knight, C. A., and Oster, G., 1947, The size of the particles of some strains of tobacco mosaic virus as shown by the electron microscope. Arch. Biochem., *15*, 289-294.

Knight, C. A., and Stanley, W. M., 1941, Preparation and properties of cucumber virus 4. J. Biol. Chem., *141*, 29-38.

Kozloff, L. M., and Knowlton, K., Putnam, F. W., and Evans, E. A., Jr., 1951, Biochemical studies of virus reproduction. V. The origin of bacteriophage nitrogen. J. Biol. Chem., *188*, 101-116.

Kozloff, L. M., and Putnam, F. W., 1950, Biochemical studies of virus reproduction. III. The origin of virus phosphorus in the *Escherichia coli* T6 bacteriophage system. J. Biol. Chem., *182*, 229-242.

Lamm, O., 1937, Measurements of concentration gradients in sedimentation and diffusion by refraction methods. Solubility properties of potato starch. Nova Acta Regiae Soc. Sci. Upsaliensis [*4*], No. 6, 10.

Lauffer, M. A., 1943a, The sedimentation rate of the infectious principle of tobacco mosaic virus. J. Biol. Chem., *151*, 627-634.

Lauffer, M. A., 1943b, Denaturation of tobacco mosaic virus by urea. II. Kinetic aspects. J. Am. Chem. Soc., *65*, 1793-1802.

Lauffer, M. A., 1944, The size and shape of tobacco mosaic virus particles. J. Am. Chem. Soc., *66*, 1188-1194.

Lauffer, M. A., and Carnelly, H. L., 1945, Thermal destruction of influenza A virus hemagglutinin. I. The kinetic process. Arch. Biochem., *8*, 265-274.

Lauffer, M. A., Carnelly, H. L., and MacDonald, E., 1947, Thermal destruction of influenza A virus infectivity. Arch. Biochem., *16*, 321-328.

Lauffer, M. A., and Dow, R. B., 1941, The denaturation of tobacco mosaic virus at high pressures. J. Biol. Chem., *140*, 509-518.

Lauffer, M. A., and Miller, G. L., 1944, The sedimentation rate of the biological activities of influenza A virus. J. Exp. Med., *80*, 521-529.

Lauffer, M. A., and Price, W. C., 1940, Thermal denaturation of tobacco mosaic virus. J. Biol Chem., *133*, 1-15.

Lauffer, M. A., and Price, W. C., 1947, Electrophoretic purification of Southern bean mosaic virus. Arch. Biochem., *15*, 115-124.

Lauffer, M. A., and Stanley, W. M., 1938, Stream double refraction of virus proteins. J. Biol. Chem., *123*, 507-525.

Lauffer, M. A., and Stanley, W. M., 1939, The physical chemistry of tobacco mosaic virus protein. Chem. Rev., *24*, 303-321.

Lauffer, M. A., and Stanley, W. M., 1943, The denaturation of tobacco mosaic virus by urea. I. Biochemical aspects. Arch. Biochem., *2*, 413-424.

Lauffer, M. A., and Stanley, W. M., 1944, Biophysical properties of preparations of PR8 influenza virus. J. Exp. Med., *80*, 531-548.

Lauffer, M. A., and Taylor, N. W., 1952, Unpublished results.

Lauffer, M. A., Taylor, N. W., and Wunder, C. C., 1952, Unpublished results.

Lauffer, M. A., and Wheatley, M., 1951, Destruction and denaturation of influenza A virus. Arch. Biochem. and Biophys., *32*, 436-447.

Lea, D. E., 1947, Actions of Radiations on Living Cells. Macmillan, New York.

Ledingham, J. C. G., 1931, The aetiological importance of the elementary bodies in vaccinia and fowl-pox. Lancet, *2*, 525-526.

Loeffler, F., and Frosch, P., 1898, Berichte der Kommission zur Erforschung der Maul-und Klauenseuche bei dem Institut für Infektionskrankheiten in Berlin. Zentralbl. f. Bakter. Abt. I. Orig., *23*, 371-391.

Longsworth, L. G., 1942, Recent advances in the study of proteins by electrophoresis. Chem. Rev., *30*, 323-340.

Loring, H. S., 1938, Properties of the latent mosaic virus protein. J. Biol. Chem., *126*, 455-478.

Loring, H. S., 1939, Properties and hydrolytic products of nucleic acid from tobacco mosaic virus. J. Biol. Chem., *130*, 251-258.

Loring, H. S., Marton, L., and Schwerdt, C. E., 1946, Electron microscopy of purified Lansing virus. Proc. Soc. Exp. Biol. and Med., *62*, 291-292.

Loring, H. S., and Schwerdt, C. E., 1946, Isolation of a macromolecular constituent with properties of the Lansing strain of poliomyelitis virus. Proc. Soc. Exp. Biol. and Med., *62*, 289-291.

Luria, S. E., Delbrück, M., and Anderson, T. F., 1943, Electron microscope studies of bacterial viruses. J. Bact., *46*, 57-76.

MacCallum, W. G., and Oppenheimer, E. H., 1922, Differential centrifugation; A method for the study of filterable viruses, as applied to vaccinia. J. Am. Med. Assn., *78*, 410-411.

MacDonald, E., Price, W. C., and Lauffer, M. A., 1949, A yellow variant of Southern bean mosaic virus. The isoelectric points of yellow and of regular southern-bean-mosaic-virus proteins. Arch. Biochem., *24*, 114-118.

Malkiel, S., 1947, Immunochemical studies on tobacco mosaic virus. II. The host-strain relationship. J. Immunol., *57*, 43-49.

McClelland, L., and Hare, R., 1941, The adsorption of influenza virus by red cells and a new *in vitro* method of measuring antibodies for influenza virus. Canad. J. Pub. Health, *32*, 530-538.

McFarlane, A. S., and Kekwick, R. A., 1938, Physical

properties of bushy stunt virus protein. Biochem. J., *32*, 1607-1613.

McIntosh, J., and Selbie, F. R., 1940, The application of the Sharples centrifuge to the study of viruses. Brit. J. Exp. Path., *21*, 153-160.

McKinney, H. H., 1927, Quantitative and purification methods in virus studies. J. Ag. Res., *35*, 13-38.

McLaren, A. D., 1949, Photochemistry of enzymes, proteins, and viruses. Adv. Enzymol., *9*, 75-170.

Miller, G. L., 1944, Influence of pH and of certain other conditions on the stability of the infectivity and red cell agglutinating activity of influenza virus. J. Exp. Med., *80*, 507-520.

Miller, G. L., Lauffer, M. A., and Stanley, W. M., 1944, Electrophoretic Studies on PR8 influenza virus. J. Exp. Med., *80*, 549-560.

Miller, G. L., and Price, W. C., 1946a, Physical and chemical studies on southern bean mosaic virus. I. Size, shape, hydration and elementary composition. Arch. Biochem., *10*, 467-477.

Miller, G. L., and Price, W. C., 1946b, Physical and chemical studies on southern bean mosaic virus. III. Electrophoretic and nucleic acid studies. Arch. Biochem., *11*, 337-343.

Miller, G. L., and Stanley, W. M., 1941, Derivatives of tobacco mosaic virus. I. Acetyl and phenylureido virus. J. Biol. Chem., *141*, 905-920.

Miller, G. L., and Stanley, W. M., 1942, Derivatives of tobacco mosaic virus. II. Carbobenzoxy, -chlorobenzoyl, and benzenesulfonyl virus. J. Biol. Chem., *146*, 331-338.

Müller, H. O., 1942, Die Ausmessung der tiefe übermikroskopischer Objekte. Kolloid Ztschr., *99*, 6-28.

Neurath, H., 1942. The investigation of proteins by diffusion measurements. Chem. Rev., *30*, 357-394.

Neurath, H., and Cooper, G. R., 1940, The diffusion constant of tomato bushy stunt virus. J. Biol. Chem., *135*, 455-462.

Neurath, H., and Saum, A. M., 1938, The diffusion of tobacco mosaic virus protein in aqueous solution. J. Biol. Chem., *126*, 435-442.

Northrop, J. H., and Anson, M. L., 1929, A method for the determination of diffusion constants and the calculation of the radius and weight of the hemoglobin molecule. J. Gen. Physiol., *12*, 543-554.

Oster, G., 1946, Molecular weights and other properties of viruses as determined by light absorption. Science, *103*, 306-308.

Oster, G., Doty, P. M., and Zimm, B. H., 1947, Light scattering studies of tobacco mosaic virus. J. Am. Chem. Soc., *69*, 1193-1197.

Oster, G., and McLaren, A. D., 1950, The ultraviolet light and photosensitized inactivation of tobacco mosaic virus. J. Gen. Physiol. *33*, 215-228.

Parker, R. F., and Rivers, T. M., 1935, Immunological and chemical investigations on vaccine virus. I. Preparations of elementary bodies of vaccinia. J. Exp. Med., *62*, 65-72.

Parker, R. F., and Rivers, T. M., 1936a, Immunological and chemical investigations of vaccine virus. III. Response of rabbits to inactive elementary bodies of vaccinia and to virus-free extracts of vaccine virus. J. Exp. Med. *63*, 69-94.

Parker, R. F., and Rivers, T. M., 1936b, Immunological and chemical investigations of vaccine virus. IV. Statistical studies of elementary bodies in relation to infection and agglutination. J. Exp. Med., *64*, 439-452.

Parker, R. F., and Rivers, T. M., 1937, Immunological and chemical investigations of vaccine virus. VI. Isolation of a heat-stable, serologically active substance from tissues infected with vaccine virus. J. Exp. Med., *65*, 243-249.

Parker, R. F., and Smythe, C. V., 1937, Immunological and chemical investigations of vaccine virus. V. Metabolic studies of elementary bodies of vaccinia. J. Exp. Med., *65*, 109-120.

Pickels, E. G., 1938, A new type of air bearing for air-driven high-speed centrifuges. Rev. Sci. Inst., *9*, 358-364.

Pickels, E. G., 1943, Sedimentation in the angle centrifuge. J. Gen. Physiol., *26*, 341-360.

Pirie, N. W., Smith, K. M., Spooner, E. T. C., and McClement, W. D., 1938, Purified preparations of tobacco necrosis virus (Nicotiana virus II). Parasitology, *30*, 543-551.

Pollard, E., 1951, Ionizing radiation as a test of molecular organization. Am. Scientist, *39*, 99-109.

Porter, K. R., and Thompson, H. P., 1948, A particulate body associated with epithelial cells cultured from mammary carcinomas of mice of a milk-factor strain. J. Exp. Med., *88*, 15-24.

Price, W. C., 1940, Thermal inactivation of four plant viruses. Arch. ges. Virusforsch. *1*, 373-386.

Price, W. C., 1946, Purification and crystallization of southern bean mosaic virus. Am. J. Bot., *33*, 45-54.

Price, W. C., Williams, R. C., and Wyckoff, R. W. G., 1945, Electron micrographs of crystalline plant viruses. Arch. Biochem, *9*, 175-185.

Price, W. C., Williams, R. C., and Wyckoff, R. W. G., 1946, Electron micrographs of crystalline plant viruses. Arch. Biochem., *9*, 175-185.

Putnam, F. W., and Kozloff, L. M., 1950, Biochemical studies of virus reproduction. IV. The fate of the infecting virus particle. J. Biol. Chem., *182*, 243-250.

Randall, R., Mills, J. W., and Engel, L. L., 1947, The preparation and properties of a purified equine encephalomyelitis vaccine. J. Immunol, *55*, 41-52.

Reed, W., Carroll, J., Agramonte, A., and Lazear, J. W., 1911, Yellow fever: a compilation of various publications, U. S. 61st Cong., 3d sess., Senate, Doc. No. 822, Washington.

Richards, A. G., Jr., Anderson, T. F., and Hance, R. T., 1942, A microtome sectioning technique for electron microscopy illustrated with sections of striated muscle. Proc. Soc. Exp. Biol. and Med., *51*, 148-152.

Ross, A. F., 1941a, Purification and properties of alfalfa-mosaic virus protein. Phytopathology, *31*, 394-410.

Ross, A. F., 1941b, The determination of some amino acids in tobacco mosaic virus protein. J. Biol. Chem., *138*, 741-749.

Ross, A. F., 1942, The fractionation of the amino acids of tobacco mosaic virus protein. J. Biol. Chem., *143*, 685-693.

Ross, A. F., and Stanley, W. M., 1938, The partial reactivation of formolized tobacco mosaic virus protein. J. Gen. Physiol., *22*, 165-191.

Ross, A. F., and Stanley, W. M., 1939, The sulphur and phosphorous content of tobacco mosaic virus. J. Am. Chem. Soc., *61*, 535-536.

Ruska, H., von Borries, B., and Ruska, E., 1939, Die Bedeutung der Übermikroskopie für die Virusforschung. Arch. ges. Virusforsch., *1*, 155-169.

Salk, J. E., 1946, Variation in influenza viruses. A study of heat stability of the red cell agglutinating factor. Proc. Soc. Exper. Biol. and Med., *63*, 134-139.

Schachman, H. K., and Lauffer, M. A., 1949, The hydration, size and shape of tobacco mosaic virus. J. Am. Chem. Soc., *71*, 536-541.

Scherp, H. W., 1933, The diffusion coefficient of crystalline trypsin. J. Gen. Physiol., *16*, 795-800.

Schlesinger, M., 1933, Reindarstellung eines Bakteriophagen in met freiem auge sichtbaren Mengen. Biochem. Ztschr., *264*, 6-12.

Schramm, G., and Bergold, G., 1947, Über das Molekulargewicht des Tabakmosaikvirus. Ztschr. f. Naturforsch., *2b*, 108-112.

Schramm, G., Born, H. J., and Lang, A., 1942, Versuch über den Phosphoraustausch zwischen radiophosphorhaltigem Tabakmosaikvirus und Natriumphosphat. Naturwiss., *30*, 170-171.

Schwerdt, C. E., and Loring, H. S., 1947, The identification of three mononucleotides from tobacco mosaic virus nucleic acid. J. Biol. Chem., *167*, 593-597.

Scott, E. M., and Lauffer, M. A., 1946a, Thermal destruction of influenza A virus hemagglutinin. III. The effect of urea. Arch. Biochem, *11*, 179-184.

Scott, E. M., and Lauffer, M. A., 1946b, Thermal destruction of influenza A virus hemagglutinin. IV. The effect of initial virus concentration. Arch. Biochem., *11*, 185-189.

Sharp, D. G., Taylor, A. R., Beard, D., and Beard, J. W., 1942, Electrophoresis of the rabbit papilloma virus protein. J. Biol. Chem., *142*, 193-202.

Sharp, D. G., Taylor, A. R., Beard, D., and Beard, J. W., 1943, Morphology of the eastern and western strains of equine encephalomyelitis. Arch. Path., *36*, 167-176.

Sharp, D. G., Taylor, A. R., McLean, I. W., Jr., Beard, D., and Beard, J. W., 1944a, Density and size of influenza virus A (PR8 strain) in solution. Science, *100*, 151-153.

Sharp, D. G., Taylor, A. R., McLean, I. W., Jr., Beard, D., and Beard, J. W., 1944b, Sedimentation velocity and electron micrographic studies of influenza virus A (PR8 strain) and B (Lee strain) and the swine influenza virus. J. Biol. Chem., *156*, 585-600.

Sharp, D. G., Taylor, A. R., McLean, I. W., Jr., Beard, D., Beard, J. W., Feller, A. E., and Dingle, J. H., 1944c, Isolation and characterization of influenza virus B (Lee strain). J. Immunol., *48*, 129-153.

Sharp, D. G., Taylor, A. R., McLean, I. W., Jr., Beard, D., and Beard, J. W., 1945, Densities and sizes of the influenza viruses A (PR8 strain) and

B (Lee strain) and the swine influenza virus. J. Biol. Chem., *159*, 29-44.

Sharp, D. G., Taylor, A. R., Hook, A. E., and Beard, J. W., 1946, Rabbit papilloma and vaccinia viruses and T2 bacteriophage of E. coli in "shadow" electron micrographs. Proc. Soc. Exper. Biol. and Med., *61*, 259-265.

Sigurgeirsson, T., and Stanley, W. M., 1947, Electron microscope studies on tobacco-mosaic virus. Phytopathology, *37*, 26-38.

Simha, R., 1940, Influence of Brownian movement on viscosity of solutions. J. Phys. Chem., *44*, 25-34.

Smadel, J. E., Pickels, E. G., and Shedlovsky, T., 1938, Ultracentrifugation studies on the elementary bodies of vaccine virus. II. The influence of sucrose, glycerol, and urea solutions on the physical nature of vaccine virus. J. Exp. Med., *68*, 607-627.

Stanley, W. M., 1935, Isolation of a crystalline protein possessing the properties of tobacco mosaic virus. Science, *81*, 644-645.

Stanley, W. M., 1936a, The inactivation of crystalline tobacco mosaic virus protein. Science, *83*, 626-627.

Stanley, W. M., 1936b, Chemical studies on the virus of tobacco mosaic. VII. An improved method for the preparation of crystalline tobacco mosaic virus protein. J. Biol. Chem., *115*, 673-678.

Stanley, W. M., 1937a, Chemical studies on the virus of tobacco mosaic. VIII. The isolation of a crystalline protein possessing the properties of aucuba mosaic virus. J. Biol. Chem., *117*, 325-340.

Stanley, W. M., 1937b, Crystalline tobacco mosaic virus protein. Am. J. Bot., *24*, 59-68.

Stanley, W. M., 1937c, Chemical studies of the virus of tobacco mosaic. IX. Correlation of virus activity and protein on centrifugation of protein from solution under various conditions. J. Biol. Chem., *117*, 755-770.

Stanley, W. M., 1938a, The isolation and properties of tobacco mosaic and other virus proteins. Harvey Lectures, Ser. 33, 170-204.

Stanley, W. M., 1938b, Aucuba mosaic virus protein isolated from diseased, excised tomato roots grown in vitro. J. Biol. Chem., *126*, 125-131.

Stanley, W. M., 1939, The isolation and properties of tobacco ring spot virus, J. Biol. Chem., 129, 405-428.

Stanley, W. M., 1940, Purification of tomato bushy stunt virus by differential centrifugation. J. Biol. Chem., *135*, 437-454.

Stanley, W. M., 1941a, Chemical properties of viruses. Sci. Month., *53*, 197-210.

Stanley, W. M., 1941b, Some chemical, medical and philosophical aspects of viruses. Science, *93*, 145-151.

Stanley, W. M., 1942a, The concentration and purification of tobacco mosaic virus by means of the Sharples super-centrifuge. J. Am. Chem. Soc., *64*, 1804-1806.

Stanley, W. M., 1942b, The preparation and use of tobacco mosaic virus containing radioactive phosphorous. J. Gen. Physiol., *25*, 881-890.

Stanley, W. M., 1943, Chemical structure and the mutation of viruses, in Virus Diseases, Ithaca, Cornell University Press, 35-59.

Stanley, W. M., 1944a, An evaluation of methods for

the concentration and purification of influenza virus. J. Exp. Med., *79*, 255-266.

Stanley, W. M., 1944b, The size of the influenza virus. J. Exper. Med., *79*, 267-283.

Stanley, W. M., 1945, The preparation and properties of influenza virus vaccines concentrated and purified by differential centrifugation. J. Exp. Med., *81*, 193-218.

Stanley, W. M., 1946, The efficiency of different Sharples centrifuge bowls in the concentration of tobacco mosaic and influenza viruses. J. Immunol., *53*, 179-189.

Stanley, W. M., 1947, Chemical studies on viruses. Chem. and Engin. News, *25*, 3786-3791.

Stanley, W. M., and Anderson, T. F., 1941, A study of purified viruses with the electron microscope. J. Biol. Chem., *139*, 325-338.

Stanley, W. M., and Anderson, T. F., 1942, Electron micrographs of protein molecules. J. Biol. Chem. *146*, 25-30.

Stanley, W. M., and Lauffer, M. A., 1939, Disintegration of tobacco mosaic virus in urea solutions. Science, *89*, 345-347.

Stanley, W. M., and Loring, H. S., 1936, The isolation of crystalline tobacco mosaic virus protein from diseased tomato plants. Science, *83*, 85.

Stanley, W. M., and Loring, H. S., 1939, Properties of purified viruses. Relazioni del IV Congresso Internazionale di patologia comparata, *1*, 45-87.

Stanley, W. M., and Wyckoff, R. W. G., 1937, The isolation of tobacco ring spot and other virus proteins by ultracentrifugation. Science, *85*, 181-183.

Steere, R. L., and Williams, R. C., 1948, A simplified method of purifying tomato bushy-stunt virus for electron microscopy. Phytopathology, *38*, 948-954.

Svedberg, T., and Pederson, K. O., 1940, The Ultracentrifuge. Oxford, Clarendon Press.

Takahashi, W. N., and Rawlins, T. E., 1932, Method for determining shape of colloidal particles; application in the study of tobacco mosaic virus. Proc. Soc. Exp. Biol. and Med., *30*, 155-157.

Takahashi, W. N., and Rawlins, T. E., 1937, Stream double refraction of preparations of crystalline tobacco mosaic. Science, *85*, 103-104.

Taylor, A. R., 1944, Chemical analysis of the influenza viruses A (PR8 strain) and B (Lee strain) and the swine influenza virus. J. Biol. Chem., *153*, 675-686.

Taylor, A. R., 1946, Chemical analysis of the T_2 bacteriophage and its host, *Escherichia coli* (strain B). J. Biol. Chem., *165*, 271-284.

Taylor, A. R., Beard, D., Sharp, D. G., and Beard, J. W., 1942, Nucleic acid of the rabbit papilloma virus protein. J. Infect. Dis., *71*, 110-114.

Taylor, A. R., Sharp, D. G., Beard, D., and Beard, J. W., 1943a, Isolation and properties of the equine encephalomyelitis virus (eastern strain). J. Infect. Dis., *72*, 31-41.

Taylor, A. R., Sharp, D. G., Beard, D., Beard, J. W., Dingle, J. H., and Feller, A. E., 1943b, Isolation and characterization of influenza A virus (PR8 strain). J. Immunol., *47*, 261-282.

Taylor, A. R., Sharp, D. G., McLean, I. W., Jr., Beard, D., and Beard, J. W., 1945, Concentration and purification of influenza virus for the preparation of vaccines. J. Immunol., *50*, 291-316.

Thornberry, H. H., 1935, Quantitative studies on the filtration of tobacco mosaic virus. Phytopathology, *25*, 601-617.

Tiselius, A., 1937, A new apparatus for electrophoretic analysis of colloidal mixtures. Trans. Faraday Soc., *33*, 524-531.

Tiselius, A., Pedersen, K. O., and Svedberg, T., 1937, Analytical measurements of ultracentrifugal sedimentation. Nature., *140*, 848-849.

Vinson, C. G., and Petre, A. W., 1929, Mosaic disease of tobacco. Bot. Gaz., *87*, 14-38.

Vinson, C. G., and Petre, A. W., 1931, Mosaic disease of tobacco. II. Activity of the virus precipitated by lead acetate. Contrib. Boyce Thomp. Inst., *3*, 131-145.

Williams, R. C., and Backus, R. C., 1949, Macromolecular weights determined by direct particle counting. I. The weight of the bushy-stunt virus particle. J. Am. Chem. Soc., *71*, 4052-4057.

Williams, R. C., and Wyckoff, R. W. G., 1944, The thickness of electron microscopic objects. J. Appl. Phys., *15*, 712-716.

Williams, R. C., and Wyckoff, R. W. G., 1945a, Electron shadow-micrography of virus particles. Proc. Soc. Exp. Biol. and Med., *58*, 265-270.

Williams, R. C., and Wyckoff, R. W. G., 1945b, Electron shadow-micrographs of haemocyanin molecules. Nature, *156*, 68-70.

Woodruff, C. E., and Goodpasture, E. W., 1929, The infectivity of isolated inclusion bodies of fowl-pox. Am. J. Path., *5*, 1-9.

Woodruff, C. E., and Goodpasture, E. W., 1930, The relation of the virus of fowl-pox to the specific cellular inclusions of the disease. Am. J. Path., *6*, 713-720.

Wyckoff, R. W. G., 1948, The electron microscopy of macromolecular crystals. Acta Crystall., *1*, 292-294.

Wyckoff, R. W. G., 1949, Electron Microscopy. New York, Interscience.

Wyckoff, R. W. G., 1951, The virus of vaccinia in chick embryo membrane. Proc. Nat. Acad. Sci., *37*, 565-569.

Zworykin, V. K., Morton, G. A., Ramberg, E. G., Hillier, J., and Vance, A. W., 1945, Electron Optics and the Electron Microscope. New York, Wiley.

JOSEPH E. SMADEL, M.D.

Army Medical Service Graduate School

3

Serologic Reactions in Viral and Rickettsial Infections

INTRODUCTION

Serologic methods provide the trellis which supports the rapidly spreading growth of knowledge of viral and rickettsial agents. Most of the basic technics have been borrowed directly from bacteriology and immunology, but these generally have been modified because of difficulties encountered in obtaining appreciable quantities of reasonably pure viral and rickettsial antigens. However, highly purified materials have become available in a number of instances and one may expect this progress to continue.

It is not the purpose of this chapter to catalogue in detail various tests employed with each viral and rickettsial agent. The objectives are: to discuss principles of broad applicability, to illustrate the methods employed in the field by providing detailed descriptions of selected technics, and to summarize in tabular form the more important serologic methods used in work on viral and rickettsial diseases of man. Students who are interested in more exhaustive accounts of the subjects which are not discussed completely here or elsewhere in this book are referred to the original publications and to the report of the American Public Health Association's Committee on Diagnostic Procedures for Virus and Rickettsial Diseases (1948).

NEUTRALIZATION

Following recovery from a viral or rickettsial disease the sera of men and animals generally contain immune substances which are capable of neutralizing the infectious agent. These protective antibodies, which are highly specific, are demonstrated by adding the serum to infectious material and then inoculating the mixture into a susceptible host which serves as an indicator of the presence or absence of active agent in the mixture. It may be mentioned that this principle was established with vaccinia (Sternberg, 1892) several years before it was used with bacteria. The neutralization test has continued to be a mainstay in the virus field but has not proved of equal value in studies on the rickettsial agents. This technic provides a method, which is not unduly complex, for detecting minute amounts of specific antibody. The information thus obtained is useful in the diagnosis of disease as well as in estimating the response of the host to certain vaccines. The technic can be used also to identify newly isolated strains of virus. When employed for this purpose potent antisera against known viruses are tested for their capacity to neutralize the unknown agent.

Neutralization tests are always costly in time and materials and frequently are difficult to interpret. An ideal test of this type would be one in which (1) a single infectious unit of the agent induces, in a highly susceptible host, a disease which is readily recognizable by death of the animal or by an obvious lesion at the site of inoculation, (2) the agent is sufficiently stable so that suspensions can be prepared, standardized, and stored until used without appreciable loss of potency, and (3) the specific antibody, which develops in the convalescent host, occurs in appreciable amounts and is relatively stable. The continued extensive use of the neutralization test in studies of most of the viral diseases indicates that it is a useful procedure even though all of the criteria just mentioned are rarely fulfilled.

No single neutralization technic is satisfactory for all the viral agents. In the search for the most suitable conditions for employing the method with each virus, many variations have been introduced. Some of these have been instituted in order to provide a dependable, relatively simple procedure which can be used for assaying large numbers of sera. The neutralization test used in the world-wide surveys on yellow fever supplies an example of such an adaptation of the principles to a specific purpose (Bugher, 1948). Other variations have been introduced to provide a high degree of accuracy for special experimental studies. One example is the influenza technic described by Kilbourne and Horsfall (1951); another is Parker's method for vaccinia which is outlined in this section. Much work has gone into studies of the neutralization phenomenon in relation to neurotropic viruses, and certain methods have been devised which are usable for routine diagnostic purposes (Olitsky and Casals, 1947; Hammon, 1948). It is evident, therefore, that there is no standard neutralization test which is applicable under all circumstances. Each technic represents a compromise in the selection of various factors which influence the final result; among these are the choice of the indicator host, the route of inoculation, the source of virus, the type of antiserum, the use of constant dilutions of serum with serial dilutions of virus or vice versa, the time and temperature of incubation of virus-antiserum mixture, and the age of the inoculated animals. An indication of the range of indicator hosts and of the sources of virus employed in neutralization tests is given in Table 6.

An example of a neutralization test in which death or survival of the animal serves to indicate the presence or absence of active virus is given below. This method, which was recommended by the Neurotropic Virus Disease Commission in 1942 for the diagnosis of epidemic viral encephalitides of North America, has yielded satisfactory results over a period of years at the Army Medical Center with these as well as several other neurotropic agents. Like other general-purpose technics it has limitations. The following detailed description of the Commission's technic is quoted from Paul (1944).

(a) Virus. Ten or more brains removed from mice showing nervous signs are ground with sand or alundum and 10 cc. of inactivated* undiluted rabbit serum are added for each gm. of brain tissue. After centrifugation at about 2000 r. p. m. for ten minutes, the supernatant fluid is drawn off and regarded as the 1 to 10 dilution of virus. Part of it is titrated immediately, and the rest is distributed in ampules in 1-cc. amounts. [2 cc. quantities are often preferable, Ed.] The sealed ampules are quickly frozen in a mixture of solid CO_2 and 95 percent alcohol and stored in a solid CO_2 refrigerator. Depending upon needs, one or more ampules are thawed and used in each test, the unused portion of the virus being discarded.

(b) Preparation of Virus Dilutions, and Control and Serum-virus Mixtures. Starting with the 1 to 10 dilution from the frozen ampule, one prepares 1 to 50, 1 to 500, 1 to 5000, etc., up to 1 to 500,000,000 or 1 to 5,000,000,000 dilutions, using 10 percent rabbit serum in saline as the diluent and a separate pipet for each dilution. Then 0.2 cc. of the selected dilutions are added to marked tubes containing either 0.2 cc. of the undiluted unknown serum or of a tested negative, undiluted rabbit serum for the control mixtures.

* Inactivation is carried out at 56° C. for one-half hour.

(c) Selection of Critical Dilutions. If the preliminary titration has indicated that the LD_{50} titre of the virus to be used is in the range of the 10^{-8} dilution, after incubation at 37° C. for two hours, then the control dilutions to be tested will be 10^{-6}, 10^{-7}, 10^{-8}, and 10^{-9} and the serum dilutions 10^{-4}, 10^{-5}, 10^{-6}, 10^{-7}. Similarly:

(1) with preliminary LD_{50} titre of virus in range of 10^{-7},
Control dilutions,
$$10^{-5}, 10^{-6}, 10^{-7}, 10^{-8}$$
Serum dilutions,
$$10^{-3}, 10^{-4}, 10^{-5}, 10^{-6}$$

(2) with preliminary LD_{50} titre of virus in range of 10^{-9},
Control dilutions,
$$10^{-7}, 10^{-8}, 10^{-9}, 10^{-10}$$
Serum . . . . $10^{-5}, 10^{-6}, 10^{-7}, 10^{-8}$

These dilutions are selected in order to be within the range of 100 percent mortality at one end, and 100 percent survival at the other in the control titration, bearing in mind the variations in titre that may be expected with virus suspensions preserved in the frozen state. When the test is to be used for diagnosis with a virus that has been found to maintain its titre well, one may dispense with the lowest dilution in the serum mixtures (i.e., the 10^{-3}. or 10^{-4}, or 10^{-5}) and use 3 instead of 4 serum-virus dilutions. [Author's Note. Stock virus preparations which have diminished in titer by 1.5 to 2.0 log dilutions during storage should be replaced by new materials.]

(d) Incubation, Numbers of Mice, and Period of Observation. Five mice are to be inoculated with each dilution. The intracerebral route of inoculation is used, employing 0.25-cc. tuberculin syringes to permit a more accurate delivery of a standard 0.03-cc. dose. If the number of mice should become limited either because of inadequate supply or the large number of sera to be tested, four mice may be used for each dilution. The controls and serum-virus mixtures are to be incubated in a water bath at 37° C. for two hours and then placed in an ice-bath until inoculated. The highest dilutions are to be inoculated first (i.e., 10^{-9}, 10^{-8}, 10^{-7}, etc.) and the control mixtures should be the last. The mice shall be observed and deaths recorded for at least ten days in the case of Western and Eastern equine encephalitis and for at least fourteen days in the case of St. Louis encephalitis virus. All deaths within twenty-four hours after inoculation shall be regarded as being due to traumatic or nonvirus causes, and in the case of St. Louis

EXAMPLE

	FINAL DILUTION OF VIRUS						LD_{50} TITRE, LOG OF DILUTION	NEUTRALIZATION INDEX	
MIXTURE	10^{-4}	10^{-5}	10^{-6}	10^{-7}	10^{-8}	10^{-9}			RESULT
Control	. . .	. . .	5/5	4/5	3/5	0/5	8.0		
Serum A	5/5	5/5	5/5	3/5	. . .	. . .	7.0+	<10	Negative
Serum B	5/5	5/5	3/5	2/5	. . .	. . .	6.5	32	Equivocal
Serum C	5/5	4/5	3/5	0/5	. . .	. . .	6.0	100	Positive

Fraction 3/5 indicates that 5 mice were inoculated and in 3 death occurred as a result of the virus infection.

PROCEDURE USED IN CALCULATING LD_{50} TITRE*
CONTROL

	DIED	SURVIVED	ACCUMULATION TOTALS			
			DIED	SURVIVED	DEATHS	% MORTALITY
10^{-6}—5/5	5	0	12	0	12/12	100.0
10^{-7}—4/5	4	1	7	1	7/8	87.5
10^{-8}—3/5	3	2	3	3	3/6	50.0
10^{-9}—0/5	0	5	0	8	0/8	0

∴ LD_{50} titre, log of dilution = 8.0.
Arrows indicate direction of addition for accumulation totals.
* The Reed-Muench formula will be used even in the absence of a zero mortality endpoint or of 2 dilutions below the 50 percent or more mortality range, with the clear understanding that the results are not absolutely accurate. This is the best available procedure for a standard method of expressing the results under circumstances which make it impractical to increase the number of dilutions to cover the strict requirements of the Reed-Muench formula.

SERUM B

	DIED	SURVIVED	ACCUMULATION TOTALS			
			DIED	SURVIVED	DEATHS	% MORTALITY
10^{-4}—5/5	5	0	15	0	15/15	100.0
10^{-5}—5/5	5	0	10	0	10/10	100.0
10^{-6}—3/5	3	2	5	2	5/7	71.4
$\overline{10^{-7}}$—2/5	2	3	2	5	2/7	28.6

$$\frac{\%\ \text{mortality above } 50\% - 50\%}{\%\ \text{mortality above } 50\% - \%\ \text{mortality below } 50\%} = \text{factor or proportionate distance}$$

or

$$\frac{71.4\% - 50\%}{71.4\% - 28.6\%} = \frac{21.4}{42.8} = 0.5$$

When tenfold dilutions are used LD_{50} titre $=$ log of dilution above 50% $+$ factor or in this case $= 6.0 + 0.5 = 6.5$.

CALCULATION OF NEUTRALIZATION INDEX FOR SERUM B

Control titre log of dilution $\quad = 8.0$
minus
Serum B titre log of dilution $= 6.5$
Neutralization index log $\qquad = \overline{1.5}$
Antilog of 1.5 $= 31.6$ or 32; therefore neutralization index $= 32$.

encephalitis virus, considering the dilutions used, all deaths during the first three days shall be regarded as non-specific.

The Commission regarded a neutralization index of 1 to 9 as negative, of 10 to 49 as equivocal, and of 50 or more as positive. Hammon (1948) discusses modifications of this method and the interpretation of results obtained. The finding of a neutralizing antibody against a virus in a single specimen of serum usually cannot be regarded as proof that the recent illness of a patient was caused by the virus in question. Neutralizing antibodies which appear following many infections persist for long periods of time. The picture is further complicated by the occurrence of neutralizing substances in sera of persons who suffered unrecognized disease in the form of inapparent or atypical infection, or who were vaccinated with active or inactive virus. In the face of these facts, the presence of a specific neutralizing antibody in a patient's serum can be looked upon as evidence of previous experience of the person with the agent but no date can be given for the episode. Therefore, it is the rule in good diagnostic work to demand at least two samples of serum for testing: the first is taken early in the disease when anti-bodies are absent or at a low level and the second at an appropriate time during convalescence. The reader is referred to other chapters in this book for detailed information on obtaining, handling and testing specimens for the diagnosis of individual diseases.

The neutralization test ordinarily employed for vaccinia illustrates the use of the dermal lesion of the rabbit as an indication of the infectivity of serum-virus mixtures. Parker (1939) introduced into this test a degree of exactitude not previously attained. It was accomplished by accurate determination of the number of infective particles of virus present before addition of antiserum and of the residual number of infective units in virus-serum mixtures. In practice, preliminary tests were performed to estimate the approximate titer of the stable, stored-virus suspension and the approximate amount of virus neutralized by a given dilution of antiserum. Then, serial twofold dilutions of the infected material were prepared in Locke's solution containing 5 per cent normal rabbit serum. The range selected included as the most concentrated virus suspension that which would be expected to induce lesions at each site of inoculation and as the most dilute that concentration at which lesions would appear at none of the sites. Two sets of such serial twofold dilutions of virus were prepared, one covering the range for virus plus normal serum and the other for virus plus immune serum. As many as 40 intracutaneous inoculations of each virus-serum mixture were made in rabbits. The presence or absence of a lesion at each site was recorded on the 5th day and the titers calculated by the 50 per cent endpoint method which was presented in detail above. The difference between the titer of virus in the presence of normal serum and of the antiserum being studied was taken as the neutralizing capacity of the latter. Such a laborious method as this has limited applicability except in studies on the fundamentals of virus-antibody reactions. A simplified version of Parker's technic used in studies of vaccinia by the writer is conducted in the following manner. Serial tenfold dilutions of stock virus suspension are prepared and portions of each dilution covering the range encompassing the expected endpoints are mixed with equal amounts of normal serum and of the antiserum to be tested. Multiple inoculations of each serum-virus mixture are made into the skin of each of several rabbits; usually two or four areas of skin on one rabbit are infiltrated with each mixture, and from two to four rabbits are used in a single test. The procedure for calculating neutralizing capacity of the antiserum is the same as Parker's. It should be obvious that animals used in neutralization tests must not previously have acquired immunity to the virus under investigation. In studies on vaccinia this point is overlooked too frequently because of failure to recognize the ease with which rabbits acquire subclinical infection, and subsequent resistance, in a laboratory where the virus is being handled. It should be standard practice to use rabbits for neutralization tests for vaccinia on the day that they arrive in the laboratory. Similarly, the normal rabbit serum employed in the test should be obtained from blood drawn from animals which are not immune.

In performing neutralization tests with certain viral agents, it may be necessary, or desirable, to arrive at an indicator reaction by a more circuitous route than death of the animal or the production of a single lesion at the site of inoculation. Burnet, Keogh and Lush (1937) evolved a technic suitable for estimating neutralizing antibodies against certain viruses which are capable of producing pocklike lesions on the chorio-allantoic membranes of embryonated eggs; this embodied a comparison of the average numbers of lesions produced by control and test mixtures of virus and serum. Hirst (1942a,b) demonstrated that neutralization tests could be achieved with egg-passage strains of influenza virus which were not well adapted to animals. He inoculated mixtures of virus and antiserum into embryonated eggs, and after a period of incubation sufficient to allow time for growth of virus, he determined the presence or absence of infection in each test egg by examining its allantoic fluid for viral hemagglutinins. Habel (1945) employed similar principles in studies on antibodies against mumps; here the finding of specific complement-fixing antigen of mumps in eggs used in the neutralization test served to indicate infectivity of the inoculated serum-virus mixture.

The nature of the reaction involved in the neutralization of viruses by antisera has been the subject of lengthy, and often heated, discussion. Following the demonstration by Andrewes (1928) that noninfectious mixtures of virus and antibody regain infectivity when diluted, or treated by other simple means, credence was given to the concepts that no in-vitro combination occurred between virus and neutralizing substance and that the dilution phenomenon was peculiar to viruses. Craigie (1939) summarized the accumulated evidence which suggested that both ideas were erroneous. Undoubtedly, the nature of the reaction will continue to provide a source of scientific interest. It may be noted that recently several workers (Kalmanson and Bronfenbrenner, 1943; Morris, 1944; McKee and Hale, 1946) have emphasized the similarity of the mechanics of the neutralization reaction regardless of whether viruses, bacteria, or toxins are acted upon by their specific antibodies.

There is justification for the general statement that in viral infections of man neutralizing substances are distinct from those antibodies detectable by in-vitro technics. Two diseases in which experimental evidence clearly indicates that such is the case are vaccinia (Craigie, 1939) and lymphocytic choriomeningitis (Smadel and Wall, 1940). Although much information on influenza leads to the conclusion that the antibody which inhibits hemagglutination by the virus in vitro is the same as that which neutralizes the virus in vivo (Hirst, 1942a), nevertheless, certain recent studies appear to show that the responsible antibodies are not identical (Walker and Horsfall, 1950).

COMPLEMENT FIXATION

The basic principles of the complement-fixation technic are identical whether employed in viral and rickettsial diseases or elsewhere. Although attempts to apply the method to viral materials were successful early in this century, the results were generally discredited. During the past decade, the method has come into progressively wider use in the field. Each additional application has invariably awaited the preparation of suitable antigen, i.e., a suspension rich in viral or rickettsial material. The numerous diseases in which the complement-fixation technic is employed in experimental and diagnostic studies are listed in Table 6. A fact not evident from the table is that the method probably has been used more frequently in the routine diagnosis of rickettsial diseases than in work on viral infections. The methods employed in complement-fixation reactions in the epidemic encephalitides and in epidemic typhus fever will be presented in detail as illustrative examples of the application of these technics in the study of viral and rickettsial diseases.

Many neurotropic viruses are obtained in largest amounts when grown in the brains of susceptible animals, and it is axiomatic that the richest available source of virus is the one most likely to yield suitable material for in-vitro testing. Crude complement-fixing antigens prepared from brain tissues have a number of disadvantages. In the first place, they react nonspecifically with certain sera. This is dependent in part on the "antigen-antibody reaction" between normal sera and tissue extracts which has been discussed by Kidd and Friedewald (1942) and which Maltaner (1946) has suggested may be entirely nonspecific in nature and due to the presence of a cephalinlike substance in the tissue extracts. In addition, they react with Wassermann-positive sera from human beings. Over and above these disadvantages, the antigens prepared from brain tissue tend to become anticomplementary and to deteriorate unless special precautions are taken. It is of interest that during the past 15 years methods for preparing complement-fixing antigens from brain tissue have gone through a complete cycle. Craigie and Tulloch (1931) demonstrated that the nonspecific flocculating material, which interfered with interpreting a specific precipitin reaction, could be removed from rabbit brain infected with vaccinia if the tissue were dried, extracted with ether, and repeatedly frozen and thawed following rehydration. Howitt (1937) adopted this method in preparing complement-fixing antigens from brains of animals infected with neurotropic viruses. Subsequently, Casals and Palacios (1941) found that the undesirable reaction could be eliminated if aqueous suspensions of infected brain were repeatedly frozen and thawed, and if the human or animal sera which were used in the test were heated at 60-65° C. Havens and co-workers (1943) preferred to eliminate nonspecific material by high speed centrifugation since with such preparations it was unnecessary to heat the serum to be tested beyond the usual 56° C. The cycle has now been closed by De Boer and Cox (1947) who have returned to lyophilization of infected brain tissue followed by extraction with a lipid solvent to remove the undesirable substance. Although sufficient time has not elapsed for adequate trial of this method for use in routine diagnosis of neurotropic virus diseases, it holds considerable promise. The methods of Casals, of Havens, and of De Boer have been used extensively for the diagnosis of human disease by a few workers; each is satisfactory in the hands of those familiar with it.

The starting substance for preparing antigens by each method is a suspension of infected brain material from moribund mice. Casals and Havens use a 10 per cent suspension in physiologic saline solution which contains 2 per cent inactivated normal serum of mice, guinea pigs, or rabbits. Casals's (1947) description of the processing of such material is as follows:

The suspension is kept overnight in the refrigerator at 2 to 4° C. It is centrifuged next day at 2500 rpm for ½ hour. The supernatant is placed in 100 x 16 mm lusteroid tubes— about 10 cc. to a tube—frozen and thawed by dipping alternately 15 minutes in a dry-ice alcohol mixture and into water at 37° C. This cycle is repeated 4 or 5 times causing a flocculate to appear. In our experience no more than 5 thawings are necessary; however, if flocculation does not occur it would be advisable to continue the treatment until it does. Finally the brain-tissue extract is centrifuged in an electrically driven angle-head centrifuge at 7000 rpm for 1 hour; the supernatant is decanted, measured and merthiolate in dilution 1:10,000 is added. These antigens can be used for as long as 4 months after preparation if kept at 2-4° C. They have been obtained with the following viruses: rabies, Eastern, Western and Venezuelan equine encephalitis, Russian tick-borne, louping-ill, Japanese B, West Nile, St. Louis, GD VII strain of Theiler, and lymphocytic choriomeningitis.

Havens and co-workers (1943) remove the large particles from the brain suspension by horizontal centrifugation and then promptly clarify the suspension by centrifugation in a refrigerated angle centrifuge at 12,000 r.p.m. for one hour. Although such antigens may be stored for some time at 5° C., it is preferable to maintain them in the frozen state at —20° C. or —70° C. Both types can be rendered noninfectious and can be lyophilized, but in the few laboratories where the methods have been used extensively neither of these procedures has been employed regularly in routine diagnostic work; thus, the antigens as used are generally infectious and unstable.

De Boer and Cox (1947) prepare a 20 per cent suspension of infected mouse brains in distilled water, lyophilize the material and then extract the dried powder several times with benzene. The extracted powder can be stored in the dried state until ready for use when it is rehydrated in saline solution and clarified by centrifugation at 10,000 r.p.m. This method is even more dangerous to the laboratory worker than the first two, since the dried powder which is manipulated during extraction is infectious.

The procedure of Casals, Olitsky and Anslow (1951) for obtaining a complement-fixing antigen from the brains of suckling mice infected with poliomyelitis virus is sufficiently different from the methods just described to warrant mention. Homogenized tissue is extracted in succession with acetone, acetone-ethyl ether and ether after which the residual solvent is removed under vacuum. The dry material is suspended in physiologic saline solution and subsequently centrifuged at 10,000 r.p.m. The supernatant material constitutes the antigen and represents a yield of about 0.6 ml. per gram of wet tissue. The authors point out that brains of infant mice contain appreciably less lipids than those of adults and regard this as an important factor in the success of their technic.

Details of the complement-fixation technic employed with the neurotropic viruses need not be gone into here. Suffice it to say that a delicate and accurate procedure is necessary, and usually overnight fixation is pre-ferred. Hammon's (1948) remarks on the interpretation of complement-fixation tests in the epidemic encephalitides are quoted from his review of the subject:

Until a great deal of experience has been gained in performing the complement-fixation test, it is recommended that all sera be tested twice or until two similar results are obtained, each test made on a different day, and prefer-ably with a different antigen. Thus, certain difficulties in interpretation will obviously be avoided. Fixation at a 1:2 level must be re-garded at any time with considerable scepti-cism. Negatives, at least with the Western equine virus, must not be given the same final evaluation as a similar finding with the neu-tralization test. If sera have been heated at 65° C. or twice at 60° C. to free them from anticomplementary or non-specific substances, negatives, for St. Louis at least, lose much sig-nificance.

Inspection of Table 6 shows that most of the complement-fixing antigens of viral origin are not derived from brain tissue. Difficulties associated with nonspecific com-ponents often encountered with antigens prepared from such sources are surmounted with relative ease. The avoidance of brain as a source of antigen is possible even with certain of the neurotropic viruses, namely, lymphocytic choriomeningitis and eastern and western equine encephalitis. It may be emphasized that with the epidemic encepha-litides, as with other viral and rickettsial infections, serologic tests which are entirely satisfactory under carefully controlled con-ditions of scientific investigation may not be generally applicable for routine diag-nosis of human infection. At the present time the widespread use of a number of the specific diagnostic methods for viral and rickettsial diseases is deterred by the rela-tive lack of availability to the ordinary laboratory of simple, noninfectious, stable antigens.

A wide variation exists in the methods employed for the preparation and use of antigens for complement-fixation tests in rickettsial diseases. Only one technic for the preparation of antigen from one agent will be discussed in detail, the others are thoroughly reviewed in recent articles by Smadel (1948a, b). The methods which Plotz and co-workers (1948) employed in their complement-fixation test for the diag-nosis of epidemic typhus are as follows: a 20 per cent suspension of infected yolk-sac tissue is prepared in buffered saline solution, pH 7.0, containing 0.5 per cent formalde-hyde, and gross particles are removed by filtration through bronze gauze. The sus-pension is stored for several days in a cold room while the material becomes noninf-ectious and the large fat particles rise to the surface. The suspension is siphoned off from beneath the yolk-fat layer and cen-trifuged at 4,000 r.p.m. in an angle machine for one hour to deposit the rickettsiae. The sedimented rickettsiae and accompanying particulate yolk-sac material are resus-pended in formol-saline solution and subse-quently extracted with a half volume of ethyl ether. The rickettsiae remain in the aqueous phase which is removed for further processing. Rickettsiae are sedimented by centrifugation, and the supernatant fluid removed and discarded. This supernatant fluid contains a specific soluble substance of typhus which reacts almost equally well with either epidemic or murine convalescent sera. The deposited rickettsiae are resus-pended in diluent, extracted with ether, and rewashed four to six times by differen-tial centrifugation in order to remove re-sidual traces of the soluble antigen. After the final resuspension, the antigen is cen-trifuged in the horizontal machine to remove large particles. Such rickettsial antigens closely approach a state of purity, i.e., com-plete freedom from contaminating material of the host which supported growth of the organism. They are highly specific sero-logically and in complement-fixation tests give cross reaction only with the sera from the closely related disease, murine typhus. In diagnostic tests two units of antigen are mixed with two full units of complement and serial dilutions of the serum to be tested; 0.25 cc. amounts, respectively, of antigen and sera are used and 0.5 cc. amounts of complement. The mixture is incubated overnight at 5° C., after which the hemolytic system is added; this consists of 0.5 cc. of an equal mixture of a 3 per cent suspension of washed sheep erythrocytes and a solution containing three minimal hemolytic doses of amboceptor. The tests are read after further incubation at 37° C. for a half hour.

The application of the complement-fixation technic to the study of individual viral and rickettsial diseases of man is discussed in other chapters in this volume. Intelligent use of the method requires familiarity not only with the technical procedures but also with the clinical features of the different infections. So much variation occurs in the time of appearance of antibodies, the maximal titers which they attain, and the length of time they remain after infection that few generalizations are warranted. Thus, in most neurotropic viral diseases complement-fixing antibodies appear later than do neutralizing substances, but in lymphocytic choriomeningitis the reverse occurs. In the neurotropic virus group, complement-fixing titers rarely exceed 1/32, whereas in the rickettsial and psittacosis groups end points of 1/128 to 1/1024 are not unusual. Furthermore, these antibodies disappear in a few weeks or months in the first group of infections but persist for years in the last two. Even the response of human beings to vaccination varies. For example, a primary course of immunization with appropriate materials rarely elicits complement-fixing antibodies for Japanese B encephalitis virus, whereas epidemic typhus vaccine induces an antibody response in more than half the persons who receive it for the first time. The complement-fixation technic sometimes serves as the means of recognizing newly isolated strains of infectious agents. Smadel and Wall (1941) used it in this manner for the rapid identification of lymphocytic choriomeningitis virus in animals inoculated with infectious material from patients. Furthermore, the method provided data for establishing the antigenic individuality of the newly recognized rickettsia of North Queensland tick typhus (Plotz et al., 1946).

The indirect complement-fixation technic has been employed for detecting antibody against the virus of Newcastle disease (Wolfe et al., 1949) and viruses of the psittacosis-lymphogranuloma venereum group (Karrer et al., 1950; Hilleman et al., 1951) in the sera of certain fowl. In this test, serial dilutions of serum, viz., chicken, containing noncomplement-fixing antibodies are incubated with standard amounts of antigen and complement. Known quantities of specific complement-fixing antibody from rabbit, pigeon, or human serum are added to the mixtures which are again incubated. Following this, the hemolytic system is introduced, and the test is completed and read in the usual manner. Chicken serum which contains psittacosis antibodies binds the antigen but not the complement. Hence, the subsequent addition of pigeon serum, containing complement-fixing antibodies, and of the hemolytic system is followed by lysis of erythrocytes. When the chicken serum is without antibodies, the pigeon serum reacts with antigen and complement, and no hemolysis occurs at the termination of the test.

Another modification of the complement-fixation procedure, namely, the conglutinating complement-absorption test (CCAT), has been adapted for use in Q fever, psittacosis-lymphogranuloma venereum, vaccinia and influenza (Wolfe and Kornfeld, 1948; Stoker et al., 1950; Hilleman et al., 1951). In this test, agglutination of erythrocytes, not their lysis, is observed. The conglutinating system contains sheep erythrocytes which have been sensitized with the natural hemagglutinin of bovine serum and also "conglutinin," a substance in fresh bovine serum, that will agglutinate such sensitized cells in the presence of non-hemolytic complement obtained from the cat or the horse. Dilutions of the serum to be tested, appropriate amounts of antigen and nonhemolytic complement are incubated, after which the conglutinating system is added. If fixation occurred in the original mixture, no complement remains for the conglutinating reaction, and agglutination of erythrocytes does not occur. While the CCAT generally gives a higher value for the titer of a serum than that obtained by ordinary hemolytic complement-fixation tests, this possible advantage is often offset by higher anticomplementary activity and by nonspecific results.

AGGLUTINATION AND PRECIPITATION

The term "flocculation" was used frequently in the earlier literature to describe in-vitro aggregation of viral and rickettsial materials by their specific antisera. There continues to be justification for employing this broad term which embodies both agglutination and precipitation, since, in some instances at least, it is difficult to decide whether the aggregating material is a suspension of particles or a solution. One may use the term "agglutination" with confidence when referring to elementary bodies of vaccinia or to *Rickettsia prowazeki*, for these relatively large structures are readily seen by ordinary microscopy. Similarly, one would not hesitate in applying the term "precipitation" to the specific aggregation obtained with the soluble LS antigen of vaccinia which is a small protein molecule no larger than serum globulins. However, difficulty is encountered in designating the type of flocculation reaction obtained with the soluble antigen of typhus; this serologically active substance consists of particulate material of minute size when compared with the rickettsial organism, but nevertheless the particles are as large as the smallest viruses. In general, "flocculation" should be used to describe specific serologic aggregations displayed by materials known to contain both large particulate structures and soluble antigen, and to designate the reaction when the physical nature of the antigen is uncertain.

The flocculation reaction with materials from a single disease, like the complement-fixation test, may involve concurrently a number of different specific antigen-antibody systems. Vaccinia provides the best example of this. The elementary bodies of vaccinia are agglutinated by at least four different antibodies which occur in convalescent sera and have been designated, respectively, L, S, NP, and X. The first three of these antibodies also react in complement-fixation and precipitation tests with their homologous soluble antigens. Therefore, a flocculation occurring in a mixture of crude antigen of vaccinia and anti-vaccinal serum might represent agglutination of virus particles by any one or all the antibodies just listed, as well as precipitation of the LS antigen by either of its antibodies. The serologic reactions of vaccinia are discussed at length in the chapter on Smallpox and Vaccinia.

In the field of viral and rickettsial diseases, as elsewhere, antigens which flocculate with their specific antisera almost invariably fix complement under appropriate conditions. However, the converse is not true. The data given in Table 6 clearly indicate that the complement-fixation technic is employed in many diseases in which a flocculation reaction has not been demonstrated. In general, less concentrated preparations of antigen are required for detectable fixation of complement than for visible flocculation. This is illustrated by the findings with stock suspensions of washed *R. prowazeki* which were described in the preceding section. Such suspensions are regularly diluted 1/80 to 1/100 when used as antigen in complement-fixation tests, whereas a 1/8 to 1/15 dilution is required for agglutination reactions. Merrill (1936) has brought together data which indicate that a concentration of antigen of the order of 0.001 mg./cc. is required in order for visible flocculation to occur in the presence of appropriate antibody. Table 6 which summarizes data on serologic reactions contains no information on the size of the etiologic agents. Therefore, it should be mentioned that at the present time specific flocculation reactions are restricted almost exclusively to the rickettsiae and large mammalian viruses. The exceptions are the agents of lymphocytic choriomeningitis and influenza among the intermediate-sized viruses and of yellow fever among the small viruses. The list will be extended no doubt when technical difficulties associated with the preparation of concentrated, purified antigens are overcome.

Antigens for use in agglutination tests with rickettsiae of the typhus fever, spotted fever and Q fever groups, and with viruses of the vaccinia-variola and psittacosis-lymphogranuloma venereum groups, as well as antigens for use in precipitin tests for yellow fever, vaccinia, psittacosis, lymphocytic choriomeningitis, influenza and typhus come from diverse sources, all of which need not be enumerated or tabulated here. Methods for preparing these antigens vary considerably as do the technics which are used to demonstrate their presence. Since more is known about the properties of vaccine virus and its antigens than of other viral or rickettsial agents which affect man, certain of the technics which have assisted in adding to our knowledge of this virus will be mentioned in detail.

Studies of the antigenic structure of vaccine virus were facilitated by the preparation of highly purified suspensions of elementary bodies and their use in agglutination tests. Although a number of investigators contributed methods for obtaining such material (Smadel and Hoagland, 1942), the technic of Craigie (1932) embodies all of the essential principles which still are employed for this purpose. His method included use of a strain of virus for seed which was well adapted to growth in the epithelial cells of the skin of rabbits; inoculation of large areas of closely clipped, unpigmented skin of healthy rabbits by gentle scratching with a fine wire brush while the site was bathed with a highly infectious suspension of virus; harvesting

the dermal pulp on the third day following inoculation by lightly scraping the surface with a dull scalpel after moistening the skin with buffered water; and finally, preparing an appropriate dilution of dermal pulp and subjecting it to an extensive process of differential centrifugation. In the last part of the process, large particulate material was removed by horizontal centrifugation; then the elementary bodies were sedimented by spinning at high speed in an angle machine. Sedimented virus was washed several times by resuspension in dilute buffer solution and recentrifugation. Finally, aggregated particles were removed from the suspension of washed virus by prolonged horizontal centrifugation. The resultant virus suspensions were stable; when stored at 5° C. they remained suitable for serologic and infectivity tests for several months. Agglutination tests, in which washed elementary bodies were used, were carried out with equal quantities of an optimal dilution of antigen and serial dilutions of antisera, or vice versa, depending on whether the titer of antigen or antiserum was desired. Tubes containing the test mixtures were incubated overnight at 50° C. in covered racks to prevent evaporation.

Craigie (1932) found that the supernatant fluid obtained by means of the first angle centrifugation in the process just described for preparing purified suspensions of elementary bodies from dermal pulp provided an excellent source of the soluble antigens of vaccinia. The supernatant fluid was freed of residual virus by passage through a Seitz filter. This "dermal filtrate" was employed as antigen in precipitin tests which were performed in the same manner as the agglutination tests. Proof that all of the serologic activity associated with Craigie's heat-labile and heat-stable soluble antigens of vaccinia was present in a single protein molecule was obtained by Shedlovsky and Smadel (1942) who used the precipitin reaction in following the various stages of purification of LS antigen from its source in crude dermal filtrate.

Many workers have attempted to develop simple diagnostic procedures which employ crude viral and rickettsial antigens in an extremely sensitive flocculation test. They added particulate material in the form of bacteria (Roberts and Jones, 1941), collodion (Goodner, 1941) or insoluble dye (Smorodintsev and Fradkina, 1944) to the crude suspension of tissue with the object of absorbing specific, serologic substances on the surfaces of the particles. Such coated particles were then aggregated by specific antibody. While these procedures have proved satisfactory for certain experimental studies they present difficulties which must be overcome before they can serve their intended purpose, i.e., diagnosis of disease.

The agglutination and precipitation technics have proved to be important tools for investigating serologic properties of certain viral and rickettsial agents, but they have been less valuable in the diagnosis of human disease than the neutralization and complement-fixation reactions. The agglutination test is listed in Table 6 as a commonly employed diagnostic aid in only two diseases, while the precipitin reaction is not mentioned in this connection. One situation in which rickettsial agglutination provides the only available serologic means of differential diagnosis occurs in those patients with murine typhus who previously have received epidemic typhus vaccine (Plotz and Wertman, 1945). Sera of such individuals when examined by the complement-fixation technic, give antibody responses which are typical of epidemic typhus, or which fail to differentiate between epidemic and murine typhus; but when the rickettsial agglutination test is used, high levels of antibody against *R. mooseri* are found.

VIRAL AND RICKETTSIAL HEMAGGLUTININS

The agglutination of erythrocytes by microbial agents, Hirst's phenomenon, has proved to be a most valuable tool in investigative and diagnostic work on a number of viral diseases. The nature of the reaction is discussed in Chapter 4. In addition, the subject is mentioned in the chapters dealing with those agents which display the property of hemagglutination. The present discussion will be limited to the diagnostic application of the hemagglutination-inhibition test.

The original hemagglutination-inhibition test for the diagnosis of influenza (Hirst, 1941) has been modified somewhat by almost every investigator who has used it. Although satisfactory results were obtained with all of these procedures (Whitman, 1947), it was difficult to compare quantitatively the data from different laboratories. In order to circumvent this situation, the U. S. Army adopted a single procedure in 1946 and supplied its laboratories with standard antigens and antisera. The technic described below is that currently employed in Army laboratories (Anonymous, 1951); it differs slightly from the earlier one (Anonymous, 1946) and conforms closely to a procedure recommended for routine diagnostic purposes for laboratories of the Armed Forces Epidemiological Board and the World Health Organization (Committee on Standard Serological Procedures in Influenza Studies, 1950).

MATERIALS

1. Saline solution (0.85 per cent NaCl in freshly distilled water).
2. Type "O" human red blood cells, either fresh or preserved in Alsever's solution.
3. Standard dried type A (PR8), type A prime (FM1) and type B (Lee) antigen.
4. Standard dried chicken antisera against each of the viruses mentioned in (3) above.
5. Kahn tubes (12 x 75 mm.) with evenly rounded bottoms.
6. Racks for Kahn tubes (flat bottom type without depressions).
7. One ml. serological pipettes, graduated in 0.01 ml., and 5.0 ml. pipettes, graduated in 0.1 ml.

Glassware must be chemically clean since traces of acid or alkali interfere with the test. Kahn tubes which do not have evenly rounded bottoms should be discarded. It is advisable to reserve specially selected and cleaned tubes for use only in influenza work.

PROCEDURE

Preparation of Standard Antigens and Antisera. Lyophilized diagnostic biologics are prepared by the method of Hilleman, Buescher and Smadel (1951). Antigens are obtained in the following manner. Nine- or ten-day embryonated eggs from chickens free of *Salmonella pullorum* infection and Newcastle disease are inoculated via the allantoic cavity with 0.4-ml. amounts of a dilution of the appropriate seed virus (usually 10^{-4} to 10^{-5}) which has been found in preliminary titrations to produce chorioallantoic fluids with hemagglutinin titers of 1:320 or greater. After further incubation at 35° C. for 44 to 48 hours, the eggs are candled and the embryos which are still alive are chilled overnight in the refrigerator at 4° C. The allantoic fluids are harvested aseptically, pooled and tested for sterility after which merthiolate is added to a final concentration of 1:10,000. Such pooled fluids, which constitute the antigen, are distributed in 5.0-ml. amounts in appropriate containers and lyophilized in a chamber or manifold drier in a manner to insure a final moisture content of less than one per cent. Such antigens when properly sealed to exclude moisture are stable during storage for at least three years at refrigerator temperature.

Control antisera are prepared in chickens. Roosters weighing 6-8 lb. are injected both intravenously and intraperitoneally with 5.0-ml. amounts of the appropriate freshly harvested allantoic fluids having hemagglutinating titers of 1:320 or greater. Ten days later, the roosters are bled to death by cardiac puncture. The clotted blood is cut into small pieces, stored overnight at 4° C. and at room temperature for four or five hours on the following day to facilitate contraction of the clot. The serum is removed following centrifugation, inactivated at 56° C. for one-half hour and dispensed in 0.5-ml. amounts into ampoules for drying by the chamber or manifold method. Satisfactory antisera are those which (1) have inhibitory titers of 1:800 or greater when tested with the homologous antigen and of not more than 1:100 when tested with the two heterologous antigens, and (2) are obtained from roosters which possess no viral inhibitor prior to immunization. Properly dried and sealed antisera are stable for at least several years.

Titration of Antigens. Prior to use, an ampoule of each standard antigen is rehydrated aseptically with 5.0 ml. of distilled water. A sample of this stock material is removed for the day's work and the remainder is stored in a stoppered bottle at 4° C. or preferably at —20° C. The sample is diluted with 19 parts of physiological saline solution and allowed to stand for one hour at room temperature; this facilitates elution of virus from the small amount of particulate matter in the preparation.

To determine the hemagglutinin titer 0.5 ml. volumes of serial twofold dilutions of antigen (1:20 to 1:5120) in physiological saline solution are mixed in Kahn tubes with 0.5 ml. volumes of a 0.5 percent suspension of human red blood cells (type "O"). The mixtures are thoroughly shaken and the pattern of the sedimented cells is read after the tubes have remained undisturbed for 60 to 70 minutes at room temperature (22 to 25° C.). In reading the results, the last tube showing complete hemagglutination is considered the end point of the titration. The diagnostic test for influenza antibodies employs four units of virus in 0.25 ml. In the above titration of virus the agent is contained in 0.5 ml.; therefore, the concentration required for the serum test is eight times that represented as the end point of the virus titer. Thus, if the last tube showing agglutination contained 0.5 ml. of a 1:320 dilution, then eight times this concentration or a 1:40 dilution, i.e., 1:2 of the day's stock or 1:40 of rehydrated antigen, would contain four units in a 0.25 ml. volume.

Erythrocyte Suspension. Human "O" blood, either fresh or preserved for up to one month in Alsever's solution, is employed. The cells are washed three times in saline solution. For the final centrifugation, the suspension is placed in a 15.0-ml. graduated tube and spun at 1,500 r.p.m. for ten minutes in a machine equipped with a horizontal head having a radius of $5\frac{1}{2}$ inches (i.e., $5\frac{1}{2}$ inches from axis to trunnion slot). The supernatant fluid is withdrawn without disturbing the packed cells, the volume of cells is read and enough saline solution is added to make a 0.5 percent suspension. This stock should be used only on the day it is prepared.

The Diagnostic Agglutination-Inhibition Test. Two serum specimens from each patient must be tested simultaneously with all three types of antigen. The first of these sera (acute phase) is obtained within two to three days after onset of illness and the second (convalescent) is obtained ten to fourteen days after onset of illness. The tests are set up as follows:

Three-tenths-milliliter amounts of the sera to be tested are inactivated at 56° C. for thirty minutes. Each is then diluted 1:8 by adding 2.1 ml. of saline solution. For each serum to be tested three rows of ten Kahn tubes are placed in a rack and 0.75-ml. amounts of saline solution are added to tubes Nos. 2 to 10 in the front row. No. 1 tube (far left) in the front row and all the tubes in the middle and back rows are left empty. Twenty-five-hundredths-milliliter amounts of the in-activated 1:8 dilution of serum are transferred to tube No. 1 of each of the three rows and 0.75 ml. of this same dilution of the serum is placed in tube No. 2 in the front row. This is mixed thoroughly and 0.25-ml. amounts are transferred to the No. 2 tubes of the middle and back rows. The operation is repeated in this manner until three identical series of two-fold dilutions have been prepared. Each tube now contains 0.25 ml. of the serum in dilutions ranging from 1:8 to 1:4096.

After the serum dilutions have been prepared, 0.25-ml. amounts of properly diluted PR8 test antigen (four units) are added to each of the tubes in the first row, FM1 antigen to those in the second row and Lee antigen to those in the third row. The racks are thoroughly shaken and 0.5-ml amounts of the 0.5 per cent erythrocyte suspension are added to the serum-antigen mixtures. The racks are shaken again and then left undisturbed at room temperature until the tests are read sixty minutes later. The titer of a serum is recorded as the highest dilution which inhibits hem-agglutination. Thus, if inhibition is observed through tubes Nos. 1 to 7 of the front row and tube No. 3 in the middle and back rows, the titer would be 1:512 with PR8 and 1:32 with FM1 and Lee antigens.

Controls. (1) Standard antisera. Antisera from roosters immunized against the PR8, FM1 and Lee strains of influenza virus are used for control purposes and are included in each day's test. Five ml. of sterile distilled water containing 1:10,000 crystalline mer-thiolate are added to a specimen of lyophilized inactivated antiserum making a 1:10 dilution of the original serum. This stock solution is stored at 4° C. in a sterile tightly stoppered container. Three-tenths ml. of stock is re-moved for the day's work and mixed with 2.7 ml. of saline solution making a 1:100 dilution of the original serum. Agglutination-inhibition tests with the standard antisera are performed in the same manner as those with patients'

sera except that the No. 1 tubes contain a 1:100 dilution instead of a 1:8 dilution. The tests with positive control sera serve two pur-poses: (1) to confirm the identity of the antigen used; and (2) to assist in correlating the results obtained in tests performed on dif-ferent days. While the titer of a given serum is inversely affected by changes in the concen-tration of virus used in the test, nevertheless, the titer of a positive control serum is more regularly reproducible than that of an antigen preparation since it is changed little by minor differences (a unit or so) in the amount of antigen employed. The end point for a given standard antiserum with its homologous anti-gen should not vary more than a single two-fold dilution from that obtained in previous tests.

(2) Retitration of test antigen. A portion of the diluted stock antigen, containing an estimated four agglutinating units in 0.25 ml. and used in the agglutination-inhibition test, must be retitered to determine its potency. This is done in the same manner as the initial antigen titration after rehydration except that tube No. 1 receives 0.5 ml. of the diluted stock. Complete agglutination should occur in the first four tubes of the titration.

Interpretation. Results are reported in terms of the titers of each of the paired sera obtained with each antigen. A fourfold or greater increase in titer with any one of the antigens during convalescence is considered of diagnostic significance. A rise in titer to both type A and type B virus should be sus-pected of being due to recent vaccination and a thorough investigation of this possibility should be made. Concurrent infection in a single individual with both type A and type B influenza virus is a rare occurrence.

A number of viral agents of human dis-ease display the phenomena of hemagglu-tination. However, it will be noted in Table 6 that in only a few instances is the hemagglu-tination-inhibition test listed as a frequently used diagnostic procedure. Information on the hemagglutinating capacities of the neurotropic viruses has developed rapidly since 1947 when Hallauer (1949) demon-strated that members of the encephalomyo-carditis group aggregated sheep erythro-cytes. Japanese encephalitis virus has a hemagglutinin which is one of the more diffi-cult to handle (Sabin and Buescher, 1950).

A particulate substance which is present in infected mouse brain along with this viral hemagglutinin destroys the latter within a few days, but when the former is removed by centrifugation at 13,000 r.p.m., the antigen is stable for some weeks at 4° C. A substance present in sera of normal animals of several species, including man and rabbit, nonspecifically inhibits the Japanese hemagglutinin. This substance can be removed by extracting serum with chloroform, a procedure which does not destroy the specific antibody which is effective in hemagglutination-inhibition tests employing sera of patients convalescent from Japanese encephalitis or antisera prepared in rabbits. Buescher (1951) obtained highly stable, noninfectious preparations of Japanese hemagglutinin by combining Warren's (1949) technic of purification by protamine-heparin precipitation with ultraviolet-light inactivation followed by lyophilization. It is to be hoped that the hemagglutination phenomenon may be employed eventually to provide useful diagnostic procedures for the neurotropic viral infections. In general, however, greater simplicity and dependability must be instilled into the present methods before they warrant careful field comparison with the neutralization and complement-fixation tests now employed.

COLD HEMAGGLUTININS AND STREPTOCOCCUS MG AGGLUTININS

These two substances appear in the sera of a considerable proportion of patients with primary atypical pneumonia and, although not specific for the disease, are helpful in its diagnosis.

Cold hemagglutinins are substances in serum which aggregate erythrocytes at low temperatures but not at 37° C. They bear no relation to the viral hemagglutinins discussed in the preceding section. The nature and occurrence of cold hemagglutinins in various normal and pathologic conditions are discussed in papers by the two groups of workers who in 1943 independently dem-

onstrated the frequent presence of these substances in sera from patients with atypical pneumonia (Finland et al., 1945c; Turner and Jackson, 1943).

The technic for demonstrating cold hemagglutinins is relatively simple. There are several satisfactory methods available, among which are those described by Turner (Turner, Nisnewitz et al., 1943), the Commission on Acute Respiratory Diseases (1944), and Finland and associates (1945b). For the past eight years the author has used the following technic, which is a slight modification of that of the first group of workers.

MATERIALS FOR COLD-HEMAGGLUTININ TEST

(1) Kahn tubes and racks
(2) Serologic pipettes, 1.0 cc. graduated in hundredths
(3) 0.9 per cent NaCl solution
(4) Cells. Sterile human O group blood is used. It may be obtained from a blood bank, or preferably, 20 cc. may be drawn from a healthy adult and added to an equal volume of Alsever's solution. Alsever's solution contains 2.05 per cent dextrose, 0.42 per cent sodium chloride, 0.8 per cent trisodium citrate, and 0.055 per cent citric acid. Twenty cc. amounts of solution are distributed in 50 cc. vaccine bottles; air is partially removed by suction applied through a needle inserted through the rubber stopper, and the evacuated bottles are autoclaved at 15 pounds for 15 minutes. A supply of bottles of solution may be kept on hand. Freshly drawn blood while still in the syringe is injected through the stopper, which has been cleaned with an iodine swab, and mixed with the sterile Alsever's solution. The sterile blood mixtures may be stored at 5° C. for two weeks and portions removed aseptically when needed to prepare suspensions of washed erythrocytes. The cells are washed three times by sedimentation in the centrifuge and resuspended in 10 volumes of 0.9 per cent NaCl solution. The final centrifugation is done in a graduated 15 cc. tube at 2,000 r.p.m. for 10 minutes, after which the supernatant fluid is pipetted off and the volume of packed cells determined by inspection. Sufficient 0.9 per cent NaCl solution is added to make a 1.0 per cent suspension of erythrocytes. Usually 5 cc. of blood-Alsever's solution mixture yields about 1.2 cc. of packed cells. Washed red cells are

unsatisfactory after storage for this type of work.

(5) Patient's serum. Cold hemagglutinins are absorbed by erythrocytes at refrigerator temperature. Therefore, venous blood should be allowed to clot at room temperature, after which the serum is removed and stored in a refrigerator. Clotted refrigerated blood will yield satisfactory serum for the cold-hemagglutinin test if it is warmed in a 37° C. water bath for half an hour prior to separation of serum.

Procedure for Test

(1) To each of a series of 10 Kahn test tubes is added 0.3 cc. of NaCl solution. 0.3 cc. of the patient's serum is added to the first tube on the left, mixed, and 0.3 cc. removed and added to the second tube, etc. In this manner serum dilutions covering the range from $1/2$ to $1/1024$ are prepared.

(2) 0.3 cc. of a 1 per cent suspension of washed O cells is added to each tube.

(3) The tubes are shaken and placed overnight in a refrigerator maintaining a temperature of 0 to 5° C. It is important that the temperature remain within this range. Upon removal from the refrigerator next morning the tests should be read promptly since disaggregation may occur quickly at room temperature.

(4) For reading, each tube is held in a good light and the bottom is flicked; if complete aggregation has occurred, a disk of erythrocytes floats up from the bottom of the tube, this is a 4 plus reaction. Tubes showing less agglutination are rotated back and forth while held vertically between the palms and then read with the aid of a hand lens.

(5) In order to be sure that the aggregation is caused by cold hemagglutinins, the test tubes are next transferred to a 37° C. water bath and reread two hours later. The agglutination should disappear under such conditions.

The relationship of cold hemagglutinin to the type of primary atypical pneumonia which the Commission on Acute Respiratory Diseases (1946) showed to be associated with a filterable agent and experimentally transmissible to human beings, has been summarized by Finland and co-workers (1945a) as follows:

Cold agglutinins are absent early in the disease. They usually make their appearance during the second or third week after the onset of symptoms and the titers increase rapidly thereafter. The maximum titers are attained in most instances between the middle of the second and the middle of the fourth weeks. The height of the maximum titer appears to be unrelated to the time when it is attained. The titers drop fairly rapidly after reaching the maximum so that significantly lower ones are already found between the third and fifth weeks. In most of the cases, the cold agglutinins can no longer be demonstrated in a significant titer by the fourth to the sixth weeks. Significant titers persist longer in cases in which the maximum titers are very high.

It may be added that the titer of cold hemagglutinins is generally proportional to the severity of the disease. While a number of factors in the different tests for cold hemagglutinins influence the exact value taken as the endpoint in the titration, there is general agreement among workers that a titer of 1/32 to 1/64 in a single convalescent serum is of some significance. The demonstration of a fourfold or greater rise in titer in serum taken in convalescence when compared with that obtained in the early stage of illness is of greater diagnostic importance than is a positive result on a single sample.

Streptococcus MG is a nonhemolytic streptococcus serologically separable from other members of the group. Agglutinins against it are specific antibodies which react with the capsular polysaccharide of the organism (Mirick et al., 1944); they are distinct from cold hemagglutinins. A positive reaction, i.e., MG titer of 1:20 or more, occurs in from 40 to 80 per cent of different series of patients with primary atypical pneumonia (Thomas et al., 1945; Horsfall, 1947; Finland et al., 1945d). A significant increase in titer is common during the course of this disease but rare in other infections. Although there is a positive correlation between the development of MG agglutinins and cold hemagglutinins in patients with primary atypical pneumonia, a sizable number shows one but not the other reaction. Therefore, it is frequently desirable that both tests be carried out when this disease is suspected. The technic described below for determining MG agglutinins is recommended by Horsfall (1951); it differs but slightly from the method employed earlier by his group (Thomas et al., 1945).

MATERIALS FOR STREPTOCOCCUS MG AGGLUTINATION TEST

(1) Kahn tubes and racks.

(2) Serologic pipettes, 1.0 ml. graduated in tenths.

(3) 0.9 per cent NaCl solution.

(4) Streptococcus MG suspension.

The bacteria for the suspension are grown for 18 hours at 37° C. in nutrient broth (Todd-Hewitt broth is recommended). The bacterial cells are washed three times by sedimentation in the centrifuge and resuspended in sufficient 0.9 per cent NaCl solution to give a turbidity approximating No. 5 in the McFarland scale. Usually the volume of NaCl solution required corresponds to about one half or one third the volume of the original culture. The bacteria then are killed by heating at 65° C. for one hour. Merthiolate, in a final concentration of 1:10,000, is added as a preservative. Suspensions prepared in this manner may be kept for two or three months at 4° C. without loss of potency.

(5) Serum specimens from patient.

It is of value to test serum obtained during the acute phase of the illness, i.e., less than five days after onset, along with serum specimens obtained at later dates, i.e., two weeks and four weeks after onset. Blood may be allowed to clot in the refrigerator because agglutinins against streptococcus MG are not absorbed by erythrocytes as are cold hemagglutinins. Serum is removed and stored at 4° C.

PROCEDURE FOR TEST

(1) To each of a series of ten Kahn tubes is added 0.3 ml. of NaCl solution. Three-tenths ml. of serum, which has not been inactivated by heating, is added to the first tube and mixed. Then 0.3 ml. of the mixture is withdrawn and added to the second tube, etc. In this manner serum dilutions from 1:2 to 1:1024 are prepared.

(2) Three-tenths ml. of the suspension of streptococcus MG is added to each tube.

(3) The tubes are shaken and kept at room temperature overnight.

(4) For reading, each tube is held in strong light, and the bottom is flicked vigorously. A hand lens is not used. Complete agglutination (four plus reaction) is shown by a solid plaque or disk of bacteria and a clear fluid. Tubes showing less agglutination are assigned values from three plus to one plus. Definite clumps of agglutinated bacteria which do not break up on shaking are taken to indicate the end point.

MG agglutinins usually appear in significant amounts on the day of defervescence or later. In general, the longer the illness, the more likely is the appearance of agglutinins and the higher is the titer of those that do appear (Curnen et al., 1945). The antibodies decrease rather quickly, beginning a month after onset of disease; by the end of the second month about 40 per cent of patients who were positive earlier have become negative. As in other serologic diagnostic procedures, a fourfold rise in titer of MG agglutinins during convalescence is of greater significance than a single positive test.

A number of viral and rickettsial agents can induce a disease picture similar in many respects to the primary atypical pneumonia associated with cold hemagglutinins (Smadel, 1943). However, the development of cold hemagglutinins and MG agglutinins is unassociated with the appearance of specific antibodies against these agents, namely, those causing influenza A and B, psittacosis, lymphocytic choriomeningitis (Curnen et al., 1945), and Q fever (Robbins, Gauld and Warner, 1946).

A more detailed discussion of the cold-hemagglutinin and MG agglutinin reactions in the diagnosis of one type of atypical pneumonia is found in Chapter 17. It may be pointed out at this time, however, that the incidence of positive cold-hemagglutinin reactions in cases of atypical pneumonia varies in different areas and at different times. Thus, 68 per cent of sera obtained from the 200 patients with atypical pneumonia studied in Boston during 1942 to 1944 gave positive reactions (Finland et al., 1945b), and 44 of 83 cases studied in England in 1942 and 1943 yielded positive results (Turner, Nisnewitz et al., 1943). In contrast, only 5 of 53 patients with atypical pneumonia in the Naples area in 1944-45 developed cold hemagglutinins; however, 30 of these developed specific antibodies against Q fever (Robbins et al., 1946). These findings bear comparison with the incidence of positive cold-hemagglutinin reactions in patients who developed atypical pneumonia after experimental inoculation (Commission on Acute Respiratory Diseases, 1946). In two experiments, the reaction appeared in 8 of the 10 and 5 of the 6 volunteers, respectively; among these same patients, 2 of the first group and none of the second developed MG agglutinins. The above facts may be interpreted as follows. In some outbreaks of atypical pneumonia, the virus which is associated with the appearance of cold hemagglutinins and MG agglutinins in a patient's serum is the most frequent etiologic agent, whereas under different circumstances, other agents assume the major role. The observations of Keitel (1950) that the majority of infants in a smoldering outbreak of gastro-enteritis developed these two types of agglutinins is of interest, especially since 8 of the 11 fatal cases also had the pathologic changes of atypical pneumonia.

RICKETTSIAL AND VIRAL TOXINS

Clinicians frequently have been impressed with the toxic appearance of patients during the acute phase of a number of the viral and rickettsial diseases. Only in the last few years has it been clearly demonstrated that toxic substances are intimately associated with certain of the agents in this group of parasitic micro-organisms. Gildemeister and Haagen (1940) were the first to show that death of mice occurred within a few hours after receiving suspensions of yolk-sac tissue containing numerous rickettsiae of murine typhus. Shortly afterward, Bengtson, Topping and Henderson (1945) in the United States and Otto and Bickhardt (1941) in Germany demonstrated a similar phenomenon with preparations of rickettsiae of epidemic typhus. The toxins

of *R. mooseri* and *R. prowazeki,* which are closely related but not identical, serve as prototypes for toxins of rickettsial and viral agents, and will be discussed in detail. Table 5 summarizes certain information about these toxins.

Typhus toxins are demonstrable only in preparations which are extremely rich in infectious rickettsial organisms, and yolk-sac tissue has almost invariably been the source of such materials. The rapid death of animals following the injection of lethal preparations leads to the conclusion that the effect is that of a toxin and not one dependent upon overwhelming infection. This idea is well substantiated by the findings in studies of murine typhus as well as in those of scrub typhus (Smadel et al., 1946a, b) and the lymphogranuloma venereum-psittacosis group of diseases (Rake and Jones, 1944). Animals which fail to succumb within a few hours may recover from their acute illness and remain well for several days to a week, after which they then develop the usual signs of infection and die. It has not yet been possible to dissociate the toxins from the infectious agents. The unsuccessful attempts to separate the toxic materials from the infectious agents may be dependent upon the fact that the toxins are extremely labile substances. For instance, in the case of rickettsiae of epidemic typhus, the addition of formaldehyde to toxic preparations of yolk sac destroys their capacity to kill mice (Bengtson et al., 1945), but such noninfectious material contains an antigen which elicits the production of antitoxin in man and guinea pigs (Topping, Henderson and Bengtson, 1945) and resistance in mice to the action of the toxin (Craigie et al., 1946). Thus, the epidemic typhus toxin itself is extremely labile, but the toxoid produced by treatment with formalin is remarkably stable. In a similar manner, the toxins of murine typhus and several diseases of the psittacosis-lymphogranuloma venereum group remain immunogenic after inactivation. Furthermore, noninfectious

TABLE 5. TOXINS ASSOCIATED WITH RICKETTSIAE AND VIRUSES

GROUP	AGENT	TEST ROUTE	TOXIC MANIFESTATIONS IN ANIMALS	SPECIFICITY OF ANTITOXIN
Rickettsiae	R. prowazeki	I.V., I.P.		Epidemic typhus toxin neutralized by murine antiserum about as well as by homologous antiserum, and vice versa.
	R. mooseri	I.V., I.P.	Dyspnea, weakness, cyanosis, convulsions and death; onset 2 hours, most deaths before 6 hours.	
	R. orientalis	I.V.		Marked.
Lymphogranuloma-Psittacosis	Lymphogranuloma venereum	I.V., I.P.		Marked.
	Psittacosis	I.V.	Lethargy, dyspnea and death; onset 4 hours, most deaths before 24 hours.	
	Meningopneumonitis	I.V., I.P.		Marked with some strains, broad crossing with others.
	Mouse pneumonitis	I.V.	Prostration and death; onset 30 minutes; most deaths at 4 hours, others at 30 hours, with same signs.	Marked.
	Feline pneumonitis	I.V., I.P.	Death 6-24 hours.	Marked.
Influenza		I.C.	Hyperirritability, convulsions, death 12-48 hours.	
	Influenza A	I.P., I.V.	Death 16-72 hours.	
		Rabbit cornea	Haziness, thickening of cornea; onset at 24 hrs., complete at 72 hours.	Each toxin neutralized by homologous but not by heterologous antiserum.
	Influenza B	I.C., I.P., I.V.	Same as influenza A.	
		Rabbit cornea	Same as influenza A.	
	Swine Influenza	I.C., I.P., I.V.	Same as influenza A.	

All toxic materials are obtained from infected yolk-sac tissue except those of influenza which are usually derived from infected chorio-allantoic fluid.

The test animal used for demonstrating toxic effect is the mouse in all instances except influenza where the rabbit is also used.

I.V. = intravenous   I.P. = intraperitoneal   I.C. = intracerebral

preparations of influenza A and B viruses are capable of immunizing mice against the toxic factors associated with the active agents (Henle and Henle, 1946).

As a rule, the toxins elicit antibodies which are highly specific. Although there is considerable crossing between the antitoxins associated with R. mooseri and R. prowazeki, they can be distinguished one from another by appropriate tests (Hamilton, 1945). The toxin of the Gilliam strain of scrub typhus is so specific that the production of antitoxin against it is limited to certain strains of R. orientalis (Smadel et al., 1946b). In a like manner, viruses of the influenza group (Henle and Henle, 1946) elicit specific antitoxins which fail to react with toxins of closely related viruses. Early studies (Hamre and Rake, 1944; Rake and Jones, 1944) showed a high level of specificity of the antitoxins against certain viruses of the psittacosis-lymphogranuloma venereum group and this proved to be useful in the immunologic separation of these agents. Subsequent investigations (Manire and Meyer, 1950) of a larger number of strains, which belonged in the general subgroup containing psittacosis and meningopneumonitis viruses, showed that some elicited quite specific antitoxins, viz., Louisiana and SF, while others provided less specific antitoxins which overlapped considerably.

Clinical and pathologic manifestations of toxins associated with different rickettsiae are similar. Animals show no signs of illness for 1 to 2 hours after inoculation, then develop weakness and dyspnea, followed rapidly by prostration and convulsive seizures which usually terminate in death within 1½ or 3 hours; all deaths from rickettsial toxins occur within 18 hours. However, toxic deaths caused by viral agents may be delayed a day or so. Mice which die rapidly from rickettsial toxins show only a general vascular congestion. Mice which succumb late to the viral toxins frequently show focal necrotic changes in their livers (Rake and Jones, 1944; Henle and Henle, 1946). While the mouse is used almost exclusively in studies of this type, some of the toxins have been demonstrated by their effects on other animals. Thus, influenza A and B viruses injected into the eye of the rabbit induce a corneal response (Evans and Rickard, 1945). It may be mentioned that the toxic factors of *R. prowazeki* recently described by Olitzki, Czaczkes and Kuzenok (1946) as being related to the endotoxins of gram-negative bacteria bear little apparent relation to the mouse lethal toxin.

Little is known about the nature of the toxins or of their importance in disease. Moreover, the viral and rickettsial toxins have not yet become of diagnostic importance in medicine.

SOLUBLE ANTIGENS

The term "soluble antigens" has been applied to a group of serologically specific substances which are found in certain viral and rickettsial diseases but which are not the infectious agents themselves. These noninfectious soluble antigens have diverse chemical and physical properties but resemble each other in having a minute size when compared with the agents with which they are associated and in possessing some, but not all, of the immunologic properties of the intact agent. Such a description suggests that soluble antigens are either fractions or products of the microbiologic agents; while this idea is speculative, it is consistent with most of the known facts. The description also implies that soluble antigens occur and are recognized most readily among the large, more complex viruses and the rickettsiae. This is indeed the case. The list of the diseases of man in which soluble antigens have been demonstrated includes five of the rickettsial infections, two groups of the elementary-body diseases, and two maladies caused by viruses of intermediate size. As one goes down the list of agents in respect to size, it becomes increasingly difficult to obtain experimental evidence which will permit the recognition of a soluble antigen separable from the virus. It is because of such technical difficulties that the noninfectious, serologically specific substance found in infections caused by the virus of yellow fever (Hughes, 1933; Lennette and Perlowagora, 1945) is not included in the present discussion of soluble antigens.

Craigie (1932), working with vaccinia, was the first to prove the existence of a soluble antigen among the viral and rickettsial agents. Extensive information has been accumulated on this protein molecule, now called LS antigen, as well as on another soluble antigen of vaccinia, i.e., one extracted from elementary bodies and designated NP because of its nucleoprotein nature (Smadel, Rivers and Hoagland, 1942). LS is common to vaccinia and variola but NP has only been searched for in the former. Immunization with these antigens neither induces protection in animals nor elicits neutralizing substances against the virus although both substances are antigenic, since they induce antibodies which fix complement or precipitate in the presence of homologous antigen. The hemagglutinin of vaccinia may also be classified as a soluble antigen since it is noninfectious and is smaller than the elementary body, i.e., 65 mμ for the former and 235 mμ for the latter (Burnet and Stone, 1946; Chu, 1948a). Moreover, the hemagglutinin is distinct antigenically from LS antigen and apparently from the material in the infectious elementary body which elicits neutralizing antibody (Chu, 1948b). Soluble antigens occur in psittacosis (Lazarus and Meyer, 1939) and in lymphogranuloma venereum (Rake et al., 1941). Indeed, a group-reactive lipid antigen is common to a number of members of the psittacosis-lymphogranuloma family (Hilleman and Nigg, 1948). Moreover, one member, i.e., meningopneumonitis virus, is associated with a hemagglutinin which is smaller than the infectious virus particle but, like the latter, reacts in serologic tests in a group-specific manner (Hilleman et al., 1951). Acid-soluble extracts of psittacosis and of lymphogranuloma viruses, although inactive in complement-fixation tests, appear to elicit strain-specific skin reactions in patients convalescent from infection with the homologous agent; this is in contrast to the group-specific reactions obtained with the heated viruses (Barwell, 1949). The soluble substance of lymphocytic choriomeningitis is useful in diagnostic complement-fixation tests with human and animal sera, but, like the soluble antigens of vaccinia, plays no role in resistance to infection (Smadel and Wall, 1940). Similarly, the soluble antigens of influenza A and B react in complement-fixation tests with homologous antibodies which appear to be unrelated to neutralizing antibodies (Wiener, Henle and Henle, 1946).

Although soluble substances were not recognized among the rickettsial agents until 1942, a considerable amount of information was quickly obtained concerning them because of their relation to military medicine. All these data have not appeared in the published literature but several recent reviews summarize much of it (Plotz, 1948; Smadel, 1948a, b). The soluble antigen of epidemic typhus is derived from crude suspensions of infected tissue from which intact rickettsiae are removed by centrifugation and probably represents more than one antigenic substance. It possesses most of the immunogenic properties of intact rickettsiae (Topping and Shear, 1945; Plotz, 1948), and for this reason was retained in the epidemic typhus vaccine employed during World War II by the military forces of the United States. This vaccine was an ether extracted 10 per cent suspension of infected yolk-sac tissue inactivated by formaldehyde.

The soluble antigens of epidemic and murine typhus are so closely related serologically that they are essentially indistinguishable. Hence, their presence in antigens intended for use in diagnostic complement-fixation tests interferes with differentiation of these two diseases. For this reason, Plotz and co-workers (1948) eliminated such materials from their rickettsial antigens by repeated washing (see section on complement fixation). The nature of the soluble antigen or antigens associated with *R. prowazeki* is better understood than those of the other rickettsiae. Apparently on rupture *R. prowazeki* liberates a nucleoprotein which behaves as a relatively type-specific antigen in complement-fixation tests. When acted upon by proteolytic enzymes, this material becomes group-specific, reacting almost equally well with epidemic and murine antisera (Chambers, Cohen and Clawson, 1950). A common soluble antigen is associated with the agents of Rocky Mountain spotted fever and boutonneuse fever (Plotz, Reagan and Wertman, 1944), and a serologically related substance may account for the cross reaction obtained in complement-fixation tests with materials from spotted fever and rickettsialpox (Huebner and co-workers, 1946). Although a serologically active substance with the general properties of a soluble antigen has been demonstrated by complement-fixation tests in materials

TABLE 6. SEROLOGIC REACTIONS USED FREQUENTLY IN DIAGNOSIS OF VIRAL AND RICKETTSIAL DISEASES OF MAN

Group	Disease	In-Vitro Tests		In-Vivo Tests		
		Type	Common Sources of Antigen	Type	Common Sources of Virus	Usual Test Animal
Viral Epidemic Encephalitides	St. Louis					
	Japanese					
	Equine western eastern Venezuelan	Complement fixation	Mouse brain	Neutralization	Mouse brain	Mouse
	Russian (Louping-ill)					
	Lymphocytic chorio-meningitis	Complement fixation	Guinea pig spleen Mouse brain	Neutralization	Mouse brain Guinea pig brain	Mouse Guinea pig
	Pseudo-lymphocytic choriomeningitis					
	West Nile					
	Bwamba			Neutralization	Mouse brain	Mouse
Other Neurotropic Viruses	Semliki Forest					
	Encephalomyocarditis (Col.-SK, MM and Mengo)					
	Poliomyelitis	Complement fixation*	Mouse brain (Lansing prototype only)	Neutralization*	Monkey cord Mouse brain (certain type only)	Monkey Mouse (certain type only)
	Coxsackie	Complement fixation*	Suckling mouse tissue	Neutralization*	Suckling mouse tissue	Suckling mouse

* Indicates procedures are satisfactory but generally not available or else not suitable for clinical work.

TABLE 6 (*Continued*)

Group	Disease	In-Vitro Tests		In-Vivo Tests		
		Type	Common Sources of Antigen	Type	Common Sources of Virus	Usual Test Animal
Variola-Vaccinia		Complement fixation	Human vesicle fluid or crusts; membranes from eggs used for isolation of virus			
Psittacosis Lympho-granuloma Venereum		Complement fixation	Yolk sac			
Influenza	A	Hemagglut.-inhibition	Allantoic fluid (Amniotic fluid for C)			
	B					
	C	Complement fixation				
Herpes	Herpes simplex	Complement fixation	Chorio-allantois	Neutralization	Mouse brain	Mouse
					Chorio-allantois	Chorio-allantois
Mumps		Complement fixation	Monkey parotid; amniotic fluid; yolk sac			
		Hemagglut.-inhibition	Amniotic fluid			
Miscellaneous Viruses	Yellow fever					
	Dengue fever	Complement fixation	Mouse brain	Neutralization	Mouse brain	Mouse
	Colorado tick fever					
	Rift Valley fever	Complement fixation	Mouse liver	Neutralization	Mouse brain or liver	Mouse
	Foot-and-Mouth disease	Complement fixation*	Guinea pig foot-pad			

TABLE 6 (*Continued*)

Group	Disease	In-Vitro Tests		In-Vivo Tests		
		Type	Common Sources of Antigen	Type	Common Sources of Virus	Usual Test Animal
	Primary atypical pneumonia	Cold hemagglutination	Human type O cells			
		Streptococcus agglut.	Streptococcus MG			
Miscellaneous Viruses (*Cont.*)	Newcastle	Complement fixation				
		Hemagglut.-inhibition	Allantoic fluid			
	Epidemic typhus	Complement fixation	Yolk sac			
	Murine typhus	Agglutination				
		Weil-Felix	*B. proteus*, OX-19			
	Scrub typhus	Weil-Felix	*B. proteus*, OX-K			
	Rocky Mountain spotted fever					
Rickettsial Diseases	Boutonneuse fever	Complement fixation	Yolk sac			
	South African tick-bite fever	Weil-Felix	*B. proteus*, OX-19 and OX-2			
	North Queensland tick typhus	Complement fixation	Yolk sac			
		Weil-Felix	*B. proteus*, OX-2			
	Rickettsialpox	Complement fixation	Yolk sac			
	Q fever					

[95]

from tissues infected with *R. orientalis* (Smadel, Rights and Jackson, 1946a), its relation to the antigens of scrub typhus, which have to do with immunity and neutralizing antibody, remains to be elucidated.

It may be noted that the soluble antigen of epidemic typhus and the hemagglutinin of vaccinia are quite large when compared with the LS antigen of vaccinia and that they could be either large molecules or small particles; with such a size the question arises as to whether they form a solution or a suspension. Here, as in the field of specific flocculation, some of the points of possible disagreement may be eliminated when a consensus is reached on the lower limit for size of particles and the upper limit for size of molecules. However, as the various antigens become fully characterized and named, the term "soluble antigen" will probably fall into disuse.

SUMMARY

Serologic reactions used in the diagnosis of viral and rickettsial diseases of man are summarized in Table 6. A number of viral diseases are not mentioned in the table because acceptable serologic procedures for them have not yet been developed, or are of doubtful value, or are too highly technical to be of general importance. The diseases which are omitted from the table are as follows: common cold, chickenpox, German measles, inclusion blennorrhea, infectious hepatitis, measles, molluscum contagiosum, trachoma, verruca and herpes zoster.

REFERENCES

American Public Health Association Committee, 1948, Diagnostic Procedures for Virus and Rickettsial Diseases, New York, Am. Pub. Health Assn.

Andrewes, C. H., 1928, The action of immune serum on vaccinia and virus III *in vitro*. J. Path. and Bact., *31*, 671-698.

Anonymous, 1946, A modified agglutination-inhibition test for the diagnosis of influenza. Bull. U. S. Army Med. Dept., *6*, 777-780.

Anonymous, 1951, Rickettsiae and viruses *in* Methods for Medical Laboratory Technicians, Departments of the Army and the Air Force TM 8-227—AFM 160-14, Washington, U. S. Government Printing Office, pp. 523-558.

Barwell, C. F., 1949, Extraction of a specific antigen from the virus of lymphogranuloma venereum. Nature, *164*, 1013.

Bengtson, I. A., Topping, N. H., and Henderson, R. G., 1945, Epidemic typhus, demonstration of a substance lethal for mice in the yolk sac of eggs infected with *Rickettsia prowazeki*. National Institute of Health Bull., No. *183*, 25-29.

Buescher, E. L., 1951. Unpublished data.

Bugher, J. C., 1948, Yellow fever *in* Diagnostic Procedures for Virus and Rickettsial Diseases, New York, Am. Pub. Health Assn., pp. 267-288.

Burnet, F. M., Keogh, E. V., and Lush, D., 1937, The immunological reactions of the filterable viruses. Austral. J. Exp. Biol. and Med. Sci., *15*, 231-368.

Burnet, F. M., and Stone, J. D., 1946, The haemagglutinins of vaccinia and ectromelia viruses. Austral. J. Exp. Biol. and Med. Sci., *24*, 1-8.

Casals, J., 1947, Complement-fixation tests for diagnosis of human viral encephalitides. J. Immunol., *56*, 337-341.

Casals, J., Olitsky, P. K., and Anslow, R. O., 1951, A specific complement-fixation test for infection with poliomyelitis virus. J. Exp. Med., *94*, 123-137.

Casals, J., and Palacios, R., 1941, The complement fixation test in the diagnosis of virus infections of the central nervous system. J. Exp. Med., *74*, 409-426.

Chambers, L. A., Cohen, S. S., and Clawson, J. R., 1950, Studies on commercial typhus vaccines. II. The antigenic fractions of disrupted epidemic typhus rickettsiae. J. Immunol., *65*, 459-463.

Chu, C. M., 1948a, Studies on vaccinia haemagglutinin. I. Some physico-chemical properties. J. Hyg., *46*, 42-48

Chu, C. M., 1948b, Studies on vaccinia haemagglutinin. II. Some immunological properties. J. Hyg., *46*, 49-59.

Commission on Acute Respiratory Diseases, 1944, Cold hemagglutinins in primary atypical pneumonia and other respiratory infections. Am. J. Med. Sci., *208*, 742-750.

Commission on Acute Respiratory Diseases, 1946, The transmission of primary atypical pneumonia to human volunteers. II. Results of inoculation. Bull. Johns Hopkins Hosp., *79*, 109-124.

Committee on Standard Serological Procedures in Influenza Studies, 1950, An agglutination-inhibition test proposed as a standard of reference in influenza diagnostic studies. J. Immunol., *65*, 347-353.

Craigie, J., 1932, The nature of the vaccinia flocculation reaction, and observations on the elementary bodies of vaccinia. Brit. J. Exp. Path., *13*, 259-268.

Craigie, J., 1939, Die Virusarten als Antigene und die erworbene Immunität gegen Virusinfektionen. I. Die Antigenfunktionen und die serologischen Reaktionen der Virusarten *in vitro*, *in* Doerr, R. und Hallauer, C., Handbuch der Virusforschung. Zweite Hälfte, Wien, Springer, 1106-1147.

Craigie, J., and Tulloch, W. J., 1931, Further investigations on the variola-vaccinia flocculation reaction. Special Report Series, No. 156, Med. Res. Council, London, His Majesty's Stationery Office.

Craigie, J., Watson, D. W., Clark, E. M., and Malcomson, M. E., 1946, The serological relationships of the rickettsiae of epidemic and murine typhus. Canad. J. Res., Sec. E, *24*, 84-103.

Curnen, E. C., Mirick, G. S., Ziegler, J. E., Jr., Thomas, L., and Horsfall, F. L., Jr., 1945, Studies on primary atypical pneumonia. I. Clinical features and results of laboratory investigations. J. Clin. Investig., *24*, 209-226.

De Boer, C. J., and Cox, H. R., 1947, Specific complement-fixing diagnostic antigens for neurotropic viral diseases. J. Immunol., *55*, 193-204.

Evans, C. A., and Rickard, E. R., 1945, The toxic effect of influenza virus in the rabbit eye. Proc. Soc. Exp. Biol. and Med., *58*, 73-74.

Finland, M., Peterson, O. L., Allen, H. E., Samper, B. A., and Barnes, M. W., 1945a, Cold agglutinins. II. Cold isohemagglutinins in primary atypical pneumonia of unknown etiology with a note on the occurrence of hemolytic anemia in these cases. J. Clin. Investig., *24*, 458-473.

Finland, M., Peterson, O. L., Allen, H. E., Samper, B. A., Barnes, M. W., and Stone, M. B., 1945b, Cold agglutinins. I. Occurrence of cold isohemagglutinins in various conditions. J. Clin. Investig., *24*, 451-457.

Finland, M., Peterson, O. L., Barnes, M. W., and Stone, M. B., 1945c, Cold agglutinins. III. Observations on certain serological and physical features of cold agglutinins in cases of primary atypical pneumonia and of hemolytic anemia. J. Clin. Investig., *24*, 474-482.

Finland, M., Samper, B. A., and Barnes, M. W., 1945d, Cold agglutinins. VI. Agglutinins for an indifferent streptococcus in primary atypical pneumonia and in other conditions and their relation to cold isohemagglutinins. J. Clin. Investig., *24*, 497-502.

Gildemeister, E., and Haagen, E., 1940, Fleckfieberstudien. I. Mitteilung: Nachweis eines Toxins in Rickettsien-Eikulteren. (Rickettsia mooseri). Deutsche med. Wchnschr., *66*, 878-880.

Goodner, K., 1941, Collodion fixation; a new immunological reaction. Science, *94*, 241-242.

Habel, K., 1945, Cultivation of mumps virus in the developing chick embryo and its application to studies of immunity to mumps in man. Pub. Health Rep., *60*, 201-212.

Hallauer, C., 1949, Agglutination von Hammelerythrocyten durch murine Poliomyelitisvirusstämme. Proc. 4th Internat. Congr. for Microbiology, July 1947, Copenhagen, Rosenkilde and Bagger, p. 257.

Hamilton, H. L., 1945, Specificity of the toxic factors associated with the epidemic and murine strains of typhus rickettsiae. Am. J. Trop. Med., *25*, 391-395.

Hammon, W. McD., 1948, Encephalitis, *in* Diagnostic Procedures for Virus and Rickettsial Diseases. New York, Am. Pub. Health Assn., pp. 187-217.

Hamre, D., and Rake, G., 1944, Feline pneumonitis (Baker), a new member of the lymphogranuloma-psittacosis group of agents. J. Infect. Dis., *74*, 206-211.

Havens, W. P., Jr., Watson, D. W., Green, R. H., Lavin, G. I., and Smadel, J. E., 1943, Complement fixation with the neurotropic viruses. J. Exp. Med., *77*, 139-153.

Henle, G., and Henle, W., 1946, Studies on the toxicity of influenza viruses. I. The effect of intracerebral injection of influenza viruses. J. Exp. Med., *84*, 623-637.

Hilleman, M. R., Buescher, E. L., and Smadel, J. E., 1951, Preparation of dried antigen and antiserum for the agglutination-inhibition test for virus influenza. Pub. Health Rep., *66*, 1195-1203.

Hilleman, M. R., Haig, D. A., and Helmold, R. J., 1951, The indirect complement fixation, hemagglutination and conglutinating complement absorption tests for viruses of the psittacosis-lymphogranuloma venereum group. J. Immunol., *66*, 115-130.

Hilleman, M. R., and Nigg, C., 1948, Studies on lymphogranuloma venereum complement-fixing antigens. IV. Fractionation with organic solvents of antigens of the psittacosis-lymphogranuloma venereum group. J. Immunol., *59*, 349-364.

Hirst, G. K., 1941, The agglutination of red cells by allantoic fluid of chick embryos infected with influenza virus. Science, *94*, 22-23.

Hirst, G. K., 1942a, The quantitative determination of influenza virus and antibodies by means of red cell agglutination. J. Exp. Med., *75*, 49-64.

Hirst, G. K., 1942b, *In vivo* titrations of influenza virus and of neutralizing antibodies in chick embryos. J. Immunol., *45*, 285-292.

Horsfall, F. L., Jr., 1947, Primary atypical pneumonia. Ann. Int. Med., *27*, 275-281.

Horsfall, F. L., Jr., 1951, Personal communication.

Howitt, B. F., 1937, The complement-fixation reaction in experimental equine encephalomyelitis, lymphocytic choriomeningitis and the St. Louis type of encephalitis. J. Immunol., *33*, 235-250.

Huebner, R. J., Stamps, P., and Armstrong, C., 1946, Rickettsialpox—a newly recognized rickettsial disease. I. Isolation of the etiological agent. Pub. Health Rep., *61*, 1605-1614.

Hughes, T. P., 1933, A precipitin reaction in yellow fever. J. Immunol., *25*, 275-294.

Kalmanson, G. M., and Bronfenbrenner, J., 1943, Restoration of activity of neutralized biologic agents by removal of the antibody with papain. J. Immunol., *47*, 387-407.

Karrer, H., Meyer, K. F., and Eddie, B., 1950, The complement fixation inhibition test and its application to the diagnosis of ornithosis in chickens and in ducks. I. Principles and technique of the test. J. Infect. Dis., *87*, 13-23.

Keitel, H. G., 1950, Occurrence of cold and streptococcus MG agglutinins in infants with gastroenteritis. J. Infect. Dis., *86*, 219-222.

Kidd, J. G., and Friedewald, W. F., 1942, A natural antibody that reacts *in vitro* with a sedimentable constituent of normal tissue cells. I. Demonstration of the phenomenon. J. Exp. Med., *76*, 543-556.

Kilbourne, E. D., and Horsfall, F. L., Jr., 1951, Mouse-egg neutralization. Neutralization in the mouse of influenza viruses not adapted to the mouse. J. Immunol., *67*, 431-436.

Lazarus, A. S., and Meyer, K. F., 1939, The virus of psittacosis. III. Serological investigations. J. Bact., *38*, 171-198.

Lennette, E. H., and Perlowagora, A., 1945, The complement fixation test in the diagnosis of yellow fever. Comparative value of the serologic and histopathologic methods of diagnosis. Am. J. Trop. Med., *25*, 11-18.

Maltaner, F., 1946, Significance of thromboplastic activity of antigens used in complement-fixation tests. Proc. Soc. Exp. Biol. and Med., *62*, 302-304.

Manire, G. P., and Meyer, K. F., 1950, The toxins of the psittacosis-lymphogranuloma group of agents. III. Differentiation of strains by the toxin neutralization test. J. Infect. Dis., *86*, 241-250.

McKee, A. P., and Hale, W. M., 1946, Reactivation of overneutralized mixtures of influenza virus and antibody. J. Immunol., *54*, 233-243.

Merrill, M. H., 1936, The mass factor in immunological studies upon viruses. J. Immunol., *30*, 169-184.

Mirick, G. S., Thomas, L., Curnen, E. C., and Horsfall, F. L., Jr., 1944, Studies on a non-hemolytic streptococcus isolated from the respiratory tract of human beings. I. Biological characteristics of streptococcus MG. II. Immunological characteristics of streptococcus MG. III. Immunological relationship of streptococcus MG to *Streptococcus salivarius* type I. J. Exp. Med., *80*, 391-440.

Morris, M. C., 1944, Analogy between the effect of complement on sensitized *E. typhosa* and the effect of tissue individuality on sensitized virus. J. Immunol., *48*, 17-24.

Olitsky, P. K., and Casals, J., 1947, Neutralization tests for diagnosis of human viral encephalitides. J. Am. Med. Assn., *134*, 1224-1228.

Olitzki, L., Czaczkes, J. W., and Kuzenok, A., 1946, Endotoxic factors of *Rickettsia prowazeki* and their immunological relationship to the endotoxins of other Gram negative microorganisms. J. Immunol., *53*, 365-370.

Otto, R., and Bickhardt, R., 1941, Über das Gift der Fleckfieberrickettsien. Ztschr. f. Hyg. u. Infektionskr., *123*, 447-462.

Parker, R. F., 1939, The neutralization of vaccine virus by serum of vaccine-immune animals. J. Immunol., *36*, 147-157.

Paul, J. R., 1944, The filtrable viruses, *in* Laboratory Methods of the United States Army, edited by Simmons, J. S., and Gentzkow, C. J., Philadelphia, Lea & Febiger, pp. 579-600.

Plotz, H., 1948, The soluble substances of the rickettsiae, *in* The Rickettsial Diseases of Man. Washington, Am. Assn. Advancement of Science, pp. 198-202.

Plotz, H., Reagan, R. L., and Wertman, K., 1944, Differentiation between Fièvre Boutonneuse and Rocky Mountain spotted fever by means of complement fixation. Proc. Soc. Exp. Biol. and Med., *55*, 173-176.

Plotz, H., and Wertman, K., 1945, Modification of serological response to infection with murine typhus by previous immunization with epidemic typhus vaccine. Proc. Soc. Exp. Biol. and Med., *59*, 248-251.

Plotz, H., Smadel, J. E., Bennett, B. L., Reagan, R. L., and Snyder, M. J., 1946, North Queensland tick typhus: studies of the aetiological agent and its relation to other rickettsial diseases. Med. J. Australia, *2*, 263-268.

Plotz, H., Bennett, B. L., Wertman, K., Snyder, M. J., and Gauld, R. L., 1948, The serological pattern in typhus fever. I. Epidemic typhus. Am. J. Hyg., *47*, 150-165.

Rake, G., and Jones, H. P., 1944, Studies on lymphogranuloma venereum. II. The association of specific toxins with agents of the lymphogranuloma-psittacosis group. J. Exp. Med., *79*, 463-486.

Rake, G., Shaffer, M. F., Jones, H. P., and McKee, C. M., 1941, Soluble antigen in lymphogranuloma venereum. Proc. Soc. Exp. Biol. and Med., *46*, 300-303.

Robbins, F. C., Gauld, R. L., and Warner, F. B., 1946, Q fever in the Mediterranean area: report of its occurrence in Allied troops. II. Epidemiology. Am. J. Hyg., *44*, 23-50.

Roberts, E. C., and Jones, L. R., 1941, Agglutination of encephalitis virus-coated-bacterial cells by virus antisera. Proc. Soc. Exp. Biol. and Med., *47*, 75-76.

Sabin, A. B., and Buescher, E. L., 1950, Unique physico-chemical properties of Japanese B. encephalitis virus hemagglutinin. Proc. Soc. Exp. Biol. and Med., *74*, 222-230.

Shedlovsky, T., and Smadel, J. E., 1942, The LS-antigen of vaccinia. II. Isolation of a single substance containing both L- and S-activity. J. Exp. Med., *75*, 165-178.

Smadel, J. E., 1943, Atypical pneumonia and psittacosis. J. Clin. Investig., *22*, 57-65.

Smadel, J. E., 1948a, Complement fixation and agglutination reactions in rickettsial diseases, *in* The Rickettsial Diseases of Man. Washington, Am. Assn. Advancement of Science, pp. 190-197.

Smadel, J. E., 1948b, Serological procedures for the diagnosis of rickettsial diseases, *in* Diagnostic Procedures for Virus and Rickettsial Diseases. New York, Am. Pub. Health Assn., pp. 311-333.

Smadel, J. E., and Wall, M. J., 1940, A soluble antigen of lymphocytic choriomeningitis. III. Independence of anti-soluble substance antibodies and neutralizing antibodies, and the rôle of soluble antigen and inactive virus in immunity to infection. J. Exp. Med., *72*, 389-405.

Smadel, J. E., and Wall, M. J., 1941, Identification of the virus of lymphocytic choriomeningitis. J. Bact., *41*, 421-430.

Smadel, J. E., and Hoagland, C. L., 1942, Elementary bodies of vaccinia. Bacteriological Reviews, *6*, 79-110.

Smadel, J. E., Rivers, T. M., and Hoagland, C. L., 1942, Nucleoprotein antigen of vaccine virus. I. A new antigen from elementary bodies of vaccinia. Arch. Path., *34*, 275-285.

Smadel, J. E., Rights, F. L., and Jackson, E. B., 1946a, Studies on scrub typhus. I. Soluble antigen in tissues and body fluids of infected mice and rats. J. Exp. Med., *83*, 133-146.

Smadel, J. E., Jackson, E. B., Bennett, B. L., and Rights, F. L., 1946b, A toxic substance associated with the Gilliam strain of *R. orientalis*. Proc. Soc. Exp. Biol. and Med., *62*, 138-140.

Smorodintsev, A. A., and Fradkina, R. V., 1944, Slide agglutination test for rapid diagnosis of pre-eruptive typhus fever. Proc. Soc. Exp. Biol. and Med., *56*, 93-94.

Sternberg, G. M., 1892, Practical results of bacteriological researches. Trans. Assn. Am. Physicians, *7*, 68-86.

Stoker, M. G. P., Coombs, R. R. A., and Bedson, S. P., 1950, The application of the conglutinating complement absorption test to virus systems. Brit. J. Exp. Path., *31*, 217-232.

Thomas, L., Mirick, G. S., Curnen, E. C., Ziegler, J. E., Jr., and Horsfall, F. L., Jr., 1945, Studies on primary atypical pneumonia. II. Observations concerning the relationship of a non-hemolytic streptococcus to the disease. J. Clin. Investig., *24*, 227-240.

Topping, N. H., and Shear, M. J., 1945, Studies of antigens in infected yolk sacs. National Institute of Health Bull., No. *183*, 13-17.

Topping, N. H., Henderson, R. G., and Bengtson. I. A., 1945, Epidemic typhus fever: studies of epidemic typhus vaccine. National Institute of Health Bull., No. *183*, 65-86.

Turner, J. C., and Jackson, E. B., 1943, Serological specificity of an auto-antibody in atypical pneumonia. Brit. J. Exp. Path., *24*, 121-126.

Turner, J. C., Nisnewitz, S., Jackson, E. B., and Berney, R., 1943, Relation of cold agglutinins to atypical pneumonia. Lancet, *1*, 765-769.

Walker, D. L., and Horsfall, F. L., Jr., 1950, Lack of identity in neutralizing and hemagglutination-inhibiting antibodies against influenza viruses. J. Exp. Med., *91*, 65-86.

Warren, J., Weil, M. L., Russ, S. B., and Jeffries, H., 1949, Purification of certain viruses by use of protamine sulfate. Proc. Soc. Exp. Biol. and Med., *72*, 662-664.

Whitman, L., 1947, Factors influencing the red cell agglutination-inhibition reaction in influenza and their application to the diagnostic test. J. Immunol., *56*, 167-177.

Wiener, M., Henle, W., and Henle, G., 1946, Studies on the complement-fixation antigens of influenza viruses types A and B. J. Exp. Med., *83*, 259-279.

Wolfe, D. M., and Kornfeld, L., 1948, Conglutinating complement absorption test compared with hemolytic complement-fixation reactions using Q fever immune bovine serum. Proc. Soc. Exp. Biol. and Med., *69*, 251-255.

Wolfe, D. M., Kornfeld, L., and Markham, F. S., 1949, Simplified indirect complement-fixation test applied to Newcastle disease immune avian serum. Proc. Soc. Exp. Biol. and Med., *70*, 490-494.

GEORGE K. HIRST, M.D.

The Public Health Research Institute of The City of New York, Inc.

4

Hemagglutination by Viruses

It was found, in 1941, that influenza virus has the capacity of agglutinating the red blood cells of the domestic fowl (Hirst, 1941; McClelland and Hare, 1941), and since then a number of other viruses have been found to possess a similar property. Those agents which at present are known to cause hemagglutination (Table 7) form a very heterogeneous group which includes viruses covering the entire range of particle size from the smallest (foot-and-mouth disease virus) to the largest (viruses inducing vaccinia and meningopneumonitis). Among the hemagglutinating viruses are agents with dominating tissue tropisms for the skin, the lung, the central nervous system and the secretory glands, as well as some which cause widespread systemic infection. This heterogeneity also extends to the kind of reaction which occurs between virus and red cell. Each virus has its own spectrum of the various species of red cells which it will agglutinate. In addition, the point of attachment of the virus to the red cell (receptor spot), as well as the nature of the force which binds the two together, probably differs from one agent to another. In many cases the site and the mode of attachment of virus to the cell is still poorly understood, and this uncertainty adds greatly to the difficulties of discussing the phenomenon as a whole.

Interest in the hemagglutination reaction has centered around two main areas: (1) the use of the reaction in the laboratory as an in-vitro method for facilitating virus research and laboratory diagnosis; (2) the study of the nature of the virus-red cell reaction from the standpoint of why it occurs and what possible meaning it may have for understanding virus-host cell relationships.

The basic phenomenon of red cell clumping is similar for all the agents under discussion. Suspensions of red cells and virus are mixed and allowed to stand. The cells, in settling out, form clumps of moderate size which are macroscopically visible. Unlike the agglutination of red cells by antibody, the viruses cause a weak type of cohesion between cells which is very readily broken up on slight shaking and requires special methods for quantitative measurement. In every case studied, the agglutination of cells is accompanied by the adsorption of virus particles onto the red cell surface, and it is believed that the virus is multivalent and forms bridges between adjacent cells. The adherence of virus to cell membrane has been confirmed in several instances by electron microscopy (Dawson and Elford, 1949).

The quantitative measurement of hemagglutination may be done in a simple manner. The virus preparation is diluted serially in twofold steps in either a saline or a suitable buffer solution. To these dilutions are added washed red cells of the proper species (0.25 to 1 per cent concentration), the reaction being carried out in standard Wassermann tubes with a final volume of 0.5 to 1.0 cc. After thorough shaking, the cells are allowed to settle out at room or refrigerator temperature; this requires from one to two hours, depending on the species of red cell used. In those tubes containing no detectable hemagglutination the cells settle out in the form of a small sharply outlined button, while agglutinated cells deposit a thin film covering the entire curved portion of the bottom of the tube. Usually the margin of this disk has a characteristic serrated appearance, and for this reason the method is often referred to as the pattern test (Salk, 1944). End points are usually sharp, and tests are read without disturbing the cells, since shaking would disperse them.

With some viruses (Group 3, Table 7) the test must be carried out in a narrow range of temperature and in a diluent of precise pH, but with agents of the influenza-mumps group this is not necessary. The pattern test is the most sensitive one in general use, and suspensions of many viruses or materials containing them may be diluted several thousand times and still give a positive reaction. The inherent error is about one tube. Much more accurate photometric methods have been devised which are applicable for use with a number of viruses in which the error has been reduced to less than 10 per cent (Hirst and Pickels, 1942).

The use of hemagglutination in virus work can be illustrated most strikingly by reviewing the changes in technic which have occurred in influenza-virus research since 1941. Prior to that time there was no practicable in-vitro method by which the virus content of suspensions could be estimated. While antigen titration by the complement-fixation test could have been used, the method was actually employed very little, presumably since it was effective only over a narrow range. Virus titrations were carried out principally in mice, a method which was not only expensive but required from 7 to 10 days for completion. New influenza-virus strains were isolated from man by

serial passage in ferrets followed by serial passage in mice, a process of adaptation often taking many weeks and probably accompanied by a change in the basic antigenic pattern of the agent. Serum-antibody studies were carried out by the neutralization test in mice and by the complement-fixation test in vitro.

With the advent of the hemagglutination test it became possible to assay a tissue suspension for its virus content by a rapid and inexpensive in-vitro method (Hirst, 1942a). Despite some limitations, the test has proved to be very useful. The influenza hemagglutinin is part of the virus particle, but noninfective as well as viable virus will give the reaction, so that the hemagglutination titer of an influenza suspension is very probably proportional to the sum of the active and the inactive virus present. In the case of virus grown under optimal conditions, that is, conditions under which most of the virus is active, the in-vitro titer is closely proportional to the content of the active agent. The in-vitro method is of course much less sensitive than in-vivo technics, and an influenza suspension which gives hemagglutination when diluted 4,000 times will usually infect chick embryos at a 100,000 times greater dilution.

It was well known before 1941 that influenza virus could infect the chick embryo, yet this host was used very little in laboratory procedures, since the presence of infection was accompanied by no readily discernible evidence. Infection in chick embryos was detected only by titration in mice. When infection of the chorio-allantoic sac is initiated even by small inocula, a rapid production of virus occurs, and high levels of the agent are reached in the chorio-allantoic fluid. It is now possible to detect the occurrence of infection rapidly by a spot test in which a drop of allantoic fluid is mixed with a drop of red-cell suspension. In this way the chick embryo may be used for in-ovo titrations of virus and provides a test which is often more sensitive than mouse titration and may be completed in

TABLE 7. HEMAGGLUTINATING VIRUSES

Group	Virus	Natural Host	Primary Tissue Tropism	Particle Size (mµ)	Reference	Characteristics of Hemagglutination
1	Influenza A, B and C	Man, swine	Respiratory	100	Hirst, 1941 McClelland and Hare, 1941 Taylor, 1949	Spontaneous dissociation of virus from cells. Receptor destruction.
	Mumps	Man	Secretory glands	170	Levens and Enders, 1945	
	Newcastle disease	Domestic fowl	General	180 x 70	Burnet, 1942	
2	Variola	Man	Skin	240 x 300	North, 1944	Hemagglutinin separable from the intact virus particle.
	Vaccinia	Mouse	Skin	220 x 280	Nagler, 1942	
	Ectromelia	Mouse	Skin	300 x 200	Burnet, 1945	
	Meningopneumonitis		Lung	354	Hilleman et al., 1951	
3	Encephalomyocarditis (Mengo, Columbia SK and MM)	Rat	CNS	10-15	Hallauer, 1947 Olitsky and Yager, 1949	Virus-cell union a reversible equilibrium. Exacting conditions for the reaction necessary. Usually few species of cells susceptible to agglutination.
	Mouse encephalomyelitis (GDVII strain)	Mouse	CNS	7-10	Lahelle and Horsfall, 1949	
	Japanese encephalitis	Man	CNS	15-22	Sabin and Buescher, 1950	
	St. Louis encephalitis	Man	CNS	20-30		
	West Nile fever	Man		21-31	Sabin, 1951	
	Russian spring summer encephalitis	Man	CNS	15-25		
	Pneumonia virus of mice	Mouse	Respiratory	40	Mills and Dochez, 1944	
	Foot-and-mouth disease	Cattle	General	10	Michelson, 1949	
	Fowl plague	Domestic fowl	General	60-90	Lush, 1943	

48 hours (Hirst, 1942b; Burnet and Beveridge, 1943). The technic may also be used for in-ovo titration of neutralizing antibody. The mouse is no longer widely used.

The isolation of influenza virus from man by means of serial passage in ferrets and mice was laborious, slow and uncertain. The usual method employed at present consists of mixing unfiltered throat-washings with antibiotics (Hirst, 1945) and inoculating the mixture into the amniotic sac of chick embryos. After three or four days the amniotic fluid is removed and tested for hemagglutinins. When a new strain has been isolated the hemagglutinin titer is often high and permits the immediate determination of serologic type by means of hemagglutination-inhibition tests with appropriate antisera. This method of isolating influenza virus is rapid and efficient and yields an agent which can be used at once for further in-vivo and in-vitro tests.

In addition to facilitating the isolation, the titration and the detection of virus, the hemagglutination test has also proved to be useful in discovering qualitative differences between strains which might otherwise remain obscure. In isolating strains from human sources, Burnet and Bull (1943) found that newly recovered virus agglutinated guinea pig cells to high titer but failed to agglutinate chicken cells. With further passage, variants appeared which agglutinated both types of cells equally well. The basic significance of this finding is not yet entirely clear, but it illustrates the kind of added information which may become available through the use of in-vitro methods. Another example of this sort is the discovery of incompletely formed virus particles (von Magnus, 1951; Schlesinger, 1950) which agglutinate red cells but are not infectious. Other factors connected with hemagglutination, such as the temperature of hemagglutinin inactivation, position of a virus in the receptor gradient, spectrum of cell species agglutinated, speed of elution from red cells, etc., may be used to characterize virus strains in greater detail, and these markers will undoubtedly be of value in genetic experiments (Burnet, 1951).

Hemagglutination has been widely used for antibody measurement, the details of which are reviewed in the chapter on Serologic Reactions. It is sufficient to record here that the hemagglutinating viruses, when mixed with sufficient homologous immune antibody, lose their ability to clump red cells. The degree of inhibition, which is readily measureable, gives an estimate of the amount of antibody in various sera. There is wide variation among the hemagglutinating viruses as to the type of antibody measured. In the case of vaccinia-immune serum, the kind of antibody measured is unknown but is definitely not a neutralizing antibody. When dealing with influenza antisera, the antihemagglutinin widely overlaps the neutralizing antibody but is more strain specific than that measured by complement fixation in the presence of nonviral (soluble) antigen.

NATURE OF THE VIRUS-RED CELL UNION

The phenomenon of red-cell clumping is secondary to the attachment of virus to red cells. Since both viruses and red cells have complex surfaces, it is not surprising that different viruses combine with cells through different surface groups or by different mechanisms; in most cases the nature of the union is obscure. For convenience of description, the viruses in Table 7 have been divided into three groups based on their attachment mechanisms. The third group is the one in which the mechanisms have been least studied and includes all those agents that have been most recently found to possess the hemagglutinating property. Further studies will doubtless lead to a reclassification of the group.

In almost all instances the evidence at hand indicates that the factor responsible for red-cell clumping by members of the third group in Table 7 is closely associated with or is a part of the virus particle. In many cases adherence to rather narrow limits of pH and salt concentration is necessary for agglutination to occur; cells may adsorb virus at one concentration and quantitatively elute it at a lower concentration, leaving both virus and red cell intact. The sensitivity of the reaction to pH changes suggests that the virus-cell union may be the result of a salt effect, possibly analogous to the initial phase of the two-stage adsorption of phage to the bacterial cell (Garen and Puck, 1951). The number of species of red cells susceptible to agglutination by many viruses of this group is very limited as contrasted with the susceptibility of many species to the action of the influenza-mumps group. Specific homologous antibody acts as an agglutinin inhibitor for all these agents, and nonspecific inhibitors are also found in many biologic fluids. In most cases the type of antibody measured and the usefulness of the inhibition test have not been fully explored.

The second group (Table 7) of viral hemagglutinating agents is distinguished by the fact that the active principle is a soluble substance completely separable from the virus particle. This group includes the viruses of vaccinia, variola and ectromelia, a spontaneous disease of mice whose etiologic agent is related antigenically to that of vaccinia (Burnet and Boake, 1946). The multiplication of vaccinia virus is accompanied by the formation of a hemagglutinin active against red cells of fowl and other species. The amount formed is not proportional to the virus titer, and by centrifugation the virus may be sedimented, leaving the hemagglutinin in the supernatant fluid (Burnet and Stone, 1946; Stone and Burnet, 1946). A number of soluble components of vaccinia virus are known (see chapter on Vaccinia) but none has been identified with the hemagglutinin. There is some evidence that the hemagglutinin is a lecithinlike phospholipid (Stone, 1946a, b): (1) lecithin from several sources will agglutinate some but not all fowl cells; (2) the susceptibility of any fowl-cell suspension to agglutination by lecithin is closely paralleled by its suscep-

tibility to vaccinia hemagglutinin; (3) the active agent in vaccinia preparations is destroyed by cobra venom and *Cl. welchii* filtrates under conditions which suggest that a lecithinase may be the active principle responsible for its destruction.

The hemagglutinins of this group are inhibited by serum containing specific antibody, and the serologic differences between ectromelia and vaccinia viruses may be demonstrated by the inhibition test (Burnet and Boake, 1946). It is not certain what antibody is measured with vaccinia hemagglutinin. While the inhibition titer of human serum rises after vaccination, it is reasonably clear that the test does not measure neutralizing antibody; hence, it is extremely doubtful that this serologic test is of any value in evaluating acquired resistance to infection. The fourth member of this group, meningopneumonitis virus, is closely related to agents of ornithosis and lymphogranuloma venereum. It is perhaps significant that only the largest viruses have hemagglutinins separable from the virus particle.

The first group of agents (Table 7) is in many ways the most interesting and has been studied thoroughly; it includes the viruses of mumps, Newcastle disease (a malady of domestic fowl) and influenza. The last includes type A, B and C strains (see chapter on Influenza) affecting man, as well as those A strains which infect swine.

The basic phenomenon which makes the virus-cell relationships of this group of more than usual interest can be very simply illustrated. When one of these viruses is mixed with suitable red cells, almost all of the active agent becomes attached to the cells within a few minutes (Hirst, 1942c). If this were a simple adsorption of virus to cell, one would expect the reaction to go rapidly at first, then slowly, and finally cease at some point of equilibrium. However, the adsorbed agents of this group spontaneously elute from red cells and under proper conditions do so completely. The virus which has been adsorbed and released is fully active and in every way resembles the original virus. The red cells, although they appear to be normal, change in several ways following adsorption and release of virus. They will no longer adsorb fresh virus of the same strain, nor will they usually adsorb viruses of different strains of the same type, presumably due to the loss of virus receptors. The electrophoretic mobility of the cells is found to have been changed markedly (Hanig, 1948), and immunologic tests show that a new antigen, hitherto undetectable, has appeared on the surface of these cells (Burnet and Anderson, 1947).

These facts strongly indicate that some active process occurs and they are best explained by the assumption that the virus possesses an enzyme which is capable of attacking a surface component of the red cell called the receptor group. Very likely, the initial combination between the virus and the cell is due to forces of attraction between enzyme and substrate, and once the receptor or substrate is destroyed the combining forces no longer exist, so that the virus particle is free to move on to other receptors. A certain amount of evidence points to the fact that receptors are probably mucoproteins, but most of what is known about them is on a less precise level.

The foregoing example is typical of the simplest type of action between a single strain of virus and red cells. When the interrelationships of a number of different strains of influenza, mumps and Newcastle disease virus are examined from the standpoint of receptor destruction, the results become exceedingly complex and do not warrant detailed description, though one or two basic phenomena are reasonably clear.

Many bacteria secrete an enzyme into the medium during growth which has the capacity of destroying the virus receptors of red cells in much the same manner as that evidenced by viruses of this group (Burnet and Stone, 1947; McCrea, 1947). Exposure of red cells to this enzyme for varying periods of time results in varying degrees of receptor destruction. If these lots of cells (Burnet, McCrea and Stone, 1946) are then tested against an array of viruses of the influenza-mumps-Newcastle disease group for their ability to adsorb or to be agglutinated by these viruses, it will be found that cells which have been exposed to the enzyme for a long time have lost their ability to adsorb or to be agglutinated by any of the viruses. Cells which have been exposed to the enzyme for a short time lose their ability to react with one or two of the strains tested while retaining almost completely their agglutinability with the other strains. The order in which agglutinability disappears constitutes a series that has been called the receptor gradient. This may well mean that the receptor spots of red cells are chemically complex and contain qualitatively different types of reaction sites. Some viruses may attach firmly only to those particular sites which are quickly destroyed, while other strains may have a much wider affinity for all the sites in the receptor area.

Destruction of receptor spots by viruses has an effect similar to that of the bacterial filtrate described above, but viruses differ in the completeness and the rapidity with which they are able to destroy receptors. If one arranges the viruses in a gradient series numbered 1 to 10 (1 meaning a virus whose reactivity with red cells is quickly lost on receptor destruction, and 10 meaning a virus that still agglutinates red cells when the other 9 will not), one may test these agents for their ability to destroy red-cell receptors. Burnet, McCrea and Stone (1946) found that strain 1 will destroy the receptors for itself only, while strain 2 destroys receptors for strains 1 and 2, etc. The ability of a virus to destroy receptors can be correlated with ability to change the electrophoretic mobility of the cells (Ada and Stone, 1950). The foregoing statements imply a fairly high degree of specificity of the virus enzyme for segments of the receptor complex, and, while Burnet and his collaborators have amassed a large amount of evidence in favor of this view, it may be noted that one investigator (Hirst, 1950a) did not find such sharp specificity. Results of the latter worker suggest that in most cases, if receptors are exposed to sufficient quantities of weak virus for a long period of time, they will be destroyed but at a slower rate than that observed when a strong virus is used. One type of virus (influenza C) belonging in this group seems to have a red-cell receptor site which is unaffected by the other viruses of influenza, mumps and Newcastle disease (Hirst, 1950b).

INHIBITORS

Another aspect of the hemagglutination reaction is the occurrence of inhibitors in various biologic fluids and tissues. These inhibitors cannot be demonstrated when typical unaltered virus is used as a hemagglutinin. However, when certain influenza strains are subjected to heat (Anderson, 1948) or chemical agents, the virus is subtly altered so that while it still attaches to and agglutinates red cells it can no longer spontaneously elute from them. A virus of this kind, called an indicator (noneluting) virus, after being mixed with certain biologic fluids will no longer agglutinate red cells (hemagglutination inhibition). The inhibitors demonstrable with an indicator strain are widespread in nature and have been found in highest concentration in egg-white, human urine, ovarian-cyst fluids, extracts of salivary glands, extracts of red cells, and serum. In lower concentration they are found in almost any tissue suspension. Study of inhibitors from various sources indicates that they are probably mucoproteins. The activity of inhibitors against indicator virus is destroyed by native but not by indicator virus, and Gottschalk (1951) has shown that the destruction of inhibitor in egg-white and human serum and urine is accompanied by the liberation of what seems to be a complex amino sugar. Certain analogies of the action of native and indicator virus on red cells and on inhibitors suggest a basic similarity between these two substrates. Inhibitors from different sources vary qualita-

tively; for example, one gives a higher inhibition titer against influenza strain PR8 than against influenza strain Melbourne, while another shows just the opposite selectivity of inhibition. As with cell receptors, inhibitors vary a great deal in regard to the ease with which they may be destroyed by various viruses.

In spite of the ubiquity of inhibitors in nature, little or nothing is known of their natural importance or function. One is tempted to think of virus inhibitors, especially those in throat-secretions, as playing a role in protection of the host against certain virus infections. However, laboratory experiments have failed to show that these inhibitors, even when used in massive amounts, have any significant effect in reducing the susceptibility of experimental animals to infection. If inhibitors represent a defense mechanism, it would appear that certain viruses have developed ways of overcoming it. On the other hand, inhibitors in body fluids may represent cast-off cell receptors, and their role as part of the cell may be more important.

Virus receptors are found not only on red cells but also on other cells of the body, including those which are susceptible to viral infection. Thus, adsorption and elution of influenza virus can be demonstrated with the excised lungs of ferrets and mice and with the allantoic cells of the chick embryo. It has been demonstrated that intact receptors on the chorio-allantoic membrane are necessary for infection to take place (Stone, 1948a). If the receptor-destroying enzymes of cholera vibrio are allowed to act on this membrane, the receptors are rapidly destroyed, and infection of the membrane is rendered notably more difficult. Similar effects have been noted in mouse lung (Stone, 1948b) and in mouse brain (Cairns, 1951). The indication is that intact receptors on host cells are probably necessary for or, at least, greatly facilitate influenza infection.

All strains of the mumps-influenza-NDV group of viruses studied so far have been found to possess receptor-destroying properties. It is a reasonable assumption that such a ubiquitous property must be of some utility for these small organisms. No one has succeeded thus far in inactivating the receptor-destroying property of a virus without destroying its ability to infect; however, at what point in the infectious cycle receptor destruction may be important is not clear. It is possible that the ability to destroy inhibitors may enable the virus to free itself from firm combination with mucopolysaccharides in body secretions in order to proceed to susceptible cells. Another possibility is that virus, which has become at-

tached to host cell receptors, destroys this surface constituent as an initial act in penetrating the cell (Hirst, 1943), or it may have some more obscure action within the cell. In any event, inhibitors and receptors are destroyed in a tissue during the course of infection (Schlesinger, 1951; Liu and Henle, 1951; Fazekas de St. Groth, 1950). The function of this receptor-destroying enzyme is of special interest since it is the only complete enzyme known to be closely associated with a virus. A complete elucidation of this problem is almost sure to reveal hitherto unsuspected mechanisms involved in virus behavior.

REFERENCES

Ada, G. L., and Stone, J. D., 1950, Electrophoretic studies of virus-red cell interaction: Mobility gradient of cells treated with viruses of the influenza group and the receptor-destroying enzyme of V. cholerae. Brit. J. Exp. Path., 31, 263-274.

Anderson, S. G., 1948, Mucins and mucoids in relation to influenza virus action. I. Inactivation by RDE and by viruses of the influenza group, of the serum inhibitor of haemagglutination. Australian J. Exp. Biol. and Med. Sci., 26, 347-354.

Burnet, F. M., 1942, The affinity of Newcastle disease virus to the influenza virus group. Australian J. Exp. Biol. and Med. Sci., 20, 81-88.

Burnet, F. M., 1945, An unsuspected relationship between the viruses of vaccinia and infectious ectromelia of mice. Nature, 155, 543.

Burnet, F. M., 1951, A genetic approach to variation in influenza viruses. 1. The characters of three substrains of influenza virus A (WS). J. Gen. Microb., 5, 46-53.

Burnet, F. M., and Anderson, S. G., 1947, The "T antigen" of guinea pig and human red cells. Australian J. Exp. Biol. and Med. Sci., 25, 213-217.

Burnet, F. M., and Beveridge, W. I. B., 1943, Titration of antibody against influenza viruses by allantoic inoculation of the developing chick embryo. Australian J. Exp. Biol. and Med. Sci., 21, 71-77.

Burnet, F. M., and Boake, W. C., 1946, The relationship between the virus of infectious ectromelia of mice and vaccinia virus. J. Immunol., 53, 1-13.

Burnet, F. M., and Bull, D. R., 1943, Changes in influenza virus associated with adaptation to passage in chick embryos. Australian J. Exp. Biol. and Med. Sci., 21, 55-69.

Burnet, F. M., McCrea, J. F., and Stone, J. D., 1946, Modification of human red cells by virus action. I. The receptor gradient for virus action in human red cells. Brit. J. Exp. Path., 27, 228-236.

Burnet, F. M., and Stone, J. D., 1946, The haemagglu-

tinins of vaccinia and ectromelia viruses. Australian J. Exp. Biol. and Med. Sci., 24, 1-8.

Burnet, F. M., and Stone, J. D., 1947, The receptor-destroying enzyme of Vibrio cholerae. Australian J. Exp. Biol. and Med. Sci., 25, 227-233.

Cairns, H. J. F., 1951, Protection by receptor-destroying enzyme against infection with a neurotropic variant of influenza virus. Nature, 168, 335.

Dawson, I. M., and Elford, W. J., 1949, The investigation of influenza and related viruses in the electron microscope, by a new technique. J. Gen. Microb., 3, 298-311.

Fazekas de St. Groth, S., 1950, Studies in experimental immunology of influenza. I. The state of virus receptors and inhibitors in the respiratory tract. Australian J. Exp. Biol. and Med. Sci., 28, 15-29.

Garen, A., and Puck, T. T., 1951, The first two steps of the invasion of host cells by bacterial viruses. II. J. Exp. Med., 94, 177-189.

Gottschalk, A., 1951, N-substituted isoglucosamine released from mucoproteins by the influenza virus enzyme. Nature, 167, 845-847.

Hallauer, C., 1949, Agglutination von Hammel-erythrocyten durch murine Poliomyelitisvirus-stämme. 4th International Congress for Microbiology, July 1947, Copenhagen 1949, p. 257.

Hanig, M., 1948, Electrokinetic change in human erythrocytes during adsorption and elution of PR8 influenza virus. Proc. Soc. Exp. Biol. and Med., 68, 385-392.

Hilleman, M. R., Haig, D. A., and Helmold, R. J., 1951, The indirect complement fixation, hemagglutination and conglutinating complement absorption tests for viruses of the psittacosis-lymphogranuloma venereum group. J. Immunol., 66, 115-130.

Hirst, G. K., 1941, The agglutination of red cells by allantoic fluid of chick embryos infected with influenza virus. Science, 94, 22-23.

Hirst, G. K., 1942a, The quantitative determination

of influenza virus and antibodies by means of red cell agglutination. J. Exp. Med., *75*, 49-64.

Hirst, G. K., 1942b, In vivo titrations of influenza virus and of neutralizing antibodies in chick embryos. J. Immunol., *45*, 285-292.

Hirst, G. K., 1942c, Adsorption of influenza hemagglutinins and virus by red blood cells. J. Exp. Med., *76*, 195-209.

Hirst, G. K., 1943, Adsorption of influenza virus on cells of the respiratory tract. J. Exp. Med., *78*, 99-109.

Hirst, G. K., 1945, Direct isolation of influenza virus in chick embryos. Proc. Soc. Exp. Biol. and Med., *58*, 155-157.

Hirst, G. K., 1950a, Receptor destruction by viruses of the mumps-NDV-influenza group. J. Exp. Med., *91*, 161-175.

Hirst, G. K., 1950b, The relationship of the receptors of a new strain of virus to those of the mumps-NDV-influenza group. J. Exp. Med., *91*, 177-184.

Hirst, G. K., and Pickels, E. G., 1942, A method for the titration of influenza hemagglutinins and influenza antibodies with the aid of a photoelectric densitometer. J. Immunol., *45*, 273-283.

Lahelle, O., and Horsfall, F. L., Jr., 1949, Hemagglutination with the GDVII strain of mouse encephalomyelitis virus. Proc. Soc. Exp. Biol. and Med., *71*, 713-718.

Levens, J. H., and Enders, J. F., 1945, The hemoagglutinative properties of amniotic fluid from embryonated eggs infected with mumps virus. Science, *102*, 117-120.

Liu, O. C., and Henle, W., 1951, Studies on host-virus interactions in the chick embryo-influenza virus system. IV. The role of inhibitors of hemagglutination in the evaluation of viral multiplication. J. Exp. Med., *94*, 269-289.

Lush, D., 1943, The chick red cell agglutination test with the viruses of Newcastle disease and fowl plague. J. Comp. Path. and Therapeutics, *53*, 157-160.

von Magnus, P., 1951, Propagation of the PR8 strain of influenza A virus in chick embryos. II. The formation of "incomplete" virus following inoculation of large doses of seed virus. Acta Path. et Microb. Scand., *28*, 278-293.

McClelland, L., and Hare, R., 1941, The adsorption of influenza virus by red cells and a new in vitro method of measuring antibodies for influenza virus. Canad. Public Health J., *32*, 530-538.

McCrea, J. F., 1947, Modification of red cell agglutinability by *Cl. welchii* Toxins. Australian J. Exp. Biol. and Med. Sci., *25*, 127-136.

Michelsen, E., 1949, Hemagglutination with foot and mouth disease virus using rat blood cells. Preliminary experiments. Nord. Vet. *1*, 905-914.

Mills, K. C., and Dochez, A. R., 1944, Specific agglutination of murine erythrocytes by a pneumonitis virus in mice. Proc. Soc. Exp. Biol. and Med., *57*, 140-143.

Nagler, F. P. O., 1942, Application of Hirst's phenomenon to the titration of vaccinia virus and vaccinia immune serum. Med. J. Australia, *1*, 281-283.

North, E. A., 1944, A study of the immunological reactions of the variola and vaccinia viruses grown in the developing egg. Australian J. Exp. Biol. and Med. Sci., *22*, 105-109.

Olitsky, P. K., and Yager, R. H., 1949, Hemagglutination by Columbia SK, Columbia MM, mengo encephalomyelitis and encephalomyocarditis viruses: experiments with other viruses. Proc. Soc. Exp. Biol. and Med., *71*, 719-724.

Sabin, A. B., 1951, Hemagglutination by viruses affecting the human nervous system. Fed. Proc., *10*, 573-578.

Sabin, A. B., and Buescher, E. L., 1950, Unique physico-chemical properties of Japanese B. encephalitis virus hemagglutinin. Proc. Soc. Exp. Biol. and Med., *74*, 222-230.

Salk, J. E., 1944, A simplified procedure for titrating hemagglutinating capacity of influenza-virus and the corresponding antibody. J. Immunol., *49*, 87-98.

Schlesinger, R. W., 1950, Incomplete growth cycle of influenza virus in mouse brain. Proc. Soc. Exp. Biol. and Med., *74*, 541-548.

Schlesinger, R. W., 1951, Studies on interference between influenza and equine encephalomyelitis viruses. Archiv. f. d. ges. Virusforschung, *4*, 501-517.

Stone, J. D., 1946a, Inactivation of vaccinia and ectromelia virus haemagglutinins by lecithinase. Australian J. Exp. Biol. and Med. Sci., *24*, 191-196.

Stone, J. D., 1946b, Lipid haemagglutinins. Australian J. Exp. Biol. and Med. Sci., *24*, 197-205.

Stone, J. D., 1948a, Prevention of virus infection with enzyme of *V. cholerae*. I. Studies with viruses of mumps-influenza group in chick embryos. Australian J. Exp. Biol. and Med. Sci., *26*, 49-64.

Stone, J. D., 1948b, Prevention of virus infection with enzyme of *V. cholerae*. II. Studies with influenza virus in mice. Australian J. Exp. Biol. and Med. Sci., *26*, 287-298.

Stone, J. D., and Burnet, F. M., 1946, The production of vaccinia haemagglutination in rabbit skin. Australian J. Exp. Biol. and Med. Sci., *24*, 9-13.

Taylor, R. M., 1949, Studies on survival of influenza virus between epidemics and antigenic variants of the virus. Am. J. Public Health, *39*, 171-178.

G. JOHN BUDDINGH, M.D.

Louisiana State University School of Medicine, New Orleans

5

Chick-Embryo Technics

INTRODUCTION

The living cells of the extra-embryonic membranes and tissues, organs and yolk sac of the developing chick embryo provide the environmental factors required for multiplication of most of the viruses and rickettsiae known to be pathogenic for man and animals. Infection of the embryo with many of the viruses, rickettsiae and pathogenic bacteria provides a useful method for the experimental analysis of problems relating to the host and host cell-parasite relationship concerned in many infectious diseases. Direct isolation of the infectious agent by the inoculation of embryos with properly collected and treated materials from patients is fast gaining recognition as a standard procedure for the etiologic diagnosis of several viral and bacterial diseases. The infected embryo has been adapted to the preparation of diagonstic antigens and the large scale production of vaccines. It has also been utilized for the analysis of factors related to immunity and for the study and biologic assay of therapeutic agents.

HISTORY

The potentialities for the experimental investigation of infectious diseases inherent in the chick-embryo method were first emphasized by Goodpasture and his collaborators (Goodpasture, 1933). Adapting the technic described by Clark (1920) for embryologic work, Woodruff and Good-

pasture (1931) initiated widespread interest and adaptation of this method when they described infection of the chorio-allantoic membrane with the virus of fowl pox. Soon thereafter Goodpasture, Woodruff and Buddingh (1931, 1932) reported infection of the chorio-allantois with the viruses of vaccinia and herpes simplex. Smallpox vaccine prepared from this source was first successfully used by Goodpasture and Buddingh (1933, 1934, 1935). Following the reports of Burnet (1933), Burnet and Ferry (1934), and Burnet and Galloway (1934) on the infection of the embryo with canarypox, fowl plague, Newcastle disease and vesicular stomatitis, Burnet and his associates were responsible for rapidly enlarging the scope to which the embryo method is applicable. The extensive work of numerous investigators who have had a part in its application cannot be reviewed here. A list of the viruses and rickettsiae responsible for human infections thus far found to be infectious for the embryo and of the authors of the original reports is presented in Table 8. The publications of Burnet (1936), Goodpasture (1938, 1939, 1940), and Beveridge and Burnet (1946) provide additional information regarding the history of the development of the chick-embryo method. Investigations in which the chick embryo was used prior to 1931 for the study of infectious agents have been reviewed by Goodpasture (1938). He states that in view of remarks by Levaditi (1906),

109

TABLE 8. VIRUSES AND RICKETTSIAE OF HUMAN INFECTIONS WHICH HAVE BEEN
PROPAGATED IN THE CHICK EMBRYO

VIRUS OR RICKETTSIA	ROUTE OF INOCULATION AND AGE IN DAYS OF EMBRYO MOST COMMONLY USED	ORIGINAL PUBLICATION
Vaccinia	Chorio-allantois, 10-14	Goodpasture et al., 1931
Herpes simplex	Chorio-allantois, 12-14	Goodpasture et al., 1931
Rift Valley fever	Chorio-allantois, 10-12	Saddington, 1934
Variola (alastrim)	Chorio-allantois, 10-12	Torres and Teixeira, 1935
Psittacosis	Yolk sac, 7-9	Burnet and Roundtree, 1935
Equine encephalomyelitis	Embryo, 7-9	Higbee and Howitt, 1935
Lymphogranuloma inguinale	Yolk sac, 6-8	Miyagawa et al., 1935
Influenza	Allantois, amnion, 10-13	Smith, 1935
Lymphocytic choriomeningitis	Chorio-allantois, 11-12	Bengtson and Wooley, 1936
Louping-ill	Chorio-allantois, 10-12	Burnet, 1936
Common cold	Chorio-allantois, 10-12	Kneeland and Mills, 1936
St. Louis encephalitis	Chorio-allantois, 10-12	Harrison and Moore, 1936
Japanese B. encephalitis	Chorio-allantois, 10-12	Taniguchi et al., 1936
Yellow fever	Embryo, 6-8	Elmendorf and Smith, 1937
Meningopneumonitis	Chorio-allantois, 10-12	Francis and Magill, 1938
Rabies	Brain, yolk sac, 7-9	Dawson, 1939
B. virus	Chorio-allantois, 10-12	Burnet et al., 1939
Measles	Chorio-allantois, 10-12	Rake and Shaffer, 1939
Durand's disease	Chorio-allantois, 10-12	Findlay, 1942
Atypical pneumonia	Amnion, 10-12	Eaton and Meiklejohn, 1944
Herpes zoster	Human skin grafts on chorio-allantois	Goodpasture and Anderson, 1944
Mumps	Allantois, 8-12	Habel, 1945
Colorado tick fever	Yolk sac, 7-8	Koprowski and Cox, 1946
Dengue	Amnion, 5-6	Schlesinger, 1950
Infectious hepatitis	Amnion, 7-8	Henle et al., 1950
Coxsackie virus	Chorio-allantois, 7	Huebner et al., 1950
R. mooseri	Yolk sac, 6-8	Zia, 1934
R. prowazeki	Yolk sac, 6-8	Zia, 1934
R. rickettsii	Yolk sac, 6-8	Bengtson and Dyer, 1935
Coxiella burneti	Yolk sac, 6-8	Burnet and Freeman, 1937
R. tsutsugamushi	Yolk sac, 6-8	Wolff, 1938
R. conorii	Yolk sac, 6-8	Alexander and Mason, 1939
R. akari	Yolk sac, 6-8	Huebner et al., 1946

Borrel may be considered to have been the first to use the chick embryo for this purpose. Other notable contributions are those of Rous and Murphy (1911) with the agent of fowl sarcoma, Jouan and Staub (1920) with fowl pest, and Gay and Thompson (1928) with vaccinia virus.

GENERAL CONSIDERATIONS

The numerous factors which influence the growth of infectious agents in the chick embryo are as yet poorly understood. Empirical observations have indicated that embryos younger than 10 or 11 days usu-ally die from infection within a relatively short period of time because of the rapidity of multiplication of infectious agents. It has thus been found convenient in many instances to use young embryos when large quantities of a particular virus are desired. Older embryos, depending to some extent on the virulence of the infectious agent introduced, are more likely to respond with characteristic cellular reactions and are more suitable for the study of details of infectious processes.

Great variation has been observed in the manner in which different viruses and rickettsiae are adapted to growth in the various cells, tissues, organs and structures of the embryo. Consequently different routes of inoculation are employed for different purposes with the same or different viruses. For example, vaccinia apparently thrives best in the chorio-allantois, influenza virus is most readily obtained in quantity following intra-allantoic or amniotic inoculation; rickettsiae, on the other hand, proliferate most readily in the yolk sac. More specific information regarding the choice of age of embryos and the route of inoculation employed with different infectious agents for specific purposes should be obtained by consulting original reports and discussions in the separate chapters of this book.

The developing embryo exhibits a remarkable tenacity of life in the face of the various manipulative procedures involved in inoculation technics. After facility and familiarity with the basic technical procedures are developed by practice, operative mortality of embryos becomes negligible. With the more commonly used technics of chorio-allantoic, allantoic, amniotic and yolk-sac inoculation, the mortality from manipulation alone can be kept below 10 per cent. The acquisition of technical facility is also by far the best defense against bacterial contamination. The aseptic precautions observed in routine bacteriologic technics are of necessity required.

More detailed accounts of the various technics involved in the chick-embryo method are to be found in the publications by Goodpasture and Buddingh (1935), Burnet (1936), Polk, Buddingh and Goodpasture (1938), and Beveridge and Burnet (1946).

MATERIALS AND EQUIPMENT

Fertile Egg Supply

Commercial hatcheries are good sources for eggs of high fertility, proper size, cleanliness and freedom from natural infections.

Incubators

Commercial poultry incubators equipped with electric heating units, temperature controls, humidifiers, forced air circulation and automatic turning devices give the best results for preliminary incubation at 38° to 39° C. and from 45 to 60 per cent relative humidity. Inoculated embryos are usually incubated at from 36° to 37.5° C. in bacteriologic incubators. Lower temperatures are required in special instances. Humidity is supplied from water in a shallow pan which is placed on or near the bottom of the incubator. The inoculated eggs are maintained in the proper position in specially designed trays or racks and are not turned.

Egg Candler

Commercial poultry supply establishments carry various satisfactory types. Improvised candlers can easily be constructed.

Eggshell Cutting Drill

Carborundum abrasive disks, such as S. S. White Dental Co. points No. 6, 9, or 11, are most useful for cutting through the eggshell. They are activated by electric motors through a flexible drive-shaft equipped with a hand piece. A rheostat with attached foot treadle is required to control the motor speed. Several types of these all-purpose machines are generally available commercially. Electric hand motors are controlled with difficulty. Sharp-pointed steel trocars, diamond-point pencils, and sharp-pointed scissor blades can be substituted but these are cumbersome.

Miscellaneous Instruments

Half-spear-point dissecting needles which can be sterilized in a flame are best suited for cutting the shell-membrane. Ten-cc., metal veterinary syringes are convenient for dispensing petrolatum-paraffin mixtures. Forceps, scissors and other instruments used for removing or dissecting various embryonic structures may be suited to individual requirements. They are most conveniently sterilized in a portable electric steam sterilizer within easy access to the operator. Metal racks which will support several eggs in proper position during inoculation can be constructed. Stands for supporting single eggs during removal of infectious material are easily made by removing the wire cutting-frame from "hard boiled egg cutters" obtainable at household supply counters.

TECHNICAL PROCEDURES PRELIMINARY TO INOCULATION

Egg Candling

Transillumination of incubated eggs by means of the candler will distinguish infertile eggs and dead embryos from living embryos. Experience alone can develop the necessary familiarity with the appearance and location of the air sac, the extra-embryonic blood vessels, the size and gross anatomical divisions of the embryo, and the position of the amniotic cavity and yolk sac.

Cleansing of the Eggshell

Washing or scrubbing with soap and water removes the outer protective gelatinous coating of the eggshell and invites contamination with surface and air-borne micro-organisms. Tincture of iodine, merthiolate or alcohol may be applied to the shell area to be penetrated as an antiseptic precaution. Obviously soiled eggs are discarded.

Drilling of the Eggshell

Individual modifications of this procedure will be developed by each operator. Figure 21 presents the best method for holding the egg and guiding the drill during the operation. The drill should be run at moderate speed. The shell should be penetrated at one point and the cut enlarged to the desired size by grinding against the uncut edge, rather than by to and fro movements over the entire extent of the cut. Injury to the underlying shell-membrane and chorio-allantois must be avoided. After the drilling is completed the isolated segment and the immediately adjacent shell is covered with a thin layer of melted paraffin, kept between 60° and 65° C.

Exposure of the Embryo and Its Membranes

Good visualization of the embryonic structures is required for properly controlled inoculation. A sufficiently large segment of shell and its adhering shell-membrane should be removed overlying the position of the structure to be inoculated as determined while candling the eggs. The "window" or "shell-flap" methods described here are most commonly used.

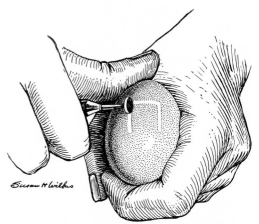

Fig. 21. Drawing illustrating method of cutting window in eggshell with dental drill.

The Window Method. A segment from 1 to 2 cm. square, as in Figure 21, is cut out of the shell with a dental drill. If the chorio-allantois is to be "dropped" a small drill hole is also made in the shell over the air sac. With the egg placed in a suitable support, the shell-membrane is cut by means of a sterile half-spear-point dissecting needle along 3 sides of the rectangle. Care is exercised to prevent injury to the underlying chorio-allantois. With the remaining uncut edge acting as a hinge, the shell segment is pried upward, grasped with forceps or the fingers and torn off. The chorio-allantois can then be dropped to provide a wide expanse of flat membrane for inoculation by puncturing the shell-membrane over the air sac. After the inoculation is completed, the window is sealed with Scotch tape. For most purposes, this method can replace the use of a glass cover-slip which must be held in place by a rim of sterile petrolatum-paraffin mixture (8 parts petrolatum, 1 part paraffin) expressed from a metal veterinary syringe. A clean cover-slip from a supply kept in 95 per cent alcohol is picked up with forceps and the alcohol adhering to it is burned off after which, while still warm, it is pressed down on the petrolatum-paraffin ring, sealing the

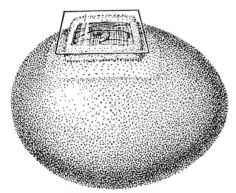

Fig. 22. Drawing illustrating closure of opening in eggshell by a cover-slip after inoculation of chick embryo.

opening (Fig. 22). Strips of adhesive tape also effectively seal the window. Squares of cellophane, sterilized in boiling water and rendered adhesive by being dipped just before use in 10 per cent egg albumen may also be used (Beveridge and Burnet, 1946).

Burnet's modification of this method is less likely to cause injury to the chorio-allantois. A triangular window is cut in the eggshell. The shell segment is carefully separated from the underlying shell-membrane. A small slit is then made through a drop of sterile saline placed in the center of the exposed shell-membrane. Suction is next applied to a drill hole over the air sac by means of a rubber bulb. The egg contents settle, separating the shell-membrane from the chorio-allantois. The

opening is then enlarged by tearing off part of or all the exposed shell-membrane. Alexander (1938) and Dunham (1942) have described technics further modified by Burnet (Beveridge and Burnet, 1946) which have been devised to reduce to a minimum accidental injury to the chorio-allantois. Exposure of the chorio-allantois and embryo through the air sac has been advocated by Taylor and Chialvo (1942).

The Shell-flap Method. The shell segment can be replaced to seal the opening. A triangular cut, 1 cm. at the base and 1.5 to 2 cm. along the sides, is made in the shell. The shell-membrane is cut along the sides of the triangle and the segment pried upward from the apex with the base acting as a hinge. Inoculations are made while the shell segment is held steady with forceps and then it is allowed to fall back to its original position. The cut is sealed carefully with melted paraffin.

INOCULATION THROUGH A SMALL DRILL HOLE

Injections into the egg can be made with a needle and syringe through a small drill hole. Where exact localization of the inoculum is not required, this procedure may be performed more or less blindly. Hirst (1942) has described injection of embryos and the amniotic sac while the egg is transilluminated by a strong light source in the candler.

METHOD OF EXPOSURE FOR REMOVAL OF LESIONS AND FLUIDS FROM THE EMBRYO

Adequate exposure through an enlarged opening in the eggshell which will provide good visualization of the embryo and its extra-embryonic structures is required for the removal of lesions, tissues and fluids. The original window can be enlarged by breaking away the shell with forceps. Contaminants will often be introduced with shell fragments by this method. When the window or shell-flap method is used the danger of contamination is greatly reduced by removing intact a large segment of shell as shown in Figure 23. With a dental drill a cut is made in the shell along the entire circumference of the long axis of the egg. Hot paraffin is spread over the entire cut. The egg is then placed on a support contained in a convenient receptacle. The shell-membrane is cut through with a sterile half-spear-point dissecting needle, leaving about 2 or 3 cm. intact at the air sac. As indicated in Figure 23, the entire top is then turned over with the intact piece of shell-membrane

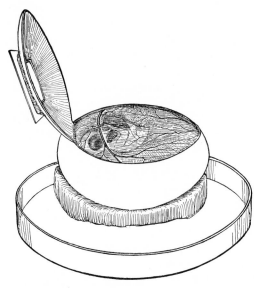

FIG. 23. Drawing illustrating an embryonated egg opened for removal of tissues and fluids.

serving as a hinge. Good exposure is thus effected. The chorio-allantois, allantoic fluid, amniotic fluid, the embryo and yolk sac are easily removed with a minimum of danger of contamination. When inoculations have been made through a small drill hole, the shell sector over the air sac should be removed by cutting around its entire circumference with a dental drill or by means of scissors.

TECHNICS OF INOCULATION

INOCULUM

It is essential that the inoculum be bacteriologically sterile. A few bacteria of low virulence which accidentally gain entrance during inoculation usually do not thrive in the embryo and rarely constitute a source of error. Spore-bearing saprophytes and the more common pathogens, however, grow rapidly, frequently killing the embryo long before any appreciable effects of virus infections can be noted. Diphtheroids and unidentified gram-positive micrococci have occasionally been encountered which have been transmitted in serial passage. Van Herick and Eaton (1945) describes pleuropneumonialike organisms as contaminants. Common molds are frequently troublesome. Attenuated live virus, propagated in embryonated eggs, for the immunization of poultry flocks may be contaminated with Newcastle disease virus. Herpes simplex virus may contaminate nasopharyngeal washings or stool suspensions.

Bacterial contaminants in an inoculum used to initiate viral infection of the embryo can be controlled by means of penicillin and streptomycin. The use of these antibiotics, introduced to inhibit the growth of bacteria in nasopharyngeal washings during the isolation of influenza virus (Rose, Pearce, and Molloy, 1946; McKee and Hale, 1947), has become widespread. Saliva, throat-washings, sputum, stool suspensions, contaminated tissues obtained by biopsy or at necropsy to which properly adjusted mixtures of penicillin and streptomycin are added can be introduced by the various routes of inoculation with minimal chances for the survival of bacterial contaminants. Filtration through Berkefeld, Zeitz or other filters, or passage through susceptible animals with aseptic removal of virus-containing tissue is required only under special circumstances.

Adequate bacterial sterility controls should be maintained on all tissues and fluids removed from infected embryos. Small portions from each individual harvest should be inoculated into appropriate media. Pools for serial passage should be made from samples which prove to be free from bacteria. If an entire passage in a series becomes contaminated, the use of penicillin-streptomycin mixtures will often prove effective in preventing the growth of the bacteria. When large amounts of infected materials are involved, sterility control is more conveniently performed on small pools or batches.

CHORIO-ALLANTOIC MEMBRANE INOCULATION

The chorio-allantoic membrane (Fig. 24) is composed of three layers, each of which represents one of the primary germinal layers. The outer or ectodermal layer con-

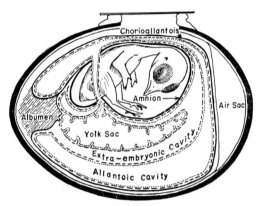

FIG. 24. Diagram of embryonated egg of 11 days' incubation showing the important structures involved in the chick-embryo technics.

sists of chorionic epithelium which arises early in embryonic development as an outgrowth of the dorsal somatopleure. Directly beneath it is the mesoderm representing a fusion of chorionic and allantoic mesoderm. The entoderm is made up of the inner lining of the rapidly expanding allantois which originates as a diverticulum from the embryonic hind gut. A rich capillary network, numerous arterioles and venules with their accompanying lymph channels are present in the mesodermal layer. No nervous tissue has been demonstrated in the membrane. The chorio-allantois provides an admirable living substrate for many viruses and micro-organisms.

AGE OF EMBRYOS

Embryos that have been incubated from 9 to 10 days can be used, but those incubated 11 or 12 days are most suitable.

CANDLING

Embryos which show a well-developed membranal circulation on transillumination are chosen. The shell is marked in the area overlying the best developed fixed blood vessels.

METHOD OF EXPOSURE

The window method including dropping of the chorio-allantois is preferred. The shell-flap method is also satisfactory.

INOCULATION

Small bits of infected tissue can be gently rubbed over the exposed membranal surface. Measured amounts of various dilutions of the inoculum can be introduced from calibrated pipettes or syringes. The inoculation fluid should be spread evenly over the available membranal surface. Volumes up to 2 cc. can be introduced.

INCUBATION AND EXAMINATION OF MEMBRANAL LESIONS

After the shell opening has been sealed the inoculated embryos are in most instances incubated at 37° C. At this temperature most virus lesions in the membrane reach maximum development in 48 to 96 hours. In those infections which spread to the embryo, death usually occurs within this period. The few observations which have been made seem to indicate that temperatures lower than 37° C. are unfavorable to virus infections of the membrane. Rickettsiae apparently are favorably influenced by temperatures as low as 32° C. (Zia, 1934). The progress of the membranal infection can be followed at regular intervals by making observations through the coverglass window either with the naked eye or with a dissecting microscope. The coverglass may be removed at any time and small bits of membranal tissue excised from more avascular areas for the purpose of making smears or transplants. Samples of exudate for smears or culture can be transferred on a sterile bacteriologic loop. Goodpasture (1933) briefly described a method for making membranal preparations in which the progress of the infection could be observed through the Leitz "Ultropak" equipment. Himmelweit (1938) independently adapted and refined this technic and made direct observations on vaccinia and ectromelia infections of the membrane.

Gross and Microscopic Appearance of Chorio-allantoic Lesions

Normal Appearance. The uninoculated chorio-allantois exposed by the window or shell-flap method incubated at 37° C. for from 48 to 96 hours retains its normal transparency and resilience. Slight, irregular opacities extending along blood vessels, which are caused by minor injuries or hemorrhage incident to the operative procedures, are frequently seen. Microscopically, normal membranes show no disturbances in the continuity of the ectodermal epithelium which is no more than one to two cells in thickness. Occasional foci of proliferating ectoderm or small ulcers at points of injury are encountered. The mesoderm is slightly thicker than in undisturbed membranes. Focal proliferations of fibroblasts and histiocytes may be observed around blood vessels or directly beneath the point where the membranal surface is injured. Accumulations of inflammatory cells are seldom if ever encountered. The entoderm usually remains undisturbed by the operative procedures.

Nonspecific Lesions. Emulsions or filtrates of noninfective foreign or embryonic tissue placed on the chorio-allantois provoke nonspecific responses of varying degree and intensity. Pin-point translucent ectodermal papules and small irregular ulcerations frequently develop. Irregular focal opacities extending along blood vessels, small hemorrhages and moderate edema develop in the mesoderm. Nonspecific changes are usually sharply confined to the area in which the inoculum is placed. Secondary foci do not develop and progressive spread of the reaction to the immediately adjacent areas does not take place. Upon microscopic examination great variation is observed in the nature and degree of these nonspecific lesions. Focal or extensive ectodermal ulcerations occcur directly beneath the debris derived from the inoculum. Various degrees of focal ectodermal proliferations especially at the ulcer edges may develop. The mesoderm shows varying degrees of edema and hemorrhage. More or less intensive proliferation of fibroblasts and mononuclear histiocytes localized directly beneath ectodermal ulcerations and in the perivascular areas develop in the mesoderm. There is usually a relatively moderate leukocytic reaction. The entoderm frequently responds with papillary or villouslike proliferative changes.

Specific Lesions. The gross and microscopic features characteristic of each virus infection to which the chorio-allantois is susceptible cannot be detailed here. The age at which the membrane is inoculated and the size of the infecting dose exert a marked influence on the appearance of the lesions. Ten- and 11-day-old membranes usually develop a diffuse confluent opacity and edema. They frequently exhibit extensive ulcers, areas of necrosis and hemorrhage regardless of the size of the inoculum. Twelve- to 14-day-old membranes are much more likely to develop focal, pocklike lesions especially if a dilute virus suspension is introduced. In the latter, differences in the gross appearance of the lesions are distinct enough to the practiced eye to permit differentiation between specific infections. Diffuse opacity and edema, hemorrhage of varying extent, focal thickenings or pocks, vesicles, ulcers, areas of necrosis and the collection of inflammatory exudate on the surface of and in the membrane are features common to most specific membranal lesions and may be regarded as indicative of infection. The progressive spread of the reaction from original foci, the development of secondary lesions and the death of the embryo are further fairly definite indications of an active infectious process.

Microscopically, the membranal lesions in many virus infections exhibit features which are specifically characteristic. The nature and intensity of the inflammatory response is usually determined by the extent of the necrosis produced by the infecting agent, and by circulatory disturbances, such as thrombosis and capillary injury. Morphologic changes in the nature of hyperplasia, hypertrophy, focal cellular proliferations associated with varying degrees of necrosis, vesicle and pock formation occur in infected membranes.

The presence of intracytoplasmic or intranuclear inclusions pathognomonic for many virus infections further aids in establishing the specificity of the lesion. Nonspecific inclusions such as keratin granules, fragments of leukocytes and erythrocytes within ectodermal and entodermal epithelial cells must be distinguished. Condensations in the cytoplasm, irregularities in staining of mesodermal fibroblasts, mononuclears and endothelial cells might be misinterpreted for specific inclusions.

In addition to careful histologic control, the specificity of the infective agent should wherever possible, be determined by inoculation into susceptible laboratory animals. Specific prevention or alteration of the membranal lesion by means of known immune serum can be demonstrated in many infections. Complement fixation with extracts prepared from membranal lesions may also be employed.

Removal, Grinding and Histologic Preparation of Membranal Lesions

Wide exposure of the egg contents by the technic previously described affords the most satisfactory means of removing membranal lesions. Forty-eight to 72 hours have been found to be the average optimum time limit with incubation at 37° C. for collecting material containing the maximum amount of the infectious agent, except in those instances where the virus is highly lethal and kills the embryo within 24 or 48 hours. Embryos which are dead within 24 hours without visible signs of infection are usually discarded.

Small quantities of membranal lesions can be ground effectively after they have been pooled in a sterile mortar covered with a Petri-dish top and frozen in a deep-freeze or in a freezing mixture of ice and salt set in a refrigerator. Removed from the deep-freeze or freezing mixture, the frozen mass is pounded with a sterile pestle until broken into small particles. As soon as thawing sets in grinding is begun and the material reduced to a smooth paste. The suspending medium is then slowly added in sufficient quantity so that the emulsion can be drawn up in a pipette.

Membranal lesions for histologic study may be removed from living embryos at any desired interval following inoculation. Small portions of the lesion for smears, bacterial control, serial passage or animal inoculation may first be cut out with sterile instruments. The infected area and a generous portion of surrounding normal membrane is completely separated with sterile scissors and forceps and spread out flat on a piece of moistened towel paper. This will prevent curling and wrinkling during fixation. After fixation in the desired fixing fluid, washing and preliminary hardening in 80 per cent alcohol strips or blocks for paraffin embedding can be cut with a sharp safety razor blade. A complete histologic study of the infectious process, which in many instances spreads to the embryo from the membrane, often provides valuable information (Buddingh, 1936; Gallavan, 1937; Buddingh and Polk, 1939). Whole embryos less than 14 days old can be fixed. Rapid fixation of the internal organs is effected by slitting the anterior abdominal and thoracic wall and the skull. After fixation, washing and preliminary hardening in 80 per cent alcohol, feathers can be easily plucked from the skin. The embryo is then sliced in any plane desired. The blocks are embedded for sectioning, mounting and staining.

TITRATION OF VIRUS SUSPENSIONS AND VIRUS-NEUTRALIZING ANTIBODIES BY THE POCK-COUNTING METHOD

Burnet and his co-workers, Keogh (1936), Burnet (1936), Burnet and Lush (1936), have introduced virus titration and virus-neutralizing antibody titration by means of the so-called pock-counting method. Several viruses such as those of variola, vaccinia, herpes, fowl pox and ectromelia, when inoculated in measured amounts of suitable dilutions on the surface of the dropped chorio-allantois of 12-day-old embryos, produce easily recognizable, discrete, focal lesions. Usually after from 36 to 72 hours of incubation following inoculation, an infected membrane can be exposed or removed and discrete lesions or pocks counted. If sufficient embryos, 4 to 6, are inoculated with standard amounts, 0.05 to 0.1 cc., of each dilution, satisfactory quantitative estimations of the relative amount of infective virus can be obtained. Serum-virus mixtures for testing the neutralizing-antibody content in immune serum can be subjected to the same procedure which will give reasonably accurate titrations. For details of the method and its application, the original papers listed and the monographs by Burnet (1936) and Beveridge and Burnet (1946) should be consulted.

AMNIOTIC INOCULATION

The amnion (Fig. 24) originates as an outgrowth from the ventral somatopleure; by the fifth day it completely envelops the embryo except at the yolk stalk. The embryo is completely submerged in the amniotic fluid which fills the amniotic sac. Introduction of infectious agents into the amniotic fluid exposes the inner epithelial lining of the amnion and the epidermal epithelium of younger embryos to infection. In embryos 12 days old and older, respiratory and swallowing movements further serve to bring the infectious agents into contact with the mucous membranes of the mouth, nose, paranasal sinuses, nasopharynx, trachea, bronchi, esophagus and the more proximal portions of the gastrointestinal tract. By this route of approach to the developing embryo infectious processes can be initiated in which the respiratory and gastro-intestinal tracts are utilized as portals of entry. Localization of the disease process in tissues and organs accessible by these routes has been found to occur in many instances.

Microscopic study of the embryos infected by the amniotic route, sacrificed and fixed at regular intervals after inoculation, in many instances provides important information regarding early stages in pathogenesis of various infectious processes. This has been done in a few instances as with influenza (Burnet, 1940), herpes simplex (Anderson, 1940), H. influenzae (Gallavan, 1938), H. pertussis (Gallavan and Goodpasture, 1938), C. diphtheriae (Cromartie, 1941), and meningococci (Buddingh and Polk, 1939).

AGE OF EMBRYOS

Embryos from 7 to 15 days' incubation can be used. The age chosen is largely determined by the virus used or the type of investigation undertaken. Slow growing viruses of relatively low virulence may be benefited by the longer period of incubation afforded by 7- to 8-day embryos. Viruses, for example those of vaccinia, influenza and herpes, proliferate in abundance when introduced into the amnion of 8- to 9-day embryos and apparently are released from the infected cells into the surrounding amniotic fluid. This fluid, when collected as soon as the embryos succumb to the infection, provides a rich, relatively cell-free source of virus adaptable to many purposes. Its virus content can be greatly increased if the infected embryos are also collected and added to the fluid. Gentle agitation will release a large proportion of the infected embryonic epidermis into the fluid. Amniotic infection at this stage of development takes advantage of the uniform susceptibility of a relatively wide expanse of naked embryonic epidermis before the feathers develop and provides an easily manageable virus suspension. When studies regarding the pathogenesis, localization, tissue reaction and course of virus, rickettsial or bacterial infection of the embryos are contemplated, 12- to 15-day-old embryos serve the purpose more usefully.

CANDLING

Embryos of the desired age are candled and the shell marked over the area where embryonic movements are most easily observed. Identification of the large mobile amniotic vein is a further aid in locating the position of the embryo and its surrounding amniotic cavity.

METHOD OF EXPOSURE

The window method is by far the most satisfactory, giving an adequate view of the course and location of the injecting needle. The shell-flap method is also adaptable. Injection through a small drill hole can be performed with proper transillumination of the egg (Hirst, 1942).

INOCULATION

Inoculation is best effected by means of a needle and syringe. Gauge 22 or 23 needles, 1¼ to 1½ inch in length, are used. With the embryo exposed by the window method, the amniotic cavity is entered by introducing the needle through the chorio-allantois as near the edge of the yolk sac as possible without entering it. While the needle is pushed forward in this position with the point directed toward the embryo it will be seen that the yolk is slightly pulled over toward the embryo by the thrust of the needle. The weight of the yolk will serve to pull the amnion over the needle and entry into the amnion is effected. This method when carefully practiced will eliminate the necessity of slitting the chorio-allantois and grasping the amnion with forceps.

INCUBATION

The period of incubation will vary with the type of virus, size of inoculum and age of embryo used. The effect of temperatures lower than 37° C. on various virus infections induced by the amniotic route has been investigated in only a few instances. Several investigators have found that influenza virus proliferates more rapidly at 35° C. in embryos inoculated into the amnion.

APPEARANCE OF AMNIOTIC FLUID AND EMBRYOS INFECTED BY THE AMNIOTIC ROUTE

Most of the changes described in embryos infected by the amniotic route have been nonspecific. If the embryo survives from 48 to 96 hours, retardation in development, subcutaneous hemorrhage, shedding of feathers, edema and cellular debris in the trachea have been described especially in influenza (Burnet, 1940). Generalized subcutaneous hemorrhage in embryos dead from infection cannot be regarded as specific as this is also observed in embryos dead from nonspecific causes. Various degrees of cloudiness of the amniotic fluid, although usually associated with infection, cannot be considered as indicative of it. The actual presence of virus must be demonstrated by the production of specific infection in susceptible animals or by suitable serologic tests.

COLLECTION OF AMNIOTIC FLUID

Amniotic fluid from infected embryos is most conveniently collected when the embryo is exposed as previously described. The fluid is most easily collected by grasping the embryo with sterile forceps introducing the point of a Pasteur pipette and manipulating the embryo and its surrounding membranes in such a way as to prevent obstruction of the pipette when suction is applied. The amount collected per embryo will vary from 1 to 5 cc. Adequate bacterial sterility controls should be run on each individual harvest or on small pools. Since amniotic fluid contains very little protein, the addition of 10 per cent inactivated normal serum is required to protect some viruses against deterioration during storage at ordinary refrigerator or dry-ice box temperatures.

ALLANTOIC INOCULATION

Allantoic inoculation is particularly useful for the propagation of influenza virus, in that it constitutes a rich source of virus for the preparation of vaccine or for general experimental work. It has also proven to be extremely useful in the titration of influenza immune bodies by the hemagglutination-inhibition test of Hirst.

AGE OF EMBRYOS AND CANDLING

Embryos that have been incubated from 10 to 11 days are usually used. During candling, the eggshell is marked at a site where the chorio-allantois appears to be well developed in an area free of large blood vessels.

INOCULATION

Exposure of the chorio-allantois by means of a window is usually not required. A small groove from 2 to 3 mm. long and 1 mm. wide is drilled into the shell without injury to the shell-membrane. The groove is covered with hot paraffin. The inoculum can then be introduced in the desired amount with a needle and syringe by piercing the shell-membrane and the chorio-allantois for a few millimeters. The opening is sealed with a thin layer of melted paraffin. Incubation is continued at 37° C. or at lower temperatures if desired.

COLLECTION OF ALLANTOIC FLUID

With influenza infection of the embryo, the fluid is collected from 36 to 48 hours after inoculation. If fluid free from red blood cells is desired, the embryos are chilled in the refrigerator for a few hours or overnight. After removing the shell over the air sac, the egg is placed in an egg cup or other convenient support. The exposed shell-membrane and chorio-allantois are cut away and the allantoic fluid is removed by means of a pipette.

No specific characteristics indicative of the presence of infectious agents can be observed in allantoic fluid. Slight cloudiness from the presence of a few inflammatory cells may be observed. If bleeding into the fluid is allowed to take place during its removal, red cell agglutination (Hirst phenomenon) may be observed in the presence of the viruses of influenza, vaccinia, ectromelia, Newcastle disease and possibly other viral infections. In embryos older than 12 days, there is a steady increase of urate concentration in the allantoic fluid. Upon standing at refrigerator temperatures these substances precipitate and produce a cloudy or milky appearance.

YOLK-SAC INOCULATION

The cells of the embryonic yolk sac are particularly susceptible to infection with various types of rickettsiae and the agents of lymphogranuloma venereum, psittacosis and mumps.

AGE OF EMBRYOS AND CANDLING

Living embryos that have been incubated from 5 to 8 days are generally used.

INOCULATION

When relatively few embryos are inoculated the window method may be used to advantage. Inoculation is performed with a 20- to 22-gauge needle and syringe. The yolk is readily recognized through the window and the site of injection visually controlled. The yolk sac can also be entered through the blunt end of the eggshell by way of a drill hole sufficiently large to admit the needle. The cut is covered with hot paraffin, tincture of iodine or merthiolate. The inoculating needle is inserted through the drill hole and directed inward along the long axis of the egg for 2 or 3 cm. so that the injection is made near the center of the egg. The drill hole is then sealed with a drop of melted paraffin. Inoculated embryos are incubated at temperatures which are found to be most suitable for the proliferation of the agent under investigation.

COLLECTION AND STUDY OF INFECTED YOLK

Removal of the top sector of the eggshell as previously described is most convenient for collecting infected yolk from embryos inoculated by the window method. The egg may also be entered through the blunt end by breaking away the shell, or separating it in one piece after cutting around the air sac with scissors or a dental drill. In either event, the embryo is first removed with sterile forceps after cutting through the membranes and umbilical stalk. The yolk sac is grasped at the umbilical stalk and transferred to a sterile Petri dish. Gentle washing with sterile saline solution will remove most of the yolk. Small samples of yolk sac can then be cut away for making smears, sterility controls or subinoculations. Pools of bacteriologically sterile yolk sac are subsequently ground, shaken with glass beads or subjected to other procedures designed to produce a suspension of the infecting agents which may be used for experimental work, vaccine or antigen production. Virus infections of the yolk sac in which the agent cannot be demonstrated in properly prepared smears require critical control to establish the specificity of the process. Subinoculation into susceptible laboratory animals, specific virus neutralization with known antiserum, specific complement fixation, and, where applicable, hemagglutination reactions have been used to good advantage. Careful histologic control of appropriately fixed and stained yolk sac should not be neglected.

INTRAVENOUS INOCULATION

Intravenous injection has found no widespread application in the study of experimental infections of the chick embryo. It nevertheless has value in studies concerned with the dissemination of disease-producing agents upon introduction into the blood stream and the pathogenesis of the infectious process under these circumstances. The method can be adapted to the study of the distribution and persistence of immune bodies following intravenous injection (Polk, Buddingh and Goodpasture, 1938). The effect of specific antibodies on the course of infection also can be studied by this means (Buddingh and Polk, 1939).

AGE OF EMBRYOS AND CANDLING

Embryos that have been incubated from 10 to 14 days are most suitable for intravenous injection. In candling, one of the larger, fixed membranal veins is located and outlined with a mark on the overlying shell.

INOCULATION

The window method is used for exposing the membranal veins. The chorio-allantois should not be dropped. Injection is performed with a sharp, 27-gauge needle and tuberculin syringe. The direction of the blood flow in the vein is determined. By careful manipulation, the needle is introduced into the vein. Considerable practice is required to perform this operation successfully. Injection is made slowly in the direction of the blood flow. From 0.05 to 0.5 cc. can be introduced. Eichhorn (1940) has introduced the following modification in this technic. The egg is candled as described and a shell segment from 1 to 2 cm. square is cut out over the location of the vein. The shell is removed carefully, leaving the underlying shell-membrane intact. A drop of sterile mineral oil applied to the shell-membrane renders it transparent. Injection into the vein is then accomplished with the intact shell-membrane serving to stabilize and fix the membranal veins. Hemorrhage subsequent to removal of the needle is reduced to a minimum by this technic. Small amounts of blood may be collected from the embryonic circulation by following either technic described. If the embryo is to be sacrificed, it is more convenient to remove it from the egg, and withdraw blood directly from the exposed heart by means of needle and syringe or capillary pipette.

INTRACEREBRAL INOCULATION

The cells of the embryonic brain are susceptible upon intracerebral inoculation to infection with the viruses of herpes (Anderson, 1940) and rabies (Dawson, 1941). Buddingh and Polk (1939) described meningococcus meningitis in embryos inoculated intracerebrally.

Age of Embryos and Candling

Embryos that have been incubated from 8 to 14 days can be used. In candling, the eggshell is marked in the area directly overlying the embryonic head which usually can be readily identified by the prominent outline of the eyes.

Inoculation

The window method is most suitable. The embryo will be found more accessible if the egg contents are not dropped by puncturing the air sac. The inoculum is introduced by means of a 1½-inch, 22 or 24 gauge needle and tuberculin syringe. In most instances the embryonic head will be visible through the window. With a sharp thrust of the needle, the injection is made directly through the skull. The usual dose is from 0.02 to 0.5 cc. If necessary, by careful manipulation, sterile forceps can be introduced through a small slit in the chorio-allantois whereupon the embryo is grasped by the beak and held in position while the injection is made.

Collection and Study of Infected Brain Tissues

Intracerebral inoculation is likely to be attended with a higher mortality rate from manipulative procedures than are other inoculation technics. From 30 to 40 per cent of embryos will frequently die, but, with increasing facility gained from practice, fatalities can be reduced to 10 per cent or less. Death resulting from the inoculation procedure usually takes place within 24 or 48 hours, and such embryos are discarded. Death of the embryos occurring later than 48 hours after intracerebral inoculation may be taken as indicative of infection. Dawson (1941) described the gross changes which occur in embryos inoculated intracerebrally with rabies virus. Hemorrhagic necrosis and atrophy of brain tissues, hydrocephalus and marked retardation in the rate of development of embryos are characteristic of this infection. Wide-spread intracranial hemorrhage and necrosis of cerebral tissues develop after 72 hours following intracerebral injection with herpes simplex (Anderson, 1940). The embryos are removed from the eggshell at any desired interval following inoculation. Sections for histologic study are best made by fixing the entire head and cutting blocks for embedding in cross and longitudinal section as described by Dawson (1941). Control of the specificity of the infectious process is obtained by the demonstration of lesions characteristic of the disease, by subinoculation into susceptible laboratory animals, or by appropriate serologic tests.

MISCELLANEOUS ROUTES OF INOCULATION

When the window method is employed, injections may be made into the embryo by the intraocular or intraperitoneal route. Accessible parts of the embryonic body wall also can be injected. In general, the same procedures indicated for intracerebral inoculations are followed.

Inoculation of Foreign Tissue Grafts on the Chorio-allantois

Many foreign tissues can be grafted successfully into the chorio-allantois. When established, these grafts can be infected with various viruses, and in a few instances have served for the propagation of viruses which are not infectious for chick-embryo tissues. TenBroeck (1941) was able to grow the virus of hog cholera in minced swine testis placed on the membrane. Goodpasture and Anderson (1942) used grafts of human skin and human fetal membranes in the study of several viruses, and succeeded in infecting sheets of human amnion with the virus of mare abortion, which does not infect the chorio-allantois.

Goodpasture, Douglas and Anderson (1938) first grafted human skin from adults or children on the chorio-allantois. Epithelium and a thin layer of corium are obtained under aseptic conditions. Small pieces, about 1 cm. square, are cut with a sharp scalpel and carefully spread, corium side down, on the surface of the chorio-allantois of 10- to 12-day embryos. The skin takes readily and can be inoculated within 24 or 48 hours after grafting. Skin from hatched chicks and from adult fowls nonimmune and immune to fowl pox could be grafted readily onto the chorio-allantois, and was found to be equally suceptible to infection with the virus of fowl pox by Goodpasture and Anderson (1940). Human fetal membranal tisue was grafted on the chorio-allantois by Goodpasture and Anderson (1942). A sheet of thin membrane, from 5 to 8 cm. square, located near the placenta is cut out with sterile instruments. It is then spread on a sterile block of cork moistened with saline. The thin layer of decidua is stripped from the chorion with forceps. The remaining thin sheet can then be easily separated by means of forceps into its component layers of chorion and amnion. Small, 1-cm. square blocks of either amnion or chorion are cut with a sharp scalpel and carefully transferred to the chorio-allantois by means of a specially designed spatula. The grafts may be inoculated before or within 24 or 48 hours after being placed on the chorio-allantois.

DE-EMBRYONATED EGGS

Bernkopf (1949) has demonstrated that influenza virus can be cultivated in the chorio-allantois of de-embryonated eggs. The method may prove to be useful for other viruses. Eggs of 14 to 15 days' incubation are candled, and the outline of the air sac is marked. The sector of shell one half centimeter above this line is removed. The exposed shell membrane with its underlying chorio-allantois is cut away. The embryo and the yolk sac are poured out, and their connections with the chorio-allantois are severed. This leaves the eggshell lined with the chorio-allantois attached to the shell membrane. All remaining yolk, albumen, and blood are thoroughly washed out with 3 changes of cold 0.85 per cent NaCl solution. The egg is then filled with from 10 to 40 cc. of Tyrode's solution containing virus and 10 units of penicillin and 40 micrograms of streptomycin per cc. The opening is sealed by means of a sterile rubber cap sealed to the shell with hot paraffin. The inoculated eggs are placed in a testtube roller which makes 6 revolutions per hour in an incubator at 37° C. Fluid can be withdrawn at desired intervals through the rubber cap by means of a sterile needle and syringe. Embryos may first be infected by the amniotic route in the usual manner. After the virus is absorbed, or as late as 48 hours after inoculation, the egg contents are poured out. The interior of the eggshell is then treated as indicated above. After further incubation increase of virus can be demonstrated.

USE OF EGGS OTHER THAN HENS'

Because of their greater availability chicken embryos have been almost exclusively used for the propagation of viruses and rickettsiae. Duck eggs and turkey eggs have an incubation period of about 4 weeks as compared with 3 weeks for the hen's egg and might prove advantageous for the study of infectious agents with long incubation periods. Most observations have been made with duck embryos which, in general, seem to exhibit the same susceptibility as do chick embryos. Brandly (1937) observed that the virus of infectious laryngotracheitis of fowls proliferates in the chorio-allantois of chick and turkey embryos but not in those of ducks, guinea-fowl or pigeons. Harris (1945) has described vaccinia infection of turtle embryos.

REFERENCES

Alexander, R. A., 1938, Studies on the neurotropic virus of horsesickness. VI. Propagation in the developing chick embryo. Onderstepoort J. Vet. Sci., *11*, 9-19.

Anderson, K., 1940, Pathogenesis of herpes simplex virus infection in chick embryos. Am. J. Path., *16*, 137-155.

Bernkopf, H., 1949, Cultivation of influenza virus in the chorio-allantoic membrane of deembryonated eggs. Proc. Soc. Exp. Biol. and Med., *72*, 680-682.

Beveridge, W. I. B., and Burnet, F. M., 1946, The cultivation of viruses and rickettsiae in the chick embryo. Spec. Rep. Series Med. Res. Counc., London, No. 256.

Brandly, C. A., 1937, Studies on certain filtrable viruses; factors concerned with egg propagation of fowl-pox and infectious laryngotracheitis. J. Am. Vet. Med. Assn., *90*, 479-487.

Buddingh, G. J., 1936, A study of generalized vaccinia in the chick embryo. J. Exp. Med., *63*, 227-240.

Buddingh, G. J., and Polk, A. D., 1939, Experimental meningococcus infection of the chick embryo. J. Exp. Med., *70*, 485-498.

Burnet, F. M., 1933, A virus disease of the canary of the fowl-pox group. J. Path. and Bact., *37*, 107-122.

Burnet, F. M., 1936, Influenza virus on the developing egg: I. Changes associated with the development of an egg-passage strain of virus. Brit. J. Exp. Path., *17*, 282-293.

Burnet, F. M., 1936, The use of the developing egg in virus research. Spec. Rep. Series Med. Res. Counc., London, No. 220.

Burnet, F. M., 1940, Influenza virus infection of the chick embryo lung. Brit. J. Exp. Path., *21*, 147-153.

Burnet, F. M., and Ferry, J. D., 1934, The differentiation of the viruses of fowl plague and Newcastle disease: Experiments using the technique of chorio-allantoic membrane inoculation of the developing egg. Brit. J. Exp. Path., *15*, 56-64.

Burnet, F. M., and Galloway, I. A., 1934, The propagation of the virus of vesicular stomatitis in the chorio-allantoic membrane of the developing hen's egg. Brit. J. Exp. Path., *15*, 105-113.

Burnet, F. M., and Lush, D., 1939, Inactivation of herpes virus by immune sera: experiments using chorio-allantoic membrane technique. J. Path. and Bact., *48*, 275-286.

Clark, E. R., 1920, Technique of operating on chick embryos. Science, *51*, 371-373.

Cromartie, W. J., 1941, Infection of normal and passively immunized chick embryos with *Corynebacterium diphtheriae*. Am. J. Path., *17*, 411-419.

Dawson, J. R., 1941, A study of chick-embryo-adapted rabies virus. Am. J. Path., *17*, 177-188.

Dunham, W. B., 1942, Egg inoculator and shell membrane teaser for virus culture. Science, *95*, 609.

Eichhorn, E. A., 1940, Technique for intravenous inoculation of chick embryos. Science, *92*, 245-246.

Gallavan, M., 1937, Encephalitis and meningitis in the chick embryo following inoculation of the chorio-allantoic membrane with *H. influenzae*. Am. J. Path., *13*, 911-926.

Gallavan, M., and Goodpasture, E. W., 1937, Infection of chick embryos with *H. pertussis* reproducing pulmonary lesions of whooping cough. Am. J. Path., *13*, 927-938.

Gay, F. P., and Thompson, R., 1929, Attempts to cultivate vaccine virus in the growing chick embryo. Proc. Soc. Exp. Biol. and Med., *26*, 556-559.

Goodpasture, E. W., 1933, Use of embryo chick in investigation of certain pathological problems. South. Med. J., *26*, 418-420.

Goodpasture, E. W., 1938, Some uses of the chick embryo for the study of infection and immunity. Am. J. Hyg., *28*, 111-129.

Goodpasture, E. W., 1939, Virus infection of the chick embryo. Ann. Int. Med., *13*, 1-11.

Goodpasture, E. W., 1940, The developing egg as a culture medium. J. Lab. and Clin. Med., *26*, 242-249.

Goodpasture, E. W., and Anderson, K., 1940, Immunity to fowlpox studied by means of skin grafts on chorioallantois of chick embryo. Arch. Path., *30*, 212-225.

Goodpasture, E. W., and Anderson, K., 1942, Virus infection of human fetal membranes grafted on the chorioallantois of chick embryos. Am. J. Path., *18*, 563-575.

Goodpasture, E. W., and Buddingh, G. J., 1933, Human immunization with a dermal vaccine cultivated on the membranes of chick embryos. Science, *78*, 484-485.

Goodpasture, E. W., and Buddingh, G. J., 1934, Immunisation de l'homme par un vaccin dermique, cultivé sur les membranes de l'embryon de poulet. Bull. mens. de l'office internat. d'hyg. pub., *26*, 1226-1232.

Goodpasture, E. W., and Buddingh, G. J., 1935, The preparation of anti-smallpox vaccine by culture of the virus in the chorio-allantoic membrane of chick embryos and its use in human immunization. Am. J. Hyg., *21*, 319-360.

Goodpasture, E. W., Douglas, B., and Anderson, K., 1938, Study of human skin grafted upon the chorio-allantois of chick embryos. J. Exp. Med., *68*, 891-904.

Goodpasture, E. W., Woodruff, A. M., and Buddingh, G. J., 1931, The cultivation of vaccine and other viruses in the chorio-allantoic membrane of chick embryos. Science, *74*, 371-372.

Goodpasture, E. W., Woodruff, A. M. and Buddingh, G. J., 1932, Vaccinal infection of the chorio-allantoic membrane of the chick embryo. Am. J. Path., *8*, 271-281.

Harris, P. N., 1945, Vaccinal infection of the chorio-allantoic membrane of the turtle embryo. Am. J. Path., *21*, 377-385.

Himmelweit, F., 1938, Observations on living vaccinia and ectromelia viruses by high power microscopy. Brit. J. Exp. Path., *19*, 108-123.

Hirst, G. K., 1942, Direct isolation of human influenza virus in chick embryos. J. Immunol., *45*, 293-302.

Jouan, C., and Staub, A., 1920, Etude sur la peste aviaire. Ann. Inst. Pasteur, *34*, 343-357.

Keogh, E. V., 1936, Titration of vaccinia virus on chorio-allantoic membrane of chick embryo and its application to immunological studies of neuro-vaccinia. J. Path. and Bact., *43,* 441-454.

Koprowski, H., and Cox, H. R., 1946, Adaptation of Colorado tick fever virus to mouse and developing chick embryo. Proc. Soc. Exp. Biol. and Med., *62,* 320-322.

Levaditi, C., 1906, La spirillose des embryons de poulet. Ann. Inst. Pasteur, *20,* 924-938.

McKee, A. P., and Hale, W. M., 1947, Streptomycin as an aid in isolating influenza virus. Science, *105,* 41-42.

Polk, A. D., Buddingh, G. J., and Goodpasture, E. W., 1938, An experimental study of complement and hemolytic amboceptor introduced into chick embryos. Am. J. Path., *14,* 71-86.

Rose, H. M., Pearce, E., and Molloy, E., 1946, Effect of penicillin and streptomycin on bacterial contamination of chick embryos inoculated with un-filtered sputums. Proc. Soc. Exp. Biol. and Med., *62,* 124-127.

Rous, P., and Murphy, J. B., 1911, Tumor implantations in the developing embryo. Experiments with a transmissible sarcoma of the fowl. J. Am. Med. Assn., *56,* 741-742.

Taylor, R. M., and Chialvo, R. J., 1942, Simplified technic for inoculating into amniotic sac of chick embryos. Proc Soc. Exp. Biol. and Med., *51,* 328-330.

TenBroeck, C., 1941, Cultivation of the hog cholera virus. J. Exp. Med., *74,* 427-432.

Van Herick, Wm., and Eaton, M. D., 1945, An unidentified pleuropneumonialike organism isolated during passages in chick embryos. J. Bact., *50,* 47-55.

Woodruff, A. M., and Goodpasture, E. W., 1931, The susceptibility of the chorio-allantoic membrane of chick embryos to infection with the fowl-pox virus. Am. J. Path., *7,* 209-222.

JOHN F. ENDERS, PH.D.

Children's Hospital, Boston, Massachusetts

6

Propagation of Viruses and Rickettsiae in Tissue Cultures

It is not surprising that attempts to propagate viruses in the presence of cells existing in vitro followed the development by Harrison (1907) of a simple method of tissue culture. For even at that time it was apparent to most observers that viruses, unlike bacteria, fail to multiply when inoculated into lifeless media. Later it was also recognized that rickettsiae could be grown only in association with living cells. Steinhardt, Israeli and Lambert (1913) re-revealed the possibilities of this new technic for the cultivation of viruses. They showed that the virus of vaccinia at least survived for several weeks in tissue cultures prepared with fragments of the cornea of guinea pigs and rabbits. They did not, however, obtain unequivocal evidence that multiplication of the agent occurred, although their results suggested that its infectivity had increased six to ten times. An increase of this magnitude is not sufficient to indicate multiplication. In fact, twelve years elapsed before data were presented by Parker and Nye (1925) which removed any doubt regarding the capacity of viruses to multiply in tissue cultures. These investigators carried vaccinia virus through a series of 11 cultures of rabbit testicular tissue and found that the last contained 51,000 times as much virus as did the initial preparation. Since this demonstration many viruses and rickettsiae pathogenic for man and lower animals have been maintained by

serial passage in tissue cultures. Lists of most of the viruses reported to have been cultivated up to 1940 will be found in reviews of Hallauer (1938), Sanders (1939) and Robbins and Enders (1950).

The technic has been applied to investigation of several fundamental problems in respect to viruses and rickettsiae, such as (a) enumeration of conditions essential for their propagation; (b) site of their multiplication; (c) interactions between the agents and the cells which they attack; (d) changes in pathogenicity which may occur as a result of cultivation in vitro; and, finally, (e) details of the mechanisms of natural and acquired immunity in infections caused by them. Already through such studies a method for the successful control of one important disease, yellow fever, has been devised. In this chapter the principal technics which have been employed for the culture of viruses and rickettsiae will be outlined, and certain of the advances which have been made toward the solution of problems mentioned above will be very briefly reviewed. Chick-embryo technics are described in Chapter 5.

METHODS OF TISSUE CULTURE EMPLOYED IN THE CULTIVATION OF VIRUSES AND RICKETTSIAE

Although various forms of culture have been used which differ in composition of the nutritive menstruum and conditions of

126

maintenance, in all of them the essential elements consist of living cells obtained from a suitable animal and a physiologic fluid. For convenience of description, the various types of culture may be divided into two categories. The first includes those in which the cells are supported in or on a semisolid or solid substrate. This usually consists of fibrin, generated from plasma at the time the culture is prepared; but agar, cellophane, long strands of cellulose, or the vessel wall itself have in some instances been employed. The second class comprises the methods in which fragments of tissue are suspended in a liquid medium. Before discussing different types of culture, the manner in which the tissues and other constituents are obtained and handled will be described.

STERILITY

Strict precautions to exclude contamination by bacteria and molds are observed in the application of any of the procedures to be described. All manipulations are carried out either in hoods into which only the hands and arms of a worker are introduced, or in rooms designed so that the bacterial content of the air can be reduced to a minimum (Parker, 1950). With the exception of tissue fragments, all constituents of the cultures are tested for sterility before they are used by inoculation into suitable bacteriologic media. Through the use of antibiotics it would appear that one of the greatest difficulties, i.e., bacterial contamination, in achieving successful results with tissue cultures has been largely overcome, since these substances have little or no effect on most viruses (Rose, Molloy and O'Neill, 1945; Weller, Robbins and Enders, 1949; Robbins, Enders, Weller and Florentino, 1951).

TISSUES

In most instances, the mincing of tissue for cultures is accomplished quickly and conveniently by repeatedly cutting through a piece of the tissue, placed in the bottom of a 50 cc. centrifuge tube, by means of long-handled scissors. If it is desired to obtain very uniform preparations, a cataract knife should be employed to cut the fragments from a small block of tissue placed on a glass or porcelain plate. In making explants from an original culture, a cataract knife is essential. Many kinds of tissue have been used. These have been obtained from avian and mammalian embryos, as well as from adult forms. Because of their availability and ease of growth in cultures, tissues of the chick embryo have been adopted for many studies. Seven- to 9-day embryos which have been incubated at from 37° to 39° C. are usually selected.

PLASMA

Although representing a heterologous element in some cultures, plasma of the fowl has been found suitable for nearly all purposes. The fibrin clot derived from it is firmer, more transparent, and more resistant to lytic enzymes which are produced during cell growth than are clots formed from mammalian plasma. Blood may be drawn from the wing vein or from the heart. Large, well-nourished birds should be selected and fasted for at least 24 hours before being bled. The blood may be collected in chilled, paraffin-lined tubes, or mixed as it is drawn into the syringe with 1:500 heparin in salt solution (1 part for each 9 parts of blood). To avoid hemolysis only dry glassware should be used. After separation, the plasma, which will stay in good condition for several weeks at 4° C., is stored in stoppered tubes. Recently it has been suggested that purified bovine thrombin and fibrinogen may be substituted for chicken plasma as a substrate for tissue cultures (Porter and Hawn, 1947). These materials might have the advantage of uniformity and can be preserved for long periods of time without alteration. Hetherington (1944; 1951) has shown that plasma, serum and embryonic extracts dried from the frozen state and stored are also suitable for tissue-culture work. As a substitute for plasma, Evans and Earle (1947) have successfully employed perforated cellophane membranes in the cultivation of certain kinds of cells.

Serum

Serum homologous for the tissue employed is often used in making up the nutrient fluid which also contains tissue extracts and balanced salt solution in variable proportions. Serum is obtained by bringing about coagulation of plasma or by allowing whole blood to clot. The supernatant serum is removed after it has been expressed from the clot. Great care should be taken to avoid hemolysis during the preparation of the serum. Instead of the crude serum, Simms and Sanders (1942) have used an ultrafiltrate of serum. This retains in part the growth-promoting attributes of the serum but does not lead to the deposition of intracellular fat granules which occurs in the presence of whole serum.

Tissue Extract

Extract of chick embryo is usually added to the nutrient fluid, although for certain purposes extracts of adult spleen or other organs have been substituted. Nine- to 11-day embryos incubated at from 37° to 39° C. are most suitable. After removal of the eyes—the rods of the retinae look like bacteria and may lead to an erroneous conclusion that a culture is contaminated—the embryos are cut into very small pieces with scissors or reduced to a pulp by grinding in a mortar. Sufficient amount of a balanced salt solution is then added to give a suspension consisting of equal parts of fluid and tissue which is allowed to stand at 37° C. for half an hour. After centrifugation, the supernatant fluid is removed and stored in stoppered tubes in an icebox.

Salt Solutions

A variety of mixtures of inorganic salts have been employed, most of which have been modifications of Tyrode's solution. Simm's salt solution is more easily prepared from stock solutions which may be pre-

served indefinitely (Sanders, 1939); it also has given excellent results.

Formula for Tyrode's Solution Parker (1938)

Freezing Point —0.62° C.

Sodium chloride	8.00 Gm.
Potassium chloride	0.20 Gm.
Calcium chloride ($CaCl_2$)	0.20 Gm.
Magnesium chloride ($MgCl_2$ 6 H_2O)	0.10 Gm.
Sodium acid phosphate ($NaH_2PO_4H_2O$)	0.05 Gm.
Sodium bicarbonate ($NaHCO_3$)	1.00 Gm.
Glucose	1.00 Gm.
Water, triply glass-distilled, to make	1,000 cc.

Extensive descriptions of procedures for the cultivation of tissues can be found in the monographs of Parker (1938; 1950), Fischer (1930) and Cameron (1950) and in the review by Sanders (1939).

METHODS INVOLVING THE USE OF SOLID OR SEMISOLID SUBSTRATES

Plasma or Hanging-Drop Cultures

This is the method originally devised by Harrison, and, next to the suspended-cell technic of Li and Rivers (1930), is the simplest of all procedures. It is chiefly useful in studying, from the histologic standpoint, the effect of viruses or rickettsiae on cells and in the determination of the viability of tissue fragments exposed to the action of such agents in other types of tissue culture where cell growth cannot be directly observed. Because of the small quantities of tissue which must be used and the necessity for frequently transferring the fragments or parts of them (explantation) to fresh media, this technic has not been employed much recently except for these purposes.

Plasma-drop cultures are prepared in the following manner. The tissue is divided into fragments measuring about 1 mm. in the longest dimension. The size of the fragment is of great significance in obtaining successful results with all types of culture; if the fragment is too large the center will become necrotic, whereas if it is too small growth of new cells may be scanty or absent. The optimal yield of virus is also correlated with the optimal size of the fragment. The fragment is centered in a drop of medium which has previously been placed on a thin coverslip and which usually consists of a mixture of equal parts of plasma and a balanced salt solution. After coagulation of the plasma, which is induced by the presence of the tissue, has occurred, the preparation is inverted over the cavity in a thick slide with a deep depression. Melted paraffin is applied to the edges of the coverslip which establishes a permanent, airtight seal. Preparations are usually maintained at 37.5° C., but for the cultivation of certain agents lower temperatures (35° and 32° C.) have been found to be suitable. Growth of cells may be stimulated or increased by the addition of tissue extract. If employed, one part of such an extract is usually added to one part of the balanced salt solution. The preparation may be examined under the oil immersion lens in the fresh state, or sections may be cut after fixing, staining, and embedding; fixation is carried out while the tissue is still adherent to the coverglass. To make explants, a fragment with its outgrowth of new cells is divided by means of a cataract knife into two or more equal parts which are then transferred to fresh plasma drops. In the presence of actively growing cells, explantation must be done every 2 or 3 days. For the propagation of viruses or rickettsiae, fragments of tissue from an embryo or an animal already infected may be employed as the original tissue, or fragments of normal tissue may be inoculated by suspending them for a short time in a suspension of the active agent or by addition of a small quantity of such suspension to the fluid constituents of a culture.

Carrel-Flask Cultures

Because of certain disadvantages inherent in the hanging-drop method, namely, small amount of tissue, necessity for frequent transfer, impossibility of altering at will the menstruum surrounding the cell and of determining changes in it induced by cell growth, Carrel designed flat-walled, circular flasks in which cultures consisting of a 4-phase system could be maintained for long periods of time. The four phases are tissue fragment or fragments, plasma coagulum, nutrient fluid which often contains blood serum, and overlying gas mixture. A shallow layer of the nutrient fluid lies over the tissue which is embedded in a thin sheet of fibrin attached to one wall of the flask. Renewal of the nutrient fluid, changes in its constituents, and adjustment of its pH may be carried out at will. Alterations in the gaseous phase may also be easily accomplished. Many studies by means of this technic have been made of the effect on cells of changes in the fluid and gaseous phases and conversely of the effect on the latter of growth of cells. Additional details of the method will not be given; those who are interested may consult Parker's monograph (Parker, 1950). For propagation of viruses and rickettsiae, however, this type of culture has not been much used, although Carrel (1926) showed in studies of the Rous sarcoma virus that it was adaptable to this purpose. It has not been used probably because the procedures for making and maintaining such cultures require considerable skill and training and are unnecessarily refined for obtaining satisfactory multiplication of these pathogens. In the future, however, it is possible that the technic or modifications of it may be very useful in further investigations of the effect of viruses on pure lines of cells, investigations which are much needed in attempts to understand such fundamental problems as species immunity and the manner in which viruses and rickettsiae injure the susceptible cell.

ROLLER-TUBE CULTURES

Most advantages of the Carrel-flask cultures are retained in the so-called roller-tube method of tissue culture. In addition, the latter permits cultivation of unlimited amounts of tissue which, in any well-equipped laboratory, may be easily maintained and handled under optimal conditions for survival and growth for months or even for years. Because of this fact, large quantities of virus-containing tissue emulsions and fluids may be obtained. The cultivation of considerable amounts of tissue for long periods of time is probably dependent upon the continual circulation of the nutrient fluid in a thin layer over the growing cells. In this way, cellular respiration is aided and harmful metabolites are not allowed to accumulate rapidly at the tissue-fluid interfaces. The method has been developed largely by Gey (1933) and Lewis (1935), although the underlying principle was earlier recognized and applied to a limited degree by Löwenstädt (1925) and Carrel (1913).

The essential constituents are the same as those usually included in Carrel-flask cultures. Details of the technic are given by Feller, Enders and Weller (1940). Special flasks have been designed by Shaw, Kingsland and Brues (1940) and by Porter, Claude and Fullam (1945). The shape of the container may be selected at will. For most purposes, pyrex test tubes (150 mm. x 15 mm.) are suitable, but various types of flasks, including reagent bottles, can be used for special purposes such as observing cell growth under a microscope or obtaining large yields of a virus. To set up a culture in a test tube, plasma is spread over most of its inner surface. The tissue fragments, of which there may be as many as 20 or more, are then distributed at appropriate intervals throughout the thin plasma layer. After coagulation of the plasma has taken place, nutrient fluid containing a small amount of phenol red is introduced and the tube closed with a rubber stopper.

The tube is then placed in an almost horizontal position in a specially designed rotating drum turning at about 7 r.p.m. The drum is enclosed in an incubator. In the case of actively growing tissue maintained at 37° C., the nutrient fluid must ordinarily be replaced every 2 or 3 days by fresh material. This interval can be extended somewhat by passing sterile air into the tube until the pH of the fluid is brought by expulsion of accumulated CO_2 to approximately 7.3 as indicated by color of the fluid. At lower temperatures where cell growth is much diminished, replenishment of fluid may be necessary only at intervals of 2 or 3 weeks. Explants may be made to freshly prepared tubes; but, by regulating conditions of growth, cells may be maintained almost indefinitely in original cultures. This is of great importance in the study of the effect of prolonged cultivation on cells and viruses.

Inoculation is accomplished most easily by incorporating the infective material in the nutrient fluid. By titrating specimens of nutrient fluid removed at intervals it is possible to obtain estimates of the rate of increase of a virus and its persistence in a culture. Fragments of tissue may also be excised and tested for their content of virus. The method is well adapted to study of the effect of immune serum on the multiplication of a virus. It is possible to obtain specimens of tissue for microscopic examination by using in the tube a coverslip, held in place by agar or coagulated plasma, on which two or three fragments are deposited (Feller, Enders and Weller, 1940), or by employing special flasks (Porter, Claude and Fullam, 1945).

Although the roller-tube method has not yet been as widely employed as those involving the use of fluid substrates for the cultivation of viruses and not at all for the growth of rickettsiae, it would seem to be well adapted to the study of many problems associated with these agents. Gey and Bang (1939) maintained the virus of lymphogranuloma venereum for more than seven months in the same roller-tube cultures of pure strains of human fibroblasts. The fluid removed from such cultures was found to give good Frei tests in patients with this disease. Feller, Enders and Weller (1940) maintained the virus of vaccinia in cultures of chick-embryo tissue for 9 weeks without transfer, and studied the concentration of virus in the fluids and tissue which was found to remain constant during the period of observation. Florman and Enders (1942) found the method produced excellent cultures of human monocytes obtained from the buffy layer of heparinized blood. The effect of these cells on the virus of vaccinia in the presence and absence of specific antibody and complement was investigated. Morgan and Wiseman (1946) showed that psittacosis virus could be readily grown in roller-tube cultures of chick-embryo tissues, and that the formalin-treated fluids when used as vaccine conferred considerable protection in mice. Robbins, Enders and Weller (1950), using fragments of several different human tissues, have been able to cultivate poliomyelitis viruses representing the three known antigenic types by this procedure. Ledinko, Riordan and Melnick similarly obtained evidence of multiplication of strains of the Lansing type of poliomyelitis virus in roller-tube cultures of monkey testis (1951).

Zinsser's Agar-Slant Cultures

In 1937, Zinsser (Zinsser, FitzPatrick and Wei, 1939), seeking a simplified technic for cultivating large quantities of typhus rickettsiae to be used in the production of vaccine, distributed numerous fragments of chick-embryonic tissue on the surface of isotonic agar slants containing horse serum and Tyrode's solution. The medium used by Zinsser and collaborators has been found to afford good yields of various species of rickettsiae as well as a number of viruses. In addition to furnishing support for the cells as well as factors necessary for their survival and possibly for limited growth, the agar may remove from the immediate proximity of the cells metabolic wastes which diffuse into it. Following inoculation of cultures with typhus rickettsiae, incubation at 35-37° C. is maintained for 10-14 days. Shorter periods suffice for maximal increase in the case of most viruses which have been studied; these agents, however, may survive for much longer periods; Pang and Zia (1940), for example, found the virus of St. Louis encephalitis to be active after being cultivated thirty-six days at 37° C.

On this medium, rickettsiae of epidemic and endemic typhus multiply fairly actively (Zinsser, FitzPatrick and Wei, 1939), but growth of spotted-fever rickettsiae occurs more abundantly (FitzPatrick, 1938). Vaccines prepared from cultures of these rickettsiae afford good protection to experimental animals. Recently, the method has been used for the production of a vaccine against scrub typhus, which was shown by Plotz and associates to protect mice against experimental infection (Plotz, Bennett and Reagan, 1946). This observation was of importance, since there had been great difficulty in demonstrating immunity following vaccination against this disease. The viruses of herpes simplex (Cheever, 1939), vaccinia (Kurotchkin, 1939), and St. Louis encephalitis (Pang and Zia, 1940) have been maintained in serial cultures on the Zinsser medium.

METHODS INVOLVING THE USE OF FLUID SUBSTRATES

Maitland Medium

Maitland and Maitland (1928) demonstrated multiplication of vaccinia virus in a medium composed of fragments of a fowl's kidney suspended in a mixture of Tyrode's solution and fowl serum. Although these authors considered that they were not working with tissue cultures, it has since been shown not only that in this general type of culture some cells may survive for as long as 30 days, but that there is sometimes evidence of cell multiplication (Rivers, Haagen and Muckenfuss, 1929; Enders and Florman, 1942). Various modifications of the original procedure described by the Maitlands have been introduced by different investigators. These have consisted in changing the proportions of serum and salt solution, or in employing tissues from other sources. The original medium described by the Maitlands consisted of 12 cc. of Tyrode's solution, 6 cc. of fowl serum, and, approximately 0.6 cc. of minced fowl kidney. These materials were placed in a flask, usually of the Erlenmeyer type, of 25 or 50 cc. capacity, which was then closed with a stopper. Inoculation of the medium with a pathogenic agent is best accomplished by preliminary exposure for a short time, e.g., one-half hour, of the tissue fragments to an emulsion containing such an agent. Cultures of this sort are usually incubated at 35° or 37° C. for 3 or 4 days. Transfers are accomplished by inoculating some of the suspending fluid into flasks containing freshly prepared medium, or by reducing some of the infected tissue fragments to an emulsion which is then used as inoculum. Sanders has considerably modified this procedure (Simms and Sanders, 1942). Instead of crude serum, a serum ultrafiltrate was used, and the cultures were kept at a lower temperature. In this way he has obtained good multiplication of several viruses and employed it for the primary isolation of the agent keratoconjunctivitis. The Maitland medium has been widely employed in the propagation of viruses. The yields of rickettsiae, however, have not been large as compared with those obtained by other methods, such as the Zinsser agar-slant technic or cultivation in the developing hen's egg.

RIVERS' MEDIUM

Li and Rivers (1930) found that vaccinia virus would multiply in a medium consisting of tissue fragments suspended in Tyrode's solution. This is the simplest form of tissue culture which has so far been devised. It has been extensively used and many viruses as well as rickettsiae have been propagated in it. For successful results, it is necessary to preserve a large ratio between the quantity of fluid and the amount of tissue.

PLOTZ' MEDIUM

By adding a few drops of chicken plasma to a Maitland type of medium, consisting of serum, Tyrode's solution, and chick-embryo tissue, Plotz (1938) found that the tissue fragments were gathered together in a network of fibrin which, in correctly prepared cultures, tended to float on the surface of the fluid. Excellent yields of many viruses have been obtained by this method which provides support for cells and permits an increased opportunity for cellular respiration.

METHODS OF DETERMINING MULTIPLICATION OF VIRUSES OR RICKETTSIAE

Allusion has been made to the difficulty encountered by earlier workers in demonstrating increase of viruses in tissue cultures. With improvements of methods, it has become relatively easy to show that a viral or rickettsial agent multiplies and to estimate with reasonable accuracy the degree of such multiplication. Evidence based upon the development of elementary bodies or inclusion bodies, although helpful, cannot be regarded as conclusive. It is necessary to secure quantitative data indicative of increase under carefully controlled conditions. In general, this is done by showing that the number of minimal infective doses of an agent present in a culture after a period of incubation or in the final culture of a series is much larger than the number of minimal infecting doses in the original inoculum. The most accurate way (Hallauer, 1938) of accomplishing this is to prepare two sets of cultures in exactly the same manner. One set is incubated at a temperature optimal for the multiplication of the agent; the other is kept in an icebox. At appropriate intervals, the number of minimal infective doses in a culture chosen from each lot is determined. For this determination, it is best to employ the entire contents of the culture vessel, i.e., fluid and tissues, and plasma if it be present. The solid elements are ground in a mortar with sand or alundum, the fluid being added slowly. From the supernatant fluid after centrifugation, a series of dilutions is prepared and aliquot portions of each are inoculated into groups of susceptible animals. If cultures are prepared with tissues from animals other than the chick embryo, an additional control must be included to eliminate the possibility that such tissues are already spontaneously infected with another active agent. This consists of cultures which have received no inoculum of the agent under study. After incubation, these cultures should fail to produce signs of infection when injected into animals susceptible to the agent under study.

With viruses that exhibit hemagglutination such as those of mumps and influenza, multiplication can be demonstrated readily in tissue cultures by employing inocula which are far below the hemagglutinating level. Accordingly, after incubation of the cultures, if specific hemagglutinins appear in the fluid phase, they may be taken as evidence that increase in the virus has occurred (Weller and Enders, 1948; Fulton, 1951). Since tests for hemagglutinins are so easily made, the tissue-culture method has been employed lately as a convenient means of titrating the activity of virus suspensions and of determining the virus neutralizing capacity of antisera.

In many instances, cells from developing chick embryos can be used for titration of viruses. Huang (1943a) reported that titration of viral activity can be accomplished by determining the smallest amount of virus which brings about death of the cells suspended in a liquid culture medium. Cell death was determined by explanting infected fragments into plasma drops and observing whether growth ensued. This procedure would appear to be quite feasible

when a virus, e.g., equine encephalomyelitis, that has a marked destructive action on tissues is selected. Many viruses, however, do not bring about the death of cells in cultures. For instance, Feller, Enders and Weller (1940) and Relova and Enders (unpublished experiments, 1940) found that the viruses of vaccinia, herpes simplex and influenza exert little or no injurious effect on embryonic chick cells growing in roller tubes. In contrast, these cells showed degenerative changes and became necrotic after inoculation with eastern equine encephalomyelitis viris.

ANALYSIS OF FACTORS INFLUENCING MULTIPLICATION OF VIRUSES AND RICKETTSIAE IN TISSUE CULTURES

SOURCE AND TYPE OF CELLS

Whether or not multiplication of a given agent takes place depends in part (a) upon the susceptibility of the species of animal from which the tissue is derived and (b) upon the types of cell that may be present, i.e., epithelium, endothelium, fibroblasts, monocytes, etc. The results of many studies with different viruses, however, have made it clear that the degree of pathogenicity exhibited by an agent for an intact animal is frequently not correlated with its capacity to increase in cultures prepared from tissues of such an animal. Thus, several viruses which do not produce signs of infection in the fowl can be cultivated in the presence of cells derived from the chick embryo, or in some instances from the chicken itself. Illustrations are to be found in the behavior of influenza A virus and the agent of equine encephalomyelitis. Influenza A virus (Melbourne strain) is easily propagated in tissue cultures prepared from embryonic tissues or from the lungs of newly hatched birds. Newly hatched birds, however, are entirely refractory to infection via the respiratory route. Similarly, equine encephalomyelitis virus increases very rapidly in cultures of chick embryonic tissue and brings about cellular death in a short time, but old hens are resistant to infection with the virus.

In instances where lack of correlation of this sort exists, it is not the cells of the intact animal which are responsible for its resistance. Extracellular inhibitory mechanisms present in the living body may be eliminated in cultures, thus permitting multiplication. For example, the lack of pathogenicity of the influenza virus for the chicken appears to be correlated with its normally high body temperature, 105°-106° F. At 104° F., the virus will not multiply in tissue cultures (Enders and Pearson, 1941), although the cells are not appreciably affected. In certain cases, however, there is a relationship between the resistance or susceptibility of an intact animal to infection and the failure or success, respectively, of an active agent to multiply in cultures of its tissues. Here would seem to be evidence for a true cellular resistance, although the factors upon which it depends have not been defined. The behavior of Virus III of Rivers affords an excellent illustration of such correlation. The virus is responsible for a characteristic disease of rabbits. No other species has been found susceptible. This strict host specificity is reflected in the ability of the virus to multiply in cultures prepared only from rabbit's tissues.

More recently, Weller, Enders, Robbins and Stoddard (unpublished experiments) have failed to cultivate the Lansing strain of poliomyelitis virus in chick, mouse or beef embryonic tissue nor in the testicular tissues of the rabbit, whereas, as previously noted, this agent may easily be propagated in cultures of human or monkey tissues, i.e., tissues of naturally susceptible species. Of other examples which could be cited, one of the most interesting is to be found in an experiment of Goodpasture and Anderson (1944), although it did not involve the cultivation of tissue in vitro. Fragments of human skin were grafted to the chorio-allantoic membrane of an embry-

onated hen's egg and inoculated with materials taken from the lesions of herpes zoster, a disease to which man alone is susceptible. Evidence for multiplication of the virus in the skin grafts was obtained, whereas there was no indication that any of the embryonic tissues became infected.

In view of the existence of these two classes of virus, one to which the animal is resistant and the cell susceptible and the other to which both behave in the same manner, it is apparent that one cannot predict a priori whether or not multiplication of an agent will take place in cultures containing tissues derived from a refractory animal. If feasible, it is best in attempting to cultivate a virus for the first time to use tissues from the natural host.

From experiments with tissue cultures, a limited amount of data has been made available which indicates quite definitely that some viruses are able to proliferate only within certain types of cell. The invitro demonstration of such cellular specificity might have been predicted from the long recognized differences in affinity of viruses for various tissues which early led to the classification of viruses according to their dermotropic, neurotropic and viscerotropic properties. Carrel (1926), who was among the relatively few investigators to work with pure strains of cells, showed that the Rous sarcoma virus would increase in cultures of fowl monocytes but not in cultures of fibroblasts. In contrast, fowl plague virus (Hallauer, 1931) apparently finds in epithelial cells alone the essential requirements for multiplication. In respect to the general problem of the specificity of the relationship between viruses and cell types, the recent development of technics for the establishment of tissue culture lines derived from single cells by Sanford, Earle and Likely (1948) may prove to have much significance. Further studies on the cellular specificity of viruses and rickettsiae by means of pure strain cultures are obviously desirable, since in this way factors involved in multiplication of these agents may be defined upon which logical approaches to chemotherapy can be based.

Biologic Activity of Tissue

Many experimental results point to a direct relationship between the degree of multiplication of viruses and the biologic activity of tissue. On the other hand, rickettsiae may continue to multiply at a time when the metabolism of tissue is much reduced. Perhaps the clearest evidence in support of these statements are the results of Zinsser and Schoenbach (1937), who showed that the rate of increase of the virus of equine encephalomyelitis in tissue cultures was greatest during the period of maximal oxygen consumption by the cells. As the latter declined, the titer of virus fell off rapidly. On the other hand, the number of typhus rickettsiae in similar cultures continued to increase during the period of diminishing oxygen consumption and attained the maximum only when tissue metabolism, as thus measured, had reached a low level. Their findings as far as viruses go are in agreement with observations of others. Cheever and Willmert (1942) found that the virus of herpes simplex would multiply only in freshly prepared, agar-slant cultures. In those which had been incubated for four days or longer before inoculation and in which cellular activity presumably was declining, the virus survived for a time but gradually diminished in concentration. Plotz (1937) working with the virus of fowl plague noted a greatly increased proliferation of the agent in the presence of cells which were growing actively as compared with cells which were merely surviving. Similar observations have been made by others. In spite of this evidence for the correlation of rapid multiplication of viruses with active cellular growth and metabolism, it should be pointed out that some viruses may continue to increase when cells are not dividing and are indeed almost in a resting state. Hecke (1930), Sanders (1940) and others have shown that the infective titers of certain viruses rose in tissue cultures maintained at temperatures low enough $(23°—30°$ C.) to prevent or reduce cell division to a minimum and to retard cell respiration. Investigators are agreed, however, that viruses do not multiply when cells are held at temperatures, e.g., 4° to 8° C., at which biologic activity of the cells is reduced to a minimum (completely resting cells).

Quantity of Tissue

The amount of tissue used in preparing certain types of culture appears to bear a rather close relationship to the multiplication of the virus. This is particularly evident in the Rivers-Li medium where an excess of tissue is inhibitory. But this effect is not so evident in cultures of the Carrel or roller-tube type. Factors which underlie the inhibitory effect in suspended-cell cultures are not clearly defined.

Effect of Temperature

Many viruses and rickettsiae of animal origin multiply only within a fairly restricted range of temperature, from about 40° C. to about 25° C. That the controlling factor may not be the temperature at which cellular activity is markedly affected appears from what has been already stated concerning cultivation at temperatures at which cell growth may proceed but viral activity is lost. Accordingly, it is probable that the limiting temperatures for multiplication are in part at least related to intrinsic properties of a virus.

SITE OF MULTIPLICATION OF VIRUSES AND RICKETTSIAE

Among the basic problems in the study of viral and rickettsial diseases is the determination of the exact site in or around cells at which multiplication of the causal agents occurs. As one approach to its solution, tissue-culture technics have been used. That multiplication is intimately associated with cells has been demonstrated by the results of many experiments (see Hallauer, 1938) in which the viral content of the tissue fragments was measured and compared with that of the noncellular portion of a culture. In general the tissue was found to contain more of the agent than did the other constituents. Indeed, under certain conditions, many investigators have failed to detect any significant quantity of virus in the medium surrounding the cells.

Such data, however, do not enable one to define precisely the place where propagation of the agents takes place, since this might occur in the vicinity of cells, on their surface or within them. Evidence that the conditions for increase are not provided within the neighborhood of cells by the establishment of a special environment resulting from their metabolic activities, is to be found in the results of Muckenfuss and Rivers (1930). They showed that vaccinia virus did not multiply in a cell-free, serum-Tyrode mixture which was separated from the tissue fragments by a semipermeable membrane. Microscopic examination of cells in cultures inoculated with elementary bodies of vaccinia (Bland and Robinow, 1939) and psittacosis (Bland and Canti, 1935) have given no indication that multiplication takes place on the surface of cells. On the contrary, such observations strongly suggest that only after the infective particles have passed through the cell membrane and entered the cytoplasm or the nucleus does an increase in their number ensue. These earlier observations have been supported by results of studies of virus-infected cells from tissue cultures by means of the electron microscope (Bang and Gey, 1949; Wirth and Athanasiu, 1949).

The investigations by Pinkerton and Hass (1932a, 1932b) on rickettsiae of typhus fever and Rocky Mountain spotted fever have left no doubt that these agents grow exclusively within cells. The typhus rickettsiae appear to multiply only in the cytoplasm. In contrast, the spotted-fever organisms exhibit a predilection for the nucleus, although limited growth may also take place in the cytoplasm.

ELEMENTARY BODIES AND INCLUSION BODIES

Elementary bodies represent the infectious unit of certain viruses, and thus are analogous to a single pathogenic bacterium. Careful studies of infected tissue cultures have supported this conception of the nature of these entities. It is apparent, however, that the manner in which the elementary bodies multiply may not always be by simple fission. For example, Bland and Canti (1935), by observing the course of events after inoculation of cultures of embryonic-chick cells with psittacosis elementary bodies, were able to describe an intracellular developmental cycle. During the first stage, extracellular bodies were numerous, but none could be definitely recognized within the cells. Subsequently, violet-staining and apparently homogeneous masses or plaques (5-10μ) were noted in the cytoplasm which thereafter increased in size. These resembled the inclusion bodies found in many virus diseases. Upon decolorization with acetone they were found to be composed of a pink-staining matrix in which were embedded many lilac-tinted bodies approximately 1μ in diameter. Later, a mixture of these forms and smaller bodies (0.25μ) which stained a deep violet were seen forming colonylike masses. The latter, which in all respects were identical with the elementary bodies originally inoculated, became progressively more numerous until by the end of three days they were usually the only visible forms. These observations, although they may be interpreted in several ways, establish the facts that (1) the elementary body of psittacosis may undergo morphologic changes during its developmental cycle and that (2) the plaque or inclusion body is essentially an aggregation or colony of elementary bodies. A somewhat similar process of intracellular development was found by Bland and Robinow (1939) to take place when elementary bodies of vaccinia were inoculated into tissue cultures containing corneal epithelium of a rabbit. Their findings indicated that the typical inclusions of vaccinia, Guarnieri bodies, are largely composed of elementary bodies. It should be strongly emphasized, however, that it would be entirely erroneous to assume that all inclusion bodies found associated with virus diseases are of this nature. Only in those instances where the infectious units are large enough to be visible, and so recognizable as components of an inclusion body, has it been possible to regard the latter in this manner.

CHANGES IN PATHOGENICITY OF VIRUSES IN TISSUE CULTURES

Just as repeated transfer in vitro may bring about alterations in the virulence or pathogenicity of bacteria, so serial passage of viruses in tissue culture has frequently led to changes in their capacity to induce disease when inoculated into a susceptible animal. Most often under these conditions a decrease in virulence has been noted. But in some cases, especially when an agent is propagated in tissues derived from its natural host, an increase in pathogenic properties may follow. Whether or not an alteration in the tropism of a virus for certain tissues can be induced by cultivation in the presence of a single type of cell or tissue is debatable. It would appear, however, that the capacity of an agent, after propagation in tissue culture, to injure one sort of tissue may be reduced while its pathogenicity for another may be retained. Thus, although it is clear enough that variation in pathogenicity frequently occurs in tissue culture and that this mode of inducing such change has proved extremely valuable, it has so far been impossible to define exactly the conditions which will induce the phenomenon. Therefore, the production at will of pathogenically modified variants is not yet feasible and at present they have in the majority of instances appeared spontaneously during the course of serial transfers.

The following well-known experiments of Rivers and Ward (1933) with vaccinia virus and those of Theiler and Smith (1937) with the virus of yellow fever will illustrate these general remarks. During the course of 88 passages in the Rivers-Li medium containing chick-embryonic tissue, the virus of vaccinia practically lost its capacity to induce typical dermal lesions in the rabbit, although it still produced mild typical vaccinial reactions in susceptible human beings. Six passages of this attenuated strain in the testicles of rabbits led to a restoration of pathogenicity for this animal. Seeking a method of vaccination against yellow fever by means of an attenuated virus, Theiler and Smith carried a strain of high virulence for man and the monkey through many serial cultures containing mouse-embryonic tissue and chick-embryonic tissue, respectively. In the mouse tissue the viscerotropic properties of the virus were moderately diminished, but the neurotropic properties for monkeys were not altered. In the chick tissue marked reduction of both properties occurred after about 114 passages. Additional passages in this medium led to further decrease in pathogenicity of the virus. This variant is now widely used in the preparation of yellow fever vaccine.

INTERFERENCE BETWEEN VIRUSES

Although as yet little used, tissue-culture technics would seem to provide an excellent tool for the analysis of the phenomena of interference between viruses. In this way extracellular factors in the living animal that might tend to obscure the basic reactions between susceptible cells and viruses to which they may be exposed can be largely or entirely eliminated. Moreover, the effect of one virus on the growth of another can be determined with considerable accuracy at any time, and the quantitative relationships between viral inocula can be controlled with precision.

A few studies are available which demonstrate the potentialities of the method. Huang (1940) observed that St. Louis encephalitis virus or Columbia-SK virus multiplied regularly in chick-embryo tissues in vitro but failed to cause visible injury to the cells. Yet the subsequent addition of equine encephalitis virus to such cultures did not induce degenerative changes in the cells which regularly ensue under the impact of this agent. Andrewes (1942) investigated in tissue culture the interfering effect of two strains of influenza A virus, one of which exhibited marked neurotropic properties. He noted that the strain that was first inoculated inhibited multiplication of the other when added subsequently to the system. Suppression of the multiplication of influenza A virus in tissue culture by yellow fever and West Nile virus has been described by Lennette and Koprowski (1946).

MECHANISMS OF IMMUNITY TO VIRUSES

Tissue cultures have proved of value in the investigation of natural and acquired immunity in virus infections. The correlation which has been shown to exist between the resistance of certain species to a viral agent and the failure of the cells of those species to support the agent's multiplication in cultures provides satisfactory presumptive evidence for the existence of a natural cellular immunity. As yet, unfortunately, there is no clue as to the factors upon which this native cellular resistance depends. It is possible to attribute it to the absence of nutritive substances or enzyme systems essential for the multiplication of the virus, or to the presence within the cell of antiviral substances, or to some other still unsuspected mechanisms.

Attempts have been made to determine whether or not a cellular immunity is established as a result of the active immunization of a susceptible animal. The results obtained by Andrewes (1929), working with Virus III of Rivers, indicate that cells of immune rabbits, when washed free of blood constituents and propagated in tissue cultures, are susceptible to the virus as shown by the development of typical inclusion bodies. Similar results were obtained when the virus of herpes simplex was employed (Andrewes, 1930). It would seem, then, that active immunization does not lead, at least in these cases, to an increased resistance of the cell itself. That acquired immunity may in part depend upon the development of specific humoral factors was strongly suggested by the results of this series of experiments. It was demonstrated that, whereas serum from normal animals failed to prevent infection of cells from a normal or from an immune animal, serum from an immune animal prevented the development of inclusion bodies in cells from both sources. Although these observations and many others obtained by different methods leave no doubt that a specific antibody plays an important role in immunity to viruses, the exact manner in which it exerts an inhibitory effect is still obscure. There is little or no evidence that antibody can directly destroy a virus. Information obtained from study of the virus of vaccinia in tissue cultures shows that immune serum alone or in the presence of complement does not completely inactivate this agent (Florman and Enders, 1942). Although apparently inhibited for a time, it can be shown to be present and capable of multiplication in the cells following the withdrawal of the antibody. Such observations are of significance in considering the general theory of infection and immunity in virus diseases.

REFERENCES

Andrewes, C. H., 1929, Virus III in tissue cultures. II. Further observations on the formation of inclusion bodies. III. Experiments bearing on immunity. Brit. J. Exp. Path., 10, 273-280.

Andrewes, C. H., 1930, Tissue-culture in the study of immunity to herpes. J. Path. and Bact., 33, 301-312.

Andrewes, C. H., 1942, Interference by one virus with the growth of another in tissue-culture. Brit. J. Exper. Path., 23, 214-220.

Bang, F. B., and Gey, G. O., 1949, Electron microscopy of tissue cultures infected with the virus of eastern equine encephalomyelitis. Proc. Soc. Exp. Biol. and Med., *71*, 78-80.

Bland, J. O. W., and Canti, R. G., 1935, The growth and development of psittacosis virus in tissue cultures. J. Path. and Bact., *40*, 231-241.

Bland, J O. W., and Robinow, C. F., 1939, The inclusion bodies of vaccinia and their relationship to the elementary bodies studied in cultures of the rabbit's cornea. J. Path. and Bact., *48*, 381-403.

Cameron, G., 1950, Tissue Culture Technique. 2nd ed., New York, Academic Press, Inc.

Carrel, A., 1913, Neue Untersuchungen über das selbständige Leben der Gewebe und Organe. Berl. klin. Wchnschr., *50*, 1097-1101.

Carrel, A., 1926, Some conditions of the reproduction *in vitro* of the Rous virus. J. Exp. Med., *43*, 647-668.

Cheever, F. S., 1939, Cultivation of *Herpes febrilis* virus on agar slant tissue cultures. Proc. Soc. Exp. Biol. and Med., *42*, 113-114.

Cheever, F. S., and Willmert, G. P., 1942, Age of tissue in agar-slant cultures and multiplication of virus of herpes simplex. Proc. Soc. Exp. Biol. and Med., *51*, 35-38.

Enders, J. F., and Pearson, H. E., 1941, Resistance of chicks to infection with influenza A virus. Proc. Soc. Exp. Biol. and Med., *48*, 143-146.

Enders, J. F., and Florman, A. L., 1942, Persistence of vaccinia virus and chick-embryonic cells in suspended cell tissue cultures. Proc. Soc. Exp. Biol. and Med., *49*, 153-155.

Evans, V. J., and Earle, W. R., 1947, The use of perforated cellophane for the growth of cells in tissue culture. J. Nat. Cancer Inst., *8*, 103-119.

Feller, A. E., Enders, J. F., and Weller, T. H., 1940, The prolonged coexistence of vaccinia virus in high titre and living cells in roller tube cultures of chick embryonic tissues. J. Exp. Med., *72*, 367-388.

Fischer, A., 1930, Gewebezüchtung, ed. 3, München, Müller Steinicke.

FitzPatrick F. K., 1938, Agar-slant tissue cultures of spotted fever rickettsiae. Proc. Soc. Exp. Biol. and Med., *39*, 501-502.

Florman, A. L., and Enders, J. F., 1942, The effect of homologous antiserum and complement on the multiplication of vaccinia virus in roller-tube cultures of blood-mononuclear cells. J. Immunol., *43*, 159-174.

Fulton, F., and Armitage, P., 1951, Surviving tissue suspensions for influenza virus titration. J. Hyg., *49*, 247-262.

Gey, G. O., 1933, An improved technic for massive tissue culture. Am. J. Cancer, *17*, 752-756.

Gey, G. O., and Bang, F. B., 1939, Experimental studies on the cultural behavior and the infectivity of lymphopathia venerea virus maintained in tissue culture. Bull. Johns Hopkins Hosp., *65*, 393-417.

Goodpasture, E. W., and Anderson, K., 1944, Infection of human skin, grafted on the chorioallantois of chick embryos, with the virus of herpes zoster. Am. J. Path., *20*, 447-455.

Hallauer, C., 1931, Über das Verhalten von Hühnerpestvirus in der Gewebekultur. Ztschr. Hyg., *113*, 61-74.

Hallauer, C., 1938, Die Züchtung der Virusarten ausserhalb ihrer Wirte. A. Die Viruszüchtung im Gewebsexplantat. *in* Doerr, R., and Hallauer, C., Handbuch der Virusforschung, Wien, Springer, Vol. 1, pp. 369-419.

Harrison, R. G., 1907, Observations on the living developing nerve fiber. Proc. Soc. Exp. Biol. and Med., *4*, 140-143.

Hecke, F., 1930, Züchtungsversuche des Maul-und Klauenseuchevirus in Gewebskulturen. Zentralbl. f. Bakt. Abt. I., Orig., *116*, 386-414.

Henle, W., and Henle, G., 1943, Interference of inactive virus with the propagation of virus of influenza. Science, *98*, 87-89.

Hetherington, D. C., 1944, Frozen-dried serum as a medium constituent for tissue cultures. Proc. Soc. Exp. Biol. and Med., *57*, 196-197.

Hetherington, D. C., 1951, In Methods in Medical Research, Vol. 4, M. B. Visscher, ed. pp. 209-210.

Huang, C. H., 1943a, Further studies on the titration and neutralization of the Western strain of equine encephalomyelitis virus in tissue culture. J. Exp. Med., *78*, 111-126.

Huang, C. H., 1943b, Titration of St. Louis encephalitis virus and Jungeblut-Sanders mouse virus in tissue culture. Proc. Soc. Exp. Bol. and Med., *54*, 158-160.

Koprowski, H., and Lennette, E. H., 1944, Propagation of yellow fever virus in tissue cultures containing sulfonamides. Am. J. Hyg., *40*, 1-13.

Kurotchkin, T. J., 1939, Cultivation of vaccinia in agar-slant tissue cultures. Proc. Soc. Exp. Biol. and Med., *41*, 407-409.

Ledinko, N., Riordan, J. T., and Melnick, J. F., 1951, Differences in cellular pathogenicity of two immunologically related poliomyelitis viruses as revealed in tissue culture. Proc. Soc. Exp. Biol. and Med. *78*, 83-88.

Lennette, E. H., and Koprowski, H., 1946, Interference between viruses in tissue culture. J. Exp. Med., *83*, 195-219.

Lewis, W. H., 1935, Rat malignant cells in roller tube cultures and some results, Carnegie Institution of Washington Publication 459. Contrib. Embryol., *25*, 161-172.

Li, C. P., and Rivers, T. M., 1930, Cultivation of vaccine virus. J. Exp. Med., *52*, 465-470.

Löwenstädt, H., 1925, Einige neue Hilfsmittel zur Anlegung von Gewebekulturen. Arch. f. exp. Zellforsch, *1*, 251-256.

Maitland, H. B., and Maitland, M. C., 1928, Cultivation of vaccinia virus without tissue culture. Lancet, *2*, 596-597.

Morgan, H. R., and Wiseman, R. W., 1946, Growth of psittacosis virus in roller tube tissue culture; use in a vaccine. J. Infect. Dis., *79*, 131-133.

Muckenfuss, R. S., and Rivers, T. M., 1930, Survival of vaccine virus separated from living host cells by collodion membranes. J. Exp. Med., *51*, 149-159.

Pang, K. H., and Zia, S. H., 1940, Studies of virus of encephalitis (St. Louis type) grown on agar tissue medium. Chinese Med. J. Supp., *3*, 446-457.

Parker, F., Jr., and Nye, R. N., 1925, Studies on filterable viruses. I. Cultivation of vaccine virus. Am. J. Path., *1*, 325-335.

Parker, R. C., 1938, Methods of Tissue Culture. New York, Hoeber.

Parker, R. C., 1950, Methods of Tissue Culture. 2nd ed., New York, Hoeber.

Pinkerton, H., and Hass, G. M., 1932a, Typhus fever. IV. Further observations on the behavior of *Rickettsia prowazeki* in tissue cultures. J. Exp. Med., *56*, 131-143.

Pinkerton, H., and Hass, G. M., 1932b, Spotted fever. I. Intranuclear rickettsiae in spotted fever studied in tissue culture. J. Exp. Med., *56*, 151-156.

Plotz, H., 1937, Étude comparative de la virulence des cultures de peste aviaire effectuées en présence de cellules non proliférantes et en présence de cellules en voie de prolifération. Compt. rend. Soc. biol., *125*, 603-604.

Plotz, H., 1938, Culture *in vitro* du virus de la rougeole. Bull. Acad. de méd., Paris, *119*, 598-601.

Plotz, H., Bennett, B. L., and Reagan, R. L., 1946, Preparation of an inactivated tissue culture scrub typhus vaccine. Proc. Soc. Exp. Biol. *61*, 313-317

Porter, K. R., Claude, A., and Fullam, E. F., 1945, A study of tissue culture cells by electron microscopy. Methods and preliminary observations, J. Exp. Med., *81*, 233-246.

Porter, K. R., and Hawn, C. v Z., 1947, The culture of tissue cells in clots formed from purified bovine fibrinogen and thrombin. Proc. Soc. Exp. Biol. and Med., *65*, 309-314.

Rivers, T. M., Haagen, E., and Muckenfuss, R. S., 1929, Observations concerning the persistence of living cells in Maitland's medium for the cultivation of vaccine virus. J. Exp. Med., *50*, 181-187.

Rivers, T. M., and Ward, S. M., 1933, Further observations on the cultivation of vaccine virus for Jennerian prophylaxis in man. J. Exp. Med., *58*, 635-648.

Robbins, F. C., and Enders, J. F., 1950, Tissue culture techniques in the study of animal viruses. Am. J. Med. Sci., *220*, 316-338.

Robbins, F. C., Enders, J. F., and Weller, T. H., 1950, Cytopathogenic effect of poliomyelitis viruses *in vitro* on human embryonic tissues. Proc. Soc. Exp. Biol. and Med., *75*, 370-374.

Robbins, F. C., Enders, J. F., Weller, T. H., and Florentino, G. L., 1951, Studies on the cultivation of poliomyelitis viruses in tissue culture. V. The direct isolation and serologic identification of virus strains in tissue culture from patients with non-paralytic and paralytic poliomyelitis. Am. J. Hyg., *54*, 286-293.

Rose, H. M., Molloy, E., and O'Neill, E., 1945, Effect of penicillin on bacterial contamination of eggs and tissue cultures inoculated with unfiltered sputums. Proc. Soc. Exp. Biol. and Med., *60*, 23-25.

Sanders, M., 1939, Cultivation of the viruses. A critical review. Arch. Path., *28*, 541-586.

Sanders, M., 1940, Studies on the cultivation of the virus of lymphogranuloma venereum. J. Exp. Med., *71*, 113-128.

Sanders, M., and Alexander, R. C., 1943, Epidemic keratoconjunctivitis. I Isolation and identification of a filterable virus. J. Exp. Med., *77*, 71-96.

Sanford, K. K., Earle, W. R., and Likely, G. D., 1948, The growth *in vitro* of single isolated tissue cells. J. Nat. Cancer Inst., *9*, 229-246.

Shaw, D. T., Kingsland, L. C., and Brues, A. M., 1940, A roller bottle tissue culture system. Science, *91*, 148-149.

Simms, H. S., and Sanders, M., 1942, Use of serum ultrafiltrate in tissue cultures for studying deposition of fat and for propagation of viruses. Arch. Path., *33*, 619-635.

Steinhardt, E., Israeli, C., and Lambert, R. A., 1913, Studies on the cultivation of the virus of vaccinia. J. Infect. Dis., *13*, 294-300.

Theiler, M., and Smith, H. H., 1937, The effect of prolonged cultivation *in vitro* upon the pathogenicity of yellow fever virus. J. Exp. Med., *65*, 767-786.

Traub, E., 1933, Cultivation of pseudorabies virus. J. Exp. Med., *58*, 663-681.

Weller, T. H., and Enders, J. F., 1948, Production of hemagglutinin by mumps and influenza A viruses in suspended cell tissue cultures. Proc. Soc. Exp. Biol. and Med., *69*, 124-128.

Weller, T. H., Robbins, F. C., and Enders, J. F., 1949, Cultivation of poliomyelitis virus in cultures of human foreskin and embryonic tissues. Proc. Soc. Exp. Biol. and Med., *72*, 153-155.

Wirth, J., and Athanasiu, P., 1949, Electron-microscopy of cells from tissue cultures infected with vaccinia virus. Proc. Soc. Exp. Biol. and Med., *70*, 59-61.

Zinsser, H., and Schoenbach, E. B., 1937, Studies on the physiological conditions prevailing in tissue cultures. J. Exp. Med., *66*, 207-227.

Zinsser, H., FitzPatrick, F., and Wei, H., 1939, A study of rickettsiae grown on agar tissue cultures. J. Exp. Med., *69*, 179-190.

KENNETH F. MAXCY, M.D.

The Johns Hopkins University
School of Hygiene and Public Health

7

Epidemiology

DEFINITION OF EPIDEMIOLOGY

By derivation, epidemiology would seem to be concerned with the explanation of epidemics of disease in human populations. While this definition still obtains, with the advance in biologic and medical science the field included under epidemiology has naturally broadened considerably (Frost, 1920; Maxcy, 1941). An epidemic is commonly a sudden increase in the prevalence of a disease which is more or less constantly present or endemic in a community. To explain the sudden increase it is necessary to understand the factors which determine the usual or interepidemic levels of prevalence and the characteristic distributions which the disease manifests in human populations.

While originally limited to infectious diseases, usage has extended the term to the study of diseases of unknown etiology, to diseases due to nutritional deficiencies, to senescence, to abnormal cell growth, and even to the casualties caused by physical and chemical agents, accidents, etc. In like manner, while originally limited to disease in human populations, usage has extended the term to the study of disease in animal populations and plant life. Although enzootic and epizootic have been used by veterinarians to describe the level of prevalence of disease in animal populations, it is now considered good usage to refer to the epidemiology of cattle plague or foot-and-mouth disease. While it is etymologically correct to use epiphytic to refer to an outbreak of disease in plants, the modern plant pathologist may prefer to describe his observations on the stem rust of wheat under the title of epidemiology.

Here it is proposed that the term epidemiology be reserved to designate the field of science dealing with the relationships of the various factors which determine the frequencies and distributions of an infectious process, a disease, or a physiologic state in a human community. For present purposes discussion will be centered on the principles of epidemiology as applied to understanding and control of the viral and rickettsial infections of man.

BIOLOGIC INTERPRETATION

The pandemic of influenza which occurred in 1918 was an appalling demonstration of man's helplessness and ignorance. It was obvious that epidemiology as a science was lacking in a valid rationale and a unifying concept. With the advances in the field of general biology and the collateral medical sciences, the needed concept gradually became evident. It was comprehensively formulated by Theobald Smith (1934) in the Vanuxem lectures delivered at Princeton. *Infectious disease is a manifestation of parasitism.* Simple though this concept seems today, its formulation marked an important transition. The medical explanation of an infectious disease in man broad-

141

ened to become a biologic one. It was finally realized and accepted that infection should not be set apart as peculiarly within the province of human medicine but should be viewed as an expression of the eternal struggle of living things for food by predation or parasitism, for shelter, and for propagation of their kind. More particularly it is a reaction between one of the higher forms of life to the invasion of its tissues by some species of microparasite. This conception carries with it implications that are fundamental and far reaching. It affords a framework or pattern into which endless scattered observations can be fitted. The explanation of epidemics is then to be sought in host-parasite relationships and the environmental factors which modify them.

HOST-PARASITE RELATIONSHIPS

As a result of centuries of host wanderings, mutation and selective adaptation, the viruses and rickettsiae considered in this book have in some degree become established in the biologic orbit of man, and are responsible for some of his ills. Their potentialities range from those which only rarely and inadvertently invade his tissues to cause an occasional sporadic case of a rare disease to those which are dependent upon human tissues for their continuous propagation, sometimes giving rise to epidemics which decimate tribes or nations and change the course of history. The importance of each viral and rickettsial species to man has been determined by a few biologic principles to which only brief reference can be made.

Man may be an obligate, a principal or an occasional host species, according to the degree of success which a particular species of parasite has in passing through four critical stages in relationship to him. A micro-organism may become completely dependent upon man for its survival if it is continuously successful (1) in finding entrance into his body through its proper portal of entry, whether it be the mucous membrane of the respiratory, the alimentary or the genito-urinary tracts, or the skin by means of trauma or insect bite: (2) in reaching the particular organ, tissue or cells in which nutritive conditions are favorable for multiplication: (3) in making an exit from the body in excretions, secretions, or by blood-sucking insects; (4) in surviving under the conditions of the external environment, or in an insect vector, a sufficient time to reach a new susceptible host. To the extent that it is unsuccessful in continuously maintaining progressive passage through these four critical stages in human populations and their environment it must be able to utilize other host species or survival mechanisms. Thus, one of the first requisites of a rational explanation of the behavior of an infectious disease in a human population is to understand to what extent man as a host bears responsibility for the continuous propagation of the causative microparasite or shares this responsibility with other species—animal, bird or insect.

INCUBATION PERIOD

The first step in infection is the incubation period, i.e., the interval of time from primary invasion through the skin or the mucous membranes to the onset of symptoms of a disease. Its length depends upon the peculiarities of each particular host-parasite relationship. It is extremely short, a matter of hours, when the symptoms are due to preformed growth products or to large numbers of micro-organisms which have already had opportunity to multiply in the ingested foodstuffs, as in some salmonella infections. It is short, a matter of days, when the microparasite has more or less direct access to the tissue in which the primary multiplication takes place, as in certain air-borne infections caused by microparasites which multiply in the epithelial cells lining the respiratory tract; influenza is an example. It is longer in those infections in which the microparasite is unable to multiply at the site of entrance into the body but must make its way through lymph channels to regional lymph nodes, after which it must travel by way of the lymphatics in a step-wise multiplication and invasion, bypassing the defensive barriers in the phagocytic activity of the host tissues, ultimately to gain admission to the general circulation and select the organs or tissue cells for which it has a predilection and in which it can multiply, as is the case in such diseases as typhus fever. Thus, the incubation period may be a matter of hours, days, weeks, or even months, but for any particular disease its length is relatively constant and predictable. However, as with any other measurable biologic attribute, the incubation period of a specific disease manifests a constant range of variation. Frequency distributions of incubaion periods bear a resemblance to the normal curve with a slight skewness, rising more abruptly on the short side of the mean and tailing off on the long side. As pointed out by Sartwell (1950), the degree of variation in relation to the magnitude of the mean has a constant statistical pattern, no matter whether the unit of time be hours, days, weeks or months. The range of the incubation period is an important epidemiologic characteristic for each disease. It determines the time interval necessary for comparison with dates of onset of cases in judging whether an outbreak is due to a common vehicle of dissemination or not; and, when an epidemic is due to transmission from person to person by contact, it determines the rapidity of spread of a disease through a population.

HOST REACTION

The second critical stage in the host-parasite relationship mentioned above is the one which may give rise to symptoms and signs of illness by which a disease is recognized. The host reaction may vary greatly, both in severity and duration. A *case* of an infectious disease is a host reaction of sufficiently characteristic intensity and duration to permit clinical diagnosis. Reactions which are less intense and of shorter duration are called *abortive* or *suspected* cases, the pattern being too indefinite

or protean in nature to permit clinical diagnosis, except in association with *frank* cases. When the subjective and objective symptoms are so slight as to pass unnoticed, the host is said to suffer from an *inapparent* infection. Infections which are below the threshold of clinical recognition are grouped together as *subclinical*. They can be identified only by laboratory procedures such as cultural recovery of the infecting micro-organism from the host's tissues, change in the response of the skin to specific antigenic material, or change in a serologic reaction from a negative to positive. It is at least theoretically possible that an infection may occur without demonstrable reaction on the part of the host, i.e., a symbiotic or a saprophytic relationship, but there is a difference of opinion as to whether the word infection should be used to describe such a condition.

INFECTIOUS PERIOD

In clinical medicine, interest is centered upon a patient during the period that he or she is more or less incapacitated by the disturbance of physiologic functions caused by the invasion of a pathogenic micro-organism, that is, from the onset of symptoms to clinical recovery or to a fatal issue. In epidemiology, interest must be broadened to include the whole duration of the host-parasite relationship, that is, from the time of the infective exposure until the microparasite is suppressed or eliminated from the host's body. Of particular importance is the *infectious period,* the time or times during which the microparasite progeny are making an exit or are potentially available for transfer to a new host.

CARRIERS

As early as 1890, Escherich noted that the infectious period of diphtheria was not necessarily coincident with the clinical course but that diphtheria bacilli might persist in the throats of patients during convalescence. In 1892, Guttmann, Rommelaere and Simonds noted that cholera vibrios might be recovered from the feces during convalescence. Credit probably belongs to Koch (Winslow, 1943) for grasping the important fact that cases which could be clinically diagnosed were not alone responsible for the spread of contagious diseases. In his studies of cholera in Germany, during the winter of 1892-93, he noted that some cases were so mild that they escaped recognition, and indeed could be detected only with the aid of a bacteriologic investigation. The term carrier thus includes two classes. First, there are those who are about to have, or have already had a clinical attack; they are designated as *incubatory, convalescent* or *chronic* carriers. Second, there are those who are suffering from a subclinical or asymptomatic infection, the so-called *healthy* carriers. It is important to distinguish between these two classes, and for the purposes of this discussion, the second class of carriers will be included in the designation *subclinical* or *inapparent* infections.

PATHOGENICITY

The characteristics of a clinical reaction and the ultimate issue of an infectious process in death or recovery are determined by the balance between the devices of aggression of a specific species of microparasite and the mechanisms of defense of the host species, capacities for both of which are transmitted genetically. The attributes of the parasite which determine the outcome of the reaction are described by such words as infectivity, pathogenicity, virulence, antigenic power. These attributes, however, cannot be considered apart from those of the host which are opposed. These host attributes are described by such words as susceptibility and resistance. Resistance, in turn, is broken down into such concepts as genetic resistance, maternal immunity, natural and artificially acquired immunity, antibody response, etc. These attributes, both of the microparasitic species and the human host, are relative to each other and subject potentially to all degrees of quanti-

tative variation, not only as between different species of microparasites and different broad population groups, but as between strains of the same microparasitic species in individuals of the same general group. For the sake of simplicity, in this discussion they will be included under a broad definition of the term pathogenicity.

In this sense, the pathogenicity of a microparasitic species for a human host population cannot be measured experimentally in animals. It is indicated only by observations on the experience of human beings exposed to a particular infection under natural conditions. To the extent that infection may result in recovery or death, pathogenicity is roughly indicated by the proportion of attacks which are fatal. Stated in different words, it is a ratio between cases and deaths (the percentage of cases which are fatal) or the *case-fatality ratio* of a disease. However, this ratio may be affected in a considerable measure by nonspecific conditions which affect the host population, such as starvation, lack of proper medical care, secondary invasion by other micro-organisms, and other factors. To the extent that the infection may result in a residual of impaired function, pathogenicity may be indicated by the proportion of cases which exhibit paralysis or other complications. Finally, and more important, it is possible, in dealing with many infectious diseases, to estimate the proportion of persons infected with a particular microparasite who manifest a characteristic clinical reaction to those who do not, the ratio of clinical to subclinical infections. For example, in measles it is of the order of 19:1; on the other hand, in poliomyelitis it has been estimated to be of the order of 1:100. Such ratios vary not only with the species of microparasites but frequently with different strains of the same species.

SUCCESSFUL PARASITISM

Successful adaptation of a species of microparasite to the human host does not imply a high order of pathogenicity. Rather the contrary is true. Success for a parasite, as for any other living organism, can only be measured by the size of the population of its kind and its ability to survive and maintain these numbers in a constantly changing natural universe. There is no advantage if its host sickens and dies, since dissemination of its progeny accordingly becomes limited and soon ceases. The opportunities for scatter and chance of productive contact are increased in proportion to the length of time it can continue to multiply and find easy egress in large numbers from a host which is ambulatory and gregarious. Accordingly, a high case-fatality rate may be a disadvantage to survival of a parasitic agent. Conversely, a low ratio of clinical to subclinical infections and a long duration of the infectious period tend to insure wide dissemination. The microparasites best adapted for survival are those which cause infection with the least inconvenience and injury to the host, and create only a low grade immunity of short duration.

COMMUNITY SUSCEPTIBILITY

A human community is made up of a number of individuals who vary not only in their genetic capacity to react, but nearly always in previous experience with the predominant strains of the particular species of microparasite or its close relatives. Some individuals have acquired a complete immunity, some a partial immunity, some none. The proportion of a population at any one time which has little or no immunity determines the theoretical *susceptibility status* or the mass susceptibility of a community for the infectious disease which a specific microparasite causes. If a micro-organism is commonly prevalent in a community, the proportion is a constantly changing one as susceptibles are infected, develop immunity, and recover. If the immunity conferred by an infection is durable then susceptibility decreases with age, and the age distribution

of cases is consequently that of a *children's* disease. If the immunity conferred is temporary, as with many acute respiratory infections, the same individual may be reinfected and consequently the disease attacks all ages, adults and old people as well as infants and children. Thus, community susceptibility has an age distribution, which is specific for each infectious agent, the range of which is indicated by the reciprocal, the age distribution of cases of the disease which it causes, provided exposure is a common experience.

With some infections it is possible by means of a skin test or a serologic test for specific antibodies, obtained on a representative sample of persons, to establish the immunity status of a community. A common example of the former is the use of the Schick test to determine a community's susceptibility to diphtheria. An illustration of the latter is the extensive use of the neutralization test as an indication of past infection with yellow fever virus in mapping out the geographic areas in which it is or has been prevalent. By ascertaining the correlation of positive sera with age, it is possible to discover whether the disease has been prevalent recently or to determine the period of time which has elapsed since the population was last exposed. Thus, with adequate representation of all ages in the sample of sera tested, if the positive sera were randomly distributed with regard to age and indicated infections in early life, it could be inferred that the exposure was continuing. If, on the other hand, the positive sera came only from persons beyond a certain age as, for example, beyond the age of 20, it could be inferred that the infection had not been prevalent in the area for the past 20 years.

CONTACT RATE

The qualitative variation taking place within the microparasitic and host populations, and the variations in conditions which affect their interrelationships with each other and with the environment, results in quantitative changes. The size of the microparasitic population depends upon the rapidity of passage from person to person and the accumulated proportion of persons harboring the infectious agent at any one time. This is determined not only by the proportion of susceptibles but by the opportunities for progressive transfer to new hosts, i.e., the *exposure* or *contact rate*. This rate is affected by a variety of conditions, depending upon the requirements for transmission. For those diseases which are transmitted from person to person by some form of direct or indirect contact, the importance of the degree of crowding, or density of population, as determined by living in urban or rural areas, in private homes, in institutions, or in military installations, is obvious. For those diseases which are transmitted to some extent at least by contamination of food, milk or water, the importance of sanitary conditions and home hygiene is evident. For diseases transmitted by insects there are a whole series of conditions which affect the numbers of the vector species, their access to man, and requirements of the microparasite for completing a cycle of development. In every community these factors are constantly changing with the habits of the people, day in and day out, from season to season, and from year to year.

OPERATION OF CHANCE

If an individual in the infectious stage of a disease arrives in a community from which the disease has been absent for some time, what happens will be determined in part by the susceptibility status, in part by exposure or contact rates, and finally by the operation of chance. For example, a person may develop measles and, since by chance the contacts immediately exposed are immune, no secondary cases will occur. Or, a second and third case may occur without further transmission of the disease to susceptibles. So the chain of propagation of an infectious agent may build up or diminish and disappear, depending on the one hand upon the continuing chance contacts between cases and susceptibles and on the other upon contacts between cases and immunes.

INCIDENCE OR PREVALENCE

The forces which create the dynamic biologic phenomena of infectious disease are, in the ultimate analysis, population pressures, i.e., the innate impulse of living micro-organisms to multiply and survive by parasitism upon *homo sapiens* and the efforts of the host species to preserve its own integrity. The balance between these two forces is constantly fluctuating, just as are the interactions between other living species, as for example, between the carnivores and their herbivorous food sources. When the equilibrium is a relatively stable one, it is manifested by an *endemic* prevalence. When the equilibrium is subject to sudden and violent disturbances, it is manifested by *epidemics*. If the balance is in favor of the host, the disease shows a downward trend and tends to disappear. If the balance is in favor of the microparasite, the disease tends to increase in prevalence, and may, in certain instances, act as a temporary human population check if it is widely distributed and highly fatal.

To facilitate reasoning, it is necessary to express these phenomena in quantitative terms. The basic elements of this statistical methodology are formulae which represent prevalence or incidence. The denominator (number of individuals in the host population) can in many situations be counted or estimated with considerable accuracy. The numerator (number of parasitic microorganisms) can only be indirectly represented. It is correlated in a rough way with the number of deaths, or cases, or infections caused by a microparasite population. The following indices schematically represented are most commonly used:

(1) A cause-specific death rate or mortality rate:

$$\frac{\text{Number of deaths from a specific disease during a calendar period}}{\text{Average population present during same calendar period}} \times 100*$$

(2) A case rate, attack rate or morbidity rate:

$$\frac{\text{Number of cases of a specific disease developing during a calendar period}}{\text{Average population present during same calendar period}} \times 100*$$

(3) Prevalence ratio:

$$\frac{\text{Number of cases of a specific disease existing at a particular time}}{\text{Population present or surveyed at that time}} \times 100*$$

Obviously, each of the three types of rate has its own implications. The one used will depend upon the questions to be answered and the availability of statistical information for the population group or groups under consideration. All are subject to errors of diagnosis and completeness of counting. Basic to effective use in reasoning is an assessment of the approximate validity of a rate. This can be done only when the accompanying text contains a clear statement of the universe of observation (denominator) in place or area, persons and time, the methods by which the deaths, cases or infections (numerator) were discovered and recorded, and the clinical and laboratory criteria employed in diagnosis and classification. The soundness of inferences drawn from biostatistical material can never exceed the level of accuracy of the original data.

To represent the *shift in balance* or *changes in equilibrium* between a microparasitic and a host population, it is necessary to show what happens in successive

periods of time. For adequate expression, the numerator of the fraction then should preferably be the number of *new* cases or *new* infections which are reported, or have their onset, or are discovered or are admitted to a clinic in successive days, weeks, months or years. If the number of host population (denominator) remains relatively stable during the period under consideration, the number of new cases or new infections alone will suffice to indicate the course of events without calculating rates. Thus the *incidence* of disease, or an *incidence rate,* is a dynamic concept. It reflects changes in the frequency with which the microparasite is spreading and gaining access to new susceptible individuals, and, accordingly, the increase or decrease in microparasitic population.

An accurate statement of incidence must take into account not only the number of new cases (numerator) but the total number of new individuals at risk (denominator) in each successive time period. It makes a great deal of difference whether it is a closed or an open universe, i.e., whether the population is composed of the same, or approximately the same, individuals throughout the period of observation or whether the individuals in the population

---

* This rate may be expressed on the basis of any population unit considered to be appropriate—per cent, per 1,000, per 10,000, per 100,000. The time unit chosen, whether it be hours, days, weeks, months, or years, is also varied according to circumstances.

are changing through immigration and emigration. For example, an incidence of cerebrospinal meningitis in one army camp ten times greater than in another when expressed on the basis of "cases per thousand strength per year," may be due to the fact that in the latter the personnel is permanent, while in the former it is periodically changing through the arrival of recruits and the departure of graduates from a course of training, so that ten times as many individuals are at risk of infection during the course of a year.

A prevalence ratio (3) is, properly speaking, a static concept. It represents how much disease there is in a given population existing at a particular time. For example, it may be desirable to know how many cases of active tuberculosis, of primary syphilis or of rheumatic heart disease have been identified and are under medical observation in a particular community as of a certain date.

COMMON-VEHICLE EPIDEMICS

The word epidemic is most commonly used to refer to the sudden or unusual appearance and/or temporary increase in incidence of a disease previously absent or occurring only sporadically in a particular population group and environment. It is conventionally represented in a graph by plotting the number of cases (ordinates) by date of report or onset according to the selected time intervals, hours, days, weeks (abscissae). The numbers usually show a regular ratio of increase in successive intervals to reach a maximum and pass over into a similar ratio of decrease so as to describe a more or less symmetrical curve, as illustrated in Chart 8.

It is to be noted that the span of time between the minimum and maximum incubation periods varies widely in different diseases. For example, in food poisoning due to staphylococcus toxin it is a matter of 1 to 8 hours; in influenza from 1 to 2 days; in measles from 12 to 16 days; in homol-

ogous serum jaundice from 2 to 6 months. By comparison of this span of time of the disease involved with the period during which the cases included in the outbreak have their onsets, an important inference can be drawn. If the onsets of all or nearly all of the cases fall within an interval no

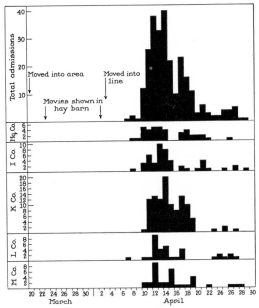

CHART 8. Outbreak of Q fever in the 3rd Battalion, 362nd Infantry, indicated by daily hospital admissions for units as a whole and for each company. (Adapted from Figs. 2 and 3, Robbins, F. C., Gauld, R. L., and Warner, F. B., 1946, A fever in the Mediterranean Area: Report of its occurrence in Allied troops. II. Epidemiology. American Journal of Hygiene, 42, 29.)

greater than that of the known variation in incubation periods, then it can be assumed that they arose from a nearly simultaneous exposure to a common vehicle of dissemination or to a single source. Or, reversing the procedure, if it be known that the group of persons selected by a disease have been together upon only a single occasion, then the common exposure must have occurred at this time and the variation in the incubation periods of different individuals can be calculated. These considerations are illustrated by studies of an outbreak of Q fever among Allied troops in the Mediterranean Area, 1944-45. The following account is paraphrased from the report of Robbins, Gauld and Warner (1946).

In April, 1945, the 3rd Battalion, 362nd Infantry Regiment, with an approximate strength of 900, experienced an explosive outbreak of Q fever. A total of 269 soldiers, or almost 30 per cent of the unit, were hospitalized between April 7th to 29th, 1945, with an illness diagnosed as primary atypical pneumonia. Early in March, the battalion was in the line where the various companies were widely dispersed. On March 20th they moved back to rest and bivouacked in an area on the northeastern slope of a ridge about 0.5 mile from Pagliana. The 4 companies camped in a semicircle about a farmhouse in which the Battalion Headquarters was located and where the headquarters officers lived. The farmer and his family remained in the house during this period. The men had pyramidal or pup tents for shelter and some slept on the ground. Some of them used hay from the barn adjacent to the house or straw from a nearby haystack as bedding. This bivouac area was occupied until April 3rd.

While in this location an intensive training program was carried on which included the presentation of numerous training films and motion pictures. These films were shown in the loft of the barn adjacent to the farmhouse and attendance of all personnel in the battalion was compulsory. The loft was large enough to accommodate one company at a time and the companies attended in rotation.

The course of the outbreak is shown in Figures 2 and 3.* The first patient was hospitalized on April 7th, 4 days after the battalion had moved back into the line and 18 days after it first occupied the area near Pagliana. The outbreak was explosive with the peak between April 12th and 14th. On April 14th there were 40 hospital admissions from the 3rd Battalion. By April 19th the outbreak was almost over and the last patient was hospitalized on April 29th. The total number of cases was 269, with 171 (63 per cent) occurring in the 6 days from April 10th to 15th.

The occurrence of the cases, by company, is shown in Figure 3.† It will be seen that the

---

* See Chart 8, an adaptation of the figures mentioned here.
† I.e., in Robbins, Gauld and Warner.

outbreak occurred in all companies at about the same time.

Only 4 cases of a similar clinical disease are known to have occurred in the other battalions of the regiment. These four men were all members of the 2nd Battalion and had all attended the showing of training film in the hay barn in the 3rd Battalion area on the night of March 25th. This was the only time 3 of them had been in the area but the other patient was a frequent visitor.

The explosive character of the outbreak would point to some common source of infection applicable to the entire battalion. Water is unlikely as a source of infection because the unit's water supply came from an engineer point which supplied other units which had no disease.

It would seem that the infection occurred during the period the battalion was bivouacked near Pagliana since this was the only time the entire unit was brought together. Assuming it to have occurred in this area, the time interval between possible exposure and onset of the outbreak fits exactly the incubation period previously estimated, 14-26 days. In speculating upon the possible sources of infection associated with the area, suspicion immediately centered around the barn where the motion pictures were shown, particularly when one considers the 3 cases in men from the 2nd Battalion who had visited this barn.

The investigation of an explosive outbreak may be relatively simple, since a priori one is concerned only with discovering the common factor. A microparasitic population has suddenly found an opportunity and a vehicle (air-borne dust particles) by which it can be disseminated to a group of host individuals in a short space of time. A certain proportion of the exposed persons is susceptible and to that extent they come down with subclinical or clinical attacks characteristic of the specific infectious agent. The problem is resolved in discovering upon what common occasion, or by what common medium, the persons so selected could have had a more or less simultaneous exposure.

If the portal of entry of the specific microparasite involved is or may be through the alimentary tract, attention is centered upon articles of food or drink, particularly water supply, milk supply or food that has been insufficiently cooked or which has been allowed to stand several hours after preparation in a warm place, allowing opportunity for growth of the pathogenic micro-organisms. The remainder of the investigation is then directed toward elucidating the conditions which permitted the contamination to occur, with the practical objective of instituting appropriate preventive measures.

If the epidemic is caused by microparasites which enter only through the respiratory tract, the investigation would seek to establish that the group affected had been exposed to a common indoor atmosphere. There is some evidence to suggest that occasionally viral or rickettsial particles liberated from a human or extrahuman source may remain viable and floating in the air in sufficient concentration and for a sufficient period of time to infect a number of individuals breathing the atmosphere at or about the same time. Outbreaks of this type, however, must be rare and nearly always obscured by the contemporary incidence of cases due to more immediate transfer of infection from person to person.

If the epidemic is due to microparasites which are transmitted to man by some arthropod, the investigation would seek to ascertain whether the group affected had been briefly exposed in a localized environment to bites of the vector species. Cook (1944) reported an instance of this kind in his studies of the epidemiology of scrub typhus:

A sharp outbreak of scrub typhus occurred in one brigade, in which 45 cases were reported over a period of four weeks. Investigation showed that infection was practically limited to two battalions operating in a particular area and within these battalions to companies patrolling a strictly limited locality. Detailed inquiry revealed the interesting fact that patrols taking different routes occasionally crossed at this spot, and bivouac or exercise here was the only common feature of epidemiological history in affected companies. Cases of typhus appeared in such patrols ten to fourteen days later, in some cases after a single visit. Companies whose patrols were limited to adjacent country escaped. The incidence in companies reported as using the site was high. Within the companies, incidence was confined to platoons which had bivouacked nearest the jungle fringe on a short section of the bank of a steep banked creek. Two patients subsequently reported from otherwise unaffected units gave a history of having visited this locality about twelve to fourteen days previous to onset.

When the epidemic is caused by microparasites whose mode or modes of transmission have not been elucidated, as is the case with Q fever cited above, all of these possibilities must be considered.

PROPAGATED EPIDEMICS

When the span of time of an epidemic wave is much greater than the average incubation period of the particular disease in question, then it can be assumed that (1) exposure to dissemination by a common vehicle has been prolonged; or that (2) the infection is being propagated by progressive host-to-host transfer (contact transmission); or that (3) there is a combination of common-vehicle dissemination with secondary contact transmission. An epidemic which is principally or solely the result of progressive host transfer is frequently called a *propagated* epidemic.

Frequently the term epidemic refers only to a peak in the oscillating incidence of a disease more or less constantly prevalent in a community. How great the increase of incidence must be before it is regarded as epidemic is a matter of judgment and is influenced by psychologic attitudes. The greater the fear of a disease, or the more unusual it is in a community, the smaller the increase needed to justify use of the descriptive term. Many statistical devices have been suggested for making the definition more objective and precise (Bundesen and Hedrich, 1925; Rich and Terry, 1946), but no definition has yet received general sanction. Dependence is placed in general upon comparing the current incidence of each specific infectious disease with its incidence in the past in the same population group and at the same time of the year. This *expected number* or *norm* is commonly expressed as a three-year or five-year median of reported cases. When current incidence exceeds this number in several successive time periods, the disease shows a tendency which, if sustained and great enough, sooner or later merits a pronouncement of the presence of an epidemic.

Each infectious disease has a seasonal variation which follows a more or less regular pattern, reaching a maximum distribution about the same time each calendar year, when conditions are most favorable to transmission. Each is subject also to an interannual variation or secular trend which may be slight or show wide fluctuations. Some diseases manifest a cycle or periodicity, epidemic years occurring at fairly regular intervals of two or three years, or perhaps four or five years or longer (Commission on Acute Respiratory Diseases, 1946). Others are entirely unpredictable in their annual behavior.

EPIDEMIC THEORY

The simplest of all infectious diseases is measles. Table 9 (Wilson and Burke, 1942, 1943) illustrates the manner in which its incidence varies in any large city. By progressive host-to-host transfer the virus

TABLE 9. MEASLES CASES BY MONTHS IN PROVIDENCE 1917-1940
(Adapted from Wilson and Burke, Proc. N.A.S., 1943)

YEAR	JAN.	FEB.	MAR.	APR.	MAY	JUNE	JULY	AUG.	SEPT.	OCT.	NOV.	DEC.	TOTAL
1917	33	47	62	109	119	36	13	7	2	1	8	55	492
1918	55	98	373	1232	1299	780	261	23	8	6	5	3	4143
1919	1	4	4	4	5	4	3	3	1	2	1	3	35
1920	125	127	136	279	404	288	146	38	45	53	190	191	2022
1921	329	585	665	390	266	99	28	10	1	2	7	26	2408
1922	89	4	3	26	25	22	23	19	7	16	131	652	1017
1923	680	1228	1470	687	383	117	29	6	3	10	7	7	4627
1924	5	6	3	11	16	30	15	2	2	1	5	2	98
1925	13	11	6	15	18	30	58	50	13	81	417	1224	1936
1926	2057	1360	648	348	196	105	48	8	1	0	0	4	4775
1927	5	2	1	1	2	2	6	2	0	9	7	23	60
1928	45	112	422	1081	883	800	508	77	18	36	36	61	4079
1929	84	189	261	399	276	111	38	4	3	2	0	0	1367
1930	2	0	1	4	23	46	22	8	1	0	2	0	109
1931	1	2	49	158	456	358	179	99	22	191	337	1548	3400
1932	2799	2037	574	199	81	11	2	0	0	0	0	0	5703
1933	0	0	0	3	3	6	5	2	4	0	1	1	25
1934	4	11	21	18	29	106	44	25	8	5	1	7	279
1935	13	57	343	1351	1953	1279	241	17	4	1	0	48	5307
1936	119	74	92	76	83	17	11	4	0	0	9	77	562
1937	422	811	1184	711	472	129	31	4	0	2	3	3	3772
1938	2	5	4	2	0	0	0	3	1	0	0	3	20
1939	33	35	40	118	317	286	157	64	20	89	267	446	1872
1940	569	495	530	462	543	372	121	20	1	0	1	1	3115
Total	7485	7300	6890	7684	7852	4934	1989	495	165	507	1435	4385	51221

Epidemics culminate in May, 1918, March, 1921, March, 1923, January, 1926, April, 1928, January, 1932, May, 1935, March, 1937, March(?), 1940. In this period of 262 months there are 9 major peaks, but we must not count both ends. The average time between peaks is 33 ± 7.9 months, not 2 years. For the mean we write 33 ± 2.8 months. In Glasgow we estimate 40 months between peaks from 1888 to 1927, incl., based on Soper's data (*J. Roy. Statist. Soc. London*, 92, 34-61 (1929)). How many peaks one counts depends on the interpretation one gives to the qualifying adjective major and what allowance one makes for seasonal interruption of an epidemic.

population maintains itself more or less continuously. If it dies out completely, before long it is reintroduced by the importation of a case in the infective stage. There is, however, a rhythmical variation in incidence correlated with the season of the year increasing to a maximum in the spring and decreasing to a minimum in the summer months. The time at which the maximum incidence is reached in each year varies within fairly wide limits. In some years, the total incidence is relatively low, in others

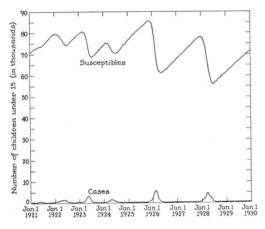

CHART 9. Secular trend of measles in Baltimore, Maryland, indicated by the estimated number of cases and susceptibles in the population under 15 years of age. (Adapted from Fig. 3, Hedrich, A. W., 1933, Monthly estimates of the child population "susceptible" to measles, 1900-1931. American Journal of Hygiene, *17*, 626.)

it rises to a level regarded as epidemic. These epidemic years appear to recur at fairly regular intervals in the same locality.

A century ago the periodicity of measles epidemics was known and discussed (Hirsch, 1883). The causes were thought to be obscure and complex, although it was generally accepted that the accumulation of susceptibles was an important factor. A more precise numerical approach to the explanation of periodicity of measles began with the contribution of Sir William Hamer (1906). Following his lead, a biometrician (Soper,

1929) in the course of an examination of possible methods of forecasting common contagious diseases "was led to adopt the simplest mathematical postulate that would describe on a first measure the generally accepted mechanism of epidemic measles, if the accumulation of susceptibles were really the prime factor, to compare the deduced results with the observed facts and then modify the primary hypothesis." Soper's work in turn stimulated W. H. Frost (unpublished), Lowell J. Reed (unpublished), Hedrich (1933), McKendrick (1940), and Wilson and Burke (1942, 1943) to elaborate the statistical approach to epidemic theory. This has elucidated quantitatively the relationships of the principal factors involved, and contributed to a rational explanation of the epidemiologic behavior of measles.

The fundamental facts with which one starts are simple. The biologic attributes of the measles virus and the requirements for infective transmission from case to susceptible remain relatively constant. The dynamics of the mass reaction are due to the flow of the virus through the human population. Susceptibles effectively exposed to cases in turn become cases; cases recovering from the infection become immunes. The susceptibles are being constantly recruited through birth and immigration, and depleted through becoming cases and immunes, or through deaths or emigration.

Upon the basis of a series of logical and reasonable approximations and assumptions, Hedrich (1933) made monthly estimates of the child population susceptible to measles in Baltimore from 1900 to 1931. As shown in Chart 9, during the 32-year period the calculated proportion of susceptibles in the population under age 15 did not rise above 53 per cent nor fall below 32 per cent. The percentage figures are only approximations, but the implications are significant. When the proportion of susceptibles was low, the incidence of measles tended to be low; consequently, susceptibles accumulated. When the proportion of accumulated susceptibles approached what McKendrick calls a *threshold density,* the situation was favorable for the support of an accelerated incidence of cases, or an epidemic. During a short period of time, the proportion of susceptibles fell rapidly as they became cases and subsequently immunes. As the proportion of immunes increased, more and more cases failed by chance to make effective contact with susceptibles and the incidence of new cases fell accordingly.

It is apparent, therefore, that the principal factor determining the occurrence of propagated epidemics of measles is the proportion of susceptibles in the population at risk, and that the termination of an epidemic wave is due to the dampening effect of the cumulation of immunes and not necessarily to the complete exhaustion of susceptibles, since many escape effective exposure. The proportion of susceptibles required to support an epidemic, and per contra the postepidemic proportion remaining, will vary in every community, and even in the same community at different times of the year. It is much easier to start an epidemic spread of the disease during the winter than in the summer, due to changes in the *contact rate,* which are only partially understood.

By utilizing the simplified premises in measles, and representing the four principal factors by appropriate symbols, it is possible to derive a dynamic equation by which, given (1) the number of cases, (2) number of susceptibles, (3) number of the total population, and (4) assuming an arbitrary value for the *contact rates* in one time period of 14 days, the number of new cases which will arise in the successive time periods of the same length can be calculated. In a community where sufficient data are available, the correspondence between cases predicted by such a formula and the cases observed is reasonably good within certain limits. The same kind of reasoning and mathematical postulations can be applied to other infectious diseases. However, the factors which go into the equation become more complex, and for an increasing pro-

portion one is unable to obtain numerical values from observations made in nature. The practical usefulness of the statistical approach to epidemic theory becomes correspondingly limited.

EXPERIMENTAL EPIDEMIOLOGY

Another approach to the discovery of laws or general principles governing the behavior of infectious diseases in human populations is through observations made upon epidemics in experimental animal colonies. Notable among the many contributions are those made by Theiler (1941) on mouse encephalomyelitis; by Traub (1939) upon choriomeningitis in mice; by Fenner (1948) upon mousepox (infectious ectromelia) of mice; by Webster and his associates (1932, 1946) on salmonella, pasteurella, pneumococcus, and Friedländer bacillus infections; by Topley and his associates (Greenwood, Hill, Topley and Wilson, 1936; Topley, 1942) on salmonella, pasteurella, and ectromelia virus infections. These studies are too extensive to permit detailed review. It will be useful perhaps to comment briefly upon the methods and observations of the two latter groups of investigators.

The general procedure was to assemble uninfected animals in unit cages, the arrangement of which could be altered to simulate a community of any desired size. A constant regime of cleaning and feeding was established, and appropriate measures taken to prevent the introduction of extraneous, pathogenic micro-organisms. An epidemic was started by introducing into an uninfected animal colony a certain number of animals infected with the microparasite selected for the experiment. The course of the subsequent epidemic was indicated by the occurrence of specific deaths, proved by necropsy and culture. Effort was made to hold all of the important factors constant except the one under examination, and to note the effect this variable had upon the course of an artificially produced epidemic.

It became evident very early in this work

that a constant genetic stock of experimental animals was fundamental to control of the host variable. As had long been known to the plant pathologists, it was found possible within certain limits by selective mating to breed out lines that were relatively resistant or relatively susceptible to infection with a particular microorganism, such as *S. enteriditis*, the cause of mouse typhoid. It was demonstrated, for example, that there may be selected promptly from a hybrid stock of mice, of which 40 or 50 per cent die, lines in which as high as 95 per cent and as low as 15 per cent succumb following a standard dose of *S. enteriditis*. This afforded experimental evidence of the importance of innate differences in resistance genetically trans-mitted in human families, lines of descent, races, to a particular microparasite, a phenomenon well illustrated by the differences in the host reaction of the white and negro race to infection with *Myobacterium tuberculosis*.

The possible importance of nutrition of the host to natural resistance to infection was appreciated. If a diet were so poor in quality or quantity as to bring about a state of debility, experimental animals whose lives were already in jeopardy from the consequences of produced deficiency would have a higher death rate than well-nourished animals if subjected to the added insult of infection. Obviously, it was desirable to hold this factor constant by providing a uniform and well-balanced diet. It was noted, however, that a diet which was well-balanced for normal growth and development, was not necessarily well-balanced in its effect upon host resistance to infection with a specific micro-organism. This question has been explored extensively by many investigators in relation to various infections experimentally produced in animals. It has been demonstrated that specific (natural) resistance can be influenced by nutrition when the stock is genetically heterogeneous and the pathogenic population to which it is exposed is heterogeneous

in the sense that it contains an array of variation in terms of capacity to produce disease (Schneider, 1951). These studies have advanced the understanding of the underlying mechanisms implied in the terms resistance and susceptibility, but diet was of very limited importance as one of the variables affecting the results of experimental epidemics produced by *Salmonella enteriditis*.

The variability in the biologic potentialities of the strains of infecting microorganism employed received considerable attention. A theory had been advanced by certain speculative epidemiologists that the rise and fall of an epidemic, such as the pandemic of influenza, are principally, if not wholly, due to a progressive increase and decrease, respectively, in virulence of the specific agent, the increase being brought about by rapid passage of the infecting agent in human beings during the early part of an epidemic and the decrease occurring because the infecting agent is subjected as an epidemic progresses to more resistance and less frequent passage as the result of increasing immunity in the host population. To test this theory, methods were devised by Webster for measuring the virulence of a specific strain of micro-organism for groups of mice by administering a fixed dosage. Sample cultures were obtained from animals dying at various times during artificially produced epidemics. Comparative titrations were made on strains from epidemics of pasteurellosis in rabbits, chickens and mice. Similar titrations of two serologic types were made during the course of mouse typhoid infections in mouse populations. A total of 300 or 400 titrations were made under many conditions to test the theory of fluctuating virulence. "The results were invariably negative and showed a constancy and fixity of disease-producing power of a given strain of organisms under all conditions of natural infection. . . ."

From his experience, Webster was inclined to believe that in all instances changes in biologic potentialities of specific microparasitic species are of little or no importance in determining the rise and fall of epidemic waves. While this may be true within certain limits for many parasitic species, there are some which are more unstable and have considerable capacity for selective variation and adaptation in those qualities which determine its pathogenicity for a human population at a particular time and place. Reference is made here in particular to recent studies on the variability of viruses of influenza (Burnet, 1951) and of poliomyelitis (Sabin, 1951). The possibility that bacterial and viral dissociation may occasionally play a role cannot be ignored (Zinsser and Wilson, 1932). The development of sulfadiazine-resistant or penicillin-resistant strains of bacteria is a pertinent indication of what may happen in nature.

Other highly suggestive experiments were conducted by Webster and associates. In one series of studies it was demonstrated that, when infected animals were introduced in a closed universe of susceptible animals, the ensuing epidemic quickly subsided as susceptibles died or became immune, although some escaped infection. An epidemic started in this manner could be maintained in an open universe if sufficient susceptible recruits were added at regular intervals. If the conditions were held relatively constant, the balance between the microparasites and the host population tended to reach a stabilized equilibrium. This was violently disturbed by a major change in the contact rate, which was accomplished by bringing a large number of animals previously dispersed in small single cages into a single colony in a large cage.

These and other experiments added support to some of the generalizations derived from experiences with epidemics in human populations under natural conditions. They emphasized particularly the accelerating effect upon incidence of an inflow of susceptibles into an infected community, and of aggregation of individuals into large groups (crowding) and per contra the

dampening effect upon incidence of accumulation of immunes. But the actual quantitative importance of each of these factors varies with the disease, its mode of transmission, the host relationships involved, and the local circumstances.

EXTRAHUMAN RESERVOIRS

In the preceding paragraphs, for the sake of simplicity in discussing factors which determine incidence, attention was concentrated upon infections which are transmissible directly from one individual to another of the same host species. These are due to microparasites which in the process of host-wandering, mutation and selective adaptation have become so highly specialized in their nutritive requirements that they can grow and multiply only when enzyme systems of certain human tissues and cells are available to them. Other disease-producing agents are sufficiently plebeian in their nutritive requirements to be able to find conditions favorable for their propagation in selected organs and tissue cells not only of man but of other mammals, birds or arthropods.

Man, along with many other species of mammal, serves only as an aberrant host for the virus of rabies, which is dependent for its continuous propagation upon the canine species. The virus of yellow fever can grow in the cells of many species of mammal, and in several species of mosquito found in the jungles of South America and Africa. Primarily, the virus is native to jungle life, apparently principally dependent upon alternation of monkey and mosquito hosts. Occasionally, it is transmitted to man, who, as an aberrant host. has "jungle" yellow fever, which is usually a sporadic disease. But if an infected human being happens to reside in a community in which there are sufficient numbers of a domesticated species of mosquito, *Aedes aegypti,* and is bitten by them, they serve as efficient vectors in propagating an epidemic of yellow fever. Since the virus cannot make an effective exit from the human host, except through the medium of blood-sucking mosquitoes, the disease is not otherwise transmissible directly from man to man.

Rickettsiae are microparasites of arthropods. In the process of evolution, they have become adapted to propagation in selected cells of man and other mammals. For example, *R. tsutsugamushi*, the cause of scrub typhus, has established a symbiotic relationship with certain species of trombiculid mites (Blake, Maxcy, Sadusk, Kohls and Bell, 1945). Mites become infected in the larval stage, and rickettsial progeny are passed from generation to generation through the successive stages of development of the mite—nymph, adult, egg, larvae, etc. This transovarial passage of the microparasite apparently does not interfere with normal growth, development and activity of the mite host. Only in the larval stage does the mite seek a meal of tissue fluids from a mammal. In the ecology of the mite vector, field rats are the most accessible source of such nutritive fluids. In the process of feeding, the larval mite infects a rat, which suffers an inapparent infection. While the rickettsiae are actively multiplying and being liberated into its peripheral circulation, the rat's tissue fluids are a medium of distribution to uninfected larval mites which happen to be feeding upon the animal at the time. The chain of transmission is thus maintained in nature without apparent detriment to either mite or rat population. When an infected mite by chance feeds upon and infects a human being, the host reaction is manifested by the clinical signs, symptoms, and course of illness classified under medical terminology variously as tsutsugamushi disease, scrub typhus, mite typhus, etc. Since larval mites have little or no opportunity to feed upon man during the stage of his illness when rickettsiae are in the peripheral circulation and since the rickettsiae fail to make an effective exit from the human host in excretions or secretions, the infection is not passed directly from man to man.

These illustrations serve to indicate the complexity of the factors which determine the incidence in human populations of diseases which are caused by microparasites with multiple host relationships. The occurrence of human cases is the visible indication of the existence of an extrahuman reservoir. There is some difference of opinion as to whether the term reservoir should be used to refer only to the principal mammalian or avian hosts or whether it should include arthropod hosts as well. Rationally, it could with advantage be used to refer to the whole underlying extrahuman mechanism by which a specific microparasitic population is continuously maintained, including the specialized ecology necessary to support the biologic relationships involved.

EVALUATION OF PREVENTIVE MEASURES

Knowledge of most of the common infectious diseases has advanced to a point where the principal factors which determine incidence and distribution are generally recognized. With many, if not all, however, there is need for epidemiologic studies which will more exactly define these factors and establish their relative (crudely quantitative) importance. One may glibly state, for example, that measles is airborne. It remains to be determined, however, to what extent the virus is conveyed on particles, more or less indirectly, by air currents from a case to susceptibles, the particle size which when inhaled will reach the mucous surfaces of the upper respiratory tract essential for infective contact, to what extent the virus is conveyed rather directly from person to person in what might be called conversational proximity, to what extent the virus is conveyed by contamination of articles with infective secretions and transferred by hands to the mouth of a susceptible, etc. The relative importance of these different routes of transmission must be evaluated if measures introduced to prevent spread are to be

TABLE 10. SECONDARY ATTACK RATES FOR POLIOMYELITIS, SCARLET FEVER AND DIPHTHERIA

AGE	POLIOMYELITIS NEW YORK CITY, 1916			SCARLET FEVER PROVIDENCE, R. I., 1904-09			DIPHTHERIA PROVIDENCE, R. I., 1904-13		
	NO. IN FAMILIES PRIMARY CASE EX-CLUDED	SUB-SEQUENT CASES	SUB-SEQUENT ATTACK RATES	NO. IN FAMILIES PRIMARY CASE EX-CLUDED	SUB-SEQUENT CASES	SUB-SEQUENT ATTACK RATES	NO. IN FAMILIES PRIMARY CASE EX-CLUDED	SUB-SEQUENT CASES	SUB-SEQUENT ATTACK RATES
0-5	10,540	335	3.18	1,493	360	24.1	2,006	295	14.9
6-10	4,575	58	1.27	1,088	279	25.7	1,410	219	15.5
11-20	4,994	10	.2	1,404	136	9.7	2,137	148	6.9
Over 20	17,191	4	.02	4,339	52	1.2	7,529	136	1.8
Total	37,300	407	1.1	8,324	827	9.9	13,082	798	6.1

(Adapted from Hygienic Laboratory Bull. No. 90, U. S. P. H. S. 1913, Tables 59 and 60, p. 125.)

maximally effective. To put the thought in more general terms, it is necessary to effectiveness that measures of prevention be directed against those conditions which are of actual importance in the particular situation rather than against the much wider range of conditions which may possibly contribute to the prevalence of a disease. Innumerable instances could be cited in which public health campaigns or measures, thought to be theoretically sound and rationally conceived, failed to accomplish the reduction which was expected.

SECONDARY ATTACK RATE

A classical example of critical evaluation of measures to prevent the spread of common contagious diseases is afforded in the development and use of the secondary attack rate, with particular reference to scarlet fever and diphtheria, by Dr. Charles V. Chapin, for many years health officer of Providence, R. I. It is related in some detail by Frost (1938) in a discussion of the familial aggregation of infectious diseases.

The principles and applications of the methods have the merit of yielding information which is easily understood and directly related to the practical problems of the health officer. The ultimate epidemiologic unit in a civil community is the

family or household, a group of people, mostly of close kinship, sharing a common environment, living in close contact in a manner easily described, and usually under the eye of a single medical or lay observer. The degree of contagiousness of different diseases can be measured by a statistical index derived from familial experience. The first case to occur is designated as a primary case. A census is made of the exposed members of the family, classified by age, sex, or other conditions which it is desired to take into account, especially with regard to their past history of having had the disease in question or specific immunization against it. A record is then kept of cases occurring in any member of the household within time limits, with reference to the primary case, set specifically for each disease, so as to include those probably infected by contact. It is then possible to summarize the observations on a large number of families and obtain an index of average experience based upon the ratio between secondary cases and exposed persons, or exposed persons specified as to age, sex, relationship, previous history, immunity status, or other quality. Table 10 illustrates the manner in which the intrafamilial spread of different diseases can be compared.

It is to be noted, however, that this index is based upon the frequency of secondary clinical cases following the occurrence of a primary clinical case. It does not take into consideration the spread by subclinical infections. It is useful nonetheless in answering certain questions: for example, (1) given a case of a communicable disease in the family, what is the risk of clinical attack borne by others in the same household within specified periods of time? (2) to what extent can risk of clinical attack be reduced by preventive measures, such as sending the primary case to the hospital or immunization of exposed susceptibles? It is pertinent to remark in this connection that a practical objective of preventive medicine is to decrease the risk of disease and death but not subclinical, immunizing infections.

While the secondary attack rate is a satisfactory device for evaluation of measures designed to reduce intrafamilial spread, it is only indirectly and by inference an indication of their effectiveness in reducing community spread. It is obvious that in dealing with a disease such as poliomyelitis it might be possible to demonstrate that by prompt isolation of the primary case the secondary familial attack rate could be measurably lowered. Yet, if there are one hundred individuals who have subclinical infections for each individual who has a paralytic attack, and both categories are involved in maintaining passage from person to person, the effect of prompt isolation of cases upon the incidence in the community as a whole may be so small as not to be measurable.

The evaluation of preventive measures in reducing the incidence of a disease in a large population unit, such as a city, is fraught with difficulty. Allowance must be made for the natural trend of the disease due to changes in complex factors other than those which are affected by the administrative measures. Occasionally, nature performs an experiment, which if brought under adequate epidemiologic perception, answers a crucial question. A classical example, which should be read by every stu-

dent of epidemiology, is presented in the observations made by John Snow (1865) on the relation of the purification of water supplies to the incidence of cholera in different districts of London during the epidemic of 1854-55.

Nature, however, seldom sets the stage for a scientific experiment in such a manner that it is possible to observe two population groups alike in all important respects except one. So it becomes necessary to set up such groups artificially if many questions as to the effectiveness of control measures are to be answered. Unusual opportunities for such studies were afforded in military organizations during the war. The many considerations which must enter into investigations of this type are illustrated by a study of the effect of oiled floors and bedding on the incidence of respiratory disease in new recruits (Commission on Acute Respiratory Diseases and Commission on Air-Borne Infections, 1946).

EVALUATION OF IMMUNIZATION AND CHEMOPROPHYLAXIS

The same kind of considerations enter into epidemiologic investigations designed to evaluate the prevention of an infectious disease by immunization or by the prophylactic administration of antibiotics or chemical compounds. The preliminary work in testing effectiveness and safety is carried out in the laboratory upon experimental animals. When sufficient evidence has been accumulated to justify the use, the final evaluation of the efficacy of such agents can be obtained only by human trial. Furthermore, these observations must be so controlled as to merit scientific acceptance of results. Failure to meet this necessity has led in many instances in the past to the exploitation of biologic products and chemical substances which was unwarranted, and at times actually detrimental. It has become painfully evident that evaluation by "clinical impressions" is unreliable.

The basic requirements of critical trials

upon human beings are well known, but the actual conduct of such an experiment is fraught with practical difficulties. Ideally, two groups of persons, a test and a control group, are placed under observation. They must be alike in all essential respects, particularly those which relate to their susceptibility at the beginning of the experiment and their exposure to natural infection throughout the period of observation. The substance to be tested must be administered without discrimination; if possible, alternate individuals should receive a placebo or blank. It is highly desirable that neither the subjects themselves nor the investigator who is responsible for their subsequent follow-up and observation should know who has received the test material and who has not. In this manner, errors due to unconscious human bias may be obviated. Individuals of both groups must be examined with equal frequency, care, and for equal periods, which are sufficiently long to insure an adequate test of the protection afforded. The criteria used in clinical diagnosis must be clearly stated. The resulting attack rates in the two groups must be sufficiently large to be statistically significant.

This is a basic outline of the kinds of problem encountered. There are always many perplexing circumstances and occurrences tending to disturb the results for which allowance must be made in some manner. Illustration of this type of epidemiologic studies designed to evaluate critically an immunization procedure is found in a report on the protective effect of vaccination against influenza A (Francis, Salk, Pearson and Brown, 1945), and in a subsequent series of reports on its protective effect under conditions of natural exposure (Francis, 1945; Rickard, Thigpen and Crowley, 1945; Hale and McKee, 1945; Eaton and Meiklejohn, 1945; Hirst, Plummer and Friedewald, 1945; Salk, Menke and Francis, 1945; Magill, Plummer, Smillie and Sugg, 1945). An example of a study planned to assess critically the value of a drug, will be found in the report on the dynamics of meningococcal infections and the effect of chemotherapy by Phair and Schoenbach (1944).

REFERENCES

Blake, F. G., Maxcy, K. F., Sadusk, J. F., Jr., Kohls, G. M., and Bell, E. J., 1945, Studies on tsutsugamushi disease (scrub typhus, mite-borne typhus) in New Guinea and adjacent islands. Am. J. Hyg., *41*, 243-373.

Bundesen, H. N., and Hedrich, A. W., 1925, Method for early detection of epidemic trends. Am. J. Pub. Health, *15*, 289-296.

Burnet, F. M., 1951, Some biological implications of studies on influenza viruses. Bull. Johns Hopkins Hosp., *88*, 119-137; 137-157; 157-180.

Commission on Acute Respiratory Diseases, Fort Bragg, N. C., 1946, The periodicity of influenza. Am. J. Hyg., *43*, 29-37.

Commission on Acute Respiratory Diseases, and The Commission on Air-Borne Infections, 1946, A study of the effect of oiled floors and bedding on the incidence of respiratory disease in new recruits. Am. J. Hyg., *43*, 120-144.

Cook, C. E., 1944, Observations on the epidemiology of scrub typhus. Med. J. Australia, *2*, 539-543.

Eaton, M. D., and Meiklejohn, G., 1945, Vaccination against influenza: a study in California during the epidemic of 1943-1944. Am. J. Hyg., *42*, 28-44.

Fenner, F., 1948, The epizootic behaviour of mouse-pox (infectious ectromelia). Brit. J. Exp. Path., *29*, 69-91.

Francis, Thomas, Jr., 1945, The development of the 1943 vaccination study of the Commission on Influenza. Am. J. Hyg., *42*, 1-11.

Francis, Thomas, Jr., Salk., J. E., Pearson, H. E., and Brown, P. N., 1945, Protective effect of vaccination against induced influenza A. J. Clin. Investig., *24*, 536-546.

Frost, W. H., 1927, Epidemiology, *in* Nelson Loose-Leaf System, Preventive Medicine, Public Health. Nelson, New York, Vol. 2, pp. 163-190; *reprinted in* Maxcy, K. F., Papers of Wade Hampton Frost. New York, Commonwealth Fund, 1941, pp. 493-542.

Frost, W. H., 1938, The familial aggregation of infectious diseases. Am. J. Pub. Health, *28*, 7-13.

Greenwood, M., Hill, A. B., Topley, W. W. C., and Wilson, J., 1936, Experimental epidemiology. Med. Res. Council, London, Special Reports, Series 209.

Hale, W. M., and McKee, A. P., 1945, The value of influenza vaccination when done at the beginning of an epidemic. Am. J. Hyg., *42*, 21-27.

Hamer, W. H., 1906, The Milroy lectures on epidemic disease in England—the evidence of variability and of persistency of type (Lecture 3). Lancet, *1*, 733-739.

Hedrich, A. W., 1933, Monthly estimates of the child population "susceptible" to measles, 1900-1931. Am. J. Hyg., *17*, 613-636.

Hirsch, August, 1883, Handbook of Geographical and Historical Pathology. London, The New Sydenham Society, Vol. 1.

Hirst, G. K., Plummer, N., and Friedewald, W. F., 1945, Human immunity following vaccination with formalinized influenza virus. Am. J. Hyg., *42*, 45-56.

Magill, T. P., Plummer, N., Smillie, W. G., and Sugg, J. Y., 1945, An evaluation of vaccination against influenza. Am. J. Hyg., *42*, 94-105.

Maxcy, K. F., 1941, Papers of Wade Hampton Frost. New York, Commonwealth Fund.

McKendrick, A. G., 1940, The dynamics of crowd infection. Edinburgh Med. J., *47*, 117-136.

Phair, J. J., and Schoenbach, E. B., 1944, The dynamics of meningococcal infections and the effect of chemotherapy. Am. J. Hyg., *40*, 318-344.

Rich, W. H., and Terry, M. C., 1946, The industrial "control chart" applied to the study of epidemics. Pub. Health Rep., *61*, 1501-1511.

Rickard, E. R., Thigpen, M., and Crowley, J. H., 1945, Vaccination against influenza at the University of Minnesota. Am. J. Hyg., *42*, 12-20.

Robbins, F. C., Gauld, R. L., and Warner, F. B., 1946, Q fever in the Mediterranean Area: Report of its occurrence in Allied troops. II. Epidemiology. Am. J. Hyg., *44*, 23-50.

Sabin, A. B., 1951, Paralytic consequences of poliomyelitis infection in different parts of the world and in different population groups. Am. J. Pub. Health, *41*, 1215-1230.

Salk, J. E., Menke, W. J., Jr., and Francis, Thomas, Jr., 1945, A clinical, epidemiological and immunological evaluation of vaccination against epidemic influenza. Am. J. Hyg., *42*, 57-93.

Sartwell, P. E., 1950, The distribution of incubation periods of infectious disease. Am. J. Hyg., *51*, 310-318.

Schneider, H. A., 1951, Nutrition and resistance—susceptibility to infection. Am. J. Trop. Med., *31*, 174-182.

Smith, Theobald, 1934, Parasitism and Disease. Princeton University Press.

Snow, John, 1865, Snow on Cholera. New York, Commonwealth Fund.

Soper, H. E., 1929, The interpretation of periodicity in disease prevalence. J. Roy. Stat. Soc., *92*, 34-61.

Theiler, Max, 1941, Studies on poliomyelitis. Medicine, *20*, 443-462.

Topley, W. W. C., 1942, The biology of epidemics. Proc. Roy. Soc., London, Ser. B, *130*, 337-359.

Traub, E., 1939, Epidemiology of lymphocytic choriomeningitis in a mouse stock observed for four years. J. Exp. Med., *69*, 801-817.

Webster, L. T., 1932, Experimental epidemiology. Medicine, *11*, 321-344.

Webster, L. T., 1946, Experimental epidemiology. Medicine, *25*, 77-109.

Wilson, E. B., and Burke, M. H., 1942, The epidemic curve. Proc. Nat. Acad. Sci., *28*, 361-367.

Wilson, E. B., and Burke, M. H., 1943, The epidemic curve. II. Proc. Nat. Acad. Sci., *29*, 43-48.

Winslow, C. E. A., 1943, The Conquest of Epidemic Disease. Princeton University Press.

Zinsser, Hans, and Wilson, E. B., 1932, Bacterial dissociation and a theory of the rise and decline of epidemic waves. J. Prevent. Med., *6*, 497-514.

R. WALTER SCHLESINGER, M.D.

The Public Health Research Institute of The City of New York, Inc.

8

Interference Between Animal Viruses

When an animal is exposed simultaneously to infection with two viruses, one of the following events may occur: (1) both viruses multiply side by side and produce characteristic manifestations of infection (dual infection); (2) one of them renders the host abnormally susceptible to the other (virus exaltation) or stimulates the proliferation of a type of cell which preferentially supports the propagation of a second, extraneous virus; (3) one virus so modifies the cells or tissues of the host that a second virus either cannot consummate its normal infectious cycle or cannot produce its characteristic pathogenic effects (viral interference). Although this chapter is primarily concerned with the third possibility, a definitive distinction between dual infection and interference is difficult to make since the latter is, in a sense, a specialized form of the former. To illustrate this point, and also to show how diverse the manifestations of interference can be, a few arbitrarily chosen examples of the phenomenon will be described in some detail.

EXAMPLES OF INTERFERENCE BETWEEN ANIMAL VIRUSES

INDEPENDENCE OF IMMUNOLOGIC SPECIFICITY

The first instance of interference recognized as such apart from classical specific immunity was the elaboration by Findlay and MacCallum (1937) of an observation made by Hoskins (1935). The latter found that a neurotropic variant of yellow fever virus, by itself causing only transitory fever in *rhesus* monkeys, could effectively protect these animals against an otherwise fatal dose of viscerotropic yellow fever virus given simultaneously. Findlay and MacCallum modified this basic observation in a number of ways and showed in particular that antibody production probably did not account for the effect. This contention was strengthened when they demonstrated that Rift Valley fever virus, which is only mildly pathogenic for monkeys, could similarly suppress the immunologically unrelated yellow fever agent.

INTERFERENCE BY VIRUSES CAPABLE OF UNRESTRICTED MULTIPLICATION

Interference Between Theiler's Virus of Mouse Encephalomyelitis and Western Equine Encephalomyelitis (W.E.E.) Virus. Intracerebral inoculation of the TO strain of Theiler's virus produces in mice, after an incubation period of about two weeks, a paralytic disease similar to that induced by mouse-adapted strains of poliomyelitis virus. The virus does not, as a rule, multiply to titers in excess of $10^{3.5}$ ID_{50}. W.E.E. virus, on the other hand, causes a rapidly fatal form of diffuse encephalomyelitis. It multiplies to titers of the order of 10^9 LD_{50}. Chart 10 shows the composite results of two experiments which illustrate what happens when these two viruses are

161

inoculated intracerebrally at varying intervals (Schlesinger, Olitsky and Morgan, 1943). If TO virus is inoculated immediately before minimal amounts of W.E.E. virus, all mice succumb to W.E.E. at the same time that the control animals die. If the interval between the injections of the two viruses is lengthened, an increasingly larger amount of W.E.E. virus is required to bring about infection. Thus, if ten days

Reciprocal Interference Between Active Type A and Type B Strains of Influenza Virus.

These two viruses were studied in embryonated eggs by Ziegler and Horsfall (1944). If relatively small amounts of each type are inoculated simultaneously into the allantoic cavity of chick embryos, both multiply. If one is given a head start of from 8 to 12 hours, the other one is suppressed. However, if the second strain is

LD$_{50}$ of WEE	Interval between intracerebral inoculations of TO and WEE viruses				
	2 days	4 days	6 days	8 days	10 days
10,000,000	—	—	—	—	[T][T][T]
100,000	—	—	■■■■[T]	■[T][T][T]	■[T][T][T][T][T]
3,000	—	■■■■	■■■■[T]	■[T][T][T]	—
1,000	■■■■[T]	■■■■■	■■■[T][T]	■[T][T][T][T]	[T][T][T][T][T][T][T]
30	—	■■[T][T][T]	■■[T][T][T]	[T][T][T][T]	—
10	■■■■■	[T][T][T][T][T]	[T][T][T][T][T]	[T][T][T][T]	—

■ mouse died of WEE virus
[T] mouse survived WEE virus inoculation but developed Theiler's disease

CHART 10. Interference between Theiler's virus and western equine encephalomyelitis virus. All mice were inoculated with 30 minimal infectious doses of TO virus and reinoculated at the stated intervals with graded doses of W.E.E. virus. (From Schlesinger, R. W., Olitsky, P. K., and Morgan, I. M., 1943, Observations on acquired cellular resistance to equine encephalomyelitis virus. Proc. Soc. Exp. Biol. and Med., *54*, 272-273; supplemented by an unpublished experiment.)

elapse between the two doses, the mice resist as much as ten million lethal doses of the far more virulent equine virus. Even after inoculation of such large amounts, no multiplication of the latter is demonstrable. The course of Theiler's disease, on the other hand, is not affected by the interposed inoculation of W.E.E. virus. In contrast to yellow fever and Rift Valley fever viruses, the viruses in this system are far apart not only immunologically but also in other biologic respects. Because of the high degree of pathogenicity of W.E.E. virus in normal mice, interference in the reverse direction cannot be readily demonstrated.

given in excessively large doses it still can establish an infection even after an interval of 8 hours.

INTERFERENCE BY VIRUSES RESTRICTED IN THEIR MULTIPLICATION

Interference Between Egg-adapted Influenza and Various Encephalitogenic Viruses.

Vilches and Hirst (1947) showed that nonneurotropic strains of influenza virus, inoculated intracerebrally in mice, interfered with various encephalitic viruses, e.g., W.E.E. virus. The time limits of this type of interference are illustrated in Chart 11. The interfering agent has to be administered either before or together with the virus that is to be suppressed. The amount of influenza virus has to be large, and if the time interval between the two inoculations exceeds 9 days, the degree of interference decreases. In this instance, it is known that the nonneurotropic strains of influenza virus are capable of only limited multiplication in mouse brain. Although after inoculation of large amounts there is no increase but rather a progressive decrease in infectious titer (Henle and Henle, 1946; Vilches and

ceptibility to the other type. In contrast, when the homologous strain is injected intracerebrally, it produces only transitory signs of infection, and viral multiplication is arrested by the intervention of a pronounced local antibody response (Schlesinger, 1949). For about three weeks, animals which have survived a challenge dose of homologous virus are also refractory to the heterologous agent. Thereafter, while immunity to the homologous virus persists, susceptibility to the heterologous agent is

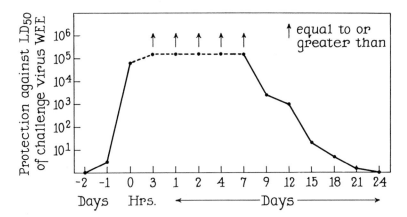

CHART 11. Interference between influenza virus (PR8 strain) and western equine encephalomyelitis virus in mice. Both viruses were inoculated intracerebrally. Influenza virus was given at time 0; W.E.E. virus earlier, simultaneously, or later, as indicated in the graph. Interference is expressed in terms of number of LD_{50} of W.E.E. virus which mice survived. (From Vilches, A., and Hirst, G. K., 1947, Interference between neurotropic and other unrelated viruses. J. Immunol., *57*, 125-140.)

Hirst, 1947), the virus undergoes a single, incomplete cycle of multiplication yielding immature virus particles which are noninfectious (Schlesinger, 1950).

Multiplication of Interfering Virus Restricted by Specific Immune Mechanism. Interference between eastern and western equine encephalomyelitis viruses, two immunologically distinct agents, is difficult to demonstrate because both of them cause rapidly fatal infections in experimental animals. This difficulty can be overcome by first immunizing the animals with formalin-inactivated virus of either type. Animals so vaccinated retain their normal sus-

fully restored (Schlesinger, Olitsky and Morgan, 1943, 1944).

INTERFERENCE BY INACTIVATED VIRUSES

It was found by Henle and Henle (1943, 1945) and by Ziegler, Lavin and Horsfall (1944) that influenza virus inactivated by ultraviolet irradiation, when inoculated in large doses into the allantoic cavity of embryonated eggs, inhibited the propagation of either homologous or heterologous types of influenza virus. Complete inhibition occurred when the irradiated virus was given simultaneously with or as long as 96 hours before inoculation of the active virus. The most interesting results were obtained when the inactivated virus was given shortly after the active virus; under these conditions the infectious cycle of the latter had already begun, but newly produced virus had not yet appeared. Here, the outcome depended upon

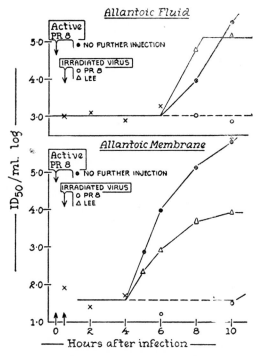

CHART 12. The effect of injection of homologous and heterologous irradiated virus, following infection, upon infectivity curves in allantoic fluids and membranes. The crosses denote mean titers during the constant periods. (From Henle, W., 1949, Studies on host-virus interactions in the chick embryo-influenza virus system. II. The propagation of virus in conjunction with the host cells. J. Exp. Med., *90*, 13-22.)

whether the irradiated virus was immunologically related or unrelated to the active virus, as is illustrated in Chart 12. Homologous inactive virus completely inhibited multiplication. Heterologous virus permitted the infectious cycle already in progress to go on to completion, but further multiplication was prevented. This resulted in one-step growth curves (Henle, Henle and Rosenberg, 1947; Henle and Rosenberg, 1949).

INTERFERENCE AS A LOCALIZED PHENOMENON

When an interfering dose of ultraviolet-irradiated influenza virus is inoculated into the allantoic cavity of embryonated eggs, the amniotic sac retains its susceptibility to infection with active virus (Henle, Henle and Kirber, 1947). This finding supports the belief that interference is not due to a systemic change in the host's response to the suppressed virus but that it is limited to those tissues or cells which have had immediate contact with the interfering agent.

INTERFERENCE WITH COMPLETION OF VIRAL MULTIPLICATION

The work of Hoyle (1948) and of Henle and Henle (1949) suggests that reproduction of influenza virus in the embryonated egg proceeds in stages. The appearance of newly produced infectious virus is preceded by an increase in complement-fixing antigen and in hemagglutinin. The hemagglutinin at this stage is considered to be an immature virus which in the last stage of the growth cycle is transformed into fully developed infectious virus. Therefore, virus harvested from eggs at different developmental stages may show variations in the ratio of infectious to hemagglutinating titers.

Samples of influenza virus consisting preponderantly of immature, noninfectious but hemagglutinating particles can be obtained from embryonated eggs inoculated with very large amounts of the active agent. In such eggs, even prolonged incubation fails to bring about a rise in infective titer, even though the hemagglutinin may rise to maximum titers (von Magnus, 1946, 1951). This phenomenon of auto-interference differs from other examples of interference described in that viral multiplication is not inhibited; instead, transformation of newly produced viral particles into complete, infectious virus is blocked. There is some evidence suggesting that the incomplete virus itself may be capable of acting as an interfering agent.

What the broader implications of this latter type of interference may be is conjectural. Its discovery in the case of influenza viruses is due entirely to the ability to identify some biologic properties of the immature virus particles. Intermediate or incomplete forms have not been recognized for other species of animal viruses. However, certain experiences in which it was found that adaptation of viruses to new hosts was facilitated by inoculating dilute rather than concentrated source materials may be related to auto-interference (Theiler, 1951, on yellow fever; Schlesinger and Frankel, 1952, on dengue fever).

It is clear from these few examples (for a more complete review see Henle, 1950) that interference between animal viruses can take many forms. It is not an all-or-none process. Inhibition of viral growth may be complete or partial. The phenomenon of auto-interference and the experiments with ultraviolet-irradiated influenza virus reveal that viral growth can be arrested by the interfering agent at various stages in the infectious cycle. Despite these diversities, a few general characteristics, which tie together many isolated observations, are evident.

GENERAL CHARACTERISTICS AND INTERPRETATION OF INTERFERENCE PHENOMENA

Manifestations of Interference. The ability of one virus to interfere with another may manifest itself in two ways: (1) protection of the host against an otherwise injurious or fatal infection; (2) partial or complete inhibition of multiplication of one virus by the other.

Reciprocity of Interference. For many viral pairs, e.g., heterologous types of influenza virus, it has been possible to show that interference is mutual; the question of success or failure of each virus depends almost entirely on quantitative conditions of the test. In other instances, only one of a pair is known to be capable of interfering with the other. This does not necessarily mean that suppression in the reverse direction could not occur. In some cases, infection with one virus of a pair is so rapidly fatal that its effect on the growth of the less-virulent agent cannot be tested. In other cases, a virus capable of multiplying in several different tissues may interfere with another virus whose activity is confined to a single organ, but the reverse cannot be shown as readily because interference could be effective only in the organ infected by both viruses.

Relation of Interference to Immunologic Phenomena. Interference has been observed between immunologically related viruses and between immunologically unrelated ones. Extreme examples are, on one hand, the phenomenon of auto-interference and, on the other, those instances where the interfering and the suppressed viruses are not only immunologically distinct but also far apart in their general biologic and physical characteristics, e.g., influenza and equine encephalomyelitis viruses. When the behavior of two immunologically related viruses is studied in animals capable of antibody production, the differentiation of resistance due to interference from that due to specific immunity is sometimes hard to make, as, for example, in the case of neurotropic yellow fever virus vs. viscerotropic yellow fever virus in monkeys, in Magrassi's *Konkurrenzphänomen* between nonencephalitogenic and encephalitogenic strains of herpes simplex virus (Doerr and Seidenberg, 1937), or in various other instances where avirulent and virulent strains of the same virus (Henle, 1950) are involved. This difficulty does not arise when interference is demonstrated in hosts incapable of antibody production, e.g., chick embryos or tissue cultures made from embryonic tissues (Lennette and Koprowski, 1946). Furthermore, in the case of interference between immunologically distinct agents, there is no reason to believe that antibodies or other humoral factors play a role.

Nature of Interfering Agents. The interfering capacity has always been found inseparable from the viral particles themselves. If the agents are noninfectious in the sense that they are incapable of multiplication, they nevertheless contain specific antigens or possess some other viral properties such as, in the case of hemagglutinating viruses, the ability to agglutinate erythrocytes. The interfering capacity is independent of reproductive capacity, which is illustrated by the fact that ultraviolet- or heat-inactivated (Isaacs and Edney, 1950a) influenza viruses are potent interfering agents. Noninfectious, incomplete influenza virus appears to play a part in the phenomenon of auto-interference. In some instances, the interfering virus is restricted in its multiplication either because it is not adapted to the particular host tissue, e.g., influenza virus in mouse brain, or because other factors, e.g., specific immunity as described above in connection with western and eastern equine encephalomyelitis viruses, intervene. Regardless of whether an agent is active or inactivated, all available evidence indicates that its interfering capacity is associated with its ability to interact in some specific way with host cells.

Time and Dosage Factors. Irrespective of its nature or of the particular way in which its interaction with host cells manifests itself, the interfering virus, in order to be successful, must have a quantitative advantage or a head start over the virus that is to be suppressed. Hence, if a mixture containing equal amounts of two viruses is inoculated into a host, the chances are that the one which infects or multiplies more rapidly will win out; or, if in a mixture one virus vastly exceeds the other in amount, it will act as the interfering agent. By the same token, viruses, which are restricted in their multiplication or have been inactivated, must be administered in large doses in order to be effective as interfering agents. Finally, the interfering agent must be given before, together with, or, as is possible in a few instances, very shortly after the virus that is to be suppressed. All interference phenomena, when compared with specific immunity, endure only for a short time.

Intimate dependence on dosage and timing most strongly suggests that the interfering virus must saturate the susceptible cell population at a time before the other virus has had an opportunity to do so. These quantitative aspects of the phenomenon and its localization support the assumption that the mechanism of interference operates at the level of the individual susceptible cell. It is not surprising, therefore, that any pair of viruses which exhibit the interference phenomenon under one set of conditions can, under changed circumstances, infect the same host simultaneously. This would be expected in hosts, which, in contrast with bacteria, are not unicellular organisms. The precise number of cells in a given animal-host system is not known or can at best be estimated for certain tissues. Thus, Hoyle (1948) estimates that the total number of endothelial cells lining the allantoic cavity of 12-day-old chick embryos is of the order of 10^8. This number seems to be in reasonably good agreement with the number of particles which apparently must be present in ultraviolet-irradiated preparations of influenza virus in order to interfere effectively (Henle, 1950). Considered in this light, the apparent conflicts between interference and dual infection with the same virus combinations may be resolved. Thus, Sugg and Magill (1948) and Sugg (1951) have reported that they were able to carry a mixture of the PR8 and the Lee strains of influenza virus through as many as 52 serial passages in chick embryos. The quantitative data here suggest that neither virus was present in the inocula in sufficiently high infectious titer to involve a large enough number of cells.

Emphasis on the importance of quantitative factors should not be taken to suggest that interference is the inevitable result of infection of a cell by two viruses.

That this is not so will be shown in the following section.

DUAL VIRUS INFECTION OF SINGLE CELLS AND VIRUS EXALTATION

Nothing is known about the specific factors which determine whether or not a given viral combination will result in interference. Why is it that egg-adapted strains of influenza virus fail to interfere with certain neurotropic viruses, e.g., 17D yellow fever, rabies and Semliki Forest viruses, under experimental conditions identical with those under which they effectively interfere with equine and other encephalitis viruses (Vilches and Hirst, 1947)? It is possible that differences such as these may not be related at all to specific inherent properties of the viruses but may be attributable to technical limitations. On the other hand, infection of single cells with two distinct types of viruses has been unequivocally demonstrated in a few instances.

Anderson (1942) and Syverton and Berry (1947a) observed two types of inclusion bodies in the same cell, e.g., intranuclear herpetic inclusions and cytoplasmic vaccinial (Guarnieri) bodies in the same cells of a rabbit's cornea inoculated with these two agents. Here, the difference in type and location of the inclusions suggests that the two viruses multiply in association with different constituents of the same cell. Syverton and Berry (1947b) also showed that the cells of the virus-induced rabbit papilloma (Shope) could be readily superinfected with several other viruses, such as B virus, vaccinia virus, or myxoma virus. The last infected the tumor even when it was inoculated at a site remote from it.

Specific susceptibility of virus-induced tumor cells to an extraneous virus was demonstrated recently by Ginder and Friedewald (1951). In tissue culture, as well as in the rabbit, the neurotropic Semliki Forest virus was found to have a selectively destructive effect on the cells of virus-induced

rabbit fibromas. The S.F. virus produced no detectable ill effects in the organs of normal rabbits, nor did it multiply in cultures of normal rabbit tissues. Both the S.F. virus and fibroma virus decreased in direct proportion to the rate of destruction of tumor tissue. Instances in which one virus stimulates a type of cell which is specifically susceptible to superinfection with another are valid examples of virus exaltation. In other examples of virus exaltation that have been reported, direct synergism in single cells between the two infecting viruses has not been proved. It has been reported that the potency of the FA strain of Theiler's encephalomyelitis virus may be increased when it is inoculated into mice together with an avirulent strain of the same virus (Gard, 1944). Lépine and Marcenac (1948) described an instance of virus exaltation in which herpes virus enhanced the susceptibility of mice to pseudorabies virus. Findlay and Howard (1949) called attention to the possibility that enhancement between two neurotropic viruses may be due to nonspecific changes affecting the transport of viruses.

A recent report by Burnet and Lind (1951) on dual infection with the neurotropic variant of the WS strain of type A influenza virus and egg-adapted strains of type A influenza virus has a more direct bearing on the interference problem. Interference between such pairs has been reported to occur in tissue cultures (Andrewes, 1942) and in the mouse brain (Burnet and Lind, 1951). However, the latter authors found that by properly adjusting the relative concentration of the two viruses in a mixture, they could obtain evidence for the appearance in inoculated mouse brains of new virus particles which incorporated properties of both parent viruses. This finding was interpreted as being closely analogous to the recombination of related bacterial viruses (see chapter on Bacterial Viruses). This interpretation would necessitate the assumption that both types of virus infect the same cell and exchange genetic markers in the course of their reproductive cycles. Such a concept would be compatible with the discovery that the egg-adapted strains of influenza virus involved go through at least a partial cycle of multiplication in the mouse brain (Schlesinger, 1950). With different combinations of these viruses, the question of whether interference or dual infection of single cells occurs would seem to depend on quantitative conditions.

MECHANISM OF INTERFERENCE

The ability of one virus to suppress infection with another has been observed among viruses pathogenic for animals, plants and bacteria. Upon superficial examination, the existence of this type of phenomenon in host-virus systems of three orders of living things seems to suggest the operation of basically similar mechanisms. It is tempting, therefore, to borrow concepts or facts pertaining to one class of viruses, especially bacterial viruses, to fill in the gaps in knowledge of another class. Analogies to the bacterial viruses have helped in formulating working hypotheses for the study of animal viruses (see collection of papers in Viruses 1950, edited by Delbrück) but they carry with them the danger of oversimplification. Each type of host system necessitates the use of totally different experimental methods, different standards of sensitivity, and different criteria for the evaluation of host-virus interaction. Methods in the study of interference (mutual exclusion) between phages, for example, are delicate enough to reveal fine differences between the behavior of serologically related and that of unrelated pairs in dual infection of single cells (see chapter on Bacterial Viruses). Technics used in work on plant viruses are relatively crude by comparison, and this perhaps accounts for the fact that acquired cross immunity of plants has been demonstrated only between serologically related viruses (Wallace, 1950).

Taking interference between animal viruses as a separate problem, and granting the validity of the assumption that it operates at the level of the individual susceptible cell, one could think of a variety of ways in which the interfering virus might act. It could prevent infection by the suppressed virus through destruction of susceptible cells; through changes in the surface of host cells resulting in loss of specific adsorptive capacity; or by the presence on the surface or release from the host cell of some deleterious factor. If one assumes that combination between host cell and suppressed virus is not prevented, one might postulate that the interfering virus inhibits multiplication of the other agent. This could be brought about by inability of the suppressed virus to penetrate from surface to interior of the cell; mobilization within the cell of antiviral substances; competition by the interfering virus for some cellular constituent essential to viral reproduction; or inability of the host cell to release newly produced viral particles.

Undoubtedly there are other theoretical possibilities. The ones mentioned indicate, however, how varied the mechanism of interference may be. Some of these alternatives, especially mere destruction of susceptible cells or release from cells of antiviral substances, have little or no experimental support. The possible merits of the other hypothetical mechanisms are more difficult to assess, since technics available for work with most animal viruses are much too crude for the delicate type of analysis required to distinguish between them. In the case of the influenza viruses, however, the hemagglutination reaction and the identification of receptorlike substances on red cells and in susceptible tissues have helped in bringing about some progress.

The analogy between tissue cell and agglutinable red cell is tempting (see chapter on Hemagglutination by Viruses). One would like to think that destruction or blockade of cellular receptors by the interfering virus is responsible for the interference phenomenon. Treatment of tissues with the receptor-destroying enzyme present in certain bacterial filtrates may indeed protect them against infection with influenza viruses (Stone, 1948a, b; Cairns, 1951). However, the blocking or destructive effect exerted by interfering viruses is less pronounced than that of bacterial filtrates. Ultraviolet-irradiated virus, while capable of destroying receptors, can interfere even when inoculated after the dose of infecting virus. This and other lines of evidence produced by Henle and co-workers (1947) strongly suggest that ultraviolet-irradiated virus retains the ability to exert effects on the host cells far more profound than those due to virus-receptor union alone. Moreover, Isaacs and Edney (1950a, b) have shown that heat-inactivated virus interferes despite its loss of receptor-destroying activity. They also found that interference by heat-inactivated virus does not prevent active virus from destroying receptors or from gaining entrance into cells. It has also been shown that receptor destruction plays no role in the interference between active influenza and equine encephalomyelitis viruses (Schlesinger, 1951).

It is probable, therefore, that interference phenomena in which influenza viruses are involved are due to disturbance of some deep-seated link in the infectious cycle. The phenomenon of auto-interference (von Magnus, 1951), related observations in mouse brain (Schlesinger, 1950), and the dramatic effects of homologous irradiated virus in arresting a growth cycle already in progress (Henle, Henle and Rosenberg, 1947; Henle and Rosenberg, 1949), all point in the direction of competition for cellular constituents which are available in limited supply. What these hypothetical constituents are and at which step in the infectious cycle they are essential, remains to be determined. Whatever information may emerge from future investigations of the interfering action of influenza virus may not be at all applicable to interference between other viruses.

RELATION OF INTERFERENCE TO NATURAL INFECTION

The conditions under which interference can be demonstrated experimentally are highly specialized with regard to suitable virus combinations, factors of dosage and timing, and opportunity to infect the same cells at the same time. It is very unlikely that these conditions would be often fulfilled in natural infection of man. In order to interfere, two viruses would have to compete with each other either at the portal of entry or in association with some cells which support their multiplication. In either case, the entire accessible cell population would have to be involved in the interfering infection. It is small wonder, therefore, that several pairs of viruses which are known to be capable of interfering in experimental hosts have nevertheless been isolated simultaneously from a patient. An example is the presence of Coxsackie and poliomyelitis viruses in the same stool from a human being (Rhodes et al., 1950; Curnen and Melnick, 1951); interference between these two viruses has been shown to occur in the mouse (Dalldorf, 1951).

RELATION TO CHEMICAL INHIBITION OF VIRAL GROWTH

All virus preparations thus far known to be effective as interfering agents have been inseparably associated with the viral particle. Therefore, it would be premature to postulate any relationship whatsoever between interference phenomena and the mechanisms by which certain chemically defined substances inhibit viral multiplication, e.g., certain bacterial polysaccharides (Ginsberg, Goebel and Horsfall, 1948), methionine analogues (Ackermann, 1951), or basic amino acids (Eaton, Magasanik, Perry and Karibian, 1951).

RELATION TO EPIDEMIOLOGIC PROBLEMS

Speculation on possible epidemiologic implications of interference are perhaps more promising. Thus, St. Louis and equine encephalomyelitis viruses interfere with each other in experimental hosts (Huang, 1943; Duffy, 1944) and it is conceivable that one of the factors limiting the spread of certain arthropod-borne viruses may have to do with their ability to interfere with each other in the arthropod vector or in some intermediate host. Such a possibility is suggested by the finding, under experimental conditions, of interference between dengue and yellow fever viruses in their common vector, *Aedes aegypti* (see chapter on Dengue). It is noteworthy that two diseases so similar in their epidemiologic character have rarely, if ever, been endemic in the same region at the same time.

REFERENCES

Ackermann, W. W., 1951, The role of *l*-methionine in virus propagation. J. Exp. Med., *93*, 337-343.

Anderson, K., 1942, Dual virus infection of single cells. Am. J. Path., *18*, 577-583.

Andrewes, C. H., 1942, Interference by one virus with the growth of another in tissue-culture. Brit. J. Exp. Path., *23*, 214-220.

Burnet, F. M., and Lind, P. E., 1951, A genetic approach to variation in influenza viruses. 3. Recombination of characters in influenza virus strains used in mixed infections. 4. Recombination of characters between the influenza virus A strain NWS and strains of different serological subtypes. J. Gen. Microbiol., *5*, 59-66; 67-82.

Cairns, H. J. F., 1951, Protection by receptor-destroying enzyme against infection with a neurotropic variant of influenza virus. Nature, *168*, 335.

Curnen, E. C., and Melnick, J. L., 1951, Poliomyelitis and Coxsackie viruses in paralytic poliomyelitis. Pediatrics, *8*, 237-248.

Dalldorf, G., 1951, The sparing effect of Coxsackie virus infection on experimental poliomyelitis. J. Exp. Med., *94*, 65-71.

Delbrück, M., Editor, Viruses 1950. Cal. Inst. of Technology, Pasadena, Calif.

Doerr, R., and Seidenberg, S., 1937, Die Konkurrenz von Virusinfektionen im Zentralnervensystem (Phänomen von Fl. Magrassi). Z. Hyg. u. Infektionskr., *119*, 135-165.

Duffy, C. E., 1944, Interference between St. Louis encephalitis virus and equine encephalomyelitis virus (Western type) in the chick embryo. Science, *99*, 517-518.

Eaton, M. D., Magasanik, B., Perry, M. E., and Karibian, D., 1951, Inhibition of influenza and mumps viruses in tissue culture by basic amino acids. Proc. Soc. Exp. Biol. and Med., *77*, 505-508.

Findlay, G. M., and Howard, E. M., 1950, Virus exaltation. Brit. J. Exp. Path., *31*, 45-50.

Findlay, G. M., and MacCallum, F. O., 1937, An interference phenomenon in relation to yellow fever and other viruses. J. Path. and Bact., *44*, 405-424.

Gard, S., 1944, Tissue immunity in mouse poliomyelitis. Acta Med. Scand., *119*, 27-46.

Ginder, D. R., and Friedewald, W. F., 1951, Effect of Semliki Forest virus on rabbit fibroma. Proc. Soc. Exp. Biol. and Med., *77*, 272-276.

Ginsberg, H. S., Goebel, W. F., and Horsfall, F. L., Jr., 1948, The inhibitory effect of polysaccharide on mumps virus multiplication. J. Exp. Med., *87*, 385-410.

Henle, G., and Henle, W., 1946, Studies on the toxicity of influenza viruses. I. The effect of intracerebral injection of influenza viruses. J. Exp. Med., *84*, 623-637.

Henle, W., 1949, Studies on host-virus interactions in the chick embryo-influenza virus system. II. The propagation of virus in conjunction with the host cells. J. Exp. Med., *90*, 13-22.

Henle, W., 1950, Interference phenomena between animal viruses: A review. J. Immunol., *64*, 203-236.

Henle, W., and Henle, G., 1943, Interference of inactive virus with the propagation of virus of influenza. Science, *98*, 87-89.

Henle, W., and Henle, G., 1945, Interference between inactive and active viruses of influenza. III. Cross-interference between various related and unrelated viruses. Am. J. Med. Sci., *210*, 362-369.

Henle, W., and Henle, G., 1949, Studies on host-virus interactions in the chick embryo-influenza virus system. III. Development of infectivity, hemagglutination, and complement fixation activities during the first infectious cycle. J. Exp. Med., *90*, 23-37.

Henle, W., Henle, G., and Kirber, M. W., 1947, Interference between inactive and active viruses of influenza. V. Effect of irradiated virus on the host cells. Am. J. Med. Sci., *214*, 529-541.

Henle, W., Henle, G., and Rosenberg, E. B., 1947, The demonstration of one-step growth curves of influenza viruses through the blocking effect of irradiated virus on further infection. J. Exp. Med., *86*, 423-437.

Henle, W., and Rosenberg, E. B., 1949, One-step growth curves of various strains of influenza A and B viruses and their inhibition by inactivated virus of the homologous type. J. Exp. Med., *89*, 279-285.

Hoskins, M., 1935, A protective action of neurotropic against viscerotropic yellow fever virus in Macacus Rhesus. Am. J. Trop. Med., *15*, 675-680.

Hoyle, L., 1948, The growth cycle of influenza virus A. A study of the relations between virus, soluble antigen and host cell in fertile eggs inoculated with influenza virus. Brit. J. Exp. Path., *29*, 390-399.

Huang, C. H., 1943, Titration of St. Louis encephalitis virus and Jungeblut-Sanders mouse virus in tissue culture. Proc. Soc. Exp. Biol. and Med., *54*, 158-160.

Isaacs, A., and Edney, M., 1950a, Interference between inactive and active influenza viruses in the chick embryo. I. Quantitative aspects of interference. II. The site of interference. Australian J. Exp. Biol. and Med. Sci., *28*, 219-230; 231-238.

Isaacs, A., and Edney, M., 1950b, Interference between inactive and active influenza viruses in the chick embryo. IV. The early stages of virus multiplication and interference. Australian J. Exp. Biol. and Med. Sci., *28*, 635-645.

Lennette, E. H., and Koprowski, H., 1946, Interference between viruses in tissue culture. J. Exp. Med., *83*, 195-219.

Lépine, P., and Marcenac, F., 1948, Exaltation de la virulence du virus d'Aujesky par association avec le virus herpétique. Ann. Inst. Past., *75*, 192-194.

von Magnus, P., 1947, Studies on interference in experimental influenza. I. Biological observations. Arkiv Kemi, Miner. och Geol., *24B*, No. 7.

von Magnus, P., 1951, Propagation of the PR8 strain of influenza A virus in chick embryos. II. The formation of "incomplete" virus following inoculation of large doses of seed virus. Acta Path. et Microbiol. Scand., *28*, 278-293.

Rhodes, A. J., Clark, E. M., Knowles, D. S., Shimada, F. S., Ritchie, R. C., Donohue, W. L., Armstrong, M. P., Wilson, F. H., McLean, W. J., and Silverthorne, N., 1950, Studies on Poliomyelitis in Ontario. III. Further observations on the association of Coxsackie and poliomyelitis viruses. Canad. J. Pub. Health, *41*, 183-188.

Schlesinger, R. W., 1949, The mechanism of active cerebral immunity to equine encephalomyelitis virus. II. The local antigenic booster effect of the challenge inoculum. J. Exp. Med., *89*, 507-527.

Schlesinger, R. W., 1950, Incomplete growth cycle of influenza virus in mouse brain. Proc. Soc. Exp. Biol. and Med., *74*, 541-548.

Schlesinger, R. W., 1951, Studies on interference between influenza and equine encephalomyelitis viruses. Arch. für die ges. Virusforschung, *4*, 501-517.

Schlesinger, R. W., and Frankel, J. W., 1952, Adaptation of the "New Guinea B" strain of dengue virus to suckling and to adult Swiss mice. A study in viral variation. Am. J. Trop. Med. and Hyg., *1*, 66-77.

Schlesinger, R. W., Olitsky, P. K., and Morgan, I. M.,

1943, Observations on acquired cellular resistance to equine encephalomyelitis virus. Proc. Soc. Exp. Biol. and Med., *54*, 272-273.

Schlesinger, R. W., Olitsky, P. K., and Morgan, I. M., 1944, Induced resistance of the central nervous system to experimental infection with equine encephalomyelitis virus. III. Abortive infection with Western virus and subsequent interference with the action of heterologous viruses. J. Exp. Med., *80*, 197-211.

Stone, J. D., 1948a, Prevention of virus infection with enzyme of *V. cholerae*. I. Studies with viruses of mumps-influenza group in chick embryos. Australian J. Exp. Biol. and Med. Sci., *26*, 49-64.

Stone, J. D., 1948b, Prevention of virus infection with enzyme of *V. cholerae*. II. Studies with Influenza virus in mice. Australian J. Exp. Biol. and Med. Sci., *26*, 287-298.

Sugg, J. Y., 1951, Further studies on serial passage of a mixture of influenza viruses in embryonated eggs. Proc. Soc. Exp. Biol. and Med., *76*, 199-202.

Sugg, J. Y., and Magill, T. P., 1948, The serial passage of mixtures of different strains of influenza virus in embryonated eggs and in mice. J. Bact., *56*, 201-206.

Syverton, J. T., and Berry, G. P., 1947a, Multiple virus infection of single host cells. J. Exp. Med., *86*, 145-152.

Syverton, J. T., and Berry, G. P., 1947b, The superinfection of the rabbit papilloma (Shope) by extraneous viruses. J. Exp. Med., *86*, 131-144.

Theiler, M., 1951, *in* Yellow Fever, G. K. Strode, Editor, McGraw-Hill Book Company, Inc., 39-136.

Vilches, A., and Hirst, G. K., 1947, Interference between neurotropic and other unrelated viruses. J. Immunol., *57*, 125-140.

Wallace, J. M., 1950, Immunological properties of plant viruses, *in* Viruses 1950, M. Delbrück, Editor, Cal. Inst. of Technology, 93-98.

Ziegler, J. E., Jr., and Horsfall, F. L., Jr., 1944, Interference between the influenza viruses. I. The effect of active virus upon the multiplication of influenza viruses in the chick embryo. J. Exp. Med., *79*, 361-377.

Ziegler, J. E., Jr., Lavin, G. I., and Horsfall, F. L., Jr., 1944, Interference between the influenza viruses. II. The effect of virus rendered non-infective by ultraviolet radiation upon the multiplication of influenza viruses in the chick embryo. J. Exp. Med., *79*, 379-400.

ALBERT B. SABIN, M.D., FRANK L. HORSFALL, JR., M.D., KARL F. MEYER, M.D., THOMAS F. McNAIR SCOTT, M.D., AND JOHN C. SNYDER, M.D.

The Children's Hospital Research Foundation, University of Cincinnati ; The Rockefeller Institute for Medical Research ; George Williams Hooper Foundation for Medical Research, University of California ; The Children's Hospital of Philadelphia, University of Pennsylvania ; Harvard University, School of Public Health

9

Diagnosis of Viral and Rickettsial Infections

INTRODUCTION

The various clinical manifestations of infection with viral and rickettsial agents and the different procedures by which each of these infections can be identified are described in detail in other chapters. However, very few maladies of viral or rickettsial etiology possess sufficiently distinctive clinical patterns to permit the physican to make an etiologic diagnosis with any degree of certainty. In most instances, the illness is of such a character that any one of a number of viral, rickettsial or other infectious agents may be etiologically involved.

An etiologic diagnosis can be established only by laboratory methods, but the physician should be able to tell the laboratory worker which disease or diseases are suspected. Accordingly, it is important to know which viral or rickettsial agents to suspect in the presence of certain clinical pictures, whether or not laboratory procedures are available for making an etiologic diagnosis. Furthermore, it is desirable to know whether these procedures are simple enough for routine performance, or whether they are so complex, costly and time-consuming that they would be justified only for research purposes. Table 11 lists the virus dis-

eases for which a completely equipped virus laboratory may offer diagnostic service, as well as the tests and the specimens which are required for this purpose. Table 12 lists the virus diseases for which diagnostic tests are either not practicable or not available as yet. All known rickettsial infections can be diagnosed by serologic methods, and the procedures of choice and diagnostic criteria are listed in Table 13.

Physicians should be aware of the evidence by which a given agent, or serologic response to it, may be etiologically related to a clinical syndrome. An etiologic diagnosis generally can be established by: (a) recovery and identification of the infectious agent; (b) demonstration of an antibody response bearing a definite time relationship to the clinical syndrome under investigation; and occasionally (c) the identification of a specific antigen (e.g., the complement-fixing antigen in the vesicles or crusts of variola or vaccinia) or morphologic structure in affected tissues (e.g., the cytoplasmic inclusions of trachoma and inclusion blennorrhea; Negri bodies in rabies). It is important to remember, however, that while these procedures establish the existence of a given infection at a given time, the actual

172

TABLE 11. VIRUS DISEASES FOR WHICH SIMPLE, SPECIFIC DIAGNOSTIC
LABORATORY PROCEDURES ARE AVAILABLE

DISEASE	SPECIMENS REQUIRED	PROCEDURES OF CHOICE
1. Influenza	Acute and convalescent serum	H-I; C-F
2. Psittacosis-ornithosis	Acute and convalescent serum	C-F*
3. Lymphogranuloma venereum	Acute and convalescent serum	C-F*
4. Trachoma	Conjunctival scrapings	Stained smear
5. Inclusion blennorrhea	Conjunctival scrapings	Stained smear
6. Variola	Contents of vesicle, pustule, or scab	(a) Use as antigen for C-F
		(b) Recover virus for identification*
7. Vaccinia	As for variola	As for variola*
8. Herpes simplex	(a) Acute and convalescent serum	(a) Neut.; C-F
	(b) Contents of vesicle	(b) Virus isolation*
9. Molluscum contagiosum	Contents of nodule	Microscopic examination
10. Yellow fever	Acute and convalescent serum	Neut.; C-F?
11. Dengue	Acute and convalescent serum	C-F; Neut.
12. Rift Valley fever	Acute and convalescent serum	C-F; Neut.*
13. Colorado tick fever	Acute and convalescent serum	C-F
14. Lymphocytic choriomeningitis	Acute and convalescent serum	C-F; Neut.
15. Mumps	Acute and convalescent serum	C-F; H-I
16. Rabies	(a) Film of brain tissue	(a) Stained smear
	(b) Brain tissue in fixative	(b) Histologic section
	(c) Brain tissue frozen or in 50% glycerol	(c) Virus isolation*
17. Arthropod-borne encephalitides:		
St. Louis†		
Western equine†	Acute	
Eastern equine	and	
Japanese B†	convalescent	C-F*
Venezuelan	serum	
Russian spring-summer		
Louping ill		

C-F = complement fixation; H-I = hemagglutination-inhibition; Neut. = neutralization.
* Recommendations for virus isolation are limited to special circumstances mentioned in text.
† Infection due to these viruses can also be diagnosed by hemagglutination-inhibition tests.

etiologic relationship of the infection to a clinical syndrome in an individual patient must frequently be based on other considerations. For example, some viruses can be recovered from the body for weeks or years after they have produced a clinically apparent or inapparent infection. Thus, the mere recovery of poliomyelitis virus from the stools or herpes simplex virus from the mouth or the throat during the course of an obscure illness could not be taken as evidence that these viruses were responsible for the disease. If the unrelated, clinically apparent disease occurs a sufficiently short time after infection with these viruses, it might even be possible to demonstrate a rising antibody titer. The point is that, together with recovery of virus and rising antibody titer, one must have a clinical pattern which repeated studies have shown to be compatible with the particular virus isolated. Another difficulty is encountered when two different viruses are either fellow travelers or are being disseminated at the same time, each possessing the capacity to give rise to either inapparent infection or recognizable symptoms. Thus, poliomyelitis virus is often disseminated in a community during an epidemic of mosquito-transmitted encephalitis. It is known that a considerable proportion of the population develops antibodies for the encephalitis viruses without exhibiting any clinical signs of infection. It is also known that during the same period there occur cases of the aseptic-meningitis syndrome due to infection with poliomyelitis virus. Thus, it is possible during such a period for a patient to have aseptic meningitis due to poliomyelitis virus and an inapparent infection with encephalitis virus.

TABLE 12. VIRUS DISEASES FOR WHICH ROUTINE SPECIFIC DIAGNOSTIC PROCEDURES
ARE NOT AVAILABLE OR PRACTICAL

GROUP	DISEASES
Viruses not available for laboratory procedures	Measles, varicella, rubella, exanthem subitum, primary atypical pneumonia,* common cold, undifferentiated respiratory disease, infectious hepatitis, phlebotomus (pappataci, sandfly) fever, herpes zoster, verrucae
Procedures available but too costly or cumbersome for routine use	Poliomyelitis
Etiologic diagnosis of clinical manifestations still a research problem	Infections due to Coxsackie viruses (herpangina, epidemic pleurodynia, etc.) Infections due to encephalomyocarditis virus Infections due to West Nile, California, Semliki Forest, Bwamba and various other viruses recovered in certain regions from mosquitoes Epidemic keratoconjunctivitis
Special problems only occasionally encountered as a result of exposure to viruses in laboratory or field	Infection due to Newcastle disease of fowl Infection due to foot and mouth disease of cattle Infection due to vesicular stomatitis of cattle and horses Infection due to B virus of monkeys Infection due to virus of ovine pustular dermatitis Infection due to virus of infectious anemia of horses Infection due to virus of cowpox

* Nonspecific procedures of cold hemagglutination and streptococcus MG agglutination can aid diagnosis of primary atypical pneumonia.

In the absence of suitable tests for infection with poliomyelitis virus, the serologic tests would indicate only infection with the encephalitis virus.

Another diagnostic problem is exemplified by the dual infection of patients with poliomyelitis virus and a Coxsackie virus. Thus, it is possible to recover a Coxsackie virus from some patients with either paralytic or nonparalytic poliomyelitis and to demonstrate antibody development or increase in antibody titer indicative of current infection. In many such cases, poliomyelitis virus can also be recovered, or antibody development in surviving patients is demonstrable. Since the Coxsackie viruses do not produce the same type of lesions in experimental animals as do the poliomyelitis viruses, and since there has been no unequivocal recovery of the Coxsackie viruses from the central nervous system or cerebrospinal fluid of human beings, there is every reason to regard the clinical manifestations of paralysis or involvement of the central nervous system without paralysis in these patients as having been caused by the poliomyelitis viruses, and the Coxsackie viruses as fellow travelers unrelated to the clinical syndrome under investigation. Because procedures for virus recovery and serologic tests for the poliomyelitis viruses are more laborious and less sensitive than those for the Coxsackie viruses, there are also examples of clinically diagnosed paralytic or nonparalytic poliomyelitis in which only infection with a Coxsackie virus has been demonstrated. This is mentioned here to illustrate the circumstances under which recovery of a virus associated with serologic evidence of current infection, cannot by itself constitute evidence that the demonstrated infection was responsible for the clinically apparent syndrome.

Generally speaking, virus recovery is too laborious and time-consuming a procedure for routine diagnostic purposes. However, there are occasions when it is either the only way, or the most rapid way, to identify an etiologic agent. Thus, vaccinia cannot be differentiated from variola by serologic methods, and when a differential diagnosis is between generalized vaccinia

TABLE 13. DIAGNOSIS OF RICKETTSIAL INFECTIONS BY SEROLOGIC TESTS

RICKETTSIAL INFECTION	COMPLEMENT-FIXATION (C-F) TESTS WITH RICKETTSIAL ANTIGENS					WEIL-FELIX (W-F) REACTION AGGLUTINATION OF PROTEUS			PROCEDURE OF CHOICE
	EPIDEMIC TYPHUS	MURINE TYPHUS	RMSF	Rpox	Q	OX19	OX2	OXK	
Typhus fever:									
Epidemic, louse-borne	++++	+ or 0	0	0	0	++++	0 or +	0	C-F and W-F
Recrudescent (Brill's disease)	++++	+ or 0	0	0	0	0[a]	0	0	C-F
Murine, flea-borne	+ or 0	++++	0	0	0	+++	0 or +	0	C-F
Rocky Mountain spotted fever (RMSF)[b]	0	0	++++	0	0	0 or ++++	++++ or 0	0	C-F and W-F
Rickettsialpox (Rpox)	0	0	++++	++++	0	0	0	0	C-F and W-F
Scrub typhus (Tsutsugamushi disease)[c]	0	0	0	0	0	0	0	++++	W-F
Q fever	0	0	0	0	++++	0	0	0	C-F

++++ = diagnostic rise in titer in serial serum specimens. See text.
+++ = rise in titer; confirmation needed from other evidence.
++ = slight rise in titer; not diagnostic.
(a) W-F may be + with OX19. See text.
(b) See chapter on Spotted-Fever Group for discussion of serologic tests in boutonneuse fever, South African tick-bite fever and North Queensland tick typhus.
(c) Antigens of scrub typhus rickettsiae suitable for general use in C-F tests are not available.

and variola, the virus must be recovered and identified. When one cannot be certain whether an eruption is due to herpes simplex or herpes zoster (particularly in persons with a history of recurrent herpes simplex), recovery of herpes simplex virus from some of the vesicles can establish the diagnosis. When Negri bodies are absent or atypical in a case of suspected rabies, isolation and identification of the virus is the only way to establish a diagnosis. When one suspects a beginning epidemic of Venezuelan equine encephalitis or Rift Valley fever, the fastest way to identify the agent is by inoculating mice with blood obtained shortly after onset of illness: the mice succumb in 2 days, and a C-F antigen prepared from their tissues can be used to identify the virus. A developing epidemic of an arthropod-borne encephalitis is often ushered in by a fatal case, and recovery of virus from the brain by mouse inoculation is the most rapid way of identifying the causative agent. Whenever virus isolation is considered necessary for identification of the etiologic agent, the person who will do the laboratory work should be consulted before specimens are obtained or sent.

With the exceptions just noted, it may be seen in Tables 11 and 13 that serologic tests on specimens of serum collected during the acute phase of illness and in convalescence are most important in routine diagnosis of viral and rickettsial infections. The need for testing both specimens is obvious when one realizes that all of the viruses for which the tests are used can cause inapparent infection and be widely disseminated in a population. Unless one can demonstrate that antibody for an agent first appeared or significantly increased in titer during the course of the illness or convalescence, it is not possible to diagnose infection by serologic procedures. As a general rule, a fourfold increase in titer of antibody (when twofold serum dilutions are tested against constant amounts of antigen or virus) is regarded as evidence of current infection. The optimum times for drawing blood for

such tests are described in the subsequent sections. It is a good rule, however, to draw 20 ml. of blood as soon as the possibility of a viral or rickettsial infection comes under consideration. To avoid loss of cold hemagglutinins, the blood should be allowed to clot at room temperature and the serum separated before refrigeration. The serum is then stored in a refrigerator, a deep freeze or a dry-ice chest until the convalescent specimen is obtained; then, both are shipped to the laboratory at the same time. A physician must indicate the diseases for which diagnostic tests are desired.

Subsequent sections of the chapter deal briefly with the crucial clinical manifestations and epidemiologic circumstances which should lead a physician to suspect the viral and rickettsial diseases which can be diagnosed by laboratory procedures listed in Tables 11 and 13. When the clinical and epidemiologic pattern of an illness does not match that of any known viral or rickettsial infection, its investigation becomes a problem for research instead of routine diagnosis.

VIRUS DISEASES OF THE NERVOUS SYSTEM

The presence of nuchal-spinal rigidity or more specific signs pointing to involvement of the central nervous system (CNS) during the course of an ill-defined, acute febrile illness generally leads a physician to suspect viral infection of the nervous system, when the cerebrospinal fluid (CSF) does not exhibit the changes associated with bacterial infection. Under these conditions, however, a variety of agents other than viruses must be considered in differential diagnosis. For practical purposes it is helpful to use the cytologic and chemical changes in the CSF for diagnostic orientation. It is useful to regard the following as abnormal: leukocytes in excess of 10 per c.mm., protein in excess of 50 mg. per 100 ml., and sugar less than 50 mg. per 100 ml., provided that the blood sugar is at least 100 mg. per 100 ml. and that the analysis is performed on fresh or iced specimens.

Conditions Associated with Normal CSF. When the CSF remains normal in at least two examinations several days apart during the first week after onset of CNS signs, two known viruses need to be considered: rabies and poliomyelitis. Although pleocytosis may occur in rabies, the CSF is frequently normal, and the progressively severe clinical manifestations, including excitement, convulsions, delirium, diffuse muscle spasm affecting particularly those of deglutition, etc. (see chapter on Rabies), associated with a history of bite by a potentially rabid animal, lead one to suspect that diagnosis. Rabies should also be suspected in patients with ascending or bulbar paralysis when the CSF is normal and the patient dies. The diagnosis of human rabies can be established by the demonstration of Negri bodies in films or histologic sections of appropriate portions of the brain (see chapter on Rabies). Normal CSF may occur in poliomyelitis, but it is uncommon during the first week of illness. Toxic manifestations of various localized or systemic bacterial infections are most often responsible for signs of involvement of the CNS associated with normal CSF, and a physician should make a thorough search for such infections in sinuses, middle ears, intestines and urogenital tracts.

Conditions Associated with Low CSF Sugar. The only viral disease of the human nervous system in this category is lymphogranuloma venereum. The other CSF features are pleocytosis with as many as 4,000 leukocytes per c.mm. early in the disease and an increase in protein, ranging from 250 mg. per 100 ml. early in the disease to 3,570 mg. per 100 ml. during the later stages. During later stages of the disease when the pleocytosis and the protein are highest, the CSF sugar may be normal. Other clinical evidence of lymphogranuloma venereum may be minimal, and bacterial meningitis, particularly tuberculous or influenzal, enters into the differential diagnosis in the early stages. Lymphogranuloma venereum infection of the CNS may take the form of a severe meningo-encephalitis, which, untreated, may last for many weeks; the marked CSF changes can persist for several months after chemotherapy and clinical improvement. The Frei test may remain negative for several months after onset. C-F antibodies for "lygranum" antigen are present in the blood in high titer early after onset, and it may not be possible to demonstrate a fourfold increase in titer in subsequent specimens. A high titer of C-F antibody may provide only suggestive evidence that the CNS signs and symptoms are due to infection with a virus of the lymphogranuloma-venereum group. Since this virus is present in the CSF for several weeks after onset, the diagnosis can be made by recovering and identifying the virus. Intracerebral inoculation of the CSF in mice is the procedure of choice.

Conditions Associated with Pleocytosis and Normal (or Increased) CSF Sugar. When there are no organisms or localizing neurologic signs suggestive of brain abscess, epidural abscess, mastoiditis, etc., the differential diagnosis and the steps that can be taken to elucidate it by virologic procedures depend to a large extent on clinical manifestations.

A. DIFFERENTIAL DIAGNOSIS OF ASEPTIC-MENINGITIS SYNDROME. If the CNS signs and symptoms remain essentially those of an aseptic-meningitis syndrome, i.e., nuchal-spinal rigidity with or without hamstring spasm but without any significant motor disturbances, the following viruses enter into consideration as potential etiologic agents:

Poliomyelitis virus is probably the commonest cause of the aseptic-meningitis syndrome during the summer and the autumn and should not be forgotten during the other seasons of the year. A pleocytosis in excess of 1,500 cells would point away from poliomyelitis.

Mumps virus should be suspected, even in the absence of involvement of the salivary glands, particularly when there is a history of exposure or of a recent epidemic of mumps in the community. Although the number of leukocytes in the CSF is usually under 1,000 per c.mm., a pleocytosis of 1,500 to 4,000, predominantly mononuclear cells, can occur. The increase in protein is much smaller than that associated with lymphogranuloma venereum. Although virus can be recovered from the CSF in mumps meningitis, serologic procedures are preferable.

Lymphocytic choriomeningitis virus is not a common cause of the aseptic-meningitis syndrome and, as a rule, does not occur during the months of greatest prevalence of poliomyelitis. The index of suspicion should be particularly high in persons living in rodent-infested houses. The C-F test on serum obtained during the acute phase and about 3 weeks after onset is recommended as the diagnostic test of choice. Since neutralizing antibodies appear later than the C-F antibodies in this infection, it may be possible to establish the diagnosis by means of the neutralization test on serum specimens obtained early in convalescence and about 6 weeks after onset.

Herpes Simplex Virus. There are no special clues for suspecting this virus as a cause of CNS infection, and only routine serologic tests are likely to pick up the occasional case of aseptic meningitis which may be caused by it. Either C-F or neutralization tests on acute and convalescent serum specimens are recommended, and the criteria for diagnosis are discussed in a subsequent section of the chapter.

Arthropod-borne encephalitis viruses receive special consideration in cases of aseptic meningitis which occur simultaneously with typical cases of encephalitis due to these agents. Reference has already been made to the diagnostic problem which arises when an arthropod-borne encephalitis virus and poliomyelitis virus are being disseminated at the same time. Until simple diagnostic tests become available for poliomyelitis virus, the role of the arthropod-borne encephalitis viruses in the causation of the aseptic-meningitis syndrome will remain obscure.

Other Viruses. Herpes zoster and infectious mononucleosis may occasionally be associated with aseptic meningitis. The etiologic relation of the Coxsackie viruses to the aseptic-meningitis syndrome is still under investigation. Since there is as yet no simple test to rule out poliomyelitis infection in a patient, one cannot be certain that a simultaneous readily detectable infection with a Coxsackie virus was responsible for the aseptic-meningitis syndrome.

Nonviral Agents. Leptospira may occasionally give rise to the aseptic-meningitis syndrome without the associated nephritis or hepatitis. A history of unusual association with potentially infected rodents, dogs, hogs and cattle, or water contaminated by them, should increase suspicion of this etiologic agent. The association of a maculopapular eruption with an aseptic-meningitis syndrome, as in swineherd's disease, should also lead to the suspicion of a leptospira.

B. DIFFERENTIAL DIAGNOSIS OF MORE EXTENSIVE CNS MANIFESTATIONS. When clinical manifestations point to more extensive involvement of the CNS than occurs in the aseptic-meningitis syndrome, and the CSF exhibits the changes mentioned above, viruses of the following diseases need consideration: poliomyelitis, the arthropodborne encephalitides, rabies and herpes simplex. The capacity of the viruses of mumps and lymphocytic choriomeningitis to be the direct cause of CNS manifestations more severe than those of the asepticmeningitis syndrome is open to question. Poliomyelitis virus receives primary consideration when the first CNS signs are those of varying degrees of flaccid paralysis associated with absent or markedly diminished deep tendon reflexes, pointing to involvement of motor neurons in the spinal cord, the medulla or the midbrain. Under exceptional circumstances, rabies and some of the arthropod-borne viruses may also exert their major effect on various lower motor neurons. Patients with severe attacks of poliomyelitis, especially those with bulbar involvement, may exhibit loss of consciousness, convulsions, muscle twitching, etc., which often lead a physician to confuse the condition with an encephalitis. In poliomyelitis, however, such disturbances are usually preceded by evidence of paralysis, while in viral encephalitis they are almost invariably the first to appear. Similarly, increased or normal deep tendon reflexes and a Babinski sign may be seen early in poliomyelitis, but if they do not disappear within a few days in the presence of marked weakness or paralysis, some other disease must be considered.

When the first signs point to involvement of portions of the CNS other than the lower motor neurons, differential diagnosis lies chiefly between encephalitis caused by the viruses mentioned above and the different forms of acute disseminated encephalomyelitis: the postvaccinal (rabies, vaccinia), postinfectious (measles, varicella, rubella, mumps, etc.) and the beginning stages of multiple sclerosis, neuromyelitis optica, etc. The important clinical signs in this category are psychic disturbances, disorientation, disturbances of speech not related to paralysis of any muscles required for speech, muscle twitching, convulsions, weakness of certain muscle groups associated with persistent increased or normal deep tendon reflexes, persistent Babinski sign, extensive spasticity of muscles other than those of the neck, spine and hamstrings, and depressed sensorium ranging from deep lethargy to coma. The clinical distinction between acute, febrile encephalomyelitis due to the known viruses and that caused by noninfectious or other as yet unknown mechanisms is often difficult and must depend to a large extent on history and course of illness. Since the known viruses attack primarily the gray matter, clinical signs pointing to early predominant involvement of the tracts are more in favor of the postinfectious and other demyelinating maladies. Furthermore, the viral encephalitides are characterized by a

relatively brief course. There is either a fatal outcome within 2 weeks or defervescence within 7 to 14 days and, as a rule, rapid disappearance of even the most severe clinical manifestations. Occasional sequelae are more likely to occur in infants, and atrophy of the shoulder girdle muscles is common in Russian Spring-Summer encephalitis. Under natural conditions, the potential etiologic relationship of the known arthropod-borne viruses to a case of encephalitis is further restricted by their limited geographic distribution and seasonal activity (see chapter on Viral Encephalitides). Should any one of these viruses migrate beyond its usual geographic distribution, its recognition and identification would become a problem for research instead of routine diagnosis. Herpes simplex virus, which is world-wide in distribution and not restricted by season, has provided no special clinical clues for its recognition in the few cases of encephalitis reported thus far on the basis of postmortem studies.

Routine diagnostic tests are not yet available for poliomyelitis, and encephalitis due to the viruses of rabies and herpes simplex has thus far been diagnosed only at necropsy. Serologic tests for herpes simplex virus, however, can be applied to serum of a patient surviving encephalitis caused by it, provided that such an infection is suspected. The most important diagnostic service which the virus laboratory can render in this field is to establish whether or not one of the arthropod-borne encephalitis viruses was responsible. Satisfactory C-F tests are now available for this whole group, and hemagglutination-inhibition tests can be used for some of the viruses. Inapparent infection is very common with this group of viruses, and the mere presence of antibodies against one of them in a patient with acute CNS disease does not constitute evidence that the clinical syndrome was caused by that virus. An etiologic diagnosis of encephalitis is possible only when antibody can be shown to appear or increase in titer at least fourfold during the illness or within a short time thereafter. The necessary rise in titer may occur at somewhat different times in different virus infections and in different individuals with the same virus infection. For routine purposes it is advisable to obtain the first serum specimen as early as possible in the acute phase of illness and the second specimen 2 weeks after onset; if antibody has either failed to appear or to increase fourfold in titer, another specimen should be tested 5 weeks after onset. When it is important to establish as quickly as possible the etiology of a developing epidemic of encephalitis, the interval between specimens may be only a few days, since diagnostic increases in antibody can occur in some patients within 7 to 10 days after onset of illness. Special care must be exercised in conducting and interpreting C-F tests for Japanese B encephalitis virus in areas where dengue, yellow fever, West Nile fever, or St. Louis encephalitis are also prevalent, because of group-specific C-F antigens shared by these viruses. Thus a fourfold or greater rise in C-F antibodies for Japanese B virus without concomitant development of neutralizing antibodies would indicate that the serologic response was not caused by Japanese B virus but by a related virus.

Although neutralizing antibodies, sometimes in high titer, are usually present at the time of death, diagnosis as a rule cannot be established by the C-F test. In fatal cases, pathologic examination of the brain can only indicate whether the character and the distribution of lesions are those of viral encephalitis, poliomyelitis, demyelinating disease or infectious polyneuritis; recovery of the virus is necessary to identify the causative agent.

SYSTEMIC VIRUS INFECTIONS

An acute, febrile illness, which cannot be readily identified with some established bacterial, protozoal, mycotic or rickettsial etiology receives consideration as a potential virus infection. Since, unfortunately, there exist no signs or general tests by which viral infections can be identified as a group, it becomes necessary to determine which of the established viral infections come closest in clinical and epidemiologic pattern to the malady under investigation. Maladies with special signs referable to the respiratory tract, skin and mucous membranes, eyes and nervous system are analyzed separately. There remain seven other viral infections without special localizing signs, most of them limited to certain geographic areas, for which virus laboratories can perform diagnostic tests. Systemic diseases of viral etiology for which diagnostic laboratory procedures are not available are listed in Table 12.

Yellow fever should be suspected in individuals who (a) live in the endemic zones of Africa and South America, (b) have returned from such areas during a period of 6, but not more than 10, days after the last potential exposure, or (c) live in the vicinity of the ports of call of airplanes coming from endemic areas. The disease is suspected when black vomit, melena and other evidences of hemorrhagic tendency, together with jaundice, albuminuria, oliguria or anuria appear several days after the onset of a febrile illness, characterized by slow pulse and leukopenia. In many instances these dramatic clinical manifestations are lacking; the disease is particularly mild in most of the Negro races of Africa. Neutralization tests on acute and convalescent serum specimens have been used to establish a diagnosis. Since antibodies develop very early in this disease, the first serum specimen should be obtained before the fourth day, and the second may be obtained during the first few days of convalescence or from 10 to 14 days after onset. The illness can be regarded as having been caused by the yellow fever virus when (a) antibodies are absent in the first specimen and present in the second, or (b) when both serum specimens have antibody, the second neutralizes the same amount of virus in at least a fourfold higher dilution than the first.

Dengue is suspected among newcomers in endemic areas, or during epidemics which occur as a result of importation of the virus in nonendemic areas which harbor *Aedes aegypti, A. albopictus,* or *A. scutellaris* mosquitoes. A morbilliform, scarlatiniform or petechial rash occurring during the course or at the end of a self-limited febrile, leukopenic illness of from 5 to 7 days' duration is characteristic of the disease. However, the illness can be shorter, milder, without rash and clinically not recognizable as dengue, particularly in persons exposed at different times to more than one type of dengue virus. No studies on the serologic diagnosis of naturally occurring cases of dengue have as yet been made. Observations on experimentally infected volunteers indicate that the C-F test, in which the immunologically distinct Hawaii and New Guinea "C" antigens are employed, can be used for diagnostic purposes. Since the C-F antibody may not reach its peak titer until 2 or 3 weeks after onset of illness, it may be possible to demonstrate the necessary fourfold increase in titer either between an acute-phase serum and one obtained 2 weeks after onset, or between a serum obtained early after defervescence and another taken 3 or 4 weeks after onset. Since the C-F antigen has group-specific components, an absolute diagnosis of the immunologic type of dengue virus responsible for the disease may be possible only by neutralization tests with the two serum specimens. If a disease that is suspected of being dengue on clinical and epidemiologic grounds yields negative C-F tests, the possibility that it may be caused by a hitherto unrecognized immunologic type of the virus must be considered. Because dengue shares a group-specific C-F antigen with the viruses of West Nile fever, yellow fever and Japanese B encephalitis, the C-F tests may need to be supplemented by neutralization tests for a definitive diagnosis in areas where the other viruses are also present.

Rift Valley fever should be suspected when a self-limited febrile illness of several days' duration characterized only by acute onset, leukopenia and malaise occurs in individuals with potential exposure to the virus either in the laboratory or in the enzootic regions of East Africa. The recent discovery of Rift Valley fever among cattle and human beings in South Africa in the vicinity of the Johannesburg airport stresses the circumstances under which this disease should be suspected in previously uninvolved areas. Diagnosis can be made most quickly by recovering the virus from a patient's blood during the febrile period. While this procedure is the method of choice for rapid identification of an epidemic or epizootic, serologic methods are preferable for routine diagnosis. Either neutralization or C-F tests can be used, and a diagnosis is possible only when antibody, which is either absent or present in low titer during the first few days after onset, appears or increases in titer during convalescence. Neutralizing antibody appears very rapidly and, for routine purposes, the convalescent serum specimen may be obtained as early as 4 days after defervescence.

Colorado tick fever should be suspected when a self-limited, febrile, nonexanthematous illness, characterized by two bouts of fever (each lasting 2 or 3 days with a fever-free interval of similar duration between them) and associated with leukopenia and malaise, occurs during the tick season in areas infested by the wood tick, *Dermacentor andersoni.* The diagnosis can be established by demonstrating the appearance of C-F antibodies in convalescent serum or a fourfold increase in titer. The first serum specimen can be obtained at any time during the febrile phase, while the second one should be collected approximately 3 weeks after onset.

Mumps. Ordinarily the diagnosis of mumps does not require laboratory confirmation. However, in cases of atypical involvement of the salivary glands and of pancreatitis or orchitis unassociated with obvious involvement of the salivary glands, and in the differential diagnosis of the aseptic-meningitis syndrome, a laboratory may be called upon to provide evidence of the etiologic role of mumps virus. For routine purposes, C-F or hemagglutination-inhibition tests on acute and convalescent serum specimens are most suitable, and a fourfold or greater rise in titer is required to establish that infection with mumps virus had occurred during the period under investigation. Most patients have C-F antibody within a week after onset of symptoms and practically all do at the end of 3 weeks.

Lymphocytic choriomeningitis virus, experimentally inoculated in volunteers, has produced a systemic illness without localizing signs, which may exhibit 2 or 3 febrile waves during a 3-week period. Since the reservoir of the virus is in rodents and dogs, it is clear that human beings are infected only under special conditions. Diagnostic procedures recommended for routine purposes are discussed in the section dealing with the differential diagnosis of the aseptic-meningitis syndrome.

Venezuelan equine encephalitis virus has produced many laboratory infections characterized by an influenzalike malady without localizing signs. It is not known whether a similar malady may occur in human beings residing in the enzootic regions of Central and South America. Diagnosis can be established by appropriate serologic tests on acute and convalescent serum specimens. Neutralizing antibody appears as early as 5 days after onset.

ACUTE INFECTIONS OF THE RESPIRATORY TRACT

The chief problem in the diagnosis of acute viral infections of the respiratory tract is to be able to designate the proper one from among a number of disease entities, many of which present similar manifestations. The major clinical categories are: (1) infections associated with pneumonia, of which a large majority can be identified with the aid of laboratory data; and (2) infections without pneumonia, of which only a small proportion can be iden-

tified satisfactorily even with the aid of laboratory data.

Infections associated with pneumonia (or pneumonitis) almost invariably produce cough and fever. Physical signs of pneumonia may be absent, minimal or definite. X-ray examination of the chest regularly shows evidence of pulmonary infiltration. Common features are relatively slow pulse rate, normal leukocyte count and differential pattern, and increased erythrocyte sedimentation rate. Recognized disease entities in this category are: (1) primary atypical pneumonia, (2) psittacosis or ornithosis, and (3) Q fever. Influenza is associated with pneumonia only in exceptional instances. None of these infections can be identified positively without laboratory data. Careful epidemiologic and clinical studies are important in each instance and may lead to a presumptive diagnosis which serves as a guide to laboratory investigations. In a thorough epidemiologic survey, infected birds or mammals should be sought. Cage pets (parrots, parakeets, canaries), barnyard fowl and birds (chickens, ducks, turkeys, pigeons) and mammals (cats, sheep, cattle, marsupials) are open to suspicion.

Laboratory procedures for establishing a diagnosis include the nonspecific serologic tests, viz., cold hemagglutination and streptococcus MG agglutination, for primary atypical pneumonia, and the specific complement-fixation tests for psittacosis and Q fever. Because some patients show an increase in titer either in the cold-hemagglutination or in the streptococcus-MG-agglutination tests but not in both, it is advisable to perform both tests in every case. Approximately 50 to 60 per cent of patients with primary atypical pneumonia show a definite increase in serum titer during convalescence as determined by one or the other test; unfortunately, negative results in both tests do not serve to exclude the diagnosis. Patients with other diseases, including psittacosis or Q fever, do not develop a significant increase in serum titer, as shown by either test, except in rare instances. There is as yet no generally accepted or satisfactory means by which the infectious agent or agents responsible for primary atypical pneumonia can be recovered from patients and identified.

The incidence of psittacosis (ornithosis) virus and Q fever rickettsiae as a cause of atypical pneumonia has not been established and can conceivably vary under different circumstances. While a good epidemiologic history can direct suspicion to one or the other of these infections, such a history is often lacking. In the absence of such a history, it is desirable that the sera of any patient with atypical pneumonia, which fail to show either a cold-hemagglutinin or streptococcus-MG-agglutinin response, be tested for C-F antibodies in the presence of psittacosis and Q fever antigens. A fourfold or greater rise in C-F titer during convalescence can be regarded as evidence of current infection with these agents; peak convalescent titers should be at least 1:32 for psittacosis and 1:80 for Q fever. At least two specimens of serum are required for all tests, and these should be collected in the manner described in the introduction to this chapter. The acute-phase serum should be obtained during the first 5 days of illness and the second specimen 2 weeks after onset. However, streptococcus MG agglutinins and Q fever C-F antibodies may not develop optimally until 4 and 3 weeks, respectively, after onset, and appropriate antibiotic therapy may delay the rise in titer of psittacosis antibodies. Accordingly, if a diagnosis cannot be made on the first two sera, a laboratory worker will probably request additional specimens. In fatal cases of atypical pneumonia, the etiologic agent may be identified only after its recovery from lung tissue obtained at necropsy. When a virus of the psittacosis (ornithosis) group is suspected, lung tissue may be sent to a laboratory either in the frozen state or in 50 per cent buffered glycerol.

Infections without pneumonia are commonly manifested by fever and malaise. Signs pointing to the respiratory tract may be slight or moderately severe. Clinical manifestations presented by this group of infectious processes are so variable as to make a brief appraisal of them misleading. In a large proportion of instances a definite disease entity cannot yet be identified, and frequently laboratory studies fail to yield data pointing to a specific diagnosis. The recognized entities in this category are: (1) influenza A, influenza B and influenza C; and (2) common cold. Several other syndromes are often unsatisfactorily designated as undifferentiated respiratory infections. Psittacosis (ornithosis), Rift Valley fever, Venezuelan equine encephalomyelitis, atypical forms of dengue, sandfly fever, abortive poliomyelitis, lymphocytic choriomeningitis and infectious hepatitis can exhibit clinical syndromes which may be mistaken for influenza.

Influenza A, influenza B or influenza C cannot be identified positively without adequate laboratory data. Critical epidemiologic and clinical study should lead to a presumptive diagnosis and indicate the desirability of laboratory investigation. Although cases of influenza A or B occur sporadically, most of them are seen during epidemics. Such epidemics may be of any dimension, i.e., small and localized or widespread. Common features in both diseases are abrupt onset, moderate fever, increased pulse rate, definite malaise, slight to mild upper respiratory symptoms, no physical or x-ray evidence of pneumonia, normal or subnormal leukocyte count, normal differential pattern, and increased erythrocyte sedimentation rate. Serologic procedures of choice are hemagglutination inhibition and CF. At least two specimens of serum are required: (1) acute-phase serum and (2) convalescent serum. Sera should be obtained shortly after onset and 2 weeks later. If the results are negative or inconclusive, a third specimen should be obtained 4 weeks after onset. A fourfold increase in antibody titer of the convalescent serum as compared with that of the acute-phase serum is significant.

The antibody titer of a single specimen of serum, however high, is of little diagnostic value. Persons who recently have been given influenza virus vaccine may show an antibody response which has no diagnostic import. Most patients with influenza A or B show a significant antibody response against the infecting agent. In the absence of such a response, diagnosis is doubtful. Patients with other diseases do not show an antibody response against either A or B virus.

Influenza A or B virus can be recovered from the upper respiratory tract, but not from the blood, of patients during the first few days of illness. If this is to be attempted, a near-by laboratory proficient in the study of viruses should be consulted before potentially infectious specimens are obtained. Adequate instructions regarding the type of specimens desired and their transportation can be obtained from the laboratory which is willing to undertake recovery and identification of the agent. Such investigations are in all cases research problems which require careful planning and the inoculation of experimental animals. Under no circumstances should infectious specimens be sent to a laboratory unaware of the problem at hand with a request for "virus studies."

Diagnosis of the common cold and of the various syndromes included in the large category of undifferentiated respiratory infections is based entirely on clinical manifestations. There are as yet no laboratory procedures which are of aid in identifying any of these conditions.

VIRAL DISEASES WITH SPECIAL EFFECT ON SKIN, MUCOUS MEMBRANES, GENITALIA AND EYES

Skin. Viral infections can produce the following manifestations in the skin: (a) generalized maculopapular, scarlatiniform or petechial eruptions as in measles, rubella, exanthem subitum, dengue, the early stages of smallpox, and occasionally also during the systemic phase of lymphogranuloma venereum; (b) generalized or localized vesicular or vesiculopustular eruptions as in smallpox, vaccinia, varicella, herpes zoster, herpes simplex, eczema herpeticum, eczema vaccinatum, lymphogranuloma venereum and, more rarely, under special circumstances, in cowpox, ovine pustular dermatitis (contagious ecthyma of sheep), foot-and-mouth disease, and B virus infections; (c) tumors as in molluscum contagiosum and warts (verrucae). Laboratory procedures for establishing an etiologic diagnosis are available for the following of the more common infections: herpes simplex, variola-vaccinia, lymphogranuloma venereum and molluscum contagiosum.

There are two main diagnostic problems relative to the virus of herpes simplex. The first one arises when herpes simplex virus forms vesicles along the cutaneous distribution of a nerve, especially on the face, and thus simulates herpes zoster. This problem can be resolved best by recovery and identification of herpes simplex virus, because it presents itself as a rule in individuals who have recurrent herpes and in whom no increase in antibody titer is demonstrable. The second problem must be faced when there is no clear history of exposure either to the virus of herpes simplex or that of vaccinia in patients with Kaposi's varicelliform dermatitis. A decision regarding this situation can be reached only by laboratory methods. A negative C-F test for vaccinia on the vesicle contents and the presence of multinucleated giant cells in stained scrapings from the base of a vesicle are compatible with a diagnosis of herpes simplex. However, an absolute diagnosis is possible only through recovery of virus or demonstration of increasing titer of antibody against it in a patient's serum.

Several diagnostic problems arise in relation to variola-vaccinia and varicella. Differentiation between generalized vaccinia or mild smallpox and varicella is not always easy on clinical grounds alone. A negative C-F test for vaccinia or smallpox on vesicle contents and the presence of multinucleated giant cells in a stained smear of material from the lesions favor the diagnosis of varicella. Differentiation between variola and vaccinia as the cause of a generalized vesiculopustular eruption, when the history is too obscure to permit a decision, can be made only through recovery of the virus and testing its behavior in rabbits and embryonated eggs (see chapter on Variola-Vaccinia).

When a scarlatiniform rash or an eruption similar to erythema multiforme is associated with a febrile illness, in which vesicular or ulcerative genital lesions and inguinal adenitis are prominent features, lymphogranuloma venereum should be suspected. Since the C-F test on the patient's serum becomes positive in high titer before the Frei test, and since the skin test may be more useful in differentiating LGV from psittacosis, both diagnostic procedures should be used.

Molluscum contagiosum should be suspected when multiple discrete nodules, usually pearly white and painless, averaging 2 mm. in diameter and limited to the epidermal layer of the skin, are found on the face, arms, legs, buttocks, genitalia and scalp, rarely in the mouth, and never on the soles and the palms. A small white core can often be seen at the top of each nodule. Diagnosis is established by finding typical molluscum bodies in the cheesy exudate that is obtained from a nodule. The expressed material is put on a glass slide, a drop of either brilliant cresyl blue (1:2,000 in saline) or Lugol's iodine is added, a coverslip is placed over it, and the preparation is examined under the microscope with the dry, high-power objective. The large, oval molluscum bodies (20 to 37 μ) stain a deep brown with Lugol's iodine and blue with brilliant cresyl blue. When material suitable for microscopic study cannot be expressed from a nodule, diagnosis can be established by finding molluscum bodies in histologic sections of an excised nodule.

Mucous Membranes. Mucous membranes of the mouth and the throat present distinct lesions in the following established viral infections: (1) measles (Koplik spots), (2) varicella and zoster (vesicles in mucosa of mouth, tongue, palate, pharynx), (3) herpangina due to a Coxsackie virus (minute vesicles or small punched-out ulcers surrounded by red areolas on the anterior pillars of the fauces, the pharynx and the palate), (4) herpes simplex (primary herpetic ginginvostomatitis), (5) variola-vaccinia (enanthem) and occasionally (6) in lymphogranuloma venereum (vesicles or ulcers on tongue and throat), foot-and-mouth disease (vesicles or ulcers on buccopharyngeal mucosa) and molluscum contagiosum. There are as yet no laboratory tests for measles, varicella and zoster, but their diagnosis seldom requires laboratory confirmation.

Herpangina should be suspected when a self-limited, febrile illness associated with sore throat, dysphagia and the lesions mentioned above occurs predominantly in children during the summertime. Although several different immunologic types of Coxsackie virus have been established as the cause of this disease, recovery of virus from the throat, its identification, and the demonstration of a rising titer of antibodies are still too laborious for routine purposes. Furthermore, since many children can be infected with a Coxsackie virus without exhibiting the syndrome of herpangina, recovery of virus and development of antibodies in an individual do not constitute absolute proof that a febrile illness with questionable mouth lesions was caused by the agent.

Primary infection with the virus of herpes simplex is the most common cause of stomatitis in children between 18 months and 3 years of age, and should be suspected in this and other age groups when a febrile illness is associated with red, swollen gums and a vesicular eruption turning to yellowish plaques on the mucous membranes of the oral cavity. It is uncommon for recurrent stomatitis to be of viral origin. Diagnosis of primary infection with the virus of herpes simplex can be established by complement-fixation or neutralization tests performed on sera obtained during the acute phase and approximately 3 weeks later. Appearance of antibody during convalescence or a significant increase in titer must be demonstrated.

Genitalia. The viruses of lymphogranuloma venereum, herpes simplex, inclusion blennorrhea, mumps, molluscum contagiosum and warts produce lesions in the genital organs. Primary lesions of lymphogranuloma venereum consist of vesicles or shallow ulcers involving the penis, the labia, the vagina and occasionally the urethra. Subsequent involvement of the lymphatics gives rise to the chronic, granulomatous inflammatory conditions of the genito-anorectal area and regional lymph nodes described in the chapter on Psittacosis-Lymphogranuloma Venereum Group. The C-F and the Frei tests are the diagnostic procedures of choice. The virus of herpes simplex is the cause of recurrent vesicles and small erosions on the penis, labia and vaginal mucous membrane. The cause of the recurrent infection can be established only by recovery and identification of the virus, since serologic methods fail to show a change in antibody titer. The virus of inclusion blennorrhea is an occasional cause of mild, nonbacterial urethritis and should be suspected, especially in fathers of children with neonatal inclusion conjunctivitis. This virus occurs in the uterine cervix as an inapparent infection. Diagnosis depends on demonstration of typical cytoplasmic inclusions in epithelial cells. Mumps virus may cause orchitis and oöphoritis, and confirmation of a diagnosis by serologic methods is desirable in patients who may have such involvement without obvious disease of the salivary glands. The virus of molluscum contagiosum can produce nodules on the penis and the vulva, which can be diagnosed in the same manner as those which occur elsewhere on the skin. Warts on the penis, the labia and the vulval orifice are of the same viral etiology as common warts elsewhere on the

skin; no diagnostic laboratory procedures are available.

Eyes. The viruses of trachoma, inclusion blennorrhea, herpes simplex, herpes zoster, epidemic keratoconjunctivitis and molluscum contagiosum produce lesions in the eyes. The eyes are also affected in the following systemic viral infections: smallpox (keratitis, iridocyclitis, hypopyon ulcers), measles (conjunctivitis), sandfly fever (marked injection of exposed ocular conjunctiva—Pick's sign), Newcastle disease (conjunctivitis) and occasionally varicella.

Trachoma and inclusion blennorrhea are considered together, because diagnosis in both involves the demonstration of indistinguishable cytoplasmic inclusions in epithelial cells. The differential diagnosis, therefore, depends on clinical considerations, which are fully discussed in the chapter on Trachoma and Inclusion Conjunctivitis. Infection with the virus of inclusion blennorrhea should be suspected in (a) newborn infants exhibiting a purulent conjunctivitis, particularly marked on the lower lid, which appears within 5 to 12 days after birth; in (b) gynecologists, obstetricians and bathers in certain swimming pools (swimming-pool conjunctivitis), who exhibit nonbacterial, acute, follicular conjunctivitis, particularly marked on the lower lid. Trachoma does not occur in the newborn during the first 2 weeks. Trachoma in adults differs from inclusion blennorrhea in forming follicles more extensively on the upper lid and giving rise to pannus and corneal scarring. Epithelial scrapings or contents of follicles, instead of exudate, should be used for preparation of smears which are fixed for 5 minutes in methyl alcohol and stained for 1 hour at 37° C. in diluted neutral Giemsa's stain. While the epithelial cytoplasmic inclusions are the same in both conditions, follicular material shows necrotic changes, e.g., cellular debris, pale-staining cells and macrophages full of cellular fragments, in trachoma but not in inclusion blennorrhea or other follicular diseases of the conjunctiva.

Herpes simplex virus can give rise to either palpebral conjunctivitis or keratoconjunctivitis, with or without fever and preauricular lymphadenitis. The palpebral conjunctivae are swollen and intensely congested with little or no purulent discharge. The cornea presents various patterns of erosions and ulcers. This virus should be particularly suspected when these manifestations are associated with the following: (1) preceding pyrexia, (2) herpetic vesicles on the lids, (3) absence of bacteria, (4) hyperesthesia of the eye, (5) rapid healing and (6) relapses or recurrences. Since the eyes are usually affected in recurrent infections with this virus, the infectious agent can be identified only after its isolation. Diagnosis of zoster ophthalmicus, resulting in scleritis, keratitis and iridocyclitis, cannot be confirmed by simple laboratory procedures. Clinical manifestations of epidemic keratoconjunctivitis are very similar to those resulting from infection with the virus of herpes simplex; results of investigation of outbreaks of this disease are still inconclusive. On rare occasions, lesions of molluscum contagiosum are found in the eyelids and may extend to involve the conjunctiva and the cornea. In some patients, the molluscum tumors are present only in the eyes, and the condition may be mistaken for trachoma. Diagnosis can be established by demonstrating molluscum bodies in material obtained from lesions.

RICKETTSIAL INFECTIONS

Fever, headache, rash, and contact with certain insects (or their excreta) are the common features which lead a physician to consider a diagnosis of typhus, Rocky Mountain spotted fever, boutonneuse fever, South African tick-bite fever, North Queensland tick typhus, rickettsialpox, or scrub typhus. The other important rickettsial disease of man, Q fever, does not produce a rash and may have no association with insects. Isolation of rickettsiae from patients by various procedures involving animals, insects, or chick embryos is a research problem. Diagnosis of the rickettsial infections of man is based upon clinical features, epidemiologic data and serologic reactions. If specific treatment is begun later than the seventh day of a rickettsial disease, no important delay in antibody development is likely, nor is the magnitude of the response reduced appreciably. When adequate treatment is given very early after onset, however, antibody response may be delayed and reduced to the extent that interpretation of serologic tests may be very difficult.

Epidemic Typhus Fever. This disease is characterized by exposure to infected human body lice (or their feces) from 10 to 14 days before onset, severe intractable headache, sustained high fever (40° C. or higher), and a diffuse macular or maculopapular rash which appears on the trunk from the fourth to the seventh day of illness and then spreads over the entire body except the face, the palms and the soles. During severe and widespread epidemics, diagnosis is usually made on the basis of the four characteristics just enumerated, without recourse to laboratory procedures. Where laboratory facilities can be utilized, the Weil-Felix test (agglutination of Proteus OX19) is the procedure of choice, either as a slide test (with careful controls to ensure specificity of the bacterial suspension) or as the standard tube reaction. The peak agglutinin response usually occurs at the end of the second week of illness. More than 95 per cent of patients with epidemic typhus develop agglutinins in their sera for OX19 in titers exceeding 1:160; values over 1:1,000 are frequently observed. Since normal persons, or those infected with *Proteus vulgaris*, may have agglutinins to OX19 in low titer, it is important to demonstrate that the titer found in the third week is 4 times greater than that found before the seventh day of illness. The C-F and rickettsial-agglutination tests, in which highly purified suspensions of epidemic typhus rickettsiae are used are more specific than the Weil-Felix test and should be used to distinguish epidemic louse-borne from murine flea-borne typhus fever. These tests are not usually available under conditions which predispose to louse infestation and epidemics of typhus. An eightfold or greater rise in C-F titer is usual (from the first week to the third week specimens); maximum titers of more than 1:320 are common. In the rickettsial-agglutination test titers above 1:200 are considered diagnostic.

Diagnosis of epidemic typhus in persons previously immunized may not be possible unless the complement-fixation and rickettsial-agglutination tests are applied, since the Weil-Felix reaction is often inconclusive after immunization. In vaccinated individuals, the C-F test may not differeniate between epidemic and murine typhus.

Brill's Disease (Recrudescent Typhus). This diagnosis is considered when fever and severe persistent headache occur in a person who has lived in a region where he might have had an attack of louse-borne typhus fever years before. A rash similar to that described for epidemic typhus may be observed, or there may be no rash. Brill's disease, unlike classic epidemic typhus, occurs in the absence of contact with infected lice or louse feces. The Weil-Felix test is usually negative (maximum titers less than 1:160) although positive reactions may be encountered occasionally. The procedure of choice is the C-F test in which highly purified epidemic typhus rickettsiae are used. Titers before the seventh day are usually less than 1:40 and rise rapidly by the twelfth day to at least 1:320; values exceeding 1:1,000 are common. When antibodies to murine typhus antigens are found, the titers are regularly lower by at least fourfold than those with epidemic typhus antigen. The rickettsial-agglutination test is also satisfactory. Rising titers with more than a fourfold change, or values in the third week in excess of 1:200 are diagnostic.

Murine, Flea-borne Typhus. This illness is suspected when a patient has fever, headache, and a history of contact, 10 to 12 days before onset, with places where rats

abound. A history of flea bites may not be elicited since some persons do not notice them; furthermore, infected flea feces may gain access to respiratory or conjunctival membranes as air-borne particles. The occurrence of a macular rash similar to that of epidemic typhus but less intense and shorter in duration is helpful but not essential for diagnosis. The laboratory procedure of choice is the C-F test in which suspensions of highly purified murine typhus rickettsiae are used as antigen. Titers before the seventh day are usually less than 1:10 and rise by the twelfth to the twentieth day to values in excess of 1:160. When antibodies to epidemic antigen also occur, the titers are regularly lower than the murine titers in unvaccinated persons. The Weil-Felix test is usually positive (maximum OX19 titers more than 1:160).

Since murine flea-borne typhus often occurs in the same areas as Rocky Mountain spotted fever, the C-F test is necessary to distinguish between the two infections; this cannot be done with the Weil-Felix reaction alone (see Table 13).

Rocky Mountain Spotted Fever. This diagnosis is suggested by sustained high fever, prostration, headache, early appearance of a maculopapular or frankly papular rash on the extremities, later over the entire body, and history of contact with ticks or tick excreta in infected areas a few days prior to onset. The laboratory procedure of choice is the C-F test with antigen derived from Rocky Mountain spotted fever rickettsiae. Serum specimens before the seventh day are usually negative or have an antibody titer less than 1:10. By the twentieth day titers are at least 1:80, and often higher. The Weil-Felix test is usually positive (> 1:160) with either OX19 or OX2, rarely with both.

There are three other diseases which belong to the spotted-fever group and are suspected in different geographic areas when a patient has fever, headache, rash and a history of exposure to ticks (or tick excreta) a few days before onset of illness. These are boutonneuse fever which has been recognized chiefly around the Mediterranean area, South African tick-bite fever in various parts of South Africa, and North Queensland tick typhus in Australia. The available serologic data are described in the chapter on the Spotted-Fever Group.

Sera from patients with Rocky Mountain spotted fever and rickettsialpox give cross reactions in complement-fixation tests. Any possible confusion between the two diseases is usually removed by consideration of epidemiologic features; furthermore, skin lesions in the two diseases are usually distinctive. The Weil-Felix reaction completes the separation if used in conjunction with C-F tests.

Rickettsialpox. A characteristic feature of this disease, as suggested by its name, is the occurrence of a small vesicle in the central area of some of the papules which are scattered rather sparsely over the trunk. The papules appear within the first week after the beginning of fever and moderate headache. In many instances an initial local lesion several millimeters in diameter develops at the site of the mite bite several days before the systemic illness is manifest; this initial lesion aids in distinguishing rickettsialpox from varicella, which must be considered in the differential diagnosis. Frequently, patients may not be aware of contact with mites, a fact which is established only by visits to their homes or places of employment after clinical findings have raised the suspicion of rickettsialpox. Laboratory procedures of choice are the C-F and the Weil-Felix tests, done concurrently. The C-F test shows at least a fourfold rise in antibody titer with both Rocky Mountain spotted fever and rickettsialpox antigens between first-week and third-week specimens, whereas the Weil-Felix titer with OX19, OX2 and OXK shows no change or at most only a twofold rise.

Scrub Typhus (Tsutsugamushi Disease). The distinctive features of this disease are fever, severe headache, transient macular rash primarily over the trunk, history of exposure to mites (chiggers) in endemic areas, and in about 50 per cent of the patients an initial eschar at the site of the mite bite. The laboratory procedure of choice is the Weil-Felix reaction with OXK. Titers rise from first-week values (usually less than 1:20) to third-week values of 1:160 or higher. Diagnosis depends on clinical and epidemiologic features as well as the Weil-Felix reaction, since relapsing fever (*Borrelia recurrentis* infection) may also induce a rise in titer to OXK.

Q Fever. This illness has been mentioned in the diagnosis of respiratory disease caused by viruses. Although Q fever may be transmitted by infected ticks or their excreta, there have been hundreds of cases in which transmission was attributed to contact with infected milk, hides, meat (cow, sheep, goat) or dust from contaminated dairies. The common features are fever, headache, cough and pneumonitis as revealed by roentgenograms. Unlike the other rickettsial diseases, there is no rash in Q fever. The infection may occur without x-ray evidence of pneumonitis and may assume other clinical forms. The laboratory procedure of choice is the C-F test. Titers in the first week are usually less than 1:10; by the third week values of 1:80 or higher are obtained. The Weil-Felix test is negative. Recovery of Q fever rickettsiae through the use of embryonated eggs or animals is hazardous to the laboratory staff and should not be undertaken except as a research procedure in a well-equipped isolation laboratory.

A. D. HERSHEY, ph.d., and J. BRONFENBRENNER, ph.d.

Carnegie Institution of Washington, and
Wake Forest College, The Bowman Gray School of Medicine

10

Bacterial Viruses: Bacteriophages

Bacteria are subject to viral infections similar to those observed in higher plants and animals. The presence of a virus is first recognized when signs of disease in bacterial cultures are noticed, the most obvious of which is dissolution or lysis of the bacterial cells. There is evidence that inapparent infections not resulting in lysis also occur, but the best known bacterial viruses destroy their host cells by lysis, because these have caught the attention of investigators. Because of the dramatic nature of lysis, bacterial viruses were named bacteriophages by d'Herelle (1917), who shares with Twort (1915) credit for their discovery. The name bacteriophage was not well chosen, since it calls attention to a relatively trivial property of these viruses, and away from important properties possessed by all viruses.

GENERAL PROPERTIES

The fundamental properties of bacterial viruses revealed by earlier studies can be summarized as follows:

The viruses multiply during growth and lysis of infected bacterial cultures, and can be propagated indefinitely through a series of cultures.

The viruses are small, pass through filters which hold back bacteria, and are not sedimented in ordinary centrifuges.

The number of infective viral particles in a lysate can be counted by allowing a portion of a highly diluted filtrate to act on a culture of susceptible bacteria spread on the surface of a nutrient agar plate. One thus counts plaques or clearings in the diffuse growth of bacteria on the agar surface, just as one counts bacterial colonies by plating on nutrient agar a highly diluted suspension of bacteria. The clearings, which result from the local growth and lytic action of the virus, arise from single viral particles in the filtrate, as shown by the proportionality between their number and the volume of lysate introduced into the Petri dish.

There are many types of bacterial virus which can be differentiated in various ways. First of all, a bacterial virus lysing bacteria of one genus does not ordinarily act on bacteria belonging to another, with the exception of some of the groups of intestinal bacteria of doubtful taxonomic standing. More interestingly, different strains of virus acting on the same bacterial species will usually be found to differ in the range of varieties of the related bacterial strains they attack. In general, a pure viral stock maintains its characteristics independently of the particular bacterial strain on which it is allowed to propagate, but genetic variation of a limited kind can readily be observed.

Bacterial viruses are extremely specific with respect to the bacterial strains on which they act. As a result of this specificity, most virus-sensitive bacterial species regularly give rise to virus-resistant variants, which grow out after the majority of the cells in an infected bacterial culture have been lysed. The resistance exhibited by these bacterial variants is often a stable hereditary characteristic and is highly specific, frequently being directed solely against the virus causing the primary lysis.

Bacterial viruses are inactivated by high temperatures, radiation, and various poisons. They are usually less susceptible to these agents than are vegetative bacteria, but more susceptible than bacterial spores. Different viruses show great and characteristic differences in stability.

Bacterial viruses are antigenic, giving rise in the tissues of experimental animals to specific neutralizing antibody of high titer. Their serologic specificity serves as an important means of classification. The viral antigens are characteristic of the virus, and are independent of those of the bacterial host. That is, antibacterial antibodies do not neutralize bacterial viruses, nor do the bacterial cells absorb virus-neutralizing antibody from antiviral sera.

References to the earlier literature and further information about bacterial viruses may be found in reviews by Adams (1950), Anderson (1949, 1950), Benzer et al. (1950), Bronfenbrenner (1928a, 1928b), Burnet (1934), Cohen (1949), Delbrück (1946a, 1946b), Fong (1949), Krueger (1936), and Wilson and Miles (1946). The one by Adams contains the only available summary of methods of studying bacterial viruses.

BIOLOGIC CLASSIFICATION

When several bacterial viruses acting on the same bacterial host are isolated from different natural sources, no two of them are likely to prove identical (Burnet, 1933a; Burnet and McKie, 1933). Usually they can be differentiated by serologic means or by analysis of host specificity, and on further examination numerous points of difference emerge. The differences focus attention on the questions: How do the many types of virus arise? To which of the differences should taxonomic significance be attached? There are two ways of tracing systematic relationships among viruses, namely, by experimental study of the evolution of new types and by correlating the properties of existing types. The first way is evidently more satisfying as far as it can be carried, but the second is easier and is a necessary adjunct to evolutionary studies. Both types of evidence will be cited in the following discussion.

It will be convenient to center this discussion about a group of bacterial viruses known as the T system, which has been thoroughly studied. The nucleus of the group consists of seven types called T1, T2, . . . T7, which were first described collectively by Demerec and Fano (1945). The property common to all members of the group is their ability to infect a particular strain of *Escherichia coli* known as B. The most obvious differences among them are the sizes of the clearings they form in bacterial cultures on agar. T1, T3, and T7 form large plaques, while T2, T4, T5, and T6 form small ones. These differences are of some taxonomic significance. As the following description of properties will show, the seven types of virus fall into four natural groups, namely, T1; T2, T4, T6; T3, T7; and T5. It is a reasonable inference that the members of any one of these groups share a comparatively recent common descent. The members of different groups, on the other hand, show no residue of common ancestry.

MORPHOLOGY AND SIZE

Perhaps the most unexpected recent finding concerning the bacterial viruses is their complexity of form revealed by the electronic microscope. Ruska (1941) and Luria and Anderson (1942) first described tadpole-shaped particles which were believed to be the virus. Luria, Delbrück and Anderson (1943) confirmed the finding of Luria and Anderson (1942) that different and characteristic images are obtained with different bacterial viruses. They also obtained a few micrographs of bacteria undergoing lysis, in which numerous, characteristically shaped particles emerging from the husk of a single bacterium were seen.

Luria, Williams and Backus (1951) have shown, by a precise method, that the num-

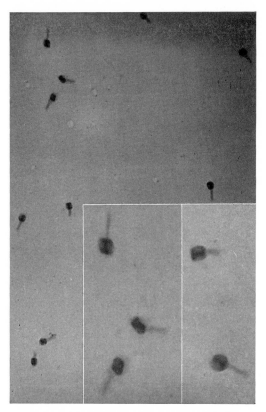

FIG. 25. Electron micrograph of the bacterial virus T2. $\times$ 20,400. The inserts show higher magnification. $\times$ 51,000. (S. E. Luria and T. F. Anderson, 1942, The identification and characterization of bacteriophages with the electron microscope. Proceedings National Academy Sciences, *28*, 127-130. Certain alterations have been made in order to combine these photographs in one plate.)

ber of plaque-forming particles in preparations of several phages is nearly the same as the number of visible particles. The same correlation had been made by Schlesinger (1933), but the importance of his observation was overlooked at the time.

These findings, together with numerous earlier measurements of size by physical

methods (Elford, 1938), put an end to an old controversy regarding the minimal particle size of certain bacteriophages (Hershey, Kimura and Bronfenbrenner 1947).

Seven of the T viruses have now been studied by means of the electronic microscope (Delbrück, 1946a). The largest are T2, T4, and T6, which are morphologically identical. They show an oval body measuring at least 65 x 80 mμ and a straight tail measuring about 20 x 120 mμ. These viruses, illustrated in Figure 25, reveal a differentiated internal structure. T5 is nearly as large as members of the group just mentioned but has a spherical body. T1 resembles T5 but has a smaller body with a diameter of about 50 mμ. T3 and T7 are smaller still and have spherical bodies about 30 mμ in diameter. Smaller viruses have been described (Elford, 1938; Frilley et al., 1944) with estimated diameters of 10 to 20 mμ. These estimates of size are not very precise and may be too low (Kerby et al., 1949; Hershey et al., 1951a), but the differences in size among different phages have been confirmed by several methods.

T2 has been found susceptible to osmotic shock, which inactivates the virus and produces "ghosts" that appear in electronic micrographs to consist of empty membranes (Anderson, 1949). A new method of preparing specimens for micrography (Anderson, 1951) has shown that T2 attaches to bacteria by the end of its tail. These facts constitute striking proof of functional differentiation in the viral substance. It is not yet known whether there is anything comparable with this in the smaller viruses.

ANTIGENIC STRUCTURE

The work of Burnet (1933a) led to the recognition of eleven different serologic groups of viruses acting on *E. coli* alone. The situation he found may be illustrated by the relationships among the members of the T system of bacterial viruses, for which the analysis has been carried further (Delbrück, 1946a; Hershey, 1946a). The seven original types fall into four unrelated serologic groups as follows: T1; T2, T4, T6; T3, T7; T5. Antiserum against a virus belonging to any one of these groups has no detectable action on viruses in any of the other groups. The relationships within groups are exemplified by the cross reactions among the even numbered viruses. Antibody against T2 neutralizes T2 much better than T4 or T6, but has some action on all three. Antiserum against T4 neutralizes T4 much better than T2 or T6, but has some action on all three. Antiserum against T6 likewise shows a strong homologous reaction and weaker heterologous reactions within the group. If antiserum against T2 is absorbed with T4 so as to remove a large part of the total antibody, the remainder still reacts to fair titer with T2, but scarcely at all with T4 or T6. This indicates that T4 and T6 have the same antigenic component in common with T2. By contrast, T4 and T6 are easily distinguished by testing with antisera against either one, showing that they also possess characteristic structures not shared with T2. Finally, if antiserum against T2 is partially absorbed with T2 itself, the remaining antibody reacts almost equally well with T2 and T4, indicating that the antibody directed toward the common structures is left. These examples suffice to show that bacterial viruses, like bacterial cells and all living tissues, contain both type-specific and group-specific antigenic determinants. On the other hand, there is no chemical or immunologic evidence that the bacterial viruses contain distinct separable antigens comparable to the protein and polysaccharide antigens of bacteria. In most respects, the virus behaves like a single antigen (Hershey, Kalmanson and Bronfenbrenner, 1943), and the multiple specificity described above may have a chemical basis similar to that revealed by the serologic cross-reactions between related proteins such as the ovalbumins of the hen and the duck.

Immunologic analysis brings out the fact that two independent methods of classification, morphologic and serologic, divide the seven viruses into precisely the same four groups: T1; T2, T4, T6; T3, T7; and T5. This result provides compelling evidence that either of these methods is sufficient to divide the bacterial viruses into genetically unrelated groups (Delbrück, 1946a). In keeping with the conclusion just stated, no experimental evidence has yet appeared to indicate that viral mutations give rise to altered antigenic character (Hershey, 1946b) Judging by the data accumulated so far, one would expect that, when antigenic variation is found, it will prove to be slight and will not be accompanied by changes in size or shape of the viral particle.

CHEMICAL COMPOSITION

For several bacterial viruses, the identification of the infectious unit with a characteristically shaped particle has been established beyond reasonable doubt. What is equally important, these particles are almost perfectly infectious, so that the plaque count on agar plates is 50 to 80 per cent of the count of visible particles (Schlesinger, 1933). These facts are crucial for practically all information concerning growth, genetic variation, and chemical composition of bacterial viruses. The importance of the high infectivity of some of the bacterial viruses becomes evident when one attempts to assess data on the chemical composition of viruses. If one finds that the weight of the isolated material per infectious unit is compatible with the estimates of size of the latter obtained by different methods, such as sedimentation and radiologic analysis, a fair state of purity is established. This correlation has now been made for the bacterial virus T2.

Hook and co-workers (1946) have analyzed preparations of the bacterial virus T2 which weighed about 10^{-15} Gm. per infectious unit, and which were shown to consist entirely of the characteristic particles. The material was composed chiefly of protein and desoxyribonucleic acid, with a remarkably high proportion of the latter—

about 40 per cent. This predominance of the one constituent known to be characteristic of cell nuclei reinforces the notion that a virus particle possesses the minimum of genetic and reproductive functions. A preparation of T2 similar to that described above has been analyzed by Cohen and Anderson (1946a). The absence of polysaccharide from this virus of relatively complex structure is notable and increases the significance of the serologic classification of bacterial viruses. Taxonomically meaningless cross reactions are often due to similar polysaccharide antigens, which seem to be distributed without plan throughout the plant, animal, and bacterial kingdoms. Protein specificity, on the other hand, seems to have developed more strictly along phylogenetic lines. Nucleic acids themselves are not known to contribute serologic specificity under any circumstances.

Several viruses closely related to T2 have been analyzed with results similar to those described. The smaller virus T7 also appears to be similar in composition to T2 (Kerby et al., 1949).

Other attempts to identify essential components of bacterial viruses have made use of enzymatic analysis. Desoxyribonuclease does not inactivate bacterial viruses, nor does it remove the nucleic acid they contain (Hershey et al., 1951a). Many bacterial viruses are resistant also to proteolytic enzymes; T2, for instance, is resistant to all enzymes that have been tested (Kalmanson and Bronfenbrenner, 1943). Certain bacterial viruses have been found susceptible to proteolytic enzymes (Northrop, 1938; Hershey, 1943), though the inactivation has not been shown to be due to enzymatic hydrolysis.

HOST-SPECIFICITY AND BAC-TERIAL MUTATION

The relation of different bacterial viruses to the cells of their hosts provides some of the most remarkable examples of biologic specificity known. In many instances, this specificity can be explained in terms of the ability of the viral particles to attach themselves to bacterial cells. The specificity of the adsorption of virus to bacterium is usually thought of as having a chemical basis analogous to that of the reaction between antigens and antibodies. Actually, the mechanism of attachment is not known, and it is possible that there are several different mechanisms. At any rate, viruses are frequently capable of distinguishing sharply between bacterial strains which are antigenically indistinguishable (Burnet et al., 1937). The specificity of the virus-bacterium reaction is most interestingly seen by examining mutants of a sensitive bacterial strain which are resistant to one or more viruses. Experiments of this sort were first described by Bail (1923). More extensive studies of the T system of bacterial viruses have been made by Demerec and Fano (1945), Luria (1946), and Hershey (1946a). A few typical results will be considered.

If an agar plate is seeded with a mixture of about 10^8 bacteria of the strain B of *Escherichia coli* and an excess of virus T1, the great majority of the bacteria are lysed. However, a few survive and grow to form colonies. These survivors are the progeny of mutants which arise about once in 10^8 divisions in every culture of the sensitive bacterial strain (Luria and Delbrück, 1943), giving rise to clones of hereditarily resistant bacteria. These resistant mutants are of several kinds. One kind, called B/1,5, is resistant to the viruses T1 and T5, but is culturally and serologically indistinguishable from the original B. A second kind (B/1) forms a small colony, is resistant only to T1, and requires tryptophane and additional sources of amino nitrogen for growth (Anderson, 1946). A third class of mutants, also resistant only to T1, can do without tryptophane. This class can be further subdivided into types whose colonies differ in size and may or may not form secondary papillae containing bacteria again sensitive to T1. There are 6 or 8 different mutations, all leading to resistance to

T1, which have been isolated repeatedly from different initially pure clones of B. It is clear that sensitivity or resistance to T1 is determined by many different genetic factors in the bacterial cell. When the acquisition of resistance to other bacterial viruses is studied in the same way, again a number of different mutations are found, each leading to resistance to the particular virus used for selection and sometimes to a few others. The total number of genetic factors in B controlling susceptibility to all its viruses is therefore very great.

Equally important from the point of view of the nature of virus sensitivity or resistance, is the question of the meaning of the linked characters, such as resistance to T1 and T5 or resistance to T1 and the tryptophane requirement, of which many examples are known (Luria, 1946). One suggestion is that there may be some metabolic connection between ability of the cell to synthesize tryptophane and to form the component of the cell-surface necessary for adsorption of T1 (Anderson, 1944). But it is also possible that this linkage depends on some wholly accidental feature of the genetic apparatus of the cell similar to the genetic linkage between sex and hemophilia in human beings (Sturtevant and Beadle, 1939). Doubtless both types of linkage contribute to the picture obtained by crude tests of virus sensitivity.

Whatever the nature of the linkage between resistance of bacteria to different viruses, it is clear that it does not furnish any useful clues to natural relationships among viruses (Delbrück, 1946a). The linkage between T1 and T5 and a stronger one between T3 and T4 bring together pairs of viruses that are morphologically and antigenically unrelated. On the other hand, bacterial mutations leading to resistance to two or more viruses of the group containing T2, T4 and T6, which are certainly very closely related (Hershey, 1946a), are rarely found. The study of viral mutations leads to similar conclusions. A mutant of T1 (Luria, 1945b) is capable of lysing certain bacteria resistant to T1 and has a range of activities identical with that of T5. This illustrates a general rule: a single mutation, representing some slight change in the structure of the virus, may lead to a new host-specificity separating the virus from the group to which it belongs and bringing it into apparent relationship with other viruses of different origin. This casual relation between viruses with respect to host-specificity may be made clear by analogy. The gamma globulins of the serum of the horse and the rabbit are generically far removed from each other and can easily be distinguished by appropriate serologic tests. But if both happen to come from animals which have been immunized against the same antigen, and if they are tested only for their specific activity as antibodies, the erroneous conclusion might be reached that they are identical proteins.

VIRUS-BACTERIUM RELATIONSHIPS

It is a prevalent but incorrect view that resistant cells fail to adsorb virus and that the attachment of virus to a bacterium is sufficient to set off a process resulting in lysis of the cell and liberation of newly formed virus. Owing to the selection of material for study, these are the virus-bacterium relationships with which one is most familiar. Some exceptional cases are instructive. In the first place, attachment of the virus to the cell involves some unknown reactions. In the simplest case, such as the attachment of T2 to *E. coli* B, fixation occurs equally well to living or dead bacteria. If the bacterium is dead, the adsorbed virus is inactivated. It is also inactivated by fragments of susceptible cells but not by those of resistant ones. T1, on the other hand, is not inactivated by such material, nor is it adsorbed to bacteria killed either by gentle heating or by brief exposure to dilute formaldehyde. It is clear that these two viruses attach to different substances in the bacterial cell and perhaps in different ways.

Reversible and irreversible phases in the adsorption of T2 to bacteria can be distinguished (Puck et al., 1951). The two phases are differently sensitive to environmental conditions, and perhaps differ in specificity.

The adsorption of phage to bacteria often requires co-factors. A high concentration of univalent cations is necessary for the adsorption of the even-numbered members of the T system, whereas several other viruses need bivalent cations. One example of an organic adsorption co-factor is known (Anderson, 1945b). Certain variants of T4 and T6 undergo a reversible transformation from infective to noninfective states as tryptophane is added or taken away (Anderson, 1948a). The kinetics of the reaction between tryptophane and phage suggest that several molecules of the amino acid must attach to the viral substance and bond together in a particular way before the virus becomes infective (Stent and Wollman, 1950). Puck et al. (1951) have found that tryptophane is also needed for the adsorption of T4 to glass. This observation disposes of the possibility that the co-factor activates a viral enzyme acting on the bacterial surface.

Once attachment of virus to a living bacterium has occurred, the ensuing reactions depend on the bacterium, the virus and environmental conditions. In certain instances nothing happens, and the virus disappears without having any detectable effect on the host. This is the case with a staphylococcal phage adsorbed to a resistant bacterial mutant (Henry and Henry, 1946), with some of the particles of T2 that have been inactivated by x-rays (Watson, 1950), and with T2 that has first been neutralized with antiserum and then adsorbed to sensitive *E. coli* (unpublished observations of the authors). It appears that in these cases the growth of the virus is blocked at an early step subsequent to adsorption. In other cases, the bacterium is killed without liberation of new virus. T2 inactivated by ultraviolet light retains its affinity for the bac-

terial cell, and the adsorption of a single particle to a bacterium is sufficient to interrupt cellular growth (Luria and Delbrück, 1942). Bacteria may also be killed by certain viruses that are adsorbed but fail to grow in media lacking calcium (Andrewes and Elford, 1932). T5 has this property. Calcium is probably necessary for an early step in the growth of T5, for if calcium is added at some time subsequent to the attachment of the virus, the ensuing latent period is about the same as that observed after adsorption in the presence of calcium (Adams, 1949). The growth of T1 is dependent on calcium in a somewhat different way (Puck, 1949). Other viruses do not appear to require calcium for growth.

More complex relationships between bacterium and virus give rise to so-called lysogenic cultures. This term has been used loosely to describe any association between bacteria and virus that permits both to persist in serial transplants. It is sometimes found that bacterial cultures recently isolated from natural sources contain virus which can be readily recovered from filtrates by testing on suitable strains of sensitive bacteria. The carrier culture may show no signs of the infection, or it may be subject to unpredictable and patchy attacks of lysis. From such cultures one can often isolate virus-free bacterial clones which may be either sensitive or resistant to the virus and the virus itself may yield lines of different activity toward the bacterial culture. It is easy to believe that carrier cultures of this description are simply unstable lines of bacteria mutating from resistance to sensitivity to a contaminating virus, which in turn mutates occasionally to a form capable of attacking all the bacteria in the culture. The known genetic properties of viruses and bacteria are sufficient to account for this condition.

More interesting are the stable virus-bacterium associations in which virus-free bacterial clones are not readily obtained. A lysogenic culture of *B. megatherium*, originally described by den Dooren de Jong

(1931), has been studied by several workers (Gratia, 1936), who agree that isolated spores of this culture always yield virus-containing lines and that spores heated to a temperature sufficient to inactivate free virus continue to give rise to lysogenic cultures. The importance of the latter observation, which at first seemed to point to the origin *de novo* of the virus, has been largely dissipated by the finding (Cowles, 1931; Adant, 1932) that virus deliberately introduced into sporulating cultures becomes thermostable within the spores. Indeed, typical lysogenic cultures can in some instances be produced experimentally by infecting them with virus (Burnet and Lush, 1936). It must be concluded that the phenomenon of lysogenesis, frequently cited as evidence for the spontaneous intracellular origin of virus, can best be explained as one type or another of association between exogenous virus and incompletely susceptible bacterium.

The association between virus and bacterium in a typical lysogenic culture has recently been clarified by the beautiful experiments by Lwoff and Gutmann (1950). They showed that the free virus in their culture came from the lysis of an occasional cell during the growth of the culture, the yield of virus being large compared with the number of bacteria lysed. A single cell, washed to remove free virus, could divide and redivide through 19 generations without liberating any virus. If a single cell was removed from the clone before free virus had appeared and was allowed to go on producing daughter cells, free virus eventually reappeared. These facts show that virus is passed from mother cell to both daughters at each cell division, and that intracellular multiplication of the virus keeps pace with the multiplication of the bacteria. Lwoff, Siminovitch and Kjeldgaard (1950) found further that the proportion of cells subject to lysis and capable of yielding phage could be greatly increased by irradiation with ultraviolet light and by certain other kinds of treatment. This system of checks and balances, evidently subject to experimental interference, is potentially of great biologic and medical importance.

Some of the virus-bacterium relationships mentioned above, particularly the co-factor requirements, provide additional criteria for tracing relationships among viral types. Thus, dependence of adsorption on univalent cations is common to members of the T2 serologic group (Hershey, 1946a), although it is found also in a few other viruses. Similarly, citrate-sensitivity, i.e., dependence on calcium, is limited to two serologic groups (Burnet, 1933b). The requirement for tryptophane in T4 and T6, but not in T2, is clarified by the finding that T4 mutates to tryptophane independence (Anderson, 1948b), and that T2 can acquire tryptophane dependence (Hershey, unpublished experiments). Evidently in these, as in several other cases, taxonomic relationships must be traced in terms of ability to undergo certain types of mutation, rather than through presence or absence of specified characters. For this reason, serologic specificity, which is a stable character, provides at present the best single taxonomic criterion.

GROWTH OF VIRUSES

Most of the current investigations of viral growth depend, directly or indirectly, on a technic known as the one-step growth experiment (Ellis and Delbrück, 1939). This consists of mixing bacteria and phage under conditions favorable for the measurement of the number of cells that become infected, and the average number of virus particles that infect each cell. A sample of this mixture is diluted sufficiently in broth to prevent further interaction between bacteria and free virus, and the liberation of new virus from the cells is followed by successive titrations of the diluted culture. The principal features of viral growth revealed by this experiment are the latent period that elapses before any of the bacteria liberate virus, and the average burst size or yield of virus per infected bacterium (Delbrück, 1946b).

The latent period of viral growth proves to be characteristic for different groups of viruses. T2, T4 and T6 have latent periods of about 21 minutes; T1, T3 and T7 of 13 minutes; and T5 of 40 minutes; all measured in nutrient broth at 37° C. (Delbrück, 1946a). The burst sizes, on the other hand, vary between 100 and 600 per bacterium and do not correlate with other known properties of the viruses. The most impressive feature of these data is the remarkable speed of growth they reveal. An increase of three hundredfold in 13 minutes corresponds to a maximum generation time of about 1.5 minutes.

Doermann (1948a) has introduced a number of important methods for studying the intracellular growth of phage. One of these methods is based on the fact that cyanide added to a suspension of bacteria infected with T4 stops the growth of phage almost instantaneously and yet allows the bacteria to be lysed passively by T6. The number of infective T4 particles released during lysis thus gives a measure of the number that were present in the cell at the moment when cyanide was added. This method of analysis divides the latent period into two equal parts. During the first half, often called the dark period, the addition of cyanide does not permit the recovery of any infective virus, as if the original infecting particles had disappeared from the cell. During the second half, or maturation period, infective virus particles reappear and increase in number up to the time of spontaneous lysis. For two reasons, these data mean something quite different from the expected intracellular growth curve. First, the starting point of the maturation period is not a number corresponding to the number of virus particles that originally entered the cell, but zero. Secondly, in mixed viral infections, genetic recombinants, which must originate by a process that is terminal to multiplication (Hershey and Rotman, 1949), are already present at the beginning of the maturation period (Doermann and Dissosway, 1949). One is forced to conclude that

the second half of the latent period is devoted to the reconversion into resting, infective phage particles of a hypothetical, noninfectious, vegetative form of virus that has multiplied during the dark period (Luria, 1950; Hershey, 1952). The existence of a "probacteriophage" has also been postulated by Lwoff and Gutmann (1950) to signalize the fact that lysogenic bacteria may lyse without yielding infective virus.

The ideas coming from the experiments just described call for a new line of inquiry into the character of the vegetative form of the virus, which is presumably liberated from the cell by lysis during the dark period of viral growth. This investigation, which may throw light on other instances of "masking" in viruses, is only beginning.

One crucial question about the growth of the virus has been answered by studying the distribution of numbers of mutants arising in small populations of multiplying virus (Luria, 1951). The results indicate that the numerical increase in virus (strictly speaking, genetic subunits of the virus) must be geometric by twos, which means that each daughter virus participates in the further growth of the population. This inference is chiefly interesting in terms of the alternative it excludes, namely, that the entering virus particle sets up a machine for the manufacture of its kind in the cell, which then turns out new virus particles one by one. Doermann's (1948a) curves of intracellular growth probably would have been interpreted on this basis in the absence of other information.

Luria and Human (1950) have described cytologic changes in bacterial cells following viral infection. T1 produces no changes visible during the first 3 or 4 minutes, after which the cells rapidly fill up with chromatin. T2 causes a rapid dispersal of the nuclei, which are replaced during the first 5 minutes by large peripheral masses of chromatin. T7 deforms the nuclei, which fuse and swell during the first 6 or 7 minutes to form a large central mass, giving the cells a spindle-shaped profile.

Cohen (1947) has measured the net rates of accumulation of protein and nucleic acid in virus-infected bacteria. Whether these approximate the actual rates of synthesis is not known. Protein accumulation continues after infection at approximately the rate characteristic of normal bacterial growth. Nucleic acid accumulation is interrupted for about one-third of the latent period and then proceeds at a considerably faster rate than it does in uninfected bacteria. All the nucleic acid formed appears to be of the desoxypentose type, as if the formation of bacterial substance had been replaced by the formation of viral substance. At the end of the normal latent period (21 to 25 minutes) the ratio of protein to nucleic acid increments is considerably larger than the ratio found in the virus, so that protein, if not also nucleic acid, is synthesized in excess of the material needs of the mature virus present at this time.

Owing to the delay of lysis under the conditions of these experiments (Doermann, 1948b), virus formation continues for several hours after the end of the normal latent period. During this time the nucleic acid content of the culture increases slowly, while the accumulation of protein ceases, and as the cells begin to lyse the total increments of protein and nucleic acid are roughly equal to the amounts eventually recovered as virus. It is not clear whether this means a remarkably efficient economy on the part of the virus or whether the unused materials are destroyed. Additional implications of these data have been summarized by Cohen (1949).

Certain questions about viral growth call for the use of isotopically labeled substrates. Kozloff et al. (1950), extending the work of Cohen (1947), have shown that only about 25 per cent of the phosphorus and nitrogen that are incorporated into phage T6 comes from materials assimilated by the bacteria before infection; the remainder gets into the bacteria after infection. Some idea of the possible intermediates in the synthesis of viral material may be learned by tracing to its source the contribution from the preassimilated bacterial substance (Kozloff et al., 1950). The general picture that emerges is the following. There is in the bacterium a small pool of relatively simple nonspecific substances that receives additions from the continual degradation of more complex substances characteristic of the bacterium and from the uptake of nutrients from the outside. This pool is normally drawn on for the synthesis of characteristic bacterial components. Viral infection interrupts this last process more or less completely (Cohen, 1949), and during viral growth the pool is drawn on for the synthesis of characteristic viral components. The following information has been gained about the route from characteristic bacterial substance to characteristic phage substance. (1) There is no evidence that any specific materials are transferred intact. That none is transferred is suggested by new evidence for the absence of serologic relationship between bacterium and virus (Cohen and Arbogast, 1950; Roesel, 1951). (2) Purines are transferred intact. (3) Equal proportions of the phage purine nitrogen and the phage thymine nitrogen come from materials assimilated before infection. If the thymine (present in DNA but not in the more abundant RNA) comes from bacterial DNA, the purines (present in both types of nucleic acid) probably come from DNA also. (4) Phage DNA receives an excess of nitrogen over phosphorus from the bacteria, showing that the transfer is not exclusively intact bacterial DNA. (5) The transfer of nitrogen to phage DNA exceeds the transfer of nitrogen to phage protein, showing that the precursors of the two fractions in the cell pool are different.

Some of the inferences stated above are trivial. We have listed them to show that the use of tracer analysis does not carry a magical guarantee of penetrating results. The general idea that emerges from these studies is nevertheless very important, namely, that the synthesis of characteristic phage substance, like the synthesis of the characteristic components of other organisms, calls upon undifferentiated materials whose fate is uniquely determined by the given biologic situation.

This idea gives rise to the following question. Is all the characteristic phage substance derived from the cell pool of undifferentiated material, or is some of it transmitted intact from the viral parents? Putnam and Kozloff (1950) have shown that when bacteria are infected with phage labeled with radioactive phosphorus, 30 per cent of the labeled atoms end up in the phage progeny and 70 per cent of them are found in nonsedimentable material. The question asked above may now be restated in the form of several alternatives. Does the 30 per cent fraction pass through the pool of undifferentiated material on its way from parent to offspring phage? If not, does it form a special hereditary part of the phage, or does it enter into all parts? Is it distributed among all the progency particles, or a few of them? Is the 70 per cent loss due to the wasteful use of specific materials, or is metabolic turnover an intrinsic feature of synthetic processes?

One of these questions has been framed in experimental terms by Cohen and answered by Maaløe and Watson (1951). When phage particles containing radioactive phosphorus are allowed to undergo two successive cycles of intracellular multiplication, 30 per cent of the initial radioactivity is conserved during the first cycle, and 30 per cent of the conserved fraction is reconserved during the second cycle. Since the seed phage used for the first growth cycle was uniformly labeled with radioactive atoms, and the first cycle progeny behaved during growth like the primary seed phage, the first cycle progeny must also have been uniformly labeled. This shows that the conserved fraction is derived from and enters into all parts of the phage that contain phosphorus. Other questions about material transfer of parental substance during multiplication of phage remain unanswered.

The one-step growth experiment provides an opportunity to study the relation between growth and metabolism of bacteria and growth of virus. In general, the growth of the virus is closely linked to that of the bacterial host. In bacteria taken from a culture in its terminal phase of growth, the latent period of virus liberation is prolonged, and the yield of virus is reduced, as compared with cultures in the rapidly multiplying condition. The effects of temperature on the latent periods of bacterial and viral growth are identical (Delbrück, 1940). Viral and bacterial growth are stopped by sulfanilamide (Wahl et al., 1946) or by 5-methyltryptophane (Cohen and Anderson, 1946b), substances presumably interfering with different specific metabolic processes. The coupling of viral growth to that of the host cells is not absolute, however. If E. coli B is grown in broth, in a glucose-NH_3 medium, or in ammonium lactate, the bacterial generation times are 19, 30 and 60 minutes, respectively, while the latent period of virus growth is little affected (Luria, personal communication). In the absence of calcium, bacteria and certain viruses can grow, but T5 cannot (Adams, 1949).

Attempts have been made to connect viral growth with specific nutrient sources by transferring infected cells into solutions containing known metabolites (Spizizen, 1943; Cohen and Fowler, 1948). Experiments of this type have shown that nitrogen, phosphorus and oxidizable carbon are needed. The specific requirements depend both on the genetic potentialities of the bacterium (whether or not it is able to synthesize its own tryptophane, for instance) and on the adaptive state of the bacterium (whether its tryptophane synthesizing apparatus is in working order at the time of infection). The dependence on the adaptive state of the bacterium is particularly strict because it appears that viral infection blocks adaptive processes, presumably as one aspect of a general interference with the synthesis of characteristic bacterial constituents (Cohen, 1949). Thus E. coli infected with phage cannot change over from glucose utilization to lactose utilization, and the infected bacteria do not lyse in the presence of lactose unless they were already prepared to utilize this substance at the time of infection (Monod and Wollman, 1947). Similarly, the only requirements for growth of virus in bacteria multiplying in an ammonium lactate medium are the constituents of that medium, but if the same bacteria from a culture in meat extract broth are infected and transferred to a synthetic medium the requirements turn out to be nearly as complex as meat extract broth (Cohen and Fowler, 1948). It appears that the requirements for viral growth are, to a first approximation, the same as the requirements for bacterial growth. This finding contradicts the idea that virus is synthesized from precursors native to the cell by reactions requiring little expenditure of energy (Krueger and Scribner, 1939). The same inference is to be drawn from the tracer experiments summarized earlier.

In principle, reactions essential to the growth of virus can be identified in terms of the metabolic blocks responsible for its failure under a variety of conditions. In naturally resistant bacteria the block is of genetic origin and presumably can be studied by the methods of biochemical genetics (Henry and Henry, 1946). Another approach seeks to identify the action of substances tolerated by bacteria but capable of blocking the growth of virus. One such substance is an acridine derivative which, in concentrations insufficient to affect bacterial growth, prevents multiplication of the virus T2 (Fitzgerald and Lee, 1946). The reactions that are blocked in this instance occur late during the latent period (Foster, 1948) and may be concerned with terminal steps in the completion of infectious particles. Low temperature (Maaløe, 1950) and pH (Gold and Watson, 1950) also may have a selective action on particular phases of viral growth. These preliminary findings point to the need for methods of study of viral growth that do not depend on the measurement of the latent period or the

burst size, which may very well have control mechanisms only indirectly influenced by important phases of viral growth. One method of this kind has been worked out (Benzer et al., 1950); it depends on changes that occur in the sensitivity to ultraviolet light of the intracellular virus colony during early stages of development.

Attempts to learn more about viral growth, whether to answer superficial questions about its control or general questions about the underlying process, have an obvious relation to medical problems. Among these, the control of typical viral infections is perhaps only one of many.

VIRAL MUTATIONS

Both hereditary and nonhereditary variations in viruses are known. The hereditary variations are called mutations, which may be described as stepwise heritable changes that occur primarily or exclusively during the growth of the virus. Nothing is known about the physical nature of mutational change. Recombination experiments show that different mutations usually occur in different localized regions of the hereditary substance of the virus. The known mutations are spontaneous ones; that is, external influences that may alter the frequency of viral mutations have not yet been found. The natural frequencies of individual mutations are unknown, but most of the recognizable ones must occur less often than one time per million duplications. Mutations are known that affect host specificity, type of plaque, latent period (Watson, unpublished), burst size (Hershey, unpublished), resistance to heat (Adams and Lark, 1950), resistance to proflavine (Foster, 1948), and the requirement for tryptophane (Anderson, 1948b). Nonheritable variations in heat resistance have also been described (Adams and Lark, 1950).

Mutations affecting host specificity, called h-mutations, are easily observed in any bacterial virus (Luria, 1945a). If, for example, one plates out a portion of a lysate containing a billion particles of T1 in a

Petri dish seeded with a suitable strain (B/1) of *E. coli* resistant to T1, a few clearings are likely to appear. The virus isolated from these clearings is not T1, for it is almost equally active on B/1 and on the original strain B. It can be shown that this virus stems from mutants arising spontaneously during the growth of T1 (Luria, 1945a). If one calls this mutant virus T1h, the original T1 may be called T1h$^+$, in conformity with the usual genetic convention. The letter h refers to the host range char-

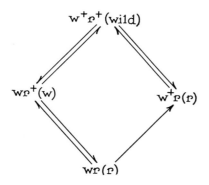

Fig. 26. Mutational pattern of the bacterial virus T2 with respect to lysis-inhibition.

acter, or to a genetic locus determining host range, and the plus sign signifies the wild-type character, or its genetic basis. In general, there are several different h-mutations which recur with characteristic frequency in a given viral stock, and the mutants themselves may undergo a second successive mutation or may revert to the original type (Hershey, 1946b). Apart from their activity on the new host, the h-mutants do not differ greatly from the parent virus. No serologic differences have been found. The mutants may or may not show a decreased infectivity toward the original host. The h-mutants of T2 are inactivated at lower temperatures than is the parent virus. The h-mutants of T3 and some other phages are so unstable that it is difficult to work with them.

Mutations affecting type of plaque have been studied chiefly in the even-numbered

viruses of the T system (Hershey, 1946a), but they occur also in T1. There are a number of recognizably different mutations affecting the plaques of T2. Some of these correspond to quantitatively different degrees of a property known as lysis-inhibition (Doermann, 1948b). The lysis-inhibiting viruses form small plaques surrounded by a ring of partial lysis. The noninhibiting mutants form larger plaques with sharp borders and are called r-mutants or rapidly lysing mutants. Intermediate mutant types have been called w-mutants or weak inhibitors (Hershey, 1946b). With reference to these two kinds of mutation, the wild type would be called w$^+$r$^+$. These two types of mutation occur independently of each other and of the h-mutations. In T2, an r-mutant arises about once per 10,000 duplications of the virus, and the w-mutation occurs with similar frequency. These frequencies tell us nothing about the rates of individual mutations because recombination experiments show that the same visible effects can result from many different mutations. Both r-mutants and w-mutants are indistinguishable from the parent type except for the characteristics mentioned. Both are relatively stable genetically, but mutation back to wild type can be demonstrated by serial passage through successive bacterial cultures, during which the wild type replaces the mutant types.

The properties described above permit a limited genetic analysis (Hershey, 1946b) which is summarized in Figure 26. The arrows indictate mutations that have been demonstrated experimentally. There are four genotypes, indicated by appropriate symbols in the figure, but only three phenotypes, as shown in parentheses. The mutant wr differs from w$^+$r in having arisen through two successive mutations. The two can be told apart by the fact that wr is replaced by the phenotype w, while w$^+$r is replaced by wild type, during serial passage. The existence of these four genotypes, together with the failure to observe single step mutations corresponding to the diagonals of

Figure 26, may be regarded as sufficient proof for the independence of the genetic loci r and w. This type of genetic analysis may be called analysis of mutational pattern.

INTERACTIONS BETWEEN VIRUSES

Genetic Recombination. A second method of genetic analysis, independent of the one just described, utilizes the phenomenon of genetic recombination in a way that is formally equivalent to the breeding tests by which inheritance is studied in sexual organisms. Genetic recombination has been studied chiefly in phages related to T2, but it occurs also in T1 (Hershey, unpublished) and T5 (Adams, 1951c). Genetic recombination was first observed by Delbrück and Bailey (1946), who were investigating the question whether related viruses could produce mixed infections (Delbrück and Luria, 1942; Hershey, 1946a). They stated that their results could be interpreted either in terms of induced mutation or genetic recombination. Following up their discovery, Hershey (1946b) tested the possibility of genetic recombination, which was finally demonstrated by Hershey and Rotman (1948, 1949).

By the application of recombination tests, it was found that different r-mutations occurring in the same stock of T2 result from alterations in different parts of the genetic material of the virus (Hershey and Rotman, 1948). The r-mutations provided a sufficient number of genetic markers to permit the construction of a genetic map, on which a position could be assigned to other mutations (Hershey and Rotman, 1949). In all instances tested, when analysis of mutational pattern has shown that two mutations occurred independently of each other, recombination tests have placed the corresponding loci at different map positions. With the discovery of an instance of multiple allelism (Hershey and Davidson, 1951), that is, two alternative mutations occurring at the same locus, the formal

proof was complete that inheritance in viruses is controlled by a number of localized genes subject to linkage restrictions.

The cross between a host-range mutant (h) and a plaque-type mutant (r) may be taken as a typical example of genetic recombination. One infects bacteria with virus in such a way that a single bacterium receives, on the average, about 5 particles of h-mutant and about 5 particles of r-mutant. This bacterium with its mixed infection can, if one wishes, be isolated in a small tube of nutrient broth, where it lyses in about 21 minutes to liberate some 200 particles of virus. The contents of the tube are then plated out on nutrient agar seeded with a mixture of bacteria capable of distinguishing between particles that are h and particles that are not h. After plaques have developed, the 200 colonies of virus can readily be classified into four true-breeding genetic types: the parental h, the parental r, the recombinant hr (mutant in character with respect to both host-range and type of plaque), and the recombinant wild type (normal in both respects). Both the total and relative numbers of the four kinds of virus in a single yield of this type are subject to large variations, but if an average is taken over the yields from many bacteria two important characteristics are noted. The numbers of the two recombinant viruses are equal, and the total number of recombinants is characteristic for the particular pair of mutants entering into the cross. These pair-specific numbers furnish the measures of linkage from which the genetic map is constructed.

The biologic significance of genetic recombination can be stated in a general way. A solution to the problem of the mechanism of genetic recombination promises to yield a clue to the more basic problem of origin of viruses; perhaps this is the only clue for which there can be legitimate hope at present. It is already clear that the genetic recombination of mutant genes and its converse, mutual exclusion, provide on the one hand a ready means for the evolution of new viral types and on the other hand an isolating mechanism for the preservation of viral species. This is a remarkable biologic situation, inasmuch as it seems to have been arrived at without any close analogue of sex. Finally, the practical problems to which genetic recombination is most closely related have to do with the rise and fall of viral epidemics and the interepidemic survival of disease.

Mutual Exclusion. Interference with the growth of one virus by another has been described for plant, animal and bacterial viruses. Detailed information can be obtained by quantitative studies of what happens when a single bacterial cell is infected with two kinds of virus (Delbrück and Luria, 1942). It turns out that there are several different kinds of interference. The first in order of discovery is called mutual exclusion (Delbrück, 1945a). This may be described as follows.

If two serologically unrelated viruses are simultaneously adsorbed to the same bacterium, only one of them is liberated when the cell is lysed. Even the original particles of the second type are lost. This mutual exclusion requires only a single particle of the excluding type, and the exclusion of the second type cannot be attributed to failure of adsorption. Which member of the virus pair will grow and which will be excluded depends on the nature of the viruses, on chance, and on the interval of time between the adsorption of the first and the second virus of the pair (Delbrück, 1945a). T2 nearly always excludes T1 or T7, but if T1 and T7 are simultaneously adsorbed, either one is equally likely to grow. If the attachment of the second virus of the pair follows that of first by several minutes, the first always excludes the second. The yield of the successful virus is often less in mixed infection than in unmixed infection. This depressor effect (Delbrück, 1945a) is less, the later the second virus reaches the cell.

When two viruses of the T2 group infect the same cell, mutual exclusion fails. Thus, if T2 and one of its mutants (Hershey, 1946a), or T2 and T4, or T2 and T6 (Delbrück and Bailey, 1946) infect the same cell, 80 or 90 per cent of the bacteria liberate both types; with the pair T4 and T6, about 20 per cent liberate both types. T1 and one of its mutants (Hershey, unpublished), T5 and one of its mutants (Adams, 1951a), and T5 and one of its serologic relatives (Adams, 1951b) also prove to be compatible pairs. The generalization that serologically related viruses form compatible pairs, while serologically unrelated ones form incompatible pairs (Delbrück and Bailey, 1946), seems to be warranted. This rule suggests one more criterion of relatedness among the bacterial viruses.

Mutual Exclusion in Lysogenic Bacteria. At present there is no adequate theory of the mechanism of mutual exclusion. The following observations either furnish a clue to the mechanism or point to another category of mutual exclusion. Bertani (1951) has studied the liberation of virus from a lysogenic bacterium carrying three distinct viruses. When an occasional cell liberates virus in this culture, the yield may contain one kind of virus or another, but not more than one. In this instance, it is clear that the vegetative forms of all three viruses multiply together in the cell. Therefore, the mutual exclusion probably has to do with the maturation of infective particles.

Weigle and Delbrück (1951) have studied mutual exclusion between T5 and an unrelated phage, lambda, carried by a lysogenic strain of *E. coli*. The lysogenic bacteria used in these experiments were irradiated with ultraviolet light, which caused them to lyse and liberate lambda after a latent period of 60 minutes. Weigle and Delbrück superinfected the irradiated bacteria with T5 at various times during this 60-minute period. They found that T5 excludes lambda when the superinfection occurs at any time up to 20 minutes before the cell is due to liberate lambda. The critical time coincides roughly with the time at which the maturation of lambda occurs in the cell in the absence of superinfection. These authors suggest that mutual exclusion in general may operate during some late step in the maturation of infective particles.

Limited Participation. When bacteria are infected with 10 to 20 particles of T2 carrying one genetic marker and very few particles carrying a second, many of the bacteria will give pure yields of the virus of the major type (Dulbecco, 1949). The proportion of bacteria liberating both types depends on the relative number of the two kinds of particles entering into the infection. Dulbecco has explained this result in terms of a limitation to the number of particles capable of initiating growth in a single cell. Other possible explanations have not been excluded.

Superinfection with Compatible Virus. If a bacterium is infected with a few particles of genetically marked T2 two or three minutes before it is infected with T2 carrying a different marker, the yield is likely to contain only the virus arriving first (Dulbecco, 1952a). This phenomenon cannot be connected with the mutual exclusion defined above, because T2 and its mutants form compatible pairs. A clue to the operation of this kind of interference comes from some novel experiments with isotopically marked viruses (Lesley, French and Graham, 1950), which show that approximately 50 per cent of the phosphorus in the superinfecting virus is very quickly eliminated from the cell. Nothing like this happens to the phosphorus in the virus of the primary infection. Apparently the cell learns how to destroy virus as well as how to make new virus in the first few minutes following infection. These experiments open up another fertile field of investigation.

Heterozygosis. Genetic recombination depends for its recognition on a two-gene difference between the interacting viruses. Other effects on the viral progeny can be seen when the two viruses differ by a single gene. These effects are not hereditary. When a bacterium is infected with the pair T2 and its h-mutant, or T2 and its r-mutant, approximately 2 per cent of the viral progeny will contain both alleles of the gene by which the parental viruses differed (Hershey and Chase, 1951). These exceptional progeny may appropriately be called heterozygotes. The heterozygous particles do not multiply as such, but immediately break down on infecting a bacterium to yield the two types of virus from which they came. Heterozygotes arise also in typical genetic crosses, in which case they do not always yield the parental viruses, but are progenitors of recombinants.

Phenotypic Mixing. Another nonhereditary effect of the interaction between viruses can be seen when the infecting pair consists of T2h and T2h+ (Hershey et al., 1951b). The effect seen is a modification of phenotype affecting both the host-specificity and the heat-sensitivity by which the two parental viruses differ. All the virus particles in the cell are affected independently of genotype, and the resulting phenotype is intermediate between those of the two pure lines of virus. If analogous effects occur in other mixed infections, it would not, in most instances, be possible to detect them. The phenomenon is presumably related to nonheritable alterations of host-specificity observed in virus coming from interspecific crosses (Delbrück and Bailey, 1946; Novick and Szilard, 1951).

Phenotypic mixing can be expected to have important effects on the composition of all viral populations. The host-range mutants, for example, in a stock of wild-type virus, must have come from bacteria also infected with wild-type virus. Similarly, a larger or smaller proportion of the wild-type virus in the same stock must have come from bacteria also infected with h-mutant virus. The stock will contain, therefore, a majority of authentic wild-type virus, and two minorities of similar but varying size consisting of phenotypically confused h-mutant virus and phenotypically confused wild-type virus. There would be few or no h-mutant particles with the phenotype characteristic of pure stocks of h-mutant virus. One consequence of this situation is that by no known method could one measure the proportion of h-mutants in such a stock, unless they were numerous enough to be sampled at random.

The possible biologic significance of phenotypic mixing is of considerable interest. Evidently the association between two viruses could result in the perpetuation of individually untenable types, in doubly lysogenic bacteria for instance, even in the absence of genetic recombination. An example would be a rare unstable mutant carried along with its stable progenitor. In this way the number of individually deleterious genes that could be preserved for trial in new combinations with other genes would be greatly increased. Presumably the long-range effect of phenotypic mixing would thus be a considerable acceleration of the evolutionary process in viruses. Here again we see a novel substitute among the viruses for a condition (diploidy) that accomplishes a specific purpose in higher organisms.

Multiplicity Reactivation. Luria (1947) has described an interaction between compatible pairs of viruses resulting in the repair of damage caused by ultraviolet irradiation. A discussion of this phenomenon, called multiplicity reactivation because it occurs only when two or more particles infect the same cell, will be found in a later section of the chapter. At this point several parallels between multiplicity reactivation and phenotypic mixing may be mentioned. Phenotypic mixing is complete; every particle of virus liberated from a mixedly infected bacterium shows the mixed phenotype. Phenotypic mixing is gene-specific; the material responsible for the h-phenotype must be produced under the influence of the h-gene. Phenotypic mixing is not readily explained as an effect of fusions between phage particles, because the data of genetic recombination (Hershey and Rotman, 1949) show that not all particles in the cell have an opportunity to exchange genes with their opposite numbers. Multiplicity reactivation is efficient; one inactive particle nearly

always reactivates another present in the same cell. Multiplicity reactivation is specific for the genome; T2 can reactivate T2 but not T5, and T5 can reactivate T5 but not T2 (Luria, 1950). Multiplicity reactivation is not readily explained as an effect of fusions between phage particles. Reactivation presumably calls for interactions taking place before multiplication starts, whereas fusions have to be terminal to multiplication (Hershey and Rotman, 1949). Both multiplicity reactivation and phenotypic mixing are best explained in terms of a shared metabolism, under the control of the viral genes, which yields metabolites that are accessible to all the viral particles in the cell.

Eight distinct types of interaction between bacterial viruses infecting the same cell have been listed. Some of these are certainly related to each other; one hopes that many of them are. Defining these relationships is one of the major tasks of viral research for the immediate future. When it has been accomplished a long step will have been taken toward an understanding of viral behavior.

EFFECTS OF RADIATIONS

The effects of radiations on viruses have been studied in a variety of ways in the hope of learning something about viral growth and structure. Several of the questions raised by these studies have been clarified; none of them has been answered. Radiobiology offers technics of great potential power (Lea, 1946; Latarjet, 1946; Luria and Latarjet, 1947; Luria, 1947). Whether these technics can be successfully employed will remain in doubt until more has been learned about the mode of action of radiant energy.

The known effects of radiations on the infectivity of bacteriophage are the following: inactivation (by x-rays, β-rays, ultraviolet light, and others); reactivation by visible light of previously irradiated virus; induction by ultraviolet light of productive lysis in lysogenic bacteria (Lwoff, Simino-vitch and Kjeldgaard, 1950); and photo-reversal of the effect last mentioned (Weigle and Delbrück, 1951). Only the inactivating effect is obtained by irradiating naked virus; the other effects are seen when infected bacteria are irradiated.

One application of the lethal effect is possible because the wave-length dependence of the absorption of light in the visible and ultraviolet regions is characteristic of particular types of chemical structure. Nucleic acids, for instance, have an absorption spectrum different from that of proteins. Thus, one can hope to learn something about the vital structures of a virus by studying the dependence on wave length of its inactivation by ultraviolet light. There are limitations to this analysis, since it is possible that one wave length may be more effective than another, not because it is absorbed by a unique vital material, but because the photons of different energy vary in efficiency of photochemical effect when absorbed by the same material. However, viruses do show different and characteristic inactivation spectra. The bacterial viruses that have been tested, including T1 and T2 (Zelle, personal communication), yield an inactivation spectrum with a maximum near 2650 AU, similar to the (nucleic acid) absorption spectrum of the phage, and to action spectra for bacteria, fungi, yeasts, influenza virus and vaccine virus. The quantum yield at the optimal wave length is said to be about one death per 10^4 photons (yielding about 5 electron volts of energy per photon) absorbed by the phages mentioned (Benzer et al., 1950). Tobacco-mosaic and chicken-tumor viruses differ from the other materials tested, giving action spectra with maxima below 2,400 AU (Hollaender and Oliphant, 1944).

It has been found that sufficient numbers of radioactive phosphorus atoms can be incorporated directly into the viral substance during growth to produce lethal effects due to the radioactive decay of the isotope (Hershey et al., 1951a). The β-particles emitted during the decay are not responsible for the effects observed. The radioactive phage particle is killed on the average by the tenth or the twelfth atomic transmutation occurring in its structure. This corresponds to the decay of one out of 50,000 atoms of viral phosphorus. The possible applications of this technic to problems of viral growth have not yet been adequately explored.

The lethal effects of ionizing radiations, x-rays for example, are produced by local absorptions of energy (about 34 electron volts per ionization) delivered nearly at random to the atoms making up the virus and its external surroundings. If the latter contain suitable protective substances it is believed that only absorptions within the particle itself are effective (Luria and Exner, 1941). On this assumption, the mean lethal dose can be expressed in ion pairs produced per cc. of viral substance. This dose turns out to be, for T2 or T4, 5 x 10^{16} ion pairs for x-rays (Luria and Exner, 1941; Latarjet, 1948) and 1 x 10^{17} for β-rays from P32 (Hershey et al., 1951a; and a subsequent check). The difference may reflect systematic errors in the measurements. In order to convert these measurements into efficiencies of killing, one has to know the volume of the phage particle. A current estimate for T2 (Hershey et al., 1951a) gives 7 x 10^{-16} cc., from which the efficiency of killing is of the order 0.02 per ionization within the particle volume. This efficiency may be raised threefold by assuming that the ionizations are delivered in clusters of three (Lea, 1946). The conventional inference from this measurement would be that killing by ionizing radiation is the result of a single local absorption of energy within a sensitive volume comprising one-fifteenth to one-fiftieth of the total volume of the phage particle. In a similar way one could infer from the experiments with assimilated P32 that about 10 per cent of the phosphorus atoms of the phage lie within this sensitive volume. Whether the sensitive volume so defined corresponds to any real structure or structures within the phage particle is the classical unsolved problem of radiobiology.

A remarkable phenomenon discovered by Luria (1947) has brought one form of the notion of the sensitive volume to a critical test. Phage inactivated by ultraviolet light retains its ability to attach to bacteria, and the adsorption of a single particle suffices to cause the death of the bacterium, though no growth of virus can be detected. When two or more individually noninfective particles attach to the same bacterium, however, growth of virus and lysis of the cell proceed in typical fashion. Luria sought to explain this phenomenon, which he has called multiplicity reactivation, in terms of the following hypothesis.

The lethal effects of ultraviolet light are assumed to be lethal mutations induced by single photon absorptions. A virus particle is noninfective after it has experienced one or more lethal mutations. Two or more virus particles attached to the same bacterium fail to grow only if each of the particles happens to have undergone a lethal mutation in the same reproductive unit. Multiplicity reactivation results, therefore, from an efficient and selective process of genetic recombination that brings together one unmutated unit of each kind from a common pool. The high efficiency of the recombination process is explained by further assumptions about the details of viral growth.

Certain qualitative and quantitative features of multiplicity reactivation supported this interpretation rather well (Luria and Dulbecco, 1949). More critical experiments have shown, however, that the repair of physiologic effects of radiation plays a large part in this phenomenon (Dulbecco, 1952b). In this instance, therefore, the doctrine of lethal mutations, which is closely connected with the idea of the sensitive volume, has not proved to be fruitful.

A second remarkable discovery (Dul-becco, 1950) is connected historically, if not logically, with the shift in interpretation of multiplicity reactivation. Dulbecco finds that phage inactivated by ultraviolet light can be revived during a short period of time after attachment to a sensitive bacterium by exposure to light of from 3,000 to 5,000 AU wave length. The photoreactivation does not result from a simple photochemical reaction taking place in the viral substance but depends for its effectiveness on a chain of reactions of which some occur in darkness.

Certain applications of radiation effects can be made without any assumptions about the nature of the effects observed. One example of this kind (Luria and Latarjet, 1947; Latarjet, 1948) is the attempt to measure the numerical increase of intracellular virus during the latent period of viral growth. The method is (or can be) based on the following empirical facts. Bacteria to which single viral particles are attached survive under irradiation (as measured by the capacity to yield virus) by a characteristic kinetic law known as exponential survival. Bacteria to which n-number of virus particles are attached survive (as virus yielders) according to a different law, known as the n-target law. It occurred to Luria and Latarjet (1947) that it might be possible to follow the intracellular growth of virus by measuring n from the shape of survival curves for infected bacteria irradiated at different times during the latent period of viral growth. Unfortunately, they found that the survival curves for bacteria infected with T2 changed not only with respect to n, but also with respect to the apparent sensitivity to irradiation of the intracellular virus and probably also as a result of the spread of n resulting from lack of synchronization of viral growth in individual bacteria. Experiments along the same lines with bacteria infected with T7 (Benzer et al., 1950) avoid some of these complications, but others remain. The failure of these experiments, and the information from other sources that intracellular virus passes through noninfective stages, suggest that questions about the number of intracellular virus particles must wait until something has been learned about the organization of the vegetative form of the virus.

REACTION OF BACTERIAL VIRUSES WITH ANTIBODY AND COMPLEMENT

The neutralization of bacterial viruses by antiserum is a direct effect of the deposition of antibody on the surface of the particle, as shown by the fact that removal of the antibody by digestion with papain restores infectivity (Kalmanson and Bronfenbrenner, 1943). It might be supposed that the antibody interferes with the attachment of the virus to the bacterial cell. This may be the case with some viruses, e.g., T1 (unpublished observations), but not with all. With C16, a virus related to T2, it has been shown by an indirect method (Burnet, Keogh and Lush, 1937) that specific neutralization does not prevent the adsorption of virus to bacteria. With T2 itself, it can be shown directly and quantitatively that the neutralized virus is adsorbed just as readily and as specifically as the active virus. In these cases, therefore, antibody neutralizes the virus by interfering with some step in its growth subsequent to attachment to the bacterial cell.

The combination of antibody with virus is irreversible, in the sense that neutralized mixtures, diluted to a concentration at which the antibody they contain would have no effect unless combined with the virus, remain noninfective indefinitely (Hershey, 1943). With the virus sufficiently dilute so that there is no agglutination of the viral particles and with antibody in sufficient excess, the proportionate inactivation of virus in a given interval of time is independent of the initial viral concentration. This fact (Burnet, Keogh and Lush, 1937), usually spoken of as the percentage law (Andrewes and Elford, 1933), is a nec-essary consequence of the physical conditions stated in any irreversible bimolecular reaction.

Sufficiently large amounts of virus adsorb all neutralizing antibody from antiviral serum. If the concentration of virus exceeds ten billion particles per cc., specific precipitation of the large viruses occurs (Burnet, Keogh and Lush, 1937). The precipitate can be analyzed for virus and for antibody (Hersey, Kalmanson and Bronfenbrenner, 1943). Data for T2 show that precipitation occurs throughout the range of from about 40 to 5,000 molecules of antibody combined per viral particle and that only about 90 molecules combined per particle are required to neutralize infectivity. The large antibody-combining capacity of the virus is compatible with its known size. The relatively small amount of surface-coating required to neutralize infectivity is consistent with the finding previously mentioned, that neutralized T2 is specifically adsorbed to bacteria. Two minutes after a bacterial virus is attached to its host, the addition of antiserum fails to neutralize the virus. Every infected cell treated with antiviral antibody during the latent period of viral growth is lysed at the expected time and liberates its normal yield of virus (Delbrück, 1945b).

Complement may either accelerate or retard the neutralization of bacterial viruses by antibody, depending on the virus and on the conditions of test. With T1 particularly, the presence of complement largely prevents neutralization by antibody. On the other hand, particularly in the case of T2, if the virus is first sensitized lightly with antibody, the subsequent exposure to complement causes considerable neutralization. Like the neutralization by antibody alone, the action of complement is largely reversed by treatment with papain (Hershey and Bronfenbrenner, 1947).

The facts listed above bring out two points. First, different bacterial viruses show different behavior in their reactions with antibody. Since this is so, it is evidently dangerous to generalize about immune reactions of bacterial viruses or about their similarities to or differences from other viruses. Second, although infectivity measurements introduce imponderable biologic factors into the study of the reaction between antibody and antigen, it is nevertheless true that attention paid to the purely physical characteristics of the reaction helps in understanding infection and immunity.

LYSIS OF BACTERIA

The lysis of *E. coli* by bacterial viruses is particularly mysterious because no known enzyme dissolves these bacteria, nor do they autolyse readily. Bacteria that have been heavily irradiated by ultraviolet light are lysed either by lysozyme from egg white or by a lysin separated from purified virus T2 (Anderson, 1945a). However, since irradiated bacteria lyse spontaneously at a suitable pH, and heat-killed bacteria are resistant to the viral lysin, the enzymatic nature of the latter is doubtful.

It has been found that lysozyme liberates virus adsorbed to killed *B megatherium* (Pirie, 1940). A similar chemical action must occur during lysis of bacteria by virus, but it remains to be determined whether the necessary enzymes are supplied by the virus or by the cell.

A hypothesis concerning the mechanism of lysis has been proposed by Bronfenbrenner (1928b). It is supported by the following observations. Bacteria undergoing lysis may show marked swelling (Hetler and Bronfenbrenner, 1932; *cf.* Delbrück, 1940), and bacterial growth and metabolism are sometimes increased in the presence of virus (Crowe and Coke, 1938; *cf.* Cohen and Anderson, 1946a). High concentrations of agar prevent the swelling of bacteria and inhibit lysis under certain conditions. Addition of urea to agar offsets these effects (Bronfenbrenner and Hetler, 1933). It is supposed, therefore, that increased bacterial metabolism following viral infection is accompanied by hydrolytic changes (Hetler and Bronfenbrenner, 1928) increasing the intracellular osmotic pressure. Swelling due to the entry of water eventually bursts the cell membrane. High concentrations of agar minimize the entry of water, and urea somehow aids it. This hypothesis attributes the lysis to an indirect effect of enzymatic action, in which the role of the virus is solely that of a stimulus to autolytic reactions.

REFERENCES

Adams, M. H., 1949, The calcium requirement of coliphage T5. J. Immunol., *62*, 505-516.

Adams, M. H., 1950, Methods of study of bacterial viruses *in* Methods in Medical Research, Vol. II, The Year Book Publishers, Chicago, pp. 1-73.

Adams, M. H., 1951a, Mixed infection with bacterial virus T5 and its heat stable mutant. J. Immunol., *66*, 131-136.

Adams, M. H., 1951b, Mixed injection of a bacterium with coli-dysentery phage T5 and a serologically related Salmonella phage. J. Immunol., *66*, 477-484.

Adams, M. H., 1951c, The hybridization of coliphage T5 and Salmonella phage PB. J. Immunol., *67*, 313-320.

Adams, M. H., and Lark, G., 1950, Mutation to heat resistance in coliphage T5. J. Immunol., *64*, 335-347.

Adant, M., 1932, Le bactériophage du *Bacillus subtilis* sporulé. Compt. rend. Soc. biol., *111*, 1055-1056.

Anderson, E. H., 1944, Incidence of metabolic changes among virus-resistant mutants of a bacterial strain. Proc. Nat. Acad. Sci., *30*, 397-403.

Anderson, E. H., 1946, Growth requirements of virus-resistant mutants of *Escherichia coli* strain "B."

Proc. Natl. Acad. Sci., *32*, 120-128.

Anderson, T. F., 1945a, On a bacteriolytic substance associated with a purified bacterial virus. J. Cell. Comp. Physiol., *25*, 1-15.

Anderson, T. F., 1945b, The role of tryptophane in the adsorption of two bacterial viruses on their host, E. coli. J. Cell. Comp. Physiol., *25*, 17-26.

Anderson, T. F., 1948a, The activation of the bacterial virus T4 by L-tryptophan. J. Bact., *55*, 637-649.

Anderson, T. F., 1948b, The inheritance of requirements for adsorption cofactors in the bacterial virus T4. J. Bact., *55*, 651-658.

Anderson, T. F., 1949, The reactions of bacterial viruses with their host cells. Bot. Rev., *15*, 464-505.

Anderson, T. F., 1950, Bacteriophages. Ann. Rev. Microbiol., *4*, 21-34.

Anderson, T. F., 1951, Techniques for the preservation of three-dimensional structure in preparing specimens for the electron microscope. Trans. New York Acad. Sci., ser. 2, *13*, 130-134.

Andrewes, C. H., and Elford, W. J., 1932, The "killing" of bacteria by bacteriophage. Brit. J. Exp Path., *13*, 13-21.

Andrewes, C. H., and Elford, W. J., 1933, Observations on antiphage sera. I. "The percentage law." Brit. J. Exp. Path., *14*, 367-376.

Bail, O., 1923, Versuche über die Vielheit von Bakteriophagen. Ztschr. f. Immunitätsforsch. u. exper. Therapie, Orig., *38*, 57-164.

Benzer, S., Delbrück, M., Dulbecco, R., Hudson, W., Stent, G. S., Watson, J. D., Weidel, W., Weigle, J. J., and Wollman, E. L., 1950, A syllabus on procedures, facts, and interpretations in phage. *In* Viruses 1950, M. Delbrück, ed. California Institute of Technology, Pasadena, pp. 100-147.

Bertani, G., 1951, Studies on lysogenesis. I. The mode of phage liberation by lysogenic *Escherichia coli*. J. Bact., *62*, 293-300.

Bronfenbrenner, J., 1928a, The bacteriophage: present status of the question of its nature and mode of action, *in* Jordan and Falk, The Newer Knowledge of Bacteriology and Immunology. University of Chicago Press, pp. 525-556.

Bronfenbrenner, J., 1928b, Virus diseases of bacteria—bacteriophagy, *in* T. M. Rivers, Filterable Viruses. Baltimore, Williams & Wilkins, pp. 373-414.

Bronfenbrenner, J., and Hetler, D. M., 1933, Effect of urea upon activity of bacteriophage. Proc. Soc. Exp. Biol. and Med., *30*, 1308-1311.

Burnet, F. M., 1933a, The serological classification of coli-dysentery phages. J. Path. Bact., *36*, 307-318.

Burnet, F. M., 1933b, A correlation of the serological classification with certain biochemical tests. J. Path. Bact., *37*, 179-184.

Burnet, F. M., 1934, The bacteriophages. Biol. Rev., *9*, 332-350.

Burnet, F. M., and Lush, D., 1936, Induced lysogenicity and mutation of bacteriophage within lysogenic bacteria. Australian J. Exp. Biol. Med. Sci., *14*, 27-38.

Burnet, F. M., and McKie, M., 1933, The differentiation by Bail's method of phages lysing a typical B. coli strain. J. Path. Bact., *36*, 299-306.

Burnet, F. M., Keogh, E. V., and Lush, D., 1937, The immunological reactions of the filterable viruses. Australian J. Exp. Biol. and Med. Sci., *15*, 227-368.

Cohen, S. S., 1947, The synthesis of bacterial viruses in infected cells. Cold Spring Harbor Symp. Quant. Biol., *12*, 35-49.

Cohen, S. S., 1949, Growth requirements of bacterial viruses. Bact. Rev., *13*, 1-24.

Cohen, S. S., and Anderson, T. F., 1946a, Chemical studies on host-virus interactions. I. The effect of bacteriophage adsorption on the multiplication of its host, Escherichia coli B, with an appendix giving some data on the composition of the bacteriophage, T2. J. Exp. Med., *84*, 511-523.

Cohen, S. S., and Anderson, T. F., 1946b, Chemical studies on host-virus interactions. II. The chemical simulation of the interference phenomenon by 5-methyl tryptophane. J. Exp. Med., *84*, 525-533.

Cohen, S. S., and Arbogast, R., 1950, Chemical studies in host-virus interactions. VI. Immunochemical studies on the purity of concentrates of various bacterial viruses prepared by differential centrifugation procedures, with an appendix on the desoxyribonucleic acid content of their viruses. J. Exp. Med., *91*, 607-618.

Cohen, S. S., and Fowler, C. B., 1948, Chemical studies in host-virus interactions. V. Some additional methods of determining nutritional requirements for virus multiplication. J. Exp. Med., *87*, 275-282.

Cowles, P. B., 1931, The recovery of bacteriophage from filtrates derived from heated spore-suspensions. J. Bact., *22*, 119-123.

Crowe, H. W., and Coke, H., 1938, The growth-stimulating effect of bacteriophage. J. Path. Bact., *47*, 157-160.

Delbrück, M., 1940, The growth of bacteriophage and lysis of the host. J. Gen. Physiol., *23*, 643-660.

Delbrück, M., 1945a, Interference between bacterial viruses. III. The mutual exclusion effect and the depressor effect. J. Bact., *50*, 151-170.

Delbrück, M., 1945b, Effects of specific antisera on the growth of bacterial viruses. J. Bact., *50*, 137-150.

Delbrück, M., 1946a, Bacterial viruses or bacteriophages. Biol. Rev., *21*, 30-40.

Delbrück, M., 1946b, Experiments with bacterial viruses. Harvey Lecture Series, *41*, 161-187.

Delbrück, M., and Bailey, W. T., Jr., 1946, Induced mutations in bacterial viruses. Cold Spring Harbor Symposia on Quant. Biol., *11*, 33-37.

Delbrück, M., and Luria, S. E., 1942, Interference between two bacterial viruses acting upon the same host, and the mechanism of virus growth. Arch. Biochem., *1*, 111-141.

Demerec, M., and Fano, U., 1945, Bacteriophage-resistant mutants in *Escherichia coli*. Genetics, *30*, 119-136.

Doermann, A. H., 1948a, Intracellular growth of bacteriophage. Carnegie Inst. Washington Yr. Bk., *47*, 176-182.

Doermann, A. H., 1948b, Lysis and lysis inhibition with *Escherichia coli* bacteriophage. J. Bact., *55*, 257-276.

Doermann, A. H., and Dissosway, C. F.-R., 1949, Intracellular growth and genetics of bacteriophage. Carnegie Inst. Washington Yr. Bk., *48*, 170-176.

den Dooren de Jong, L. E., 1931, Ueber Bac. megatherium und den darin anwesenden Bakteriophagen. Zentralbl. f. Bakt., Abt. 1, Orig., *120*, 1-15.

Dulbecco, R., 1949, The number of particles of bacteriophage T2 that can participate in intracellular growth. Genetics, *34*, 126-132.

Dulbecco, R., 1950, Experiments on photoreactivation of bacteriophages inactivated with ultraviolet radiation. J. Bact., *59*, 329-347.

Dulbecco, R., 1952a, Mutual exclusion between related phages. J. Bact., *63*, 209-217.

Dulbecco, R., 1952b, A critical test of the recombination theory of multiplicity reactivation. J. Bact., *63*, 199-207.

Elford, W. J., 1938, The sizes of viruses and bacteriophages, and methods for their determination *in* Doerr and Hallauer, Handbuch der Virusforschung, Berlin, Springer, pt. 1, pp. 126-231.

Ellis, E. L., and Delbrück, M., 1939, The growth of bacteriophage. J. Gen. Physiol., *22*, 365-384.

Fitzgerald, R. J., and Lee, M. E., 1946, Studies on bacterial viruses. II. Observations on the mode of action of acridines in inhibiting lysis of virus-infected bacteria. J. Immunol., *52*, 127-135.

Fong, J., 1949, Bacteriophage. Ann. Rev. Microbiol., *3*, 423-444.

Foster, R. A. C., 1948, An analysis of the action of proflavine on bacteriophage growth. J. Bact., *56*, 795-809.

Frilley, M., Bulgakov, N., and Bonet-Maury, P., 1944, Recherches sur la taille et la structure du bactériphage φ-X-174. Actions des Rayons X. (K du molybdène). Compt. rend. Soc. biol., *138*, 726-727.

Gold, W., and Watson, D. W., 1950, Studies on the bacteriophage infection cycle. II. Phage infection and lysis of *Clostridium madisonii*, a function of pH. J. Bact., *59*, 17-27.

Gratia, A., 1936, Des relations numériques entre bactéries lysogènes et particules de bactériophage. Ann. Inst. Pasteur, *57*, 652-676.

Henry, J. E., and Henry, R. J., 1946, Studies on the relationship between bacteriophage and bacterial host cell. I. Absorption of phage by resistant variants of staphylococcus. J. Bact., *52*, 481-486; 527-538.

d'Herelle, F., 1917, Sur un microbe invisible antagoniste des bacilles dysentériques. Compt. rend. Acad. sci., *165*, 373-375.

Hershey, A. D., 1943, Experiments with bacteriophage supporting the lattice-hypothesis. J. Immunol., *47*, 77-87.

Hershey, A. D., 1946a. Mutation of bacteriophage with respect to type of plaque. Genetics, *31*, 620-640.

Hershey, A. D., 1946b. Spontaneous mutations in bacterial viruses. Cold Spring Harbor Symposia on Quant Biol., *11*, 67-76.

Hershey, A. D., 1952, Reproduction of bacteriophage. Exp. Cell Research, in press.

Hershey, A. D., and Bronfenbrenner, J., 1947, Effects of complement on the specific neutralization of bacteriophage. Fed. Proc., *6*, 428.

Hershey, A. D., and Chase, M., 1951, Genetic recombination and heterozygosis in bacteriophage. Cold Spring Harbor Symp. Quant. Biol., *16*, in press.

Hershey, A. D., and Davidson, H., 1951, Allelic and nonallelic genes controlling host specificity in a bacteriophage. Genetics, *36*, 667-675.

Hershey, A. D., Kalmanson, G., and Bronfenbrenner, J., 1943, Quantitative relationships in the phage-antiphage reaction. J. Immunol., *46*, 281-299.

Hershey, A. D., Kamen, M. D., Kennedy, J. W., and Gest, H., 1951a, The mortality of bacteriophage containing assimilated radioactive phosphorus. J. Gen. Physiol., *34*, 305-319.

Hershey, A. D., Kimura, F., and Bronfenbrenner, J., 1947, Uniformity of size of bacteriophage particles. Proc. Soc. Exp. Biol. and Med., *64*, 7-12.

Hershey, A. D., Roesel, C., Chase, M., and Forman, S., 1951b, Growth and inheritance in bacteriophage. Carnegie Inst. Washington Yr. Bk., *50*, 195-200.

Hershey, A. D., and Rotman, R., 1948, Linkage among genes controlling inhibition of lysis in a bacterial virus. Proc. Nat. Acad. Sci., *34*, 89-96.

Hershey, A. D., and Rotman, R., 1949, Gentic recom-

bination between host-range and plaque-type mutants of bacteriophage in single bacterial cells. Genetics, *34*, 44-71.

Hetler, D. M., and Bronfenbrenner, J., 1928, Evidence of hydrolysis of bacterial protein during lysis. J. Exp. Med., *48*, 269-275.

Hetler, D. M., and Bronfenbrenner, J., 1932, Further studies on the mechanism of transmissible lysis of bacteria. Proc. Soc. Exp. Biol. and Med., *29*, 806-808.

Hollaender, A., and Oliphant, J. W., 1944, The inactivating effect of monochromatic ultraviolet radiation on influenza virus. J. Bact., *48*, 447-454.

Hook, A. E., Beard, D., Taylor, A. R., Sharp, D. G., and Beard, J. W., 1946, Isolation and characterization of the T2 bacteriophage of *Escherichia coli*. J. Biol. Chem., *165*, 241-258.

Kalmanson, G. M., and Bronfenbrenner, J., 1943, Restoration of activity of neutralized biologic agents by removal of antibody with papain. J. Immunol., *47*, 387-407.

Kerby, G. P., Gowdy, R. A., Dillon, E. S., Dillon, M. L., Csáky, T. Z., Sharp, D. G., and Beard, J. W., 1949, Purification, pH stability and sedimentation properties of the T7 bacteriophage of *Escherichia coli*. J. Immunol., *63*, 93-107.

Kozloff, L., Putnam, F. W., and Evans, E. A., Jr., 1950, Precursors of bacteriophage nitrogen and carbon. *In* Viruses 1950, M. Delbrück, ed. California Institute of Technology, Pasadena, pp. 55-63.

Krueger, A. P., 1936, The nature of bacteriophage and its mode of action. Physiol. Rev., *16*, 129-172.

Krueger, A. P., and Scribner, E. J., 1939, Intracellular phage precursor. J. Gen. Physiol., *22*, 699-717.

Latarjet, R., 1946, L'effet biologique primaire des radiations et la structure des microorganismes. Rev. canadienne de biol., *5*, 9-47.

Latarjet, R., 1948, Intracellular growth of bacteriophage studied by Roentgen irradiation. J. Gen. Physiol., *31*, 529-546.

Lea, D. E., 1946, Actions of Radiations on Living Cells. 402 pp., Cambridge University Press.

Lesley, S. M., French, R. C., and Graham, A. F., 1950, Breakdown of infecting coliphage by the host cell. Arch. Biochem., *28*, 149-150.

Luria, S. E., 1945a, Mutations of bacterial viruses affecting their host range. Genetics, *30*, 84-99.

Luria, S. E., 1945b, Genetics of bacterium-bacterial virus relationship. Ann. Missouri Bot. Garden, *32*, 235-242.

Luria, S. E., 1946, Spontaneous bacterial mutations to resistance to antibacterial agents. Cold Spring Harbor Symposia on Quant. Biol., *11*, 130-137.

Luria, S. E., 1947, Reactivation of irradiated bacteriophage by transfer of self-reproducing units. Proc. Nat. Acad. Sci., *33*, 253-264.

Luria, S. E., 1950, Bacteriophage: an essay on virus reproduction. Science, *111*, 507-511.

Luria, S. E., 1951, The frequency distribution of spontaneous bacteriophage mutants as evidence for the exponential rate of phage reproduction. Cold Spring Harbor Symp. Quant. Biol., *16*, in press.

Luria, S. E., and Anderson, T. F., 1942, The identification and characterization of bacteriophages with the electron microscope. Proc. Nat. Acad. Sci., *28*, 127-130.

Luria, S. E., and Delbrück, M., 1942, Interference between inactivated bacterial virus and active virus of the same strain and of a different strain. Arch. Biochem., *1*, 207-218.

Luria, S. E., and Delbrück, M., 1943, Mutations of bacteria from virus sensitivity to virus resistance. Genetics, *28*, 491-511.

Luria, S. E., Delbrück, M., and Anderson, T. F., 1943, Electron microscope studies of bacterial viruses. J. Bact., *46*, 57-78.

Luria, S. E., and Dulbecco, R., 1949, Genetic recombinations leading to production of active bacteriophage from ultraviolet inactivated bacteriophage particles. Genetics, *34*, 93-125.

Luria, S. E., and Exner, F. M., 1941, The inactivation of bacteriophages by x-rays—influence of the medium. Proc. Nat. Acad. Sci., *27*, 370-375.

Luria, S. E., and Human, M. L., 1950, Chromatin staining of bacteria during bacteriophage infection. J. Bact., *59*, 551-560.

Luria, S. E., and Latarjet, R., 1947, Ultraviolet irradiation of bacteriophage during intracellular growth. J. Bact., *53*, 149-163.

Luria, S. E., Williams, R. C., and Backus, R. C., 1951, Electron micrographic counts of bacteriophage particles. J. Bact., *61*, 179-188.

Lwoff, A., and Gutmann, A., 1950, Recherches sur un *Bacillus megatherium* lysogène. Ann. Inst. Pasteur, *78*, 711-739.

Lwoff, A., Siminovitch, L., and Kjeldgaard, N., 1950, Induction de la lyse bactériophagique de la totalité d'une population microbienne lysogène. Compt. rend. Acad. Sci., *231*, 190-191.

Maaløe, O., 1950, Some effects of changes of temperature on intracellular growth of the bacterial virus T4r. Acta Pathologica et Microbiologica Scandinavica, *27*, 680-694.

Maaløe, O., and Watson, J. D., 1951, The transfer of radioactive phosphorus from parental to progeny phage. Proc. Nat. Acad. Sci., *37*, 507-513.

Monod, J., and Wollman, E., 1947, L'inhibition de la croissance et de l'adaptation enzymatique chez les bactéries infectées par le bactériophage. Ann. Inst. Pasteur, *73*, 937-956.

Northrop, J. H., 1938, Concentration and purification of bacteriophage. J. Gen. Physiol., *21*, 335-366.

Novick, A., and Szilard, L., 1951, Virus strains of identical phenotype but different genotype. Science, *113*, 34-35.

Pirie, A., 1940, The effect of lysozyme on the union between a phage and the susceptible *Bacillus megatherium*. Brit. J. Exp. Path., *21*, 125-132.

Puck, T. T., 1949, A reversible transformation of T1 bacteriophage. J. Bact., *57*, 647-655.

Puck, T. T., Garen, A., and Cline, J., 1951, The mechanism of virus attachment to host cells. I. The role of ions in the primary reaction. J. Exp. Med., *93*, 65-88.

Putnam, F. W., and Kozloff, L. M., 1950, Biochemical studies of virus reproduction. IV. The fate of the infecting virus particle. J. Biol. Chem., *182*, 243-250.

Roesel, C. E., 1951, Antibody molecules with two specificities produced by animals exposed to mixtures of antigens. Thesis, Washington University, St. Louis.

Ruska, H., 1941, Über ein neues bei der bakteriophagen Lyse auftretendes Formelement. Naturwiss., *29*, 367-368.

Schlesinger, M., 1933, Beobachtung und Zählung von Bakteriophagenteilchen im Dunkelfeld—Die Form der Teilchen. Ztschr. f. Hyg., *115*, 774-780.

Spizizen, J., 1943, Biochemical studies on the phenomenon of virus reproduction. I. Amino acids and the multiplication of bacteriophage. J. Infect. Dis., *73*, 212-221.

Stent, G. S., and Wollman, E. L., 1950, Studies on activation of T4 bacteriophage by cofactor. II. The mechanism of activation. Biochim. and Biophys. Acta, *6*, 307-316.

Sturtevant, A. H., and Beadle, G. W., 1939, An Introduction to Genetics. Philadelphia, Saunders, p. 33.

Twort, F. W., 1915, An investigation of the nature of ultramicroscopic viruses. Lancet, *2*, 1241-1243.

Wahl, R., Nitti, F., and Faguet, M., 1946, Relations entre la lyse bactériophagique et la multiplication microbienne étudiées à l'aide des sulfamides. Ann. Inst. Pasteur, *72*, 290-293.

Watson, J. D., 1950, The properties of X-ray-inactivated bacteriophage. I. Inactivation by direct effect. J. Bact., *60*, 697-718.

Weigle, J. J., and Delbrück, M., 1951, Mutual exclusion between an infecting phage and a carried phage. J. Bact., *62*, 301-318.

Wilson, G. S., and Miles, A. A., 1946, The bacteriophage *in* Topley and Wilson's Principles of Bacteriology and Immunity, ed. 3. Baltimore, Williams & Wilkins, pp. 325-350.

PETER K. OLITSKY, M.D., AND J. CASALS, M.D.

The Rockefeller Institute for Medical Research

11

Viral Encephalitides

Encephalitis means inflammation of the brain. When the brain is inflamed, the spinal cord also is usually involved either primarily or secondarily; therefore, the word encephalomyelitis is often employed instead of encephalitis. These designations, based on location of pathologic changes, are in contradistinction to the words polioencephalitis which denotes that the gray matter of the brain is essentially involved, poliomyelitis which indicates that the principal lesions are in the gray matter of the cord, and leuko-encephalitis which points to the fact that the cerebral white matter is the tissue most affected.

Encephalitis may be caused by physical means, chemical substances, and infective agents or their toxins. The infective agents may be protozoa, fungi, bacteria, spirochetes, rickettsiae, or viruses; when the last-mentioned agents are the incitants, the term viral encephalitides is applied to the diseases induced and viruses causing them are referred to as being neurotropic. A neurotropic virus attacks nervous tissue, but it may also affect other tissues; a neuronotropic virus attacks chiefly neurons. There are degrees of neurotropism, so that a distinction is made between highly neurotropic viruses, such as those of poliomyelitis and rabies, and ordinary neurotropic viruses, for example, those causing equine and Japanese B encephalitis. Highly neurotropic viruses are found in the central nervous system (CNS) and not at all or with difficulty in other tissues, blood, secretions, or excretions, except for that of poliomyelitis which can readily be found in the feces. Moreover, the isolation of a highly neurotropic virus from nonneural materials, e.g., the saliva in rabies and pharyngeal secretions, feces, or lymphatic glands in poliomyelitis, does not necessarily indicate that such an agent multiplies elsewhere than in nervous structures in vivo.

Levaditi (1929) named the then-known encephalomyelitic viruses ectodermic (*ectodermoses*) neurotropes. From this viewpoint, now only of historical interest, such viruses showed an elective affinity for the tissues derived from the ectoderm (cutaneous, mucous or corneal membranes) and for those derived from the invaginated ectoderm (the central nervous system) (Levaditi and Voet, 1935). These viruses, however, attack cells of other embryonic origins and the classification is, therefore, not acceptable at the present time. As the viral encephalitides became better known, certain ones were classified on the basis of common characteristics, and were designated as summer encephalitides, endemic or epidemic virus infections of CNS, and, finally, arthropod-borne virus encephalitides.

To show how the subject of viral encephalitides has developed within the past few years, one need refer only to a review of viruses written in 1928 by Rivers. The various human encephalitides then known, with the exception of rabies and poliomyelitis, were listed as (1) von Economo's (lethargic) ; (2) following vaccination (jennerian prophylaxis) ; (3) Japanese 1924; (4) Koritschoner; and (5) Australian X. At that time, from none of these diseases had a virus been recovered and definitely proved to be the causal agent. Eight years later the virus of Japanese encephalitis had been found; the Koritschoner disease had been shown to be identical with rabies; and now the Australian X malady is assumed to be Japanese B encephalitis. From different parts of the world, many epidemic viral encephalitides have been reported since 1930.

It is impossible at the present time to classify the encephalitides. For convenience, however, one might group them in various ways: one such tentative grouping appears below. Dates in parentheses after each name refer to the year of the first epidemic or isolation of the virus; when two dates are given, the second refers to the year in which the virus was first isolated.

CNS infections caused by neurotropic viruses which invade along axonal pathways:

Poliomyelitis (1840, 1909; *v.* Chap. 13)
Rabies (1881; *v.* Chap. 12)

Arthropod-borne encephalitides so called first by Hammon and Reeves (1945):

St. Louis encephalitis (1933)
Japanese B encephalitis (1924, 1936)
Australian X disease 1917 (possibly Japanese B encephalitis)
Western equine encephalitis (1930)
Eastern equine encephalitis (1933)
Venezuelan equine encephalitis (1938)
Louping-ill (1930)
Russian Far East or tick-borne encephalitis (1937)

Encephalitides transmitted to man by direct contact with lower animals (in addition to rabies):

B virus (monkey; 1934)
Lymphocytic choriomeningitis (mice; 1934)

Encephalitides produced by viruses ordinarily nonencephalitogenic:

Herpes simplex (*v.* Chap. 25)
Lymphogranuloma venereum (*v.* Chap. 20)
Mumps (*v.* Chap. 28)
Measles (*v.* Chap. 22)
Infectious mononucleosis (viral? *v.* Chap. 29)

Viruses which are encephalitogenic in experimental animals but as yet not definitely known to cause encephalitis in man:

A. "Tropical" viruses (1940 to date)

West Nile	Ilhéus
Semliki Forest	Anopheles A
Bunyamwera	Anopheles B
Bwamba fever	Wyeomyia

(At present, 9 others from Africa and South America are being studied; among them are the Ntaya, Zika, Uganda S and Kumba viruses)
B. California
Miscellaneous group:
Durand's disease (not as yet established as an encephalitis, 1940)
Pseudolymphocytic choriomeningitis (1939)
Encephalomyocarditis family (so named by Warren, Smadel and Russ in 1949):
Col. SK virus infection, 1940; Col. MM virus infection, 1943; encephalomyocarditis, 1945, and Mengo encephalomyelitis, 1949 (*v.* Chap. 39 for description and references)
Coxsackie group (1948; *v.* Chap. 14)

Neurologic maladies possibly having a viral etiology but for which as yet no infective agent has been identified:

von Economo's disease (1915)
Guillain-Barré syndrome (infectious polyneuritis; 1859?)
Herpes zoster (1862?; *v.* Chap. 27)

Demyelinating encephalitides, for which viral etiology has been proposed without convincing evidence, are grouped here tentatively for aid in differential diagnosis:

Acute primary hemorrhagic encephalitis or leuko-encephalitis (1881, 1944)

Disseminated encephalitis (1906; 1946)

Multiple sclerosis (1835, 1913 and later)

Postinfection or postvaccination encephalitides

Postinfection encephalitides, which occasionally arise shortly after smallpox or rabies vaccination or after recognizable infections caused by different nonencephalitogenic viruses, is an important group. Here also a viral etiology has not been established; in fact, their causation still remains obscure. In recent times, cases have been more frequently reported and occur after several viral infections, for examples, measles, influenza, mumps, varicella, variola, infectious hepatitis, dengue, rubella, lymphocytic choriomeningitis and yellow fever.

The clinical picture presented by an encephalitis depends on the areas of the CNS damaged instead of upon the kind of virus involved. While a definite clinical picture may be found during an epidemic, one may encounter great difficulty, from the clinical picture alone, in diagnosing the kind of encephalitic virus responsible for the outbreak. Workers in the laboratory are, therefore, called upon to identify the causal agent.

The general pathologic picture of the viral encephalitides depends on the fact that viruses are obligate cellular parasites and that the first evidence of injury due to their presence appears in susceptible cells. Nerve cells or neurons are the most important elements in the CNS and are susceptible to the action of many viruses. Some viruses attack not only neurons but cells of the supporting tissues also. Reaction of susceptible cells to viruses is evidenced by their degeneration or death. Injury and death of susceptible cells are followed by an inflammatory reaction; one finds neuronophagia, cellular infiltration about the blood vessels, proliferation of glial cells, infiltration of polymorphonuclear and mononuclear cells into the meninges and nervous tissues, and areas of hemorrhage and necrosis in the ground substance of the gray or white matter. Variations in the above picture that may be observed in different kinds of encephalitis depend on the fact that a certain sort of lesion may be more prominent in one type of encephalitis than in another and that similar pathologic lesions may have different localizations in the different encephalitides. In any event, it is impossible or very difficult, from a pathologic examination of the central nervous tissues alone, to make a definite diagnosis of a particular type of encephalitis in individual patients (Fig. 27; Fig. 28, *top, right and left; bottom, left*).

VON ECONOMO'S DISEASE

(Synonyms: *Encephalitis lethargica;* type A encephalitis; epidemic encephalitis; sleepy or sleeping sickness)

Introduction

Von Economo's disease is a meningo-encephalomyelitis which is probably infectious and characterized by a wide variety of signs and symptoms in different individuals and in the same person at different stages of the malady; often associated with ophthalmoplegia and residual parkinsonism, and occurring chiefly in spring and winter months. None of the names given to this malady is satisfactory. Certainly many of the patients are far from being sleepy and now it is obvious that several encephalitic viruses cause epidemics. Since it was the first of the epidemic encephalitides to be recognized, it is the first to be described here, even though the causal agent has not been discovered.

History

What happened before 1915, according to Flexner (1935), "is lost in that haze of the history of the diseases of the nervous system which up to a hundred years ago consisted of a medley of 'hardenings and soft-

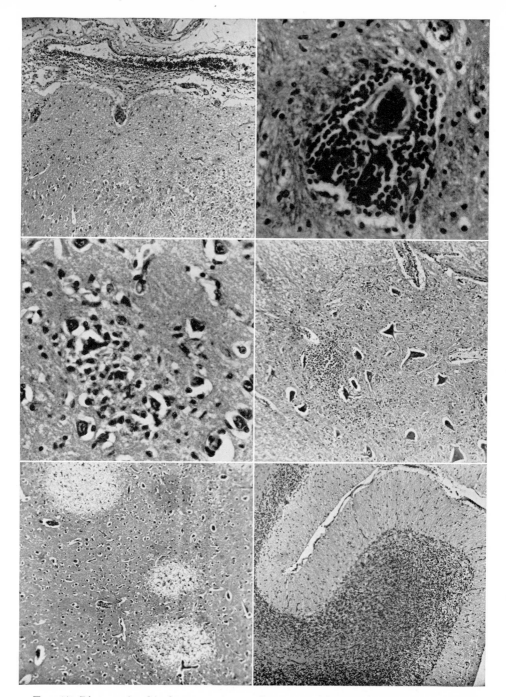

FIG. 27. Pictures in this figure represent the essential lesions found in human CNS in Japanese B encephalitis and are characteristic of the pathologic picture seen in the viral encephalitides in general. All are stained with hematoxylin-eosin.

(*Top, left*) Lymphocytic infiltration of the cerebral meninges. × 80. (*Top, right*) Perivascular infiltration. × 280.

(*Center, left*) Cortical neuronal disintegration, exhibiting lymphocytic, polymorphonuclear and microglial cell reaction. × 280. (*Center, right*) Glial focus, lymphocytic cell infiltration and degeneration of neurons. × 80.

(*Bottom, left*) Multiple acellular plaques of necrosis in cortex. × 80. (*Bottom, right*) Complete destruction of Purkinje cells. × 68. (Zimmerman, H. M., 1946, The pathology of Japanese B encephalitis. American Journal of Pathology, *22*, 965-991.)

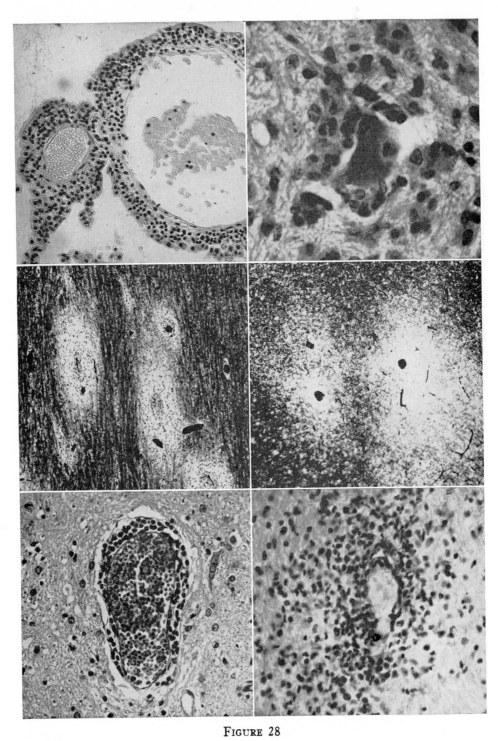

FIGURE 28

enings.' " It may well be that the "sleeping sickness" associated with the influenza epidemic of 1712 and "nona" of about 60 years ago may have been von Economo's disease, but the first modern cases were probably observed in 1915 in Rumania (Urechia, 1921). Many patients were noted in France in 1916 (Cruchet et al., 1917) and the first elaborate work on the disease as it occurred in Vienna in 1917 was by von Economo (1917). It appeared in 1918 in the United States in New York City, Iowa and West Virginia (Neal et al., 1942). Epidemics were reported from different parts of the world until 1926 when they apparently ceased and have not been heard of to the present time, although now and again a single case is seen; the diagnoses of such cases are always under suspicion since they are made on clinical findings alone. Why epidemics have ceased is a mystery. No specific virus has as yet been recovered. Earlier reports indicated that there might be a connection between the outbreaks of encephalitis and those of influenza; however, no direct relationship between the two maladies has been proved.

Clinical Picture

The precise incubation period is un-known, but it is assumed to be from 4 to 15 days. The clinical picture as described follows that given by Barker and revised by Rivers (1943). There is a marked diversity of signs and symptoms during the course of the affection so that any type of neurologic syndrome can be simulated. In general the symptom-complex is divided into three stages; the first exhibits many types, but two are well defined and common: (1) a somnolent-ophthalmoplegic syndrome, and (2) an irritative, hyperkinetic complex, either choreiform or myoclonic. The somnolent-ophthalmoplegic type is characterized by a brief initial stage with fever, meningeal irritation, drowsiness, and ocular paralyses. Other symptoms may develop, such as rigidity, paralyses of other members and psychotic disturbances. The hyperkinetic type is initiated by fever and excitement which is followed by choreiform movements or myoclonic contractions. Other types seen at times during the first stage are: the psychotic, with patients exhibiting a variety of signs ranging from those found in simple mental impairment to those seen in conditions simulating general paresis or schizophrenia; the poliomyelitic type with lower motor neuron paralyses; the type with involvement of

---

FIG. 28. All pictures, except *top right,* were obtained from the collection of Dr. T. M. Rivers, Director, Hospital of The Rockefeller Institute; *top left* with permission of the Journal of Experimental Medicine. Center and bottom rows photographed by J. B. Haulenbeek.

(*Top, left*) Lymphocytic infiltration of the choroid plexus in a monkey having experimental lymphocytic choriomeningitis. H. and E. stain. × 207.

(*Top, right*) Neuronophagia from a case of von Economo's disease. H. and E. stain. × 575.

(*Center, left*) Perivascular demyelination in postvaccinal encephalitis. Weigert's stain. × 54.

(*Center, right*) Perivascular demyelination in postmeasles encephalitis. Weigert's stain. × 54. The center frames should be compared with Figure 27 (*bottom, left*) in which the demyelination is not perivascular.

(*Bottom, left*) Engorged vessel of the brain showing perivascular cuffing limited to the Virchow-Robin space; from a case of St. Louis encephalitis. H. and E. stain. × 270.

(*Bottom, right*) Infiltration around a cerebral vessel, from a case of postvaccinal encephalitis. To be compared with frame to left and to be noted is the spreading disposition of the perivascular infiltrating cells, not limited to the Virchow-Robin space. The cells consist of monocytes, lymphocytes and altered phagocytic glial cells. H. and E. stain. × 270.

posterior root ganglia; tabetic type with ataxia; an epileptomaniacal type; cataleptic type; amyostatic-akinetic form (apathy, rigidity, akinesia, amimia, slow motion and tremor); and finally, the fulminating type from which the patient succumbs within a few hours after the onset.

Of importance is the fact that during an epidemic a large number of patients may show aberrant forms and inapparent disease. In the latter case, the first suspicion of an encounter with the malady is the appearance of definite parkinsonism.

The second stage (pseudopsychoneurotic) may persist for months or years and is characterized by subjective symptoms such as headache, insomnia, irritability, dizziness, and fatigue. Often objective signs of CNS lesions may be lacking.

The third stage (chronic) at times immediately follows the first and consists of motor disturbances of the type seen in parkinsonism. There also may be vegetative disturbances (sialorrhea, dacryorrhea and seborrhea) or psychotic signs.

During all stages of the disease, the blood count is of little diagnostic value. The cerebrospinal fluid is usually clear and shows pleocytosis (lymphocytosis), normal or slightly increased amounts of sugar, and slight increase in protein. It should be emphasized that the fluid is often completely normal.

PATHOLOGIC PICTURE

Macroscopically, the CNS may show hyperemic areas in the meninges and hyperemia accompanied by small hemorrhages in the basal ganglia, midbrain and pons. Microscopically, the lesions of von Economo's disease are as a rule slower in developing and are of a more chronic, productive type than are those of the established viral encephalitides. They are usually found in the gray matter, particularly in the mesencephalon and diencephalon (von Economo, 1917), and are (a) degenerative and (b) inflammatory and infiltrative. The former are revealed by degeneration and necrosis of neurons associated with neuronophagia (Fig. 28, *top, right*), the latter are evidenced by perivascular cuffings, focal glial cell proliferation and lymphocytic infiltrations, especially in the gray matter. The perivascular reaction consists of accumulation of small and large mononuclear cells and plasma cells in the sheaths of the vessels and in the perivascular spaces. Hemorrhages may be seen in limited areas of the cerebral cortex, basal ganglia, midbrain and pons. Demyelination is not prominent, nor are lesions in the spinal cord marked.

ETIOLOGY

The cause of the malady has not been discovered even though its general aspect conforms with that of a viral infection. Levaditi (1929) proposed herpes simplex virus as the causal agent. This virus occasionally induces encephalitis in man but such an encephalitis is quite distinct (*v. infra*) from von Economo's disease.

DIAGNOSIS

There are no laboratory tests available at present for specific diagnosis; the disease is recognized on clinical or pathologic grounds alone and for that reason diagnoses are not always accurate.

TREATMENT

No specific treatment is available.

EPIDEMIOLOGY

The disease has been widespread throughout the world. It has a definite seasonal incidence, occurring chiefly in winter and early spring months. Thus, its spread is probably not dependent on insects. It has been suggested that the malady is spread by contact or droplet infection. People of all ages may be attacked, but most patients are under 40 years of age; 25 per cent of cases occur in people from 10 to 20 years old. The incidence is slightly higher in males than in females. The average mortality rate is 30 per cent. Residual symptoms occur in 20 per cent of patients. At present no one knows how to prevent the spread of the disease in a population.

ST. LOUIS ENCEPHALITIS

(SYNONYMS: American encephalitis used by Japanese and Europeans; S. L. E. as abbreviation)

INTRODUCTION

St. Louis encephalitis is a meningo-encephalomyelitis, endemic and epidemic in central and western United States, having a varied symptomatology, prevailing in the summer, and caused by a specific virus. The disease differs in many respects from von Economo's encephalitis, but is similar in certain respects to the western type of equine encephalitis and to Japanese B encephalitis, two of the so-called summer encephalitides.

HISTORY

In the summer of 1932 an epidemic of encephalitis, which was first regarded as von Economo's disease, occurred in Paris, Illinois. During the following summer a similar epidemic occurred in and around St. Louis and Kansas City, Missouri; 1,130 cases were reported in St. Louis County. The disease was then believed to be a nosologic entity different from von Economo's encephalitis. Muckenfuss, Armstrong and McCordock (1933) by inoculation of infected human brain tissue into monkeys, recovered the causal virus. Webster and Fite (1933) obtained similar results by using albino mice as experimental hosts. The malady appeared again in St. Louis in 1937; thereafter only small outbreaks or sporadic cases have been encountered in limited parts of the United States.

CLINICAL PICTURE

After an incubation period, estimated to range from 4 to 21 days, the disease develops and presents a clinical picture somewhat different from that of von Economo's encephalitis. The picture presented by persons attacked during the epidemic of 1933 has been described by Hempelmann, revised by Rivers (1943), as follows:

Group One. Individuals in this group showed an abrupt onset of illness with fever, nausea, vomiting, constipation, headache, vertigo, nuchal rigidity, Kernig's sign, lethargy, ataxia, difficulty with speech, mental confusion, and tremor. Paralyses were not common, and when they occurred they were of the spastic type; ocular muscles were, as a rule, spared.

Group Two. In this group, patients showed from 1 to 4 days prodromata of headache, malaise, abdominal and muscular pains, chills and fever, sore throat and conjunctivitis with photophobia. Following this, the encephalitic syndrome described under Group One developed.

Group Three included the mild and abortive cases with headache and fever which might have been missed except for abnormalities in the cerebrospinal fluid. However, such illnesses should be differentiated from poliomyelitis.

Hammon (1943b) described the clinical syndrome in recent small epidemics and in sporadic cases in accordance with its occurrence in infants and in children and adults; he further subdivided the cases into mild and severe types. In infants the onset is sudden with rapidly developing fever, 105-106° F. or higher, and neurologic disturbances, especially those involving the motor systems. The disease may be fulminating and may end in death from 2 to 4 days after onset. Not infrequently an infant recovers within 5 or 7 days; 10 to 40 per cent under 6 months of age in certain outbreaks show signs of permanent injury to the CNS in the form of mental retardation, hydrocephalus, epileptiform seizures and similar states. In children and adults the disease is generally not so severe, but sometimes a fulminating type is seen. Convalescence requiring months in severe cases and weeks in milder ones, is the rule. Recovery in the older group is usually complete; less than 5 per cent of the survivors have sequelae, such as tremor, weakness and mental deficiency; parkinsonism is rare.

Blood counts exhibit, as a rule, 10,000 to 14,000 white blood cells with a shift to the left in the polymorphonuclear elements. The spinal fluid is clear, under slight pressure and with pleocytosis, up to 300 cells or more, lymphocytes and monocytes predominating; protein is slightly increased; normal amount of sugar is found.

PATHOLOGIC PICTURE

Gross examination of the brain and cord reveals edema, vascular congestion and small hemorrhages. Microscopic examination shows a cellular infiltration, chiefly of lymphocytes, and engorgement of blood vessels in the meningeal layers. In other tissues of the CNS there are evidences of acute inflammation, such as engorgement of the blood vessels, perivascular lymphocytic infiltration (Fig. 28, *bottom, left*) small hemorrhages, focal glial proliferation, and diffuse infiltration of lymphocytes, polymorphonuclear leukocytes, and plasma cells; lymphocytes predominate. The outstanding lesions are the degeneration and necrosis of neurons associated with neuronophagia; exceptionally, small sterile abscesses and areas of necrosis of the gray and white matter occur. Perivascular edema with loculation of the adjoining parenchyma may occur. Perivascular demyelination is not seen.

The histopathologic picture of St. Louis encephalitis differs from that of von Economo's disease. In the former the meningeal reaction is more pronounced than in the latter; the inflammatory foci are more widely scattered through the cerebral cortex than in the basal ganglia and midbrain; neuronal necrosis and neuronophagia are more marked; and the spinal cord is more extensively involved.

EXPERIMENTAL INFECTION; HOST RANGE

Rhesus monkeys respond to intracerebral inoculation of only certain strains of the virus by showing 8 to 14 days later fever, excitement, tremors, paresis, and even prostration, followed as a rule by recovery. At necropsy one observes neuronal degeneration and necrosis, perivascular cuffing, and focal cellular infiltration of the nervous tissues. It is difficult to propagate the virus in monkeys, since it becomes lost on passage; moreover, cebus monkeys are wholly insusceptible.

Mice are susceptible to the virus. It was with this species that Webster in 1937 developed a strain particularly susceptible to St. Louis, louping-ill and Russian Far East viruses; the strain has been designated albino Swiss-W mouse (Casals and Schneider, 1943). Mice can be infected regularly by intracerebral or intranasal route and occasionally by feeding them virus suspensions (Harford and Bronfenbrenner, 1942). When mice are infected by the cerebral or nasal route, the virus is found regularly in the CNS, blood and spleen, and in practically all other organs during the terminal stages of the infections (Peck and Sabin, 1947). Virus may be found in the spleen for 30 days after a subcutaneous dose. The active agent can be propagated in the testicles of mice without diminution of its virulence. After intranasal or intracerebral infection of Swiss-W mice, an incubation period of from 3 to 4 days is followed by ataxia, ruffled fur, convulsions and paralysis; prostration and death occur from 1 to 5 days later. The pathologic picture resembles that seen in the human disease.

Mice develop the experimental disease when mouse-adapted virus diluted to 10^{-7} or 10^{-8} is given intracerebrally or when it is diluted to 10^{-3} and introduced intranasally. To induce experimental St. Louis encephalitis in mice, brain tissue containing virus is removed under sterile conditions and a sufficient amount of physiologic saline solution, or hormone broth at pH 7.4, or 10 per cent normal rabbit serum in saline solution is added to make a 10 per cent suspension. It is ground in a sterile mortar or in a Waring blendor. The suspension is then centrifuged at 2,000 r.p.m. for 10 minutes and the supernate is drawn into a tuberculin syringe having a 27 gauge, ¼ inch needle. Anesthetized mice are then injected intracerebrally at a point half way between the external ocular canthus and the auditory canal, just without the sagittal suture. The needle to half its length is directed through the skull and meninges and 0.03 cc. is slowly injected. For nasal instillation, a similar amount is dropped into each nasal cavity through a blunt needle so as not to injure the tissues. To infant mice, which are much more susceptible to the virus by intraperitoneal and subcutaneous inoculation than are adults, 0.1 to 0.25 cc. of the suspension is given (Olitsky and Harford, 1938; Schabel et al., 1947).

Rats (7 or 8 days old) and wild mice (gray house mice) are also susceptible to experimentally inoculated virus which induces a lethal encephalitis; but hamsters and horses are susceptible only to certain strains of the active agent. Adult rats, sheep, kittens, and ferrets are insusceptible. Chickens, doves, ducks, guinea pigs, and rabbits and other vertebrates may develop only an inapparent infection during which virus is found in their blood stream. Monkeys, horses and mice react with this type of infection after subcutaneous injection of minute amount of the virus. As will be shown later, the fact that animals in apparent health can harbor virus in the blood which in turn may infect insect vectors is of prime epidemiologic importance.

Etiology

The diameter of the virus as determined by filtration through gradocol membranes is 20 to 30 millimicrons. It passes readily through Berkefeld V and N, and Seitz filters. It is not so stable as are certain other encephalitic viruses, since it deteriorates rapidly on standing at room temperature. It is best preserved by being kept frozen at about −70° C., in buffered 50 per cent glycerol at 4° C., or lyophilized. In preparing virus for storage in the form of

a suspension, it is best to use undiluted or 50 per cent rabbit serum inactivated at 56° C. for 30 minutes as suspending fluid. The virus in 10 per cent suspensions of brain tissue is inactivated by 1 per cent formalin in from 12 to 18 hours at room temperature, but not by 1 per cent phenol within at least 25 days. Soft x-rays inactivate it within 4 hours in suspensions of brain tissue or in clear supernates. Filtered virus is inactivated when held at 56° C. for 30 minutes. The pH at which the active agent is most stable at 4° C., viz., 8.8 in glycine-phosphate buffer, is similar to that for the virus of Japanese B encephalitis: it remains active for 3 weeks at pH 8.4-8.8, but not above or below these values (Duffy, 1946).

The virus multiples in minced chick- or mouse-embryo tissue medium, in Li-Rivers (1930) medium, in modifications of the Maitland tissue medium, and in chick embryos. The latter can be infected by the yolk-sac or chorio-allantoic routes. The most commonly used procedure at the present time is that of inoculating the chorio-allantoic membrane of a 10- to 12-day-old chick embryo. For this purpose is employed a suspension of virus, usually 10 per cent, prepared as described above; or, if the virus material is contaminated, a Berkefeld V or Seitz filtrate is used. Of the suspension or its filtrate, 0.05 cc. is inoculated under sterile precautions through a puncture in the shell or placed on the membrane through a window made in the shell which after inoculation is sealed with a coverslip and paraffin. After incubation at from 35 to 37° C. for 3 or 4 days or longer, the egg is opened; the membrane is edematous and opaque and exhibits a diffuse proliferation of the ectodermal layers and focal necrosis. The St. Louis encephalitis virus is one that does not produce definite, discrete pocks, or localized lesions. The virus is recoverable from the membrane, brain, lungs, liver, kidney or spleen, and by intracerebral mouse test usually has a titer of 10^{-2} or 10^{-3}. This titer persists up to the time of hatch-ing. Chick embryos are little affected by the virus, although only few hatch successfully. The virus also multiplies in suspended-cell or agar-slant medium prepared from mouse-embryo tissue.

In the blood of human beings infected by St. Louis virus, neutralizing and complement-fixing antibodies are detectable on approximately the seventh day after the onset of illness. The neutralizing antibody can endure for many years, if not for a lifetime; complement-fixing antibody, for at least 1 to 3 years. In monkeys, mice, hamsters, and rabbits, the neutralizing antibody can be produced following injections of active virus or virus inactivated by formalin or ultraviolet radiation; depending on the route of injection and the species of animal, it may be found as early as 48 hours after injection. In mice and hamsters complement-fixing antibody is produced and appears, as a rule, somewhat later and endures for a shorter period than does the neutralizing antibody. Rabbit antiserum containing neutralizing antibody can be prepared not only against St. Louis encephalitis virus but also against most of the encephalitic viruses and is useful as a positive control in serologic work and studies of passive immunity. Sabin (1951) disclosed that the virus under certain conditions hemagglutinates sheep or newly hatched chick erythrocytes.

Several interesting immunologic phenomena have been reported in connection with this active agent which may have a general application to viral encephalitides. For example, Slavin (1943) showed that occasionally (3 of 14 pairs of mice) virus, administered intranasally to passively immunized young mice, may persist in the CNS, but not in the spleen or nasal mucosa, for as long as 162 days; the animals during the periods mentioned were in good health. Smith (1943) demonstrated in mice virus-neutralizing antibody in the milk and placental transmission of antibody. She also showed that young mice under 2 weeks of age are susceptible to the virus introduced

intraperitoneally; in older mice a resistance is developed to the virus inoculated in this manner but not to that introduced by intracerebral or intranasal routes (cf. equine encephalitis virus; Lennette and Koprowski, 1944). Hodes (1939) found that pregnancy in mice not only interferes with the development of immunity following vaccination but also causes a diminution in the amount of a previously established immunity; between 2 and 7 weeks postpartum the response to vaccination returns to the type seen in virgin mice. Finally, it has been reported that there is a marked difference in the increase of the virus in the brain tissue of innately susceptible and resistant mice. In the former, the virus reaches a higher titer on culture in vitro; the difference was believed to be due to some factor in the brain tissue itself and not to specific antibody (cf. discussion by Morgan, 1941, and Olitsky and Casals, 1945).

DIAGNOSIS

From clinical and pathologic observations alone, the only diagnosis that can be made with assurance is that of an encephalitis. A diagnosis of the specific type of encephalitis can be made only through laboratory tests which consist of serologic determinations and isolation and identification of the virus. Paired specimens of serum from each patient are necessary for the serologic tests. The first specimen should be taken as early as possible after the onset of illness; the second, late in convalescence. Then, the paired specimens are tested at the same time for the presence of neutralizing and complement-fixing antibodies. If antibodies against the St. Louis virus are absent from the first specimen and present in the second, the patient has had St. Louis encephalitis. If they are absent from both specimens, the patient probably did not have the disease. On the other hand, he might have had it, because a few patients fail to produce antibody against this virus during the period of observation. If the first specimen was taken sufficiently early in the course of the illness and antibodies of the same titer are present in both specimens, the current illness was not St. Louis encephalitis, the antibodies against the St. Louis virus having been acquired through an infection at some previous time. Frequently, serum from animals immunized against St. Louis encephalitis and occasionally serum from human patients convalescent from the disease contain antibodies against Japanese B and West Nile viruses as well as against St. Louis virus. In such cases it must be remembered that antibodies for a homologous virus, are, as a rule, at a higher level than they are for heterologous agents.

Now in regard to the isolation and identification of the virus. The active agent has not been recovered from the spinal fluid of human beings and only very rarely has it been recovered from the blood. Consequently, for diagnostic purposes it is not worth while looking for it in these materials. If a patient dies and necropsy is obtained, a search for the virus in the brain and cord is made. Specimens of brain and cord are collected under aseptic conditions. With these a 10- to 20-per cent emulsion is made in physiologic saline solution and 0.03 cc. of the emulsion is injected intracerebrally, as described, into each of at least 6 albino Swiss mice. If a transmissible filterable agent free from bacteria is obtained, it is then identified in the usual manner, namely, by neutralization and complement-fixation tests in which known antisera are used and by inoculation tests in which mice immune to known viruses are employed.

TREATMENT

There is no specific treatment of the disease. Antibiotic substances have been ineffective in experimental infections.

EPIDEMIOLOGY

Seasonal incidence of the disease is definite; most cases occur in late summer and early fall instead of spring and winter as is the case with von Economo's encephalitis. The disease is found mainly in mid- and southwestern United States (Woolley and Armstrong, 1934); streams, ponds and weeds in an area seem to favor its appearance (Casey and Broun, 1938). In the St. Louis 1933 epidemic, the attack rate was highest in those living in the suburbs of the city. In the epidemic of 1933, no age was exempt but the highest incidence occurred in persons older than 45 years. In the more recent small epidemics and sporadic cases in western United States, the incidence has been high in infancy, lowest in children from 5 to 12 years, and relatively high in persons from 15 to 50 years old; in the last class, rates were higher for males. The mortality rate varies with the epidemic and with facilities for nursing, since the latter is believed to be of great consequence in recovery (Hammon, 1943b); it increases directly with age and is reported to range from 5 to 30 per cent (Neal, 1942; Hammon, 1945).

The chief vectors of the disease as it exists in America are possibly, according to Hammon and Reeves (1943) and Hammon (1945, 1948), *Culex tarsalis* and *Culex pipiens*. In the laboratory, transmission of the virus to animals has been effected by 9 species of mosquitoes from 3 genera: *Culex, Aedes* and *Culiseta*. While the reservoir of the virus is not definitely known, mites feeding on infected chickens or other birds are suspected. After birds are infected by the bite of mites or mosquitoes, the virus circulates in their blood without affecting their health, and they develop neutralizing antibodies. The seasonal activity of *Culex tarsalis* mosquitoes from which the virus was isolated in nature correlates with the season of human epidemics and no other mosquito has shown as yet such a correlation. Moreover, they feed on birds in which, in nature, specific antibody against the virus is found. For these reasons the case for *Culex tarsalis* as vector is strong. It should be borne in mind that no transmission experiments in man have been performed. Consequently the evidence that mosquitoes are directly involved in the human disease is circumstantial. Reeves (1951) points out that *Culex tarsalis* is a primary vector of western equine and St. Louis encephalitis viruses only in certain areas. Recently it has been reported that the virus was isolated from chicken mites (*Dermanyssus gallinae*) collected in St. Louis County during a nonepidemic period (Smith, Blattner and Heys, 1944). This would indicate the possibility of the overwintering of the virus in the mites of chickens or other birds, especially since transovarian infection of the mite has been demonstrated (Smith et al., 1948). Finally, the virus has been passaged to the third generation in the eggs of *Dermacentor variabilis*, the American dog tick (Blattner and Heys, 1944).

The close similarity between St. Louis encephalitis and western equine encephalitis in respect to clinical, pathologic and epidemiologic phenomena is worthy of note. Hammon (1943b) states the case for the two viruses involved. Both are found in *Culex tarsalis* caught in nature and can be passaged in the laboratory by means of such mosquitoes; both infect horses and produce inapparent infection in other vertebrates; moreover, mosquitoes can acquire both viruses by feeding on infected fowl which show no apparent disease; both are disseminated through central and western United States; and finally, both cause disease in human beings in summer and may operate simultaneously in the same epidemic area.

Control Measures

Immunization by means of a vaccine devised by Sabin and collaborators (1943), which consists of formalin-inactivated virus, has not as yet had an adequate trial in human beings. It has been shown, however, capable of inducing a high degree of immunity in mice to active virus inoculated peripherally or intracerebrally; and in a small series of human tests it caused the appearance of neutralizing antibody. A vaccine prepared through inactivation of the active agent by means of ultraviolet radiation has also been used successfully in mice. Neither of these vaccines is available for general use as yet. A logical program for the protection of individuals and communities should always include measures for the control of arthropods.

JAPANESE B ENCEPHALITIS

(Synonyms: Russian autumnal encephalitis; Japanese encephalitis; summer encephalitis; probably identical with Australian X disease)

Introduction

Japanese B encephalitis is one of the summer encephalitides, chiefly prevalent in the Far East especially on the Japanese mainland, characterized by varied clinical pictures, diffuse neuronal necrosis, and inflammation of the brain and cord, and is caused by a virus similar in some respects to that of St. Louis encephalitis. In view of the fact that von Economo's disease has occurred in Japan, it is designated by the Japanese as type A to distinguish it from their type B. Australian X disease is assumed to be similar to, if not identical with, Japanese B encephalitis; and at one time Russian autumnal encephalitis was regarded as a distinct nosologic entity but later it was shown to be Japanese B encephalitis.

History

While epidemics of encephalitis have occurred in Japan since 1871, the one that appeared in 1924 was particularly noticeable because more than 6,000 people were known to be attacked of whom 60 per cent died. From 1924 to 1940, outbreaks arose each summer resulting in more than 27,000 victims. These records are from Japanese sources and do not represent the numbers of proved cases of Japanese B encephalitis; in all probability they include a number of other CNS infections such as poliomyelitis. In the summer of 1945, an outbreak of

Japanese B encephalitis took place on Okinawa among natives and American military personnel. In 1948, another extensive epidemic was recorded in which more than 8,000 Japanese civilians and about 35 American soldiers were affected. These epidemics were studied by several groups of American workers (Sabin, 1947; Tigertt et al., 1950).

Hayashi (1934) transmitted to monkeys a CNS infection by means of intracerebral inoculation of brain tissue from persons who had succumbed to encephalitis. In the summer of 1935, during an explosive epidemic, Kasahara et al. (1936), Kawamura et al. (1936), and Taniguchi et al. (1936), using mice as experimental animals and finding specific neutralizing antibody in recovered patients, established the fact that a virus is the cause of the disease.

CLINICAL PICTURE

The clinical picture is that of the viral encephalitides in general, and as in the other forms, three clinical types can be distinguished: meningo-encephalomyelitis of severe, moderate or mild degree; the abortive type; and the clinically inapparent cases.

Meningo-encephalomyelitic Type. After an incubation period of unknown duration, probably 8 to 15 days, the prodromal signs of anorexia, nausea, headache, fever, and nervousness occur and endure for 1 to 4 days. The onset may be sudden or gradual and is characterized by fever, vomiting, and apathy which may turn into mental confusion or disorientation, lethargy or even coma. The fever of 104° F. or higher, reaches, as a rule, its height within the first day or two after the onset. It then continues for about 5 days when it falls by lysis. The temperature becomes normal from 5 to 10 days after onset, although in certain instances it may remain elevated for several weeks. With the febrile reaction are associated nuchal and spinal rigidity, spasticity of the legs, disturbed deep and cutaneous reflexes, difficulties of speech, tremors, convulsions and pareses or pa-

ralyses. In the Japanese epidemic of 1924, about 30 per cent of the attacked persons were reported to have had either spastic or flaccid paralysis of the limbs; in some, the paralysis involved the facial muscles. When signs of lower motor neuron paralysis are encountered, the possibility of poliomyelitis should be considered. In the Okinawan epidemic, definite paralyses were rarely seen. Cerebellar type of in-co-ordination is noted, but ocular paralyses, in contradistinction to von Economo's disease, are infrequent. Sensory and psychic disturbances may arise. The acute phase lasts from a few days to 2 weeks or longer, depending on the severity of the attack. In mild cases, the neurologic and psychotic signs are less marked. When recovery follows an attack, it is usually complete; parkinsonism and other sequelae are, therefore, infrequent. In a study of two epidemics, 2,000 cases in each, only 3.1 and 10 per cent, respectively, of the survivors exhibited neurologic or psychotic changes.

Other Types. The abortive type is one in which the signs and symptoms may be fleeting or mild and consist of fever alone or in association with the prodromal signs as mentioned. The clinically inapparent or missed cases comprise those in which the only indication of infection is the development of antibody in the serum of patients.

During the acute phase the white blood cell count shows a moderate polymorphonuclear leukocyte increase, with a shift to the left; the average white blood cell count is 10,000 to 25,000 or higher. The cerebrospinal fluid, as a rule, is clear; the pressure is slightly increased; and pleocytosis, to 250 or more cells, chiefly of lymphocytes is present. Early in the course of the disease, polymorphonuclear cells may be found in the fluid. The protein content is somewhat increased; the amount of sugar is usually normal; the amounts of chlorides and calcium are increased and decreased, respectively.

PATHOLOGIC PICTURE

Macroscopically, the brain and coverings

show edema and congestion especially in the cortical gray matter, basal nuclei, pons, and medulla. Microscopically are seen perivascular cuffing and meningeal infiltration chiefly with lymphocytes and some polymorphonuclear leukocytes. Neuronal degeneration and necrosis with associated neuronophagia are noted especially in the substantia nigra, red nuclei, basal ganglia, cerebral cortex, cerebellar cortex and horns of the spinal cord, along with diffuse or focal infiltration of various parts of brain and cord with mononuclear and polymorphonuclear cells. The most striking pathologic change is the destruction of the Purkinje cells in the cerebellum, a lesion also observed in the experimental disease and in louping-ill. In addition, there are patches of encephalomalacia, acellular plaques of spongy appearance in which medullary fibers, dendrites and axons are destroyed, and focal microglial proliferation (Fig. 27). In chronic cases, focal and diffuse deposition of calcium salts leading to a foreign body response may occur (Zimmerman, 1946). The topography of the lesions in all regions of the cortical gray matter and in the molecular and Purkinje-cell layers of the cerebellum is different from that observed in poliomyelitis (Haymaker and Sabin, 1947).

EXPERIMENTAL INFECTION; HOST RANGE

Lower animals susceptible to the virus and showing signs of disease, as reported by the Japanese, are in order of susceptibility from highest to lowest, mouse, monkey, horse, cow, goat, sheep, hamster, young dog, young rat, pig, cat, and vole. Viremia is noted in the horse, dog, goat, rabbit, duck, adult rat, and sparrow; the latter three show, however, no visible signs of infection. The guinea pig is partially resistant, showing only a febrile reaction. Recently, Hammon, Reeves and Burroughs (1946) demonstrated that chickens reveal a viremia for 1 to 7 days after being inoculated subcutaneously with the virus, the birds in the meanwhile being otherwise unaffected in health. After being fed virus, hamsters develop viremia; some of them succumb from encephalitis, while others survive and are immune (Schabel et al., 1947). The epidemiologic implication of the finding that an animal on exposure to the virus remains apparently healthy but harbors virus in the blood is that it may be a reservoir in nature from which blood-sucking arthropods can pick up the virus for infection of man. On Okinawa, also in Japan and Korea, Sabin (1947) found, however, that native chickens were free from infection. Young horses in nature have encephalitis due to Japanese B virus but most of them, as in human beings, develop inapparent infection and antibody. Recently, Hodes, Thomas and Peck (1946a) have shown that, during an outbreak of the disease on Okinawa, apparently normal horses exhibited in their sera complement-fixing and neutralizing antibodies; they suggested that this animal may have played an important epidemiologic role in the spread of the Okinawa epidemic.

White mice develop the experimental disease after intracerebral injection of mouse-adapted virus in dilutions up to 10^{-8} or even higher; they become infected after intranasal instillation and intraperitoneal inoculation of the virus. In the case of the latter type of inoculation, infection occurs with 10^{-2} to 10^{-7} dilutions of the active agent, depending on the age of the animals. They show within 3 to 8 days after injection a rapidly developing lethal encephalomyelitis with paralyses, tremors and convulsions. This host develops with age an increasing resistance to the virus given peripherally which appears at the time of weaning. Mice are experimentally infected in the manner described in the section on St. Louis encephalitis.

Young rhesus monkeys develop an experimental encephalomyelitis within 4 to 8 days after intracerebral, intraocular or intranasal inoculation of dilutions of the virus similar to those given to mice. They show nystagmus, nuchal rigidity, salivation, convulsive seizures, unequal pupils, paralyses of various members including the eyelids, cerebellar ataxia and in-co-ordination, and, finally, prostration ending in death. The virus can be propagated indefinitely by monkey to monkey passage in which respect this active agent differs from that of St. Louis encephalitis (*v. supra*). For intracerebral injection of monkeys the following method is used: the monkey's scalp is shaved, tincture of iodine is applied and then removed by means of alcohol, and the animal is anesthetized. A quarter-inch incision of the scalp is made, and the skull is trephined for a 22 to 25 gauge needle at a point 1 cm. to the right or left of the sagittal suture and 1 cm. in front of the coronal suture. Through this opening the injection is made with a ⅝ inch needle, gauge 22 for suspensions and 25 for filtrates of the inoculum prepared as indicated for St. Louis virus (*v. supra*). The needle is inserted to the hilt and reaches the right or left frontal lobe; the dose, inoculated slowly, is usually 0.5 to 1 cc.

Etiology

Japanese B virus is said to have a diameter of from 15 to 22 millimicrons as determined by ultrafiltration through gradocol membranes (Sabin and Duffy, personal communication; Yaoi et al., 1939). The size as determined by ultracentrifugation of infected mouse brains is not as yet definitely settled since all the components found by this technic are present also in normal mouse brains, except one which has a sedimentation constant of about 5 Svedberg units—a unit is a sedimentation rate of 10^{-13} cm. per second per unit centrifugal field. If this should be the virus itself, and if it were spherical and had a density of protein, it would have a diameter considerably less than 10 millimicrons. This component may, however, correspond to one found in normal mouse brains having a sedimentation constant of 8 Svedberg units; further work is needed therefore to settle this point (Duffy and Stanley, 1945). The virus passes through Seitz and Berkefeld V and N filters. Filtered virus is inactivated

at 56° C. within 30 minutes. The virus in infected mouse brains is preserved by storage on dry ice at about −70° C., by immersion in 50 per cent buffered glycerol at 4° C., and by lyophilization. For preservation of diluted virus, the recommended diluent is undiluted normal rabbit serum, 50 per cent normal rabbit serum in saline solution, or sterile undiluted skim milk adjusted to pH 8.4 (Duffy and Stanley, 1945). For dilution of virus in neutralization tests 10 per cent normal rabbit serum or 10 per cent skim milk in saline is employed. The optimum pH for stability of the active agent at 4° C. is about 8.5 in acetate-glycine-phosphate buffer; the virus is inactivated rapidly at pH 10 and pH 7.

The virus has been cultivated in embryonated hens' eggs, first by Taniguchi et al. (1936) and later by Warren and Hough (1946), Koprowski and Cox (1946) and others. Recent investigators have been able to bring the titer of cultivated virus up to $10^{-7.5}$ or even to $10^{-8.5}$. The method of propagating the virus in the embryos is similar to that used for St. Louis virus. The most satisfactory yields are obtained by inoculation of the chorio-allantois (*v. supra*, St. Louis encephalitis) and yolk sac. By the latter method, 7- to 9-day incubated eggs are inoculated with 0.5 cc. of 10^{-4} dilution of infected mouse-brain suspension having a high titer of virus. The eggs are then incubated at 35.5 to 36° C. for 48 hours when the maximum amount of virus is obtainable; within 48 to 72 hours all embryos die; virus is found throughout the egg but chiefly in the embryo itself.

Neutralizing and complement-fixing antibodies are developed after clinically apparent infection. The neutralizing antibody can be observed as early as 3 days (Sabin, 1947) after the onset of symptoms in certain patients; in others, it is detectable within 1 or 2 weeks. It has been shown to endure at least for 4 years, if not for life. Complement-fixing antibody has been found as early as 5 days and as late as 5 months after onset of illness, but at present no one knows how long it can be detected. Antibody is also developed after inapparent infection. Hammon and Sabin (personal communication) have found that Japanese natives, who give no history of having had encephalitis but have neutralizing antibody and no complement-fixing antibody in their serum, respond with a marked titer of complement-fixing antibody, even after a single injection of low-potency vaccine of the Japanese B encephalitis virus which by itself produces neither neutralizing nor complement-fixing antibody in controls. Positive complement fixation indicates recent infection; this antibody does not persist so long as that responsible for virus neutralization—a generality applicable to all viral encephalitides. It is of interest to note that the type of virus operating in the 1945 epidemic on Okinawa was first determined by complement-fixation tests on patients' serum (Hodes, Thomas and Peck, 1946b; Sabin, 1947). Antibodies are also found in lower animals immunized by vaccination with inactivated virus or convalescent from infection with active virus. Serum from immunized animals may show crossing with St. Louis and West Nile viruses in serologic tests, but no relationship among the three can be demonstrated by cross-immunity tests, i.e., by intracerebral tests in immunized animals (Smithburn, 1942; Casals, 1944). When serologic crossing occurs, the homologous reaction is always stronger than the heterologous. Sabin and Buescher (1950) have reported that the virus in mouse brain contains a specific hemagglutinin for chick and sheep cells, which is demonstrable by special technic (*v.* Chap. 3).

DIAGNOSIS

Clinical and pathologic pictures by themselves point to a diagnosis of encephalitis, but the type can be determined only by isolation and identification of the virus or by serologic and immunologic tests. The procedures of laboratory diagnosis are similar to those outlined in the section on St. Louis encephalitis (*v. supra*). As indi-

cated there, CNS tissue is the best material in which to look for the active agent. Nevertheless, Japanese and Russian workers state that virus can be recovered from the blood, cerebrospinal fluid, and even urine, feces or saliva. Recovery of virus from these latter materials must be considered as uncommon or problematic and not an established practical procedure. Since Russian Far East encephalitis and Japanese B encephalitis may be found occasionally in the same areas of Russia an aid to the differential diagnosis is the fact that 6-weeks old or older albino mice are resistant to Japanese B virus administered by the subcutaneous route but are highly susceptible to the Russian Far East virus given in this manner.

The time required for routine determination of the etiologic agent, by means of virus isolation and rise with time of the specific antibody level in the serum, is from 10 to 21 days or even longer; this also applies to other forms of viral encephalitis. If trained workers in a prepared laboratory are available, tentative diagnosis, derived chiefly from results of complement-fixation tests, may be had within a few days (Sabin et al., 1947).

TREATMENT

No specific treatment is at present available.

EPIDEMIOLOGY

The disease arises in epidemic form during the warmest months. Over a period from 1924 to 1937, there were recorded by the Japanese 21,355 cases in Japan with a fatality rate of about 57 per cent. As in the 1933 epidemic of St. Louis encephalitis, the greatest number of people attacked was usually in the older age group; over 60 per cent being more than 50 years old and among them the fatality rate was 65 to 80 per cent as against 50 to 55 per cent among younger persons. The ratio of males to females having the encephalitis was 124:100. On Okinawa during 1945 to 1949, American workers (Rivers, personal communication; Sabin, 1947; Tigertt and Hammon, 1950) recorded about 400 suspected cases among natives, of whom about 35 per cent died, and 21 among American personnel, of whom 28 per cent died. On this island the age distribution was, however, greatest in the 5- to 9-year group. Both Japanese and American observers believe that the incidence of the disease in certain areas is limited by the presence of populations of immunes, an idea supported by their finding of virus-neutralizing antibody in the serum of persons not giving a history of having had encephalitis. People with antibodies under these conditions must at some time have had an inapparent or abortive infection; in some areas (Korea) they constitute from 90 to 100 per cent of the population (Deuel et al., 1950). In Korea, as in North and Middle China, antibody surveys revealed a widespread dissemination of the virus, even more so than in Japan; only sporadic cases arise in Korea, while extensive epidemics are noted in Japan (Sabin et al., 1947). The disease is found in Japan, especially in the coastal areas bordering on the Inland Sea; the maritime provinces of the Soviet Union and Manchuria; the Ryukyus (Okinawa); Formosa; North, Middle and East China; Korea; Indo-China; Java; the Philippines; Guam; Malay Peninsula and Sumatra.

Japanese, Russian and American workers have reported infection of many genera and species of mosquitoes with the virus (reviewed by Hammon, et al., 1949a). The latter showed, in confirmation of earlier Japanese findings, that *Culex tritaeniorhynchus* and *C. pipiens*, var. *pallens* can experimentally transmit the virus; thus, with both species positive results were obtained in young mice bitten by mosquitoes 8 days and later after their blood-virus meal. Hammon et al. (1949b) also disclosed that *C. tritaeniorhynchus* was found naturally infected during an epidemic in Japan. A significant observation is that certain species of experimentally infected mosquitoes after being kept for 66 to 91 days at 8 to 13° C.—a temperature prevailing in the temperate-zone environments selected by mosquities for hibernation—can transmit infection to mice by biting (Hurlbut, 1950). Reeves and Hammon (1946) demonstrated experimentally that the virus can be transmitted by 7 species, representing 3 genera, of mosquitoes indigenous to North America. Even though they failed to demonstrate transovarian infection in them, this continent may, nevertheless, be faced with the problem of the entrance and dissemination of the virus within its boundaries. The reservoirs of the virus are also unknown. Many mammals and birds, especially chickens, have been suspected mainly because they develop only viremia after inoculation of the virus. From observations made on Okinawa and in Japan (Hodes et al., 1946a; Sabin, 1947) it would appear that the active agent can be widespread among horses, cattle, swine, sheep, goats, dogs, and other mammals at a time when it is absent or only very occasionally present in chickens and in human beings.

CONTROL MEASURES

Since certain arthropods may be vectors, their abatement and the screening of dwellings should be placed first on a program of prevention. Health officers at maritime or air ports receiving passengers from the Far East should be alerted for the possibility of the entry of immigrants ill with the disease. Such patients may become reservoirs for possible dissemination of the virus by means of indigenous mosquitoes which can be infected (v. supra; Reeves and Hammon, 1946). Indeed, at least two persons having become ill with Japanese B encephalitis while en route from epidemic centers in the Far East have already been detected at a West Coast port. One should realize, however, that man-to-man transmission of the malady by way of arthropods has not as yet been proved; the source of virus for arthropods is considered at present to be lower animals.

Prevention by use of specific antiserum

has not as yet been applied to man, although hyperimmune horse serum has been found to be effective in experimental infections. At the present time a chick-embryo vaccine (Warren and Hough, 1946; Koprowski and Cox, 1946) is being tested in the field to determine its ability to protect human beings. A mouse-brain vaccine prepared by Sabin and collaborators (1943) and Sabin (1947) has been effective for prevention of experimental infection. Russian observers report that a mouse-brain vaccine has shown promising results in man in Siberia. A chick-embryo type of vaccine is now prepared by the United States Army Medical School for use only in immunization of laboratory personnel (Smadel, 1951; Warren, Smadel and Rasmussen, 1948).

AUSTRALIAN X DISEASE

(SYNONYM: Australian acute polioencephalomyelitis)

INTRODUCTION

Australian X disease is a viral encephalitis, limited to Australia, which is now believed to be similar to if not identical with, the Japanese B type; at least it had many of the characteristics of the latter.

HISTORY

During a hot, dry summer in 1917-1918 an epidemic of acute encephalomyelitis broke out in Australia involving 134 persons of whom half were less then 5 years of age; 70 per cent of the patients succumbed (Cleland and Campbell, 1917). The disease reappeared in 1922, 1925 and 1926 but in milder form; it has not been encountered as a definite clinical entity since 1926. A virus was isolated from cerebral tissue of 3 patients (Cleland and Campbell, 1917, 1919) and from the cerebrospinal fluid of another; the active agent was lost before a comparative study of its properties could be made. This form of encephalitis was at first thought to be acute anterior poliomyelitis, then louping-ill; at

present it is believed to have been caused by the virus of Japanese B encephalitis.

CLINICAL PICTURE

After an incubation period of from 5 to 12 days, symptoms of malaise, headache and gastro-intestinal disturbances were noted; these were rapidly followed by fever, vomiting and neurologic reactions characterized by tremors, twitchings, ataxia, convulsions, and rarely ophthalmoplegia or other paralyses. The disease in the original epidemic was fulminating; some children died within 24 hours after onset of illness; others within 4 to 6 days. Those who survived, recovered completely. The blood showed a slight leukocytosis, and the spinal fluid, a pleocytosis.

PATHOLOGIC PICTURE

The pathologic changes conformed to those seen in the viral encephalitides with the exception of a noticeable destruction of the Purkinje cells of the cerebellum, a lesion similar to that seen in louping-ill and Japanese B encephalitis. Otherwise the brain was more involved than the cord with neuronal degeneration and necrosis, perivascular infiltration, glial accumulations and small capillary hemorrhages.

EXPERIMENTAL INFECTION; HOST RANGE

The virus was active in rhesus monkeys; through them it was passaged 14 times before it was lost. Sheep, a horse, a foal, and a calf were found susceptible. In monkeys the incubation period after intracerebral injection of the virus was 5 to 23 days, at which time signs of lethal meningoencephalitis developed. Insusceptible animals were dogs, kittens, rabbits, guinea pigs, and fowls.

ETIOLOGY

The virus not being available for study, its properties are far from being wholly known. It is not identical with poliomyelitis virus, as was first thought, because its host range is different and its clinical and pathologic pictures are those of encephalitis instead of poliomyelitis. Moreover, of 40 patients only 3 exhibited paralysis (Neal, 1942). It is not likely to be identical with the virus of louping-ill of sheep because neither that agent nor its vector, *Ixodes ricinus,* is present in Australia. On the tenuous grounds of similarity in clinical and pathologic features and in host range, the disease caused by this active agent is for the present classified as Japanese B encephalitis. Another point in favor of this opinion is the recovery of a virus either identical with or closely related to that of Japanese B encephalitis from patients of a 1951 epidemic of encephalitis in Australia ("Murray Valley encephalitis"). It is of interest that during this epidemic evidence that horses and dogs were naturally infected (*v*. Japanese B encephalitis) was obtained.

WESTERN EQUINE ENCEPHALITIS

(SYNONYMS FOR THE EQUINE ENCEPHALITIDES OR ENCEPHALOMYELITIDES: *Die Amerikanische Encephalitis* [*beim Pferde*]; epizootic equine encephalomyelitis; W. E. E.)

INTRODUCTION

Western equine encephalitis is a summer viral disease of lower animals, especially of horses and mules, the virus of which is transmissible to human beings in whom a malady is produced closely resembling that of St. Louis encephalitis. It is distinct in several features from the maladies brought about by infection with the eastern and the Venezuelan equine viruses.

HISTORY

For more than 75 years, epizootics of encephalitis have been observed in equine animals in the United States. Meyer, Haring and Howitt (1931) isolated the causal agent from the CNS of affected horses in California by transmission experiments in which horses, monkeys, rabbits, guinea

pigs, rats, and mice were used. The agent is now known as the western equine encephalitis virus. Meyer (1932) was the first to record the possibility of human infection with this agent, but Howitt (1938) was the first to recover the virus from the CNS tissue and blood of man by means of intracerebral inoculation of mice. The most extensive human epidemic occurred in 1941, chiefly in North Dakota, Minnesota and adjacent provinces of Canada; over 3,000 persons were attacked with a mortality rate of 8 to 15 per cent. At the present time there exists an endemic focus along our Pacific coast. For example, in 1945 and 1946 there were 57 and 149 cases, respectively, diagnosed as neurotropic virus infections at the Kern County (California) Hospital; of these, 18 and 9 patients, respectively, were definitely shown to have had western equine encephalitis; from 1947 to 1951 the incidence was still low.

CLINICAL PICTURE

The incubation period is from about 5 to 10 days but may be from 4 to 21 days. The clinical picture varies considerably in different patients, from negligible signs and symptoms to acute comatose states developing within 24 hours.

In the common epidemic type, patients exhibit prodromata of headache, drowsiness, fever and gastro-intestinal disturbances. Then suddenly, less often gradually, fever appears with neurologic signs and symptoms which consist of severe headache, insomnia, and marked pain in the muscles, especially in those of the back. Lethargy, disturbances of speech, ataxia, nystagmus, tremor, convulsions, mental confusion, amnesia, and even coma may supervene. Paralysis is not common, occurring in about 15 per cent of those attacked; ophthalmoplegia and ptosis are still more uncommon. The acute febrile phase endures from 7 to 10 days. Most patients recover completely; residuals such as parkinsonism are rare. Clinically it cannot be differentiated from St. Louis encephalitis (*v. supra*). Abortive forms may be seen; here some of the prodromal symptoms, such as fever and headache, may be the sole indications of infection. Clinically inapparent cases, i.e., those in which no obvious signs except development of serum antibody are discernible, frequently are observed during epidemic and interepidemic periods.

The white blood cell count exhibits, as a rule, a slight polymorphonuclear leukocytosis; the total count ranges from 10,000 to 16,000. The cerebrospinal fluid shows a pleocytosis of 10 to more than 400 cells; early, polymorphonuclear leukocytes are in evidence, but about 3 days after the onset mononuclear cells begin to predominate. Protein is usually increased and sugar may be slightly increased or normal in amount.

Pathologic Picture

Macroscopic and microscopic changes in the CNS closely resemble those of St. Louis encephalitis and are essentially meningoencephalitic; the cord is often not involved, except in some instances in which a few small lesions are seen in the upper cervical region. As a rule, only a slight lymphocytic infiltration of the meninges occurs. In the gray matter there are widespread lesions consisting of focal accumulations of glial cells, perivascular lymphocytic infiltration, spongy disintegration of the ground substance, neuronal degeneration, and a varying degree of neuronal necrosis with neuronophagia. A diffuse infiltration of polymorphonuclear and mononuclear cells may be observed. The lesions are extensive in the gray matter, but scattered microglial aggregations and plaques of myelomalacia without a surrounding inflammatory reaction can be seen in the white matter. Some blood vessels show an inflammatory reaction in their walls and occasionally thrombi are seen.

Experimental Infection ; Host Range

The western virus has a very wide host range. In nature, human beings, horses and mules have shown signs of infection. The experimental infection with signs of illness can be induced in albino mice, hamsters, rats, guinea pigs, domestic and wild rabbits, monkeys, squirrels, cotton rats, kangaroo rats, wood rats, wild mice, puppies, deer, pigs, gophers, calves, goats, prairie chickens, and pigeons. Sheep and cats are resistant. Barnyard fowl and certain wild birds exhibit, after exposure to the virus, a viremia but are otherwise unaffected (Hammon and Reeves, 1945).

The animal of choice for experimental work is the white mouse. After intraperitoneal or intramuscular inoculation of 15-day-old mice, virus appears in the blood and in the majority of instances it migrates from the blood to the nasal mucosa, whence it invades the CNS by the olfactory route. Most old mice are resistant to the virus given by peripheral routes other than the nasal (Sabin and Olitsky, 1938a and b; for similar studies in guinea pigs and monkeys, see Hurst, 1936). Old and young mice are equally susceptible to the virus given intracerebrally and intranasally. Mouse-adapted virus, when given intracerebrally, produces disease in dilutions of 10^{-8} and rarely 10^{-10}; dilutions of 10^{-3} are effective by intranasal instillation. From 2 to 6 days after inoculation mice show signs of meningoencephalomyelitis, for example, generalized spastic muscular contractions, spastic paralyses, wild or in-co-ordinated movements, torpor, prostration, and death. Death may ensue within a few hours after onset of signs or at any time up to two days later. The pathologic picture simulates that observed in man.

The method of inoculating mice and of preparing inocula has already been described (*v. supra*, St. Louis encephalitis). For intracerebral inoculation of other susceptible animals such as rabbits, hamsters, rats, and guinea pigs, the procedure follows that used in monkeys (*v. supra*, Japanese B encephalitis). For hamsters, rats and guinea pigs, a 25 gauge, $\frac{1}{4}$ inch needle is inserted to the hilt through a trephined opening; the amount of inoculum is 0.1 or 0.2 cc.; and the site of inoculation corresponds to that designated for the mouse (*v. supra,* St. Louis encephalitis). For rabbits, a 25 gauge, ⅜ inch needle is used; the inoculum varies from 0.3 to 1 cc., depending on the size of the animal.

ETIOLOGY

The diameter of the virus, estimated from results of filtration through gradocol membranes, is about 25 millimicrons; according to results from electron micrography and from ultracentrifugation, it is about 40 millimicrons. It is filterable through Berkefeld V, N and W candles and through Seitz filters. The active agent grown on chick embryos exhibits on ultracentrifugation two components. One has a sedimentation constant of about 79 Svedberg units or a diameter of about 25 millimicrons; such a component is also found in normal chick-embryo tissue. The other component has a sedimentation constant of about 265 Svedberg units or a diameter of about 45 millimicrons; this component carries all of the infectivity (Beard, 1945). The chemical constitution of the infective particles as purified by ultracentrifugation was reported by Beard (1945) and colleagues to be 54 per cent fat-solvent extractable material, 4 per cent carbohydrate, and the remainder ribonucleoprotein; thus the virus was said to be a ribonucleo-lipoprotein complex. One should consider the limitations of a technic which may not yield a pure material; the chemical results stated above may therefore need revision when in the future pure virus preparations become available. Electron micrography of the virus is said to reveal images resembling those of the active agent of papilloma, i.e., round particles with ill-defined edges having internal structures some of which are rounded and dense, some oblong, and others vacuolated, located centrally or eccentrically (Beard, 1945). Ninety-nine per cent of the virus can be adsorbed on Willstaetter's Type C aluminum hydroxide from which it can be eluted.

The maximum stability of the virus at icebox temperature is between pH 7 and pH 8.5; its infectivity is rapidly lost in suspensions more acid than pH 6.5. In suspensions the virus withstands a temperature of 70° C., and in filtrates, a temperature of 60° C. for 10 minutes. It resists undiluted ether, 0.2 per cent choloroform, 1 or 2 per cent phenol, 0.05 per cent bichloride of mercury, and 1:500 merthiolate; the latter and phenyl mercuric borate can be used as bacteriostatic preservatives of viral suspensions in 1:10,000 and 1:50,000 dilution, respectively. In the preparation of vaccines, the virus is inactivated by keeping the suspension in the presence of 0.4 per cent formalin for 2 days at 20° C. and then for 2 days at 4 or 5° C. It can be preserved in cold 50 per cent buffered glycerol at a pH 7.4 or 7.5, by being held in the frozen state on dry ice, by lyophilization, or by being held in 2 per cent bovine-serum albumin at −20 to −25° C. (Olitsky et al., 1950). The virus is rapidly inactivated by K and Li periodate (Goebel, Olitsky and Saenz, 1948).

The western virus grows readily in the Maitland type of tissue culture and in the developing chick embryo. All methods of inoculation of embryonated eggs are effective in producing large yields of virus, titers being 10^{-7} to 10^{-9}. The methods of inoculation are the following: directly into the embryo, on the chorio-allantois, into the yolk sac, into allantoic and amniotic cavities, and into the brain of the embryo. After inoculation by any of these routes, the embryo dies within 18 to 24 hours, showing widespread hemorrhage, thrombosis and necrosis throughout all tissues. The rapidly developing lethal infection of chick embryos is characteristic of the action of this virus.

After natural or experimental infection, the virus induces a solid immunity, which can also be achieved by the use of vaccines consisting of virus inactivated by formalin (Shahan and Giltner, 1934; Cox and Olitsky, 1936; Beard et al., 1940). Both complement-fixing and virus-neutralizing antibodies are associated with this immunity. Thus, in human beings ill with the infection, neutralizing antibody certainly is found within 7 days after the onset and, according to Hammon (personal communication), even on the day of onset of the disease, and may persist for at least 2 years; complement-fixing antibody is also found within 7 days after the onset but in the majority of cases it is not found 12 to 14 months after recovery. After vaccination of human beings, neutralizing antibody lasts for at least 2 years but little or no complement-fixing antibody is produced. In experimental animals after vaccination, neutralizing antibody appears within 3 days and endures for at least 6½ months; complement-fixing antibody develops on the ninth day and lasts for at least 4 months. The duration of antibody as stated here is based on the longest time after vaccination at which tests were made.

Cox and Olitsky (1936) and Morgan et al. (1942) demonstrated that mouse-brain vaccines can be used for the experimental production of solid and enduring immunity to challenge doses of the virus given intracerebrally and peripherally. In such vaccinated animals there is a correlation between the amount of neutralizing antibody in the serum and the immunity against viral infection. Furthermore, Morgan, Schlesinger and Olitsky (1942) reported that neutralizing antibody can be found in the cerebrospinal fluid of rabbits after immunization and that a correlation exists between the levels of serum and of spinal fluid antibody and cerebral immunity. This work points to the availability of antibody to the CNS as being an important factor in the manifestation of such immunity. Vaccination of guinea pigs to a degree at which they resist 1,000 cerebral lethal doses fails to protect the CNS against the initial effects of the virus given intracerebrally; an abortive infection of 20 to 30 hours' duration ensues, characterized by fever and histopathologic changes simulating those which occur in control animals at a very early period after infection. In addition, recovered guinea pigs or mice are resistant for about 2 weeks to certain heterologous agents, such as eastern equine and vesicular stomatitis virus, given intracerebrally, i.e., they reveal the so-called interference phenomenon or something similar to it, which has been designated by the investigators as an "acquired nonspecific cellular resistance" (Schlesinger et al., 1944). Schlesinger (1949) has found that vaccinated mice may be resistant to large intracerebral inocula of a slowly growing strain of the virus but not to a rapidly growing derivative. Also, if their immunity is of a low grade, they are more resistant to a large than to a small amount of virus, a result, perhaps, of the antigenic booster effect of the excess of virus in the large inocula over that needed for initiating infection.

DIAGNOSIS

As with other viral encephalitides, the clinical and pathologic findings indicate a diagnosis of encephalitis but the type can only be determined by isolation and identification of the virus or by serologic and immunologic tests; the laboratory procedures involved in diagnosis have already been described (v. supra, St. Louis encephalitis). As stated there, the most satisfactory source of virus is CNS tissue; even though the western equine virus has been recovered from the blood and cerebrospinal fluid of patients, it has been found so rarely as to make viral studies on such material inadvisable as a diagnostic measure.

TREATMENT

There is no proved specific treatment of the disease. Olitsky, Schlesinger and Morgan (1943) have shown in experiments with mice and guinea pigs that hyperimmune rabbit serum is ineffective if treatment is begun after onset of definite signs of encephalitis; however, if the antiserum is given to guinea pigs 24 to 48 hours after inoculation of virus and before the signs of disease are obvious, treatment can prevent lethal infection. Moreover, in certain serum-treated animals there occurred typical, fatal encephalitis after an incubation period of 13 to 47 days; in such instances it was assumed that the virus persisted within the CNS during the prolonged incubation period, and, when the content of antibody of the CNS reached a low level, even though still demonstrable, it became ineffective and could no longer prevent the active agent from passing to and infecting other cells. These findings may have application to other neurotropic virus infections; at any rate they support the conclusions of Rivers (1939) that treatment with immune sera is, with few exceptions, valueless if it is begun after onset of definite clinical signs of a viral infection. Sulfonamide compounds and ACTH do not affect the virus or the experimental disease induced by it (Olitsky and Saenz, 1948).

Epidemiology

The main epidemiologic features of the disease are similar to those of St. Louis encephalitis; indeed, mixed epidemics have been reported. Epidemics of the disease and poliomyelitis have occurred simultaneously in the same area as was the case in Manitoba during the summer of 1941, when, without serologic tests, it was not always easy to differentiate one infection from the other. The disease prevails chiefly from mid-July to mid-September in the United States west of the Mississippi River, but lately it has been reported from Michigan, Alabama and Florida. It also occurs during the summer in Canada and the Argentine Republic. Most victims of infection are adult males, 20 to 50 years of age, who work outdoors. In the epidemic in Manitoba in 1941, a high attack rate was also noted in infants under 1 year of age. In the San Joaquin Valley in California, attack rate in infants is also comparatively high. The mortality rate is said to be from 7 to 20 per cent, the average being about 10 per cent.

The vector is considered by Hammon and Reeves (1945) and others to be culicine mosquitoes, of which *Culex tarsalis* may be the most important species; at least such mosquitoes caught in nature have frequently been shown to harbor the virus. Kelser (1934) in 1932 demonstrated experimentally that *Aedes aegypti* mosquitoes can transmit the western virus from infected guinea pigs to normal guinea pigs and horses and from an infected horse to normal guinea pigs. The reservoir of the virus is unknown, but chickens and other birds are suspected. *Culex tarsalis* mosquitoes have a predilection for fowl which after infection by the bite of the arthropod show a viremia, their health otherwise being unaffected. The infection from fowl to fowl may be carried on by mosquitoes or perhaps by some other blood-sucking insect or by the wild bird mite (Hammon, 1948) or the chicken mite (Sulkin, 1945). No one has as yet proved the presence of virus in mosquitoes caught on horses ill with the natural disease; nor have transmission experiments with infected insects been attempted in man. The evidence that mosquitoes are the vectors of the human disease, although strong, is therefore incomplete; Hammon and Reeves (1945) indicate that the vector may not be identical in different epidemic areas. Syverton and Berry (1941) succeeded in transmitting the disease to animals by means of experimentally infected wood ticks, *Dermacentor andersoni*; ticks so infected could in turn convey, through transovarian passage, the virus to their progeny. The active agent has been recovered from a conenosed bug, *Triatoma sanguisuga*, caught in nature. To conclude, the present concept of the probable way of spread of this disease and of St. Louis encephalitis is: Two blood-sucking arthropods are involved, a bird mite which maintains the virus in nature and a mosquito which conveys the infection from birds to birds and to other vertebrates including horse and man; the latter may be accidental hosts (Hammon, 1948; Smith et al., 1948).

CONTROL MEASURES

A formolized vaccine made from nervous tissue of animals was prepared by Shahan and Giltner (1934) and Cox and Olitsky (1936). A formolized chick-embryo vaccine is available at the present time for the prevention of the disease in equine animals (Beard et al., 1940). It has received the approval of the U. S. Bureau of Animal Industry as an effective means of prophylaxis. Recommendations concerning the use of such a vaccine in man await the results of controlled tests in the field under epidemic conditions. In the meantime, it is being used for workers in laboratories or those especially exposed to the virus. Specific antiserum for passive immunization has been used successfully in experimental animals, but no satisfactory trial has been made in human beings. Since arthropods, especially mosquitoes, are considered as possible vectors, their control should always be undertaken first.

EASTERN EQUINE ENCEPHALITIS

(SYNONYMS: Similar to those for western equine encephalitis; E. E. E.)

INTRODUCTION

Eastern equine encephalitis is a summer disease of equine and avian animals which is transmissible to man in whom it is characterized, as a rule, by extensive inflammation and destruction of the CNS. The eastern virus should not be regarded merely as another serologically distinct strain capable of inducing equine encephalitis, but, as is the case also with the Venezuelan type, more as a virus capable of inducing a nosologic entity.

HISTORY

During the summer of 1933, TenBroeck and Merrill (1933) recognized an encephalitis in horses on farms in Virginia, Delaware, New Jersey, and Maryland. These workers and, at about the same time, Giltner and Shahan (1933) isolated a virus from the brains of affected animals; this active agent was serologically and immunologically distinct from the western virus and was designated eastern equine encephalitis virus. It was first recovered from human CNS tissue by Fothergill et al. (1938) and by Webster and Wright (1938). In 1938, an epidemic occurred in Massachusetts which involved 34 persons, mostly children, with a mortality rate of 74 per cent. In the same area and at the same time, 90 per cent of 248 horses which had encephalitis died. A laboratory worker suffered a severe attack in Indiana in 1939 (Olitsky and Morgan, 1939) and three other persons had the disease in Texas during 1941-1942 (Hammon, 1943a). In 1947, in Louisiana an explosive epidemic involved 14,000 horses, of which 90 per cent died, and about 15 human beings, of whom 9 died.

CLINICAL PICTURE

The disease as it occurred in the Massachusetts epidemic was severe and fulminating. As a rule, there were 2 phases. The first began suddenly with nausea, vomiting, headache, and fever which lasted 24 to 36 hours and was followed by a short period of well-being. After this came the second phase with high fever reaching 106° F. at times, gastro-intestinal disturbances, drowsiness or coma, convulsions, generalized rigidity or opisthotonos, paralyses, bulging fontanelles, edema of legs and face, and cyanosis. As a rule, the acute manifestations lasted about a week, extremes being from 1 day to 3 weeks. Of the survivors only one recovered completely; the others exhibited sequelae varying from emotional instability to various types of paralyses and mental deterioration (Farber et al., 1940; Ayres and Feemster, 1949).

Leukocytosis of 14,000 to 66,000 cells per c.mm. of which 90 per cent were polymorphonuclear cells, was present. The cerebrospinal fluid was under increased pressure with a pleocytosis up to 1,000 cells of which polymorphonuclear cells predominated during early stages of the disease; later mononuclear cells predominated. Protein was increased and the sugar was normal in amount.

In spite of the severity of the average attack, there is a certain number of human beings who, as first shown by Olitsky and Morgan (1939) and later by others, develop no clinical reaction after infection with the virus but show specific neutralizing antibody; how frequently such clinically inapparent infections occur is unknown.

Pathologic Picture

On macroscopic examination, generalized visceral congestion and pulmonary edema were observed. The brain showed marked congestion, edema and flattening of the convolutions. On microscopic examination, inflammation of the meninges was noted and lesions were found widespread throughout the brain but mainly in the brain stem and basal ganglia, the cord often being spared or exhibiting only mild changes. The pathologic changes in the nervous tissue consisted of severe destruction of neurons and ground substance, perivascular cuffing, and plaques of encephalomalacia. In acute cases the infiltrating cells were polymorphonuclear leukocytes; in patients succumbing a week after onset of illness, mononuclear cells predominated. Small blood vessels revealed disorganization of their walls and endarteritis with deposition of fibrin and formation of thrombi.

Experimental Infection ; Host Range

The eastern virus is, in general, more invasive and has a greater degree of virulence in experimental animals than has the western; this is reflected by a shorter incubation period, more rapid death and a higher titer of virus in CNS tissues. Otherwise it induces an experimental disease similar to that caused by the western virus and the host range is also similar with the exception that sheep, cats, hedgehogs, and quail have been shown to be susceptible to the virus given intracerebrally (v. supra, western equine encephalitis). A detailed description of the lesions noted in the CNS of several animal species having the experimental disease is given by Cepero (1949).

Etiology

The properties of the eastern virus are in general similar to those of western (v. supra). The size of both active agents is approximately the same; Beard (1945) reports that the component obtained by ultracentrifugation which carries the eastern agent has a sedimentation constant of 273 Svedberg units instead of 265 which was found for the western virus. Beard (1945) also states that the number of particles of eastern virus per 0.05 cc. necessary for infection of mice is of the order of 250. It should be borne in mind, however, that the accuracy of such a statement necessarily depends on the purity of the preparation of virus being studied (v. supra, Japanese B and western equine encephalitis). Bang and Gey (1949) found by electron microscopy diplococcuslike bodies in chick-embryo cultures similar to those described by Beard in purified preparations of the virus. It has been reported that the active agent (Ten-Broeck and Herriott, 1946) is inactivated by one of the mustard compounds, bis (beta-chloroethyl) sulfide, without losing its antigenicity.

Although the eastern and western viruses are similar in many respects, even to the sort of antibodies produced and the time of their appearance (v. supra), they are, nevertheless, serologically and immunologically distinct. When the eastern agent was injected extraneurally in young and old mice, it was found (Morgan, 1941) that the capacity to be immunized increased with the age of the animal; i.e., old mice produced a higher level of antibody at a more rapid rate than did young ones. With the eastern and western viruses Olitsky, Sabin and Cox (1936) and Sabin and Olitsky (1938a) demonstrated the development with age in the tissues of mice of a physiologic, if not an anatomic, barrier beyond which peripherally inoculated virus did not pass. In this way they account for the fact that old mice do not die after peripheral inoculation of eastern and western equine viruses.

DIAGNOSIS

The procedures for diagnosis are similar to those mentioned for St. Louis and western equine encephalitis (*v. supra*).

TREATMENT

No specific treatment is available. Sulfonamide and antibiotic compounds are ineffective in experimental infections.

EPIDEMIOLOGY

The disease in horses and mules is at present distributed over the Eastern United States and Canada (Ontario), Mexico, Panama, Cuba, Dominican Republic, Brazil, and perhaps the Philippines. Only 4 states of the Union, Alabama, Michigan, Arkansas, and Texas, are known to harbor both eastern and western forms. Apparently eastern virus is spreading westward and the western eastward. In Massachusetts during July through October, 1938, the disease attacked human beings and horses; the median date for reported deaths in horses was August 27th, two weeks earlier than a similar date for human deaths. Of the human beings attacked in this outbreak, 70 per cent were under 10 years of age; 25 per cent were less than one year, the youngest being one month old; and 15 per cent were more than 21 years of age. Both sexes were equally attacked. During the fall of that year the disease was detected in pheasants and a pigeon caught in the same area. The results of experiments with the eastern agent led TenBroeck (1938, 1940) to conclude that birds are more likely than horses to act as reservoir hosts; he also demonstrated that birds may have viremia without apparent signs of infection. Indeed, from 1938 to 1946, 13 epizootics occurred among pheasants in New Jersey (Beaudette and Black, 1948). Evidence indicates that certain *Aedes* mosquitoes, especially those that infest the salt

marshes where the greatest numbers of equine cases arise (TenBroeck), may serve as vectors of the disease. Merrill, Lacaillade and TenBroeck (1934) showed that the western virus multiplies in *Aedes aegypti* mosquitoes while the eastern virus multiplies in the *Aedes sollicitans* mosquitoes, thus demonstrating for the first time multiplication in mosquitoes of a virus derived from animals. The virus has been recovered from chicken mites (*Dermanyssus gallinae*) and a mixture of lice (*Eomenacanthus stramineus* and *Menopon pallidum*) in an epidemic area by Howitt et al. (1948), who infer that these may be the important vectors among birds; the vector among horses and human beings is still unknown. Howitt et al. (1949) found the eastern virus in mosquitoes (*Mansonia perturbans*) caught wild in Georgia during an epizootic among horses.

CONTROL MEASURES

Specific antiserum prevents the disease in experimental animals; its use in man must await further tests. Formalin-inactivated vaccines prepared from infected chick embryos have been used successfully for prevention of the disease in equine animals. The general principles of active immunization with such vaccines have been described by Olitsky and Cox (1936) and by Cox and Olitsky (1936). While the vaccine has not as yet had a trial in human beings in the face of an epidemic, it has been given to persons who from the nature of their work are exposed to the virus; it is not as yet recommended for mass immunization of human populations. Mosquito control should be considered in any program for prevention of the disease.

VENEZUELAN EQUINE ENCEPHALITIS
(SYNONYM: *Peste loca*)

INTRODUCTION

Venezuelan equine encephalitis is a disease primarily of equine animals; its causal agent is distinct from that of eastern and western equine encephalitis; it is transmissible to human beings in whom it usually induces a mild disease of a varied syndrome.

History

During 1935, an encephalitis was observed in horses and mules in Colombia. In 1938 a severe epizootic swept over Venezuela; the agent responsible for this outbreak was recovered by Beck and Wyckoff (1938) and Kubes and Rios (1939) from the brains of animals that had died of the disease. Later the disease was reported in Ecuador and Trinidad, and recently in Panama (A. B. Sabin, personal communication). Human infections have been reported by Casals, Curnen and Thomas (1943) and by Lennette and Koprowski (1943); they occurred in laboratory workers and were mild. Other nonfatal human infections were observed in Argentina in 1944. In 1943, two fatal infections in human beings occurred in Trinidad (Randall and Mills, 1944; Gilyard, 1945).

Clinical Picture

The precise incubation period of the disease is unknown; it is probably short, from two to five days. As a rule persons infected with this virus during laboratory investigations do not show definite neurologic or encephalitic signs or symptoms; on the contrary, they present the picture seen in acute febrile infections such as influenza; the symptoms are generally mild; headache and fever are prominent. In addition, gastrointestinal disturbances, tremor, myalgia, diplopia, and lethargy may be noted. Signs and symptoms persist for 3 to 5 days in mild cases and for 8 days in more severe attacks, after which prompt and complete recovery takes place. In the two cases in Trinidad, acquired under natural conditions, the onset was acute with definite signs and symptoms of encephalitis which were followed by coma and death. Neutralizing antibody has been found in persons without any history of having had the disease; these are assumed to represent instances of clinically inapparent infections. Little is known as yet concerning changes in the blood and spinal fluid. The pathologic picture in human beings has not been sufficiently studied to warrant comments.

Experimental Infection; Host Range

In addition to equine animals, the virus is pathogenic by intracerebral route for mice, guinea pigs, rabbits, rats, dogs, cats, sheep, goats, and partially so for pigeons. Chick embryos are susceptible. Cattle are resistant. The pathology of the experimental infection is that of a nonpurulent inflammation of the brain characteristic of the viral encephalitides. A distinctive feature of the virus is its high virulence for adult animals when inoculated by peripheral (nonneural) routes; when administered in this way as little as 10^{-9} or 10^{-10} dilutions of mouse-adapted virus may infect mice. In the natural disease of man and equine animals and in experimental infections, the virus has been found in the CNS and also in the blood under the latter conditions. The active agent is recovered not only from the nasopharynx of human beings infected accidentally in the laboratory but also from their blood; this is a characteristic feature of the malady.

Etiology

Little is known of the properties of the virus. It is filterable through Berkefeld N and Seitz filters; it can be preserved in 50 per cent buffered glycerol, by being held in the frozen state at $-70°$ C., and by lyophilization. It grows well in the Maitland type of tissue culture and in embryonated hens' eggs. Convalescent human beings and lower animals immunized with vaccines develop specific neutralizing and complement-fixing antibodies; they appear from 1 to 2 weeks after onset of infection, but how long they endure is still to be determined.

Diagnosis

A specific diagnosis can be made only by

laboratory procedures, i.e., by identification of the virus isolated from CNS tissue, blood or nasopharyngeal washings, or by finding neutralizing or complement-fixing antibodies during convalescence (*v. supra,* St. Louis encephalitis).

TREATMENT

There is no specific treatment.

EPIDEMIOLOGY

The known distribution of the natural disease is at present in northern South America, Trinidad and Panama. The reservoir of the virus is still to be found. Its mode of transmission in man may vary; in certain instances, such as in laboratory infection, it may be by droplet or dust infection. Gilyard (1944) considers that *Mansonia titillans,* a culicine mosquito, and *Aedes taeniorhynchus* may transmit the disease to horses and human beings. Since man may become infected through the upper respiratory tract and since the virus is found in the nasopharyngeal washings of infected human beings, at some future date an epidemic may occur in a human population without the aid of an insect vector.

CONTROL MEASURES

A formalin-inactivated vaccine prepared from infected chick embryos (Kubes and Rios, 1939) has been used in Venezuela for prevention of the disease in horses. Randall et al. (1949) prepared a partially purified vaccine which has been shown to produce a high level of antibody. This vaccine has been used only for protection of laboratory workers (Smadel, 1951). Any program for prevention should include insect control.

LOUPING-ILL

(SYNONYMS: Ovine encephalomyelitis; thwarter-ill; trembling-ill; *la tremblante du mouton*)

INTRODUCTION

Louping-ill is a natural disease of sheep characterized chiefly by cerebellar ataxia and on occasions has attacked man in whom is induced a mild nonfatal type of encephalitis. It should be differentiated from tick-borne fever of sheep (Gordon et al., 1932).

HISTORY

The disease in sheep, which has been known in Scotland and North England since 1807 or even earlier, produces a diphasic fever. During the first phase, viremia occurs; in the second, no viremia is present but neurologic disturbances appear, especially cerebellar ataxia characterized by a leaping motion, whence the name louping-ill. The causal virus was discovered in 1930 by Pool, Brownlee and Wilson at the Moredun Institute in Scotland, where the major studies on the veterinary disease have been conducted. Rivers and Schwentker (1934) were the first to report infection of human beings by the virus; it occurred accidentally in workers investigating the active agent. In 1943, a close serologic relationship between the virus of louping-ill and that of Russian Far East encephalitis was demonstrated (Casals, 1944). Russian observers (Sergeev, 1944; Silber and Shubladze, 1945) have reported the presence of louping-ill in White Russia, not only in sheep, but in man. The disease has been reported in farmers along England's northern borders (Davison et al., 1948) and possibly in Czechoslovakia (Edward, 1950). Those handling fleece likely to be tick infested develop specific neutralizing antibody after clinically apparent or inapparent infection (Hurst, personal communication).

CLINICAL PICTURE

The incubation period of the disease in persons infected during laboratory investigations on the virus is unknown. If it is similar to the natural or experimental infection in lower animals, it would be 5 to 14 days. The disease in man is diphasic as in sheep. A preliminary episode, enduring about a week, of fever, headache, gastrointestinal derangement, malaise, and prostration is followed by clinical improvement which may also last a week. Then follows a recrudescence characterized by fever, headache, diplopia, lethargy, nuchal rigidity, blurring of the optic disks, and weakened deep reflexes; mental confusion may be present. The disease endures for 4 or 5 weeks and terminates in complete recovery. The malady in Russia called louping-ill is clinically indistinguishable from Russian Far East encephalitis (*v. infra*) and an unknown number of patients have died (Sergeev, 1944).

White blood cell counts may be as high as 17,000 per c.mm. The cerebrospinal fluid is under increased pressure; there is a pleocytosis usually of mononuclear cells; the amount of protein is greater than normal.

PATHOLOGIC PICTURE

In the natural or experimental infection of sheep and in the experimental disease of laboratory animals, the lesions are those of a diffuse meningo-encephalomyelitis. The outstanding feature is the pronounced, often complete, destruction of the Purkinje cells of the cerebellum (Hurst, 1931), which is also present in Japanese B encephalitis (Fig. 27, *bottom, right*). Cytoplasmic inclusion bodies in monkeys and mice, but not in sheep, have been described by Hurst (1931). In fatal human cases in Russia (Sergeev, 1944) the cerebellum is said to reveal considerable neuronal destruction (Silber and Shubladze, 1945).

EXPERIMENTAL INFECTION; HOST RANGE

Lambs, sheep, horses, mice, rhesus monkeys, hamsters, and voles are susceptible to experimental infection; all show viremia and therefore their organs, as well as CNS tissue, yield virus. Rats develop inapparent infection with multiplication of the virus in the CNS; rabbits and guinea pigs are wholly resistant. Pigs are susceptible, but serial passage in them is limited. There is evidence that cattle contract the disease if kept in infected areas.

Mice are the experimental animals of choice and can be infected intracerebrally with 10^{-7} dilutions of virus suspensions; when inoculated by peripheral routes they are only moderately susceptible. From 5 to 14 days after inoculation, mice develop apathy or hyperesthesia, ruffled fur, tremor, ataxia, and paresis; thereafter, within 1 to 5 days, prostration develops which is followed by death. Virus can be found in the blood on the second day after intracerebral or intranasal inoculation; it can be found in the brain on the first day after inoculation or about 2 to 4 days before clinical signs of infection are manifested.

ETIOLOGY

The diameter of the virus as determined by filtration through gradocol membranes is 15 to 22 millimicrons; as estimated from results of ultracentrifugation, 22 to 27 millimicrons. It is filterable through Berkefeld V, N and W candles, through Seitz pads, and through Chamberland L_2 and L_3 filters. It can be preserved in 50 per cent buffered glycerol, by being held in the frozen state at about $-70°$ C., and by lyophilization. It retains its activity best at pH 7.5 to 8.5 in the cold; it is rapidly inactivated at room temperature, a 90 per cent drop in infectivity occurring within 24 hours even at pH 7.6. In a suspension of mouse-brain tissue the virus is inactivated at $80°$ C. in 30 seconds, at $60°$ C. in 2 minutes, and at $58°$ C. in 10 minutes. In a similar suspension at pH 7.3 it is electronegatively charged (Lépine, 1931). It is rapidly inactivated by methylene blue in the presence of light and by bile salts.

The virus can be cultivated in Li-Rivers medium of minced viable chick-embryo tissue suspended in Tyrode's solution. The inoculation of the chorio-allantoic membrane of 10-day-old chick embryos with large amounts of virus may cause their death within 6 days, at which time necrosis of the liver, generalized edema, and jaundice are found. Virus is present in the blood 2 to 6 days after inoculation and in the chorio-allantoic membrane it reaches a titer of 10^{-7} within 2 days.

Convalescent human beings, or those having had clinically inapparent infection, exhibit neutralizing (Rivers and Schwentker, 1934) and complement-fixing (Casals and Palacios, 1941) antibodies. The exact time of their appearance is not known, but they persist for at least eight years. Neutralizing antibody has been found in mice, monkeys and sheep after infection or immunization: complement-fixing antibody has also been found in mice (Casals, 1944).

DIAGNOSIS

If the observations on the occurrence of the disease in White Russia are confirmed, then one can say that fatal human infection with the virus occurs. A specific diagnosis of the malady cannot be made from the clinical signs or symptoms or from the pathologic picture. It can be determined, however, by the identification of the virus from the blood or cerebrospinal fluid during life, or from the CNS tissue secured at necropsy; it can be made also by means of the proper serologic tests. It is of interest in this relation to mention the fact that Rivers and Schwentker (1934) failed to isolate the virus from the first recorded human infections, but by the application of the neutralization test they were able to show that this veterinary malady does attack man. At present, both neutralization and complement-fixation tests are available for diagnosis in the manner described for St. Louis encephalitis. It should be noted, however, that louping-ill virus and the Russian Far East virus are closely related as evidenced both by neutralization and complement-fixation tests and by cross-immunity tests. Edward (1950) and Smadel (personal communication) have shown that, with their strains of Russian Far East and louping-ill viruses, essentially the same degree of protection is displayed when homologous or heterologous materials are used in cross-neutralization and cross-immunity tests, whether performed by the intracerebral or the intraperitoneal route. Casals (1944), on the other hand, found that,

although some difficulty may arise in differentiating one of these agents from the other, it can be resolved if one keeps in mind the fact that an antiserum gives a more pronounced reaction with its homologous virus than with the heterologous agent and that in cross-immunity tests the crossing occurs only when the challenge doses of virus are injected into immune animals by peripheral routes instead of intracerebrally.

EPIDEMIOLOGY

The tick, *Ixodes ricinus,* is the vector responsible for the disease which occurs in sheep most frequently in the spring and summer. The active agent through transovarian passage goes from one generation of infected ticks to the next. By what means the laboratory infections in man have arisen has not been determined; one can postulate the possibility of droplet or dust infection. It is reported (Silber and Shubladze, 1945) that the tick, *Ixodes ricinus,* is found in White Russia and harbors the virus of louping-ill.

CONTROL MEASURES

Formolized suspensions of virus have been used successfully in Scotland for prevention of the disease in sheep. Tick control is an important preventive measure.

RUSSIAN FAR EAST ENCEPHALITIS

(SYNONYMS: Russian spring-summer encephalitis; Russian spring or summer encephalitis; Russian forest-spring encephalitis; Russian tick-borne encephalitis; Russian endemic encephalitis)

INTRODUCTION

Russian Far East encephalitis is a disease occurring in spring and early summer, mainly in the Far East provinces of the Soviet Union and less frequently in European and Siberian Russia; the vector of the virus, which is closely related to that of louping-ill, is a wood tick.

History

The disease was observed in Far East Russia in 1932. The causal virus was discovered in 1937 (*cf.* Silber and Soloviev, 1946) and was shown to be present in the brain, blood, spinal fluid, liver, and spleen of infected human beings. Smorodintsev (1940) reported that Russian workers regard this agent to be closely related to the virus responsible for Japanese B encephalitis; however, Casals (1944) showed that no such relationship exists.

Clinical Picture

After an incubation period of 10 to 14 days, the disease in human beings suddenly manifests itself by headache, nausea, vomiting, hyperesthesia, photophobia, and fever. Fever usually lasts for 5 to 7 days, sometimes for 13, and falls either by lysis or by crisis; during the febrile period viremia may exist. Soon after onset of illness, patients exhibit signs and symptoms of meningo-encephalitis or polioencephalitis, the development of particular signs and symptoms depending on the location of lesions in the central nervous system. Flaccid paralysis of the shoulder-girdle muscles is a distinctive feature of this disease. In an epidemic may be seen (a) abortive infections causing fever for 3 to 5 days and ending in full recovery of the patients; (b) moderately severe meningo-encephalitis followed by recovery of 80 per cent of the patients within 1 or 2 months, or by permanent neurologic or psychotic sequelae without parkinsonism in 20 per cent of the patients; and (c) severe or fulminating meningo-encephalitis with death usually within 1 to 7 days.

The white blood cell count is usually about 10,000 per c.mm. The spinal fluid is clear and under pressure and shows a lymphocytic pleocytosis of 50 or more cells; the amount of protein is increased; the amount of sugar is not significantly changed.

Pathologic Picture

At necropsy, the CNS reveals a meningo-encephalomyelitis in which neuronal necrosis and neuronophagia in the spinal cord, and mesodermal and glial reactions throughout the brain and cord are more pronounced than are such phenomena in most of the other viral encephalitides. The blood vessels of the CNS are said to show a thrombovasculitis; the spleen shows hyperplasia; parenchymatous degeneration is found in the liver, kidney and heart.

Experimental Infection; Host Range

The virus is pathogenic for rhesus monkeys especially after intracerebral inoculation. Guinea pigs show only fever after inoculation, and the disease in them is not transmissible in series. Sheep, goats, hamsters, linnets, siskins and goldfinches are susceptible. Rabbits, pigeons and rats are insusceptible; at times gray rats may exhibit viremia after intracerebral inoculation. Many kinds of wild rodents and birds are found in nature with a viremia but appear to be otherwise unaffected by the natural infection (Silber and Soloviev, 1946). Albino mice are the experimental animals of choice; irrespective of their age, peripheral and intracerebral inoculations of virus are about equally effective, as little as 10^{-9} dilutions of mouse-adapted virus sufficing for infection. In this species, the incubation period is from 5 to 13 days, depending on route of inoculation and dose of virus given; the disease manifests itself by convulsions and paralysis, which are followed by death within a day or two after the first signs of illness. In man the virus is found in the blood, spinal fluid, brain and other organs; according to Silber and Soloviev (1946), it is also present in the urine.

Etiology

The diameter of the virus, as determined by filtration through gradocol membranes, is from 15 to 25 millimicrons. It passes through Berkefeld V and N and Chamberland L_2 and L_3 filters. The virus is inactivated by a temperature of 60° C. within

10 minutes, by 0.5 per cent formalin within 48 hours, by 3 per cent lysol within 20 minutes, and by 1 per cent phenol within 10 days. Its maximum stability is at pH 7.4 to 7.8; it can be preserved in 50 per cent glycerol in the cold, by being held at a temperature of —70° C., and by lyophilization. It is cultivable in the Maitland type of tissue cultures and in embryonated hens' eggs.

Complement-fixing and neutralizing antibodies are detectable in human beings 15 to 20 days after onset of illness; the neutralizing antibody and the complement-fixing antibody are known to persist for at least 2 years. Casals and Olitsky (1945) demonstrated that neutralizing antibody and complement-fixing antibody appeared in mice on the second and sixth days, respectively, after immunization with formolized virus; the former persisted practically throughout the life of mice, but the latter endured for only 4 months. They also reported that 2 injections of the vaccine induce in mice a solid immunity to virus given peripherally that endures almost throughout life; active Far East virus is therefore not essential for production of a lasting, staunch immunity. Moreover, a correlation was found to exist between the level of neutralizing antibody in the blood, as determined by the peritoneal test, and the degree of immunity to virus introduced peripherally, but not to virus inoculated intracerebrally. The cross-reactions between the Far East and louping-ill agents have already been described (*v. supra*, louping-ill). The virus has been shown to hemagglutinate specifically sheep erythrocytes (Sabin, 1951).

DIAGNOSIS

Diagnosis of Russian Far East encephalitis can be made only by isolation and identification of the virus or by serologic methods, as described in the section on St. Louis encephalitis. The serologic and immunologic reactions of the Far East agent must be differentiated from those of louping-

ill virus since there are cross-reactions between the two (*v. supra*, louping-ill).

TREATMENT

Specific serotherapy has been used by Russian workers who gave hyperimmune goat serum in the early phases of the disease; there is at present no uniformity of opinion on its value.

EPIDEMIOLOGY

The disease appears most frequently in May and June and continues through the summer at a diminishing rate; thus, it is unlike the Japanese and St. Louis encephalitis which usually appear in July or August. Epidemics break out in forest industrial centers, such as lumber camps, or among forest workers living in villages, but not among people inhabiting cities. The highest mortality is among males 20 to 30 years old; children under 5 years of age are rarely attacked. Difference in morbidity rates observed in different groups of a population may be accounted for by differences in exposure to infected wood ticks. The overall mortality rate is 30 per cent. The vector is suspected to be a wood tick, *Ixodes persulcatus*. Virus has been found in nymphs and adult ticks caught in nature and is transmitted to their progeny by transovarian infection. The disease has been produced experimentally in mice by the bites of infected ticks. The reservoir of the virus in nature is believed by Russian observers to be woodland mammals and birds.

CONTROL MEASURES

It has been reported (cf. Silber and Soloviev, 1946) that the experimental disease can be prevented in mice by giving them hyperimmune goat or human convalescent serum 1 to 10 days before exposure to the virus or during the incubation period. The use of immune serum is advised by Russian workers, especially after laboratory accidents or tick bites in endemic zones. Smorodintsev (1944) perfected a vaccine consisting of formalin-inactivated virus in mouse-brain tissue which he states is effective for prevention of the disease. A vaccine is prepared at the United States Army Medical School; it is available for immunization only of laboratory personnel engaged in handling this virus (Smadel, 1951). Tick control is important as a preventive measure.

LYMPHOCYTIC CHORIO-MENINGITIS

(SYNONYMS: LCM; choriomeningitis; *maladie d'Armstrong*)

INTRODUCTION

Lymphocytic choriomeningitis is an endemic viral infection of lower animals, especially the mouse, in which the CNS and particularly the meninges and choroid plexuses are involved; it is transmissible to man in whom the infection produces a marked diversity of signs and symptoms.

HISTORY

Wallgren (1925) used the term acute aseptic meningitis to designate a clinical syndrome in man that he thought was a nosologic entity. He described it as an acute febrile, nonfatal malady characterized by symptoms and signs of meningeal irritation and associated at times with infection of the upper respiratory tract. Now it is known that acute aseptic meningitis is not a nosologic entity but represents a clinical syndrome which may be caused by more than one etiologic agent, one of which is the virus of lymphocytic choriomeningitis. This virus was accidentally discovered by Armstrong and Lillie (1934) in a monkey being used for study of the virus of St. Louis encephalitis. The name lymphocytic choriomeningitis virus was given to the agent because of the marked reaction produced by it in the choroid plexus and meninges of monkeys. Traub (1935) showed that normal-looking albino mice harbor the virus and he voiced the opinion that the mouse is the natural host. Rivers and Scott (1935) recovered the active agent from the cerebrospinal fluid of

human beings ill with what had been diagnosed as Wallgren's acute aseptic meningitis. Lépine et al. (1937) demonstrated that by subcutaneous injection of virus from mice, performed as a therapeutic measure, lymphocytic choriomeningitis could be induced in human beings and that the disease is transmissible from man to man by means of intramuscular inoculations of infected blood.

CLINICAL PICTURE

Infection by this virus may assume a number of different clinical forms (Smadel et al., 1942), such as aseptic meningitis, "grippe," meningo-encephalomyelitis, and acute fatal systemic disease; often it is clinically inapparent. In most instances the meningeal and grippal types prevail. After an unknown period of incubation, the onset is sudden, frequently with symptoms and signs similar to those of influenza. In many patients, this is all that happens and recovery ensues promptly. In others, the grippal phase is followed by definite signs of meningitis which may endure for about 2 weeks; complete recovery is the rule. During the febrile period, virus is found in the blood, the cerebrospinal fluid, urine, and nasopharyngeal secretions. In the other neurologic or systemic forms, which are seen only occasionally, the disease takes on the syndrome referable to the extent and location of lesions in the CNS or other organs; these forms are sometimes fatal. The virus can be recovered from the CNS or from the lungs of patients dying of the disease. There are many instances in which neutralizing antibody is found in the blood of a person who gives no history of an attack of the ailment; these are examples of clinically inapparent infection.

In the experimental disease in man (Lépine et al., 1937), the incubation period was from 36 to 72 hours which was followed by 2 or 3 febrile waves enduring over a three-week period; the last febrile reaction was accompanied in about 50 per cent of the subjects by headache, vomiting and positive Kernig sign that lasted for 2 or 3 days.

During the acute phase the blood count reveals a mild polymorphonuclear leukocytosis. The cerebrospinal fluid is under increased pressure; protein is slightly increased but the amount of sugar is normal; pleocytosis occurs with usual counts of 150 to 400 lymphocytes per c.mm.; and sometimes as many as 1,700 to 33,000 per c.mm have been reported.

Pathologic Picture

The occasional fatal case of the encephalitic or myelitic type showed inflammatory changes in the meninges, ependyma and choroid plexuses characterized by marked infiltration with lymphocytes (Fig. 28, *top, left*). Otherwise the lesions corresponded to those observed generally in the viral encephalitides. In rare fatal cases of the acute systemic type of the disease, the lungs and liver showed inflammatory reactions (Smadel et al., 1942).

Experimental Infection; Host Range

The virus is transmissible to man, albino mice, guinea pigs, monkeys, dogs, rats, gray mice, chimpanzees, and chick embryos. Rabbits, pigs and birds are apparently insusceptible. The laboratory animals of choice for inoculation of the virus are the guinea pig and the albino mouse. Mice are best infected by intracerebral and intranasal routes, infection being obtained by these routes with 10^{-7} and 10^{-3} dilutions of virus, respectively. Mice, 5 to 12 days after inoculation, develop tremors and convulsions which characteristically terminate in a few seconds in generalized rigidity; death occurs in 1 to 3 days after onset of illness. If small doses of the virus are inoculated peripherally, a nonfatal infection may be induced which immunizes the animals; large doses may cause fatal infection after intraperitoneal administration. Guinea pigs, like mice, are best infected by the intracerebral route; after subcutaneous or intraperitoneal inoculation, death may occur

within 9 to 16 days. The virus can be found in the brain, blood, spleen, lungs and urine of mice and guinea pigs, and, according to Shwartzman (1944a), is firmly associated with their erythrocytes. The pathologic picture is one of a meningoplexal and perivascular infiltration by lymphoid cells, plasmacytes, macrophages and other cells, with occasional areas of focal gliosis. Lymphoid-cell infiltrations are present in the kidney, the salivary gland and the pancreas. In mice, also, there is often serous pleurisy, serous peritonitis and hepatitis; and necrosis, hemorrhage and serofibrinous exudate are observed in the lymphatic organs. Hepatitis is seen also in infected guinea pigs and monkeys. Thus, in experimental infection, the virus is generalized through the CNS and viscera and is associated with inflammatory lesions which persist for a long time during convalescence (Lillie, 1950). Different strains of the virus vary greatly in their pathogenicity for and behavior in experimental animals.

The virus occurs naturally in several species of animals; mice, guinea pigs, monkeys and dogs have been found to harbor it. Traub (1935) found that the spontaneous disease in mice is transmitted by mothers to their young in utero or shortly after birth and that the virus is propagated or maintained in a colony by normal-appearing carriers.

Etiology

The diameter of the virus is from 40 to 60 millimicrons as determined by filtration through gradocol membranes, and from 37 to 55 millimicrons as estimated from results of ultracentrifugation. It passes through Berkefeld V, N and W candles and Seitz filters. It is preserved in 50 per cent buffered glycerol, by being kept in the frozen state at $-70°$ C., and by lyophilization; in a brain suspension it is not stable at room temperature. It can be cultivated in vitro in minced mouse- or chick-embryo tissue suspended in a mixture of salt solution and serum, on the chorio-allantois, or in the yolk sac of 11- or 12-day-old chick embryos. The membranes and brains yield virus with a titer of up to 10^{-7} by intracerebral titration in mice. Infected embryos hatch, however, and the chicks survive. Smadel and Wall (1941) have demonstrated the presence of a specific soluble substance separable from the active virus in the organs, chiefly spleens, of infected guinea pigs and mice.

Complement-fixing and neutralizing antibodies appear in the serum of convalescent human beings; the former is first noted from about 1 to 3 weeks after onset of illness, the latter not until 6 to 10 weeks. Neutralizing antibody is known to persist for at least 3 years in persons who have had the disease, while the amount of complement-fixing antibody begins to decline 3 to 6 weeks after the onset of an attack. Both kinds of antibody are also produced in experimental animals after infection with active virus or after immunization with inactive virus; both appear within 10 days; how long they endure is not known.

DIAGNOSIS

The diagnosis is made by the isolation and identification of the virus and by serologic tests. The active agent may be obtained from the blood or cerebrospinal fluid of patients; at necropsy it is found in CNS tissues. One should be certain that the stock of animals used for diagnostic purposes is free from the virus. Serologic tests are performed with paired sera, acute phase and convalescent, as indicated in the section on St. Louis encephalitis. Since complement-fixing antibody appears before neutralizing antibody, the second or convalescent serum should be collected about 3 weeks after onset of illness for complement-fixation tests and about 6 to 10 weeks for neutralization tests.

TREATMENT

There is no specific treatment. Sulfonamide compounds influence neither the virus nor the experimental disease induced by it.

EPIDEMIOLOGY

The disease occurs chiefly in persons from 20 to 30 years of age, males and females being equally affected. Most cases occur during the winter and spring. Its incidence in the United States can be inferred from the fact that 11 per cent of 2,000 sera collected at random from persons who offered no history of being attacked, showed neutralizing antibody (Armstrong, 1940-1941). The disease, moreover, assumes an important role in public health because its virus is present in certain lower animals commensal with man, such as the gray or house mouse (*Mus musculus*). The virus escapes from the mouse by way of the nasal secretions, semen, urine and feces, thus possibly contaminating the habitat of man. It is conceivable that dust may be effective in transmitting the disease to man (Armstrong. 1940-1941). The virus most likely enters man by way of the upper respiratory tract. Shaughnessy and Milzer (1939) suggested that arthropods, such as culicine mosquitoes, stable flies, wood ticks, and body lice, serve as vectors for transmitting the disease from infected rodents to normal rodents and from infected rodents to man; this has not as yet been proved. Another way of conveying infection from mouse to mouse and from mouse to man has been suggested by Syverton et al. (1947), namely, through superinfected *Trichinella spiralis* or its larvae.

CONTROL MEASURES

The elimination of mice or other animal carriers of the virus from human habitations is an important measure for control of the disease in a population. A patient's excretions should be disinfected since they may contain the virus.

PSEUDOLYMPHOCYTIC CHORIOMENINGITIS

MacCallum, Findlay and Scott (1939) inoculated mice intracerebrally with spinal fluid obtained from two patients having the signs and symptoms of acute aseptic meningitis and recovered an active agent which they called the virus of pseudolymphocytic choriomeningitis. It induced in mice, guinea pigs and rhesus monkeys an experimental disease which was similar in many respects to that of lymphocytic choriomeningitis. It had, however, a shorter incubation period in mice, about 5 days instead of 5 to 12 days, and produced in all animals less pronounced pathologic changes. It was shown to be immunologically distinct from the virus of lymphocytic choriomeningitis and much larger, being from 150 to 225 millimicrons in diameter, as determined by filtration through gradocol membranes, instead of 40 to 60. It is filterable through Berkefeld V but not N candles and through Seitz filters. The virus can be propagated readily on the chorio-allantoic membrane of developing chick embryos. It is preserved in 50 per cent glycerol and by lyophilization; it is inactivated at a temperature of 56° C. within 30 minutes and by 0.05 per cent formalin at 4° C. within 48 hours.

DURAND'S DISEASE
(Synonym: D virus infection)

In 1940, in Tunis, during a febrile illness, Durand isolated from his blood a virus the properties of which were studied further by Findlay (1942), who was also attacked as a result of a laboratory infection. In man, after experimental inoculation, there develops after from 2 to 4 days a local cutaneous lesion associated with viremia, fever, the presence of the virus in the cerebrospinal fluid, cough, vomiting and lethargy. The symptoms persist for from 6 to 8 days, after which neutralizing and complement-fixing antibodies are found in the serum. The experimental animal of choice is the guinea pig, which is susceptible by intracerebral and peripheral inoculations of virus. It exhibits fever, adenopathy, enlarged spleen and pneumonitis. Monkeys, dogs, cats, merions, mice, hamsters and voles are also susceptible. The virus is found in their blood, organs and spinal fluid; on recovery, infected hosts develop neutralizing and complement-fixing antibodies. The virus multiplies in Maitland-type tissue cultures, and chick embroys show a lethal infection after introduction of virus into the yolk sac or chorio-allantois. The virus is about 65 millimicrons in diameter as determined by ultrafiltration through gradocol membranes. It is preserved by glycerolation, by being held in the frozen state, or by lyophilization.

B VIRUS INFECTION

B virus infection of human beings is an acute ascending myelitis associated with focal necrosis of the internal organs and is caused by the bite of normal-appearing monkeys which harbor the causal virus in their saliva (Sabin, 1934, 1949). The virus was isolated by Sabin and Wright (1934) and insofar as is known only 4 human cases, all fatal, have been recorded; of these, 2 were proved by isolation of virus.

The outstanding features of the case studied by Sabin, Patient B., hence the name B virus infection, were the appearance of vesiculopustular lesions at the site of the monkey bites, developing within three days, followed within another three days by regional lymphangitis and adenitis. A week later began a series of motor and sensory disturbances first noted in the lower extremities and bladder and followed by an acute ascending myelitis with death in a few days. The pathologic picture was that of focal necrosis in the spleen, adrenals, regional lymph glands, and a meningo-encephalomyelitis comparable to that of the viral encephalitides in general. From the brain, cord and spleen a virus was isolated by intraperitoneal and intracerebral inoculation of suspensions of these tissues into rabbits. The experimental disease, especially after intracerebral inoculation in monkeys and peripheral injection in rabbits, patterns itself after the human malady, and in the induced lesions herpetic-type

(Cowdry Type A) intranuclear inclusions and multinucleated giant cells are found. In monkeys that have received the virus intravenously, the striking feature of infection is the development of an exanthem chiefly about the forehead, eyes, conjunctivae and face and an enanthem on the buccal mucosa, tongue and palate, that closely resemble the eruption produced by intravenous inoculation of vaccine virus. Guinea pigs are susceptible, but mice are only irregularly so. B virus is pathogenic only for mice less than 3 weeks of age, while herpes virus is highly pathogenic for young and old mice. The rabbit is the animal of choice for primary isolation of the virus and experimental work (Sabin, personal communication).

The diameter of the virus is about 125 millimicrons as determined by filtration through gradocol membranes; it is filterable through Berkefeld V and N, Chamberland L₃ and a single disk Seitz filters; most of it is sedimented from a suspension at 14,000 r.p.m. for $3\frac{1}{4}$ hours. It can be preserved in 50 per cent glycerol, by being stored on dry ice at about −70° C., and by lyophilization. The active agent is cultivable on the chorio-allantois of the developing chick embryo, on which it produces lesions, or pocks, indistinguishable from those of herpes simplex. Egg-adapted virus kills embryos within 6 days; they show focal lesions in the viscera, which have a high concentration of the active agent. Neutralizing antibody is found in apparently normal monkeys; the number of animals possessing the antibody varies with the stock examined.

B virus has features common to the active agents of herpes simplex and pseudorabies. These viruses are not identical even though they are serologically related in a way somewhat similar to that demonstrated for West Nile, St. Louis and Japanese B viruses, i.e., the crossing is of a low degree and the homologous reactions are more marked than are the heterologous. It was recently shown, however, that B virus is a more inclusive antigen than is the virus of herpes simplex (Burnet et al., 1939). The serologic crossing that occurs between herpes simplex virus and B virus is frequently observed in normal human sera; whenever neutralizing antibody is present against the former agent there is also regularly a small amount of such antibody against the latter (Burnet et al., 1939). Pseudorabies agent is more pathogenic for guinea pigs and mice than is B virus; both are pathogenic for rhesus monkeys, while herpes simplex virus is, as a rule, innocuous for this animal. There is no specific treatment, and prevention of infection consists of protection against bites by monkeys.

TROPICAL VIRUSES IMPORTANT IN HUMAN INFECTIONS

The miscellaneous viruses here described comprise a group recovered by members of the research staff of The Rockefeller Foundation and associates while in pursuit, from 1937 to 1949, not directly of these infective agents but of the causative agent of yellow fever in Africa, Brazil and Colombia. The properties of these agents and still others not mentioned, which are serologically and immunologically distinct, are still being studied; one of them, the Mengo encephalitis virus, is described in Chapter 39. The West Nile and the Bwamba fever viruses were obtained from the blood of Africans mildly ill; the others were secured from mosquitoes by means of inoculation of mice in which encephalomyelitis was produced. It should be stressed, however, that viruses which are encephalitogenic in an experimental animal need not necessarily be disease-producing or neurotropic in man. Some of the tropical viruses produce under experimental conditions encephalitis in human beings. The viruses are widespread and numerous, and it is likely that still others await discovery. Finally, they are described here for convenience until more is known about them and the diseases they produce. The name "tropical viruses" is an expedient one: the group was first isolated in the tropics, but with time one or all of them may be introduced into or prevail in the temperate zone.

West Nile Virus

The virus (Smithburn et al., 1940) was isolated from an African woman with a mild fever by intracerebral inoculation of her blood serum into mice. Rhesus monkeys are also susceptible. Mice and monkeys given the virus intracerebrally exhibit encephalitis, characterized by acidophilic degenerative changes in the Purkinje cells. Rabbits, guinea pigs and hedgehogs are not susceptible. The diameter of the virus as determined by filtration through gradocol membranes is from 21 to 31 millimicrons. It can be propagated in a medium containing suspended, minced chick-embryo tissue and in chick embryos after inoculation of the yolk sac, the allantois or the chorioallantoic membranes. It is related to St. Louis and Japanese B viruses as revealed by neutralization and complement-fixation tests, but not by cross-resistance tests (Smithburn, 1942; Casals, 1944). The degree of crossing is generally small, and, while shown mainly by animals artificially immunized against the viruses, it is occasionally observed in human sera. Sera from natives in widely separated localities in central Africa showed neutralizing antibody. The virus hemagglutinates sheep or chick erythrocytes (Sabin, 1951). Clinically apparent disease of the human CNS induced by this virus has been noted.

In 1950, 3 strains of a virus, found by neutralization and complement-fixation tests to be related to the West Nile virus and to a lesser degree to Japanese B and St. Louis encephalitis viruses, were isolated by Melnick et al. (1951) from the serum of apparently normal children living in the vicinity of Cairo, Egypt. The strains were recovered by intracerebral inoculation of the serum into mice and by infection of the chorioallantoic membrane of chick embryos. The Egyptian virus was not neutralized by gamma globulin collected in the United States, but in the Egyptian area from which the virus was isolated 70 per cent of the inhabitants, aged 4 or more years, revealed both neutralizing and complement-fixing antibodies.

Bwamba Fever

Smithburn, Mahaffy and Paul (1941) described in natives of Bwamba, Uganda, a mild disease of 4 or 5 days' duration characterized by fever, headache, generalized pains, and conjunctivitis. From the blood of 9 natives, a virus was isolated by intracerebral inoculation of mice. Four or 5 days after intracerebral or intranasal inoculation of the virus, mice show a viremia and an encephalitis characterized by degeneration of pyramidal cells in the cortex which have acidophilic intranuclear bodies resembling inclusions. Rhesus monkeys react with a mild illness or an inapparent infection; rabbits and guinea pigs are not susceptible. The diameter of the virus as determined by filtration through gradocol membranes is from 113 to 150 millimicrons. It can be preserved by lyophilization and by being kept frozen at −70° C. It is inactivated at 50° C. within 30 minutes. Blood serum of the 9 persons from whom virus was isolated showed no neutralizing antibody during the acute phase of the disease, but did possess it in convalescence, i.e., between the 12th and 576th day after the onset of illness. Smithburn and Bugher (personal communication) have tested over 1,400 sera against this virus and found antibody to be widespread among East and West African natives.

Semliki Forest Virus

Smithburn and Haddow (1944) described the isolation of this virus from *Aedes abnormalis* group of mosquitoes caught in nature in Uganda. Mice receiving the virus by various routes develop a viremia and an encephalitis characterized by lesions resembling those of experimental equine encephalitis. It also induces a lethal encephalitis in guinea pigs, rabbits, rhesus and redtail

(*Cercopithecus nictitans*) monkeys only after intracerebral inoculation; it can be propagated in chick embryos by various routes of inoculation. It is unusually resistant to heat, and a temperature of 60° C. for one hour is needed for its complete inactivation. It has not as yet been isolated from man. Human contact with this virus, however, was shown by the fact that neutralizing antibody was found in 47 normal persons out of 313 tested from different localities in Uganda. Among wild animals, only primates were found to possess neutralizing antibody.

Bunyamwera Virus

The isolation of this virus was accomplished by Smithburn, Haddow and Mahaffy (1946) by the inoculation of a filtered emulsion of naturally infected *Aedes* mosquitoes into a rhesus monkey. The active agent was easily adapted to mice which are susceptible by various routes of inoculation and show viremia, convulsions and paralysis which terminate rapidly in death. The main pathologic changes are in the brain and consist of congestion, hemorrhage and neuronal necrosis chiefly in Ammon's horn and in the basal ganglia. In rhesus monkeys the infection is not always lethal. Rabbits are insusceptible. The virus has not as yet been shown to cause in nature a clinically apparent disease in man or lower animals. But that it has produced clinically inapparent infection in human beings is shown by the fact that 28 of 298 healthy residents of Uganda were found to have neutralizing antibody in their serum.

Other Viruses

Recently a number of viruses, in addition to those mentioned, that are neurotropic in experimental animals have been isolated from mosquitoes caught in nature in South America, among them being those isolated by Roca-Garcia (1944) and called by him *Anopheles A, Anopheles B* and *Wyeomyia* viruses. Their relation to infection of man is still unknown.

Laemmert and Hughes (1947) recovered a virus from *Aedes* and *Psorophora* mosquitoes caught in the vicinity of Ilhéus, Bahia, Brazil, which possesses serologic specificity, produces encephalitis in laboratory animals, and against which neutralizing antibody is found in the human beings of that locality. Ilhéus virus is interesting because it appears, as demonstrated by cross-serologic reactions, to fall into the group of West Nile-St. Louis-Japanese B viruses.

At the present time, nine other viruses are being investigated by members of the staff and associates of The Rockefeller Foundation; among them are the Ntaya, Zika, Uganda S and Kumba viruses.

California (Hammon-Reeves) Virus

This recently discovered virus has been found three times in *Aedes dorsalis* and *Culex tarsalis* caught in San Joaquin Valley, California; other parts of the state have not as yet been surveyed. The active agent is pathogenic for the mouse and cotton rat, causing lethal CNS infection. Monkeys, guinea pigs and chickens are resistant. Ground squirrels and rabbits receiving the virus subcutaneously reveal an inapparent infection associated with viremia. The virus is transmissible to the latter by bites from infected mosquitoes. It is cultivable in chick embryos. In California, neutralizing antibody is frequently found in man, rodents and large domestic mammals, but not in birds; complement-fixing antibody has been demonstrated in horses but not in man. This virus was thought to be the cause of a severe case of encephalitis in a child in whom was shown a rising titer of antibody during convalescence (Hammon and Reeves, 1945).

ENCEPHALITIS DURING THE COURSE OF OTHER VIRAL DISEASES

The encephalitides which occur as a phase of primary infections with viruses that are ordinarily nonencephalitogenic, i.e., those causing herpes simplex, lympho-granuloma venereum, mumps, measles, and infectious mononucleosis which is probably a viral infection, will be discussed in chapters given to these viral maladies. They should, however, be differentiated from the postinfection encephalitides which arise after a primary viral attack, as happens sometimes after influenza, measles, vaccinia or other viral maladies (*v. infra,* postinfection encephalitis). In the encephalitis arising during a primary viral attack, the virus causing the initial infection may be still active and detectable while the encephalitic process goes on, whereas in the postinfection group the primary virus is, as a rule, no longer recoverable and the primary viral syndrome has disappeared or is rapidly dropping into the background. Finally, the basic pathologic pictures of the former are those caused by the direct action of a virus, while in postinfection encephalitides the pathologic picture is dominated by the characteristic perivascular demyelination (*v. infra,* postinfection encephalitis).

ACUTE PRIMARY HEMORRHAGIC MENINGO-ENCEPHALITIS

(SYNONYMS: Strümpell's disease; acute epidemic leuko-encephalitis)

Acute primary hemorrhagic meningo-encephalitis is a malady characterized by predominance of large or small hemorrhagic foci and perivascular demyelination throughout the CNS. It is of interest that a hemorrhagic encephalitis occurs spontaneously in horses, acute epizootic leuko-encephalitis, first described in 1901. Since diagnosis is based on clinical or pathologic findings and not on specific etiology, it is impossible to say at this time whether or not the equine disease has any connection with that of man and whether or not all the reports of the human malady concern the same disease. The human malady was first noted in 1881. In western Europe in 1891, cases occurred which were regarded as secondary to influenza. Thereafter, sporadic cases were observed in Russia, Australia, England, United States and elsewhere (Hurst, 1941; Margulis, Soloviev and Shubladze, 1944). Margulis et al. (1944) reported a study of 9 Russian cases conducted during 1939-1940; CNS tissue, blood or spinal fluid from four patients injected intracerebrally in mice yielded a virus which the investigators regarded as the causal agent of the malady.

The length of the incubation period is unknown. The onset is acute with fever, anorexia, dullness, or irritability for a day or two. Then, follows an acute and stormy syndrome of convulsions, delirium, nuchal rigidity, coma, and death within a week, or recovery after 7 to 20 days of illness. Survivors who pass into a chronic stage show frequent exacerbations, varying paralyses, ataxia, and nystagmus. Pupillary or ocular palsies are rare. Survivors may also exhibit permanent sequelae, such as athetoid movements, paralyses and psychoses. The blood count reveals a moderate polymorphonuclear leukocytosis of 10,000 to 20,000 cells per c.mm., and the spinal fluid is clear, blood-tinged, under increased pressure, with moderate pleocytosis and increased protein. The pathologic picture in the CNS is one of congestion of arterioles and capillaries; the walls of many vessels are broken and surrounding tissues are infiltrated with blood. The vascular walls may be necrotic and the vessels may be filled with thrombi. There are concomitant gliosis, degeneration and necrosis of neurons, and inflammatory reaction in the gray and white matter, especially in the latter, with perivascular infiltration with round and plasma cells. The distinctive feature is a perivascular demyelination. The diagnosis should be made guardedly since it is based at present only on clinical and pathologic pictures that are not markedly different from those occurring generally in the postinfection encephalitides (*v. infra*). The report on the causal agent (Margulis et al., 1944) needs confirmation. The problem here is the differentiation of this malady from other demyelinating diseases, especially since the latter are also associated with a greater or lesser degree of hemorrhagic reaction. Persons of all ages can be attacked, but morbidity is highest in young people. Mortality rates vary in different outbreaks from 15 to 70 per cent. There is no specific treatment, and control measures are unknown.

POSTINFECTION ENCEPHALITIS

(SYNONYMS: Acute demyelinating encephalomyelitis; acute disseminated encephalomyelitis; postvaccinal [or postmeasles, etc.] encephalitis; acute perivascular myelinoclasis; acute primary myelinoclasis)

INTRODUCTION

Postinfection encephalitis is an acute affection of the CNS occasionally arising during convalescence from infectious diseases, especially those caused by viruses, or following vaccination against such diseases as smallpox and rabies, or developing spontaneously in certain instances without a prior history of disease or vaccination.

HISTORY

A record of demyelination can be found in an atlas of pathology published in England in 1838 to show certain primary forms of disease processes. In 1872, acute disseminated encephalomyelitis, which is now known generally as postinfection encephalitis, was observed following smallpox; it was noted in 1886 following measles; in 1887 following preventive inoculation against rabies; and in 1907 after vaccination against smallpox. Outbreaks of postvaccinal encephalitis, which assumed epidemic proportions, occurred in England and Holland during 1922 and 1924, respectively. In more recent times, cases of postinfection encephalitis have been observed following several other virus diseases, especially mumps, varicella and influenza.

CLINICAL PICTURE

The clinical picture seen in encephalitis that develops during convalescence from viral infections depends on the type, extent and location of the lesions in the CNS. In general, it is encephalitic, myelitic, or encephalomyelitic. The encephalitic form is commonly seen following vaccination against smallpox; the myelitic type usually occurs after antirabic treatment; and both kinds are seen with equal frequency after variola. Most cases of postinfection encephalitis follow measles and vaccination against smallpox, and the picture seen under these conditions will be described in detail.

Postvaccinal encephalitis usually develops abruptly from 2 to 24 days, average 10 days, after vaccination. In the encephalitic type, fever, headache, vomiting and drowsiness occur which may be followed by photophobia, delirium, convulsions, trismus, paralyses, transient muscular weakness, inco-ordination, ataxia, and a variety of disturbances of deep and superficial reflexes. In the myelitic type, paralyses and sensory disturbances are usually present. The course of the disease is fairly rapid and terminates in recovery within 7 to 14 days, or in the death of from 37 to 58 per cent of the patients. In most instances recovery is complete; this is a striking feature of postvaccinal encephalitis when compared with postmeasles encephalitis which not infrequently is followed by sequelae.

The first indication of the development of postmeasles encephalitis is usually noted after the rash has disappeared, 4 to 6 days after defervescence. In infants, the first sign of CNS involvement may be convulsions. In older children, the disease is ushered in by drowsiness, stupor, meningismus, and convulsions at times. Muscular twitchings, rigidity, choreiform movements, ataxia, spastic paralyses, aphasia, and psychic disturbances may be observed. Of particular note is the occurrence of cerebellar ataxia and, in certain instances, flaccid paralyses. Infants and children usually recover, but sequelae, such as spastic paralysis, tremors, choreic or athetoid movements, and psychic derangements may occur.

Encephalitis rarely follows German measles but, when it does, the clinical picture is not essentially different from that of postvaccinal encephalitis. Such is also true of the rare cases of encephalitis following dengue fever, smallpox and yellow fever. The encephalitis that follows varicella is more common and is somewhat similar to postmeasles encephalitis, i.e., cerebellar forms are prominent. Postmumps encephalitis must be differentiated from mumps meningitis and mumps meningoencephalitis. The former disease is not caused by the direct action of mumps virus and perivascular demyelination is prominent in the pathologic picture, while the latter conditions are due to the direct action of mumps virus on CNS tissue and perivascular demyelination is not a part of the pathologic changes observed. The symptomatology and course of the demyelinating encephalitis, which follows antirabies vaccination and bacterial infections or which arise spontaneously, are similar in most respects to the postinfection encephalitis that follow viral infections.

The cerebrospinal fluid of patients with postinfection encephalitis is clear, under increased pressure, free from infective agents, contains a normal amount of sugar and a slightly increased amount of protein, and usually reveals a lymphocytic pleocytosis which may be as high as 300 cells.

Pathologic Picture

The pathologic picture in postinfection encephalitis is one predominantly of demyelination, which is usually found around small veins in the white matter. Associated with this are vascular lesions and thrombus formation which may be seen most frequently in small vessels. Hemorrhages and perivascular infiltration with lymphocytes and glial cells are found; the glial cells exhibit proliferation and active phagocytosis of fat and myelin material. A gliosis is also found diffusely scattered throughout the CNS. Degeneration and necrosis of neurons is not marked. One or another of the lesions

may predominate or may be absent in any single case (Findlay, 1940). The main features are, therefore, the perivascular demyelination in the gray and white matter of the brain and cord, which may occur with or without hemorrhage, and only a slight amount of neuronal degeneration and necrosis (Fig. 28, *center and bottom frames*). Rivers (1932) holds that the pathologic changes in postinfection encephalitis are not those usually produced by the direct action of a virus on the CNS where, as in St. Louis encephalitis, the lesions are mostly in the gray matter and neuronal damage and death are a prominent part of the picture. Hurst (1944) regards the changes as nonspecific, i.e., as reactions to different agents. According to Roizin, Helfand and Moore (1946) and others, the lesions are in many respects similar to those observed in other demyelinating maladies, for example, multiple sclerosis.

Etiology

Postinfection encephalitis has not been transmitted to experimental animals (Rivers, 1932). There has been much speculation concerning the etiology of this demyelinating process and the matter has been discussed at length by Hurst (1944) and Ferraro (1944).

Among the theories advanced are: (1) the infection theory which implies that the disease is caused through action on the CNS by the virus causing the primary disease, e.g., measles, or by the activation of a latent virus already present in the host. Recently, Margulis, Soloviev and Shubladze (1946) reported the isolation of a virus from the blood of one patient and from the CNS tissue of another with acute sporadic disseminated encephalomyelitis and state that the virus may possibly be the etiologic agent not only of this demyelinating malady but also of multiple sclerosis. The active agent is different from that of acute primary hemorrhagic meningo-encephalitis recovered by Margulis et al. (1944). The writers point out the fact that this work is far from complete. At the present time it is safe to say that no one has definitely shown the direct action of a virus to be the cause of postinfection encephalitis. Therefore, caution must be used in the interpretation of the role of the occasional virus reported to have been recovered from patients with this disease.

(2) Another theory relates to toxins or poisons as the etiologic agents which are assumed to be developed during the course of the primary viral attack. In this group of agents belong poisons that induce cerebral anoxia (Ferraro, 1944; Hurst, 1944). This theory was advanced because of the fact that lesions produced in the CNS by CO, KCN and tetanus toxin resemble those of postinfection encephalitis.

(3) The enzyme theory assumes that myelin-destroying agents are produced in the patient or that those already present are activated by the viral infection; this theory has at present little support.

(4) The theory relating to vascular thrombi is actively advanced at present, especially by Putnam (1941) and his colleagues. Encephalitis and plaques of demyelination have been produced experimentally by the intravenous injection of oil or various blood coagulants into animals.

(5) The idea that phenomena of immunity or allergy play a role in the causation of postinfection encephalitis arose as the result of experimental investigations. Demyelination and inflammation of the CNS of monkeys was produced by the intramuscular injections of emulsions of normal rabbit brain tissue (Rivers, Sprunt and Berry, 1933). This work has been expanded by Morgan (1947) and by Kabat, Wolf and Bezer (1947) who injected intramuscularly into monkeys a mixture of normal monkey-brain tissue, dead tubercle bacilli and oil, and by others who successfully used rabbits, guinea pigs and mice (Olitsky and Yager, 1949). The view that the pathologic processes in postinfection encephalitis are the expression of phenomena of allergy or immunity receives support

from the fact that encephalitis sometimes follows the use of immune sera or vaccines or develops in the course of antirabic treatment (Rivers, 1932; Findlay, 1940; Putnam, 1941; Ferraro, 1944; Hurst, 1944).

DIAGNOSIS

Diagnosis is ordinarily made from clinical findings and a history of convalescence from a viral infection or of having been vaccinated recently. Postinfection encephalitis should be distinguished from an encephalitis that may occasionally arise during the course of a viral disease, for example, measles and mumps. In the latter case, the encephalitis may be caused by the virus responsible for the primary disease and the pathologic picture is wholly different from that seen in the demyelinating postinfection encephalitides. The diagnosis is, therefore, difficult and confirmation can be had only by finding the characteristic perivascular demyelination in the CNS at necropsy. The disease should also be differentiated from spontaneous demyelinating maladies of multiple sclerosis, diffuse sclerosis, Schilder's disease, neuromyelitis optica, acute hemorrhagic leuko-encephalitis, and more than a score of other encephalopathies listed by Roizin, Helfand and Moore (1946) who believe that from a histopathologic point of view all types of demyelinating diseases, including postinfection encephalitis and acute hemorrhagic meningo-encephalitis (v. supra), belong to one group of primary demyelinating processes, and that differences among them can be ascribed to age of the patient, duration of the affection, distribution of lesions, and degrees of host resistance to the causal agent. The differences therefore may be only apparent, not real (Ferraro, 1944; Hurst, 1944).

TREATMENT

There is no specific treatment.

EPIDEMIOLOGY

The occurrence of postinfection encephalitis has no relationship to the severity of the primary viral attack or to the immediate reactions after vaccination against smallpox or rabies. In postvaccinal encephalitis, moreover, there is no relationship to the strain of vaccine virus used. Encephalitis rarely follows the second or subsequent vaccinations against smallpox; there is no relation between morbidity and and the amount of vaccine virus used or the manner of its insertion into the body. Encephalitis following vaccination against smallpox occurs in people of all ages, but the disease is more common in children than in infants or adults, e.g., the largest number of cases occur in children from 2 to 14 years of age. In England 93 cases of postvaccinal encephalitis were observed between 1922 and 1928; in Holland 150 between 1924 and 1928; in the United States 71 between 1923 and 1932. Up to 1943, more than 200 cases of postmeasles encephalitis were recorded throughout the world (Haymaker and Smadel, 1943), and by 1935, 121 cases of postvaricellar encephalitis had been reported. The incidence of encephalitis following antirabic treatment or immunization varies widely depending on the material used; 1 of 17,620 persons receiving antirabic vaccination with heat-inactivated virus exhibited paralysis (Casals, 1945), while in China, 5 of 201 persons who were vaccinated developed neurologic syndromes, and two of them died. The general mortality rate is from 10 to 58 per cent; high in postvaccinal encephalitis, from 37 to 58 per cent, and low in the postmeasles and other types, 10 per cent. The rate for each type, however, varies from year to year.

Control Measures

Since the cause of postinfection encephalitis has not been definitely established, it is difficult to say much about control measures. Vaccines made from nervous tissues and particularly those containing nervous tissue to which killed tubercle bacilli and oil have been added, should be used with great care (Rivers et al., 1933; Morgan, 1947; Kabat et al., 1947). Since infants are least often attacked by postvaccinal encephalitis, primary vaccination against smallpox should be performed at the age of about 6 months and revaccination on entering school.

INFECTIOUS POLYNEURITIS

(Synonyms: Guillain-Barré disease; Landry's paralysis; encephalomyeloradiculitis; infectious neuronitis; acute polyneuritis with facial diplegia)

Infectious polyneuritis is characterized by neurologic signs referable to the peripheral spinal and cranial nerves and sometimes by involvement of the adrenals, liver, heart, and kidneys. The outstanding features of the condition are a protein-cell dissociation observed in the cerebrospinal fluid, progression of the neurologic symptoms, tachycardia and gastro-intestinal disturbances. It occurs after diseases associated with known bacterial toxins as in diphtheria and scarlet fever, after infections of unknown etiology involving the respiratory or the intestinal tracts, and occasionally without any recognized antecedent infection. The malady usually endures for several weeks or rarely may last for three years or longer. Except in elderly people in whom the disease may be fatal, complete recovery is the rule. Certain patients, however, may show permanent weakness of one side of the face or other paretic and paralytic sequelae. The mortality rate is about 20 per cent and death often occurs within the first two weeks usually as a result of paralysis of the intercostal muscles. Fatal cases in children may be wrongly diagnosed as poliomyelitis. There is a mild polymorphonuclear leukocytosis of 10,000 to 15,000 cells; in the early stages of the disease, however, from 25 to 80 per cent of the white blood cells may be lymphocytes (Haymaker and Kernohan, 1949). Changes in the cerebrospinal fluid are characteristic; pressure is increased, cells may be normal in numbers or at times slightly increased, the amount of protein is usually greater than normal and may at times be as much as 800 mg. per 100 cc. This increase of protein may persist for a long time.

There is marked edema, congestion and focal inflammation of involved nerves and spinal roots. Swelling and beading of the myelin sheaths occur as well as fragmentation, beading and dissolution of axons associated with marked proliferation of the neurilemmal cells. No inflammation is found in the CNS; neuronophagia is absent. Neurons in the medulla, cord and ganglia may exhibit changes similar to those following section or damage of axons, viz., chromatolysis, eccentricity of nucleus, vacuolization of cytoplasm, and appearance of acidophilic bodies in the cytoplasm, a picture somewhat similar to that observed by Olitsky (1939) and others in avian encephalomyelitis. Focal degeneration and necrosis associated with infiltration by mononuclear cells may be present in the adrenals, liver, heart and kidneys.

Attempts to transmit the disease to lower animals have failed (Sabin and Aring, 1941). The etiology is as yet unknown, although it has been considered an infective agent, perhaps a virus. The recent studies of Sabin and Aring (1941) have led them to suspect that the disease is produced by a toxic substance developed during the infection which usually precedes the polyneuritic attack. Outbreaks of the disease do occur, chiefly in the colder months. Persons of all ages may be attacked, but the morbidity is highest in those between 20 and 30 years of age; both sexes are equally affected. Diagnosis is made on clinical findings, particularly a protein-cell dissociation in the cerebrospinal fluid. There is no specific treatment or control measure.

GENERAL CONSIDERATIONS

Epidemiologic Generalizations Concerning the Arthropod-borne Encephalitides

A variety of arthropods have been suspected of serving as vectors of the summer encephalitides, and many kinds of lower animals have been considered as reservoirs of the virus so that a cycle of transmission has been deduced of infection from a warm-blooded lower animal to arthropod to animal or man. It should be stressed, however, that so far the determination of the vector for any of the encephalitides has been based either on laboratory experiments or on the detection of an arthropod naturally infected with the virus in question. The crucial tests, namely, the ability of an arthropod naturally infected with a virus to transmit to man the disease caused by that virus and the decline or disappearance of the disease as correlated with the abatement or elimination of a particular arthropod, are still to be made.

There are probably 2 phases in the epidemiologic pattern of the arthropod-borne encephalitides. One is the maintenance and dissemination of the viruses in nature. Several of the incitants have been found in normal-appearing birds or other domestic or woodland fauna which may be considered reservoirs of the agents. Animal-to-animal transmission may occur through the bites of indigenous arthropod vectors, in some of which the viruses may pass from generation to generation by the transovarian route. Under such conditions, one can regard the arthropods as hosts or reservoirs of the viruses as well as vectors. The other phase in the epidemiologic cycle concerns the infection of man and may follow the pattern: lower animal → animal-adapted arthropod → man. Thus, for equine encephalitis, the mite perhaps maintains the virus in nature and in the course of this maintenance infects birds. Another arthropod, the mosquito, transmits it to other birds, to man, and to horses. Subsequently, the spread of the disease to the new hosts, man or horse, is by mosquitoes which feed on infected human beings or horses. For Russian Far East encephalitis, however, ticks may be the vectors among woodland animals as hosts, as well as among human beings. It would appear that at least some of these viruses are normally infectious agents of lower animals or arthropods and that man is infected accidentally during the efforts of the viruses to survive in nature.

An interesting problem concerns the interrelationship of the summer encephalitides. They show themselves generally in definite areas of the globe, each form of disease attacking within specific geographic boundaries. Moreover, there is a serologic overlapping among certain viruses of this group. Other points of similarity relate to the uniformity of size of most of the active agents, to the clinical and pathologic pictures which are not much different in the various types, to prevalence of the maladies during the warm months when arthropod populations reach their peak. For these reasons it has been postulated that the viruses may have had a common ancestor which on dissemination over the world has been acted upon by environmental factors; perhaps the latter served to impress certain changes reflected in serologic and immunologic reactions. The environmental factors are assumed to be insect vectors and animal reservoirs in newly invaded areas to which the virus became in time adapted (cf. Stanley, 1941; Shwartzman, 1944b; Silber and Soloviev, 1946).

A similar situation may perhaps exist here as among the *Rickettsioses:* European typhus is louse-borne; New World typhus, flea-borne; East African typhus, tick-borne; and Far East typhus, mite-borne (Olitsky, 1946).

Pathogenesis of the Viral Encephalitides

The pathogenesis of the viral encephalitides as they occur in nature has not as yet been thoroughly studied, only a few fragmentary findings are available. The progression of some of the viruses from the site of their introduction into the body to the CNS, however, has been studied experimentally. TenBroeck et al. (1935) demonstrated that, in the horse inoculated intracutaneously with eastern equine encephalitis virus, there was a high content of the agent in the blood stream during the first febrile period of a diphasic syndrome, 3 days before the first signs of an involvement of the CNS were visible. The circulating virus decreased rapidly and was absent from the blood 24 hours before signs of encephalitis appeared. This finding is believed by TenBroeck to be characteristic of the natural malady in the horse and may be similar to what occurs in the viral encephalitides of man. In man, however, the period of viremia may be lengthened in certain infections, e.g., Russian Far East encephalitis.

Hurst (1936) showed that the infection in guinea pigs and monkeys following peripheral (nonneural) injection of the eastern or western equine encephalitis virus is at first visceral, during which time the viruses multiply in nonneural tissues, including those of the vascular system; then appears a second or nervous phase in which viruses progress through and multiply in the CNS. Sabin and Olitsky (1937-1938) demonstrated that both young and old mice are susceptible to these viruses administered by the intracerebral route but that only the young ones succumb after receiving them by the peripheral route. It was postulated that, in old mice, age affects the nonneural tissues in some subtle way to make them incapable of supporting viral multiplication, while the tissues of young mice are capable of supporting virus multiplication. Moreover, in old mice a resulting infection may not induce visible illness, but will produce antibody and immunity. In other words, resistance can be regarded as the capacity of an individual's tissue to suppress or to reduce viral multiplication sufficiently to prevent development of clinically apparent illness, or to convert a violent nervous malady into a mild one. Morgan (1941) found that young mice develop antibody slowly and at a low level, while adults produce it rapidly and at a high level; this difference is sufficient in part to account for the relative resistance of the old mice and the susceptibility of the young to peripherally introduced virus. It may be, therefore, that both factors, age of the tissues and rate of antibody production, control the spread of virus in the body. Whatever the mechanism may be, the commonest type of infection induced by these "encephalitis" viruses is abortive or inapparent.

The progression of a virus to the CNS varies with the species of experimental animal and with the type of virus used (Sabin and Olitsky, 1937-1938; Sabin, 1941). For example, in the case of viruses highly neurotropic for mice, such as that of vesicular stomatitis, the virus progresses after intranasal instillation to the CNS in a closed system, the olfactory-nerve pathway; in this pathway it appears to progress through the synapses from neuron to neuron. Eastern equine virus progresses in the mouse in a similar way, yet, as a rule, in the guinea pig it invades the CNS by traversing the walls of the blood vessels (Hurst, 1950). The Venezuelan equine and Russian Far East viruses, after peripheral inoculation, can induce encephalitis both in old and in young mice.

It should be stressed that the pattern of pathogenesis observed in the experimental animal is not necessarily that found in man. However, in certain instances the picture seen in the naturally occurring disease in lower animals may afford a model for the study of the malady in man. Thus the equine encephalitides in horses are diphasic; the early phase is visceral, the later one nervous (TenBroeck et al., 1935). During the visceral phase the virus circulates in the blood and the signs are those of a systemic infection, while during the nervous phase— the two phases may overlap at times—the active agent multiplies in nervous tissues, injury and destruction of which give rise to signs and symptoms of an encephalitis. A diphasic type of infection certainly occurs in some of the human viral encephalitides. Whether the virus passes directly from the blood into the CNS, whether, after leaving the circulation, it is deposited on the nasal mucosa whence it progresses via neurons and their processes to the CNS, or whether it goes directly by way of nerves to the CNS from the point of introduction into the body, is not as yet definitely known for most of the agents producing encephalitis in man. Noran and Baker (1943) suggest, however, that the pathogenesis of encephalitis in man caused by the eastern and western equine viruses is based on a vascular spread of the active agents. Lymphocytic choriomeningitis is in the majority of instances a systemic disease; consequently most patients suffering from it do not show signs of involvement of the brain and cord (Rivers, 1939; Armstrong, 1940-1941). The reason for this is attributed by Armstrong to barriers which protect the CNS from various infections.

REFERENCES

Armstrong, C., 1940-1941, Studies on choriomeningitis and poliomyelitis. Harvey Lectures, *36*, 39-65.

Armstrong, C., and Lillie, R. D., 1934, Experimental lymphocytic choriomeningitis of monkeys and mice produced by a virus encountered in studies of the 1933 St. Louis encephalitis epidemic. Pub. Health Rep., *49*, 1019-1027.

Ayres, J. C., and Feemster, R. F., 1949, The sequelae of eastern equine encephalomyelitis. New England J. Med., *240*, 960-962.

Bang, F. B., and Gey, G. O., 1949, Electron microscopy of tissue cultures infected with the virus of eastern equine encephalomyelitis. Proc. Soc. Exp. Biol. and Med., *71*, 78-80.

Beard, J. W., 1945, The ultracentrifugal, chemical, and electron micrographic characters of purified animal viruses. Proc. Inst. Med. Chicago, *15*, 294-313.

Beard, J. W., Beard, D., and Finkelstein, H., 1940, Vaccination of man against the virus of equine encephalomyelitis (eastern and western strains). J. Immunol., *38*, 117-136.

Beaudette, F. R., and Black, J. J., 1948, Equine encephalomyelitis in New Jersey pheasants in 1945 and 1946. J. Am. Vet. Med. Assn., *112*, 140-147.

Beck, C. E., and Wyckoff, R. W. G., 1938, Venezuelan equine encephalomyelitis. Science, *88*, 530.

Blattner, R. J., and Heys, F. M., 1944, Blood-sucking vectors of encephalitis: Experimental transmission of St. Louis encephalitis (Hubbard strain) to white Swiss mice by the American dog tick, *Dermacentor variabilis* Say. J. Exp. Med., *79*, 439-454.

Burnet, F. M., Lush, D., and Jackson, A. V., 1939, The relationship of herpes and B viruses: immunological and epidemiological considerations. Australian J. Exp. Biol., *17*, 41-51.

Casals, J., 1944, Immunological relationships among central nervous system viruses. J. Exp. Med., 79, 341-359.

Casals, J., 1945, A current view of the rabies problem. Ann. Int. Med., 23, 74-78.

Casals, J., Curnen, E. C., and Thomas, L., 1943, Venezuelan equine encephalomyelitis in man. J. Exp. Med., 77, 521-530.

Casals, J., and Olitsky, P. K., 1945, Enduring immunity following vaccination of mice with formalin-inactivated virus of Russian spring-summer (Far Eastern, tick-borne) encephalitis. Correlation with serum-neutralizing and complement-fixing antibodies. J. Exp. Med., 82, 431-443.

Casals, J., and Palacios, R., 1941, The complement fixation test in the diagnosis of virus infections of the central nervous system. J. Exp. Med., 74. 409-426.

Casals, J., and Schneider, H. A., 1943, Natural resistance and susceptibility to Russian spring-summer encephalitis in mice. Proc. Soc. Exp. Biol. and Med., 54. 201-202.

Casey, A. E., and Broun, G. O., 1938, Epidemiology of Saint Louis encephalitis. Science, 88, 450-451.

Cepero, E. B., 1949, Histopatologia experimental del sistema nervioso central en la encefalitis equina del este. Trab. Inst. Cajal Inv. Biol., 41, 164-275.

Cleland, J. B., and Campbell, A. W., 1917, The Australian epidemics of an acute polio-encephalomyelitis (X disease). Rep. Director-General of Public Health, New South Wales, pp. 150-280.

Cleland, J. B., and Campbell, A. W., 1919, An experimental investigation of an Australian epidemic of acute encephalo-myelitis. J. Hyg., 18, 272-316.

Cox, H. R., and Olitsky, P. K., 1936, Active immunization of guinea pigs with the virus of equine encephalomyelitis. J. Exp. Med., 63, 745-765.

Cruchet, R., Moutier and Calmettes, 1917, Quarante cas d'encéphalo-myelite subaiguë. Bull. et mém. Soc. méd. hop. Paris, 41, 614-616.

Davison, G., Neubauer, C., and Hurst, E. W., 1948, Meningo-encephalitis in man due to the louping-ill virus. Lancet, 255, 453-457.

Deuel, R. E., Bawell, M. B., Matumoto, M., and Sabin, A. B., 1950, Status and significance of inapparent infection with virus of Japanese B encephalitis in Korea and Okinawa in 1946. Am. J. Hyg., 51, 13-20.

Duffy, C. E., 1946, pH stability of St. Louis encephalitis virus. Proc. Soc. Exp. Biol. and Med., 63, 333-334.

Duffy, C. E., and Stanley, W. M., 1945, Studies on the biochemical, biophysical, and immunogenic properties of Japanese B type encephalitis virus and vaccines. J. Exp. Med., 82, 385-410.

von Economo, C., 1917, Encephalitis lethargica. Wien. klin. Wchnschr., 30, 581-585.

Edward, D. G. ff., 1950. The relationship of a newly-isolated human encephalitis virus to louping-ill virus. Brit. J. Exp. Path., 31, 515-522.

Farber, S., Hill, A., Connerley, M. L., and Dingle, J. H., 1940, Encephalitis in infants and children caused by the virus of Eastern variety of equine encephalitis, J. Am. Med. Assn., 114, 1725-1731.

Ferraro, A., 1944, Pathology of demyelinating diseases as an allergic reaction of the brain. Arch. Neur. and Psych., 52, 443-483.

Findlay, G. M., 1940, Nervous affections in man and animals. Proc. Roy. Soc. Med., 33, 161-168.

Findlay, G. M., 1942, Durand's disease: a virus infection transmissible to animals and man. Trans. Roy. Soc. Trop. Med. and Hyg. 35, 303-318.

Flexner, S., 1935, Virus diseases of the central nervous system: their extent and mode of infection. Proc. Inst. Med. Chicago, 10, 278-288.

Fothergill, L. D., Dingle, J. H., Farber, S., and Connerley, M. L., 1938, Human encephalitis caused by the virus of the eastern variety of equine encephalomyelitis. New England J. Med., 219, 411.

Giltner, L. T., and Shahan, M. S., 1933, The 1933 outbreak of infectious equine encephalomyelitis in the Eastern states. N. Am. Vet., 14, 25-27.

Gilyard, R. T., 1944, Mosquito transmission of Venezuelan virus equine encephalomyelitis in Trinidad. Bull. U. S. Army Med. Dept., No. 75, 96-107.

Gilyard, R. T., 1945, A clinical study of Venezuelan virus equine encephalomyelitis in Trinidad, B. W. I. J. Am. Vet. Med. Assn., 106, 267-277.

Goebel, W. F., Olitsky, P. K., and Saenz, A. C., 1948, The inactivation of biologically active proteins and the virus of western equine encephalomyelitis by periodic acid. J. Exp. Med., 87, 445-455.

Gordon, W. S., Brownlee, A., Wilson, D. R., and MacLeod, J., 1932, Studies in louping-ill. J. Comp. Path. and Therap., 45, 106-140.

Hammon, W. M., 1943a, Encephalitis. Eastern and western equine and St. Louis types, as observed in 1941 in Washington, Arizona, New Mexico and Texas. J. Am. Med. Assn., 121, 560-564.

Hammon, W. M., 1943b, The epidemic encephalitides of North America. Med. Clinics of N. America. New York Number, 27, 632-650.

Hammon, W. M., 1945, The encephalitides of virus origin with special reference to those of North America. Clinics, 4, 485-503.

Hammon, W. M., 1948, The arthropod-borne virus encephalitides. Am. J. Trop. Med., 28, 515-525.

Hammon, W. M., Rees, D. M., Casals, J., and Meiklejohn G., 1949a, Experimental transmission of Japanese B encephalitis virus by Culex tritaeniorhynchus and Culex pipiens var. pallens, suspected natural vectors. Am. J. Hyg., 50, 46-50.

Hammon, W. M., and Reeves, W. C., 1943, Laboratory transmission of St. Louis encephalitis virus by 3 genera of mosquitoes. J. Exp. Med., 78, 241-253.

Hammon, W. M., and Reeves, W. C., 1945, Recent advances in the epidemiology of the arthropod-borne virus encephalitides including certain exotic types. Am. J. Pub. Health, 35, 994-1004.

Hammon, W. M., Reeves, W. C., and Burroughs, R., 1946, Japanese B encephalitis virus in the blood of experimentally inoculated chickens. Proc. Soc. Exp. Biol. and Med., 61, 304-308.

Hammon, W. M., Tigertt, W. D., Sather, G., and Schenker, H., 1949b, Isolations of Japanese B encephalitis virus from naturally infected Culex tritaeniorhynchus collected in Japan. Am. J. Hyg., 50, 51-56.

Harford, C. G., and Bronfenbrenner, J., 1942, Infection of mice by feeding with tissues containing the virus of St. Louis encephalitis. J. Infect. Dis. *70*, 62-68.

Hayashi, M., 1934, Übertragung des Virus von Encephalitis epidemica auf Affen. Proc. Imp. Acad. Japan, *10*, 41-44.

Haymaker, W., and Kernohan, J. W., 1949, The Landry-Guillain-Barré syndrome. Medicine, *28*, 59-141.

Haymaker, W., and Sabin, A. B., 1947, Topographic distribution of lesions in central nervous system in Japanese B encephalitis. Arch. Neur. and Psych., *57*, 673-692.

Haymaker, W., and Smadel, J., 1943, The pathology of the viral encephalitides. Army Med. Museum, Washington, D. C., June (not paginated).

Hodes, H. L., 1939, Effect of pregnancy upon the immunity of mice vaccinated against St. Louis encephalitis virus. J. Exp. Med., *69*, 533-543.

Hodes, H. L., Thomas, L., and Peck, J. L., 1946a, Complement-fixing and neutralizing antibodies against Japanese B virus in the sera of Okinawan horses. Science. *103*, 357-359.

Hodes, H. L., Thomas, L., and Peck, J. L., 1946b, Cause of an outbreak of encephalitis established by means of complement-fixation tests. Proc. Soc. Exp. Biol. and Med., *60*, 220-225.

Howitt, B., 1938, Recovery of the virus of equine encephalomyelitis from the brain of a child. Science, *88*, 455-456.

Howitt, B. F., Dodge, H. R., Bishop, L. K., and Gorrie, R. H., 1948, Virus of eastern equine encephalomyelitis isolated from chicken mites *(Dermanyssus gallinae)* and chicken lice *(Eomenacanthus stramineus)*. Proc. Soc. Exp. Biol. and Med., *68*, 622-625.

Howitt, B. F., Dodge, H. R., Bishop, L. K., and Gorrie, R. H., 1949, Recovery of the virus of eastern encephalomyelitis from mosquitoes *(Mansonia perturbans)* collected in Georgia. Science, *110*, 141-142.

Hurlbut, H. S., 1950, The transmission of Japanese B encephalitis by mosquitoes after experimental hibernation. Am. J. Hyg., *51*, 265-268.

Hurst, E. W., 1931, The transmission of "louping-ill" to the mouse and the monkey; histology of the experimental disease. J. Comp. Path. and Therap., *44*, 231-245.

Hurst, E. W., 1936, Infection of the Rhesus monkey *(Macaca mulatta)* and the guinea pig with the virus of equine encephalomyelitis. J. Path. and Bact., *42*, 271-302.

Hurst, E. W., 1941, Acute haemorrhagic leucoencephalitis; previously undefined entity. Med. J. Australia, *2*, 1-6.

Hurst, E. W., 1944, A review of some recent observations of demyelination. Brain, *67*, 103-124.

Hurst, E. W., 1950. Some observations on the pathogenesis of eastern equine encephalomyelitis and louping-ill in young and old animals. J. Comp. Path. and Ther., *60*, 237-262.

Kabat, E. A., Wolf, A., and Bezer, A. E., 1947, The rapid production of acute disseminated encephalomyelitis in *rhesus* monkeys by injection of heterologous and homologous brain tissue with adjuvants. J. Exp. Med., *85*, 117-130.

Kasahara, S., Ueda, M., Okamoto, Y., Yoshida, S., Hamano, R., and Yamada, R., 1936, Experimental studies on epidemic encephalitis. Kitasato Arch. Exp. Med., *13*, 48-65.

Kawamura, R., Kodama, M., Ito, T., Yasaki, T., and Kobayakawa, Y., 1936, Studies concerning the virus of epidemic encephalitis, Japanese type. Kitasato Arch. Exp. Med., *13*, 281-323.

Kelser, R. A., 1934, Mosquitoes as vectors of the virus of equine encephalomyelitis. Proc. 12th Internat. Vet. Cong., New York, *2*, 336-347.

Koprowski, H., and Cox, H. R., 1946, Propagation of Japanese B encephalitis virus in the developing chick embryo. J. Immunol., *52*, 171-186.

Kubes, V., and Rios, F. A., 1939, The causative agent of infectious equine encephalomyelitis in Venezuela. Science, *90*, 20-21.

Laemmert, H. W. and Hughes, T. P., 1947, The virus of Ilhéus encephalitis. Isolation, serological specificity and transmission. J. Immunol., *55*, 61-67.

Lennette, E. H., and Koprowski, H., 1943, Human infection with Venezuelan equine encephalomyelitis virus. A report on 8 cases of infection acquired in the laboratory. J. Am. Med. Assn., *123*, 1088-1095.

Lennette, E. H., and Koprowski, H., 1944a, Influence of age on the susceptibility of mice to infection with certain neurotropic viruses. J. Immunol., *49*, 175-191.

Lennette, E. H., and Koprowski, H., 1944b, Neutralization test with certain neurotropic viruses. A comparison of the sensitivity of the extraneural and intracerebral routes of inoculations for the detection of antibodies. J. Immunol., *49*, 375-385.

Lépine, P., 1931 Étude des propriétés du virus de la tremblante du mouton. Compt. rend. Soc. biol., *108*, 476-478.

Lépine, P., Mollaret, P., and Kreis, B., 1937, Réceptivité de l'homme au virus murin de la chorioméningite lymphocytaire. Reproduction expérimentale de la méningite lymphocytaire bénigne. Compt. rend. Acad. sci., *204*, 1846-1848.

Levaditi, C., 1929, Etiology of epidemic encephalitis. Its relation to herpes, epidemic poliomyelitis and postvaccinal encephalopathy. Arch. Neurol. and Psych., *22*, 767-803.

Levaditi, C., and Voet, J., 1935, Nouvelle classification des ectodermoses neurotropes. Compt. rend. Acad. sci., *201*, 743-745.

Li, C. P., and Rivers, T. M., 1930, Cultivation of vaccine virus. J. Exp. Med., *52*, 465-470.

Lillie, R. D., 1950, The pathology of lymphocytic choriomeningitis virus infection: a discussion, in Kidd, J. G., ed., The Pathogenesis and Pathology of Viral Diseases, New York, Columbia Univ. Press, pp. 181-193.

MacCallum, F. O., Findlay, G. M., and Scott, T. M., 1939, Pseudo-lymphocytic choriomeningitis. Brit. J. Exp. Path., *20*, 260-269.

Margulis, M. S., Soloviev, V. D., and Shubladze, A. K., 1944, Acute primary hemorrhagic meningo-encephalitis. Am. Rev. Soviet Med., *1*, 409-427.

Margulis, M. S., Soloviev, V. D., and Shubladze, A. K.,

1946, Aetiology and pathogenesis of acute sporadic disseminated encephalomyelitis and multiple sclerosis. J. Neur., Neurosurgery and Psych., 9, 63-74.

Melnick, J. L., Paul, J. R., Riordan, J. T., Barnett, V. H., Goldblum, N., and Zabin, E., 1951, Isolation from human sera in Egypt of a virus apparently identical to West Nile virus. Proc. Soc. Exp. Biol. and Med., 77, 661-665.

Merrill, M. H., Lacaillade, C. W., and TenBroeck, C., 1934, Mosquito transmission of equine encephalomyelitis. Science, 80, 251-252.

Meyer, K. F., 1932, A summary of recent studies on equine encephalomyelitis. Ann. Int. Med., 6, 645-654.

Meyer, K. F., Haring, C. M., and Howitt, B., 1931, The etiology of epizootic encephalomyelitis of horses in the San Joaquin Valley, 1930. Science, 74, 227-228.

Morgan, I. M., 1941, Influence of age on susceptibility and on immune response of mice to eastern equine encephalomyelitis virus. J. Exp. Med., 74, 115-132.

Morgan, I. M., 1947, Allergic encephalomyelitis in monkeys in response to injection of normal monkey nervous tissue. J. Exp. Med., 85, 131-140.

Morgan, I. M., Schlesinger, R. W., and Olitsky, P. K., 1942, Induced resistance of the central nervous system to experimental infection with equine encephalomyelitis virus. I. Neutralizing antibody in the central nervous system in relation to cerebral resistance. J. Exp. Med., 76, 357-369.

Muckenfuss, R. S., Armstrong, C., and McCordock, H. A., 1933, Encephalitis: Studies on experimental transmission. Pub. Health Rep., 48, 1341-1343.

Neal, J. B., et al., 1942, Encephalitis. A Clinical Study, New York, Grune & Stratton, pp. 1-563.

Noran, H. H., and Baker, A. B., 1943, Sequels of equine encephalomyelitis. Arch. Neur. and Psych., 49, 398-413.

Olitsky, P. K., 1939, Experimental studies on the virus of infectious avian encephalomyelitis. J. Exp. Med., 70, 565-582.

Olitsky, P. K., 1946, Epidemic primary virus infections of the central nervous system of man. Am. Naturalist, 80, 401-409.

Olitsky, P. K., and Casals, J., 1945, Concepts of the immunology of certain virus infections. Bull. N. Y. Acad. Med., 21, 356-374.

Olitsky, P. K., and Cox, H. R., 1936, Active immunization of guinea pigs with the virus of equine encephalomyelitis. I. Quantitative experiments with various preparations of active virus. J. Exp. Med., 63, 311-324.

Olitsky, P. K., and Harford, C. G., 1938, Intraperitoneal and intracerebral routes in serum protection tests with the virus of equine encephalomyelitis. I. A comparison of two routes in protection tests. J. Exp. Med., 68, 173-189.

Olitsky, P. K., and Morgan, I. M., 1939, Protective antibodies against equine encephalomyelitis virus in the serum of laboratory workers. Proc. Soc. Exp. Biol. and Med., 41, 212-215.

Olitsky, P. K., Sabin, A. B., and Cox, H. R., 1936, An acquired resistance of growing animals to certain neurotropic viruses in the absence of humoral anti-bodies or previous exposure to infection. J. Exp. Med., 64, 723-737.

Olitsky, P. K., Schlesinger, R. W., and Morgan, I. M., 1943, Induced resistance of the central nervous system to experimental infection with equine encephalomyelitis virus. II. Serotherapy in western virus infection. J. Exp. Med., 77, 359-374.

Olitsky, P. K., and Saenz, A. C., 1948, Serum treatment of western equine encephalitis in mice determined by the course of viral infection. Proc. Soc. Exp. Biol. and Med., 68, 200-204.

Olitsky, P. K., and Yager, R. H., 1949, Experimental disseminated encephalomyelitis in white mice. J. Exp. Med., 90, 213-224.

Olitsky, P. K., Yager, R. H., and Murphy, L. C., 1950, Preservation of neurotropic viruses, U. S. Armed Forces Med. J., 1, 415-417.

Peck, J. L., Jr., and Sabin, A. B., 1947, Multiplication and spread of the virus of St. Louis encephalitis in mice with special emphasis on its fate in the alimentary tract. J. Exp. Med., 85, 647-662.

Pool, W. A., Brownlee, A., and Wilson, D. R., 1930, The etiology of "louping-ill." J. Comp. Path. and Therap., 43, 253-290.

Putnam, T. J., 1941, Newer conceptions of postinfectious and related forms of encephalitis. Bull. N. Y. Acad. Med., 17, 337-347.

Randall, R., Maurer, F. D., and Smadel, J. E., 1949, Immunization of laboratory workers with purified Venezuelan equine encephalomyelitis vaccine. J. Immunol., 63, 313-318.

Randall, R., and Mills, J. W., 1944, Fatal encephalitis in man due to the Venezuelan virus of equine encephalomyelitis in Trinidad. Science, 99, 225-226.

Reeves, W. C., 1951, The encephalitis problem in the United States. Am. J. Pub. Health, 41, 678-686.

Reeves, W. C., and Hammon, W. M., 1946, Laboratory transmission of Japanese B encephalitis virus by seven species (three genera) of North American mosquitoes. J. Exp. Med., 83, 185-194.

Rivers, T. M., editor, 1928, Filterable Viruses. Baltimore, Williams & Wilkins, pp. 1-428.

Rivers, T. M., 1932, Relation of filterable viruses to diseases of the nervous system. Arch. Neur. and Psych., 28, 757-777.

Rivers, T. M., 1939, Viruses and Virus Diseases. Stanford University Press, pp. 1-133.

Rivers, T. M., 1943, Virus diseases, in Cecil, R. L., Textbook in Medicine, ed. 6. Philadelphia, Saunders.

Rivers, T. M., and Schwentker, F. F., 1934, Louping ill in man. J. Exp. Med., 59, 669-685.

Rivers, T. M., and Scott, T. F. M., 1935, Meningitis in man caused by a filterable virus. Science, 81, 439-440.

Rivers, T. M., Sprunt, D. H., and Berry, G. P., 1933, Observations on attempts to produce acute disseminated encephalomyelitis in monkeys. J. Exp. Med., 58, 39-53.

Roca-Garcia, M., 1944, The isolation of three neurotropic viruses from forest mosquitoes in eastern Colombia. J. Infect. Dis., 75, 160-169.

Roizin, L., Helfand, M., and Moore, J., 1946, Disseminated, diffuse and transitional demyelination of the central nervous system. A clinico-histopathologic study. J. Nerv. and Ment. Dis., 104, 1-50.

Sabin, A. B., 1934. Studies on the B virus. III. The experimental disease in *Macacus rhesus* monkeys. Brit. J. Exp. Path., *15*, 321-334.

Sabin, A. B., 1941, Constitutional barriers to involvement of the nervous system by certain viruses, with special reference to the role of nutrition. J. Pediat., *19*, 596-607.

Sabin, A. B., 1947, Epidemic encephalitis in military personnel. Isolation of Japanese B virus on Okinawa in 1945, serologic diagnosis, clinical manifestations, epidemiologic aspects and use of mouse brain vaccine. J. Am. Med. Assn., *133*, 281-293.

Sabin, A. B., 1949, Fatal B virus encephalomyelitis in a physician working with monkeys. J. Clin. Investig., *28*, 808 (Abst.).

Sabin, A. B., 1951, Hemagglutination by viruses affecting the human nervous system. Fed. Proc., *10*, 573-578.

Sabin, A. B., and Aring, C. D., 1941, Visceral lesions in infectious polyneuritis. Am. J. Path., *17*, 469-482.

Sabin, A. B., and Buescher, E. L., 1950, Unique physico-chemical properties of Japanese B encephalitis virus hemagglutinin. Proc. Soc. Exp. Biol. and Med., *74*, 222-230.

Sabin, A. B. and collaborators, Duffy, C. E., Warren, J., Ward, R., Peck, J. L., and Ruchman, I., 1943, The St. Louis and Japanese B types of epidemic encephalitis. Development of noninfective vaccines: report of basic data. J. Am. Med. Assn., *122*, 477-486.

Sabin, A. B., and Olitsky, P. K., 1937-1938, Influence of host factors on neuroinvasiveness of vesicular stomatitis virus. J. Exp. Med., *66*, 15-34, 35-57; *67*, 201-228, 229-249.

Sabin, A. B., and Olitsky, P. K., 1938a, Variations in pathways by which equine encephalomyelitic viruses invade the CNS of mice and guinea pigs. Proc. Soc. Exp. Biol. and Med., *38*, 595-597.

Sabin, A. B., and Olitsky, P. K., 1938b, Age of host and capacity of equine encephalomyelitic viruses to invade the CNS. Proc. Soc. Exp. Biol. and Med., *38*, 597-599.

Sabin, A. B., Schlesinger, R. W., Ginder, D. R., and Matumoto, M., 1947, Japanese B encephalitis in American soldiers in Korea. Am. J. Hyg., *46*, 356-375.

Sabin, A. B., and Wright, A. M., 1934, Acute ascending myelitis following a monkey bite, with the isolation of a virus capable of reproducing the disease. J. Exp. Med., *59*, 115-136.

Schabel, F. M., Jr., Miller, S., Abendroth, M., and Gordon, F. B., 1947, Susceptibility of the hamster to St. Louis and Japanese encephalitis viruses by feeding. Proc. Soc. Exp. Biol. and Med., *66*, 332-333.

Schlesinger, R. W., 1949, The mechanism of active cerebral immunity to equine encephalomyelitis virus J. Exp. Med., *89*, 491-505; 507-527.

Schlesinger, R. W., Olitsky, P. K., and Morgan, I. M., 1944, Induced resistance of the central nervous system to experimental infection with equine encephalomyelitis virus. III. Abortive infection with western virus and subsequent interference with the action of heterologous viruses. J. Exp. Med., *80*, 197-211.

Sergeev, J. S., 1944, Clinical aspect of tick-borne encephalitis in the northwest provinces of the Soviet Union. Neuropatologiya i psykhiatriya, *13*, No. 2, (each number paged separately) 54-57 (in Russian).

Shahan, M. S., and Giltner, L. T., 1934, Some aspects of infection and immunity in equine encephalomyelitis. J. Am. Vet. Med. Assn., *84*, 928-934.

Shaughnessy, H. J., and Milzer, A., 1939, Experimental infection of *Dermacentor andersoni* Stiles with the virus of lymphocytic choriomeningitis. Am. J. Pub. Health, *29*, 1103-1108.

Shwartzman, G., 1944a, Recovery of the virus of lymphocytic choriomeningitis from the erythrocytes of infected animals. J. Immunol., 48, 111-127.

Shwartzman, G., 1944b, Some recent advances in bacteriology and virus research with special reference to electron microscopy. J. Mt. Sinai Hosp., *11*, 137-158.

Silber, L. A., and Shubladze, A. K., 1945, Louping-ill in the USSR. Am. Rev. Soviet Med., *2*, 339-341.

Silber, L. A., and Soloviev, V. D., 1946, Far Eastern tick-borne spring-summer (spring) encephalitis. Am. Rev. Soviet Med., Special Suppl., 1-80.

Slavin, H. B., 1943, Persistence of the virus of St. Louis encephalitis in the central nervous system of mice for over 5 months. J. Bact., *46*, 113-116.

Smadel, J. E., 1947, Research in virus diseases. Bull. U. S. Army Med. Dept., *7*, 795-808.

Smadel, J. E., 1951, The hazard of acquiring virus and rickettsial diseases in the laboratory. Am. J. Pub. Health, *41*, 788-795.

Smadel, J. E., Green, R. H., Paltauf, R. M., and Gonzales, T. A., 1942, Lymphocytic choriomeningitis: Two human fatalities following an unusual febrile illness. Proc. Soc. Exp. Biol. and Med., *49*, 683-686.

Smadel, J. E., and Wall, M. J., 1941, Identification of the virus of lymphocytic choriomeningitis. J. Bact., *41*, 421-430.

Smith, M. G., 1943, Placental transmission of immunity to St. Louis encephalitis virus inoculated intraperitoneally in mice. Proc. Soc. Exp. Biol. and Med., *52*, 83-85.

Smith, M. G., Blattner, R. J., and Heys, F. M., 1944, The isolation of the St. Louis encephalitis virus from chicken mites (*Dermanyssus gallinae*) in nature. Science, *100*, 362-363.

Smith, M. G., Blattner, R. J., Heys, F. M., and Miller, A., 1948, Experiments on the role of the chicken mite, *Dermanyssus gallinae,* and the mosquito in the epidemiology of St. Louis encephalitis. J. Exp. Med., *87*, 119-138.

Smithburn, K. C., 1942, Differentiation of the West Nile virus from the viruses of St. Louis and Japanese B encephalitis. J. Immunol., *44*, 25-31.

Smithburn, K. C., and Haddow, A. J., 1944, Semliki forest virus, I. Isolation and pathogenic properties. J. Immunol., *49*, 141-157.

Smithburn, K. C., Haddow, A. J., and Mahaffy, A. F., 1946, A neurotropic virus isolated from *Aedes* mosquitoes caught in the Semliki forest. Am. J. Trop. Med., *26*, 189-208.

Smithburn, K. C., Hughes, T. P., Burke, A. W., and Paul, J. H., 1940, A neurotropic virus isolated from the blood of a native of Uganda. Am. J. Trop. Med., *20*, 471-492.

Smithburn, K. C., Mahaffy, A. F., and Paul, J. H., 1941, Bwamba fever and its causative virus. Am. J. Trop. Med., *21*, 75-90.

Smorodintsev, A. A., 1940, The spring-summer tick-borne encephalitis. Arch. ges. Virusforsch., *1*, 468-480.

Smorodintsev, A. A., 1944, Tick-borne encephalitis. Am. Rev. Soviet Med., *1*, 400-408.

Stanley, W. M., 1941, Some chemical, medical and philosophical aspects of viruses. Science, *93*, 145-151.

Sulkin, S. E., 1945, Recovery of equine encephalomyelitis virus (western type) from chicken mites. Science, *101*, 381-383.

Syverton, J. T., and Berry, G. P., 1941, Hereditary transmission of the western type of equine encephalomyelitis in the wood tick, *Dermacentor andersoni* Stiles. J. Exp. Med., *73*, 507-530.

Syverton, J. T., McCoy, O. R., and Koomen, J., 1947, The transmission of the virus of lymphocytic choriomeningitis by *Trichinella spiralis*. J. Exp. Med., *85*, 759-769.

Taniguchi, T., Hosokawa, M., and Kuga, S., 1936, A virus isolated in 1935 epidemic of summer encephalitis of Japan. Jap. J. Exp. Med., *14*, 185-196.

TenBroeck, C., 1938, Birds as possible carriers of the virus of equine encephalomyelitis. Arch. Path., *25*, 759.

TenBroeck, C., 1940, Transmission of equine encephalomyelitis. Report of Proceedings, 3rd Internat. Cong. for Microbiol., New York, 300-301.

TenBroeck, C., and Merrill, M. H., 1933, Serological difference between Eastern and Western equine encephalomyelitis virus. Proc. Soc. Exp. Biol. and Med., *31*, 217-220.

TenBroeck, C., Hurst, E. W., and Traub, E., 1935, Epidemiology of equine encephalomyelitis in the eastern United States. J. Exp. Med., *62*, 677-685.

TenBroeck, C., and Herriott, R. M., 1946, Viruses inactivated by mustard (Bis(beta-chloroethyl) sulfide) as vaccines. Proc. Soc. Exp. Biol. and Med., *62*, 271-272.

Tigertt, W. D., and Hammon, W. M., with collaborators, 1950, Japanese B encephalitis: A complete review of experience on Okinawa 1945-1949. Am. J. Trop. Med., *30*, 689-722.

Traub, E., 1935. A filterable virus recovered from white mice. Science, *81*, 298-299.

Urechia, C. L., 1921, Dix cas d'encéphalite épidémique avec autopsie. Arch. internat. de neurol., 2e partie 65-78.

Wallgren, A., 1925, Une nouvelle maladie infectieuse du sysème nerveux central? Acta paediat., *4*, 158-182.

Warren, J., and Hough, R. G., 1946, A vaccine against Japanese B encephalitis prepared from infected chick embryos. Proc. Soc. Exp. Biol. and Med., *61*, 109-113.

Warren, J., Smadel, J. E., and Rasmussen, A. F., 1948, The antibody response in human beings inoculated with Japanese encephalitis vaccine, chick embryo type. J. Immunol., *58*, 211-221.

Warren, J., Weil, M. L., Russ, S. B., and Jeffries, H., 1949, Purification of certain viruses by use of protamine sulfate. Proc. Soc. Exp. Biol. and Med., *72*, 662-664.

Webster, L. T., 1937, Inheritance of resistance of mice to enteric bacterial and neurotropic virus infections. J. Exp. Med., *65*, 261-286.

Webster, L. T., and Fite, G. L., 1933, A virus encountered in the study of material from cases of encephalitis in the St. Louis and Kansas City epidemic of 1933. Science, *78*, 463-465.

Webster, L. T., and Wright, F. H., 1938, Recovery of eastern equine encephalomyelitis virus from brain tissue of human cases of encephalitis in Massachusetts. Science, *88*, 305-306.

Wooley, J. G., and Armstrong, C., 1934, The distribution of immunity against encephalitis virus of the St. Louis type in the United States as determined by the serum-protection test in white mice. Pub. Health Rep., *49*, 1495-1505.

Yaoi, H., Kanazawa, K., Murai, M., and Arakawa, S., 1939, On size of Japanese epidemic encephalitis virus as estimated by "gradocol" membrane. Jap. J. Exp. Med., *17*, 375-378.

Zimmerman, H. M., 1946, The pathology of Japanese B encephalitis. Am. J. Path., *22*, 965-991.

HARALD N. JOHNSON, M.D.

Laboratories of the Division of Medicine and Public Health

The Rockefeller Foundation, New York City

12

Rabies

(SYNONYMS: Hydrophobia, *rage, Tollwut, Lyssa, rabbia, rabia, raiva*)

INTRODUCTION

Rabies is an acute infection of the central nervous system caused by a virus and is, as a rule, propagated in dogs and related wild animals such as the wolf, fox, coyote, and jackal. Man and all warm-blooded animals are susceptible. The virus is often present in the saliva of rabid animals and consequently is most commonly transmitted by a bite. Under favorable conditions the virus, when introduced into a wound, becomes established in nerve tissue and migrates to the brain where, after an incubation period of from 10 days to several months, it produces an acute, almost invariably fatal encephalitis.

HISTORY

Rabies has been known in Europe and Asia since ancient times, and has maintained a characteristic symptomatology and high fatality rate. As far as is known, rabies has always been primarily associated with the canine species. The period of summer reckoned by the heliacal rising of the dog star, Sirius, has since antiquity been referred to as dog days, when dogs are supposed to be especially liable to spells of madness. It is easy to understand why people of ancient Egypt, Greece, and Rome ascribed the disease to supernatural causes, because animals ordinarily docile and friendly became extremely vicious and aggressive without evident cause, and, after a period of maniacal behavior, developed convulsive seizures and paralysis, which were followed by death. Rabies in dogs and domestic animals was described by Democritus (500 B.C.) and Aristotle (322 B.C.). Celsus (A.D. 100) recognized the relationship of hydrophobia in man to rabies in animals and recommended cauterization of wounds produced by rabid dogs. Galen (A.D. 200) favored surgical resection of the wound area.

Prior to the 18th century, rabies was primarily a disease of wild animals, and domestic dogs played no significant part in its maintenance and spread. Rabies was known in western Europe as early as 1271, at which time it was prevalent among wolves in France. The first recorded epizootic of rabies among domestic dogs in urban centers occurred in Italy during 1708; by 1728 the disease had appeared in epizootic proportions in most of the major cities of Hungary, Germany and France. Rabies was known in England as early as 1613 (Mullett, 1945), but did not occur in epizootic proportions among dogs until 1734. There is no evidence to indicate that the disease existed in North or South America before colonization. Historical archives

267

of the State of Virginia contain references to rabies as early as 1753 and those of North Carolina as early as 1762; by 1785 the disease was prevalent among dogs throughout New England. Rabies was unknown in South America until 1803 when it appeared among dogs in Peru; in 1806, an outbreak was observed among hunting dogs imported by English officers into La-Plata, Argentina, (Bouley, 1863).

The transmission of rabies from a rabid dog to a normal dog by inoculation of saliva was reported by Zinke in 1804 and by Gruner and by Salm-Reifferscheidt in 1813. These experimental studies showed that the disease was infectious, and on the basis of this evidence it was assumed that destruction of stray dogs and quarantine of other domestic dogs would eliminate the disease. Sanitary measures including these provisions were adopted in Norway, Sweden and Denmark, and by 1826 these countries were free from rabies. Although rabies was eliminated from some urban centers in continental Europe by dog-control regulations, these frequently became reinfected after a few years, because the disease was established in wild animals in many regions. For those interested in obtaining references and more complete information concerning the early history of rabies, Högyes (1897), Kraus et al. (1926) and Koch (1930) are recommended.

Galtier (1879) introduced the use of domesticated rabbits as experimental animals for the diagnosis and study of rabies, but the modern concept of this disease, and virus diseases in general, was developed by Pasteur and his associates. The first publication by this group of investigators relative to the etiology of rabies is of interest in that it illustrates a problem which has repeatedly confused the study of virus diseases, that is, the isolation of a pathogen unrelated to the disease in question but transmissible in series in an experimental host. In this particular case, they isolated an organism from the saliva of a human being with rabies which produced hemor-

rhagic septicemia in rabbits (Pasteur et al., 1881a). The subsequent discovery that the true infective agent of rabies could be recovered in a relatively pure state from the brain of an animal that has died of the disease and the development of intracerebral inoculation by Roux, whereby animals could be infected consistently, opened the way for an extensive study of the disease (Pasteur et al., 1881b). Since the infective agent as obtained from brains of diseased animals could not be identified with certainty by microscopic examination and could not be cultivated in media used for the growth of ordinary bacteria, it was called a virus, from the Latin word for poison. The ultramicroscopic nature of the infective agent was postulated by Pasteur, but this was not established until Remlinger (1903) showed that it would pass through Berkefeld filters impervious to visible bacteria.

Pasteur et al. (1884) were the first to modify the pathogenicity of a virus for its natural host by serial intracerebral passage in another species of host. In an attempt to develop a variety of rabies virus which could be used safely for vaccination, they passaged the agent intracerebrally in rabbits and other animals. This resulted in the development of an infection characterized by a short incubation period; such modified viruses were called fixed, to distinguish them from the natural, or so-called street, virus. Though the virus maintained in rabbits at first appeared to become more virulent for dogs, it soon began to show a gradual loss of pathogenicity, and, after 100 passages, the fixed virus had little capacity to infect dogs when given subcutaneously. Pasteur had noted previously that cultures of the chicken-cholera organism, when stored for several weeks at room temperature, lost their pathogenicity but still retained their immunizing capacity. In an attempt to reproduce this phenomenon with rabies virus, he exposed the spinal cords of rabbits infected with fixed virus to drying at room temperature; then, by means of a series of 10 daily subcutaneous injections of fixed virus, graded from no infectivity to maximum infectivity as determined by intracerebral tests in rabbits, dogs were made resistant to experimental infection with the natural virus. During 1885, a peasant boy, who had been severely bitten by a rabid dog, was taken to Pasteur, and, in view of the serious nature of the exposure and the plea that something be done, the boy was vaccinated in a manner similar to that used for immunization of dogs, the theory being that, if dogs could be immunized in a 2-week period so that they would resist infection with the natural virus, the long incubation period of rabies in human beings would allow the development of a high grade of immunity before the potential onset of the disease. The treatment appeared to be without ill effects and the boy remained well (Pasteur, 1885). This became known and other persons were taken to Pasteur for treatment; and the vaccine treatment for rabies soon was adopted as a routine procedure in medical centers throughout the world.

Högyes (1897) introduced the dilution method of obtaining graded doses of rabbit-fixed virus comparable to those given in the desiccated tissue vaccine. Roux (1887) introduced the use of glycerol as a preservative for maintaining the viability of virus in specimens of infected tissue. This discovery was applied to the production of vaccine by Calmette (1891), whereby desiccated spinal cord tissue of varied infectivity could be kept on hand at treatment centers by storage in glycerol. Fermi (1908) was the first to use chemical treatment of tissue suspensions of fixed virus for the preparation of vaccine. He introduced the use of phenol for this purpose, and Semple (1919) by modification of Fermi's method showed that the phenol-treated tissue vaccine could be rendered completely noninfectious and still retain its immunizing capacity.

No microscopic method for the diagnosis of rabies was available until Negri (1903, 1907) described the occurrence of characteristic intracytoplasmic inclusion bodies in the nerve cells of human beings and animals proved to have been infected with rabies by isolation of the virus. This discovery made it possible to arrive at a prompt microscopic diagnosis of most cases of animal rabies and has been used as a guide for human treatment. Though intracerebral inoculation had been successfully employed for many years in the experimental study of rabies in other species of laboratory animals, it was not adapted to the study of the disease in the white mouse until 1930 (Hoyt et al., 1930). This animal has been found particularly useful for diagnostic work because of the short incubation period of the disease in it and the regular production of Negri bodies in its brain following intracerebral inoculation of street virus (Webster et al., 1935).

The discovery of rabies among vampire bats in Brazil (Haupt et al., 1921) marks a new era in the history of the malady. Whereas all other known vectors transmit the disease for a limited period of time and then die of the infection, the vampire bat is capable of transmitting rabies for several months as a symptomless carrier (Pawan, 1936b).

CLINICAL PICTURE

The incubation period of rabies may be as short as 10 days or as long as 7 or more months, but it is rarely less than 15 days or more than 5 months. When persons have developed rabies 1 to 2 years after they were known to have been bitten by a rabid animal, it is usually impossible to be certain that there had not been a more recent exposure, possibly a minor wound which had been forgotten because it had been produced by an animal not obviously ill. There is no evidence to support the theory that the incubation period depends on the linear distance the virus must travel from the point of infection in order to reach the brain. The relatively high attack rate and short mean incubation period of rabies following hand and face wounds is more readily accounted for by the severe lacerations in such exposures and the abundant sensory innervation and superficial aspect of the muscle tissue in such areas. In the experimental disease, the length of the incubation period varies inversely in proportion to the amount of active virus introduced instead of in relation to the location of the inoculation. Even when the virus is introduced into the brain, the latent period may be as long as 90 days. It is, therefore, evident that long incubation periods are largely dependent on a temporary arrest of virus multiplication, either at the site of infection or at some place in the nervous system. The observed short, mean incubation period for persons developing rabies despite vaccine treatment may be explained by the failure to protect those individuals in whom the disease develops before vaccination has had a chance to exert its maximum immunologic effect. For example, through the courtesy of Dr. T. F. Sellers, director of laboratories for the Georgia State Department of Health, it has been possible to study the records of the rabies treatment service of that state for the period from 1921 through 1945. More than 45,000 persons were given vaccine treatment and, of these, 35 developed rabies with a mean incubation period of 28 days. This can be compared with the mean incubation period of 56 days in a group of 30 untreated persons who developed the disease during the years mentioned above. Prior to the introduction of the postexposure vaccination for rabies, a study was made of 224 cases of the disease observed in France during the period from 1852 through 1862 (Tardieu, 1863). Of these, 40 developed the disease within 1 month after exposure, 143 in 1 to 3 months, 30 in 3 to 6 months, and 11 in 6 to 12 months. It is evident from this study, as well as others (Kraus et al., 1926), that the incubation period of rabies in untreated individuals will be less than 30 days in approximately 20 per cent of the cases and that in the majority of individuals the disease develops from one to three months after exposure.

The onset of the disease is marked by 2 to 4 days of prodromal symptoms, such as fever, headache, malaise, anorexia, nausea, and sore throat. The temperature is elevated from 1° to 3° F. and shows no marked fluctuation. Headache, when it occurs, is localized most often in the occipital region or over the vertex. Vomiting may be protracted or even projectile. Respiration tends to be shallow, and speech may be interrupted by sighing inspirations. Most patients exhibit increasing nervousness, irritability, anxiety, and insomnia, but some show marked depression and melancholia. The early symptom of most diagnostic significance is some abnormal sensation about the site of infection. This will occur in about 80 per cent of the cases and, when present, favors a diagnosis of rabies. There may be pain, burning, sensation of cold, pruritus, tingling, or formication about the wound. The pain may be local or radiating. The patient may complain of a dull, constant pain referable to the nervous pathways proximal to the location of the wound or there may be intermittent, stabbing pains radiating distally to the region of inoculation. Referred pain in the neck, back, chest, or abdomen has been noted in some cases. Inflammation about the site of exposure, so often noted in rabies, appears to result from scratching or rubbing by the patient because of the abnormal sensations, but it is also possible that some type of urticarial or angioneurotic skin reaction may occur. In general, the early symptoms may be ascribed to the stimulative action of the virus affecting various groups of neurons, predominantly those of the sensory system. Though there is apt to be decreased sensitivity to local pain, such as that caused by the introduction of a needle, the patient may complain bitterly of drafts and bed clothes which produce a general stimulation of the skin. There is apt to be sensitivity to other types of stimulation such as those produced by bright light and loud noise. Objective signs include increased activity of muscle reflexes and general increase in muscle tone. Muscle tics may be present. Facial expression is apt to be overactive. The pulse rate is rapid. Symptoms referable to stimulation of the sympathetic nervous system include dilatation of the pupils, lacrimation, increased salivation, and excessive perspiration.

In most cases, the excitation phase is predominant up to the time of death. However, depressive or paralytic symptoms may be predominant from the beginning or may supervene at any stage of the disease. The onset of the acute excitement phase is gradual and is marked by increasing nervousness, anxiety and apprehension. There is a strong desire to be up; wandering aimlessly about and speaking in disconnected sentences are not unusual. A sense of impending death is frequent. Despite great fear and anxiety, a patient rarely bursts into tears. The outstanding clinical symptom of rabies is related to the act of swallowing; when fluid comes in contact with the fauces, it is expelled with considerable violence, and painful, spasmodic contractions of the muscles of deglutition and of the accessory muscles of respiration are produced. Subsequently, the sight, smell, or sound of liquids, by suggesting the act of swallowing may precipitate spasm of the muscles of the throat. The name hydrophobia, or fear of water, has been used to designate the disease since ancient times because of the frequent occurrence of this symptom in those developing the disease. In some cases, the reflex irritability of the throat muscles is not so intense, and the patient exhibits no fear of water, though there may be difficulty in swallowing and a sense of constriction in the throat when the fluid or food passes the fauces. In order to avoid the act of swallowing, a patient is apt to allow the saliva to drool from the mouth between attempts at expectoration. Due to difficulty in taking fluids by mouth, a patient is apt to develop progressive dehydration so that the mouth and tongue become dry and parched. As the disease progresses, the stimulation of the muscular system becomes more pronounced, and vermiform and fibrillar muscular contraction and general tremor may occur. Choking when attempting to swallow may result in such severe spasm of the respiratory muscles that prolonged apnea develops with cyanosis and gasping attempts at respiration. Convulsive seizures are common and may be so extreme as to produce opisthotonus. Maniacal behavior, such as tearing clothes and bedding, is not uncommon, but vicious and murderous action, such as biting and fighting, is rare, though it may occur. Periods of intense excitement are interspersed with those of relative quiet at which time a patient is well oriented and answers questions intelligently. In the majority of cases, a patient dies in the acute excitement phase of the disease during a convulsion. Therefore, the paralytic phase caused by degeneration of motor neurons usually is not very evident. However, weakness of muscle groups related to the site of infection may be present early in the course of the disease. Ocular palsies, leading to strabismus and inco-ordination of ocular muscles, may occur. Weakness of the facial and masseter muscles may be present so that a patient has difficulty in closing the eyes or mouth, and the face becomes less expressive. Weakness of the muscles of phonation may be recognized by the development of hoarseness or loss of voice. Examination of the eyes may show partial blindness of central type, and, though the pupils may have been dilated and may have reacted poorly to light early in the disease, they at times become constricted or show inequality. Hippus, nystagmus, diplopia, or strabismus may be noted. Vertigo may be present, indicating middle ear disease, and, though this is apt to be an early symptom, it may develop at any period of the disease. The corneal reflex is decreased or absent, and the corneae become dry. The pulse rate may continue to be rapid with a rate of 100 to 120 at bed rest, but this may shift to bradycardia with a rate of 40 to 60 per minute. Cheyne-Stokes respiration is observed in most cases.

Though there may be stiffness of the neck, Kernig's and Brudzinski's signs are not elicited. A positive Babinski reaction may be obtained. Weakness of an extremity is preceded by loss of tendon reflexes. Paralysis, when it develops, is of the flaccid type and the muscles are not tender. Local sensation to pin prick, heat, and cold is diminished and in-co-ordination may be noted. The disease, when it develops as described above, appears to be invariably fatal, and a patient seldom lives longer than three days after the onset of the acute excitement phase.

If the acute excitement phase is survived, muscle spasms cease and the patient becomes quiet. The fear of water may disappear, if previously present, and the patient may be able to swallow, though with great difficulty. The face becomes expressionless and anxiety and excitement are replaced progressively by apathy, stupor and coma. In some cases, there may be a period of a few hours during which it may seem that a patient is getting better, but this apparent remission is followed rapidly by progressive paralysis. Depressive or paralytic symptoms may become predominant at any time during the course of the disease, and in some instances evidence of excitation of the nervous system may be absent. Though a patient may complain of fever, headache, nausea, and general discomfort at the beginning, the first significant sign is a sudden onset of weakness of one or more extremities. In rare instances, the course of the paralysis follows the pattern of Landry's syndrome and, beginning with the muscles of the legs, a progressive ascending paralysis develops with no relation to the site of the infection. Patients developing the predominantly paralytic form of rabies seldom have difficulty in swallowing until the terminal phase of the disease. The innervation of the musculature of the bladder and intestinal tract is affected so that retention and obstipation develop early. Incontinence may develop, especially in patients with a prolonged ill-

ness. There may be abnormal stimulation of the sex organs. Consciousness is retained until late in the course of the disease. In this type of rabies, a patient may live as long as ten days after the onset of paralysis. There were 55 cases of rabies in Trinidad, British West Indies, during the period from 1929 through 1935, among persons bitten by vampire bats. Most of these persons were bitten on the toes, and in such cases they regularly exhibited an ascending type of paralysis. Nerve root pain preceded or accompanied the spreading paralysis in some cases. Difficulty in swallowing was noted in only one case. Some of the Trinidad patients survived for more than two weeks and one lived for thirty days following the onset of paralysis (Verteuil et al., 1936).

The red blood cell count is not altered in rabies except where excessive dehydration occurs and the blood is concentrated. The white blood cell count is increased and may reach 20,000 or 30,000 cells per c.mm. Blood smears are apt to show a relative increase in the percentage of polymorphonuclear and large mononuclear cells. Examination of the urine may show a slight albuminuria, and hyaline casts may be found in the sediment. A reaction for glucose and acetone is noted in most cases. There is no marked increase in the spinal fluid pressure, but the level ordinarily will be above the average figure. The fluid is consistently clear, though tests may show a slight increase in the amount of protein. The cell count usually is within normal limits; more than 100 cells are encountered rarely; if there is an increase, the cells are predominantly of the mononuclear type.

If a patient is known to have been bitten by a rabid animal and the symptomatology is characteristic, there is little difficulty in making a correct clinical diagnosis. However, in some cases it is impossible to obtain a history of exposure due largely to the failure of a patient or his relatives to recollect a minor wound produced by an apparently healthy dog. In such cases, unless the clinical course is typical, the diagnosis may be missed. The clinical course of rabies may at times be very similar to that of poliomyelitis, either the bulbar or spinal type. Other viral and rickettsial agents that produce encephalitis or encephalomyelitis must be considered in the differential diagnosis. Tetanus may develop following bites by animals, but the incubation period is shorter than that of rabies, ordinarily from 6 to 14 days. Trismus, though a very constant symptom of tetanus, is rarely present in rabies, and the muscular spasticity in tetanus is constant and general while in rabies it is intermittent and affects chiefly the muscles of the throat. Where there has been a definite history of dog bite or other exposure to rabies, it is not uncommon to encounter rabies hysteria. In such cases, a patient ordinarily attempts to emulate convulsive seizures. Patients receiving rabies vaccine treatment may develop paralysis attributable to a sensitization caused by the rabbit brain material in the vaccine. This paralysis may simulate paralytic rabies, and may produce symptoms referable to cranial nerves, such as difficulty in swallowing, paralysis of the masseter muscles and unilateral or bilateral facial paralysis. Encephalitis without paralysis may be caused by the vaccine treatment, and in such cases the disease begins with high fever and headache which may be followed by convulsions and coma.

There is no proved instance of a human being having recovered from rabies. One might therefore assume that it is always fatal. However, when one considers the fact that isolation of the virus from living human beings depends on inoculation of saliva into animals, which is rarely done, it may well be that nonfatal infections do occur. The nonfatal or so-called abortive type of rabies described by Koch (1930) is uniformly a paralytic disease. On clinical grounds it is difficult, if not impossible, to differentiate treatment paralysis occurring as the result of rabies vaccination from paralytic rabies. Failure to demonstrate rabies virus in the brain at necropsy is considered evidence in favor of a diagnosis of paralysis due to the vaccine. In dealing with animals, however, isolation of the virus becomes increasingly difficult the longer an animal lives after the onset of the disease, and when death is delayed for a week or more it may be impossible to isolate the virus. Histologic examination of the brain and spinal cord in fatal cases of paralysis caused by vaccination may not aid in differentiating the condition from paralytic rabies, and, in the absence of specific inclusion bodies, one may be left in doubt as to the cause of death. Furthermore, the problem of differentiating the two conditions cannot be solved by immunologic tests, since the vaccine treatment as well as the disease results in the development of specific antibodies to rabies virus.

PATHOLOGIC PICTURE

There are no gross abnormalities which can be regarded as diagnostic of rabies. The meninges are normal except for vascular congestion, and the spinal fluid is clear and colorless. The surface of the brain and spinal cord usually exhibits a pink or red discoloration caused by marked engorgement of the blood vessels. There is slight to moderate cerebral edema as shown by flattening of the cerebral convolutions and partial obliteration of the sulci. On section, the cut surface of the brain and spinal cord has a pink cast. Ordinarily this is most marked in the thalamus, medulla and cervical spinal cord. Perivascular hemorrhage is rarely evident on gross examination. When the site of the bite is located on one of the extremities, the cut surface of the spinal cord may show unilateral, pinkish-gray discoloration and obliteration of the normal markings. This lesion, when present, is most marked in the posterior horn. The lungs usually show some atelectasis and the mucosa of the trachea and bronchi is congested. The thymus may be enlarged and edematous. The small intestine sometimes presents the picture of paralytic ileus. The mucous membrane of the gastro-intestinal tract is congested, and local digestion of the gastric mucosa, with perforation of the stomach wall and diaphragm and the presence of stomach contents in the abdominal or pleural cavities, is a frequent finding.

When examined histologically the meninges usually appear normal. A variable degree of hyperemia and slight perivascular infiltration with mononuclear cells may be seen. The cerebral and cerebellar cortex show general hyperemia and acute neuronal degeneration. The white matter exhibits variable demyelinization and degeneration of axis cylinders. In the midbrain, basal ganglia and pons, the neuronal degeneration generally is severe and is associated with marked hyperemia. Small perivascular hemorrhages, most noticeable in the thalamus and subependymal neuroglial tissue, are seen frequently. Neuronal degeneration is especially severe in the thalamus, hypothalamus, substantia nigra, and the nuclei of cranial nerves. These areas show a slight perivascular and perineuronal mononuclear cell infiltration. The medulla uniformly presents the maximum pathologic alteration. The cranial nerve nuclei exhibit marked neuronal degeneration and the infiltration by mononuclear cells is proportionally greater than elsewhere. The spinal cord shows hyperemia and perivascular infiltration, which are especially marked in the cervical portion at the decussation of the motor tracts. The neuronal degeneration is apt to be extensive in the posterior horns. When the site of the bite is located on one of the extremities, the corresponding posterior horn is apt to show marked hyperemia, neuronophagia and cellular infiltration; the corresponding tracts of Goll and Burdach and the posterior funiculus exhibit extensive degeneration of axons and myelin sheaths. The contiguity of the axon is disrupted so that it appears beaded, and the myelin sheath is vacuoloated. The dorsal root ganglia from the same region show marked neuronal degeneration and moderate to marked mononuclear cell infiltration.

In general the leukocytic infiltration is largely perivascular, but clusters of mononuclear cells are found about degenerating neurons, especially in the cranial nerve nuclei. The leukocytes found in the neuroglial tissue are, for the most part, of the small and large mononuclear types, but in some cases polymorphonuclear cells are present. There is apt to be a slight diffuse mononuclear cell infiltration of the interstitial tissue of the pons, medulla, and cervical spinal cord, varying in proportion to the degree of neuronophagia. Cellular infiltration may be very scanty when a patient dies soon after the onset of the disease and is proportionally greater the longer the duration of the disease. The neuroglial cells of the substantia gelatinosa about the central canal show a variable degree of proliferation; this is especially evident in the spinal cord. The neuroglia about degenerating neurons become more prominent than usual, and, though this may result from an increase in their size, it is suggestive of proliferation. The oligodendroglia throughout the brain show swelling, a manifestation of the moderate cerebral edema which is present in all cases. Most of the neurons of the central nervous system show some pathologic alteration. The main change consists of pyknosis of the nucleus and ballooning of the cytoplasm. The Nissl substance is decreased in amount and the cytoplasm exhibits variable vacuolar and granular degeneration. Some neurons show condensation of the cytoplasm seen in coagulative necrosis, while others exhibit fragmentation of the cytoplasm and general loss of cellular detail.

The inclusion bodies which can be demonstrated in the neurons of the majority of cases of rabies generally are referred to as Negri bodies (Plate 1). These structures when present are pathognomonic of rabies. The specific inclusion bodies are found in the cytoplasm of large neurons which present the ballooning type of degeneration and consist of sharply defined, spherical, oval or elongated eosinophilic bodies, ordi-

PLATE 1

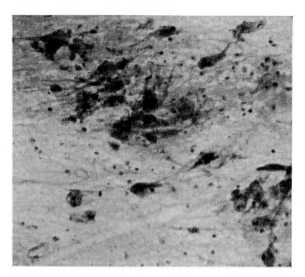

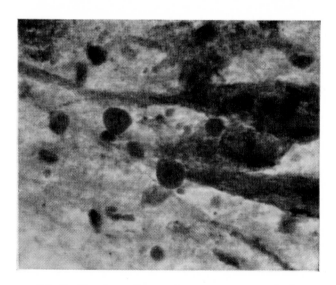

(*Top*) Routine diagnostic smear prepared from Ammon's horn of a dog that had died of rabies. Sellers' stain. × 200.

(*Bottom*) Higher magnification of the illustration above, showing internal structure of Negri body. Sellers' stain. × 900. (Photographs by R. F. Carter)

narily 2 to 10 microns in diameter. Several inclusion bodies, usually of variable size, may be present in one neuron and are found most often in the cytoplasm between the nucleus and the dendritic prolongations of the cell. They also may be found in the first part of the dendrite and in such instances are elongated. The characteristic inclusion body contains an inner structure of basophilic granules, which vary from 0.2 to 0.5 microns in diameter and are surrounded by a clear zone in preparations stained by Wolbach's modification of Giemsa's stain. Large inclusion bodies have a central granule and one or more concentric layers of these inner bodies, separated by a finely granular ground substance or matrix. Small inclusion bodies may contain a central basophilic granule, but some are uniformly acidophilic and, in the absence of large forms, cannot be regarded as specific because of their similarity to inclusion bodies found in other diseases. Characteristic inclusion bodies of rabies are apt to be more abundant in Ammon's horn of the hippocampus than elsewhere in the nervous system, but may be found in large numbers in the pyramidal cell layer of the cerebral cortex, the Purkinje cell layer of the cerebellum and in the large neurons of the basal ganglia and cranial nerve nuclei. They may be found also in neurons of the spinal cord, dorsal root ganglia, the ganglionic cell layer of the retina, and ganglia of the sympathetic nervous system. Negri (1903, 1907) believed that the intracytoplasmic inclusion bodies of rabies represented one stage in the development of a protozoan parasite. Subsequent studies of the inclusion bodies of rabies, as well as those found in other viral diseases, indicate that, while they may contain infective units of the virus, they are composed largely of a matrix derived from the cytoplasm of degenerating cells. The absence of thymonucleic acid from the Negri body as shown by the Fuelgen stain conforms with the characteristics of other inclusion bodies due to infection with a virus. The matrix contains considerable lipid

material as shown by selective staining methods. The Negri body may be derived in part from the neurofibrillar apparatus of the neuron (Goodpasture, 1925). Coccoid bodies in the cytoplasm of degenerating neurons which stain in a manner similar to that of the matrix of the Negri body were noted by Koch (1930), but they cannot be regarded as diagnostic of rabies.

Neurons of ganglia of the sympathetic nervous system and the dorsal root ganglia of the spinal cord show degenerative changes similar to those of the brain. Marked ballooning and vacuolation of the cytoplasm may be present. The interstitial tissue of the ganglia may show moderate to extensive infiltration of mononuclear cells. The degenerating neurons are surrounded by large cuboidal cells which appear to be derived from cells of the sheath of Schwann. The peripheral nerves, particularly those related to the site of the bite, show coalescence of neurofibrillae and fragmentation of axis cylinders, vacuolation of the myelin sheath and a variable degree of mononuclear cell infiltration in the perineural lymphatics.

If the salivary glands contain virus, there is moderate to marked degeneration of acinar cells of the mucus-secreting tissue. This lesion is associated with mononuclear cell infiltration of the interstitial tissue. The ducts of the salivary glands may be markedly distended with amorphous material containing cellular debris. The lacrimal glands show a similar lesion when infected with the virus. Acute degeneration of the medullary cells of the adrenal gland can be correlated with the presence of the virus and, when present, is associated with mononuclear cell infiltration of the interstitial tissue of the adrenal medulla. Acute degeneration of the acinar epithelium of the pancreas and the epithelial cells of the renal tubules may be found in some cases of rabies. The gastro-intestinal tract may show congestion and edema of the mucosa, and the neurons of the sympathetic plexuses may show degenerative changes similar to those of the sympathetic ganglia elsewhere in the nervous system.

In the absence of specific inclusion bodies in the neurons of the central nervous system, a definite diagnosis of rabies cannot be made with certainty on the basis of the pathologic picture, because the lesions produced by rabies virus are similar to those found in other viral encephalitides.

EXPERIMENTAL INFECTION; HOST RANGE

Rabies virus is pathogenic for all mammals. Infection does not take place through intact skin or by ingestion. It is difficult to infect animals by intraperitoneal inoculation, but injection of the virus into the skin, subcutaneous tissue, muscle, or nervous tissue, in that order, is increasingly efficacious in producing disease. Intracerebral inoculation of the natural virus obtained from dogs will, with rare exceptions, produce a fatal infection in all mammals. Inoculation of the virus onto the scarified cornea may produce infection. Dogs can be infected by intravenous injection and high mortality may be obtained if large doses of virus are given. Infection can be obtained by intranasal inoculation, and mice are susceptible to both street and fixed virus given in this way. Ducks, geese, doves, and domestic fowl of all types are susceptible, but less so than mammals. Young birds ordinarily develop a fatal paralytic disease following intracerebral inoculation, but recovery from rabies is relatively frequent in adult birds. The disease is not transmissible by arthropods or insects.

The domestic dog is the principal source of human infection, and the nature of the virus can be determined best by study of the disease in this host. A normal dog bitten by a rabid animal may develop rabies within 10 days, or it may show no signs of the disease until several months later. The usual incubation period varies from 21 to 60 days. Following inoculation with the natural virus obtained from infected salivary-gland tissue, the incubation period depends to a large degree on the amount of active virus introduced. For example, dogs inoculated in each masseter muscle with 0.06 cc. of the supernate of a 10 per cent suspension of infected salivary-gland tissue ordinarily develop rabies within 15 or 25 days, with a mean latent period of from 19 to 21 days. A mortality rate of 90 to 100 per cent is obtained if the natural virus is present in high titer in the infected tissue. When a 10^{-3} dilution of the same virus preparation is inoculated into dogs in the volume and manner just described, the mortality rate is not reduced markedly, but the mean incubation period may be increased to 40 to 50 days. The same type of natural virus, when titrated in dogs by the intracerebral method, may show an LD_{50} of 0.5 cc. $\times 10^{-5.5}$. In this instance, the incubation period may be as short as eight days, but, with rare exceptions, the disease will develop within 10 or 20 days after inoculation; however, a latent period of from 2 to 3 months may be observed in some dogs. Dogs infected with the natural virus by intradermal or subcutaneous inoculation are apt to have an incubation period of 30 days or more, with a mean latent period of from 40 to 50 days. The mortality rate following these methods of exposure is low, and, even in small groups of animals, it rarely exceeds 50 per cent.

The picture of rabies in dogs infected by peripheral inoculation is similar to that observed in man. For practical purposes, rabies in dogs is classified as furious or dumb type, depending upon the signs shown by the animal. In the former type, the excitation phase is prolonged, while in the latter, the paralytic phase develops early. Most infected dogs show some manifestation of both types, that is, a short excitation phase characterized by restlessness, nervousness, and viciousness, followed rapidly by depression and paralysis. The incidence of the two types of the disease is not constant and depends on the character of the natural virus. Sudden death of dogs from rabies, without appreciable signs of illness, is not uncommon. Dogs that develop the predominantly excited type of rabies invariably die of the infection within a period of 11 days from the onset of illness. The acute phase of the disease usually terminates in death within 3 or 5 days. Apparent recovery has been noted in dogs developing the paralytic type of rabies, but this is a rare occurrence. The behavior observed during the prodromal phase of the disease in dogs is of two types; most infected animals become increasingly apprehensive and nervous, while others seek solitude and become increasingly apathetic. In the former type, a dog may appear unusually friendly, which is probably a manifestation of fear. This is the most dangerous phase of the disease, as the dog is usually very excitable and will bite at the slightest provocation. A rabid dog is more likely to bite a stranger than its master during the early stage of the disease, but with the onset of the acute excitement phase it may show no recognition of its master and exhibits only an insane desire to attack and bite. The symptom of hydrophobia does not occur in canine rabies, but difficulty in swallowing is common. Partial or complete paralysis of the muscles of phonation occurs in most rabid dogs as shown by a characteristic change in their bark or growl or by inability to make any sound. This may be the reason why rabid animals so often attack without warning. The tendency of rabid dogs to eat dirt, straw, bedding, and wood is well known. If caged, the animal may break off its teeth in attempts to free itself. During the prodromal phase, the physical signs include fever, a decrease or loss of the corneal reflex, decreased sensation to painful stimuli, dilatation of the pupils, and an increase in muscle tone which gives the animal an alert appearance. As the disease progresses, a dog may be unable to close its eyes completely which take on a glazed appearance resulting from dryness of the corneae. An animal may show twitching of muscles, a general muscular tremor, in-co-ordination, and convulsive seizures. If

a dog does not die at this stage, progressive paralysis and coma precede death. Dogs infected experimentally by inoculation of virus into the masseter muscles, ordinarily develop paralysis of these muscles early, which is spastic at first, making it difficult for the animals to open their jaws after biting. The initial febrile period may last one or two days and then the temperature drops to normal or subnormal levels. A second febrile period is uncommon, but some animals develop a high terminal fever.

Transmission of rabies in nature depends on the ability of the virus to reach and to multiply in the salivary glands of a rabid animal. The virus may be present also in the lacrimal glands, pancreas, kidney, and breast tissue; it shows little affinity for tissue of mesodermal origin and has not been demonstrated with certainty in the blood, spleen, liver, lymph nodes, bone marrow, or sex glands of animals infected in nature. The virus is demonstrable in the central nervous system of nearly all animals that have died of rabies. When the disease is of long duration, autosterilization may take place. The medulla and thalamus usually contain the greatest concentration of virus. The submaxillary glands are the best source of virus from tissue other than that of the nervous system, and may contain more virus than the brain as determined by titration. The adrenal glands of rabid animals are likely to contain virus, but cellular degeneration is confined to the medulla and is evidently a part of the general involvement of nervous tissue. It is true that virus may be present in the saliva of dogs that appear entirely normal upon casual observation, but, if examined carefully, they will show some signs of infection, such as fever, irritability, and various types of abnormal behavior. Nicolas (1906) found that the appearance of virus in saliva coincided with the initial febrile response to infection but that the infected dog might not show classical signs of rabies until five days later. Nearly all those who have studied experimental rabies in dogs have noted apparent recovery from the paralytic disease. However, there is no record of isolation of rabies virus from the saliva of a naturally infected dog that eventually recovered. Furthermore, with the possible exception of the dog reported by Remlinger (1907), it has been impossible to isolate virus from saliva of experimentally infected dogs that did not succumb. The case of nonfatal paralytic rabies described by Remlinger occurred in a dog that had been inoculated with fixed virus. The reputed isolation of virus from the saliva of this dog is questionable. At least, other investigators have been unable to isolate virus from the salivary glands of dogs infected with fixed virus, and the data, as presented, suggest that the guinea pigs inoculated with the dog saliva died of a disease other than rabies.

The ability of the virus to invade salivary glands varies with different strains and different species of host. In a joint study carried on by the Georgia State Department of Health and the rabies laboratory of the International Health Division of The Rockefeller Foundation, an attempt was made to determine the frequency with which salivary glands are invaded by rabies virus in animals infected in nature. Of 28 dogs proved to be rabid by isolation of virus from the brain, 21 (75 per cent) had demonstrable virus in the salivary glands. Of 150 foxes proved to have rabies, 130 (87 per cent) were found to have virus in the salivary glands. Virus was isolated from the salivary glands of 16, or approximately 50 per cent, of 34 head of infected cattle. Strains of rabies virus, isolated from foxes during an epizootic (Johnson, 1945a), varied in their ability to invade salivary glands of mice infected by intramuscular inoculation. When groups of 25 or more mice were infected with the natural viruses, some strains were able to invade the salivary glands of only 30 per cent of the animals, while others were capable of such invasion in 80 per cent. Tropism of virus for the salivary glands, as determined by this method, was markedly reduced by a few serial, intracerebral passages in mice. Rabies virus maintained in vampire bats may be especially adapted to multiplication in salivary glands, as these animals at times transmit the disease by bite for weeks or months and then become noninfectious without at any time having shown signs of illness (Pawan, 1936b).

In summary, it may be said that the natural or so-called street-virus rabies is characterized by a long and extremely variable incubation period and a rather constant production of Negri bodies. Infection with the virus often results in a prolonged excitement state associated with irritability and viciousness. In a variable but high percentage of cases, the virus is able to reach the salivary glands and be excreted in the saliva. There is no satisfactory evidence of antigenically different strains of rabies virus. The natural virus may be altered by rapid passage in the natural host as shown by the character of the disease produced, that is, by increased speed of multiplication in the brain, more general distribution of virus in this organ, and less invasiveness for the salivary glands. This undoubtedly acts as a check on the spread of rabies, since animals infected with highly virulent strains of the virus uniformly develop a paralytic type of disease and do not propagate it by bite.

The term fixed virus has been applied to strains of the agent that have been propagated by serial intracerebral passage in some experimental animal, usually the rabbit, in which the incubation period has become short and constant. Rabies caused by fixed virus is characterized by an incubation period of 4 to 6 days following intracerebral inoculation; absence of Negri bodies in the brain; wide dissemination of the virus in the central nervous system with consequent high titer; and a rapidly-progressing, paralytic disease. Such strains have lost to some degree their ability to migrate centrifugally or centripetally along nerves, and apparently are unable to multiply in nonnervous tissue, such as that of salivary glands.

The variety of fixed virus most widely used for human vaccination is the Pasteur strain, which has been maintained by serial passage in rabbits since its isolation in 1882 (Pasteur, 1885). Most of its substrains, which are available today, have been through 2,000 or more passages in rabbits. Some substrains have a shorter incubation period than others, which may be accounted for by factors such as age of animal used, time of harvest of the passage virus respective to the onset of symptoms, and constant versus intermittent passage. Each substrain has a very constant incubation period in any group of animals of uniform age given the same inoculum. Titration of fixed virus shows that the incubation period varies inversely in proportion to the amount of virus given. In general, the maximum amount of active virus in the brain of a rabbit is found about 24 hours after onset of illness, and laboratories producing vaccine sometimes take temperature readings on the rabbits as fever marks the onset of the disease. The virus to be used for a vaccine should have an LD_{50} of 0.03 cc. $\times 10^{-5.5}$ or better, when tested in mice. Titer of the virus may be slightly higher if tested in rabbits, but it is seldom possible to obtain an LD_{50} of more than 0.25 cc. $\times 10^{-6}$. The Pasteur strain, when given by intracerebral inoculation, is highly pathogenic for all laboratory animals, as well as dogs and large domestic animals such as sheep, horses, calves, and goats. However, it appears to be unable to infect human beings when given subcutaneously, and dogs seem to be almost equally resistant to the agent inoculated peripherally. On the other hand, approximately 100 per cent mortality can be obtained in rabbits, guinea pigs, and mice by intramuscular inoculation of large doses of rabbit-fixed or mouse-fixed virus. Rabies virus adapted to mice by constant serial intracerebral passage has an LD_{50} of about 0.03 cc. $\times 10^{-7}$, when titrated intracerebrally in mice. Such strains appear to have the same pathogenicity range for laboratory animals and dogs as does the rabbit-fixed virus. The capacity of the natural virus to form Negri bodies ordinarily is lost following 25 serial intracerebral passages in mice.

A variety of fixed virus has been developed by serial intracerebral passage in baby chicks, and this chick-brain-fixed virus (Flury) when passaged in chick embryos by yolk-sac inoculation was found to be nonpathogenic for rabbits when given intramuscularly (Koprowski et al., 1948). This modification of pathogenicity of the virus for rabbits after cultivation in chick embryos had been noted by Bernkopf et al. (1940), and Dawson (1941). The low pathogenicity for rabbits may have been brought about by prolonged cultivation in baby chicks, as rabbits were refractory to intramuscular inoculation with large doses of chick-embryo virus regardless of the passage level. Continued passage of the virus in chick embryos did bring about an alteration of the pathogenicity of the virus for hamsters inoculated intramuscularly as shown by an increased incidence of nonfatal paralytic rabies. Guinea pigs were more refractory than hamsters to intramuscular inoculation with the Flury chick-embryo-adapted virus, and dogs were entirely refractory (Koprowski, 1949). Fixed varieties of rabies virus will propagate in tissue culture when chick-embryo brain is used, but serial passage is difficult and the virus is apt to be lost after 20 passages. However, these strains can be maintained indefinitely in tissue culture when mouse-embryo brain is used, but the species pathogenicity of the virus remains constant.

ETIOLOGY

The diameter of rabies virus has been estimated to be 100 to 150 millimicrons (Galloway et al., 1936) and, as is the case with other large viruses, the agent is not readily filterable. It will pass through diatomaceous earth and unglazed porcelain filters which hold back common varieties of bacteria but is not readily filterable through Seitz EK filter pads.

Resistance of the virus to various physical and chemical agents depends on the source of the infected material and the method of its preparation. In testing the survival of the virus at various temperatures, one must be cognizant of certain factors, such as the original infectivity of tissues as determined by titration, the percentage and type of tissue which contains the virus, and the diluent used in the preparation of the material to be tested. Infected brain or salivary-gland tissue are the best sources of virus. The virus, when infected tissues are stored in undiluted neutral glycerol, retains its infectivity for several weeks at room temperature or for several months at refrigerator temperature. The infectivity of tissues exposed to the air at room temperature is lost in one or two weeks depending on the prevailing temperature and relative humidity, but at refrigerator temperature the virus may remain active for several weeks and at subfreezing temperatures for one or more years. In order to study the nature of the virus and its response to physical and chemical agents, it must be liberated from cells by grinding. Physiologic saline solution is added to make a 10 per cent suspension by weight of tissue and this material is then subjected to centrifugation. The freed virus is present in the supernate. Intracellular enzymes are liberated with the virus which may have an unfavorable effect on its activity, while certain other substances freed from the cells appear to have a protective effect. In dilutions containing less than 0.1 per cent tissue extract, the virus deteriorates rapidly unless normal serum is added to the diluent. Though in higher dilutions the virus is inactivated more rapidly in physiologic saline solution than in distilled water, there is no significant difference in the survival of the virus in the two diluents if serum is added. Physiologic saline solution is preferable to distilled water, as the latter causes precipitation of protein in cell-free supernates,

thus making it difficult to maintain a uniform suspension of the virus. A large proportion of active virus is found in the sediment following centrifugation of macerated tissue as shown by regrinding the sedimented tissue and titrating the supernate. For routine inoculation, it is preferable to use the supernate, as the suspension of tissue may quickly kill experimental animals when injected into the brain. By intraperitoneal or intramuscular injection, a tissue suspension is more infectious than the supernate. Physiologic saline solution containing at least 2 per cent inactivated normal guinea pig serum is the most satisfactory diluent for studies of rabies virus; there is no significant loss of infectivity in the higher dilutions over a period of a few hours at room temperature or 24 hours at 4° C. When exposed to a temperature of from 54° to 56° C., aqueous suspensions of virus are inactivated in an hour or less. The best method of preserving the virus is through desiccation while in the frozen state followed by storage at refrigerator temperature; under such conditions it may remain infective for several years. Dried virus is less sensitive to heat and may prove infective after 24-hours' exposure to a temperature of from 54° to 56° C. Repeated freezing and thawing of virus suspensions results in loss of infectivity. Variation in subfreezing temperature has a harmful effect on the virus and saturation with carbon dioxide inactivates it. If a standard virus is to be used, it should be tubed in desired amounts in pyrex glass ampoules, sealed, frozen rapidly, and stored in a dry-ice chest.

Rabies virus, as obtained in serum-saline suspensions of infected tissue, may be concentrated and purified to some degree by the common methods of selective precipitation of serum proteins, namely, fractional precipitation with ammonium sulphate and isoelectric precipitation; it is found in the globulin-type fraction. Cox et al. (1947) have reported purification and concentration of rabies virus by means of alcohol precipitation.

Rabies virus is rapidly destroyed by sunlight or by ultraviolet irradiation (Hodes et al., 1940). It is readily inactivated by formalin, bichloride of mercury, and strong acids and bases. The virus is moderately resistant to ether and chloroform and very resistant to phenol. Bacteriostatic concentrations of merthiolate and sodium sulfadiazine do not harm the virus.

Rabies virus adapted to laboratory animals may be cultivated in tissue cultures in which the Maitland type of medium containing minced mouse-embryo brain is used (Kanazawa, 1936; Webster et al., 1936). The virus has not been adapted to multiplication in media containing little or no nervous tissue. It can be cultivated in the developing chick embryo. Infection is obtained by chorio-allantoic-membrane inoculation (Kligler et al., 1938; Bernkopf et al., 1940) or by direct inoculation of the embryo (Dawson, 1941). Recent studies have shown that chick embryos can be infected by injection of the virus into the yolk sac, and serial passages have been accomplished in this manner. The unusual feature of the infection in embryos is that virus may be demonstrated in the blood (Koprowski et al., 1948).

Immunologic and serologic tests are of little value for the diagnosis of rabies, but infection does give rise to specific antibodies which may be demonstrable in the blood early in the course of the disease. Neutralization and complement-fixation tests are useful for studying the mechanism of immunity to the disease, particularly the response to vaccination. The virus as it occurs in nature can, with rare exceptions, be identified readily by its ability to produce Negri bodies. Fixed virus, however, does not give rise to specific inclusion bodies, and such strains must be identified by cross-neutralization, complement-fixation, or protection tests.

For the neutralization test, it is preferable to have a standard virus, against constant amounts of which undiluted and various tenfold dilutions of serum may be tested. Preliminary titration of a standard virus makes it possible to use a definite amount, ordinarily 200 LD_{50} per 0.03 cc. for mice. The LD_{50} endpoint is determined by the method of Reed et al. (1938). When the virus is mixed with an equal volume of serum or serum dilution, its concentration will be 100 LD_{50} per 0.03 cc. In parallel with a known immune serum control, unknown sera are tested undiluted and in tenfold dilutions in physiologic salt solution through 10^{-3} against the standard virus. The normal serum control is tested undiluted against the standard virus and against standard virus diluted tenfold, i.e., 10 LD_{50}. Incubation of the mixtures for one hour at 38° C. and another hour at 4° C. with agitation of the tubes at 15-minute intervals is sufficient for satisfactory neutralization of the virus by known immune serum. At least 4 mice should be injected intracerebrally with 0.03 cc. of each serum-virus mixture. There are rarely any survivors in the 10 LD_{50} control group. Survival of more than 50 per cent of the mice in the 100 LD_{50} group tested against undiluted serum is regarded as satisfactory evidence of immunity to rabies. Immune serum may be prepared by immunization of guinea pigs, and it is possible to obtain neutralization of 100,000 LD_{50} of fixed virus per 0.015 cc. of serum. The neutralization test is of value for the identification of unknown strains of rabies virus, particularly those modified by serial intracerebral passage in laboratory animals.

The complement-fixation test is applicable to the study of rabies (Casals et al., 1941), but it has not as yet been adapted to diagnosis of the disease. Animals immunized with active, fixed virus develop complement-fixing antibodies; these tend to disappear within three months, while virus-neutralizing antibodies persist and the animals remain immune to peripheral exposure with rabies virus.

The immunizing potency of rabies vaccine can be estimated by parallel intracerebral titrations of fixed rabies virus in vaccinated and unvaccinated mice (Webster, 1936, 1939). Rabies vaccines marketed in the United States for use in human beings and lower animals must be tested for immunizing potency according to a method developed by the U. S. Public Health Service (Habel, 1940; Habel et al., 1948). Mice receive 6 intraperitoneal injections of 0.25 cc. of vaccine diluted so as to contain 0.5 per cent brain tissue. The vaccine is given on alternate days, and on the fourteenth day following the first dose the mice are challenged in groups of 10, serial tenfold dilutions of fixed virus covering the expected infectivity range from 1 to 100,000 LD_{50} being used. The LD_{50} endpoint of virus for the vaccinated and unvaccinated animals is determined. The vaccinated mice must show an endpoint titer of at least 1,000 LD_{50} less than the controls in order for the vaccine to be approved. A 100 per cent protection is not obtained regularly in vaccinated mice tested intracerebrally with 100 LD_{50}, even though the animals have been immunized with vaccine containing active virus; yet it is not uncommon for from 50 to 100 per cent of the vaccinated mice to survive tests with all dilutions of the virus. Vaccinated mice may be tested for resistance to rabies by intramuscular inoculation of fixed virus (Webster, 1939). Almost 100 per cent mortality may be obtained in normal mice which receive in the muscles of each thigh an inoculum of 0.03 cc. of an uncentrifuged 10 per cent suspension of mouse brain infected with fixed virus. Three intraperitoneal injections, spaced a week apart, of 0.25 cc. of undiluted commercial vaccine containing phenol-inactivated virus should produce a solid immunity to active fixed virus given intramuscularly 3 weeks following the first dose of vaccine. Whatever type of vaccination schedule is used, the peak of immunity is not reached until three or four weeks following the first dose of vaccine. The intracerebral challenge was adopted for routine potency tests, because it gives a more accurate index of the amount of antigen in the vaccines than does an intramuscular challenge. The challenge inoculation is given 14 days following the first dose of vaccine in order to limit the time of observation before a finished vaccine can be released for distribution.

It is also possible to rate the antigenicity of a vaccine by the amount of tissue virus in milligrams, which, given in two doses by intraperitoneal injection 10 days apart, will protect more than 50 per cent of the vaccinated animals when these are challenged at 14 or 21 days after the first dose of vaccine by intracerebral inoculation of 10 to 50 LD_{50} standard rabbit-fixed rabies virus. This obviates the booster effect of the large doses of virus in the 10^{-1} through 10^{-3} dilutions when the challenge virus is titrated in vaccinated mice for comparison with the control-group titer. A sharper endpoint will be obtained if the challenge virus is given by intramuscular inoculation.

The remarkable susceptibility of hamsters to street virus inoculated intramuscularly (Koprowski, 1949; Koprowski et al., 1950) makes this animal particularly suitable for testing the protective value of various types of vaccine and also for testing the potency of rabies antiserum.

DIAGNOSIS

History of exposure, clinical symptoms and signs, and outcome of an illness often play an important part in the diagnosis of rabies in man and lower animals. The development of specific diagnostic methods for determining whether or not animals have rabies was necessitated by the frequency with which human beings are bitten, especially by dogs which in most instances do not have rabies. If a biting dog fails to develop signs of rabies or die within a period of 7 days, a bitten person can be assured that exposure to rabies did not occur. The laboratory diagnosis of rabies is based on the finding, at necropsy, of Negri bodies in the nerve cells of man or lower animals infected in nature or in the brains of laboratory animals inoculated with saliva or infected tissue from such sources. The finding of Negri bodies is sufficient for diagnosis of rabies, but when they cannot be found it is necessary to resort to animal inoculation.

Negri bodies are readily demonstrated in impression preparations of brain tissue stained by Sellers' (1927) method. Though Negri bodies usually are more abundant and characteristic in Ammon's horn than elsewhere in the brain, it is advisable to make preparations also from the cerebral and cerebellar cortex. The impression method is of particular value because the anatomical orientation of nerve cells is retained and there is little distortion and rupture of cells. Ammon's horn is exposed by cutting through the cortex over the posterior horn of the lateral ventricle. A cross section, 1 to 2 mm. in thickness, is removed from the middle of the horn where it bulges up from the floor of the ventricle and is placed on an absorbent surface, such as a tongue depressor or paper towel. Several impressions are obtained by touching clean glass slides to the surface of the section. While still moist, the slide is immersed in the staining solution for about 5 seconds after which it is washed in water. The preparation is ready for examination as soon as it is dry. While fresh preparations stained in this way give the best results, impression preparations fixed in absolute methyl alcohol and allowed to dry before being stained can be used. Tap water, if not contaminated with certain mineral salts, is satisfactory for washing the stained preparations. If tap water cannot be used, uniform results are obtained by washing in M/150 phosphate buffer solution, pH 7.0, prepared in distilled water.

SELLERS' STAIN

Basic fuchsin, saturated absolute
    methyl alcohol solution . . . . 2-4 cc.
Methylene blue, saturated absolute
    methyl alcohol solution . . . . 15 cc.
Methyl alcohol, absolute, acetone free . 25 cc.

It is convenient to keep the staining solution in a Coplin jar which can be sealed with vaseline to prevent evaporation. Because of variability in the dye content of different lots of stain, an excess of the powdered dye should be used in preparing stock solutions. A properly stained smear, when light passes through it, should appear reddish-violet in thin areas and purplish-blue in thick portions. If in the trial stain the thin parts are bluish, add 0.5 cc. of the fuchsin solution. Negri bodies are stained cherry red and stand out in sharp relief (Plate 1); the basophilic inner structure is colored deep blue. The cytoplasm of nerve cells is stained blue to purplish-blue; nuclei and nucleoli are deep blue; the stroma is rose pink, while nerve fibers are colored a deeper pink; neural sheaths are not stained; bacteria, if present, are stained deep blue; and erythrocytes are copper color. For the demonstration of Negri bodies in paraffin sections, brain tissue should be fixed in Zenker's fluid containing 5 per cent glacial acetic acid, and the sections should be stained with phloxine-methylene blue or Wolbach's modification of Giemsa's stain as described by Mallory (1938).

In human specimens, there is little chance of confusing the inclusion bodies of rabies with those which occur in other diseases. In dog brains, however, inclusion bodies caused by distemper virus may be encountered which are similar to those occurring in rabies. The distemper inclusion bodies are pale red, are more refractile than those caused by rabies, and have no inner structure. They may be irregular in outline, and occur more frequently in the thalamus and lentiform nuclei than in Ammon's horn. Intracytoplasmic inclusions may be found in the brains of mice which do not have rabies. These are small, pink to bright red in color, very refractile, uniformly round, and have no inner structure.

Diagnosis of rabies by isolation of the virus depends on the injection into animals of saliva taken during the disease or brain tissue obtained at necropsy. In the past, saliva has been rarely used because of bacteria encountered. Now that antibiotics are available, attempts should be made to isolate virus from saliva of human beings suspected of having rabies, particularly those suffering from the paralytic type which is so difficult to differentiate from paralysis caused by rabies vaccine. Since the submaxillary salivary glands are most likely to contain virus, specimens of saliva should be taken from under the tongue. The saliva then may be diluted in a serum-saline mixture containing penicillin and streptomycin and tested by intracerebral inoculation into mice. Though undiluted saliva is apt to cause immediate death when injected intracerebrally into laboratory animals, it may be injected intramuscularly into hamsters or guinea pigs. The Syrian hamster is very susceptible to street virus given by intramuscular inoculation (Koprowski, 1949; Koprowski et al., 1950). Brain tissue obtained at necropsy should be preserved in undiluted, neutral glycerol; portions of the medulla, basal ganglia, and cerebral cortex should be used. If the disease was of long duration, there may be little or no virus in the brain. There is considerable variation in the distribution and concentration of virus in various portions of the cerebral cortex, spinal cord, and nerve trunks of human beings who have died of rabies. The spinal fluid rarely contains virus (Leach et al., 1940). Fresh or glycerolated specimens of brain tissue are prepared for inoculation by grinding in a mortar and adding physiologic saline solution to make a 10 per cent suspension. The supernatant fluid, following centrifugation, is used for inoculation of mice. When bacteria are seen in preparations, small portions of the brain should be placed in glycerol for a few days, or, if it is necessary to avoid delay, the tissue may be suspended in physiologic salt solution containing 0.5 per cent phenol and stored in a refrigerator for 24 hours before testing. The virus may be separated from bacteria by filtration, but much of it is retained in fine filters unless the tissue-virus suspension is subjected to a preliminary clarification by passing it through a coarse filter. Treatment with merthiolate or with a mixture of penicillin and streptomycin may be used also for counteracting bacterial contamination.

All of the various strains of albino mice are suitable as test animals (Johnson et al., 1940); there is no significant decrease in susceptibility to intracerebral infection with increasing age. If a specimen is positive, some of the mice ordinarily will show tremors, in-co-ordination, or paralysis from 6 to 8 days after inoculation. Convulsions are common, and an animal may die during such a seizure. Most mice infected with the natural virus develop flaccid paralysis of the legs which progresses to complete prostration. Frequently, Negri bodies can be demonstrated in the brain five days after inoculation. Occasionally, the incubation period is prolonged, particularly when specimens have been obtained from patients living several days after onset of illness. In such cases, the mice may not show signs of infection until two or three weeks after inoculation. It is necessary to confirm a diagnosis of rabies in mice by finding Negri bodies, since several viruses produce a disease picture in this host similar to that of rabies.

Rabbits and guinea pigs may be used for diagnostic inoculation. In general, the incubation period of rabies caused by street virus is from 15 to 30 days for rabbits and from 10 to 20 days for guinea pigs when the virus is introduced into the brain; the latent period ordinarily is shorter in immature than in mature animals. At times, the incubation period may be as long as 90 days. The disease in rabbits and guinea pigs is similar to that described in mice.

Since Negri bodies become more numerous with progression of the disease, it is advisable to hold biting dogs in quarantine. Negri bodies can be found in approximately 90 per cent of naturally infected animals that have died of rabies (Koch, 1930); they are demonstrable in about 70 per cent of human beings who have died of rabies (Johnson, 1942). There is a considerable variation from month to month in the percentage of rabid dogs showing Negri bodies as deter-

TABLE 14. SUMMARY OF MICROSCOPIC AND MOUSE-INOCULATION STUDIES OF DOG BRAINS, GEORGIA STATE DEPARTMENT OF HEALTH, 1937

MONTH	NEGRI +	NEGRI O	NEGRI O MOUSE +	TOTAL +	PER CENT OF TOTAL POSITIVE THAT WAS NEGRI O
January	62	37	5	67	7.5
February	50	38	1	51	2.0
March	67	48	13	80	16.2
April	76	48	6	82	7.3
May	77	93	7	84	8.3
June	58	76	9	67	13.4
July	73	68	8	81	9.9
August	39	63	11	50	22.0
September	48	39	4	52	7.7
October	45	35	6	51	11.8
November	53	45	7	60	11.7
December	42	33	4	46	8.7
Total	690	623	81	771	10.5

mined by mouse-inoculation tests. Table 14 shows the results of a routine study of dog brains received by the Georgia State Department of Health during 1937; the specimens were sent in from many different foci of rabies. Suggestive evidence of variation in the strains of virus was obtained; this was based on the ability of the different strains to promote the formation of Negri bodies. Some strains obtained from the brains of naturally infected dogs nearly always produce a paralytic disease in experimentally infected dogs, which is characterized by a rapid course and absence of Negri bodies. In this connection, it may be noted that 26 per cent of 35 brains of rabid foxes, which were obtained during the peak month of an epizootic, contained no Negri bodies, while all the brains of 59 foxes suffering from enzootic rabies were shown to contain virus and Negri bodies (Johnson, 1942; 1945a).

Animals examined for rabies are usually those which develop the excited form of the disease and become vicious and bite. Dogs developing the paralytic type are not apt to be examined, as ordinarily there is no question of human exposure. Among dogs infected experimentally with street virus, some die suddenly without showing signs of excitation, and, as a rule, about 50 per cent of them develop the paralytic form of the disease and seldom live more than one or two days after onset of illness; less than 50 per cent of such infections are characterized by the formation of Negri bodies (Johnson, 1942).

When characteristic Negri bodies cannot be demonstrated in the brains of mice infected with a virus otherwise characteristic of rabies virus, it may be identified by determining whether or not it is neutralized by rabies-immune serum. When a person, who has not been given the vaccine, develops rabies, it is possible to demonstrate an increase in the titer of neutralizing antibody in the blood serum during the course of the infection.

TREATMENT

There is no specific treatment for rabies once the disease develops. Barbiturates are better than morphine for relieving anxiety, because patients exhibit a marked tolerance for morphine and small doses actually increase the excitement in some cases. If sedatives cannot be given by mouth, phenobarbital-sodium given by subcutaneous injection is indicated. Anesthesia may be used to control convulsive seizures. Dehydration develops rapidly in most patients; this may be controlled by intravenous injection of physiologic salt solution.

Human beings exposed to rabies ordinarily know when the exposure occurred and where the virus was deposited. Local treatment of wounds inflicted by rabid animals has been used for centuries, and this is probably the most important means for preventing the disease. Ekstrom (1830) introduced the use of acid for local treatment of such wounds, and during an epizootic of rabies in Stockholm treated 106 persons who had been bitten. Preliminary treatment consisted of washing the wound with dilute hydrochloric acid; the wound was opened surgically in some cases. Secondary treatment included either actual cautery, or cautery with concentrated hydrochloric acid or fused potassium hydroxide. One person treated 24 hours after exposure died 18 months later; this was considered a possible failure of treatment, although the symptoms were not characteristic of rabies. None of the other treated persons developed rabies, but a few cases of the disease occurred among a limited number of persons who were exposed but did not receive the treatment. The use of nitric acid for the treatment of wounds inflicted by rabid animals is based on the experimental studies of Cabot (1899), Poor (1911), and Rosenau (1935). These studies, which show an almost complete protection through cauterization with nitric acid 24 hours after inoculation of the virus in subcutaneous or intramuscular tissues of guinea pigs, indicate that the virus remains localized for a time at the point of introduction. When virus is introduced into an open wound in guinea pigs (Shaughnessy et al., 1943), thorough washing with 20 per cent soft soap solution 2 hours later is as effective as nitric acid in preventing infection. The object of

local treatment is to remove or inactivate virus that may have been deposited in the wound, and thorough washing with a concentrated soap solution undoubtedly is the best method of accomplishing this. Whether or not acid cautery should be used depends on time after exposure and the type of wound which may be too deep for cleaning with soap solution.

The use of vaccines for the prevention of rabies following exposure is recommended by public health authorities throughout the world because of the remarkably low mortality rate among treated persons. Controlled clinical tests of the effectiveness of combined local and vaccine treatment as compared with local treatment alone, have not been done, and satisfactory experimental evidence of the efficacy of vaccine treatment is lacking (Webster, 1942). Soon after the introduction of the vaccine treatment, it became evident that the disease could not be prevented if the incubation period was short; this led to the adoption of the absolute and reduced fatality rate in statistics on such treatment. The reduced, or treatment-failure, rate includes only those cases that develop the disease 2 or more weeks following the completion of the treatment. McKendrick (1940), in his ninth review of the statistics on rabies treatment, gave a reduced fatality rate of 0.34 for 152,899 cases treated with a vaccine prepared from desiccated spinal cords and 0.48 for 490,670 cases treated with the Semple vaccine containing inactivated virus. Failure to demonstrate a clear-cut superiority of the vaccine with active virus by such statistics and the possible, though extremely rare, occurrence of rabies (Remlinger, 1935) caused by vaccines containing active, fixed virus have discouraged their use.

For details of preparing the various types of rabies vaccine, the reader is referred to the article by Kraus et al. (1926). All early methods of treatment were similar in that they consisted of the administration of increasing doses of active, rabbit-fixed virus. By the original method, graded amounts of active virus were obtained by drying infected rabbit spinal cords for varying periods of time in a jar containing sticks of potassium hydroxide. A similar range of infectivity was obtained by Högyes through serial dilution of fresh fixed virus and by Babes through a 15-minute exposure of fresh fixed virus to temperatures ranging from 80° to 45° C. In all these methods of treatment, the total dosage of virus was increased for severe exposures such as those resulting from wounds of the face. Harris et al. (1911) introduced the modern method of desiccation from the frozen state to obtain a supply of fixed virus of known infectivity. Certain vaccines treated with phenol contain active virus, and, of these, the Fermi vaccine and that of Sellers (1923) are still in use. The studies of Semple (1919), Harvey et al. (1923), Covell et al. (1936), and Shortt et al. (1937) have shown that fixed virus inactivated in the presence of phenol retains its capacity to immunize. Vaccines have been developed in which the virus is inactivated by formalin (Cumming, 1914), ether (Remlinger, 1919), chloroform (Kelser, 1930), and ultraviolet irradiation (Hodes et al., 1940). The unbound formaldehyde in Cumming's vaccine is removed by dialysis. In the preparation of the Semple vaccine, the infected tissue is exposed to 1 per cent phenol during the period of inactivation; later this concentration is reduced by dilution. An excess of phenol appears to denature the antigen, and now it is recommended that the final product contain no more than 0.25 per cent phenol. The antigenicity of the Semple vaccine is better when the inactivation is carried out at room temperature instead of at 37° C. Vaccines prepared by treatment with ether or chloroform are kept at refrigerator temperature until the virus is inactivated; ordinarily several weeks are required for complete inactivation. Variation in survival time of the virus may necessitate several safety tests before a vaccine can be released for use. Inactivation of the virus by physical means, such as ultraviolet irradiation, has

the advantage that the inactivating agent is not incorporated in the vaccine. Tissue enzymes liberated from brain material used in the preparation of rabies vaccine undoubtedly have a deleterious effect on the antigenicity of the virus. The chemicals used for vaccine production possess some enzyme-inhibiting properties, but they also decrease the antigenicity of the virus if used in high concentrations.

Passive immunization against rabies by the administration of immune serum has been shown by Hoyt et al. (1938), Habel (1945), and Koprowski et al. (1950) to be effective in animals. The most extensive studies of the value of such treatment for the prevention of rabies in man are those of Shortt et al. (1935) and Covell et al. (1936). In an attempt to obtain clinical evidence of the efficacy of serum treatment, they limited its application to severely exposed persons; in rotation, three of every four severely bitten persons coming to the Pasteur Institute in Kasauli, India, received an injection of 20 cc. of immune serum on arrival which was followed by the regular treatment with Semple vaccine. Thus, 25 per cent of the severely exposed individuals received only the vaccine treatment. Of 584 persons treated with serum and vaccine, 12 or 2.05 per cent developed rabies as compared with 7 or 3.6 per cent of the 194 who were treated with vaccine alone. The failures following the use of both serum and vaccine, reported by Shortt et al. (1935), occurred in persons who presented themselves for treatment 2 or more days after exposure, and one would suspect that in such cases the use of immune serum would not be of much value. Proca et al. (1940) also observed a reduction in mortality by the combined use of immune serum and vaccine for the treatment of severely bitten persons.

There are only a few laboratories outside of France and the French colonies that continue to prepare vaccines from desiccated spinal cords. It has been found that rabbit brain is a much better source of fixed virus than is the spinal cord, and other methods of vaccine production are more practicable and economical.

On the basis of clinical evidence, there seems to be no doubt that rabies vaccine is effective in preventing the disease in the majority of the instances in which there is an expected incubation period of more than 1 month. Because local treatment may fail at times and since it usually takes several weeks for rabies to develop in man, it is advisable to resort to vaccination as an added safeguard. For persons known to have been bitten or scratched, vaccine treatment should be started immediately (1) when the animal is apprehended and presents clinical signs of rabies, (2) when the animal is killed and the brain is found positive for rabies by microscopic examination, (3) when the animal is killed, and, though the brain is negative by microscopic examination, the animal is suspected of being rabid, and (4) when a person is injured by a stray animal that escaped or by one that cannot be identified. Vaccine treatment is rarely indicated when there is no satisfactory evidence of a person having been bitten.

The Semple vaccine has been the one most commonly used in the United States. It is packaged in 7 or 14 doses of 2 cc. of 5 per cent or 0.5 cc. of 20 per cent rabbit-brain suspension in physiologic saline solution and contains 0.25 per cent phenol. The usual treatment consists of 14 daily injections of vaccine given into the subcutaneous tissue of the abdominal wall; a different site should be used for each injection.

The studies of Levinson et al. (1945) and Habel (1947) show that fixed virus inactivated by exposure to ultraviolet irradiation retains much of its antigenicity. The "U V" type vaccine is now licensed and available for clinical use. It is packaged in 7 doses of 2 cc. of 5 per cent or 1 cc. of 10 per cent rabbit-brain suspension in physiologic saline solution. Merthiolate is added as a preservative. It is a very effective vaccine.

The studies of Webster (1939) and others have shown that small doses of active fixed virus do not immunize animals and that the degree of immunity produced is proportional to the amount of virus given. Though the Semple and "U V" vaccines are very effective, the lyophilized active fixed virus vaccine has the advantage of eliminating the physical or chemical treatment which is necessary to inactivate the virus. Such procedures always induce some denaturation of antigen, and a liquid vaccine is not so stable as a lyophilized active virus vaccine.

Vaccine treatment should not be given unless there is good evidence of exposure to rabies. Sensitization to rabbit-brain tissues may produce serious allergic reactions. Acute reactions, such as syncope, generalized urticaria, or angioneurotic edema, may occur soon after an injection of vaccine in persons who have been sensitized by previous vaccination. Persons who have not been sensitized previously are not apt to show any reaction until seven or eight days after the first dose of vaccine. The most common reaction is the development of erythema and edema about the site of vaccination with accompanying pruritus and pain. These reactions tend to subside in a few days despite the continuation of treatment; however, in the 21-day treatment they may recur 15 to 16 days after the first dose of vaccine. If local reactions are accompanied by fever, headache, nausea, lymphadenopathy, and malaise, it is wise to stop the treatment. This type of reaction is uncommon, but usually precedes the development of more serious complications, such as encephalitis and paralysis. The paralytic phenomena, which may follow the administration of rabies vaccine, include peripheral neuritis, dorso-lumbar myelitis, and paralysis of Landry's type. Reactions characterized by paralysis seldom develop until five days after the first dose of vaccine, but may occur as late as two weeks after the completion of treatment. The peripheral neuritis most often involves the facial nerves, but other cranial nerves may be affected; recovery usually occurs in two or three weeks. Individuals who develop dorso-lumbar myelitis ordinarily recover. This reaction is characterized by fever and gradual onset of weakness, numbness, and tingling of the lower extremities; there may be urinary retention. In cases of paralysis of the Landry's type the onset is abrupt with high fever, headache, nausea, vomiting, girdle pain, urinary retention, and ascending paralysis. The paralysis may extend to involve the bulbar nuclei and terminate fatally. More often a patient recovers rapidly, though in rare instances there may be permanent disability. Acute encephalitis caused by vaccine is characterized by high fever, delirium, convulsions, and coma which may terminate in death. Nonfatal cases ordinarily recover without sequelae. Results of the studies of Stuart et al. (1928), Rivers et al. (1933), Morgan (1947), and Kabat et al. (1947) show that brain tissue functions as an organ-specific instead of a species-specific antigen. Paralysis caused by rabies vaccination must, therefore, be considered as a specific sensitization to brain material. Reactions of the paralytic type are most apt to occur in persons who have had a previous course of rabies vaccine (Horack, 1939; Sellers, 1947). A history of allergy in his immediate family can ordinarily be obtained from a patient who develops a reaction to the vaccine. McKendrick (1940) recorded 45 cases of vaccine paralysis, with 5 deaths, among 152,899 persons treated with vaccine prepared from desiccated spinal cords. There were 55 cases of vaccine paralysis, with 14 deaths, among 488,795 persons treated with vaccines containing phenol-inactivated virus. Sellers (1947) recorded 7 cases of vaccine paralysis among approximately 50,-000 persons treated with a phenol-treated vaccine containing active fixed virus; of these 7 cases, 5 occurred in persons who had been treated with rabies vaccine previously.

EPIDEMIOLOGY

There are two epidemiologic types of rabies, the natural disease as it occurs in wild animals and the urban type which is maintained in domestic dogs. The current world-wide distribution of rabies is due to the general popularity of dogs as pets. Domestic dogs revert easily to a semiwild or scavenger existence, and stray dogs increase rapidly in any urban community unless an organized effort is made to destroy them. The propagation of rabies in dogs is dependent to a large extent on the presence of many stray dogs in cities and towns.

The early history of rabies in Europe indicates that the disease was enzootic in wild animals in certain densely forested regions which served as starting points for recurrent migrating epizootics of the disease. The natural disease was limited by certain geographic barriers, such as mountain ranges and water, as well as by the abundance and distribution of suitable hosts capable of spreading the infection. Once established in domestic dogs, these limiting factors were much less effective, as dogs could travel with their masters from city to city and from country to country; furthermore, these animals were sufficiently numerous in any large city to maintain the disease once it was introduced. Thus, canine rabies was introduced into all thickly settled regions of Europe and into the European colonies in the western hemisphere. The disease in dogs reached its greatest intensity in Europe during the first half of the 19th century, and rabies in man reached epidemic proportions in some countries (Koch, 1930). For example, in Prussia there were from 200 to 260 human cases of rabies each year from 1800 to 1810. The most recent summary of the incidence of rabies in Europe is that of Koch (1930), who found that during 1924 and 1925 canine rabies was very prevalent in France, Germany, Italy, Austria, Hungary, Poland, Czechoslovakia, the Balkan countries, and the Union of Soviet Socialist Republics. The fox appears to be the principal wild-animal vector of rabies in western Europe, and seven major epizootics of the disease in this species were observed during the period from 1803 to 1925. The wolf is also an important host and vector of rabies in eastern Europe. Denmark, Norway, and Sweden have been free from rabies for more than 100 years. Rabies was eradicated from the British Isles in 1903. It became established again in England in 1918 by one or more dogs which were illegally imported. By 1922, Great Britain was again free from the disease, and no further outbreaks have occurred (Galloway, 1945). There have been no reported cases of rabies in the Netherlands or Switzerland for several years.

Rabies occurs in all sections of Asia. Canine rabies is very common in India, probably because of many semiwild dogs which are found in all sections of the country. The jackal is the principal wild host and vector in India, and the disease is enzootic in this species in the southern and northern parts of the country. The mongoose has a wide distribution in India, and animals of this species occasionally are found to be infected with rabies. The disease is enzootic among dogs throughout China and in Tibet, Burma, Thailand, French Indo-China, Netherlands Indies, and the Philippine Islands. In Japan, rabies has been effectively controlled by vaccination of dogs; in 1924 there were 3,205 proved cases of canine rabies and 235 persons died of the disease, while in 1932 only 63 cases of rabies were identified in dogs and no human cases were reported (McKendrick, 1933).

In Egypt and the Anglo-Egyptian Sudan, rabies is enzootic among jackals and is common in dogs. Canine rabies is relatively common in all the coastal cities of North Africa. The disease has been known for a long time in the South Kavirondo Province of Kenya, and occurred in epizootic proportions among jackals from 1912 to 1916 (Hudson, 1944). A disease of dogs, known as oulou fato, which exists in West Africa, has been identified as rabies, but it seems improbable that the dog is the principal host and vector of the disease in this region. At least, human rabies is seen rarely in

West Africa and the disease is not very common in dogs (Nicolau et al., 1933). Furthermore, the occurrence of paralytic rabies in dogs that are kept confined in compounds and not exposed to other dogs suggests that a small rodent may be the vector of the disease in some sections of West Africa. In 1949, a variety of rabies virus of the oulou-fato type was isolated in Elisabethville, Belgian Congo (Delville et al., 1950). In South Africa, rabies has become established in small veld carnivora (meercat type) belonging to the family of *Viverridae*. The disease was recognized for the first time in South Africa in 1892 when it appeared in dogs and cats in and around Port Elizabeth. In 1902, it appeared in dogs in southern Rhodesia and spread rapidly; preventive measures included the destruction of 40,000 dogs in that year and 60,000 the following year. Thereafter, the incidence of rabies remained low until 1911 when another severe outbreak occurred. Dog-control regulations were enforced for a period of 2 years, and after 1914 no further cases of rabies were observed in dogs. In 1929, there was one human case of rabies in the Orange Free State of South Africa, and during the same year a yellow mongoose (*Cynictus penicillata*) was proved to be infected with the disease. Subsequently, it was found that rabies was established in wild carnivora in Transvaal, Orange Free State, and Cape Province and that the yellow mongoose was the principal host and vector, although the stockstert (*Suricata suricatta*), wild cat (*Felina cafra*), and the pepper-and-salt meercat (*Myonax pulverulentus*) were found to be involved. There have been many outbreaks of rabies in cattle attributable to infection from the mongoose. Most of the human cases have occurred in children who were bitten when they attempted to pick up what appeared to be a tame meercat or mongoose. Rabies has not occurred in dogs during recent years, and a campaign of destruction of the wild vectors has reduced its incidence in man and domestic animals; nevertheless, there is little chance of eradicating the disease (Snyman, 1937) in this locality.

In North America, rabies has become increasingly prevalent since it was first recognized. It apparently was introduced by importation of dogs from Europe, and until 1800 was limited to the states along the eastern seaboard. By 1870 the disease had been reported in Greenland and had become prevalent in dogs in all densely settled regions east of the Mississippi River (Stimson, 1910). The disease did not become prevalent in dogs in California until 1898 (Geiger, 1916), and the appearance of rabies in coyotes of northern Mexico in 1892 (Seton, 1925) suggests that the disease was introduced into California from Mexico where historical archives contain references to rabies in man prior to 1800. The disease is known to have been epizootic in foxes in Massachusetts during the first decade of the 19th century (Thacher, 1812), in Alabama in 1890 (Wilkinson, 1894), and in Alaska in 1915 (Ferenbaugh, 1916). An epizootic of rabies in skunks, which began in Kansas in 1873, was responsible for the death of at least 40 persons, mostly cowboys and hunters, who were bitten by rabid skunks when camping on the plains (Seton, 1925). Another epizootic of skunk rabies occurred in Arizona; it began in 1907 and at least 10 persons died after they were bitten by infected skunks (Yount, 1910). The small spotted skunk of the genus *Spilogale* appears to have been the principal vector; these animals are often referred to as phobey cats in western United States, because they were known to have been the source of hydrophobia in human beings. In 1915 and 1916, rabies appeared in epizootic proportions in wild animals in California, Oregon, and Nevada (Mallory, 1915; Geiger, 1916), and, though the coyote appeared to be the most important vector, the disease was also identified in bobcats, mountain lions, skunks, and a wide variety of small wild animals. Coyotes were very abundant over a large region, and the disease persisted for many years despite an extensive campaign to reduce the number of known vectors. Large numbers of domestic animals died as a result of attacks by rabid coyotes. In Nevada, the disease was not eliminated from wild life until 1931, and it was necessary to destroy more than 89,000 coyotes, bobcats, and mountain lions and several thousand small animal vectors before this was accomplished (Records, 1932). Since 1940, rabies has again become prevalent in foxes of the United States; this vector is now so widely distributed that there is no immediate prospect of eradicating the disease from it. Repeated epizootics of fox rabies have occurred in North Carolina, South Carolina, Georgia, Alabama, Mississippi, and Louisiana, and the disease has been identified in foxes of 16 other states (Johnson, 1945a). The focus of fox rabies which developed in New York State in 1945 (Korns et al., 1948) is still active, although dog rabies has been controlled effectively since 1947.

In 1908, there were 111 human cases of rabies in the United States (Stimson, 1910). There are no official records of the annual mortality from rabies in this country prior to that year. Only 10 states were reported as being free from rabies in 1908; they were California, Idaho, Maine, Montana, Nevada, New Mexico, Oregon, Utah, Washington, and Wyoming. From 1908 to 1938 the annual human mortality from rabies varied from 33 to 103, with the lowest incidence in 1916 and the highest in 1928. In 1938, the Bureau of Animal Industry of the U. S. Department of Agriculture began collecting information as to the number of proved cases of rabies in animals. Table 15 shows the reported cases of rabies in human beings and animals in the United States during the period 1938-1949 (Brueckner, 1950).

Thirteen states were reported free from rabies during 1949, namely, Delaware, Idaho, Maine, Montana, Nevada, New Hampshire, North Dakota, Oregon, Rhode Island, Utah, Vermont, Washington and Wisconsin. Connecticut, Maryland, Massa-

TABLE 15. REPORTED CASES OF RABIES IN THE UNITED STATES, 1938-1949

YEAR	DOGS	CATTLE	HORSES	SHEEP	SWINE	CATS	GOATS	OTHER ANIMALS	MAN	TOTAL
1938	8,452	413	32	164	42	207	11	44	47	9,412
1939	7,386	358	36	17	38	269	10	172	30	8,316
1940	6,194	326	25	53	71	260	4	277	28	7,238
1941	6,648	418	39	68	159	294	9	212	30	7,877
1942	6,332	288	15	48	32	250	12	160	28	7,165
1943	8,515	349	35	45	60	316	19	310	41	9,690
1944	9,067	561	32	40	43	419	14	311	53	10,540
1945	8,505	487	46	11	30	466	10	373	35	9,963
1946	8,384	962	44	15	22	455	12	956	22	10,872
1947	6,949	766	40	15	20	393	9	728	26	8,946
1948	6,610	599	34	14	36	378	5	819	13	8,508
1949	5,237	639	24	22	54	413	6	1,192	10	7,597

chusetts, Minnesota, Nebraska, New Mexico and South Dakota were almost free from the disease. Though the majority of the wild animals found to be infected with rabies during 1949 belonged to the gray fox species, the disease was identified also in the coyote, rabbit, mouse, gopher, ground squirrel, rat, squirrel, skunk, wild cat, raccoon, opossum, muskrat and deer.

Canada appears to be free from rabies. There have been a few small outbreaks in the provinces of Ontario and Quebec during the past 15 years, when the disease was introduced from the United States, but these foci have been eliminated (Hall, 1940). Rabies was prevalent among arctic fox and sled dogs in the Northwest Territories in 1947 (Plummer, 1947a, 1947b). Vaccination of all dogs in the area was required, and the disease did not spread further among domestic dogs. There appears to be some association between lemming migrations and outbreaks of rabies in arctic fox.

Rabies is prevalent among dogs in most of the major cities of Mexico, and Central and South America. The discovery that vampire bats are infected with rabies in some sections of Mexico and South America is of considerable epidemiologic importance in that this animal may transmit rabies as a symptomless carrier. True vampire bats are found only in Mexico, Central and South America. The principal vector is *Desmodus rotundus murinus*-Wagner. Bats of this species are gray or reddish-brown with a body length of from 7 to 8 cm. and a wingspread of from 30 to 40 cm. They subsist solely on blood, which they lap up after inflicting a craterlike wound with their sharp incisor teeth. Members of the species are easily identified by their long thumbs, which are 19 to 20 mm. in length, a cleft lower lip, absence of a tail, and a poorly developed interfemoral membrane. They are known to feed on man when other hosts are scarce, and their ability to do so without awakening a victim is the source of numerous imaginative stories. The existence of rabies among vampire bats was recognized first in the state of Santa Catharina in southern Brazil. A paralytic disease of cattle and other livestock called *mal de caderas* appeared in epizootic form in that region in 1908. Some of the animals were proved to be infected with rabies virus (Carini, 1911), and, since rabies was prevalent in dogs, a vigorous program for the control of the disease in dogs was initiated, but it failed to affect the incidence and spread of the paralytic disease of cattle. From the beginning of the outbreak, ranchers had observed that bats were flying in the daytime and fighting one another, unusual phenomena, and that cattle bitten by bats during the day ordinarily developed paralysis and died within a few weeks. In 1916, a virus was isolated from a bat captured while feeding on cattle during the day (Haupt et al., 1921), and Negri bodies were demonstrated in the brains of rabbits and guinea pigs infected with this virus. On the basis of this finding, it was concluded that the repeated epizootics of paralytic rabies, which occurred in livestock in Brazil from 1908 to 1918, were due to infection induced by the bites of vampire bats.

In 1925, a paralytic disease of livestock appeared in and around Port-of-Spain, Trinidad, B.W.I. During the period from 1925 to 1929, several thousand animals died of the disease which was diagnosed as botulism. In 1929, in the village of Siparia, Trinidad, 13 persons died of acute ascending myelitis, which was diagnosed as acute anterior poliomyelitis. In 1930, there were 4 more fatal cases of ascending myelitis, and from one of these, brain tissue was submitted to The Rockefeller Institute in New York and the Lister Institute in London. Rabies virus was isolated from this material by workers in both laboratories (Hurst et al., 1931, 1932). There had been no canine rabies in Trinidad since 1914 and stringent quarantine regulations had been kept in force to prevent its importation. Furthermore, there had been no cases of suspected rabies in dogs coincident with the outbreaks of paralysis in cattle. Subsequently, it was shown that the vampire bat, *Desmodus rotundus murinus*-Wagner, was the vector of rabies in Trinidad. Rabies virus was isolated from the salivary glands of vampire bats, and cross-protection and serum-virus neutralization tests showed that the bat virus was closely related to the Pasteur strain of fixed rabies virus (Pawan, 1936a). A study of the disease in bats showed that some of them could transmit rabies by bite for as long as 83 days before dying. A high proportion of the experi-mentally infected bats developed signs of rabies following an incubation period of 9 to 38 days. With the onset of the disease, bats would often show excitement and viciousness, and these signs would persist for several days, following which animals would either recover or more often would develop progressive paralysis and die (Pawan, 1936b). An epidemiologic study of the disease in Trinidad indicated that it had been introduced by vampire bats which had migrated to Trinidad from South America. Fifty-five human cases of paralytic rabies were recorded. Control measures included immunization of livestock by means of rabies vaccine, bat-proofing of homes and stables, vaccination of persons bitten by bats, and destruction of vampire bats. These measures proved successful in eliminating the disease and no further outbreaks have been recorded in Trinidad (Verteuil et al., 1936).

During the period 1931-1934, there were repeated epizootics of paralytic rabies among livestock in the states of Santa Catharina and Matto Grosso, Brazil, and virus was isolated from naturally infected vampire bats (Torres et al., 1935). Epizootics of paralytic rabies in livestock have been observed in Paraguay, Uruguay, Brazil, Argentina, Venezuela and Mexico; the first sign of infection is usually sudden paralysis of the posterior quarters. The disease of livestock called derriengue, which has been prevalent in the Pacific coast states of Mexico for at least 37 years, has been shown to be due to infection with rabies virus transmitted by vampire bats. In the course of a field study in the State of Michoacan, Mexico, during 1944, active agents later identified as rabies virus (Giron, 1944; Johnson, 1948) were isolated from a paralyzed cow and from the salivary glands of vampire bats captured in a cave located near the place where cattle were dying of paralysis.

It is evident that rabies can flourish in any climate, because suitable hosts and vectors are present on all the major continents.

Rabies has not become established in Australia or Hawaii, but this appears to have been due to quarantine regulations which were in force prior to the development of large urban centers having the usual complement of dogs. The old superstition that dog days of July and August mark the season of maximal incidence of rabies is without scientific basis. Epizootics of rabies may develop during any season of the year; in the United States, however, the incidence of the disease is somewhat higher in the late winter and spring seasons than at other times (Table 14).

Periods of rapid geographic distribution of rabies have coincided with major wars or with mass movement of people. There is no evidence of racial differences in susceptibility to the disease. Female animals are as susceptible as males, and from this fact one might assume that a higher rate of infection in male human beings than in females is due to a more frequent exposure of the former. Most human cases of rabies occur in children, but this cannot be considered as evidence of a greater susceptibility in them than in adults; children are more liable to be bitten because of their fondness for playing with dogs and cats and their lack of defense if attacked.

While exceedingly rare, infection from man to man is possible. As maniacal and murderous activity is uncommon in human rabies and since heavy sedation is given routinely in such cases, there is little danger of a person obtaining the disease from an infected human being. Laboratory infections are uncommon and have occurred only when investigators or their assistants have been bitten by animals infected with the natural virus or when they have been accidentally injured while performing necropsies (Koch, 1930).

The attack rate of rabies in human beings bitten by rabid animals depends on several factors: for example, a rabid animal may not have virus in its salivary glands, protection provided by clothing may be so great that little or no virus enters the wound produced, and virus may be removed from open wounds by cleansing with soap and water. Susceptibility of man to rabies appears to be relatively great: Koch (1930), for example, cites Bauhin's observation that 9 of 12 persons were infected by the bites of one rabid wolf. Likewise, Fetherston et al. (1932) observed 4 cases of rabies in 8 sailors bitten on their hands by a stray dog which they had picked up in a Chinese port and taken on board a destroyer of the U. S. Navy. The danger of bites about the head and face is great as is shown by Kraus et al. (1926), who reported a mortality of 11 per cent for children and 3 per cent for adults bitten on the head by animals suspected of being rabid, despite treatment with vaccine. Of the first 214 patients with face bites treated at the Pasteur Institute in Paris, 12 or 5.6 per cent died of rabies despite vaccine treatment. A false sense of security is given by European statistics on vaccination against rabies, as they ordinarily include only the reduced mortality rate, which takes into account only those cases of rabies that develop 2 or more weeks after the completion of the treatment, the assumption being that those developing before that time do not represent failures of treatment. The most extensive statistics as to attack rate of rabies for man are those of Schuder which, as quoted by Kraus et al. (1926), list 1,325 deaths from rabies in a group of 14,959 persons bitten by rabid animals, a rate of 9 per cent. This information was obtained from records antedating vaccine treatment.

CONTROL MEASURES

Measures necessary for the eradication of rabies from domestic dogs have been known for more than 100 years; they are measures which prevent any dog from biting another for a period of the longest latency of the disease. Essential regulations include licensing of dogs and taxation of their owners, seizure and destruction of all stray dogs, quarantine or muzzling of all owned dogs while rabies prevails and for a period of at least 6 months after the last reported case, and subjection of all imported dogs to quarantine for 6 months. When rabies is prevalent in a community, any dog that has bitten a person should be confined in a veterinary hospital or dog pound for at least 7 days to allow observation for signs of rabies and to insure that the animal does not escape if it has rabies. When a rabid dog is discovered, every effort should be made to locate all other animals that were exposed to it so that they may be destroyed or kept in quarantine.

In order to eradicate rabies from a country, efforts must be co-ordinated so that control measures will be carried out at the same time in all infected regions. This requires centralized authority and makes for uniformity of methods. In Scandinavian countries, the British Isles, and Canada, where the disease has been eliminated, the Ministry of Agriculture was given the authority to carry out the necessary control provisions. There has been considerable criticism of quarantining imported dogs for 6 months; nevertheless, this provision is justified as shown by the fact that during the period of from 1919 to 1939, 16 cases of rabies were identified in dogs imported into England. Five of the 16 animals developed the disease 4 or more months after arrival in Great Britain, and one dog held for an additional period at the owner's request developed rabies 6 months and 24 days after arrival (Galloway, 1945).

In view of the fact that rabies is maintained solely in animals, primarily the dog, control work should be supervised by the Bureau of Animal Industry of the U. S. Department of Agriculture. As yet, this bureau does not have authority to enforce rabies control on a national basis. Under existing conditions, rabies control in the United States is under the jurisdiction of the State Health Department, the State Department of Agriculture, or both. For the most part, control work is conducted on a municipal or county basis, and is maintained only so long as an emergency exists.

Past experience has shown that the disease is apt to be of epizootic proportions in a locality before the state authorities are aware of the outbreak. It is the local veterinarian who will first learn of the presence of the disease, and he should be required to report immediately all suspected cases of rabies in dogs to the proper state official. In Canada, outbreaks of rabies are controlled entirely by quarantine restrictions, and all suspected cases of rabies are reported to the nearest veterinary inspector or to the veterinary director general of the department of agriculture.

Rabies in wild animals may be combatted by hunting and trapping. The U. S. Fish and Wildlife Service, division of predatory animal control, has trained personnel to supervise this type of work. If the hosts and vectors among the wild animals are drastically reduced in number in and around a focus of rabies, the disease cannot persist. If this is not done, the disease will kill most of the animals anyway, and in the meantime the infection will have spread to other regions.

The development of a vaccine for immunization of dogs by Umeno et al. (1921) has added another means for combating rabies. The Umeno and Doi vaccine was a modified Fermi vaccine in that it contained 0.5 per cent phenol. There was 20 per cent of brain tissue in the vaccine and glycerol was added as a preservative. The chemically treated virus was exposed to room temperature for two weeks or was held at refrigerator temperature for a month before use. The fixed virus may remain active for two or three months in this type of vaccine. Vaccination consisted of the subcutaneous injection of a single dose of 5 cc. of the vaccine; this was the equivalent of an entire course of vaccination in human beings. Results obtained in the large-scale use of the vaccine in dogs in Japan (Umeno et al., 1921; McKendrick, 1933) showed clearly that it was very effective. This type of vaccine was used on a large scale in the United States during the period from 1922 to 1928; it is estimated that more than 2,000,000 dogs were immunized. The studies of Eichhorn et al. (1924) confirmed the experimental work of the Japanese investigators. Since vaccination of dogs was not conducted by official agencies in the United States, it was impossible to obtain statistics regarding its effectiveness. One possible case of rabies caused by the vaccine was observed in approximately 30,000 dogs immunized in Japan, and in the United States it was observed that, in extremely rare instances, the vaccine could produce infection (Schoening, 1925). This led to a ruling by the U.S. Department of Agriculture that rabies vaccines used for immunization of dogs must contain no active virus as determined by standard safety tests. The fear of spreading rabies by vaccination of dogs with active, fixed virus was unjustified in that fixed virus does not propagate in salivary glands and is not found in saliva; furthermore, the disease produced in this way is uniformly of the paralytic type. In order to meet the requirement of safety tests, the commercial laboratories prepared a canine vaccine of the Semple type in which the concentration of brain tissue was 20 per cent. Results of experimental studies of immunization of animals with this vaccine were reported, and, since they were almost uniformly negative, immunization of dogs against rabies was criticized by medical and lay persons. The chloroform-treated vaccine of Kelser (1930) gained favor because of the clearcut positive results obtained in intramuscular potency tests conducted in rabbits. When tested in dogs this vaccine was found to produce a high degree of resistance to experimental inoculation; furthermore, if stored for as long as 16 months at refrigerator temperature, it still retained its immunizing capacity (Leach et al., 1942). Canine vaccine of the Semple type has been improved since the introduction of the mouse-potency test and has been shown to be an effective immunizing agent when tested in dogs; immunity produced by a single injection of the vaccine persists for at least a year (Johnson, 1945b; Korns et al., 1948). The Semple type vaccine is the only killed virus vaccine used extensively at the present time for the immunization of dogs. The newly developed chick-embryo-adapted living rabies virus vaccine (Flury) is now available for immunization of dogs. Laboratory studies and large-scale field trials have shown that this vaccine virus is nonpathogenic for dogs yet it produces a high grade of immunity (Koprowski, 1949; Cox, 1949; Tierkel et al., 1949).

Vaccination of dogs is recommended for use in places where quarantine of such animals cannot be enforced effectively or where the disease is present in wild animals. In order to be highly effective as a means of controlling rabies, vaccination of dogs must be combined with other control regulations such as licensing of all owned dogs and collection of all unlicensed dogs found at large. In order to secure prompt recession of the disease and simplify the collection of stray dogs, it is advisable to enforce a 90-day quarantine for all dogs. During this period owned dogs may be vaccinated, and, since some of these will have been exposed prior to vaccination, spread of the disease by such animals will be limited.

REFERENCES

Bernkopf, H., and Kligler, I. J., 1940, Characteristics of a fixed rabies virus cultivated on developing chick embryos. Proc. Soc. Exp. Biol. and Med., 45, 332-335.

Bouley, H., 1863, Rapport sur la rage. Bull. Acad. imp. méd., Paris, 28, 702-767.

Brueckner, A. L. (Chairman, Committee), 1950, Report of committee on rabies. Proc. 54th Annual Meeting U. S. Livestock San. Assn., 216-218.

Cabot, F., 1899, The cauterization of wounds infected with the virus of rabies after an interval of twenty-four hours. Med. News, 74, 329-331.

Calmette, A., 1891, Notes sur la rage en Indo-Chine. Ann. Inst. Pasteur, 5, 633-641.

Carini, A., 1911, Sur une grande épizootie de rage. Ann. Inst. Pasteur, 25, 843-846.

Casals, J., and Palacios, R., 1941, The complement fixation test in the diagnosis of virus infections of the central nervous system. J. Exp. Med., 74, 409-426.

Covell, G., McGuire, J. P., Stephens, E. D., and Lahiri, B. N., 1936, Notes on antirabic immunization. Indian J. Med. Res., *24*, 373-388.

Cox, H. R., Van der Scheer, J., Aiston, S., and Bohnel, E., 1947, The purification and concentration of influenza-virus by means of alcohol precipitation. J. Immunol., *56*, 149-166.

Cox, H. R., 1949, Review of chick-embryo adapted living rabies virus vaccines, with primary emphasis on use in dogs. Proc. 53rd Annual Meeting U. S. Livestock San. Assn., 264-272.

Cumming, J. G., 1914, Rabies-hydrophobia. J. Infect. Dis., *14*, 33-52.

Dawson, J. R., Jr., 1941, A study of chick-embryo-adapted rabies virus. Am. J. Path., *17*, 177-187.

Delville, J. P., and Jezierski, A., 1950, Isolement à partir d'un cerveau de chien d'un virus neurotrope pathogène pour de nombreuses espèces animales. Ann. Soc. Belge Méd. Trop., *30*, 405-409.

Eichhorn, A., and Lyon, B. M., 1924, Prophylactic rabies immunization by the one-injection method. J. Am. Vet. Med. Assn., *64*, 690-696.

Ekstrom, F. A., 1830, Rabies epidemic at Stockholm in 1824. London Med. Gaz., *6*, 689-691.

Ferenbaugh, T. L., 1916, A note concerning the occurrence of hydrophobia in the foxes of Alaska. Military Surg., Washington, *38*, 656-657.

Fermi, C., 1908, Uber die Immunisierung gegen Wutkrankheit. Ztschr. f. Hyg. u. Infektionskr., *58*, 233-276.

Fetherston, J. E., and Cooper, G. F., 1932, Rabies. Report of four deaths resulting from bites on the fingers by the same rabid animal. U. S. Naval Med Bull., *30*, 314-321.

Galloway, I. A., and Elford, W. J., 1936, Size of virus of rabies ("fixed" strain) by ultrafiltration analysis. J. Hyg., *36*, 532-535.

Galloway, I. A., 1945, Rabies. A review of recent articles. Trop. Dis. Bull., *42*, 674-683.

Galtier, V., 1879, Études sur la rage. Compt. rend. Acad. sci., *89*, 444-446.

Geiger, J. C., 1916, Is rabies under control in California? California State J. Med., *14*, 58-60.

Giron, A. T., 1944, El vampiro portador de virus del derriengue. Revista de la Soc. Mexicana Hist. Natural, *5*, 35-42.

Goodpasture, E. W., 1925, A study of rabies. Am. J. Path., *1*, 547-582.

Habel, K., 1940, Evaluation of a mouse test for the standardization of the immunizing power of antirabies vaccines. Pub. Health Rep., *55*, 1473-1487.

Habel, K., 1945, Seroprophylaxis in experimental rabies. Pub. Heath Rep., *60*, 545-560.

Habel, K., 1947, Ultraviolet irradiation in the production of potent antirabies vaccines. Pub. Health Rep., *62*, 791-800.

Habel, K., and Wright, J. T., 1948, Some factors influencing the mouse potency test for rabies vaccine. Pub. Health Rep., *63*, 44-55.

Hall, O., 1940, Rabies. Canad. J. Comp. Med., *4*, 146-149.

Harris, D. L., and Shackell, L. F., 1911, The effect of vacuum desiccation on the virus of rabies, with remarks on a new method. J. Infect. Dis., *8*, 47-49.

Harvey, W. F., and Acton, H. W., 1923, An examination into the degree of efficacy of anti-rabic treatment. Indian J. Med. Res., *10*, 1020-1077.

Haupt, H., and Rehaag, H., 1921, Durch Fledermäuse verbreitete seuchenhafte Tollwut unter Viehbeständen in Santa Catharina (Süd-Brasilien). Ztschr. f. Infektionskr., *22*, 104-127.

Hodes, H. L., Webster, L. T., and Lavin, G. I., 1940, The use of ultraviolet light in preparing a non-virulent antirabies vaccine. J. Exp. Med., *72*, 437-444.

Högyes, A., 1897, Lyssa, *in* Nothnagel, H., Spezielle Pathologie und Therapie, Alfred Holder, Wien., v. 5, pt. 5. Abt. 2, 1-240.

Horack, H. M., 1939, Allergy as a factor in the development of reactions to antirabic treatment. Am. J. Med. Sci., *197*, 672-682.

Hoyt, A., and Jungeblut, C. W., 1930, Experimental rabies in white mice and attempted chemotherapy. J. Infect. Dis., *47*, 418-424.

Hoyt, A., and Gurley, M. K., 1938, Experimental street virus rabies in white mice. Studies on passive immunization. II. Proc. Soc. Exp. Biol. and Med., *38*, 40-42.

Hudson, J. R., 1944, A short note on the history of rabies in Kenya. East African Med. J., *21*, 322-327.

Hurst, E. W., and Pawan, J. L., 1931, An outbreak of rabies in Trinidad. Lancet, *2*, 622-628.

Hurst, E. W., and Pawan, J. L., 1932, A further account of the Trinidad outbreak of acute rabic myelitis. J. Path. and Bact., *35*, 301-321.

Johnson, H. N., and Leach, C. N., 1940, Comparative susceptibility of different strains of mice to rabies virus. Am. J. Hyg., Sect. B, *32*, 38-45.

Johnson, H. N., 1942, The significance of the Negri body in the diagnosis and epidemiology of rabies. Illinois Med. J., *81*, 382-388.

Johnson, H. N., 1945a, Fox rabies. J. Med. Assn. Alabama, *14*, 268-271.

Johnson, H. N., 1945b, Experimental and field studies of canine rabies vaccination. Proc. 49th Annual Meeting U. S. Livestock San. Assn., 99-107.

Johnson, H. N., 1948, Derriengue. Vampire bat rabies in Mexico, Am. J. Hyg., *47*, 189-204.

Kabat, E. A., Wolf, A., and Bezer, A. E., 1947, The rapid production of acute disseminated encephalomyelitis in *rhesus* monkeys by injection of heterologous and homologous brain tissue with adjuvants. J. Exp. Med., *85*, 117-130.

Kanazawa, K., 1936, Sur la culture in vitro du virus de la rage. Japanese J. Exp. Med., *14*, 519-522.

Kelser, R. A., 1930, Chloroform-treated rabies vaccine. J. Am. Vet. Med. Assn., *77*, 595-603.

Kligler, I. J., and Bernkopf, H., 1938, Cultivation of rabies virus in the allantois of the developing chick embryo. Proc. Soc. Exp. Biol. and Med., *39*, 212-214.

Kligler, I. J., and Bernkopf, H., 1941, Studies on the cultivation and antigenic characters of rabies virus. Am. J. Hyg., Sect. B, *33*, 1-8.

Koch, J., 1930, Lyssa, *in* Kolle, W., Kraus, R., and Uhlenhuth, P.: Handbuch der pathogenen Mikroorganismen ed. 3. Jena, Fischer, Vol. 8, 547-673.

Koprowski, H., and Cox, H. R., 1948, Studies on chick embryo adapted rabies virus. I. Culture characteristics and pathogenicity. J. Immunol., 60, 533-554.

Koprowski, H., 1949, Experimental studies of rabies virus. Canad. J. Pub. Health, 40, 60-67.

Koprowski, H., Scheer, J. van der, and Black, J., 1950, Use of hyperimmune antirabies serum concentrates in experimental rabies. Am. J. Med., 8, 412-420.

Korns, R. F., and Zeissig, A., 1948, Dog, fox, and cattle rabies in New York State. Evaluation of vaccination in dogs. Am. J. Pub. Health, 38, 50-65.

Kraus, R., Gerlach, F., and Schweinburg, F., 1926, Lyssa bei Mensch und Tier. Berlin, Urban.

Leach, C. N., and Johnson, H. N., 1940, Human rabies, with special reference to virus distribution and titer. Am. J. Trop. Med., 20, 335-340.

Leach, C. N., and Johnson, H. N., 1942, Effect of prolonged storage on the antigenicity of chloroform-inactivated canine rabies vaccine. Am. J. Pub. Health, 32, 1380-1382.

Levinson, S. O., Milzer, A., Shaughnessy, H. J., Neal, J. L., and Oppenheimer, F., 1945, A new method for the production of potent inactivated vaccines with ultraviolet irradiation. II. Sterilization of bacteria and immunization with rabies and St. Louis encephalitis vaccines. J. Immunol., 50, 317-329.

Mallory, F. B., 1938, Pathological Technique. Philadelphia, Saunders.

Mallory, L. B., 1915, Campaign against rabies in Modoc and Lassen counties, California. California State Board Health Bull., 11, 273-277.

McKendrick, A. G., 1933, Rabies. A review of recent articles. Trop. Dis. Bull., 30, 575-587.

McKendrick, A. G., 1940, A ninth analytical review of reports from Pasteur Institutes on the results of anti-rabies treatment. Bull. Health Organ., League of Nations, 9, 31-78.

Morgan, I. M., 1947, Allergic encephalomyelitis in monkeys in response to injection of normal monkey nervous tissue. J. Exp. Med., 85, 131-140.

Mullett, C. F., 1945, Hydrophobia, its history in England to 1800. Bull. Hist. Med., 18, 44-65.

Negri, A., 1903, Beitrag zum Studium der Aetiologie der Tollwuth. Ztschr. f. Hyg. u. Infektionskr., 43, 507-528.

Negri, A., 1907, Sulla morfologia e sul ciclo evolutivo del parassita della rabbia. Rendiconti della R. Accad. dei Lincei, 16, 800-810.

Nicolas, M. J., 1906, Apparition de la virulence dans la salive mixte des animaux rabiques. Compt. rend. Soc. biol., 60, 625-626.

Nicolau, S., Mathis, C., and Constantinesco, V., 1933, La rage autochtone (maladie du chien fou) en Afrique occidentale française (étude critique et expérimentale). Ann. Inst. Pasteur, 50, 778-839.

Pasteur, L., Chamberland and Roux, 1881a, Sur une maladie nouvelle, provoquée par la salive d'un enfant mort de la rage. Compt. rend. Acad. sci., 92, 159-165.

Pasteur, L., Chamberland, Roux, and Thuillier, 1881b, Sur la rage. Compt. rend. Acad. sci., 92, 1259-1260.

Pasteur, L., Chamberland and Roux, 1884, Nouvelle communication sur la rage. Compt. rend. Acad. sci., 98, 457-463.

Pasteur, L., 1885, Méthode pour prévenir la rage après morsure. Compt. rend. Acad. sci., 101, 765-772.

Pawan, J. L., 1936a, The transmission of paralytic rabies in Trinidad by the vampire bat (Desmodus rotundus murinus Wagner, 1840). Ann. Trop. Med. and Parasitol., 30, 101-130.

Pawan, J. L., 1936b, Rabies in the vampire bat of Trinidad, with special reference to the clinical course and the latency of infection. Ann. Trop. Med. and Parasitol., 30, 401-422.

Plummer, P. J. G., 1947a, Preliminary note on arctic dog disease and its relationship to rabies. Canad. J. Comp. Med., 11, 154-160.

Plummer, P. J. G., 1947b, Further note on arctic dog disease and its relationship to rabies. Canad. J. Comp. Med., 11, 330-334.

Poor, D. W., 1911, The late cauterization by means of nitric acid of wounds infected with rabies virus. Collected studies from the Research Laboratory, Department of Health, City of New York, 6, 25.

Proca, G., and Bobes, S., 1940, Anti-rabic immunisation: living vaccines and killed vaccines. Bull. Health Organ., League of Nations, 9, 79-130.

Records, E., 1932, Rabies. Its history in Nevada. California and West. Med., 37, 90-94.

Reed, L. J., and Muench, H., 1938, A simple method of estimating fifty per cent endpoints. Am. J. Hyg., 27, 493-497.

Remlinger, P., 1903, Le passage du virus rabique à travers les filtres. Ann. Inst. Pasteur, 17, 834-849.

Remlinger, P., 1907, Persistence du virus rabique dans la salive du chien guéri de la rage. Compt. rend. Soc. biol., 62, 800-802.

Remlinger, P., 1919, Action de l'éther sur le virus rabique. Ann. Inst. Pasteur, 33, 616-633.

Remlinger, P., 1935, La rage dite de laboratoire. Ann. Inst. Pasteur, 55, (Suppl.), 35-68.

Rivers, T. M., Sprunt, D. H., and Berry, G. P., 1933, Observations on attempts to produce acute disseminated encephalomyelitis in monkeys. J. Exp. Med., 58, 39-53.

Rosenau, M. J., 1935, Preventive Medicine and Hygiene. ed. 6, New York, Appleton, p. 353.

Roux, E., 1887, Note sur un moyen de conserver les moelles rabiques avec leur virulence. Ann. Inst. Pasteur, 1, 87.

Schoening, H. W., 1925, Studies on the single-injection method of vaccination as a prophylactic against rabies in dogs. J. Agricultural Research, 30, 431-439.

Schoening, H. W., 1946, Report of the committee on rabies. Proc. 50th Annual Meeting U. S. Livestock San. Assn., 39-42.

Sellers, T. F., 1923, A simple modification of Högyes dilution method of preparing antirabic treatment. Am. J. Pub. Health, 13, 813-815.

Sellers, T. F., 1927, A new method for staining Negri bodies of rabies. Am. J. Pub. Health, 17, 1080-1081.

Sellers, T. F., 1947, Complications of antirabic treatment. J. Med. Assn. Georgia, 36, 30-35.

Semple, D., 1919, On the nature of rabies and antirabic treatment. Brit. Med. J., 2, 333-336.

Seton, E. T., 1925, Lives of Game Animals. Doubleday, Doran, Garden City, 1, 2.

Shaughnessy, H. J., and Zichis, J., 1943, Prevention of experimental rabies. J. Am. Med. Assn., 123, 528-533.

Shortt, H. E., McGuire, J. P., Brooks, A. G., and Stephens, E. D., 1935, Anti-rabic immunization: Probable lines of progress in improvement of methods. Indian J. Med. Res., *22*, 537-556.

Shortt, H. E., McGuire, J. P., Brooks, A. G., Stephens, E. D., and Lahiri, B. N., 1937, The relative immunizing values of different forms of antirabic vaccine and the duration of immunity in experimentally immunized animals. Indian J. Med. Res., *25*, 483-497.

Snyman, P. S., 1937, Rabies in South Africa. J. South African Vet. Med. Assn., *8*, 126-133.

Stimson, A. M., 1910, Facts and Problems of Rabies. Government Printing Office, Washington, D. C. (Hyg. Lab. Bull. 65).

Stuart, G., and Krikorian, K. S., 1928, The neuroparalytic accidents of anti-rabies treatment. Ann. Trop. Med. and Parasitol, *22*, 327-377.

Tardieu, M., 1863, Rapport sur la rage. Bull. Acad. imp. méd., Paris, *28*, 1146-1162.

Thacher, J., 1812, Observations on Hydrophobia. Joseph Arey, Plymouth, Mass.

Tierkel, E. S., Koprowski, H., Black, J., and Gorrie, R. H., 1949, Preliminary observations in the comparative prophylactic vaccination of dogs against rabies with living virus vaccines and phenolized vaccine. Am. J. Vet. Res., *10*, 361-367.

Torres, S., and Lima, E. de Queiroz, 1935, A raiva nos morcegos hematophagos (Desmodus rotundus murinus). Revista do Departamento Nacional da Producção Animal. Rio de Janeiro, *2*, 385-398.

Umeno, S., and Doi, Y., 1921, A study on the antirabic inoculation of dogs. Kitasato Arch. Exp. Med., *4*, 89-108.

Verteuil, E. de, and Urich, F. W., 1936, The study and control of paralytic rabies transmitted by bats in Trinidad, British West Indies. Trans. Roy. Soc. Trop. Med. and Hyg., *29*, 317-347.

Webster, L. T., and Dawson, J. R., Jr., 1935, Early diagnosis of rabies by mouse inoculation. Measurement of humoral immunity to rabies by mouse protection test. Proc. Soc. Exp. Biol. and Med., *32*, 570-573.

Webster, L. T., 1936, Diagnostic and immunological tests of rabies in mice. Am. J. Pub. Health, *26*, 1207-1210.

Webster, L. T., and Clow, A. D., 1936, Propagation of rabies virus in tissue culture and the successful use of culture virus as an antirabic vaccine. Science, *84*, 487-488.

Webster, L. T., 1939, A mouse test for measuring the immunizing potency of antirabies vaccines. J. Exp. Med., *70*, 87-106.

Webster, L. T., 1942, Rabies. Macmillan, New York.

Wilkinson, D. L., 1894, Rabies and hydrophobia in Alabama. Alabama Med. & Surg. Age, *6*, 557-584.

Yount, C. E., 1910, Rabies, with reports of cases from skunk bites. South. California Pract., *25*, 105-116.

HOWARD A. HOWE, M.D.

Poliomyelitis Laboratory, The Johns Hopkins University

13

Poliomyelitis

(SYNONYMS: Acute anterior poliomyelitis, infantile paralysis, Heine-Medin disease, *Kinderlähmung, poliomyélite*)

INTRODUCTION

Poliomyelitis is a common virus disease which usually runs a mild course characterized by upper respiratory or gastro-intestinal symptoms, but occasionally the picture is complicated by signs indicating invasion of the CNS. Under the latter conditions the virus is widely disseminated through the neuraxis but the clinical picture of the disease is dominated by flaccid paralysis of voluntary muscles resulting from destruction of motor neurons in the spinal cord.

HISTORY

Although the disease was clearly recognized during the latter part of the 18th century, the first systematic description of it was made by Heine in 1840. During the next 50 years, many cases of infantile paralysis were recorded in the literature, but Medin's account in 1891 was the first chronicle of an epidemic of any magnitude (44 cases). While there is no doubt that poliomyelitis has existed from antiquity, it is conceivable, for reasons which will be discussed later, that the disease was gradually changing from an endemic to an epidemic status during the 19th century, and that the Stockholm epidemic of 1887, described by Medin, was possibly the first outbreak of paralytic poliomyelitis to occur on a sufficiently large scale to attract notice. Wickman (1913) who studied an epidemic in Sweden in 1905 was the first to marshal evidence of the infectious nature of poliomyelitis and show a chain of transmission from one person to another. Landsteiner and Popper (1909) succeeded in producing a febrile illness characterized by flaccid paralysis in a monkey by the injection of an emulsion of the spinal cord from a fatal case of poliomyelitis. Shortly after the finding of a suitable experimental animal, a virus was demonstrated to be the cause of the disease and the foundation for modern investigations was laid.

CLINICAL PICTURE

The incubation period of poliomyelitis is not definitely known, but it probably ranges from 5 to 35 days, with the majority of the cases occurring 7 to 14 days after exposure. The disease may simulate a mild upper respiratory infection, with headache or a nonexudative pharyngitis, or it can be ushered in by what appears to be a simple gastro-intestinal disturbance with nausea and vomiting. Constipation is much commoner, however, than diarrhea. Fever is almost invariably present. There may be a slight polymorphonuclear leukocytosis. This mild syndrome may be present without other localizing signs and in itself constitutes evidence of infection with poliomyelitis virus. However, it cannot be diagnosed as such outside of an epidemic setting except by the isolation of virus or by a demonstration in paired sera of increase in antibody titer against the virus concerned. The latter has rarely been done. Even in a family where paralytic poliomyelitis exists, these minor illnesses cannot be classified as poliomyelitis with complete assurance in the absence of virus studies. Yet epidemiologic evidence shows beyond doubt that most poliomyelitis infections do not produce paralysis or even symptoms referable to the CNS. This phase of poliomyelitis infection may subside entirely or reappear in a few days (dromedary type), or progress during the next few hours into a condition in which CNS signs play a role. These may be nothing more than pain and stiffness in the muscles of the axial skeleton, chiefly those of the neck and the back, with increased discomfort when an attempt is made to place the chin on the chest. There is frequently increased tone in the hamstring muscles, and extension of the knee with the thigh flexed produces painful spasm (Kernig's sign). Slight retraction of the neck may also be observed so that when a patient is raised the head drops back as though the anterior neck muscles were weak. Lumbar puncture at this stage usually shows an increase in the amount of protein and in the number of granulocytes or lymphocytes in the cerebrospinal fluid. This syndrome constitutes nonparalytic poliomyelitis and may mark the clinical maximum of the infection. On the other hand, these signs may represent the prelude to paresis or paralysis. Premonitory signs of the latter are increasing muscle tenderness and stiffness, sometimes accompanied by fibrillary twitching. Cutaneous paresthesias are not uncommon but are usually mild. A patient is frequently drowsy, the face is flushed, and there may be profuse sweating. When paralysis or weakness is apparent a mononuclear pleocytosis is nearly always present in the CSF, but the counts are low,

ranging from 15 to 200 cells per c.mm. and seldom exceeding 400 or 500. Increased protein is usually demonstrable and persists for some weeks after the cell count has returned to normal (Gammon et al., 1948). The amount of sugar in the CSF is normal. The colloidal gold curve is often shifted to the left, but shows nothing peculiar to poliomyelitis. Horstmann (1949) reported that, in two large epidemics studied by the Yale Group, the onset of CNS signs was sudden in the majority of children under 9 years of age, while the reverse was true in older persons. Pain as an initial symptom was found to be twice as frequent in persons over 15 years of age as in younger people.

Fever may subside shortly before or after the appearance of paralysis and seldom persists for more than three or four days in the absence of intercurrent infection. Paralysis is of the flaccid lower motor neuron type with diminution or abolition of tendon reflexes. The final picture presented by a patient usually is a mixture of hypertonia and hypotonia of the muscles. Hypotonia and complete flaccidity dominate in proportion to the loss of function in the lower motor neurons, while hypertonia may be apparent in muscles where the effector portion of the reflex arc is still sufficiently intact to discharge impulses to them. Pollock et al. (1950), who repeatedly examined 481 patients during the early stages of clinically apparent involvement of the CNS, report that early disappearance of abdominal reflexes presaged severe paralysis of one or both legs in 85 per cent of them. While it is customary to speak of involvement of various muscle groups, this is, of course, secondary to interference with their innervation. There is no evidence that poliomyelitis viruses act directly upon muscle fibers.

About half of the paralyzed patients show involvement of the legs alone, and from 80 to 90 per cent have leg paralysis in conjunction with that of arms, trunk, etc. Isolated paralysis of arms is relatively rare (about 10 per cent). The muscles most commonly involved in the arm are those of the shoulder girdle, but the opponens pollicis is affected more frequently than are the muscles of the forearm. In the leg, the muscles of the hip are more frequently affected than those of the lower leg, with the intrinsic muscles of the foot least involved (Nitshke, 1950). It must be recognized, however, that these patterns are not invariable, depending to some degree on the age of the patient and the strain of virus. Paralyses of the diaphragm and of intercostal, abdominal or back muscles, or muscles supplied by cranial nerves are less common than are those of the limbs.

The clinical picture of poliomyelitis was very ably discussed by Peabody, Draper and Dochez in 1912, and little has been added to their observations except greater emphasis on the so-called spasm of unparalyzed or partially paralyzed muscles. This clinical entity, in reality a hyperirritable stretch reflex, is most commonly seen in the hamstrings and the muscles of the axial skeleton, but is less intense than that which accompanies true meningitis. Spasm may affect many other muscles, however, and not infrequently constitutes a block to movement which is resolved with difficulty. There is considerable disagreement among clinicians regarding the frequency of spasm; this is apparently based upon the fact that it varies quantitatively in different epidemics. See Pollock et al. (1949) and Caughey and Malcolm (1950) for opposing views.

Signs of destructive or irritative processes in the autonomic nervous system are not infrequent. In addition to sweating, urinary retention is by no means rare. It is self-limiting and usually subsides in a few days, but is said to respond favorably to certain drugs which will be discussed under treatment. Obstinate constipation is almost always the rule but does not persist for extended periods. Transient hypertension and changes in the electrocardiogram have been described (Bradford and Anderson, 1950). A more common complication is cyanosis, edema, and coldness of extremities, particu-

larly the lower ones. Transient diminution in cutaneous sweating, as measured by increased skin resistance, has also been described (Brown and Bruesch, 1949). Hypertrichosis of severely paralyzed limbs has been noted. Some patients with bulbar poliomyelitis show signs of involvement of vasomotor centers of the brainstem as evidenced by flushing of the skin, rapid pulse, or cardiac disturbances such as arrhythmia, or sudden arrest (Brown et al., 1947a). Failure of peripheral vasodilator mechanisms has also been described (Lundbaek, 1943).

Paralysis appears during the febrile period or as it is subsiding. Of 148 patients, Lassen and Skinhøj (1948) found that 83 per cent were paralyzed before the fifth day after the onset of the meningeal phase; only 5 per cent showed progression of paralysis after the temperature became normal; in the majority of patients, 71 per cent, paralysis increased for 24 hours or less after its initial appearance. From the time that paralysis is no longer progressive, the titer of virus in the spinal cord falls very rapidly and becomes negligible within a week (Bodian and Cumberland, 1947). A patient may, however, continue to eliminate virus in the stools for a much longer period, even though the disease in the CNS is probably arrested. Also, a patient may continue to have muscle spasm and tenderness for weeks and even months, although these are not in themselves necessarily an indication of continued virus activity. Relapses have been recorded but are not well documented. It is not uncommon, however, for patients to suffer exacerbation of weakness during unrelated febrile illnesses.

The clinical features of poliomyelitis may be summarized in the following manner. The disease has a wide range of manifestations and severity. While it is possible for human beings to harbor the virus in their throats or intestinal tracts without any consciousness of illness, it is difficult to say that these episodes are true infections leading to immunity, although this sequence has been repeatedly demonstrated in chimpanzees (Melnick and Horstmann, 1947; Howe et al., 1950). The generally recognized forms of human poliomyelitis are the abortive, the nonparalytic and the paralytic. The abortive type may equally well be called a minor illness, since there is nothing about its symptomatology which is unique to poliomyelitis. Nonparalytic poliomyelitis, on the other hand, is a syndrome in which there is evidence of invasion of the CNS without localizing signs beyond those of meningeal irritation and abnormally high cell counts in the spinal fluid. While the latter is certainly not always present, it must be insisted that, for the sake of uniformity in diagnosis and reporting, this sign be present.

ground of the various manifestations of the disease will be discussed.

There are many imperfectly understood factors which determine the severity of poliomyelitis. While the dose of virus is doubtless of importance, it is difficult to document this in human disease. Certainly there is also great variability in the severity of the disease induced by different strains of virus in experimental animals, and it is likely that the same is true in man. Excessive chilling and exercise are said to increase the susceptibility of monkeys to the virus administered intracerebrally, and Russell (1947) and Horstmann (1950) have presented evidence that fatigue in the nor-

TABLE 16. RECOVERY FROM POLIOMYELITIS IN RELATION TO AGE (AFTER LENHARD, 1950)

AGE	GOOD RECOVERY	PER CENT OF TOTAL	POOR RECOVERY	PER CENT OF TOTAL	DEATH	PER CENT OF TOTAL	TOTAL CASES
0-4	68	82	13	15.5	2	2.5	83
5-9	108	82.5	20	13.5	3	2.3	131
10-14	80	82	14	14.3	4	4.1	98
15-19	33	59	20	35.7	3	5.3	56
20+	19	51.4	14	38	4	10.7	37
All	308	76	81	20	16	4.	405

formity in diagnosis and reporting, this sign be present.

Even paralytic poliomyelitis is often not a clearly defined clinical entity, since such signs as excitement, apprehension, disorientation and coma are not infrequently more conspicuous in the early stages than paralysis. In fact, each patient presents a mixture of signs and symptoms indicative of damage to various parts of the CNS. Thus, disturbances of consciousness, flaccid paralysis, weakness, in-co-ordination, spasticity, muscle tenderness, hyperesthesia, or various combinations of these phenomena may be observed in one patient. No useful purpose appears to be served by separating cases of poliomyelitis into various clinical types as has been done in the past. Instead, in the section on pathology, the anatomic back-

mal physiologic range predisposes to paralysis in man. The fatigue, however, must be experienced after signs of CNS involvement have appeared. Furthermore, Brahdy and Katz (1951) have reported that the case-fatality rate in patients admitted to the Willard Parker Hospital, New York City, was nearly three times higher in patients transported long distances (average of 85 miles) than in local patients.

There is no longer doubt that age plays a role in determining the severity of paralysis. Table 16, modified from Lenhard (1950), shows clearly the increase in severe disability and case-fatality rate with increasing age. The latter trend is dramatically demonstrated by Olin's (1952) figures based upon 3,602 deaths during 4 decades in Sweden; fatality rates for adults over

25 years were from 2 to 5 times greater than for children under 7 years. This is particularly true for the bulbar form as shown in Table 17 (Longshore et al., 1951) for 1,138 cases collected during 1948-49 by the California State Department of Public Health. Children under 5 years had a 22 per cent mortality rate, while, in patients 15 years of age and over, the rate rose to 47 per cent. While mortality from spinal paralysis was low, it, nevertheless, was roughly 5 times higher in patients over 15 years of age than in those under 5.

That the type of disease may also be conditioned by age is shown by the data of Longshore et al. (1951). Only 19 per cent of

pertussis and diphtheria vaccines) within a period of 35 days before their appearance (Hill and Knowelden, 1950). According to reports, this occurred very largely in children under 3 years, and it is by no means clear that the immunization procedures increased the incidence of paralysis, although they may have been a factor in localizing it. In any event, attack rates are so low in children of this age group that any additional risk is insignificant compared with that of interrupting a pertussis or diphtheria immunization program.

Although inanition seems to increase the resistance of mice to the Lansing strain of virus inoculated intracerebrally (Foster et

TABLE 17. POLIOMYELITIS IN CALIFORNIA 1948-1949 (AFTER LONGSHORE, EDWARDS AND HOLLISTER, 1951)

	BULBAR AND BULBO-SPINAL				SPINAL				TOTAL CASES
		PER CENT OF				PER CENT OF			
AGE	CASES	P. CASES	DEATHS	C.F.R.	CASES	P. CASES	DEATHS	C.F.R.	
0-4 ...	292	19.0	65	22.3	1,240	81	4	0.3	1,532
5-9 ...	302	26.1	62	20.5	854	73.9	2	0.2	1,156
10-14 ..	133	28.4	42	31.6	335	71.6	3	0.9	468
15-24 ..	166	28.4	76	45.8	419	71.6	8	1.9	585
25+ ...	245	34.0	117	47.7	476	66.0	5	1.0	721
Total ..	1,138	25.5	362	31.8	3,324	74.5	22	0.7	4,462

the patients under 5 years had the bulbar type, while those with this type made up 34 per cent of the group over 24 years of age. Olin's very impressive tabulation of 15,303 carefully investigated paralytic cases shows an even more striking percentage of patients with respiratory difficulty in the higher age groups. Conversely, there was an almost equally marked preponderance of leg paralysis in young children. Arm, trunk and cranial nerve paralyses were equally distributed in the different age groups. Greenberg's (1951) figures for 2,446 cases in New York City during 1949 are much less dramatic but show a similar trend as regards bulbar poliomyelitis.

Localization of paralyses seems to be influenced in some obscure fashion by the administration of antigenic materials (chiefly

al., 1944), and certain vitamin deficiencies appear to enhance it in monkeys (Bodian, 1948a), it is difficult to apply these findings to human disease. Evidence has been advanced for genetic factors which predispose to paralysis in family lines (Aycock, 1942a; Addair and Snyder, 1942), but attempts to correlate paralytic poliomyelitis with constitutional or endocrinologic types are much less convincing; this is true in spite of the fact that cortisone or ACTH appear to enhance the susceptibility of certain laboratory animals to the Lansing strain of virus (Shwartzman, 1950).

PATHOLOGIC PICTURE

In asymptomatic carriers and in patients with abortive poliomyelitis, virus localizes and probably multiplies primarily in the alimentary tract from which it is shed in the oropharyngeal secretions and stools. It is not known whether the myenteric plexuses or other elements of the intestinal wall are invaded. At any rate, it is unlikely that the virus propagates in the intestinal contents, or that its invasion extends as far as the CNS. While hypertrophy of Peyer's patches has been described, its relationship to the disease is far from clear. Patients with nonparalytic and abortive poliomyelitis show the same alimentary localization of virus, but, in addition, evidence of varying degrees of invasion of the CNS. There is frequently a nonexudative pharyngitis which occasions no discomfort to a patient but suggests the pharyngeal mucosa as a site of early virus proliferation (Horstmann, 1949—see below). Rarely has virus been demonstrated in lymph glands or in the blood, but recent findings of early viremia in orally inoculated monkeys and chimpanzees (Horstmann, 1952; Bodian, 1952a) suggest that the preparalytic period has not been sufficiently studied in man. At any rate, no characteristic lesions are found outside the nervous system except in the voluntary muscles where changes are secondary to nerve degeneration. Observations of myocardial lesions (Peale and Lucchesi, 1943) do not appear to be controlled in an adequate manner.

It has recently been shown by Enders et al. (1949) that poliomyelitis virus can be propagated in cultures containing viable bits of human embryonic muscle, skin, gut or CNS. It has also been possible to grow virus in cultures of other tissues; foreskin obtained postnatally (Weller et al., 1949), monkey testes (Scherer et al., 1951; Evans et al., 1951) and certain tumors of human testicular tissue (Smith et al., 1951). Since cells in tissue cultures invariably undergo varying degrees of change from normal, it is not clear to what extent these findings describe the growth characteristics of poliomyelitis virus in the postnatal primate. A great body of evidence has now been accumulated from experiments on monkeys and chimpanzees which shows that the virus is highly neurotropic and that it spreads centripetally and to some extent centrifugally along the axons of peripheral nerves. In man, the best evidence for the axonal spread of the virus from the periphery to the CNS is derived from the many instances on record in which bulbar poliomyelitis has occurred very dramatically within 1 to 4 weeks following the removal of tonsils (Francis et al., 1942). It has also been found that cases of poliomyelitis occurring within 60 days of tonsillectomy show a marked concentration of bulbar types during the first month, whereas spinal poliomyelitis is randomly distributed over the entire period (Aycock, 1942b). Furthermore, comparisons of rates for bulbar poliomyelitis among recently tonsillectomized children were observed to be about 10 times as high as in unoperated individuals of the same age groups (Anderson et al., 1950). Since it is known that virus can be isolated from the tonsils and the throats of apparently healthy children (Kessel and Moore, 1945; Howe and Bodian, 1947), it is difficult to escape the conclusion that the trauma of operation plays a part in the inoculation of exposed fibers of the glossopharyngeal nerve.

Lesions of poliomyelitis are found wherever neurons have undergone destruction by virus. They consist of neuronal necrosis which excites considerable reaction among the various types of mesodermal cells participating in inflammation. The site of neuronal injury or destruction becomes infiltrated with lymphocytes, plasma cells, and macrophages which are often clustered about disintegrating neurons (Fig. 29, *top, left*). Granulocytes are occasionally present but do not usually form an important part of the exudate. Neighboring small venules and arterioles present adventitial infiltrations of lymphocytes which are called perivascular cuffs; these are nearly always present and may be very heavy (Fig. 29, *top, right*). Despite the mushrooming of the ends of a cut spinal cord from a patient who has succumbed to the disease, there is con-

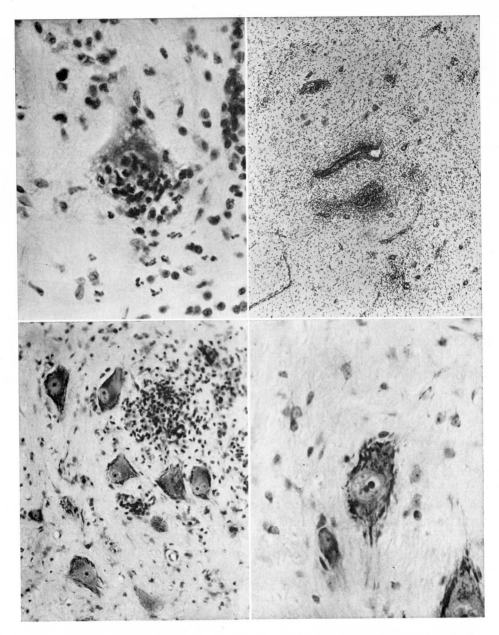

Fig. 29. (*Top, left*) Anterior horn cell of spinal cord undergoing neuronophagia. Monkey B474. Gallocyanin stain × 400.

(*Top, right*) Anterior horn of spinal cord of chimpanzee A392 showing acute perivascular cuffing and focal areas of lymphocytic infiltration. Gallocyanin stain × 40.

(*Bottom, left*) Anterior horn of monkey spinal cord showing chromatolytic anterior horn cells adjacent to a focus of phagocytes marking the site of a virus-killed neuron. Note disappearance of Nissl bodies and eccentricity of nuclei. Monkey B32. Gallocyanin stain × 400.

(*Bottom, right*) Recovering anterior horn cell showing nucleolus and intranuclear inclusion (latter surrounded by clear zone). Monkey B32. Gallocyanin stain × 400.

PLATE 2

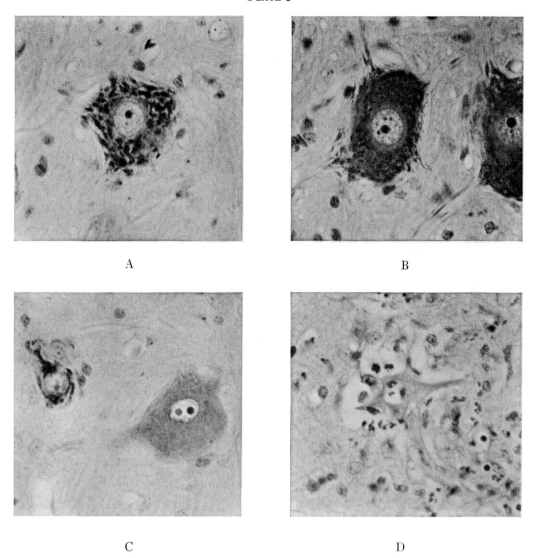

A

B

C

D

Regressive stages in spinal cord motoneurons in poliomyelitis: early acute stage. Haematoxylin-eosin-azure stain. Rhesus spinal cord. × 500. (Photographs by Chester F. Reather)

A. Normal anterior horn cell. Note massive Nissl bodies in cytoplasm, central position of nucleus, large basophilic nucleus and dispersed chromatin.

B. Early change due to virus activity. Note diffuse decrease in size of Nissl bodies (chromatolysis) and tendency for aggregation of oxychromatin in nucleus.

C. Severe diffuse chromatolysis, with disappearance of Nissl bodies. Cytoplasm shows faint diffuse basophilia. Nucleus is shrunken and contains a large eosinophilic inclusion body, as well as an intact nucleolus. The inclusion body is apparently formed by clumping of oxychromatin but does not occur in all injured cells. Note absence of inflammatory cells in vicinity, or of "edema."

D. Irreversibly injured motoneuron, showing neuronophagia by polymorphonuclear leukocytes and macrophages. All basophilia is usually lost at this stage of necrobiosis.

(Bodian, D., 1949, Poliomyelitis: pathologic anatomy, in Poliomyelitis: Papers and Discussions Presented at the First International Conference. Lippincott, Philadelphia.)

siderable anatomic and physiologic evidence that edema does not play an important role in the pathologic process. Neurons which are attacked but not destroyed occasionally show acidophilic intranuclear inclusions (Fig. 29, *bottom, right*; Plate 2, C). There are, however, no inclusions which are pathognomonic of poliomyelitis, nor does the virus interact to any significant degree with the neuroglia, myelin, or blood vessels of the CNS (Bodian and Howe, 1941a). In this respect, with the possible exception of rabies virus, the causative agents of poliomyelitis are more highly neuronotropic than are the other neurotropic viruses which infect man, for example, those of the equine encephalomyelitis group or Japanese B encephalitis.

The chief locus of activity for poliomyelitis is in the neuron, and the changes which follow in the peripheral nerves and the voluntary muscles are, in general, secondary to the destruction of the body of the nerve cell. The succession of regressive changes in a neuron is illustrated in Plate 2, A, B, C, D, taken from Bodian (1949a); a normal anterior horn cell is shown in A, while an infected cell portrayed in B has lost much of the clumped basophilic Nissl substance which ordinarily characterizes its cytoplasm. This is the phenomenon of chromatolysis and represents a reaction to injury which is reversible. A further stage of regression is seen in C where severe chromatolysis is illustrated; an acidophilic intranuclear inclusion may be observed. It is not clear whether such cells are capable of survival, although the presence of occasional inclusions in the nuclei of cells from convalescents suggests that this occurs (see Fig. 29, *bottom, right* and Fig. 31, F). D of Plate 2 illustrates a dead neuron; its nucleus is gone, the cytoplasm no longer shows any basophilia, and the first phagocytes have already arrived. See Figure 29, *top* and *bottom, left*, for later stages of neuronophagia.

Poliomyelitis virus is capable of progres-sion in the axons of the rhesus monkey's sciatic nerve at a rate approximating 2.4 mm. per hour (Bodian and Howe, 1941b). It also follows nerve-fiber pathways within the CNS, and in patients who succumb achieves a distribution which is conditioned by the susceptibility of certain nerve centers and their anatomic connections. Thus, terminally one finds a distribution of lesions (Howe and Bodian, 1941a) and of virus (Sabin and Ward, 1941) which is characteristic of polioymelitis alone. Lesions are found in the anterior horns of the spinal cord and, to a lesser extent, in the autonomic and sensory columns of the cord. Although flaccid paralysis dominates the clinical picture, there is, nevertheless, an extensive encephalitis. Indeed, the distribution of lesions in the brain is so characteristic that it distinguishes poliomyelitis from other neurotropic virus diseases perhaps even more clearly than do the lesions in the cord. The centers thus involved in the hindbrain are the motor cells of the reticular formation of the medulla and the pons, the vestibular nuclei, and their related centers in the roof and the vermis of the cerebellum. The pontine nuclei and the cerebellar hemispheres (the neocerebellar complex) are spared. Equally characteristic is the distribution of lesions in the cerebral cortex. Here the areas of destruction are confined to the motor and the premotor areas. They stop sharply at the bottom of the central sulcus (Fig. 30, *top*) and rarely extend into the somesthetic, or postcentral, cortex. Lesions are not found in any part of the visual system including the optic nerve, nor do they occur in the auditory projection areas or in any of the cortical association areas. Distribution of lesions in the primate CNS is summarized in Fig. 32 (after Bodian and Cumberland, 1947).

In none of the virus encephalitides so far investigated is this selection observed, but instead an apparently random distribution of lesions throughout the brain. Even in poliomyelitis characterized by encephalitic symptoms, namely coma, disorientation, delirium, etc., the lesions are extraordinarily intense in the brainstem, but the cortex is not involved throughout as in the virus encephalitides. Cortical hypoxia appears to be the most logical explanation of the encephalitic manifestations of poliomyelitis, since they usually recede rather rapidly when adequate respiratory exchange is effected (Brown and Baker, 1949). There is no clear anatomic basis for permanent impairment of intellect or personality, nor have such been more than occasionally described as sequels of poliomyelitis. While abnormal changes have been noted in the E.E.G. in poliomyelitis (Goldbloom et al., 1948), these have not been consistently observed (Ebaugh and Hoekstra, 1947), and such studies are not complete enough to make interpretation possible. It should be clearly appreciated that motor experience is vital for the normal intellectual and emotional development of a child. Deprivation at this level, whether because of temporary immobilization or lasting motor impairment, is sure to be reflected to a greater or lesser degree in the growth and the organization of a child's intellect and emotion. Fleeting attention and apparent slowness in learning are probably expressions of this situation rather than evidence of primary intellectual deficit. Emotional instability has been frequently noted in children convalescent from poliomyelitis, but it seems likely that in most cases this represents a reaction of children to the situation created by their hospitalization and disabilities and to the emotional attitudes of their families, rather than an evidence of damage to cortical or subcortical centers. Psychiatric evaluation of the emotional impact of paralytic poliomyelitis is in its incipient stages, and therapy in this field is still largely haphazard. For a general review see Seidenfeld (1952) and for a common-sense discussion of the family's contribution to this problem consult Rice (1949).

Ability of the virus to spread centrifugally and its wide distribution in the CNS of human beings who have succumbed to it have greatly complicated the neuropathologic demonstration of its portal of entry. For example, the fact that virus may migrate from the neuraxis into the gasserian and the spinal ganglia has made it impossible to attach any significance to the finding of lesions in them. On the other hand, the consistent absence of lesions or of virus in the olfactory bulbs virtually rules out the olfactory mucosa as a portal of entry. Simi-

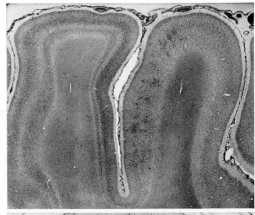

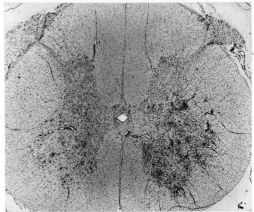

Fig. 30. (*Top*) Paracentral lobule of human cortex, case H12, showing central sulcus (center). Note lesions in precentral (motor) cortex and their absence from the postcentral cortex. Gallocyanin stain $\times$ 3. (Johns Hopkins Hospital Bulletin.)

(*Bottom*) Cervical cord of nonparalytic chimpanzee A434 showing extensive involvement of anterior horn and intermediate gray. Gallocyanin stain $\times$ 9.

larly, the rare occurrence of virus in human celiac ganglia (Sabin and Ward, 1941) and the paucity of lesions in them (Bodian and Howe, 1947) indicate that this is not an important route from the gut to the CNS. The only remaining nerve pathways from the gastro-intestinal tract are the vagus and the visceral afferent fibers, the latter entering through the dorsal roots. Unfortunately, the frequent localization of paralysis in the legs is not reliable evidence for any particular route, nor is there any indication of the role

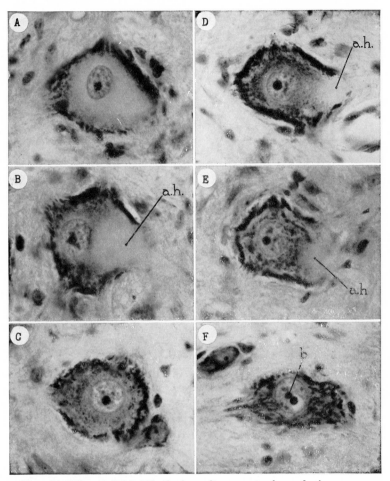

Fig. 31. Rhesus B32. Ninth day after onset of paralysis.

A. Severe central chromatolysis, with normal-appearing nucleus, and accumulation of heavy masses of Nissl substance near cell membrane. Regeneration of Nissl substance may or may not occur near the nuclear membrane.

B-E. Similar cells but with small Nissl bodies in central area. This appearance suggests regeneration of Nissl bodies from the periphery inward, with the area around the axon hillock (a.h.) last to show recovery (B, D and E).

F. Motoneuron of essentially normal appearance except for presence of acidophilic inclusion body (b) in nucleus. In the acute stage such inclusion bodies are seen only in cells with severe chromatolysis, suggesting almost complete recovery of such a cell.

(Bodian, D., 1949, Poliomyelitis: pathologic anatomy, in Poliomyelitis: Papers and Discussions Presented at the First International Poliomyelitis Conference. Lippincott, Philadelphia, pp. 62-84.)

played by these two pathways. It is conceivable that the virus may gain initial entrance to the CNS via the blood (Bodian, 1952a).

There is no mystery about the cause of all motor neurons, leaving a patient little or no functional voluntary musculature, it is commoner for the effects of the disease to be spotty, with certain muscle groups or even entire extremities appearing to be spared.

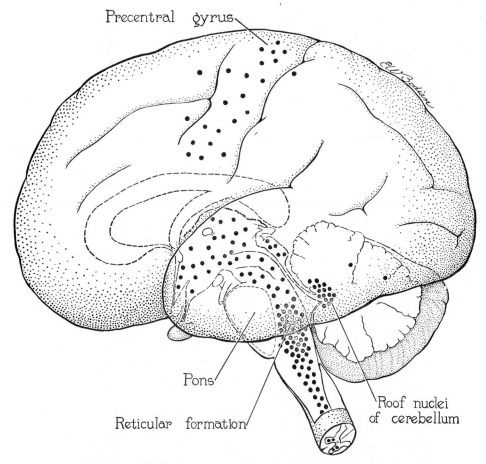

Precentral gyrus

Pons

Reticular formation

Roof nuclei of cerebellum

Fig. 32. Lateral view of human brain, with schematic transparent projection of the midsagittal surface of the brainstem. General distribution of lesions of poliomyelitis is indicated by large dots. Lesions in the cerebral cortex are largely restricted to the precentral gyrus, and those in the cerebellum to the roof nuclei. Lesions are generally found widespread in the brainstem centers, with a number of striking exceptions, such as the nuclei of the basis pontis, and the inferior olivary nuclei.

(Bodian, D., 1949, Poliomyelitis: pathologic anatomy, *in* Poliomyelitis: Papers and Discussions Presented at the First International Poliomyelitis Conference, Lippincott, Philadelphia, pp. 62-84.)

flaccid paralysis of skeletal muscles. It results from destruction of their somatic motor nerve supply, and the atrophy and the contractures which follow paralysis are entirely in keeping with this fact. While occasionally the virus wipes out practically Nevertheless, it is a constant finding, in experimental poliomyelitis and at human necropsies, that lesions are more widespread than would have been predicted on the basis of clinical findings. This seeming paradox is due to the fact that extensive destruction of neurons may take place without producing disability, if it is scattered in the anterior horn and is not concentrated in a neuron pool which innervates a functionally related group of muscles. This is illustrated in Fig. 30, *bottom,* which was made from a series of sections of the cord of a chimpanzee in which no paralysis or weakness could be detected (Bodian and Howe, 1945). While lesions are very striking in the section portrayed, the cord a few millimeters above or below this point was relatively normal in appearance. It is, therefore, possible to have many scattered lesions in the spinal cord without much functional disturbance.

Despite the fact that poliomyelitis may completely paralyze voluntary muscles by destroying their nerve supply, there are many unanswered questions regarding the anatomy and the physiology of this process and its counterpart, recovery of function. For example, it is far from clear why nerves to certain muscles are more frequently involved than others, although neuron pools innervating these muscles do not appear to be singled out for destruction (Elliott, 1947). Among others, Howe and Bodian (1942, Chap. 3) have pointed out striking differences in the inherent susceptibility of the neurons of the cerebrum. Hodes et al. (1949) have shown a relative increase in the number of small cells in the anterior horns of convalescent rhesus monkeys which led them to postulate elective destruction of large cells. This is in keeping with the observation (Hodes, 1949) that the nerves to chronically weakened muscles of poliomyelitis patients conduct more slowly than do nerves to normal muscles; it is recognized that conduction velocity varies directly with fiber diameter. Further light is thrown on this problem by Clark's (1931) work on innervation ratios, in which he showed a much higher ratio of nerve fibers to muscle fibers in a muscle capable only of gross movements in comparison with a muscle which performs delicate movements. It is, therefore, possible that selection of

proximal muscles of the extremities may be accounted for on the basis of their being innervated by large cells having large axons and a high innervation ratio. Perhaps some explanation may be found for the apparent exceptions, e.g., the vulnerability of the neuron pool innervating the opponens pollicis.

Further questions and some answers in the field of nerve-muscle pathology have been presented through improved methods of recording action potentials. See Buchthal (1949) for a good review of this subject. Diagnostic advances have been made by electrical methods, such as the determination of curves for the thresholds of muscle excitability through intact skin with sine waves at varying frequencies (Bouman et al., 1951). Aid in diagnosis may come from the study of fibrillation potentials (Huddleston and Goldseth, 1948). These authors have made use of the fact that totally denervated muscle fibers are in a continuous state of fine rapid fibrillation during which they discharge feeble but rapid potentials. These fibrillation potentials are augmented by prostigmine (Weddell et al., 1944), a drug which will be considered in the section on therapy. Buchthal and Høncke (1944) have observed that poliomyelitis muscle shows rapid diminution in the amplitude of individual action potentials with fatigue. These are partially restored by neostigmine, according to Hodes (1948) who postulated that it spares acetylcholine as in myasthenia gravis. Buchthal (1949), on the other hand, was unable to demonstrate abnormal sensitivity of poliomyelitis muscle to acetylcholine.

Reciprocal innervation appears frequently to be abrogated so that potentials are emitted simultaneously by opposing muscles; see Watkins and Brazier (1945) for a good demonstration of this and its resolution. Potentials are often discharged synchronously by muscles of poliomyelitis patients (Buchthal and Høncke, 1944), whereas normal muscles discharge asynchronously. The physiologic significance of these phenomena is obscure, and it is not known whether they are referable to the central or the peripheral nervous system. Although it seems probable that defects of the CNS account for most of them, Hodes (1948) has interpreted the rapid fatigue of poliomyelitis muscles and the early failure of their potentials as evidence of a block at the myoneural junction.

The genesis of spasm or tightness, which is noted in many unparalyzed muscles, has been the subject of much recent speculation. Such muscles are also painful when stretched or palpated; tenderness is said to outlast spasm. The spasm occurs frequently in those muscles most regularly involved in meningitis or meningismus of toxic or infectious etiology but is by no means confined to them. The muscles are electrically silent except when stretched, at which time they produce electric potentials of longer duration than normal (Bouman, 1947). Disturbances of reciprocal innervation, as noted above, are thought to be concomitants of the hyperirritable stretch reflex. There are few facts bearing upon the pathogenesis of this syndrome available from human poliomyelitis, since the nature of fatal disease usually makes adequate muscle checks difficult and sharp pathologic localization impossible. While lesions are found in the intermediate gray matter of the cord and probably involve internuncial neurons, they are seldom present except where there is also extensive destruction of motor cells. It is, therefore, difficult to show that lesions in this area are responsible for the genesis of spasticity (Bodian, 1947). Bodian (1946) has shown that monkeys in the preparalytic stage following intracerebral inoculation may have striking increases in the tone of the leg muscles before either virus or lesions can be demonstrated in the lumbosacral cord. At this stage, virus has reached the brainstem and has attacked the large motor cells of the reticular formation. These are precisely the cell groups which on stimulation yield arrest of movement and relaxation of muscle tone in the extremities

(Magoun, 1944). Spasticity may, thus, be characterized as a release phenomenon resulting from lesions in the brainstem. While this does not represent the entire mechanism of the so-called muscle spasm, it is the only modus operandi which has so far been satisfactorily demonstrated. At the same time, it calls attention to the influence of the brainstem lesions which are later masked by flaccid paralysis but doubtless play a greater role in the symptomatology of poliomyelitis than is generally recognized; for example, the literature contains occasional descriptions of spastic or upper-motor-neuron poliomyelitis. Lesions in the anterior portion of the motor cortex, area 4 s (Hines, 1936), are known to produce spasticity, but in poliomyelitis such lesions are insignificant as compared with the massive involvement of the centers in the brainstem which also regulate muscle tone. Similarly, in so-called ataxic cases (Peabody, Draper and Dochez, 1912, p. 67), signs may be accounted for by a predominance of lesions in the vestibulocerebellar system. Nevertheless, it must be emphasized that, at least in severe cases, lesions are present in practically all susceptible levels of the cord and the brain, even though paralysis or weakness may not be clinically apparent everywhere (Bodian, 1947).

The underlying pathology of muscle tenderness is as yet unexplained. It may in part be due purely to peripheral factors incidental to continued spasticity, namely, those which produce stiffness and tenderness after unusual exercise, or it may represent irritative or release phenomena resulting from lesions in the spinal ganglia, the posterior horn of the cord or the brainstem. There is as yet no acceptable evidence that virus is present or propagates in the voluntary muscles of the postnatal individual. It has also been suggested that vasospasm may be responsible for the continued pain and tenderness of muscles which is frequently observed; severely paralyzed extremities, particularly legs, are very often cold and cyanotic as well as tender. Whether this is due to lesions of the autonomic nervous system or passive circulatory stagnation in a flaccid limb is undetermined. Among others, Collins et al. (1947) noted that paravertebral sympathetic block relieved the symptoms and produced objective improvement in circulation.

Bulbar poliomyelitis really represents a concentration of lesions in those parts of the medulla containing the motor nuclei of cranial nerves. Involvement of the eye-muscle nuclei is rare, facial and jaw paralyses are more common, and localization of lesions in the nucleus ambiguus is still more frequent. Familiar early signs of the last are nasal voice, difficulty in speaking, deviation of the uvula, and regurgitation of fluids through the nose. These may be followed by complete paralysis of the muscles of deglutition, including occasionally those of the vocal cords, and at times by involvement of the respiratory and vasomotor centers. Cases have been described (Baker et al., 1950) in which the physical findings were attributed to bilateral damage to one or both of these medullary centers; they include cardiac arrhythmia or failure, decrease or increase in blood pressure, a variety of peripheral vasomotor phenomena, and respiratory arrhythmia or arrest. Bulbar poliomyelitis may exist without obvious signs of cord involvement, yet it is very questionable whether the cord ever completely escapes injury; at least bulbar patients admitted without obvious paralysis and dying within a few hours are frequently found to have many lesions in the cord if numerous levels are examined microscopically.

Recovery of motor neurons is depicted in Fig. 31 taken from Bodian (1948b, 1949a). In an examination of these cells in sequence from A to F, one will see various stages in the regeneration of Nissl material in the cell cytoplasm. A full explanation of these stages may be found in the classic presentation by Bodian (1948b). By statistical analysis of these cell types in paralytic monkeys sacrificed at various periods of convalescence, Bodian has shown that cells exhibiting chromatolysis, perhaps as severe as that shown in C of Plate 2, survive and recover their Nissl substance over a period of about 30 days. This time corresponds closely to that of the early rapid-recovery phase during which there is invariably restitution of muscle function if any viable motor cells remain in the spinal cord. There is further evidence to indicate that this process is essentially the same in man as in susceptible laboratory primates. From this point, further recovery is probably achieved through hypertrophy of muscle fibers and functional adjustments within the CNS itself which compensate for permanent deficits. Little or nothing is known about the latter, but there is some evidence that they may take place.

EXPERIMENTAL INFECTION; HOST RANGE

Until comparatively recent years it was believed that only primates were susceptible to poliomyelitis. However, the Lansing strain of virus (Armstrong, 1939) and certain other members of the same immunologic group have been shown capable of infecting rodents on intracerebral inoculation. Li and Habel (1951) have reported the adaptation of the Leon strain, which belongs to another immunologic group, to mice, but sufficient time has not elapsed for confirmation of this finding. It must be realized that experimental infections in rodents and in most species of primates are induced only by direct contact of the virus with nervous tissue. This involves intraneural inoculation of some sort, the intracerebral or intranasal routes being most frequently used. Success of the intranasal method gave rise, by analogy, to the erroneous belief that human beings are infected by the olfactory portal. It is now realized that some of the primates are susceptible to infection not only by the methods just mentioned, but also following the feeding of virus. While this group includes several species of old-world monkeys, it appears that these animals are highly susceptible only to certain strains

(Melnick and Ledinko, 1951) and do not have the receptivity characteristic of the chimpanzee, which is such a favorable host that it has been accidentally infected in the laboratory (Howe and Bodian, 1944a). Furthermore, chimpanzees are susceptible to oral inoculation of a wide range of strains of poliomyelitis virus. While the paralytic rate is relatively low, close to 100 per cent of the chimpanzees so inoculated become alimentary carriers of virus and develop antibody against the virus which they have received (Howe and Bodian, 1941b; Melnick and Horstmann, 1947; Howe et al., 1950). The chimpanzee, therefore, simulates man very closely in its reaction to the virus and is a most favorable animal for experiments in which this quality is of paramount importance. While resistance to the virus at various portals differs among the primates, once infection has been produced, the character and the distribution of lesions in the CNS are identical in the monkey, the chimpanzee and man.

ETIOLOGY

The etiologic agent of human poliomyelitis is a virus which passes easily through ordinary bacteria-tight filters. Its smallest diameter is estimated to be from 8 to 12 mμ on the basis of filtration experiments with gradocol membranes (Elford et al., 1935). There is no agreement at present about its shape (Gard, 1943; Loring et al., 1946). Efforts have been made to determine the physical and chemical characteristics of the virus by studies of relatively pure samples obtained through ultracentrifugation. Difficulties of bio-assay and of obtaining sufficient quantities of purified virus have greatly hampered these studies. The virus is thought to contain nucleoprotein.

The virus of poliomyelitis is relatively stable in the pH range of 4 to 10 (Loring and Schwerdt, 1944). It is inactivated in 10 minutes at pH 6.85 to 7.4 in the presence of 0.05 parts per million of free chlorine (Lensen et al., 1947). A chlorine residual of

0.2 p.p.m. after 20 minutes is recommended by the U.S.P.H.S. for disinfection of drinking water. Virus in a 10 per cent suspension of infected cord is inactivated in 3.5 days at icebox temperature by 0.3 per cent formalin, but resists 0.2 per cent formalin and 1 per cent phenol for 10 days (Brodie, 1935). It is inactivated within 12 to 24 hours at 25° C. by 0.1 per cent formalin (Schwerdt et al., 1951). Schultz and Robinson (1942) have tested in a cursory fashion a great many chemical compounds for virucidal activity. Among the most successful was mercuric chloride which, in a concentration of 0.01 gram per cent inactivated 20 minimal infective doses of virus within 2 hours at 37° C. Potassium permanganate also inactivated the virus under similar conditions. These, of course, are not the minimum inactivation times. The virus is quite sensitive to oxidizing agents, ultraviolet light (Jungeblut, 1937; Milzer et al., 1945; Dick et al., 1951), and heat, being inactivated by the latter within 3 minutes at a temperature of 50° C. (Shaughnessy et al., 1930). It resists freezing at —70° or —20° C. for 12 months without loss of titer (Melnick, 1946) and can survive with apparently undiminished titer for 8 years while exposed to CO_2 gas at a temperature of —70° C. (Howe, unpublished data). Activity still remains after treatment by sonic vibrations of 9,000 cps. for 1 hour (Scherp and Chambers, 1936), and after exposure to such bactericidal agents as ether and merthiolate (Brodie, 1935). The accuracy of determinations of susceptibility of virus to chemical agents depends upon the size of particles in virus-containing suspensions; this fact received little or no attention in the studies cited above.

Immunity and Types of Poliomyelitis Virus. Monkeys convalescent from paralytic attacks are highly resistant to second paralytic episodes when reinoculated with the same strain of virus (Howe and Bodian, 1941c; 1942, Chap. X). Nevertheless, immunity is relative, since, in some animals, reinoculation with homologous virus after an interval of a year produces clinical symptoms accompanied by the presence of virus in the spinal cord (Bodian, unpublished data). Similarly, a second alimentary infection with homologous virus can be induced in a small percentage of chimpanzees (Melnick and Horstmann, 1947; Howe et al., 1950). This latter situation appears to be analogous to alimentary infections of adult human beings who are in intimate contact with a paralyzed patient (Langmuir, 1942; Pearson et al., 1945; Gordon et al., 1948). Such individuals, although belonging to the age group in which paralytic rates are 2 or less per 100,000, are, during a lifetime, possibly subjected to repeated alimentary infections which do not involve the CNS.

In addition to the potentialities for reinfection with the same strain of virus (homologous reinfection), it must be realized that three immunologically distinct types of poliomyelitis virus are currently recognized (Bodian et al., 1949), and that reinfection may be caused by one of the heterologous types. Types I, II and III, more familiarly known as Brunhilde, Lansing and Leon, respectively, are the designations used for the different viruses. These types have been identified because of their failure to produce significant cross protection against paralysis in laboratory animals and the inability of each to be neutralized by immune sera specific for the others. These criteria are somewhat artificial, being based only upon laboratory experience, and it is at least possible that, under conditions of natural exposure, some cross immunity among the types may be produced. Although epidemiologic surveys are still very incomplete, evidence is accumulating to show that all three types are world-wide in distribution. See the report of the Committee on Typing of The National Foundation for Infantile Paralysis (1951) for a detailed account of this subject.

The fact that there are multiple immunogenic types of poliomyelitis virus has important implications in relation to immunity. Under these circumstances, it is not surprising that second paralytic attacks have been observed, although attempts to show that the two episodes were caused by different virus types have not been entirely successful (Bodian, 1951a). It has been suggested that second attacks bear roughly the same ratio to first paralytic attacks as the latter do to the population as a whole, thereby indicating a total lack of immunity (Bridge et al., 1946). Granting that these assumptions are true, which is doubtful, the reasoning is fallacious except as it may indicate that persons who have already suffered a paralytic episode may be in greater jeopardy than the population as a whole. It is obvious that an overwhelming majority of persons acquires an effective immunity relatively early in life, else poliomyelitis would be a disease affecting all ages equally. This argues for a limited number of immunologically different virus types which are met and conquered before the age of 20 years. Further discussion of this subject will be found in the section on epidemiology.

DIAGNOSIS

Fever, accompanied or followed by flaccid paralysis and with an increase of mononuclear cells and protein in the CSF, is pathognomonic of poliomyelitis, especially if it occurs in an epidemic setting. However, Nelson and Aycock (1944) have shown that in the state of Massachusetts there have been marked deficits in the reporting of paralytic poliomyelitis in young children and during the winter months. Infectious neuronitis, postdiphtheritic polyneuritis, and the various peripheral neuritides of toxic or metabolic origin generally have a slower onset and produce more intense and varied sensory symptoms than are characteristic of poliomyelitis. In addition, postdiphtheritic palatal paralysis is frequently associated with loss of accommodation in the muscles of the eyes, a condition never seen in poliomyelitis. The Guillain-Barré syndrome may produce flaccid paralysis but is characterized by the absence of an increased number of cells and the presence of an increased amount of protein in the spinal fluid. In this respect, however, it is indistinguishable from the late stages of poliomyelitis in which only increased protein is found in the CSF. Amyotrophic lateral sclerosis can be excluded on the basis of its chronic progressive character. Where there are encephalitic signs, such as coma, disorientation and hyperactivity, a diagnosis of poliomyelitis is still relatively secure if there are flaccid paralyses of the extremities. Such a clinical picture is invariably associated with respiratory difficulty if caused by poliomyelitis virus and should clear rapidly with improvement of respiratory exchange while paralyses persist.

When paralyses are slight or absent, various possibilities must be considered, including the virus encephalitides, lethargic encephalitis, postvaccinal or postinfection encephalitis, rabies, multiple sclerosis, cerebral malaria, cerebrospinal meningitis, tuberculous meningitis, brain tumor, or any acute infection in a young child. To distinguish nonparalytic poliomyelitis clinically from the meningism which often accompanies dysentery, sinusitis and otitis, or from mumps meningitis is frequently difficult, if not impossible. For example, Kilham et al. (1949) have reported that 6 of 17 patients diagnosed in a hospital as nonparalytic poliomyelitis developed complement-fixing and hemagglutination-inhibiting antibodies against mumps virus. Virus was isolated from the CSF of 3 patients despite the absence of parotitis. An increase of mononuclear cells and protein in the spinal fluid is helpful in making a diagnosis of poliomyelitis, but an increase is also found in most of the known virus infections of the CNS.

One of the newly recognized Coxsackie or C viruses (Dalldorf et al., 1949) and a poliomyelitis virus have on occasions been isolated from stools of patients with undoubted paralytic or nonparalytic poliomyelitis. The C viruses have been frequently isolated from the stools of human beings during poliomyelitis epidemics and are said to produce clinical pictures indistinguishable from those of nonparalytic poliomyelitis (Curnen et al., 1949). There is no question that the two viruses may exist concurrently in a community and in the stools of the same patients who respond by developing neutralizing antibody against both (Melnick et al., 1951), but it is not clear that the C viruses have produced symptoms of nonparalytic poliomyelitis. In fact, accidental laboratory infections with a C virus seem to resemble epidemic pleurodynia or Bornholm disease and are characterized by fever, headache, thoracic and abdominal pain (Kilbourne, 1950). Furthermore, C viruses have been isolated from patients diagnosed as having epidemic pleurodynia (Weller et al., 1950) and herpangina (Huebner et al., 1951). The latter condition is a benign febrile illness lasting 2 or 3 days and is accompanied by headache, abdominal pain, sore throat, vomiting and faucial ulcers. It is likely that C-virus infections might be confused with poliomyelitis at the minor-illness level where neither can be diagnosed with assurance in the absence of virus isolation or serologic studies. There is no crucial evidence that infection with a Coxsackie virus exerts any effect upon an infection with a poliomyelitic virus, or vice versa, when the two exist concurrently in the same human being.

Arthritis, particularly of the spine, and scurvy are occasionally confused with poliomyelitis by the uninitiated. The presence of spasticity with a Babinski sign practically rules out poliomyelitis and suggests brain tumor, brain abscess, epidural abscess of the spinal cord, intracranial hemorrhage, birth injury, cerebral palsy, or multiple sclerosis. The occurrence of optic neuritis or any defect of vision definitely excludes poliomyelitis, as do such residua as mental retardation, marked personality changes or epilepsy. Of aid in diagnosing a suspected case is its occurrence in a general epidemic setting, or in a family with a frank paralytic case. The surest means of diagnosis, however, is the isolation of virus from the stools or the pharyngeal secretions of the patient. Failing this, it is often impossible to diagnose nonparalytic poliomyelitis with assurance. It is also impossible to diagnose abortive poliomyelitis outside an epidemic setting and in the absence of successful isolation of virus or demonstration of increase of antibody in paired sera. A complement-fixation test has been described for poliomyelitis by Casals and Olitsky (1951) and elaborated by Lahelle (1951), but the extent of its usefulness as a routine diagnostic tool is not yet apparent.

Diagnosis of fatal poliomyelitis may be made from the presence of typical lesions in the anterior horns of the spinal cord or on the basis of the localization of lesions in the motor cortex and their absence from other cortical areas. The latter is the more important for the differentiation of cases showing encephalitic signs. If cord or brainstem is available and can be obtained with sterile precautions, it is often possible to isolate virus from it when the duration of paralysis has been less than a week. Material may be preserved for months in 50 per cent glycerol-saline solution at ordinary icebox temperature. It is usually inoculated intracerebrally into an old-world monkey as a 10 or 20 per cent emulsion in sterile saline solution or distilled water in quantities of 1 or 2 cc. As a source of virus, stool is far superior to nervous tissue, since the virus may be recovered in this medium for weeks after the onset of disease. A portion of the stool is emulsified in sterile saline solution or distilled water, clarified by centrifugation at 3,000 r.p.m., and inoculated into monkeys intraperitoneally, intracerebrally or intranasally. The first two routes have been extensively employed by Trask et al. (1938) and others, who treated the material with anesthetic ether for 24 to 48 hours to render it bacteriologically sterile. This results in the loss of less virus than does the removal of bacteria by filtration. Limitations of the method are the low susceptibility of animals by the intraperitoneal route and the high incidence of toxic deaths and brain abscesses following intracerebral inoculation. Melnick (1948) has greatly improved the method by treatment of stools in the ultracentrifuge, but his modification is available to comparatively few laboratories. Howe and Bodian (1944b) have described successful isolation of virus by intranasal inoculation into rhesus monkeys of untreated, distilled-water suspensions of stools on five successive days. With this method there is practically no mortality except from virus activity. When two animals are inoculated with material from each specimen, the method compares favorably with the intracerebral one. Poliomyelitis virus has been isolated by direct inoculation of tissue cultures with material from stools of human subjects (Robbins et al., 1951). This method also permits the direct typing of the virus with specific immune sera which electively inhibit the growth of the homologous virus type; it is still far from being available for routine diagnosis. Poliomyelitis virus may be isolated from nasopharyngeal washings and oropharyngeal swabs taken from patients within six days of the onset of illness. Methods for its recovery under such conditions are essentially those described for isolation of virus from stools (Horstmann et al., 1946a; Howe et al., 1945).

TREATMENT

Specific Therapy. The only specific therapy which has rationally recommended itself for the treatment of acute poliomyelitis is immune serum. In America, at least, this procedure has lost general favor, even though it still has its proponents. While there have been almost no well-controlled tests of its efficacy, a number of studies all force the same conclusion. The best and most recent one (Bahlke and Perkins, 1945) demonstrated that 56 patients with preparalytic poliomyelitis treated with gamma globulin fared no better at the end of 5 to 7 months than did alternately selected and untreated controls. Children, 1 to 12 years of age, were given graded doses of from 20 to 100 cc. of gamma globulin, the equivalent of from 460 to 2,300 cc. of plasma. Treatment, therefore, was much more intensive than in any previously reported series of patients; the antibody levels achieved, however, were probably inferior to those which have been observed in convalescents (Bodian, unpublished data). While the gamma globulin used was not tested against a strain of virus isolated during the epidemic, this is probably not a serious objection, since a large gamma-globulin pool collected in the U.S.A. has been shown to neutralize all of the three known types of virus (Bodian, 1949c).

Other forms of therapy, such as intravenous injection of hypertonic solutions, spinal puncture, spinal drainage, antibiotics, vitamins, hormones, etc., have had no proven success, and some of them constitute insults to the CNS. Since nonparalytic and low spinal paralytic forms of the disease present no immediate hazard to life, bed rest, adequate diet and good nursing care are the chief forms of treatment employed.

Muscle Spasm and Pain. In recent years, various methods have been proposed for the relief of the acute muscle spasm and pain, the rationale being that early mobilization will reduce atrophy and fibrous contractures. Such therapeutic agents, for the most part, act peripherally on the muscle or myoneural junction and include neostigmine (Kabat and Knapp, 1943), curare (Ransohoff, 1945) and hot woolen packs (Pohl and Kenny, 1943). Adequately controlled clinical trial of these procedures is still lacking, but numerous observers have recorded their impressions.

Eveleth and Ryan (1944) noted some relaxation of muscle spasm following the administration of neostigmine in a series of 12 patients, but remark that the drug produced either fasicular twitching of muscles or vomiting in all of them. Brainerd et al. (1945) found that undesirable reactions could be controlled with atropine, but Jones and Dickson (1947) were unable to confirm this. Levine et al. (1942) reported that neostigmine enhanced fibrillation and atrophy in denervated skeletal muscles of the rat, while atropine had the opposite effect. All observers are agreed that there is no correlation between response to the drug and final outcome of the disease. On the other hand, Hodes (1948) observed that neostigmine produced partial restoration in the falling amplitude of potentials recorded from weak muscles undergoing progressive fatigue. This led him to postulate a partial block at the myoneural junction which was benefited by the sparing effect of the drug on acetylcholine. The block could, of course, be secondary to changes in the lower motor neuron rather than the result of virus activity at the motor endplate, for which there is as yet no acceptable evidence. Procaine or priscol hydrochloride, originally reported as a muscle relaxant in an uncontrolled study by Smith et al. (1948), was found to be ineffective for reducing the pain in tense muscles by Reilley and Barsanti (1950) and Lawson (1949). The latter investigator has reported that furmethide, a parasympathetic stimulant, produced relaxation of the bladder sphincters and shortened the period of urinary retention.

Fox (1946) and Rosenberg and Fischer (1948) found no objective improvement of muscle spasm following the use of curare and emphasized the danger of its action on the respiratory mechanism. When used in relaxing doses, it also produced difficulty in swallowing and so much mental confusion that many patients were unable to cooperate with the physiotherapist. The latter authors, however, tried to maintain therapeutic concentrations by giving the drug twice in 24 hours instead of three times as recommended by its advocates. Other observers (Richards et al., 1947; Kottke et al., 1948; Bower et al., 1950) have reported that curare relaxed muscle spasm but did not facilitate the recovery of muscle function. Paul and Couch (1949) found that the time required to overcome stiffness and pain evoked by muscle stretching was much reduced in curare-treated patients.

Hot packs, and to a lesser extent hot baths, have come into common use during the acute stage of poliomyelitis. Their effectiveness, which is not universal, is probably partly physiologic and partly psychologic. The most enthusiastic proponents of the hot pack claim that by reducing painful spasm, it hastens the time when active and passive movement may be begun. More conservative workers believe that there is no advantage in forcing this time, but there is, nevertheless, distinctly greater emphasis than a decade ago on allowing a patient during the acute phase as much freedom of movement in bed as is permitted by muscle tenderness. Whether these differences in procedure are reflected in the eventual recovery of muscle function is questionable, since it is very difficult to set up extensive and well-controlled studies in man. However, a cursory glance at the illustrations in the monograph on treatment by Lovett (1917) should convince anyone that considerable progress has been made in the prevention of deformities.

Treatment of Paralyzed Muscles. Electrical stimulation of muscles during the acute as well as the chronic stages has had its proponents for many years and has recently experienced a convincing revival. Among others, Osborne et al. (1949), who used a sinusoidal wave of variable frequency (2,000-6,000 cycles/minute), reported that stimulation, especially in the high frequency range, was well tolerated even by small children. Although their series was not extensive (7 patients in acute phase and 13 in the chronic), measurement of limb circumference indicated that atrophy was retarded during the acute phase and some hypertrophy induced during the chronic. This therapeutic approach rests on a firmer experimental basis than any of the others previously cited, since there is a considerable body of knowledge dealing with muscle denervated by neurotomy which may be considered a fair model for the flaccid paretic muscle of poliomyelitis. It is generally agreed that contractions induced by electric stimulation, both galvanic (Gutmann and Guttmann, 1944) and faradic (Hines et al., 1945), lessen the loss of strength in denervated muscle and retard its atrophy. In general, the stronger the stimulation which can be tolerated the better the result.

There is no question that experimental animals develop fewer contractures of leg muscles if they are allowed freedom of movement instead of being confined in small cages. It is also quite clear that voluntary muscle decreases in bulk when immobilized or tenotomized, even in the presence of normal innervation. However, one of the moot questions which confronts the therapist is: How much exercise? It was held by Lovett (1917) and some others since his time that exercise may on occasion be excessive and damage weak muscles. The writer has never seen this happen in hundreds of monkeys which have been observed through convalescence from severe paralytic poliomyelitis. Challenges to the concept of muscle damage through fatigue in human poliomyelitis have come from DeLorme et al. (1948) and Krusen (1949), who objectively recorded the increases in bulk and strength of the quadriceps of paralyzed patients under progressive resistance exercises. Despite fatigue, which may be accompanied by clonic tremors as it is in normal subjects, continuous increase in strength was noted. Perhaps the most dramatic evidence bearing on this point is the story of an anonymous British physician (Poliomyelitis, 1948) whose rehabilitation from prostrating paralysis apparently resulted from repeated exercise maintained for about 6 years to the point of exhaustion.

The methods just detailed for the treatment of muscle can scarcely be expected to exert any appreciable effect upon the recovery of the CNS unless some type of sensory stimulation is involved, such as that caused by passive stretch, or contraction induced by the patient or by electricity.

Under these conditions, it is conceivable that where remaining CNS connections permit, old pathways may be reactivated or new ones established. In keeping with the idea of the use of exercises for promoting co-ordination, are the clinical impressions of many physiotherapists and Osborne et al. (1949) who believe that electric stimualtion alone of muscles improved a patient's sense of co-ordination.

The difficulties of evaluating any type of treatment are legion, not only because the severity of poliomyelitis varies from year to year and from one region to another, but also because the spontaneous recovery rate is high and different observers vary in their estimates of disability. The reader is referred to papers by the following authors which illustrate these difficulties: Davis et al. (1941); McCarroll (1942); Toomey (1944); Pohl (1945); Sherman (1945); Wood (1947); Lenhard (1948). From these reports, it becomes obvious that, regardless of which of the current methods of treatment is used, from 45 to 100 per cent of poliomyelitis patients made satisfactory recoveries.

It is not within the scope of this chapter to discuss the types of corrective exercises or the surgical measures which frequently must be taken in the chronic stages of poliomyelitis. Perhaps the most important factor in recovery, granting the survival of some anterior horn cells, is the determination of an individual to overcome his handicap. Except in the case of the exceptional individual, this introduces professional psychiatry into the picture. There is no doubt of the value of the intuitive though untrained psychiatrist in the form of the attending physician, nurse, physiotherapist or the parent, but at times something more is clearly needed (Seidenfeld, 1952). For example, in a study of 500 patients over 16 years of age, Deaver (1951) found satisfactory social adjustments in two thirds of them, which is not a strikingly large proportion, considering the fact that the criteria employed in the study were relatively crude and that most of the patients were adults. Naturally those in comfortable, happy homes came out the best. Little has been done about the serious problem of the child handicapped by motor difficulties which actually retard the process of learning at many integrative levels, not to mention the emotional hazard of rejection by playmates, or the more elusive and far more devastating changes in family attitudes. Human beings invariably make adjustments of some sort but they are not always healthy ones. It appears that the adjustment of the poliomyelitis patient at a deep emotional level is just beginning to receive professional attention.

Treatment of Respiratory Insufficiency. Respiratory paralysis is the gravest threat to life in poliomyelitis. It may ensue because of paralysis of intercostal muscles and diaphragm, or from failure of the respiratory center in the medulla. Both types of disease have been extensively treated in the Drinker respirator. The immediate outlook for life appears to be better in patients with the spinal respiratory syndrome than in those with the bulbar form. However, the ultimate prognosis is much worse for the first group, since members of it are not only more likely than are those of the latter to have severe paralysis of the limbs but frequently fail to recover enough vital capacity to keep their airways clear after discharge from a respirator. Of a group of 35 such patients, Landon (1934) found that 18 months after removal from a respirator 45 per cent were dead. Similarly, Brahdy and Lenarsky (1936) reported that 48 per cent of a group of discharged spinal-respirator patients had died within 2.5 years. All but one were respiratory deaths, and massive atelectasis was the commonest finding at necropsy. Of 14 survivors, 2 were without residua, 7 were able to get about enough to attend school, and the rest were totally incapacitated. It is not known to what extent this picture has been modified by the advent of antibiotics.

The percentage of patients with respiratory difficulties arising from virus invasion of the medulla, or associated with it, may vary from 10 to 45 per cent in different epidemics (Lenarsky, 1950). Although results of the invasion also vary in severity from mild palatal weakness to malignant involvement of the vasomotor and the respiratory centers, they still account for an overwhelming preponderance of deaths (94 per cent in California in 1947-48, Longshore et al., 1951, Table 17). Even in the latter type, however, the outlook is not unfavorable if a patient survives for a week. Grulee and Panos (1947) reported that all of the deaths in the Minneapolis epidemic of 1947 occurred in the bulbar group but that the "majority of the survivors made good recoveries." Many of these favorable outcomes were ascribed to recently developed methods of treatment, while others undoubtedly represented mild types of illness. However, damage of cranial nerves, like that of other nerves, may cause lasting effects, usually in the form of facial palsies or palatal weakness (Lenarsky, 1950).

Since the introduction of the tank respirator, treatment of respiratory insufficiency has been expanded into a specialty of continuously increasing complexity which can be covered only partially in this account. Students are referred to the excellent summary by Wilson (1952) which forms an important basis of the discussion presented here.

Since the virus itself is out of control, treatment of respiratory insufficiency is entirely symptomatic. The chief difficulty lies in detecting and evaluating a patient's symptoms, many of which represent profound disturbances in the physiology of respiratory exchange. Perhaps mild respiratory insufficiency should be treated outside a respirator, since, although this machine may solve some problems by virtue of its ability to alter the intrathoracic volume, it creates certain difficulties, many of which are imperfectly understood, hence the subject of controversy. To quote Wilson, "Luckily, in most patients control of alveolar ventilation is not wholly lost so that a reasonable regualtion of respiration can be carried out by the crude adjustments of pressure and rate possible in these machines." Time has produced many new and essentially untried technical changes in the respirator, such as special cams for modifying the character of its excursions, masks and other devices for administering positive pressure, pulsating mattresses, and a host of other adjuncts (Bower et al., 1950).

An important advance in respirator treatment was made when the oximeter was used to detect the degree of oxygen saturation in a patient's blood (Brown et al., 1947b). Wilson, however, believes that this vital information can be determined with great accuracy by an astute clinician who studies the respiratory movements of a sleeping patient. Furthermore, the oximeter does not measure changes in the CO_2 combining power of the blood so that severe degrees of acidosis or alkalosis may go undetected unless other tests are employed. Since these tests now involve considerable delay, control of artificial respiration would be greatly improved by a method for the instantaneous determination of alveolar CO_2 levels.

An important complication introduced by respirator treatment is the alkalosis which is the result of continuous overventilation and to which the patient becomes adapted without his knowledge. This is doubtless an important factor in the development of dependence upon the respirator which occurs in certain patients. It is, therefore, essential that the machine be operated at the minimum level which will produce adequate alveolar ventilation. This does not contraindicate the well-controlled early use of a respirator to avoid fatigue, and numerous observers have suggested spirometer measurement of tidal-air volumes to determine incipient respiratory difficulty; this is more sensitive than clinical observation or a patient's subjective state (Stafford and Gurney, 1951).

Certain other shortcomings of the respirator arise out of the restrictions which it places upon the movements of a patient and his attendants. It is obvious that frequent changes of position are essential for the avoidance of the pneumonias and bedsores which result from circulatory stasis, the muscle atrophy, contractures, and joint and bone changes which follow immobilization, especially in the prone position. Therapists are hampered by the respirator, since opening it even for a few minutes leads to a measurable decrease in the oxygen saturation of a patient's peripheral blood (Elam et al., 1948). Despite the serious disadvantages of the tank respirator, rooms with alternating pressure have remained in the developmental stage presumably because of their high cost and the single-purpose utilization of hospital space. Critical evaluation of the cuirass respirator (Plum and Lukas, 1951) and the rocking bed (Lenarsky, 1949) indicate that they do not take the place of the tank respirator, although they are of value as adjuncts to it.

If a patient with pharyngeal paralysis is placed in a respirator, constant vigilance must be maintained lest the machine force him to aspirate pooled pharyngeal secretions or regurgitated gastric contents. Control of this situation is usually first attempted through postural drainage, pharyngeal suction and parenteral feeding, but, if these measures fail, tracheotomy is indicated. Some advocate tracheotomy as a prophylactic measure (Priest et al., 1947) to avoid the possible (and imperfectly evaluated) damage of the CNS by generalized hypoxia.

Pulmonary edema, atelectasis and emphysema are other hazards of respirator treatment; this may be true only because it permits life to continue long enough for their development. Further study of the pathologic mechanisms involved will doubtless bring greater agreement on their prevention and treatment. Positive pressure is said to reduce the risk of pulmonary edema (Masland et al., 1950) and dry up excessive bronchial secretions (Bower, 1950). It seems logical, however, that the latter might be the result of drying of the tracheobronchial tree and might, therefore, be reduced ultimately by humidification of the inspired air. A device for this has been described by Kubicek et al. (1947) for use with a tracheotomy tube through which antibiotics may also be nebulized. It is clear that the use of drugs to control pharyngeal and pulmonary secretion by depressing the autonomic nervous system is harmful, since they make the secretions ropey and viscous. Dehydration has the same effect. Mucous plugs in bronchi, which lead to hypoxia and atelectasis, often can be removed by manipulating respirators and teaching patients how to produce effective coughs; a bronchoscope should be used as a last resort.

Indications for respirator treatment (condensed from Wilson, 1952) are: (1) paralysis of primary respiratory muscles (diaphragm and intercostals); (2) uncomplicated pharyngeal paralysis only when other measures fail (the carefully planned respirations of a patient who is trying to avoid aspiration of mucus from the pharynx are sometimes difficult to distinguish from the irregular inefficient respirations due to disturbances of the respiratory centers); (3) central disturbances of respiration (characterized by irregular, occasionally slow, or hiccoughing respiration). The above conditions, however, seldom exist singly, so that constant watchfulness and ready improvisation are required. For patients who cannot adjust their respiratory rhythm to that of a respirator, direct electrical stimulation of the phrenic nerve has been used with success for limited periods (Whittenberger et al., 1949). This method, however, is still in the experimental stage.

While there is disagreement as to whether tracheotomy is a prophylactic or a last-ditch measure, indications for the operation as listed by Priest et al. (1947) are the following: (1) respiratory distress as evidenced by recurrent cyanosis, coarse rales in the chest and laryngeal stridor; (2) excitement and intractability, causing a patient to resist pharyngeal aspiration; (3) stupor of degree sufficient to make a patient oblivious of accumulation of secretion in his airway; (4) inability to cough effectively; (5) pharyngeal pooling of mucus, vocal-cord paralysis, or intralaryngeal hypesthesia demonstrable by laryngoscopy.

Treatment of three respirator patients who had long and stormy courses but finally recovered is described by Monke et al. (1951). Among other things, the cost of treating one of these patients was estimated to be slightly over $10,000, which provides a rough index of the financial load entailed. According to a survey of respirator patients made by The National Foundation for Infantile Paralysis as of November, 1950, and believed to be incomplete, there were nearly 600 in respirators (Howe, 1952a). Two hundred spent 20 or more hours per day in respirators. The median duration of respirator treatment was 4 months, and the average cost of such care in hospitals was $19.20 per day, thus bringing the average cost per patient to $2,304. The survey also showed that, as compared with November, 1949, the number of full-time respirator patients had increased by nearly 40 per cent. Since 1947 it had increased by about 300 per cent, which corresponds rather closely to the ratio of increase in reported cases of poliomyelitis. However, the two may not have been correlated, and the increase in respirator patients may reflect the improved treatment of bulbar patients, who in former times, uniformly died when placed in respirators. The average number of patients in respirators between April, 1949, and November, 1950, was 390; this represented an average yearly expenditure of roughly $2,700,000.

EPIDEMIOLOGY

Poliomyelitis attacks children with greater frequency than adults, the highest incidence being in the age group under 10 years. According to Aycock (1941), pregnancy predisposes to paralysis in the mother. The disease is rare in infants under 6 months, presumably because of the carrying over of maternal antibodies, but it is also possible that during this period there is less exposure to the virus than at later ages. Newborn children may be susceptible (Mouton et al., 1950), which is to be expected if the serum of the mother does not contain type specific antibody (Howe, unpublished data). During epidemics, age-specific attack rates usually range from 1 to 10 per thousand in the two most susceptible age groups, 0 to 4 and 5 to 9 years, and from 1 to 3 per hundred thousand in people 20 years of age and older. Average annual rates are naturally much lower as may be seen in Chart 13, yet

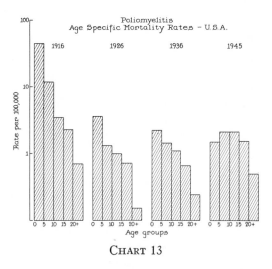

CHART 13

Collins (1946) in a study of 20,258 individuals up to 24 years of age found a history of antecedent poliomyelitis (including death) in 1.1 per cent of the group.

During the period from 1920 to 1945 in the U. S. there was a definite shift in age selection, so that children were being attacked at an older age than formerly (Chart 13). Whereas 30 years ago the highest attack rates were recorded in the 0 to 4 age group, they were later found in the next higher age group (5 to 9). This shift in age incidence has involved all the countries in which poliomyelitis is epidemic (Dauer, 1948; Maclean, 1950). A difference in age selection has also been consistently seen in a comparison of rural and urban areas, there being a definite trend toward a higher average age of those attacked in rural districts (Aycock, 1929; Olin, 1952). These differences, however, have become less marked as the distinctions between rural and urban life have been partially obliterated. For a more detailed discussion, see Howe (1949).

These facts are consistent with a single explanation, namely, that exposure is postponed longer in rural communities than in

Poliomyelitis
Per Cent Distribution of Cases by Age Groups

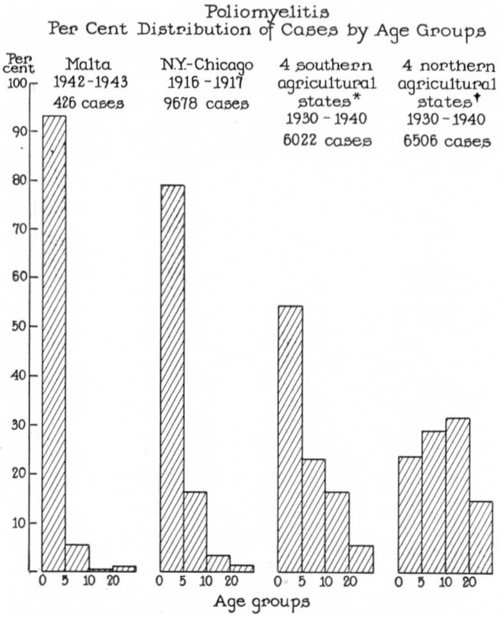

CHART 14

* Alabama, Georgia, Louisiana and North Carolina.
† Kansas, Minnesota, Montana and Vermont.
    For sake of brevity, the age group 20 and over is presented as a quinquennium, whereas it should be shown as embracing a 50-year span.

cities, and in present populations than in those of past generations. There is no longer any doubt that poliomyelitis is world-wide in distribution, although in some areas it may be of small importance as an epidemic disease. To be convinced of this, it is necessary only to study accounts of poliomyelitis in Cuba, Equador, India, Japan, Malta, Mauritius, Puerto Rico, or Venezuela. The findings are practically the same for these diverse regions, and a summary of them by Paul (1947) shows that epidemics are relatively small and infrequent, and that from

80 to 90 per cent of the reported paralytic cases occur in children less than 5 years of age. There seems to be only one explanation for these facts, namely, in these countries the virus of poliomyelitis is so ubiquitous that virtually everyone comes in contact with it before the age of 5 years. In Chart 14, the age selection in the Malta outbreak of 1942-43 (Seddon et al., 1945) is compared with that in New York and Chicago in 1916 and 1917 and with that of 4 southern and 4 northern agricultural states. The age selection in the southern states has considerable similarity to that of relatively primitive countries, e.g., Malta, or to that of large northern cities a generation ago. That those who do not succumb to paralysis gain immunity is likewise apparent. For example, in the Malta outbreak reported by Seddon et al (1945), there were 57 cases among British troops and 397 among Maltese children, but none in the Maltese soldiers even though they were equally exposed.

Reasons for discrepancies in the age selection of paralytic disease, therefore, appear to lie in differences of exposure and immunization which are conditioned by human cultural habits, climate and possibly genetic factors; most of these were outlined in the classic monograph of Wickman (1913). More extensive documentation was provided by Lavinder, Freeman and Frost (1918) in their report of the epidemic of 1916 in New York City. From that time it has been fairly clear that poliomyelitis is disseminated by human contact, although there is still disagreement as to the precise nature of the contact. Wickman was mainly concerned with small rural communities where he believed that evidence of a chain of transmission from one patient to another could be established. Since his time, many others have reported remarkable chains of contact, yet the fact remains that the possibility of obtaining this kind of evidence is relatively rare (Perkins, 1945). Lavinder, Freeman and Frost showed that in greater New York City a radial spread of the disease from an original focus appeared to take place. Thus, from the locality of the first case in Brooklyn they could plot concentric zones, each greater in radius by a mile, in which the median case occurred progressively later than in the preceding zone. While this pattern is not invariably apparent in all epidemics, it is a frequently observed phenomenon, and, when one considers the number of cases of nonparalytic and asymptomatic poliomyelitic infections which are not reported, it is surprising that the paralytic ones make any pattern at all. Wickman was conscious of the infections existing at the clinical threshold as well as below it, although he did not have a clear idea of their number.

Modern research has provided a more accurate measure of the number of silent infections in the human population. For example, an indirect estimate of them may be obtained in the following manner. Poliomyelitis would not selectively attack young children unless adults were either not exposed to the virus or were immune. Since adults and children live in the same homes, the first alternative need not be considered further. However, it is possible that adults may become resistant to the virus in a nonspecific fashion by virtue of growing older. If this were true, one would expect that age selection would be identical throughout any given climatic zone, since physiologic maturity should be reasonably uniform in all persons of a given age group. On the contrary, it is constantly observed that the average age of poliomyelitis patients is higher in rural areas than in large cities. This fact suggests that there is a postponement of exposure in sparsely settled regions and indicates that the immunity of adults is acquired by exposure to the virus. Yet Collins (1946) in a survey involving 174,850 persons of all ages found that only 1.1 per cent of those from 20 to 24 years old gave a history of a paralytic attack of poliomyelitis (including death) while 0.64 per cent showed detectable residua. Since the attack rates of paralytic poliomyelitis are negligi-

ble above this age, it appears that the immunity of most adults has been gained at a price of about one paralytic illness per hundred nonparalytic or abortive infections.

The problem may be approached in another manner. Poliomyelitis and measles have roughly the same age selection, although the former tends to affect very young children slightly more than does the latter. Chart 15 shows a comparison of the two diseases with respect to age in the counties of Maryland during the period from 1920 to 1945; it is obvious that in both

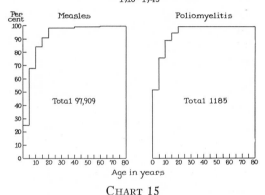

Cumulative Per Cent Age Distribution of Cases
Counties of Maryland
1916-1943

CHART 15

diseases at least 90 per cent of the cases occurred in persons of 20 years or younger. Yet there were reported 97,909 cases of measles and only 1,185 cases of paralytic poliomyelitis. In measles, most cases are diagnosed without difficulty, and about 60 per cent are reported. It is, therefore, clear that the reported cases of this disease as compared with reported cases of poliomyelitis show a ratio of roughly 200 to 1. Consequently, it is difficult to escape the conclusion that during this period there were approximately 200 nonparalytic and abortive cases of poliomyelitis to every paralytic one. This figure is in amazing agreement with that arrived at by Collins' method.

There is an entirely different and possibly even more convincing line of evidence for the existence of a large subclinical human reservoir of infection in the fact that virus has been demonstrated in the sewage of New York City from a drainage tree serving 625,000 people when only 4 cases had been reported in the area (Melnick, 1947). It was estimated that more than 6 per cent of this population were carriers. Furthermore, virus has been found in the raw sewage of Toronto, Canada, one month before a case was recognized (Rhodes et al., 1950), and from the sewage of Johannesburg, South Africa, two months after the last reported case (Mundel et al., 1946).

Evidence thus far presented clearly supports the earlier conclusions of Wickman (1913) and those who followed, namely, that human beings serve as a reservoir of virus, and that asymptomatic carriers must be extremely numerous during epidemics. It has also been shown that even outside of tropical countries poliomyelitis infection may be demonstrated throughout the year (Nelson and Aycock, 1944; Ward and Sabin, 1944). The failure to detect infections in lower mammals, despite many vigorous attempts, is in conformity with the idea that poliomyelitis is primarily a human disease which is spread by intimate human contact.

The concept of widely disseminated virus is also in complete harmony with observations on the distribution of active immunity as evidenced by the presence of antibodies which neutralize the virus. This derives chiefly from the demonstration that antibody against the Lansing strain (Type II) is world-wide and that antibodies against Type I (Brunhilde) and Type III (Leon) have been found not only in pools of gamma globulin obtained in the U. S. A. (Bodian, 1949c) but also in the sera of north Alaskan Eskimos (Paul et al., 1951), of native Egyptians (Paul et al., 1952) and of remote African tribes residing in virtual isolation from European civilization (Howe and Dick, unpublished data). That antibody is indeed correlated with immunity is indicated by the close correspondence between the curves of age-specific attack rates and those showing the distribution of Lansing

antibody in the various age groups (Turner et al., 1950).

The fact that three immunologically different types of virus (Committee on Virus Typing of The National Foundation for Infantile Paralysis, 1951) have been identified has important epidemiologic implications. Findings in the few serum pools studied thus far suggest that these, at least, are widely distributed. Furthermore, it does not seem likely that many more types exist, else it would be impossible for the majority of persons the world over to meet and surmount them before the ages of 5 to 20 years, depending upon where they live.

For many years it has been known to laboratory workers that strains of poliomyelitis virus isolated from different patients in different localities at different times differ in the severity of disease evoked by them in experimental animals. Some of these strains may be postulated as being relatively benign in man. Furthermore, it is now apparent that differences in virulence are independent of antigenic type. Thus, there is a mechanism for explaining all the vagaries of poliomyelitis which do not fit the so-called rules, most especially the continuation of subclinical immunization in the absence of clinically demonstrable infection and the occasional occurrence of unusually severe epidemics.

The epidemicity of poliomyelitis has been one of its outstanding characteristics in countries of the temperate zones. There is reason, however, for believing that the disease has not always had this character. For example, about a hundred years elapsed from the time that poliomyelitis was first noted in Europe until epidemics became apparent. Likewise, in the United States, epidemics were first described shortly before the turn of the century, although the disease was known to occur sporadically in much earlier times. It seems very probable, therefore, that until the beginning of what is known as the modern era, poliomyelitis had the endemic characteristics which it now displays in so-called primitive countries (Paul, 1947). This belief is strengthened by reports of the age selection in the late nineteenth century. Admittedly, these are crude and contain many diagnostic errors, but they are suggestive. From various European sources, for example, Starr (1899) tabulated a series of 609 cases of which 86 per cent occurred in children under 5 years of age. The first outbreak of any size to be reported in the U. S. A. took place in 1894 and was characterized by 67 per cent of children under 6 years (Caverly, 1924). It is also not irrelevant that in the outbreaks of 1916 and 1917 in New York and Chicago there was an even more marked selection of very young children (Chart 14).

Epidemics of poliomyelitis recur with considerable regularity during the summer in the temperate zones. In large metropolitan areas the disease smolders throughout the year with summer outbreaks from every 3 to 5 years. Small communities may experience poliomyelitis "epidemics" with the recognition of only 1 or 2 cases, since the small population involved would be unlikely to produce more paralytic infections. Under these conditions, however, the actual age-specific paralytic rates are usually somewhat higher than those observed in large cities. Olin (1952) has shown convincingly that paralytic rates increase with decreasing population density, possibly because there is delayed exposure in sparsely settled areas, and virus reaches susceptible persons at ages when the disease is more severe. A most dramatic example of the effects of almost complete isolation has been observed among the Eskimos of Hudson's Bay (Peart, 1949). In this instance the introduction of the virus into a previously unimmunized population of 275 persons resulted in 57 paralytic cases (a rate of 20 per cent) which were distributed among old and young alike with the exception of the age group of 0 to 4 years where the paralytic rate was only 4 per cent!

The seasonal incidence of poliomyelitis in temperate zones is a phenomenon for which there is no ready explanation. The relatively small outbreaks in warm countries may take place at any time of the year. In the northern United States a seasonal increase in cases begins in June, while August through October are the months of highest incidence. In the southern part of the United States, the disease approaches more closely an endemic status with less-marked seasonal fluctuations than in the North. Although epidemics may run their entire course during the winter (Leake et al., 1917) even at subzero temperatures (Peart, 1949), the transmission of the virus is obviously facilitated by warm weather. This may favor the parasite by altering the conditions of human contact, the extrahuman survival and dissemination of the virus, or the resistance of the host.

While it is generally agreed that the virus is spread largely through human contact, the nature of this contact has remained obscure. It has been recognized for many years that virus could be demonstrated in the pharyngeal secretions and stools of paralyzed patients and symptomless carriers. The high infection rate among familial associates and slow propagation of the disease from one household to another suggest that rather intimate conditions of personal association are usually necessary. The fact that many members of a family are found to be infected at the time the index case is recognized (Zintek, 1947) has been interpreted as indicating simultaneous exposure, but, in view of the technical difficulties of demonstrating virus, this could also mean that the virus was introduced by one individual who was still a carrier at the time of the survey. No one who has watched children at play can doubt that many opportunities exist for direct transfer of either pharyngeal secretions or feces not only among the children themselves but also to their adult associates.

Virus can be demonstrated in the pharyngeal secretions of roughly half of the patients studied early in the course of illness, while fecal virus is found in an even higher percentage. Furthermore, virus has rarely been isolated from the pharynx except during a period 7 to 10 days before or after the onset of symptoms (Howe et al., 1945; Wenner and Tanner, 1948; Schabel et al., 1950), while it may be present in stools 12 to 19 days before onset (Brown et al., 1945; Gear and Mundel, 1946; Schabel et al., 1948) and for many weeks thereafter (Horstman et al., 1946b). This finding may be of some biologic significance, since the period during which virus is obtained from the pharynx coincides quite closely with the calculated infectious period arrived at from secondary cases presumably arising from a single contact with an extra-familial primary case (Casey, 1942; Aycock and Kessel, 1943; Silverthorne et al., 1949). Although documentation is not extensive, young children are implicated as the chief pharyngeal virus carriers. This is consistent with the fact that antibody is found in pharyngeal secretions only if also present in the blood serum (Bell, 1948) and that the incidence of serum antibodies increases with age. The fact that the continued elimination of the virus in stools for a longer period of time has not been connected more frequently with the appearance of late secondary cases constitutes evidence which favors spread of virus by pharyngeal secretions. Both poliomyelitis and measles spread radially and appear to reach children in the same age groups, yet patients with poliomyelitis do not have the cough and the coryza which are so effective as propagating mechanisms in measles. If, however, the virus were occasionally present in saliva, it would not be necessary to postulate any other vehicle for its transfer. On the other hand, the apparent multiplication of the virus in the alimentary tract and the excretion of large quantities of it in the feces argues with equal force for this medium of transfer. The analogy between poliomyelitis and the enteric diseases arises from the fact that poliomyelitis behaves seasonally very much as do such infections as typhoid fever and dysentery. However, it is a striking fact that during the past generation, which has seen so much improvement in community hygiene and home sanitation, dysentery has almost been eliminated, while there has been only a slight shift in the age selection of poliomyelitis, mainly into the school-age group, which, perhaps, is chiefly due to a decrease in family size, affording less opportunity for introduction of virus into a family.

Whatever the general mode of spread of poliomyelitis is, there are also accessory means of transfer. For example, virus can frequently be recovered from house-flies and filth-flies during epidemic periods (Melnick, 1949). These insects are thought to be passive carriers and for the most part have been trapped in areas where they had ready access to human feces. Whether flies in urban areas with good sewage disposal are likewise frequently infected remains to be demonstrated. Furthermore, the increased incidence of poliomyelitis during the summer months in temperate zones corresponds roughly with the season of increased fly-prevalence. Quite obviously, if flies play a role in transmission it is only an accessory one, and their relative importance will vary enormously with climate, season, sanitation and other factors (Seddon et al., 1945; Leake et al., 1917; Peart, 1949). Efforts to suppress fly-populations with DDT sprays during urban epidemics of poliomyelitis have not resulted in any demonstrable control of the disease. In fact, epidemics of poliomyelitis have been built up and apparently run their course during fly-control programs instituted for other reasons (Gear, 1952).

Repeated attempts to recover poliomyelitis virus from blood-sucking arthropods have been negative. This is not surprising, since viremia appears to be infrequent in man (Ward et al., 1946), unless it occurs during the earliest hours of the prodromal illness, a period which needs more thorough investigation.

Diligent search has failed to reveal epidemics traceable to contaminated food or water supplies despite the fact that virus has been demonstrated in raw sewage

(Maxcy, 1949). Although 5 small outbreaks have been attributed to the consumption of raw milk infected with virus, this indicates the vigilance of epidemiologists far more than a dangerous route of transmission.

CONTROL

Since there is no specific therapy for poliomyelitis and since the virus is widely disseminated through personal contact at epidemic times, it is obvious that the ultimate control of this disease must come by furthering the process of immunization. Artificial induction of active immunity appears to offer the greatest chance of success, but there are several qualifying circumstances which must be considered. Natural infection under the modifying influence of passively introduced antibody appears to be successful in such diseases as measles but has offered little promise in poliomyelitis. Indeed, the evidence so far accumulated indicates that active-passive immunization does not take place under conditions of natural exposure even in countries where the virus reaches children at such early ages that maternally transmitted antibody should still be present (Sabin, 1951). On the other hand, it has been possible, under laboratory conditions, to induce active-passive immunization in chimpanzees (Bodian, 1952a). Chimpanzees can be immunized against homologous strains of poliomyelitis virus if alimentary infection is induced by the feeding of active virus (Melnick and Horstmann, 1947; Howe et al., 1950). The process, however, carries with it a certain risk of paralysis. Koprowski et al. (1952) have shown that human volunteers fed a presumably mild strain of Type II (Lansing type) virus developed a benign alimentary infection which was followed by the production of serum neutralizing antibody in titers similar to those observed in chimpanzees. It is doubtful, however, whether the use of active virus can be justified in man, even though it has been shown that the administration of human gamma globulin permits the development of active immunity and at

the same time greatly reduces the risk of paralysis in experimental animals (Bodian, 1951b). Similarly, cynomolgus monkeys fed active virus were protected against paralysis even though only 0.1 ml. of gamma globulin per kilo of body weight was given prior to challenge (Bodian, 1952b). Reservations regarding the use of vaccines containing active virus arise from the fact that the normal process of immunization (at least in the larger cities of the U.S.A.) goes on at the rate of one paralytic accident in 100 or more immunizations. A vaccine containing live virus would have to offer greater safety than the natural process; this would be difficult to guarantee at the inception of a vaccination program. For this reason, therefore, inactivated-virus preparations, though admittedly far less efficient than active virus, seem to offer the best chance of ultimate success.

Virus may be inactivated with formalin, ultraviolet light or high intensity electron bombardment and still retain sufficient antigenicity to immunize mice (Milzer et al., 1945), cotton rats (Loring et al., 1947; Schwerdt et al., 1951; Dick et al., 1951), monkeys (Morgan, 1948), and chimpanzees (Howe, 1951) against many paralyzing doses of active virus. Certain levels of serum antibody are consistently associated with immunity in experimental animals (Morgan, 1949) and probably also in man (Howe, 1952b). Furthermore, it seems likely that these levels can be approximated by the use of inactive virus combined with adjuvants. Methods for growing poliomyelitis virus in tissue culture (Enders et al., 1949) may solve serious problems of human vaccination. A vaccine must contain the three presently recognized types of poliomyelitis virus. That other types may suddenly crop up is relatively unlikely.

Until mass immunization is possible, poliomyelitis will continue to be a terrifying disease. Reason points out that ultimate escape from infection is impossible and that temporary escape may actually be undesirable in so far as it postpones infection to later ages when its consequences may be more severe. However, irrational fear frequently dictates popular reactions and creates pressure for unnecessary restrictions of community life. It is encouraging to note that the rational approach appears to be gaining ground. For example, poliomyelitis patients are now admitted to many general hospitals. Ordinary isolation procedures are followed with disinfection of objects which may be contaminated by respiratory secretions or fecal material. There is a tendency to shorten the period of isolation to 7 days and to discharge patients to their homes whenever they may continue to receive good medical care. In some hospitals, parents are now allowed to enter their children's rooms instead of standing hopelessly outside the door as formerly.

To pursue the rational approach further, the large number of unrecognized infections make it unlikely that any control measure will materially affect the course of an epidemic. Nevertheless, in individual instances, the risk of exposure may be somewhat reduced. For example, it would obviously be inadvisable to condone the association of healthy individuals (especially children) with those who are sick or have had known exposures. Yet it is not practical to quarantine adult family contacts or do much more than discourage movements of the normal children. Travel into epidemic areas should be interdicted. There is no good reason for closing schools or prohibiting public gatherings unless they definitely increase the risk of exposure by drawing children together from a large sparsely populated area. The decision to close a camp or a boarding school is difficult. It should be noted that, by the time a case is recognized in such a situation, many other children would have already been infected (Rubenstein et al., 1948), and to close the camp or school would spread the virus over a wide area to many susceptible children and young adults. Ingalls and Rubenstein (1950) have shown that average rates for camps and other children's institutions are about the same as general community rates for the same age groups. Nevertheless, this does not lessen the panic caused by an outbreak in which 5 paralytic cases occur in a group of 31 children (Rubenstein et al., 1948).

While there is no indication that common media such as food or drink are implicated, this possibility should never be forgotten. This applies especially to that common bathtub, the swimming pool. Control of flies and abatement of sewage pollution are in themselves desirable, but there is no evidence that they affect the course of an epidemic. Appeals to the press to avoid sensationalism have met with success in some cities and have definitely reduced ill-considered and irrational behavior.

During epidemics, children with unexplained fevers should be given bed rest. On the other hand, undue fear should not be aroused by sensational warnings against exercise or chilling, for there is no evidence that either of these, under ordinary conditions, has any effect upon the extent of paralysis unless experienced after signs of CNS invasion are apparent. Elective nose and throat operations should be postponed in the face of an epidemic but not at other times.

REFERENCES

Addair, J., and Snyder, L. H., 1942, Evidence for an autosomal recessive gene for susceptibility to paralytic poliomyelitis. J. Hered., 33, 307-309.

Anderson, G. W., Anderson, G., Skaar, A. E., and Sandler, F., 1950, The risk of poliomyelitis after tonsillectomy. Ann. Otol., Rhinol. and Laryngol., 59, 602-613.

Armstrong, C., 1939, The experimental transmission of poliomyelitis to the eastern cotton rat. Pub. Health Rep., 54, 1719-1721.

Aycock, W. L., 1929, A study of the significance of geographic and seasonal variations in the incidence of poliomyelitis. J. Prev. Med., 3, 245-278.

Aycock, W. L., 1941, The frequency of poliomyelitis in pregnancy. New England J. Med., 225, 405-408.

Aycock, W. L., 1942a, Familial aggregation in policmyelitis. Am. J. Med. Sci., 203, 452-465.

Aycock, W. L., 1942b, Tonsillectomy and poliomyelitis. I. Epidemiologic considerations. Medicine, 21, 65-94.

Aycock, W. L., and Kessel, J. F., 1943, The infectious period of poliomyelitis and virus detection. Am. J. Med. Sci., *205*, 454-465.

Bahlke, A. M., and Perkins, J. E., 1945, Treatment of preparalytic poliomyelitis with gamma globulin. J. Am. Med. Assn., *129*, 1146-1150.

Baker, A. B., Matzke, H. A., and Brown, J. R., 1950, Poliomyelitis. III. Bulbar poliomyelitis; a study of medullary function. Arch. Neurol. and Psychiat., *63*, 257-281.

Bell, E. J., 1948, The relationship between the anti-poliomyelitic properties of human nasopharyngeal secretions and blood serums. Am. J. Hyg., *47*, 351-369.

Bodian, D., 1946, Experimental evidence on the cerebral origin of muscle spasticity in acute poliomyelitis. Proc. Soc. Exp. Biol. and Med., *61*, 170-175.

Bodian, D., 1947, Poliomyelitis: Neuropathologic observations in relation to motor symptoms. J. Am. Med. Assn., *134*, 1148-1154.

Bodian, D., 1948a, Poliomyelitis in an uninoculated rhesus monkey, and in orally inoculated monkeys, receiving desoxypyridoxine. Am. J. Hyg., *48*, 87-93.

Bodian, D., 1948b, The virus, the nerve cell, and paralysis; a study of experimental poliomyelitis in the spinal cord. Bull. Johns Hopkins Hosp., *83*, 1-107.

Bodian, D., 1949a, Poliomyelitis: Pathologic anatomy, *in* Poliomyelitis: Papers and Discussions Presented at First International Poliomyelitis Conference. J. B. Lippincott Co., Phila., pp. 62-84.

Bodian, D., 1949b, Neutralization of three immunological types of poliomyelitis virus by human gamma globulin. Proc. Soc. Exp. Biol. and Med., *72*, 259-261.

Bodian, D., 1951a, Second attacks of paralytic poliomyelitis in human beings in relation to immunity, virus types and virulence, with a report of two cases, and four other individuals in Baltimore, 1944, infected with virus of the Leon type. Am. J. Hyg., *54*, 174-190.

Bodian, D., 1951b, Experimental studies on passive immunization against poliomyelitis. I. Protection with human gamma globulin against intramuscular inoculation, and combined passive and active immunization. Am. J. Hyg., *54*, 132-143.

Bodian, D., 1952a, A reconsideration of the pathogenesis of poliomyelitis. Am. J. Hyg. In press.

Bodian, D., 1952b, Experimental studies on passive immunization against poliomyelitis. II. The prophylactic effect of human gamma globulin on paralytic poliomyelitis in cynomolgus monkeys after virus feeding. Am. J. Hyg. In press.

Bodian, D., and Cumberland, M. C., 1947, The rise and decline of poliomyelitis virus levels in infected nervous tissue. Am. J. Hyg., *45*, 226-239.

Bodian, D., and Howe, H. A., 1941a, Neurotropism and the genesis of cerebral lesions in poliomyelitis: an experimental study. Bull. Johns Hopkins Hosp., *68*, 58-79.

Bodian, D., and Howe, H. A., 1941b, The rate of progression of poliomyelitis virus in nerves. Bull. Johns Hopkins Hosp., *69*, 79-85.

Bodian, D., and Howe, H. A., 1945, Non-paralytic poliomyelitis in the chimpanzee. J. Exp. Med., *81*, 255-274.

Bodian, D., and Howe, H. A., 1947, The significance of lesions in peripheral ganglia in chimpanzee and in human poliomyelitis. J. Exp. Med., *85*, 231-242.

Bodian, D., Morgan, I. M., and Howe, H. A., 1949, Differentiation of types of poliomyelitis viruses. III. The grouping of fourteen strains into three basic immunological types. Am. J. Hyg., *49*, 234-245.

Bouman, H. D., 1947, Some physiological aspects of infantile paralysis. Physiotherapy Rev., *27*, 221-227.

Bouman, H. D., Baumgartner, B. S., and Shaffer, K. J., 1951, Frequency-intensity curves of human muscle. A new method for quantitative electro-diagnosis. Fed. Proc., *10*, 18.

Bouman, H. D., and Schwartz, R. P., 1944, The degree, the extent, and the mechanism of muscle spasm in infantile paralysis. N. Y. State J. Med., *44*, 147-153.

Bower, A. G., 1950, Concept of poliomyelitis based on observations and treatment of 6000 cases in 4-year period. Northwest. Med., *49*, 103-107, 187-190, 261-266.

Bower , A. G., Bennett, V. R., Dillon, J. B., and Axelrod, B., 1950, Investigation on the care and treatment of poliomyelitis patients. Ann. Western Med. and Surg., *4*, 561-582, 686-716.

Bower, A. G., Huddleston, O. L., and Hovsepian, D., 1950, Use of curare in the treatment of anterior poliomyelitis. Am. J. Med., *8*, 160-168.

Bradford, H. A., and Anderson, L. L., 1950, Electro-cardiographic observations during a poliomyelitis epidemic. Ann. Int. Med., *32*, 270-278.

Brahdy, M. B., and Katz, S. H., 1951, Effect of transportation on severity of acute poliomyelitis. J. Am. Med. Assn., *146*, 772-774.

Brahdy, M. B., and Lenarsky, M., 1936, Respiratory failure in acute epidemic poliomyelitis. Late results and complications. J. Pediat., *8*, 420-433.

Brainerd, H., Katz, H. J., Rowe, A. P., Jr., and Geiger, J. C., 1945, The clinical manifestations of poliomyelitis. Treatment with neostigmine and the Kenny method. J. Am. Med. Assn., *128*, 718-719.

Bridge, E. M., Clarke, G. H., and Abbe, D., 1946, Clinical immunity in poliomyelitis. Am. J. Dis. Child., *72*, 501-509.

Brodie, M., 1935, Active immunization in monkeys against poliomyelitis with germicidally inactivated virus. J. Immunol., *28*, 1-18.

Brown, F. M., and Bruesch, S. R., 1949, Patterns of increased electrical skin resistance in acute human poliomyelitis. Arch. Neurol. and Psychiat., *62*, 766-777.

Brown, G. C., Francis, T., Jr., and Pearson, H. E., 1945, Rapid development of carrier state and detection of poliomyelitis virus in stool nineteen days before onset of paralytic disease. J. Am. Med. Assn., *129*, 121-123.

Brown, J. R., and Baker, A. B., 1949, Poliomyelitis. I. Bulbar poliomyelitis: a neurophysiological interpretation of the clinicopathological findings. J. Nervous and Mental Dis., *109*, 54-78.

Brown, J. R., Baker, A. B., Adams, J., and McQuarrie, I., 1947a, The bulbar form of poliomyelitis. I. Diagnosis and the correlation of clinical with physiological and pathological manifestation. J. Am. Med. Assn., *134*, 757-762.

Brown, J. R., Baker, A. B., and McQuarrie, I., 1947b, The bulbar form of poliomyelitis. II. Therapeutic measures based on pathological and physiological findings. J. Am. Med. Assn., *135*, 425-428.

Buchthal, F., 1949, Problems of the pathologic physiology of poliomyelitis. Am. J. Med., *6*, 579-591.

Buchthal, F., and Høncke, P., 1944, Electromyographical examination of patients suffering from poliomyelitis ant. ac. up to 6 months after the acute stage of the disease. Acta med. Scand., *116*, 148-164.

Casals, J., Olitsky, P. K., and Anslow, R. O., 1951, A specific complement-fixation test for infection with poliomyelitis virus. J. Exp. Med., *94*, 123-137.

Casey, A. E., 1942, Observations on an epidemic of poliomyelitis. Science, *95*, 359-360.

Caughey, J. E., and Malcolm, D. S., 1950, Muscle spasm in poliomyelitis; a study of a New Zealand epidemic. Arch. Dis. Childhood, *25*, 15-21.

Caverly, C. S., 1924, Infantile Paralysis in Vermont 1894-1922. Vermont State Department of Public Health, Burlington, 1924.

Clark, D. A., 1931, Muscle counts of motor units: a study in innervation ratios. Am. J. Physiol., *96*, 296-304.

Collins, S. D., 1946, The incidence of poliomyelitis and its crippling effects, as recorded in family surveys. Pub. Health Rep., *61*, 327-355.

Collins, V. J., Foster, W. L., and West, W. J., 1947, Vasomotor disturbances in poliomyelitis, with special reference to treatment with paravertebral sympathetic block. New England J. Med., *236*, 694-697.

The Committee on Typing of the National Foundation for Infantile Paralysis, 1951, Immunologic classification of poliomyelitis viruses. I. A cooperative program for the typing of one hundred strains (and 8 other papers on typing). Am. J. Hyg., *54*, 191-274.

Curnen, E. C., Shaw, E. W., and Melnick, J. L., 1949, Disease resembling nonparalytic poliomyelitis associated with a virus pathogenic for infant mice. J. Am. Med. Assn., *141*, 894-901.

Dalldorf, G., Sickles, G. M., Plager, H., and Gifford, R., 1949, A virus recovered from the feces of "poliomyelitis" patients pathogenic for suckling mice. J. Exp. Med., *89*, 567-582.

Dauer, C. C., 1948, Trends in age distribution of poliomyelitis in the United States. Am. J. Hyg., *48*, 133-146.

Davis, D. J., Weber, F. J., and Arey, M. S., 1941, A clinical study of poliomyelitis in Charleston County, South Carolina, 1939. Pub. Health Rep., *56*, 1007-1017.

Deaver, G. G., 1951, A study of the adjustment of 500 persons over sixteen years of age with disabilities resulting from poliomyelitis. N. Y. Med., *7*, No. 7, 16-18; 33-36.

DeLorme, T. L., Schwab, R. S., and Watkins, A. L., 1948, The response of the quadriceps femoris to progressive-resistance exercises in poliomyelitis patients. J. Bone and Joint Surg., *30-A*, 834-847.

Dick, G. W. A., Schwerdt, C. E., Huber, W., Sharpless, G. R., and Howe, H. A., 1951, Immunization of cotton rats with inactivated Lansing poliomyelitis virus. II. Inactivation by physical methods. Am. J. Hyg., *53*, 131-138.

Ebaugh, F. G., and Hoekstra, C. S., 1947, Psychosomatic relationships in acute anterior poliomyelitis. Am. J. Med. Sci., *213*, 115-121.

Elam, J. O., Hemingway, A., Gullickson, G., and Visscher, M. B., 1948, Impairment of pulmonary function in poliomyelitis; oximetric studies in patients with spinal and bulbar types. Arch. Int. Med., *81*, 649-665.

Elford, W. J., Galloway, I. A., and Perdrau, J. R., 1935, The size of the virus of poliomyelitis as determined by ultrafiltration analysis. J. Path. and Bact., *40*, 135-140.

Elliott, H. C., 1947, Studies on the motor cells of the spinal cord. V. Poliomyelitic lesions in the spinal motor nuclei in acute cases. Am. J. Path., *23*, 313-325.

Enders, J. F., Weller, T. H., and Robbins, F. C., 1949, Cultivation of the Lansing strain of poliomyelitis virus in cultures of various human embryonic tissues. Science, *109*, 85-87.

Evans, C. A., Smith, W. M., and Chambers, V. C., 1951, Multiplication of poliomyelitis virus in monkey testicular tissue. Bact. Proc., to be published in J. Bact.

Eveleth, M. S., and Ryan, A. J., 1944, Prostigmine in acute anterior poliomyelitis. Yale J. Biol. and Med., *17*, 351-357.

Foster, C., Jones, J. H., Henle, W., and Dorfman, F., 1944, The effect of vitamin B_1 deficiency and of restricted food intake on the response of mice to the Lansing strain of poliomyelitis virus. J. Exp. Med., *79*, 221-234.

Fox, M. J., 1946, Curare in the treatment of acute poliomyelitis. J. Am. Med. Assn., *131*, 278-280.

Francis, T., Jr., Krill, C. E., Toomey, J. A. and Mack, W. N., 1942, Poliomyelitis following tonsillectomy in five members of a family. J. Am. Med. Assn., *119*, 1392-1396.

Gammon, G. D., Todd, J. C., Lucchesi, P., LaVoccetta, A., Chance, B., Jr., Silverstein, A., and Sunderman, F. W., 1948, The spinal fluid in poliomyelitis. Arch. Neurol. and Psychiat., *59*, 551-554.

Gard, S., 1943, Purification of poliomyelitis viruses: experiments on murine and human strains. Acta Med. Scandinav. supp., *143*, 1-173.

Gear, J. H. S., and Mundel, B., 1946, Studies in poliomyelitis. II. The study of an outbreak of poliomyelitis occurring in a suburb of Johannesburg. South African Med. J., *20*, 106-110.

Gear, J. H. S., 1952, The extrahuman sources of poliomyelitis, *in* Poliomyelitis: Papers and Discussions Presented at Second International Poliomyelitis Conference. To be published.

Goldbloom, A., Jasper, H. H., and Brickman, H. F., 1948, Electroencephalographic studies in poliomyelitis. J. Am. Med. Assn., *137*, 690-697.

Gordon, F. B., Schabel, F. M., Jr., Casey, A. E., and Fishbein, W. I., 1948, Laboratory study of the epidemiology of poliomyelitis. J. Infect. Dis., *82*, 294-301.

Greenberg, M., 1951, An epidemic experience report on poliomyelitis. Hospitals, J. Am. Hosp. Assn., *25*, 52-54.

Grulee, C. G., Jr., and Panos, T. C., 1948, Epidemic poliomyelitis in children; clinical study, with special reference to symptoms and management of bulbar polioencephalitis. Am. J. Dis. Child., *75*, 24-39.

Gutmann, E., and Guttmann, L., 1944, The effect of galvanic exercise on denervated and re-innervated muscles in the rabbit. J. Neurol., Neurosurg. and Psychiat., 7, 7-17.

Heine, J., 1840, Beobachtungen über Lähmungszustände der untern Extremitäten und deren Behandlung. Stuttgart, Köhler.

Hill, A. B., and Knowelden, J., 1950, Inoculation and poliomyelitis; a statistical investigation in England and Wales in 1949. Brit. Med. J., *2*, 1-6.

Hines, H. M., Melville, E. V., and Wehrmacher, W. H., 1945, The effect of electrical stimulation on neuromuscular regeneration. Am. J. Physiol., *144*, 278-283.

Hines, M., 1936, The anterior border of the monkey's (*Macaca mulatta*) motor cortex and the production of spasticity. Am. J. Physiol., *116*, 76.

Hodes, R., 1948, Electromyographic study of defects of neuromuscular transmission in human poliomyelitis. Arch. Neurol. and Psychiat., *60*, 457-473.

Hodes, R., 1949, Selective destruction of large motoneurons by poliomyelitis virus. I. Conduction velocity of motor nerve fibers of chronic poliomyelitis patients. J. Neurophysiol., *12*, 257-266.

Hodes, R., Peacock, S. M., Jr., and Bodian, D., 1949, Selective destruction of large motoneurons by poliomyelitis virus. II. Size of motoneurons in the spinal cord of rhesus monkeys. J. Neuropath. and Exp. Neurol., *8*, 400-410.

Horstmann, D. M., 1949, Clinical aspects of acute poliomyelitis. Am. J. Med., *6*, 592-605.

Horstmann, D. M., 1950, Acute poliomyelitis; relation of physical activity at the time of onset to the course of the disease. J. Am. Med. Assn., *142*, 236-241.

Horstmann, D. M., 1952, Poliomyelitis virus in blood of orally infected monkeys and chimpanzees. Proc. Soc. Exp. Biol. and Med., *79*, 417-419.

Horstmann, D. M., Melnick, J. L., and Wenner, H. A., 1946a, The isolation of poliomyelitis virus from human extra-neural sources. I. Comparison of virus content of pharyngeal swabs, oropharyngeal washings, and stools of patients. J. Clin. Investig., *25*, 270-274.

Horstmann, D. M., Ward, R., and Melnick, J. L., 1946b, The isolation of poliomyelitis virus from human extra-neural sources. III. Persistence of virus in stools after acute infection. J. Clin. Investig., *25*, 278-283.

Howe, H. A., 1949, Epidemiology of poliomyelitis in the light of modern research. Am. J. Med., *6*, 537-550.

Howe, H. A., 1951, Limitation of alimentary virus carriage in chimpanzees immunized against poliomyelitis. Fed. Proc., *10*, 410.

Howe, H. A., 1952a, Poliomyelitis. Proc. Nat. Conf. on Chronic Disease: Preventive Aspects, 1951. To be published.

Howe, H. A., 1952b, Antibodies and immunity to poliomyelitis, *in* Poliomyelitis: Papers and Discussions Presented at the Second International Poliomyelitis Conference. To be published.

Howe, H. A., and Bodian, D., 1941a, Neuropathological evidence on the portal of entry problem in human poliomyelitis. Bull. Johns Hopkins Hosp., *69*, 183-215.

Howe, H. A., and Bodian, D., 1941b, Poliomyelitis in the chimpanzee: A clinical pathological study. Bull. Johns Hopkins Hosp., *69*, 149-181.

Howe, H. A., and Bodian, D., 1941c, Second attacks of poliomyelitis. An experimental study. J. Exp. Med., *74*, 145-166.

Howe, H. A., and Bodian, D., 1942, Neural Mechanisms in Poliomyelitis. The Commonwealth Fund, New York.

Howe, H. A., and Bodian, D., 1944a, Poliomyelitis by accidental contagion in the chimpanzee. J. Exp. Med., *80*, 383-390.

Howe, H. A., and Bodian, D., 1944b, The efficiency of intranasal inoculation as a means of recovering poliomyelitis virus from stools. Am. J. Hyg., *40*, 224-226.

Howe, H. A., and Bodian, D., 1947, Isolation of poliomyelitis virus from the throats of symptomless children. Am. J. Hyg., *45*, 219-222.

Howe, H. A., Bodian, D., and Morgan, I. M., 1950, Subclinical poliomyelitis in the chimpanzee and its relation to alimentary reinfection. Am. J. Hyg., *51*, 85-108.

Howe, H. A., Bodian, D., and Wenner, H. A., 1945, Further observations on the presence of poliomyelitis virus in the human oro-pharynx. Bull. Johns Hopkins Hosp., *76*, 19-24.

Huddleston, O. L., and Golseth, J. G., 1948, Electromyographic studies of paralysed and paretic muscles in anterior polioymelitis. Arch. Physical Med., *29*, 92-98.

Huebner, R. J., Cole, R. M., Beeman, E. A., Bell, J. A., and Peers, J. H., 1951, Herpangina; etiological studies of a specific infectious disease. J. Am. Med. Assn., *145*, 628-633.

Ingalls, T. H., and Rubenstein, A. D., 1950, Expectancy for outbreaks of poliomyelitis in camps and schools. Am. J. Pub. Health, *40*, 555-560.

Jones, A., and Dickson, F. D., 1947, An analysis of one hundred cases of poliomyelitis. J. Missouri Med. Assn., *44*, 881-882.

Jungeblut, C. W., 1937, Effect of ultraviolet irradiation on poliomyelitis virus *in vitro*. Proc. Soc. Exp. Biol. and Med., *37*, 160-162.

Kabat, H., and Knapp, M. E., 1943, The use of prostigmine in the treatment of poliomyelitis. J. Am. Med. Assn., *122*, 989-995.

Kessel, J. F., and Moore, F. J., 1945, Occurrence of poliomyelitis virus in tonsils and stools of noncontacts during an interepidemic period. Am. J. Hyg., *41*, 25-29.

Kilbourne, E. D., 1950, Diverse manifestations of infection with a strain of Coxsackie virus. Fed. Proc., *9*, 581-584.

Kilham, L., Levens, J., and Enders, J. F., 1949, Non-paralytic poliomyelitis and mumps meningoencephalitis. Differential diagnosis. J. Am. Med. Assn., *140*, 934-936.

Koprowski, H., Jervis, G. A., and Norton, T. W., 1952, Immune responses in human volunteers upon oral administration of a rodent-adapted strain of poliomyelitis virus. Am. J. Hyg., *55*. To be published.

Kottke, F. J., Tiegen, B. S., Siegel, S., and Knapp, M. E., 1948, Evaluation of aids to muscle reeducation in the treatment of poliomyelitis. Arch. Physical Med., *29*, 141-147.

Krusen, E. M., 1949, Functional improvement produced by resistive exercise of quadriceps muscles affected by poliomyelitis. Arch. Physical Med., *30*, 271-277.

Kubicek, W. G., Holt, G. W., Elam, J. O., Brown, J. R., and Gullickson, G., 1948, Oxygen therapy in poliomyelitis; a tracheotomy inhalator incorporating humidification and the optional use of positive pressure for oxygen therapy in patients with tracheotomy. Arch. Physical Med., *29*, 217-225.

Lahelle, O., 1951, Complement-fixation test for the Lansing strain of poliomyelitis virus. Am. J. Hyg., *54*, 391-401.

Landon, J. F., 1934, An analysis of 88 cases of poliomyelitis treated in the Drinker respirator with a control series of 68 cases; I. clinical studies in poliomyelitis. J. Pediat., *5*, 1-8.

Landsteiner, K., and Popper, E., 1909, Uebertragung der Poliomyelitis acuta auf Affen. Ztschr. f. Immunitätsforsch. u. exper. Therap., *2*, 377-390.

Langmuir, A. D., 1942, Carriers and abortive cases in a rural poliomyelitis outbreak. Am. J. Pub. Health, *32*, 275-281.

Lassen, H. C. A., and Skinhøj, E., 1948, The immediate prognosis in poliomyelitis. Ugesk. F. Laeger, *110*, 905-907.

Lavinder, C. H., Freeman, A. W., and Frost, W. H., 1918, Epidemiologic studies of poliomyelitis in New York City and the northeastern United States during the year 1916. Pub. Health Bull., No. 91, July. 309 pp.

Lawson, R. B., 1949, Therapeutic problems encountered in acute poliomyelitis. Minnesota Med., *32*, 693-696.

Leake, J. P., Bolten, J., and Smith, H. F., 1917, Winter outbreak of poliomyelitis. Elkins, W. Va., 1916-17. Pub. Health Rep., *32*, 1995-2015.

Lenarsky, M., 1949, The rocking bed—its use in poliomyelitis. Arch. Pediat., *66*, 339-348.

Lenarsky, M., 1950, Bulbar poliomyelitis. Arch. Pediat., *67*, 250-266.

Lenhard, R. E., 1950, Prognosis in poliomyelitis. J. Bone and Jt. Surg., *32A*, 71-79.

Lensen, S. G., Rhian, M., and Stebbins, M. R., 1947, Inactivation of partially purified poliomyelitis virus in water by chlorination. Am. J. Pub. Health, *37*, 869-874.

Levine, R., Goodfriend, J., and Soskin, S., 1942, The influence of prostigmine, atropine and other substances on fibrillation and atrophy in the denervated skeletal muscle of the rat. Am. J. Physiol., *135*, 747-751.

Li, C. P., and Habel, K., 1951, Adaptation of Leon strain of poliomyelitis to mice. Proc. Soc. Exp. Biol. and Med., *78*, 233-238.

Longshore, W. A., Edwards, G. B., and Hollister, A. C., Jr., 1951. Personal communication.

Loring, H. S., Marton, L., and Schwerdt, C. E., 1946, Electron microscopy of purified Lansing virus. Proc. Soc. Exp. Biol. and Med., *62*, 291-292.

Loring, H. S., and Schwerdt, C. E., 1944, Studies on purification of poliomyelitis virus. 2. pH stability range of MVA strain. Proc. Soc. Exp. Biol. and Med., *57*, 173-175.

Loring, H. S., Schwerdt, C. E., Lawrence, N., and Anderson, J. C., 1947, Preparation of formaldehyde-inactivated poliomyelitis virus and its use as an immunizing agent in cotton rats. Science, *106*, 104-105.

Lovett, R. W., 1917, The treatment of infantile paralysis. P. Blakiston's Son and Co., Phila., 2nd ed.

Lundbaek, K., 1943, Experimental investigations on the function of the autonomic nervous system during the acute phase of poliomyelitis. Acta med. Scand., *114*, 565-583.

Maclean, F. S., 1950, Poliomyelitis in New Zealand, 1947-49. New Zealand Department of Health, Annual Report of the Director General, 1949-1950, 90-112.

Magoun, H. W., 1944, Bulbar inhibition and facilitation of motor activity. Science, *100*, 549-550.

Masland, R. L., Lawson, R. B., and Kelsey, W. M., 1950, The use of positive pressure as an aid in the handling of respiratory paralysis from anterior poliomyelitis. J. Pediat., *36*, 31-34.

Maxcy, K. F., 1949, Supposed involvement of water supplies in poliomyelitis transmission. J. Am. Water Works Assn., *41*, 696-704.

McCarroll, H. R., 1942, The role of physical therapy in the early treatment of poliomyelitis. J. Am. Med. Assn., *120*, 517-519.

Medin, O., 1891, Ueber eine Epidemie von spinaler Kinderlähmung. Verhandl. d. 10. Internat. med. Kongr., 1890, 2: Abt., 6, 37, 47.

Melnick, J. L., 1946, Storage of mouse-adapted strains of poliomyelitis virus and Japanese B encephalitis virus at subfreezing temperatures. J. Infect. Dis., *79*, 27-32.

Melnick, J. L., 1947, Poliomyelitis virus in urban sewage in epidemic and in non-epidemic times. Am. J. Hyg., *45*, 240-253.

Melnick, J. L., 1948, Chemical and physical methods for the preparation of clinical samples for virus study. Proc. 4th Int. Cong. Trop. Med. and Malaria, pp. 401-407.

Melnick, J. L., 1949, Isolation of poliomyelitis virus from single species of flies collected during an urban epidemic. Am. J. Hyg., *49*, 8-16.

Melnick, J. L., and Horstmann, D. M., 1947, Active immunity to poliomyelitis in chimpanzees following subclinical infection. J. Exp. Med., *85*, 287-303.

Melnick, J. L., and Ledinko, N., 1951, Immunity following oral administration of poliomyelitis virus to monkeys. J. Immunol., *67*, 213-217.

Melnick, J. L., Kaplan, A. S., Zabin, E., Contreras, G., and Larkum, N. W., 1951, An epidemic of paralytic poliomyelitis characterized by dual infections with poliomyelitis and Coxsackie viruses. J. Exp. Med., *94*, 471-492.

Milzer, A., Oppenheimer, F., and Levinson, S. O., 1945, A new method for the production of potent inactivated vaccines with ultraviolet irradiation. III. A completely inactivated poliomyelitis vaccine with the Lansing strain in mice. J. Immunol., *50*, 331-340.

Monke, J. V., Shapiro, S. K., and Baker, A. B., 1951, Problems in the treatment of bulbar poliomyelitis. Neurol., *1*, 99-110.

Morgan, I. M., 1948, Immunization of monkeys with formalin-inactivated poliomyelitis viruses. Am. J. Hyg., *48*, 394-406.

Morgan, I. M., 1949, Level of serum antibody associated with intracerebral immunity in monkeys vaccinated with Lansing poliomyelitis virus. J. Immunol., *62*, 301-310.

Mouton, C. M., Smillie, J. G., and Bower, A .G., 1950, Report of ten cases of poliomyelitis in infants under six months of age. J. Pediat., *36*, 482-492.

Mundel, B., Gear, J. H. S., and Wilson, D., 1946, Studies in poliomyelitis. IV. The distribution of the virus of poliomyelitis in a sewage purification works in Johannesburg. South African Med. J., *20*, 336-338.

Nelson, N. B., and Aycock, W. L., 1944, A study of the reporting of paralytic poliomyelitis in Massachusetts, 1928-1941. Am. J. Hyg., *40*, 163-169.

Nelson, N. B., and Green, W. T., 1943, Second attacks of anterior poliomyelitis; report of four cases. Am. J. Dis. Child., *65*, 757-762.

Nitshke, R. A., 1950, Frequency of paralysis in various muscles during poliomyelitis. Phys. Ther. Rev., *30*, 131-134.

Olin, G., 1952, The epidemiologic pattern of poliomyelitis in Sweden, *in* Poliomyelitis: Papers and Discussions Presented at Second International Poliomyelitis Conference. To be published.

Osborne, S. L., Kosman, A. J., Bouman, H. D., McElvenny, R. T., and Ivy, A. C., 1949, Electrical stimulation of muscles in treatment of acute and chronic forms of anterior poliomyelitis. Phys. Therap. Rev., *29*, 63-68.

Paul, J. R., 1947, Poliomyelitis in Japan. Am. J. Hyg., *45*, 206-218.

Paul, J. R., Melnick, J. L., Barnett, V. H., and Goldblum, N., 1952, A survey of neutralizing antibody to poliomyelitis virus in Cairo, Egypt. Am. J. Hyg. In press.

Paul, J. R., Riordan, J. T., and Melnick, J. L., 1951, Antibodies to three different antigenic types of poliomyelitis virus in sera from north Alaskan Eskimos. Am. J. Hyg., *54*, 275-285.

Paul, W. D., and Couch, O. A., Jr., 1949, Preliminary report on the treatment of anterior poliomyelitis with exercise and curare. Arch. Physical Med., *30*, 277-285.

Peabody, F. W., Draper, G., and Dochez, A. R., 1912, A Clinical Study of Acute Poliomyelitis. Monograph No. 4, New York, Rockefeller Institute for Medical Research.

Peale, A. R., and Lucchesi, P. F., 1943, Cardiac muscle in poliomyelitis. Am. J. Dis. Child., *65*, 733-738.

Pearson, H. E., Brown, G. C., Rendtorff, R. C., Ridenour, G. M., and Francis, T., Jr., 1945, Studies of the distribution of poliomyelitis virus. III. In an urban area during an epidemic. Am. J. Hyg., *41*, 188-210.

Peart, A. F. W., 1949, An outbreak of poliomyelitis in Canadian Eskimos in wintertime. Canad. J. Pub. Health, *40*, 405-417.

Perkins, J. E., 1945, The epidemiology of poliomyelitis. N. Y. State J. Med., *45*, 159-168.

Plum, F., and Lukas, D. S., 1951, An evaluation of the cuirass respirator in acute poliomyelitis with respiratory insufficiency. Am. J. Med. Sci., *221*, 417-424.

Pohl, J. F., 1945, The Kenny concept and treatment of infantile paralysis: report of five year study of cases treated and supervised by Miss Elizabeth Kenny in America. Journal-Lancet, *65*, 265-271.

Pohl, J. F., and Kenny, E., 1943, The Kenny Concept of Infantile Paralysis and its Treatment. Minneapolis and St. Paul, Bruce Pub. Co.

Poliomyelitis, 1948, Lancet, *2*, 582-583.

Pollock, L. J., Boshes, B., Finkelman, I., Chor, H., Hiller, F., Brown, M., Arieff, A. J., Liebert, E., Tigay, E. L., Schiller, M., and Sherman, I. C., 1949, Absence of spasm during onset of paralysis in acute anterior poliomyelitis. Arch. Neurol. and Psychiat., *61*, 288-296.

Pollock, L. J., Boshes, B., Finkelman, I., Hiller, F., Chor, H., Brown, M., Arieff, A. J., Liebert, E., Tigay, E. L., Schiller, M., and Sherman, I. C., 1950, Evolution of neurologic signs of early anterior poliomyelitis. Am. J. Dis. Child., *79*, 973-987.

Priest, R. E., Boies, L. R., and Goltz, N. F., 1947, Tracheotomy in bulbar poliomyelitis. Ann. Otol., Rhinol. and Laryngol., *56*, 250-263.

Ransohoff, N. S., 1945, Curare in the acute stage of poliomyelitis. J. Am. Med. Assn., *129*, 129-130.

Rasmussen, A. F., Jr., Clark, P. F., and Smith, S. C., 1951, Effect of 6-methyl tryptophan on Lansing poliomyelitis in mice. Bact. Proc., to be published in J. Bact.

Reilley, W. A., and Barsanti, A. H., 1950, Priscoline for pain in poliomyelitis. J. Pediat., *36*, 711-714.

Rhodes, A. J., Clark, E. M., Knowles, D. S., Shimada, F., Goodfellow, A. M., Ritchie, R. C., and Donohue, W. L., 1950, Poliomyelitis virus in urban sewage; an examination for its presence over a period of twelve months. Canad. J. Pub. Health, *41*, 248-254.

Rice, E. P., 1949, The families of children with poliomyelitis, *in* Poliomyelitis: Papers and Discussions Presented at the First International Poliomyelitis Conference. J. B. Lippincott Co., Phila., pp. 308-311.

Richards, R. L., Elkins, E. C., and Corbin, K. B., 1947, Curare in the treatment of poliomyelitis. Proc. Staff Meeting Mayo Clinic, *22*, 31-38.

Robbins, F. C., Enders, J. F., Weller, T. H., and Florentino, G. L., 1951, Studies on the cultivation of poliomyelitis viruses in tissue culture. V. The direct isolation and serologic identification of virus strains in tissue culture from patients with non-paralytic and paralytic poliomyelitis. Am. J. Hyg., *54*, 286-293.

Rosenberg, D., and Fischer, A. E., 1948, Curare (intocostrin) in the acute stage of anterior poliomyelitis. Pediatrics, *1*, 648-656.

Rubenstein, A. D., Milnor, J. P., von Magnus, H., and Melnick, J. L., 1948, A study of virus carriers from a poliomyelitis outbreak at a boys' camp. New England J. Med., *238*, 218-222.

Russell, W. R., 1947, Poliomyelitis. The pre-paralytic stage, and the effect of physical activity on the severity of paralysis. Brit. Med. J., *2*, 1023-1028.

Sabin, A. B., 1951, Paralytic consequences of poliomyelitis infection in different parts of the world and in different population groups. Am. J. Pub. Health, *41*, 1215-1230.

Sabin, A. B., and Ward, R., 1941, The natural history of human poliomyelitis. I. Distribution of virus in nervous and non-nervous tissues. J. Exp. Med., *73*, 771-793.

Schabel, F. M., Jr., Casey, A. E., Fishbein, W. I., and Smith, H. T., 1948, Isolation of poliomyelitis virus from human stools during the incubation period. Proc. Soc. Exp. Biol. and Med., *68*, 593-594.

Schabel, F. M., Jr., Casey, A. E., Fishbein, W. I., and Smith, H. T., 1950, Isolation of the virus of poliomyelitis from the stools, oropharynx and nose of contacts. J. Infect. Dis., *87*, 152-157.

Scherer, W. F., Butorac, G., and Syverton, J. T., 1951, Cultivation of poliomyelitis virus in monkey testicular tissue. Fed. Proc., *10*, 417.

Scherp, H. W., and Chambers, L. A., 1936, Resistance of the viruses of poliomyelitis, human influenza and swine influenza to intense vibration. Proc. Soc. Exp. Biol. and Med., *35*, 495-500.

Schultz, E. W., and Robinson, F., 1942, The *in vitro* resistance of poliomyelitis virus to chemical agents. J. Infect. Dis, *70*, 193-200.

Schwerdt, C. E., Dick, G. W. A., Herriott, R. M., and Howe, H. A., 1951, Immunization of cotton rats with inactivated Lansing poliomyelitis virus. I. Inactivation by chemical agents. Am. J. Hyg., *53*, 121-130.

Seddon, H. J., Agius, T., Bernstein, H. G. G., and Tunbridge, R. E., 1945, The poliomyelitis epidemic in Malta 1942-3. Quart. J. Med., *14*, 1-26.

Seidenfeld, M. A., 1952, Psychological aspects of poliomyelitis, *in* Poliomyelitis: Papers and Discussions Presented at the Second International Poliomyelitis Conference. To be published.

Shaughnessy, H. J., Harmon, P. H., and Gordon, F. B., 1930, The heat resistance of the virus of poliomyelitis. J. Prev. Med., *4*, 149-155.

Sherman, Mary S., 1945, Acute anterior poliomyelitis. Final report on seventy cases treated in 1943. J. Am. Med. Assn., *128*, 722-723.

Shwartzman, G., 1950, Enhancing effect of cortisone upon poliomyelitis infection (strain MEF1) in hamsters and mice. Proc. Soc. Exp. Biol. and Med., *75*, 835-838.

Silverthorne, N., Armstrong, M. P., Wilson, F. H., Donohue, W. L., Goodfellow, A. M., Roy, T. E., McClelland, L., Clark, E. M., and Rhodes, A. J., 1949, Studies on poliomyelitis in Ontario. I. Ob-

servations on the apparent infectiousness of the acute case. Canad. Med. Assn. J., *61*, 241-250.

Smith, E., Graubard, D. J., Goldstein, N., and Bikoff, W., 1948, A new method in the management of acute anterior poliomyelitis. N. Y. State J. Med., *48*, 2608-2611.

Smith, W. M., Chambers, V. C., and Evans, C. A., 1951, Growth of neurotropic viruses in extraneural tissues. IV. Poliomyelitis virus in human testicular tissue *in vitro*. Proc. Soc. Exp. Biol. and Med., *76*, 696-700.

Stafford, W. F., Jr., and Gurney, R., 1951, Respiratory failure in poliomyelitis: a simple method for its recognition and control. Ann. Int. Med., *34*, 203-211.

Starr, M. A., 1899, Poliomyelitis anterior acuta, *in* T. C. Allbutt, System of Medicine, London, Macmillan, Vol. 8, pp. 186-206.

Toomey, J. A., 1944, Observations on the treatment of infantile paralysis in the acute stage. Transactions and Studies of the College of Physicians of Philadelphia, *12*, 14-25.

Trask, J. D., Vignec, A. J., and Paul, J. R., 1938, Poliomyelitis virus in human stools. J. Am. Med. Assn., *111*, 6-11.

Turner, T. B., Hollander, D. H., Buckley, S., Kokko, U. P., and Winsor, C. P., 1950, Age incidence and seasonal development of neutralizing antibodies to Lansing poliomyelitis virus. Am. J. Hyg., *52*, 323-347.

Ward, R., Horstmann, D. M., and Melnick, J. L., 1946, The isolation of poliomyelitis virus from human extra-neural sources. IV. Search for virus in the blood of patients. J. Clin. Investig., *25*, 284-286.

Ward, R., and Sabin, A. B., 1944, The presence of poliomyelitis virus in human cases and carriers during the winter. Yale J. Biol. and Med., *16*, 451-459.

Watkins, A. L., and Brazier, M. A. B., 1945, Studies on muscle innervation in poliomyelitis and nerve injuries. Arch. Physical Med., *26*, 69-75.

Weddell, G., Feinstein, B., and Pattle, R. E., 1944, The electrical activity of voluntary muscle in man under normal and pathological conditions. Brain, *67*, 178-257.

Weller, T. H., Enders, J. F., Buckingham, M., and Finn, J. J., Jr., 1950, The etiology of epidemic pleurodynia: a study of two viruses isolated from a typical outbreak. J. Immunol., *65*, 337-346.

Weller, T. H., Robbins, F. C., and Enders, J. R., 1949, Cultivation of poliomyelitis virus in cultures of human foreskin and embryonic tissues. Proc. Soc. Exp. Biol. and Med., *72*, 153-155.

Wenner, H. A., and Tanner, W. A., 1948, Poliomyelitis in families attacked by the disease. I. Distribution of virus in stool and oropharynx of members in households. Am. J. Med. Sci., *216*, 258-269.

Whittenberger, J. L., Sarnoff, S. J., and Hardenbergh, E., 1949, Electrophrenic respiration. II. Its use in man. J. Clin. Investig., *28*, 124-128.

Wickman, O. I., 1913, Acute Poliomyelitis. Nervous and Mental Disease Monograph Series No. 16, New York, J. Nervous and Mental Disease Pub. Co.

Wilson, J. L., 1952, Management of respiratory insufficiency, *in* Poliomyelitis: Papers and Discussions Presented at the Second International Poliomyelitis Conference. To be published.

Wood, C. F., 1947, Two-year follow-up on one quarter

of 1944 epidemic of poliomyelitis in Kentucky. Southern Med. J., *40*, 76-81.

Zintek, A. R., 1947, The rapid infection of a family after introduction of poliomyelitis virus. Am. J. Hyg., *46*, 248-253.

JOSEPH L. MELNICK, ph.d., and EDWARD C. CURNEN, m.d.

Yale University School of Medicine

14

The Coxsackie Group

INTRODUCTION

A variety of acute, self-limited diseases, as exemplified by aseptic meningitis, pleurodynia, herpangina, and brief fever without distinctive features, is caused by the Coxsackie or C viruses which represent a loosely assembled group of filterable agents having in common certain biologic and physical properties and an unusual pathogenicity for infant mice and hamsters. These viruses are widely distributed and represent multiple, distinct entities which differ antigenically and in other respects one from another. The relative importance of individual Coxsackie viruses as causative agents of human disease has not yet been fully appraised.

HISTORY

Attention was first directed to this group of viruses by Dalldorf and Sickles (1948) who isolated in suckling mice strains of a filterable agent obtained from the feces of two children with paralysis. The agent seemed to be unusual and differed from poliomyelitis viruses in that it induced fatal disease with paralysis and destructive lesions of striated muscles in unweaned mice but not in adult mice, adult hamsters or rhesus monkeys. As the children from whom the agent was isolated lived in the town of Coxsackie, New York, Dalldorf (1949) proposed that the term "Coxsackie group of viruses" be used as a provisional designation for this agent and other viruses resembling it. Melnick, Shaw and Curnen (1949) found a similar but not identical virus in the feces, and neutralizing antibodies against it in the serum of patients from southern New England during an unusual prevalence of acute illness resembling nonparalytic poliomyelitis or aseptic meningitis. They isolated other strains from the pharynx and the feces of patients, and from sewage and flies collected in various parts of the United States; by neutralization tests it was found that some of these agents differed antigenically one from another. Coxsackie or C viruses have since been detected in many parts of the world. Their existence as multiple antigenic types has been firmly established (Melnick, Shaw and Curnen, 1949; Melnick and Ledinko, 1950; Dalldorf, 1951). Whereas the strains which were first isolated (Dalldorf and Sickles, 1948) appeared to attack only the muscles of experimentally infected baby mice, other totally unrelated strains were soon encountered which induced lesions not only in muscle but also in the brain and other tissues (Melnick, Shaw and Curnen, 1949; Dalldorf, 1950; Melnick, 1950; Pappenheimer et al., 1950; Melnick and Godman, 1951).

Although Coxsackie viruses were first encountered in patients with illnesses resembling poliomyelitis, considerable evidence indicates that some of these agents may cause other forms of human disease. The finding of four isolated patients in whom a Conn.-5 type of C virus appeared to be responsible for an illness characterized by severe thoracic or muscular pains suggested that the virus might be a causative agent of epidemic myalgia or pleurodynia (Curnen, Shaw and Melnick, 1949; Curnen, 1950). This acute, self-limited malady of hitherto unknown etiology, also called Bornholm disease (Sylvest, 1933), has occurred in many parts of the world since it was apparently first observed in 1856 by Finsen in Iceland. Weller, Enders, Buckingham and Finn (1950) showed that a Conn.-5 type of C virus was the etiologic agent in a typical outbreak of epidemic pleurodynia in Massachusetts. Kilbourne (1950) detected evidence of infection by the same antigenic type of virus in New York among patients with diverse manifestations of illness including pleurodynia. Findlay and Howard (1950) reported that the instillation of a C virus (type 2) into the nose of a volunteer resulted in the development of pleural pain and complement-fixing antibodies against the agent.

Different C viruses were isolated from patients during outbreaks of brief acute febrile illnesses variously described as three-day fever or summer grippe (Webb, Wolfe and Howitt, 1950; Melnick, Ledinko, Kaplan and Kraft, 1950; Huebner, Armstrong, Beeman and Cole, 1950). More recently Huebner, Cole, Beeman, Bell and Peers (1951) reported the recovery of six antigenically different C viruses from patients with fever, mild sore throat and faucial lesions, and attributed to these agents a causative role in this syndrome, which had been described in 1924 by Zahorsky and designated herpangina.

CLINICAL PICTURE

The incubation period of infection by viruses of the Coxsackie group appears to range from 2 to 9 days with a mean between 3 and 5 days (Curnen, 1950; Findlay and Howard, 1950; Huebner et al., 1951). The manifestations of infection by individual viruses of this group are not uniform and, indeed, may represent different disease en-

tities. Information concerning the clinical features of infection by many of the viruses of the group is still meager or lacking, and in numerous accounts of disease associated with C viruses the antigenic type was not identified or the relation of the virus to the associated illness was not definitely determined. An attempt at this time to present a comprehensive description of the clinical picture of infection by these viruses would, therefore, be premature. Nevertheless, it is possible to point out certain patterns of disease which have been associated with particular types of virus and which may serve as a basis for the development of a more complete clinical picture. Evidence of infection in each of the pateints cited is based on the recovery of virus or the development of specific neutralizing antibodies or both in relation to the illness in question.

Aseptic Meningitis

Some patients infected with the Conn.-5 type of Coxsackie virus have aseptic meningitis (Curnen, Shaw and Melnick, 1949; Curnen, 1950). The onset may be sudden or gradual. Fever, malaise, headache, nausea and abdominal pain are common early symptoms. Stiffness of the neck or the back and vomiting tend to appear a day or two later but are not invariably present. The temperature elevation ranges to a maximum of 40.3° C. and lasts from 3 to 9 days with a mean of about 5 days. The febrile course of illness is occasionally diphasic. On physical examination, patients do not appear particularly ill and reveal few objective indications of disease. Hyperemia of the pharynx may be present during the acute stage. Stiffness of the neck or the back is usually evident but rarely persists for longer than the fever. Signs of muscular weakness are equivocal or lacking. Reflexes remain normal. Examination of the cerebrospinal fluid early in the acute phase of illness reveals an increase in the number of leukocytes which, in most instances, does not exceed 100 per c.mm. The percentage of polymorphonuclear cells ranges from 10 to 50. The protein content is normal or only slightly elevated. The total and differential white blood cell counts are usually within normal limits. The course of illness is uncomplicated and terminates with complete recovery. The isolation of C viruses from the feces or the pharynx of patients with similar illnesses has been reported by von Magnus (1949) and by Gard (1949), who, in one case, also recovered a strain from cerebrospinal fluid.

EPIDEMIC MYALGIA OR PLEURODYNIA (BORNHOLM DISEASE)

In patients infected with a single (Conn.-5) type of virus whose illnesses resembled pleurodynia (Curnen, Shaw and Melnick, 1949; Curnen, 1950; Weller, Enders, Buckingham and Finn, 1950; Kilbourne, 1950; Shaw, Melnick and Curnen, 1950), the clinical features corresponded generally to those encountered in the past (Sylvest, 1933) and in a recent typical outbreak in Massachusetts (Finn, Weller and Morgan, 1949). Fever and pain which are almost invariably present together are usually abrupt in onset, although they may be preceded for several hours or days by malaise, anorexia and other vague prodromal symptoms. The pain is most commonly thoracic, often accompanied by headache. The thoracic pain, which may be located on either side or substernally, varies considerably in character and severity, is intensified by movement and may last from two days to almost two weeks. Abdominal pain occurs in approximately half the cases and may be present in the absence of thoracic pain. It is frequently periumbilical or located on the right side more commonly than on the left. Aches in the trunk or the extremities are sometimes noted. Stiffness of the neck or the back is an occasional complaint. Nausea and vomiting are infrequent. Cutaneous hyperesthesia is unusual. The range and the duration of fever correspond to those noted in the patients with aseptic meningitis. The course of acute illness is sometimes diphasic. Tenderness, which may be present over the site of pain, particularly in the abdomen,

appears to be superficial, suggesting localization in the muscular wall rather than in the viscera. In occasional patients with stiffness of the neck or the back, the complaint is manifested by resistance to anterior flexion. The number of leukocytes in the blood is usually normal. As a lumbar puncture is rarely performed on patients with pleurodynia, little information is available concerning alteration of the cerebrospinal fluid. In one case (Curnen, Shaw and Melnick, 1949), the fluid was normal. On the other hand, a laboratory worker who contracted infection with an Ohio-1 type virus had clinical manifestations of both pleurodynia and aseptic meningitis; her cerebrospinal fluid contained 375 leukocytes per c.mm. with 49 per cent polymorphonuclears (Curnen, 1950; Shaw, Melnick and Curnen, 1950). Thélin and Wirth (1950) described patients in Switzerland from whom Coxsackie viruses were recovered who had illnesses with the combined features of pleurodynia and aseptic meningitis, including pleocytosis of the cerebrospinal fluid. In patients with C virus infection manifesting the clinical features of pleurodynia, illness is self-limited, and recovery is complete.

HERPANGINA

The clinical features of this syndrome in patients infected by C viruses of six different antigenic types have been described by Huebner et al. (1951) and by Parrott, Ross, Burke and Rice (1951). The illness is characteristically initiated by a relatively abrupt onset of fever which ranges to a maximum of 40.5° C. and lasts from 1 to 4 days with a mean of about 2½ days. Anorexia and dysphagia are frequently present. A majority of patients over two years of age complain of a moderately sore throat. Vomiting and abdominal pain are present in about one fourth of the cases. Headache and generalized aches are infrequent. Patients with herpangina do not appear very ill. The pharynx is usually hyperemic and discrete characteristic lesions may be seen. These range to 14 in number and average about 5 per patient. They are commonly located on the anterior pillars of the fauces, less frequently on the palate, the uvula, the tonsils or the tongue, and not characteristically on the gingival or buccal mucosa. Early individual lesions are grayish-white papules or vesicles about 1 to 2 mm. in diameter, each surrounded by a red areola. During the next 2 or 3 days the areolae become more intensely red; the vesicles enlarge (rarely to more than 5 mm. in diameter) and subsequently have the appearance of shallow grayish-yellow ulcerations. Vesicular and ulcerative lesions may be present concomitantly and are usually evident for 4 to 6 days after the onset of illness; they are, however, not invariably a feature of the infection. Among closely associated individuals infected by the same type of virus, characteristic vesicles or ulcers may be present in some and not in others. Diarrhea, cough, rhinitis, otitis media and signs of meningeal irritation are not features of this syndrome. Cultures of the oropharynx and the feces usually reveal normal flora, although occasionally pneumococci or beta hemolytic streptococci may be present. The blood-leukocyte counts are usually normal or slightly elevated. In a fourth of the patients studied by Parrott et al. (1951), total white-cell counts ranged from 15,000 to 21,000 per c.mm. In some of these patients the leukocytosis may have been attributable to the presence of pathogenic bacteria. The course of illness in herpangina is benign and self-limited.

The recovery of C viruses from patients with acute, febrile illnesses of short duration and without distinctive features occurring during the spring, the summer or the fall has been reported on a number of occasions (Melnick, Ledinko, Kaplan and Kraft, 1950; Shaw, Melnick and Curnen, 1950; Huebner et al., 1950; Rhodes et al., 1950; Webb, Wolfe and Howitt, 1950). Information is lacking on the frequency of oropharyngeal lesions in these patients whose illnesses in other respects resembled herpangina. It is possible that brief, acute,

febrile episodes of this nature, including the syndrome of herpangina, may represent the commonest form of disease induced in man by a number of different C viruses.

PATHOLOGIC PICTURE

Except for the characteristic findings in herpangina, no distinctive lesions have been observed in patients infected by Coxsackie viruses. At present, information is lacking concerning the histopathologic picture in man of infection by any of these agents, because no deaths attributable to them have been reported. Because infections with Coxsackie and poliomyelitis viruses have a similar seasonal incidence and may occur simultaneously in persons with or without disease and in view of evidence suggesting that even slight trauma may favor the development of paralysis during infection with poliomyelitis virus, the removal of bits of skeletal muscle for study from patients suspected of infection by a C virus may be hazardous.

EXPERIMENTAL INFECTION; HOST RANGE

Viruses of the Coxsackie group induce overt disease in infant mice and hamsters. When injected into chimpanzees or monkeys or when ingested by them, the active agents cause inapparent infection, manifested by a virus carrier-state and the development of specific antibodies.

Experimental infections with C viruses have been studied most extensively in infant mice (Dalldorf, 1950; Melnick, 1950). In these animals signs of disease generally appear within 2 to 10 days after inoculation and are usually manifested by weakness and paralysis of one or more extremities and of the neck. With certain strains, tremors, particularly of the head, and spasticity of the extremities may be observed. In very young mice marked ataxia may be the only sign before death, which usually occurs within 24 hours of the onset of disease. Older mice may survive, and the rate of recovery is relatively higher with some strains of the virus than with others.

Mice are susceptible to infection by the intracerebral, the intraperitoneal and the subcutaneous routes and to a much less extent (approximately 10,000 times) by the oral route (Kaplan and Melnick, 1951). The susceptibility of mice to infection by C viruses diminishes progressively from the time of birth as shown in Figure 33. After the fifth day of life they appear to be in-

bility to infection by the Conn.-5 type virus (Kilbourne and Horsfall, 1951).

The variability in their pathogenic capacities has been recognized by Dalldorf (1950, 1951) in his classification of the C viruses into two groups, based chiefly on the histopathologic features of disease induced by different strains in infant mice. In this scheme, strains which cause only generalized myopathy are classified in Group A, while those which induce focal

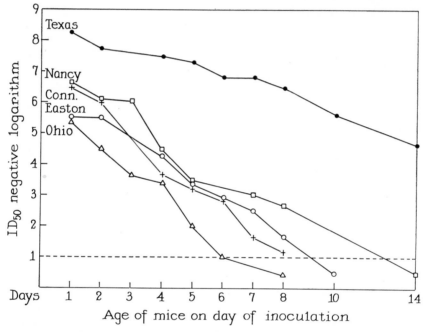

FIG. 33. Decreasing susceptibility with age of infant mice inoculated with five antigenically distinct C viruses: Texas-1, Nancy, Conn.-5, Easton-2, and Ohio-1. For each virus type, the same suspension was titrated in mice of different ages. (Goldblum, N., Unpublished data.)

susceptible to infection by some C viruses, for example the Ohio-1 type. Other C viruses, for example the Texas-1 type, have the capacity to cause paralysis and destructive lesions of muscle when injected into mice up to 3 weeks of age. Although adult mice may be infected and occasionally develop disease following the injection of certain types, serial passage of C virus in adult mice by the conventional transfer of muscle tissue has not been demonstrated. The administration of cortisone to adult mice has been reported to increase their suscepti-

myopathy, together with lesions of the central nervous system and other tissues, are included in Group B. The results of other studies (Godman, Bunting and Melnick, 1952), however, suggest that antigenically different viruses are not clearly divisible into these two categories, but instead exhibit a gradient of pathogenic activity ranging from the Conn.-5 type, which induces variable injury to muscle and severe lesions of the central nervous system, fat, liver and pancreas to the Texas-1 type, which causes severe muscular and cardiac damage but only rarely induces lesions of the nervous system, viscera or fat. Effects intermediate between these extremes are produced by other C viruses, particularly the Ohio-1 and Nancy types. In studies of the histologic changes induced in infant mice, destructive changes in skeletal muscle were detected following infection by each of 120 strains representing 14 antigenically different types. The findings indicated that skeletal muscle is the tissue most consistently affected by the agents.

Typical lesions of striated muscle in infant mice infected by a C virus resemble Zenker's hyaline degeneration, irrespective of the antigenic type virus involved (Dalldorf, Sickles, Plager and Gifford, 1949; Dalldorf, 1950; Melnick and Godman, 1951). The earliest alteration in the muscle is a proliferation of nuclei. Tinctorial changes and swelling of segments of fibers then occur, followed by nuclear pyknosis and fragmentation. At the same time, cross-striations disappear, and the myofibrils thicken and fuse. These form longitudinal striations which tend to fade and disappear as the degenerating segments become homogeneous, refractile, hyaline masses. The sarcolemma usually remains intact. The relatively short diseased segments are sharply demarcated from the contiguous ends of the normal parts of muscle fibers. With the occurrence of segmental necrosis, interstitial edema and infiltrating histiocytes appear. The mononuclear phagocytes enter into the sarcolemmal sheaths of the necrotic segments and ultimately remove the hyalinized muscle. At the height of the process, the affected segment forms a tube containing many histiocytes, remnants of hyaline substance, and fine regenerating muscle fibers or cells which have begun to grow into the sacrolemmal sheath. The regenerating muscle originates as outgrowths from the ends or peripheries of the intact parts of muscle fibers, particularly from the ends abutting on the necrotic segments, but occasionally also within the degenerating segments from those nuclei which have

escaped lethal injury. It grows out in the form of fine, thin fibers with basophilic cytoplasm, each with a central row of closely spaced nuclei, whose characteristic structure constitutes a readily identifiable feature of regeneration. These nuclei are elongate, heavily outlined, vesicular and have two large nucleoli, one of which is typically rodlike. Growth of the regenerating fibers is guided by the persistent sarcolemmal sheaths. Although restoration of the muscle is evident about a week after paralysis, residua of injury are often present in the form of partly mineralized or hyalinized derivatives of necrotic material. Typical lesions are illustrated in Figures 34 and 35.

The occurrence of lesions in tissues other than muscle is also closely related to the age of the mice as well as to the antigenic type of virus. Hepatitis, which develops in 60 to 70 per cent of mice infected during the first 3 days of life by strains of the Conn.-5 type, was not induced when infection was delayed until the fourth day or later. Pancreatitis occurs in newborn mice infected by strains of the Conn.-5 type, and also in mice over 3 weeks of age as shown recently by Pappenheimer et al. (1951), who successfully maintained the agent in adult mice by serial passage of infected pancreas. In adult mice the pancreatic acinal tissue becomes necrotic and is replaced by fat in surviving animals. It is remarkable that pancreatitis does not occur during the suckling period from the fourth to the twenty-first day of life. Infant mice with hepatitis or pancreatitis may not develop encephalitis, and involvement of other tissues is usually absent or not extensive, possibly because the animals die too early in the course of their disease.

Necrotizing steatitis in mice is characteristic of infection with certain types (Conn.-5, Ohio-1) and involves principally the maturing fetal fat lobules (interscapular pads, cervical and cephalic pads, and rarely the fat in the mesentery). Early in the course of infection the fat lobules show a

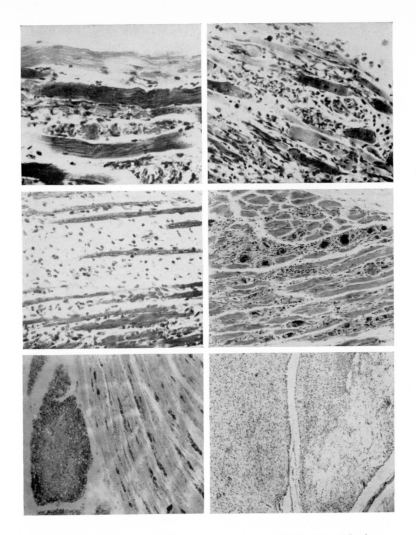

Fig. 34. Lesions of C virus infection in infant mice (Godman, Bunting and Melnick, 1952).

(*Top, left*) Striated muscle. Segmental necrosis in two fibers, illustrating early changes. The upper fiber shows the earliest lesion: nuclear proliferation and pyknosis, accentuation of cross-striations, and fissuring. The adjacent segment of muscle to the right has proliferated to form a regenerating strand. The lower fiber shows a more advanced degree of degradation, with conspicuous crumbling of the hyaline blocks within the sarcolemma. Texas-1 strain, first day of signs. H. and E. stain. × 300.

(*Top, right*) Striated muscle. Segmental necrosis, inflammation and sarcolemmal tube formation. In the center are sarcolemmal tubes in intermediate stages of development, continuous with the degenerated segments of which they form a part. Hyaline segments are present, separated by elements of the inflammatory exudate. Conn.-5 strain, second day of signs. Hematoxylin-eosin-azure stain. × 250.

(*Middle, left*) Slips of regenerating and differentiating muscle. Slender plasmodial fibers with typical nuclear alignment are separated by marked edema and an inflammatory exudate of mononuclear cells. Easton-2 strain, second day of paralysis. H. and E. stain. × 200.

(*Middle, right*) Regenerated muscle. Partly mineralized residual

narrow outer zone of vaguely outlined necrotic cells, which stains with hematoxylin
or basic dyes, and an acidophilic or fuch-
sinophilic center composed of discrete embryonal cells (Fig. 34, *lower left*). As the
lesion evolves, the outer basophilic zone
widens at the expense of the inner area.
Histiocytic phagocytes and lymphocytes in-
filtrate the lobules and soon outnumber the
recognizable fat cells and their remnants.
In animals which have survived the acute
infection, regeneration of fat cells and deposition of calcium in areas of necrosis may
be noted (Pappenheimer et al., 1950;
Dalldorf, 1950; Godman et al., 1952).

Lesions of the CNS may be induced in
baby mice by certain types of C virus
(Conn.-5, Ohio-1) and are more common
following intracerebral injection but are not
invariably a feature of infection by these
strains. Characteristically, an acute encephalomyelitis develops which affects all
parts of the CNS, particularly the cortical
gray matter. Focal leptomeningitis and
perivascular accumulations of lymphocytic
round cells are noted. Large areas of localized necrosis may be present in both the
gray and the white matter, often with little
adjacent inflammatory reaction. This local
encephalomalacia frequently evolves into
liquefaction and porencephaly (Fig. 34,
lower right) (Pappenheimer et al., 1950;
Dalldorf, 1950; Levaditi, 1951; Godman et
al., 1952).

Distribution of the Conn.-5 strain in different tissues was determined quantitatively after inoculation of mice from 4 to 5
days of age (Melnick and Godman, 1951).
High titers of virus developed by the second
day in the blood, heart, liver, muscle, intestine and its contents and were maintained through the eighth day, except in the
blood where the level of virus diminished
earlier. The highest titers occurred in muscle and brain and only in these tissues was
virus present through the ninth day of illness. Pathologic changes appeared after the
virus had reached peak levels (Fig. 36).
Acute necrosis of muscle occurred first on
the fourth day and reached maximal intensity on the eighth day. Mice showed clinical
signs of disease, paralysis, beginning on the
fifth day, and the highest incidence of illness occurred on the eighth day. After the
eighth day the number and the intensity of
lesions rapidly diminished, although scattered acute lesions continued to appear for
the next 4 days. With the decrease in myopathy there was a concomitant decrease in
the incidence of clinical signs of disease.
The regenerative phase, which began one
day after the first lesions were noted,
reached its maximal development on the ninth
and the tenth days. It is noteworthy that
the regenerating sarcoblasts suffered no injury, despite high viral concentrations.

It is evident that the distribution of lesions in mice is influenced by many factors
including the type and the dose of virus, the
route of inoculation, the strain and the age
of mice and the interval between inoculation and the fixation of tissue for histologic
examination. These variables make the histopathologic classification of C virus sug-

masses are present with the remainder of the muscle being completely
restored. Texas-1 strain, 11 days after onset of paralysis. Phloxine-
methylene-blue stain. $\times$ 100.

(*Lower, left*) Vital staining to illustrate fat necrosis and localized
muscle necrosis. Selective destruction of the peripheral part of the fat
lobule (dark area) and the preservation of the central part (light
area) with normal cellular architecture are shown. Selective involvement of muscle is evidenced by the dark-staining, necrotic areas. Mice
inoculated subcutaneously with trypan blue 5 hours before being
sacrificed. Conn.-5 strain.

(*Lower, right*) Brain. Rarefaction and porencephaly following circumscribed necrosis in the cerebrum. Conn.-5 strain, third day of
signs. H. and E. stain. $\times$ 125.

gested by Dalldorf more difficult and less certain than one based exclusively on immunologic criteria.

Although no obvious clinical disease has been produced in monkeys following the in-

geal and intestinal carriers of virus and developed specific neutralizing and complement-fixing antibodies against the agent. Chimpanzees can also be infected by the oral route (Melnick, Kaplan and Kraft,

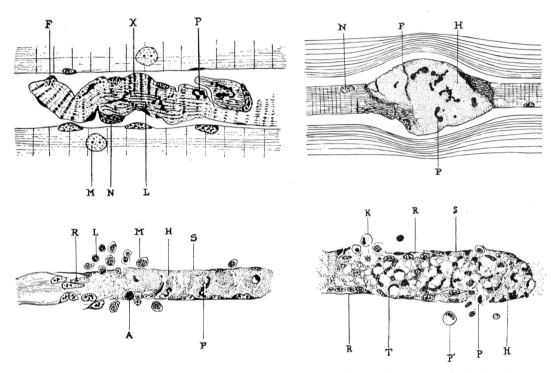

Fig. 35. Freehand drawings by Dr. Gabriel C. Godman, illustrating the lesion in striated muscle in C virus infection of mice.

(*Top, left*) Earliest appearance of segmental degeneration, showing irregular accentuation of cross striations (X), nuclear proliferation and pyknosis (P), muscle nucleus of intact fiber (M), sacrolemmal nuclei (N), longitudinal strial accentuation of myofibrils (L).

(*Top, right*) Demarcated segmental degeneration in stage of hyalinization. Increased numbers of pyknotic nuclei (P), fissure in hyalinized segment (F), hyalinized material (H), muscle nucleus in intact part of fiber (N) are present in the segment.

(*Bottom, left*) Earliest stage of sarcolemmal tube formation, illustrating ingress of phagocytes and sarcoblastic slips into the demarcated segment of degenerated muscle. There are fissures in the hyaline material (H), sarcolemma (S), mononuclear histiocyte (M), polymorphonuclear leukocyte (L), regenerating muscle elements (R), phagocyte with cytoplasmic inclusions (A).

(*Bottom, right*) Later stage of development of sarcolemmal tube, showing vacuolar sarcolysis of hyaline material (H), by phagocytes (P), regenerating muscle elements (R), sarcolemma (S), mitosis in histiocyte (K).

jection of a C virus, these animals may develop a subclinical infection (Melnick and Ledinko, 1950). Following oral administration of the Ohio-1 strain, cynomolgus (but not rhesus or cercopithecus) monkeys had pyrexia for brief periods, became pharyn-

1952), and the infection in them is inapparent or subclinical and is manifested by viremia for 2 or 3 days, a pharyngeal carrier-state of from 3 to 7 days, and an intestinal carrier-state lasting from 12 to 35 days. Specific neutralizing antibodies appear in about 12 days and persist for at least 2 years. During this period it has not been possible to cause reinfection with strains of the same type. The animals are susceptible to subsequent infection by other types, however, and when an unrelated strain is fed, the chimpanzees respond in the same manner as they did to the first type. The reaction of these animals to the feeding of C viruses is similar to that observed following the feeding of poliomyelitis virus.

Cockroaches, *Periplaneta americana*, fed a single meal containing a C virus, excrete the agent for as long as 15 days (Fischer and Syverton, 1951). Although it is possible that C viruses may be disseminated by flies and cockroaches, it has not been shown that multiplication of virus occurs within them.

ETIOLOGY

Viruses of the Coxsackie group are relatively small and pass readily through bacteria-tight filters (EK Seitz and Corning

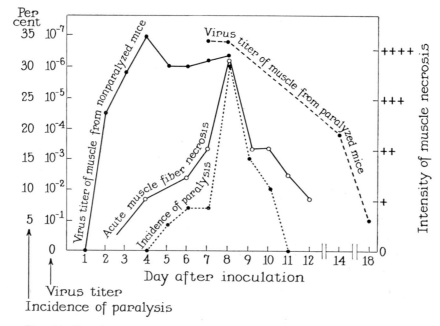

FIG. 36. Correlation of virus concentration of muscle tissue in nonparalyzed and in paralyzed mice with intensity of muscle fiber necrosis and with incidence of apparent disease; Conn.-5 strain. (Melnick, J. L., and Godman, G. C., 1951.)

C viruses have not been found to propagate readily in other laboratory animals, although their host range has by no means been thoroughly explored. One strain (type 2) has been adapted to developing chick embryos (Huebner, Ransom and Beeman, 1950), and another strain has been grown in tissue culture (Slater and Syverton, 1950). C viruses have been isolated from flies collected in nature (Melnick, 1950) and can be detected for 12 days in the excreta of flies which have been fed virus experimentally (Melnick and Penner, 1952).

glass fritted UF) without significant loss in titer. Results of filtration through gradocal membranes of known porosity indicate that the diameters of three different immunologic types of C virus (Conn.-5, Ohio-1, Texas-1) are of the order of 15 to 23 mμ (Melnick, Rhian, Warren and Breese, 1951). This was true of virus contained in the brain or the muscle of experimentally infected mice and in naturally infected human feces. It is possible that C viruses may not be uniform in size, because in two laboratories a strain belonging to another type

(TT type 1) was found to pass through filters indicating a particle diameter of approximately half that of the other types (Quigley, 1949; Melnick et al., 1951). Slightly different results were obtained by Himmelweit, Findlay and Howard (1950). Ultracentrifugation in the partition cell of the analytical rotor, or in tubes in an angle rotor, yielded sedimentation constants of 100 to 160 (S_{20}) and estimated diameters of about 25 to 30 mμ for the Conn.-5, the Texas-1, the Ohio-1 and type 1 viruses (Melnick et al., 1951). These figures were arrived at by following the sedimentation of the infective particle and of the complement-fixing antigen, which may be identical. The discrepancy in the results obtained by filtration and sedimentation with the type 1 virus cannot be resolved at present. Direct examination of purified preparations of the Texas-1 type in the analytical ultracentrifuge and in the electron microscope also yielded values of 25 to 35 mμ (Warren and Breese, 1951).

C viruses are relatively stable. Suspensions of virus may be preserved frozen at −70° or −20°C. for long periods without significant loss in titer. Viral activity is also maintained when specimens of infected tissue are stored in 50 per cent glycerol or horse serum at room temperature for as long as 70 days, and in a refrigerator for over a year (Melnick and Ledinko, 1950). Like poliomyelitis viruses, these agents withstand exposure to a wide range of pH, i.e., pH 2.3 to 9.4 for one day and 4.0 to 8.0 for seven days (Robinson, 1950). Aqueous suspensions of certain strains of C virus were inactivated between 50° and 55° C. when heated for 30 minutes; temperatures 5 to 20° C. higher were required for inactivation when the virus was suspended in milk, cream, or ice cream (Kaplan and Melnick, 1952). C viruses were not inactivated or not inhibited in vitro or in vivo by a variety of chemotherapeutic agents, including penicillin, streptomycin, chloramphenicol, terramycin and viscosin. Certain commonly used antiseptics, including

ethanol (70 per cent), Lysol (5 per cent), Roccal (1 per cent), and ether, also failed to inactivate the agents. Treatment with 0.1 N HCl or 0.3 formaldehyde, however, effected rapid inactivation (Melnick, 1951).

At least 15 different immunologic types of C virus (Table 18) are now recognized and, as many strains have not yet been classified, it seems probable that additional types will be found. Convincing evidence for the existence of multiple distinct immunologic types has been obtained by means of cross-neutralization tests in infant mice (Sickles and Dalldorf, 1949; Melnick and Ledinko, 1950), cross-complement-fixation tests (Casals, Olitsky and Murphy, 1949; Kraft and Melnick, 1950), cross-protection tests in infant mice born of immunized mothers (Melnick, Clarke and Kraft, 1950) and by cross-protection tests in chimpanzees (Melnick, Kaplan and Kraft, 1952). In identifying strains of C virus the results obtained by each of these different methods have been in close agreement.

For use in neutralization tests suspensions containing chiefly muscle and bone can be prepared from mice infected with a C virus during the first 48 hours of life and sacrificed on the first day of illness. These suspensions which cause fatal disease in susceptible baby mice stimulate a specific immune response when injected into adult mice or other animals. Each type of virus is readily neutralized by immune animal serum prepared against strains of the same type but not by immune serum against different types (Table 18) or by specific antisera against other viruses.

Antigens for complement-fixation tests can be prepared from the tissue of infant mice infected with C viruses, but the methods of preparation have not yet been standardized. Relatively crude antigens may be employed for strains of high titer. Casals, Olitsky and Murphy (1949) utilized infected tissue successively extracted with acetone and ethyl ether to eliminate nonspecific reactions. Treatment with protamine sulfate (Warren, Weil, Russ and

TABLE 18. NEUTRALIZATION OF STRAINS OF C VIRUS AND DEMONSTRATION OF EIGHT ANTIGENIC TYPES*

STRAIN OF VIRUS	CONTROL ID_{50}	IMMUNE SERUM: LOG OF NEUTRALIZATION INDEX									
		Conn.-5	Ohio-1	Texas-1	Hi. Pt.	Easton-2	Type 1	Type 2	Type 3	Nancy	Alaska-5
Conn.-5	$10^{-5.7}$	4.7	0	0	0	0	0	0	0	0	0
Ohio-1	$10^{-5.2}$	0	4.2	0	0	0	0	0	0	0	0
Texas-1	$10^{-7.0}$	0	0	6.0	5.0	0	0	0	0	0	0
NHF-43	$10^{-7.5}$	0	0	6.0	6.0	0	0	0	0	0	0
High Point	$10^{-6.5}$	0	0	4.6	5.0	0	0	0	0	0	0
Easton-2	$10^{-6.0}$	0	0	0	0	5.0	5.0	0	0	0	0
NY-5	$10^{-5.5}$	0	0	0	0	4.5	4.5	0	0	0	0
Type 1	$10^{-6.0}$	0	0	0	0	5.0	5.0	0	0	0	0
Type 2	$10^{-6.5}$	0	0	0	0	0	0	6.0	0	0	0
Type 3	$10^{-5.0}$	0	0	0	0	0	0	0	4.0	0	0
Nancy	$10^{-6.0}$	0	0	0	0	0	0	0	0	5.0	0
Alaska-5	$10^{-6.5}$	0	0	0	0	0	0	0	0	0	6.0

* From Melnick and Ledinko (1950). Additional data in this laboratory demonstrate the existence of seven additional antigenic types: Texas-12, Texas-13, Texas-14, Texas-15, Easton-10, Easton-14, and Israel-7.

Jeffries, 1949) to remove extraneous interfering substances and concentration by sedimentation in the ultracentrifuge have been recommended, especially with strains of low titer (Kraft and Melnick, 1950). Results of recent work have shown that even with strains of low titer satisfactory antigens can be prepared without concentration from the carcasses of newborn mice harvested 48 hours after the injection of a large dose of virus (Contreras and Melnick, 1952). A micromethod (Fulton and Dumbell, 1948) in which reacting mixtures totaling only 0.1 ml. are distributed on lucite plates has been found particularly useful in identifying strains of virus in complement-fixation tests with specific immune animal sera (Kraft and Melnick, 1950).

Occasionally two types of C virus have been isolated in the same mice from specimens of sewage, flies, or pooled human feces (Contreras and Melnick, 1952). With isolates containing multiple C viruses, neutralization cannot be demonstrated with any one specific antiserum. When these isolates are investigated by means of the complement-fixation test, however, reactions with different specific antisera indicate the identity of the strains contained in the mixture, and when antisera against these strains are used together, complete neutralization of the mixture can be achieved. This illustrates the value of utilizing both neutralization and complement-fixation technics for the identification of recently isolated strains of C virus.

Because mice early in life acquire a natural resistance to infections by C viruses, it is not possible to vaccinate newborn mice and later test for immunity by direct challenge; but, by challenging infant mice, which are less than 48 hours of age and born of mothers previously vaccinated, cross-protection tests can be carried out. Strains of virus studied in this way showed the same type-specificity as that observed in neutralization and complement-fixation tests (Melnick, Clarke and Kraft, 1950). In the course of these experiments, it was demonstrated that so long as a vaccinated mother lactates, sufficient protection is afforded by a short (one day) nursing period to prevent a nonimmune foster litter from being infected by a challenge injection of homologous virus. The immunity conferred by the milk of the foster mother is type-specific. Together with the transfer of immunity, there is a simultaneous transfer of complement-fixing antibodies from mother to the young. It is noteworthy that in the human population a passive transfer of neutralizing and complement-fixing antibodies from the mother to the offspring also occurs (Melnick and Ledinko, 1951).

Chimpanzees fed a C virus develop subclinical infection which is followed by the appearance of specific neutralizing antibodies and resistance to reinfection by the same type but not to primary infection by different types. The type-specificity of strains demonstrable in this manner corresponds to that determined by other methods.

Complement fixation in the presence of antigens, prepared from different C viruses, and serial specimens of serum, collected from chimpanzees over a period of two years during the course of successive different infections, has been studied (Melnick, Kaplan and Kraft, 1952). Following the initial feeding of each virus complement-fixing and neutralizing antibodies against that strain appeared. Unexpected, however, was the appearance or increase in the titer of complement-fixing antibody which developed at the same time against other types, usually those which had been fed to the animals previously and against which they had thereby acquired active immunity. The responses to heterologous strains, which had not been fed experimentally, might be attributable to earlier but unrecognized infections by these strains in the laboratory or elsewhere. The explanation of this phenomenon is not clear. Its existence is noteworthy, however, particularly as it also occurs in man.

C viruses are capable of causing infection and of stimulating an immune response in the human host. Evidence for the latter has been obtained by the detection and the measurement of specific neutralizing and complement-fixing antibodies in specimens of human serum. This is illustrated by the results of studies upon six laboratory workers who became infected while investigating the viruses. A strain of C virus was recovered from each worker during the acute febrile illness; three different types (Conn.-5, Ohio-1 and Texas-1) were represented. Sera collected from these patients prior to illness had no antibodies against the infecting type of virus, while all sera collected during convalescence possessed type-specific neutralizing antibodies (Shaw, Melnick and Curnen, 1950; Melnick and Ledinko, 1950). Results of complement-fixation tests, conducted in the presence of sera from these patients and the proper antigens, revealed, in addition to the development of antibody against the infecting virus, the appearance or enhancement of antibodies against unrelated types (Kraft and Melnick, 1952). It is evident that in man, as in chimpanzees, an increase in the titer of complement-fixing antibodies against several different types of C virus may follow infection by a single type. In view of this fact, the results of complement-fixation tests with human serum have limited value in diagnosis and may be misleading.

The duration of immunity in man following infection by any of the Coxsackie viruses is not known. No evidence has been obtained that the C viruses are serologically related to the poliomyelitis viruses or that immunity against any of the former agents confers protection against any of the latter. Studies on a strain of C virus (type 1) and a strain of poliomyelitis virus, which were found together in the feces of a child with paralysis, revealed no indication that the agents were related (Curnen and Melnick, 1951).

Many attempts have been made to demonstrate interference between poliomyelitis viruses and C viruses. One group of investigators failed to detect interference in mice or primates (Melnick, 1950). The incidence of paralysis in cynomolgus monkeys was not affected when poliomyelitis virus was fed to them simultaneously with, or within one week after, the administration of different C viruses. The establishment of subclinical infection in chimpanzees by feeding C viruses did not prevent the animals from becoming intestinal carriers of poliomyelitis virus when this agent was subsequently fed to them. On the other hand, Dalldorf (1951) has reported that the Nancy and the Conn.-5 types of C virus interfere with the activity of Lansing poliomyelitis virus in mice. The occurrence in man of simultaneous infection with poliomyelitis and C viruses has been detected (Melnick et al., 1950; Rhodes et al., 1950; Melnick et al., 1951; Curnen and Melnick, 1951), but evidence of interference between these agents in the human host is lacking.

DIAGNOSIS

Diagnosis of infection by a C virus is suggested by the clinical manifestations of aseptic meningitis, pleurodynia or herpangina. Confirmation, however, must be obtained in the laboratory by the recovery of virus from specimens of feces or oropharyngeal swabbings collected during the acute phase of illness and by the demonstration of the appearance or of an increase in neutralizing antibodies against the virus in sera collected from patients at appropriate times in relation to the onset of illness.

Differentiation of aseptic meningitis caused by a C virus from mumps meningoencephalitis, lymphocytic choriomeningitis and other forms of viral infection of the central nervous system may be indicated by clinical and epidemiologic findings. Diagnosis of the latter infections can usually be established by appropriate serologic tests and also, in some instances, by recovery and identification of the responsible virus. In view of the acute, self-limited course of infection with a C virus and the paucity of associated abnormal neurologic signs, differentiation from bacterial meningitis, mul-

tiple sclerosis, or space-occupying intracranial lesions, such as tumor, abscess or hemorrhage, should usually not be difficult.

Differentiation of C-virus infection from nonparalytic poliomyelitis in individual patients with aseptic meningitis does not appear to be possible on the basis of clinical findings alone and may be difficult even with assistance from the laboratory. Although C viruses have been recovered frequently from patients with the clinical picture of paralytic poliomyelitis, a causal relation to this form of disease is not evident, and the association may be coincidental. Coxsackie and poliomyelitis viruses have been found together in the feces of individuals with or without paralysis. Evidence is lacking, however, to show whether in man C viruses can either cause paralysis or influence the course of simultaneous infection by poliomyelitis virus. On the basis of present knowledge, it seems reasonable for the clinician or the epidemiologist to diagnose and treat any acute febrile illnesses with flaccid paralysis as poliomyelitis until convincing evidence to the contrary is made available.

Myalgia or pleurodynia attributable to a C virus has to be differentiated from other causes of thoracic pain, particularly pneumonia, pleurisy and coronary thrombosis, and from other causes of abdominal pain, including acute appendicitis, peptic ulcer, disease of the gallbladder and acute pancreatitis. The superficial character of the pain, the absence of deep abdominal or rectal tenderness, the relatively normal blood leukocyte count, and the absence of abnormal roentgenologic findings should aid in the diagnosis of infection by a C virus which can be established eventually by recovery of the virus and demonstration of a type-specific antibody response against it in the patient's serum.

A diagnosis of herpangina is suggested by the acute, self-limited course of disease and the presence of typical faucial lesions. Lesions of herpes simplex are more commonly, but not invariably, located at mucocutaneous borders. Coxsackie and herpes simplex viruses are readily isolated in baby mice and can be identified and differentiated by serologic methods. They may also be distinguished one from the other by the capacity of herpes virus, but not most C viruses, to propagate readily on the chorio-allantoic membrane of developing chick embryos, on the cornea of the rabbit's eye or in the brain of adult mice, and by the ability of C viruses, but not herpes virus, to remain active after the emulsification of virus-containing suspensions in ether. Furthermore, histopathologic pictures caused by these agents in infant mice are markedly different; intranuclear inclusions which occur in lesions induced by herpes virus are not found in lesions caused by C viruses (Curnen and Godenne, 1952). Typical lesions of herpangina, unlike those of apthous stomatitis, do not occur on the gingival or buccal mucous membranes. Follicular tonsillitis due to hemolytic streptococci and the pseudomembrane of diphtheria do not resemble herpangina and can be correctly identified by culture.

TREATMENT

No form of therapy is known which specifically affects infection induced by viruses of the Coxsackie group. Various supportive and symptomatic measures may ameliorate certain features of the illnesses.

EPIDEMIOLOGY

Viruses of the Coxsackie group have been encountered in many parts of the Western Hemisphere as well as in Europe, Asia, Africa and Australia. Isolations have been made mainly from human feces, pharyngeal swabbings, sewage and flies. Data accumulated in one laboratory on the distribution of different types of C viruses are summarized in Table 19. That C viruses are widely distributed is also indicated by the detection of antibodies against certain types in serum from individuals collected in different parts of the world and by the capacity of gamma globulin prepared from pooled human serum obtained either in the United States or in

Denmark to neutralize all of the C viruses which have been identified and tested (Melnick and Ledinko, 1950). Evidence that the capacity of gamma globulin to neutralize C viruses is an indication of previous specific antigenic experience is supported by the results of neutralization tests with serum collected from Eskimos in northern Alaska (Banker and Melnick, 1951). As shown in Figure 37, this population appears to have been heavily exposed to the Alaska-5 and High Point (Texas-1) types, less so to an Easton-2 strain (type 1), and not at all to the Conn.-5 and Ohio-1 types. In tests with specimens of feces which were collected in the same area, strains of the Alaska-5 type were isolated from each of two Eskimo children.

Information concerning the geographic and temporal distribution of individual types of C virus in relation to human disease is still meager and fragmentary. Strains of the Conn.-5 type were recovered from one boy with pleurodynia and from 5 acutely ill patients with pleocytosis of the cerebrospinal fluid but without paralysis during an unusual prevalence of aseptic meningitis in the summer of 1948 in Connecticut and Rhode Island (Curnen, Shaw and Melnick, 1949). During the same summer, antigenically related strains were recovered from 8 patients in various parts of New York state who likewise had acute nonparalytic illnesses associated with pleocytosis of the cerebrospinal fluid (Dalldorf and Gifford, 1951). A virus of this type was apparently responsible at the same time for a small outbreak in New York City of acute illnesses some of which resembled pleurodynia (Kilbourne, 1950). A Conn.-5 type also appeared to be the etiologic agent in an outbreak of pleurodynia which occurred during the summer of 1947 in Massachusetts (Weller et al., 1950). Thus, this single type of virus was apparently prevalent during the summers of 1947 and 1948 in New England and New York and caused aseptic meningitis or pleurodynia. In these early studies, relatively few attempts were made

TABLE 19. DISTRIBUTION OF ANTIGENICALLY DISTINCT C VIRUSES IN MATERIAL COLLECTED IN DIFFERENT AREAS FROM 1942 TO 1951*

AREA	YEAR	No. of ISOLATIONS	CONN.-5	OHIO-1	NANCY	TEXAS-1	TEXAS-12	TEXAS-13	TEXAS-14	TYPE I (EASTON-2)	EASTON-10	EASTON-14	TYPE 2	TYPE 3	ALASKA-5	ISRAEL-7
Texas	1942	1	0	0	0	0	0	0	1	0	0	0	0	0	0	0
Connecticut	1943	1	0	0	0	1	0	0	0	0	0	0	0	0	0	0
Ohio	1947	5	2	3	0	0	0	0	0	0	0	0	0	0	0	0
Massachusetts	1947	1	1	0	0	0	0	0	0	0	0	0	0	0	0	0
Connecticut	1948	6	6	0	0	0	0	0	0	0	0	0	0	0	0	0
Texas	1948	33	4	0	4	7	5	1	2	1	3	6	2	12	2	0
Laboratory workers	1949	6	3	1	0	2	0	0	0	0	0	0	0	0	0	0
Connecticut	1949	3	1	0	2	0	0	0	0	0	0	0	0	0	0	0
Easton, Pennsylvania	1949	28	0	0	1	0	0	0	0	24	1	1	0	0	0	0
Kansas	1949	24	1	0	0	0	0	0	0	3	1	8	4	1	1	10
North Carolina	1948	19	15	0	0	5	0	0	0	4	0	0	0	0	0	0
New York	1949	2	0	0	0	0	0	0	0	2	2	0	0	0	0	0
Michigan	1949	33	0	0	0	0	0	0	0	25	0	5	0	0	1	0
France	1950	2	0	0	0	0	0	0	0	1	0	0	1	0	0	0
Cuba	1950	1	0	0	0	1	0	0	0	0	0	0	0	0	0	0
Alaska	1950	2	0	0	0	0	0	0	0	0	0	0	0	0	2	0
Egypt	1951	7	0	0	1	2	0	0	0	1	0	0	1	1	1	3
Israel	1950	8	0	0	0	0	0	0	1	0	2	0	0	0	0	5
West Virginia	1951	8	0	0	0	0	0	0	0	0	0	0	8	0	0	0
Totals		190	33	4	8	18	5	1	4	61	9	20	16	14	7	18

* The typing of strains included in this table was carried out in one laboratory; combined complement-fixation and neutralization tests were used. Some isolates from sewage and from flies collected in Kansas, North Carolina, Texas and Egypt were found to contain two strains of different antigenic types. (Contreras, Melnick and Barnett, 1952.)

to recover the agent from patients with other forms of illness or from healthy persons. It is noteworthy that strains of this type were not encountered among a large number of specimens tested in Albany, N. Y., during 1949 (Dalldorf, 1952), in Washington, D. C., during 1949 and 1950 (Huebner et al., 1950, 1951), in only one case in New Haven during 1949, and in none during 1950 and 1951. An Ohio-1 type

poliomyelitis or minor illnesses without distinctive features. A relation of other individual types of C virus to particular forms of disease has not been clearly established.

Most Coxsackie viruses have been recovered from specimens collected during the summer and the early fall. Although this reflects to some extent the fact that these agents were first detected and later sought in the course of investigations on poliomye-

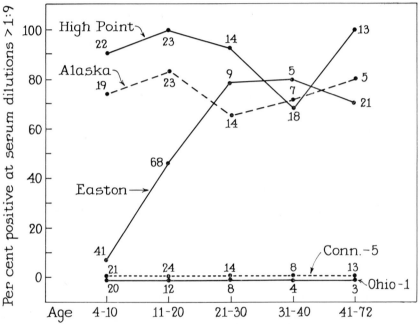

Fig. 37. Results of neutralization tests with sera of North Alaskan Eskimos expressed in terms of percentages of positive neutralization tests with 5 antigenically distinct C viruses: Conn.-5, Ohio-1, Easton-2, High Point (Texas-1) and Alaska-5. The figures at each point indicate the number of sera tested in the indicated age group. (Banker and Melnick, 1951)

was found together with poliomyelitis virus in representative patients during an outbreak of summer grippe which occurred in 1947 in Ohio (Melnick et al., 1950). Additional strains of this type have not been encountered since that time. Six other antigenically different C viruses were isolated during 1949 and 1950 from patients with herpangina in the vicinity of Washington, D. C. (Huebner et al., 1951; Cole, Bell, Beeman and Huebner, 1951). At least two of the latter types (type 2, Texas-1) have also been recovered from patients with either

litis, additional evidence has been obtained to indicate that C viruses actually are encountered more frequently during the summer months. In epidemiologic surveys during 1949 and 1950, investigators (Huebner et al., 1950, 1951; Cole et al., 1951) tested samples of feces collected at different times from individual inhabitants of a residential community near Washington, D. C. Isolations of virus were made almost exclusively in July, August and September. In another study, results of tests with paired samples of human serum collected in the spring and the fall from approximately 200 persons of different ages in North Carolina revealed that, between samplings, an appreciable percentage of the children developed neutralizing and complement-fixing antibodies against the High Point strain (Texas-1 type), indicating that infection by this agent occurred during the interval (Melnick and Ledinko, 1951). Results of tests on specimens of sewage collected each month from different areas in the United States also indicate that C viruses are encountered more frequently and in greater quantity during the summer and fall (Melnick et al., 1952). An attempt was made to recover C viruses from 860 patients in New Haven, Conn., who had acute febrile illnesses between March, 1950 and March, 1952. Forty-four strains were isolated, 36 of which were encountered in the periods from July through October (Curnen and Godenne, 1952).

C viruses have been recovered from persons of both sexes and more frequently from children than from adults (Dalldorf and Gifford, 1951; Curnen, 1951; Cole et al., 1951). Sufficient data are not yet available, however, to determine accurately the incidence according to sex, race or age-specific attack rates; this is particularly true of infections caused by different types.

The simultaneous occurrence of both poliomyelitis virus and C virus in feces from the same individual has been noted in patients with summer grippe during 1947 in Ohio (Melnick et al., 1950); in persons with paralysis, mild illness or inapparent infection during 1949 in Canada (Rhodes et al., 1950); and in patients with paralytic poliomyelitis in New York City (Curnen and Melnick, 1951). During the peak of an explosive outbreak of poliomyelitis which occurred in Easton, Pa., in 1949, patients who entered the hospital consecutively were selected for detailed study (Melnick et al., 1951). Of 36 patients (28 paralytic and 8 nonparalytic) whose stools were tested for the presence of both poliomyelitis and C

viruses during the acute stage of illness, 20 harbored both viruses, 7 had only poliomyelitis virus, 6 carried only C virus, and 3 had neither virus. Additional evidence that these patients were actually infected with C virus and not simply excreting the agent is provided by the results of tests on serum obtained during the acute and convalescent stages of illness. Of the 26 patients from whom a C virus was recovered, 23 responded with a rise in neutralizing antibodies to the prevalent Easton-2 strain or to a different strain isolated from the patient. Of 15 patients from whom a C virus could not be isolated, only 3 showed an increase in antibody against strains of C virus isolated during the epidemic. With the development of antibodies against C virus during the month after onset of illness, there was a concomitant disappearance of C virus from the stools. In 2 paralytic patients who were studied, antibodies against both poliomyelitis and C viruses increased during the 4 weeks following the onset of illness.

Similarities in the epidemiology of poliomyelitis and infection by C viruses may be briefly summarized. Both poliomyelitis and C viruses induce in man infections associated with specific antibody responses. In the human host both agents may be carried for some time and may cause either recognizable disease or inapparent infection. They are encountered most frequently at the same time of year. Both agents may be recovered not only from man but also from flies and sewage, and at times may be found together in the same specimen. Evidence is lacking, however, that poliomyelitis viruses are related to C viruses even when both are recovered from the same source. When both kinds of virus are found together in a patient with or without paralysis, it is not possible to determine precisely the extent to which each agent contributes to the observed manifestations of the dual infection. Certainly all infections caused by C viruses do not resemble poliomyelitis, nor are all cases of poliomyelitis complicated by concurrent infection with a C virus. It is evident, however, that infections by C viruses and poliomyelitis have many features in common and that studies on the epidemiology of either may require consideration of the other.

CONTROL MEASURES

Specific measures to control infection by Coxsackie viruses have not been devised. These agents may be distributed by means of the oropharyngeal secretions and feces of infected persons, many of whom remain undetected. Flies and cockroaches may harbor and transport C viruses, but whether they are of importance in the transmission of C-virus diseases from person to person has not yet been determined. Because of the unusual stability of C viruses at ordinary temperatures and their resistance to alcohol and other substances commonly used as antiseptic solutions, decontamination of objects which cannot be boiled or autoclaved may not be achieved by conventional methods. C viruses can be inactivated rapidly, however, by 0.1 N hydrochloric acid or 0.3 per cent formaldehyde. No reports have appeared on the efficacy of vaccines in prophylaxis.

REFERENCES

Banker, D. D., and Melnick, J. L., 1951, Isolation of Coxsackie virus (C virus) from North Alaskan Eskimos. Am. J. Hyg., 54, 383-390.

Casals, J., Olitsky, P. K., and Murphy, L. C., 1949, Hemagglutination and complement-fixation with types I and II. Albany strains of Coxsackie virus. Proc. Soc. Exp. Biol. and Med., 72, 636-638.

Cole, R. M., Bell, J. A., Beeman, E. A., and Huebner, R. J., 1951, Studies of Coxsackie viruses: Observations on epidemiological aspects of group A viruses. Am. J. Pub. Health, 41, 1342-1358.

Contreras, G., Melnick, J. L., and Barnett, V. H., 1952, Typing of Coxsackie viruses by immunological methods. To be published.

Curnen, E. C., 1950, Human disease associated with the Coxsackie viruses. Bull. N. Y. Acad. Med., 26, 335-342.

Curnen, E. C., 1952, Immunology, epidemiology and clinical aspects of Coxsackie virus infection. Symposium II. The Coxsackie group of viruses. Second International Poliomyelitis Conference, Copenhagen, Denmark.

Curnen, E. C., and Godenne, M. O., 1952. Unpublished data.

Curnen, E. C., and Melnick, J. L., 1951, Poliomyelitis and Coxsackie viruses in paralytic poliomyelitis. Pediatrics, 8, 237-248.

Curnen, E. C., Shaw, E. W., and Melnick, J. L., 1949, Disease resembling nonparalytic poliomyelitis associated with a virus pathogenic for infant mice. J. Am. Med. Assn., 141, 894-901.

Dalldorf, G., 1949, The Coxsackie group of viruses. Science, 110, 594.

Dalldorf, G., 1950, The Coxsackie viruses. Bull. N. Y. Acad. Med., 26, 329-335.

Dalldorf, G., 1951, The sparing effect of Coxsackie virus infection on experimental poliomyelitis. J. Exp. Med., 94, 65-71.

Dalldorf, G., 1952, The Coxsackie viruses: Isolation and properties. Symposium II. The Coxsackie group of viruses. Second International Poliomyelitis Conference, Copenhagen, Denmark.

Dalldorf, G., and Gifford, R., 1951, Clinical and epidemiologic observations of Coxsackie-virus infection. New England J. Med., 244, 868-873.

Dalldorf, G., and Sickles, G. M., 1948, An unidentified, filterable agent isolated from the feces of children with paralysis. Science, 108, 61-62.

Dalldorf, G., Sickles, G. M., Plager, H., and Gifford, R., 1949, A virus recovered from the feces of "Poliomyelitis" patients pathogenic for suckling mice. J. Exp. Med., 89, 567-582.

Findlay, G. M., and Howard, E. M., 1950, Coxsackie viruses and Bornholm disease. Brit. Med. J., 1, 1233-1236.

Finn, J. J., Weller, T. H., and Morgan, H. R., 1949, Epidemic pleurodynia: Clinical and etiologic studies based on one hundred and fourteen cases. Arch. Int. Med., 83, 305-321.

Fischer, R. G., and Syverton, J. T., 1951, The cockroach as an experimental vector of Coxsackie virus. Am. J. Trop. Med., 31, 238-242.

Fulton, F., and Dumbell, K. R., 1949, The serological comparison of strains of influenza virus. J. Gen. Microbiol., 3, 97-111.

Gard, S., 1950, "C-virus" som orsak till "barnförlamning" utan pareser. Svenska Läkartidningen, 47, 285-290.

Godman, G., Bunting, H., and Melnick, J. L., 1952, The Histopathology of Coxsackie virus infection in mice. I. Morphological observations with four different viral types. Am. J. Path., 28, 223-258.

Himmelweit, F., Findlay, G. M., and Howard, E. M., 1950, The size of Coxsackie viruses as estimated by filtration through gradocol membranes. Brit. J. Exper. Path., 31, 809-812.

Huebner, R. J., Armstrong, C., Beeman, E. A., and Cole, R. M., 1950, Studies of Coxsackie viruses. Preliminary report on occurrence of Coxsackie virus in a southern Maryland community. J. Am. Med. Assn., 144, 609-613.

Huebner, R. J., Cole, R. M., Beeman, E. A., Bell, J. A., and Peers, J. H., 1951, Herpangina, etiological studies of a specific infectious disease. J. Am. Med. Assn., 145, 628-633.

Huebner, R. J., Ransom, S. E., and Beeman, E. A., 1950, Studies of Coxsackie virus. Adaptation of a strain to chick embryos. Pub. Health Rep., 65, 803-806.

Kaplan, A. S., and Melnick, J. L., 1951, Oral administration of Coxsackie viruses to newborn and adult mice. Proc. Soc. Exp. Biol. and Med., 76, 312-315.

Kaplan, A. S., and Melnick, J. L., 1952, Thermal inactivation of Coxsackie viruses. To be published.

Kilbourne, E. D., 1950, Diverse manifestations of infection with a strain of Coxsackie virus. Fed. Proc., 9, 581-584.

Kilbourne, E. D., and Horsfall, F. L., Jr., 1951, Lethal infection with Coxsackie virus of adult mice given cortisone. Proc. Soc. Exp. Biol. and Med., 77, 135-138.

Kraft, L. M., and Melnick, J. L., 1950, Immunological reactions of the Coxsackie viruses. II. The complement fixation test. J. Exp. Med., 92, 483-497.

Kraft, L. M., and Melnick, J. L., 1952, Complement fixation tests with homologous and heterologous types of Coxsackie virus in man. J. Immunol., 68, 297-310.

Levaditi, C., 1951, La "coelogenese" nevraxique du virus Coxsackie. Ann. Inst. Pasteur, 81, 260-274.

von Magnus, H., 1949, Isolering af tre virus stammer af Coxsackie-gruppen fra patienter med meningeale symptomer. Ugeskrift for Laeger, 111, 1451-1453.

Melnick, J. L., 1950, Studies on the Coxsackie viruses: Properties, immunological aspects and distribution in nature. Bull. N. Y. Acad. Med., 26, 342-356.

Melnick, J. L., 1951, Poliomyelitis and poliomyelitis-like viruses of man and animals. Ann. Rev. Microbiol., 5, 309-332.

Melnick, J. L., Clarke, N. A., and Kraft, L. M., 1950, Immunological reactions of the Coxsackie viruses. III. Cross-protection tests in infant mice born of vaccinated mothers. Transfer of immunity through the milk. J. Exp. Med., 92, 499-505.

Melnick, J. L., Coffey, J., and Schoof, H., 1952, Unpublished studies on the seasonal occurrence of Coxsackie viruses in sewage and flies in cities in Arizona, Connecticut, Kansas, Michigan, New York and West Virginia.

Melnick, J. L., and Godman, G. C., 1951, Pathogenesis of Coxsackie virus infection. Multiplication of virus and evolution of the muscle lesion in mice. J. Exp. Med., 93, 247-266.

Melnick, J. L., Kaplan, A. S., and Kraft, L. M., 1952, A quantitative study of Coxsackie virus infections in chimpanzees. To be published.

Melnick, J. L., Kaplan, A. S., Zabin, E., Contreras, G., and Larkum, N. W., 1951, An epidemic of paralytic poliomyelitis characterized by dual infections with poliomyelitis and Coxsackie viruses. J. Exp. Med., 94, 471-492.

Melnick, J. L., and Ledinko, N., 1950, Infection of cynomolgus monkeys with the Ohio type of Coxsackie virus (C virus). J. Immunol., 64, 101-110.

Melnick, J. L., and Ledinko, N., 1950, Immunological reactions of the Coxsackie viruses. I. The neutralization test: Technic and application. J. Exp. Med., 92, 463-482.

Melnick, J. L., and Ledinko, N., 1951, Social serology: Antibody levels in a normal young population during an epidemic of poliomyelitis. Am. J. Hyg., 54, 354-382.

Melnick, J. L., Ledinko, N., Kaplan, A. S., and Kraft, L. M., 1950, Ohio strains of a virus pathogenic for infant mice (Coxsackie group). Simultaneous occurrence with poliomyelitis virus in patients with "summer grippe." J. Exp. Med., 91, 185-195.

Melnick, J. L., and Penner, L. R., 1952, Excretion of Coxsackie virus by experimentally infected flies. To be published.

Melnick, J. L., Rhian, M., Warren, J., and Breese, S. S., Jr., 1951, The size of Coxsackie viruses and Lansing poliomyelitis virus determined by sedimentation and ultrafiltration. J. Immunol., 67, 151-162.

Melnick, J. L., Shaw, E. W., and Curnen, E. C., 1949, A virus isolated from patients diagnosed as non-paralytic poliomyelitis or aseptic meningitis. Proc. Soc. Exp. Biol. and Med., 71, 344-349.

Pappenheimer, A. M., Daniels, J. B., Cheever, F. S., and Weller, T. H., 1950, Lesions caused in suckling mice by certain viruses isolated from cases of so-called non-paralytic poliomyelitis and of pleurodynia. J. Exp. Med., 92, 169-190.

Pappenheimer, A. M., Kunz, L. J., and Richardson, S., 1951, Passage of Coxsackie virus (Connecticut-5 strain) in adult mice with production of pancreatic disease. J. Exp. Med., 94, 45-64.

Parrott, R. H., Ross, S., Burke, F. G., and Rice, E. C., 1951, Herpangina. Clinical studies of a specific infectious disease. New England J. Med., 245, 275-280.

Quigley, J. J., 1949, Ultrafiltration and ultracentrifugation studies of Coxsackie virus. Proc. Soc. Exp. Biol. and Med., 72, 434-435.

Rhodes, A. J., Clark, E. M., Knowles, D. S., Shimada, F. S., Ritchie, R. C., Donohue, W. L., Armstrong, M. P., Wilson, F. H., McLean, W. J., and Silverthorne, N., 1950, Studies on poliomyelitis in Ontario. III. Further observations on the association of Coxsackie and poliomyelitis viruses. Can. J. Pub. Health, 41, 183-188.

Robinson, L. K., 1950, Effect of heat and of pH on strains of Coxsackie virus. Proc. Soc. Exp. Biol. and Med., 75, 580-582.

Shaw, E. W., Melnick, J. L., and Curnen, E. C., 1950, Infection of laboratory workers with Coxsackie viruses. Ann. Int. Med., 33, 32-40.

Sickles, G. M., and Dalldorf, G., 1949, Serologic differences among strains of the Coxsackie group of viruses. Proc. Soc. Exp. Biol. and Med., 72, 30-31.

Slater, E. A., and Syverton, J. T., 1950, The cultivation of Coxsackie virus. Proc. Soc. Exp. Biol. and Med., 74, 509-510.

Sylvest, E., 1933 (Den Bornholmske syge. Myalgia epidemica. Levin and Munksgaards Forlag, København. [English translation]: Epidemic myalgia. Bornholm disease. Humphry Milford, Oxford University Press, London, 1934).

Thélin, F., and Wirth, J., 1951, La myalgie épidémique (maladie de Bornholm). Isolement d'un virus au cours d'une épidémie récente. Revue Médicale de la Suisse Romande, 71, 44-51.

Warren, J., and Breese, S. S., Jr., 1951. Unpublished data.

Warren, J., Weil, M. L., Russ, S. B., and Jeffries, H., 1949, Purification of certain viruses by use of protamine sulfate. Proc. Soc. Exp. Biol. and Med., 72, 662-664.

Webb, C. H., Wolfe, S. G., and Howitt, B. F., 1950, "Three day fever": An acute febrile disease of childhood (further observations). Am. J. Dis. Child., 80, 245-253.

Weller, T. H., Enders, J. F., Buckingham, M., and Finn, J. J., Jr., 1950, The etiology of epidemic pleurodynia: A study of two viruses isolated from a typical outbreak. J. Immunol., 65, 337-346.

Zahorsky, J., 1924, Herpangina (a specific infectious disease). Arch. Pediat., 41, 181-184.

W. PAUL HAVENS, JR., M.D., AND JOHN R. PAUL, M.D.

Jefferson Medical College and Yale University School of Medicine

15

Infectious Hepatitis and Serum Hepatitis

There are probably several forms of viral infections of the liver which are variants of one general group. Two major members of the group are represented by (a) *infectious hepatitis* (IH) for which the synonyms *infective hepatitis* and *epidemic jaundice* have been used; and (b) *serum hepatitis* (SH) for which the synonyms *homologous serum jaundice, syringe jaundice, postvaccinal hepatitis, inoculation jaundice, transfusion jaundice* and *late arsphenamine jaundice* have been used. The first section of this chapter will deal almost entirely with the virus of infectious hepatitis and the disease which it causes, and the second section will deal with serum hepatitis. Although scant knowledge concerning the exact relationship between these two forms of hepatitis may make such a division appear arbitrary, there are immunologic differences as well as certain differences in pathogenesis and epidemiology between these two clinically similar diseases which make it desirable.

INFECTIOUS HEPATITIS

INTRODUCTION

Infectious hepatitis is a subacute viral infection in which there is a diffuse involvement of the liver. It is common and apparently world-wide in distribution, occurring in endemic and epidemic forms. The clinical disease is characterized by fever, anorexia, nausea, vomiting, abdominal distress and jaundice.

HISTORY

Infectious hepatitis has been long recognized in civilian and military personnel. Numerous accounts of it were recorded by military surgeons attached to the armies which fought through Europe in the eighteenth and the nineteenth centuries. It was common in the Union troops in the American Civil War. During World War I, the disease was prevalent in British and French forces in the Mediterranean area, where it was epidemic again in troops of various armies in World War II. More recently, it has been common among American troops in the war in Korea. It has long been termed "catarrhal jaundice," and in particular it has often been confused with Weil's disease, which was differentiated from infectious hepatitis on clinical grounds in 1886. Pioneers, in clarifying the identity of infectious hepatitis as a clinical entity, include Quincke (1903) and Cockayne (1912). Blumer (1923) was among the first in the United States to point out that infectious hepatitis probably represents the epidemic form of "catarrhal jaundice," and as such is unrelated to leptospiral hepatitis. Rich (1930) again drew attention to the fact that at necropsy nearly all cases of "catarrhal jaundice" show a diffuse hepatitis and that mucous plugs in the ampulla of Vater are rarely if ever seen.

The modern concept of the viral etiology of infectious hepatitis comes, in part, from the work of Findlay et al. (1939) but is largely a product of investigations attendant upon World War II. Voegt (1942) was the first to report its transmission to human volunteers by feeding them duodenal contents from a patient with the malady. Subsequently, others demonstrated the etiologic agent of the disease to be present in the blood (Cameron, 1943) and stools (MacCallum and Bradley, 1944; Havens et al., 1944) of patients in the acute phase of disease; to be capable of passing bacteria-tight filters; and to be transmissible serially in human volunteers (Havens, 1945a).

Clinical Picture

The incubation period ranges from 10 to 40 days, with an average of about 25. In

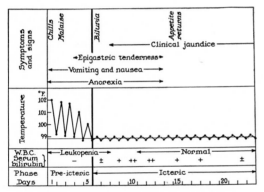

CHART 16. Schematic diagram illustrating the clinical course of an average case of infectious hepatitis in an adult. (Paul, J. R., and Havens, W. P., Jr., 1946, Recent advances in the study of infectious hepatitis and serum jaundice. Transactions of the Association of American Physicians, *59*, 133-141.)

childhood, the course of disease is shorter and milder than it is in the adult, and in young infants it may be so mild as to escape notice (Capps et al., 1950). In both children and adults jaundice may be absent, quite fleeting, or may persist as long as several weeks. Estimates of the ratio of nonicteric to icteric cases differ in various epidemics, but a conservative ratio in adults would be 1:1. The course of disease in adults is separated into two phases in most instances: preicteric and icteric, with characteristic symptoms and signs (Chart 16), but some

patients have only jaundice as a presenting complaint. The preicteric phase may range from 1 to 21 days, with an average of 5 days. The onset may be abrupt or insidious, and this early phase of the disease is characterized by anorexia, nausea, headache, lassitude, and abdominal distress; a large proportion of patients has fever at this stage, often accompanied by chills or chilly sensations. Posterior cervical lymphadenopathy is common (Barker et al., 1945a), and splenomegaly may be present. Although the liver is not usually enlarged in this stage, tenderness may often be elicited by palpation. Leukopenia is a characteristic finding at this time, and toward the end of the preicteric phase many large, atypical lymphocytes, similar to those found in patients with infectious mononucleosis, are often seen (Havens and Marck, 1946). Many patients have subjective improvement toward the end of the preicteric phase, lasting one or two days until jaundice appears, when they again experience a return of gastro-intestinal symptoms.

The icteric phase is ushered in with an exacerbation of some of the original symptoms. It may last from 1 to 10 weeks, averaging 6 weeks; some patients may have low-grade jaundice for several months. Major symptoms and signs in the icteric phase are again abdominal discomfort, usually related to pain in the right upper quadrant or epigastrium, anorexia, nausea, and often vomiting. The liver becomes enlarged and more tender, and is usually easily palpable. The spleen is palpable and tender in a fair percentage of patients. These symptoms and signs may last only a short time or as long as a month, although the usual experience is improvement in 2 weeks after jaundice attains its maximum degree of intensity. During this time, the stools may be clay colored. As jaundice wanes, a sense of well-being and appetite return. Convalescence is generally uneventful and rapid. Even in the mild cases, weight loss of 5 to 10 pounds may occur, while in the more severely sick this may be as much as 25 pounds. Complications are rare, but occasionally patients develop pneumonia and, rarely, lymphocytic meningitis or myelitis. The death rate is low, particularly in children; and in adults, in the series of military cases reported by Barker et al. (1945a), the case-fatality rate was 1.8 per 1,000, although it may be considerably higher, particularly in older persons (Müller, 1947). Death may occur early in the disease, after 3 to 10 days of illness, or later, 3 to 8 weeks after onset. Sudden appearance of restlessness, mental confusion, loss of emotional control, coma and hemorrhagic phenomena carry a grave prognosis.

The frequency of relapse ranges from 0.6 to 18 per cent of the adult cases, although the low rates are more common. In a fair percentage of relapses, the only evidence is furnished by recurrent abnormality of tests of hepatic function. In another group of patients, a relapse manifests itself as a duplication of the icteric phase of disease, although it is usually less severe than the initial illness. Complete recovery occurs in most patients.

A few patients have a prolongation of hepatic dysfunction, with or without signs or symptoms of disease, beyond the usually expected time of recovery (Havens and Ginder, 1948). A large portion of this group is asymptomatic, and the most common and reliable manifestations of hepatic insufficiency are chronic or recurrent hyperbilirubinemia and abnormal retention of bromsulphalein (Post et al., 1950). In most of these cases, the degree of functional impairment of the liver and the clinical condition are apparently compatible with full activity and eventual complete recovery (Klatskin and Rappaport, 1947; Kunkel et al., 1947). Another smaller group of patients has anorexia, lassitude and epigastric discomfort, with jaundice, enlargement of the liver, and spider angioma. The spleen may be palpable. Clinical jaundice need not be present, but in such cases results of the bromsulphalein-retention test are usually abnormal. Barker et al. (1945b) empha-

sized the importance of this syndrome in debilitated troops who had received inadequate treatment. Improvement usually follows therapy, although a small percentage of such patients have a progression of disease and develop postnecrotic cirrhosis (Watson and Hoffbauer, 1946; Sherlock, 1948; Kunkel and Labby, 1950). In these, the ultimate prognosis is poor. Jersild (1945) described the clinical course of chronic hepatitis particularly in women beyond the menopause. Remissions and exacerbations of jaundice with edema, ascites and hemorrhagic manifestations were common; death frequently occurred in as many as 50 per cent of cases from 6 to 18 months after the appearance of jaundice.

Conditions which cause relapse or prolongation and progression of disease are poorly defined. It has been suggested that inadequate rest, poor diet, intercurrent infections, previous hepatic disease and indulgence in alcohol may be predisposing factors. In addition, the disease is apparently more severe among older age groups, particularly in women beyond the menopause and in previously debilitated patients. However, in a large percentage of young adult patients with relapse or chronic hepatitis, it is impossible to find factors which can be defined with certainty as having contributed to the continued hepatic disease. It is not yet known whether relapse or chronic hepatitis is caused by the continued presence and activity of virus in the body or whether such occurrences merely represent the progressive functional inadequacy of a liver damaged by the initial infection.

Pathologic Picture

Knowledge of pathologic changes has been acquired from biopsies of the liver taken at various stages throughout the course of the disease and at necropsy (Roholm and Iversen, 1939; Dible et al., 1943; Mallory, 1947). Early changes consist of swelling and irregularity of shape of hepatic cells and numerous mitotic figures.

A tremendous amount of parenchymal destruction has already occurred by the time jaundice is evident. Biopsies later in the course of disease reveal regeneration of hepatic parenchyma with complete restoration in most cases at the end of 2 or 3 the periphery of the lobule, particularly in the portal stroma. This response is mononuclear in type with a predominance of lymphocytes, plasma cells, and monocytes, although neutrophiles and eosinophiles are also in evidence. The lobular remnant con-

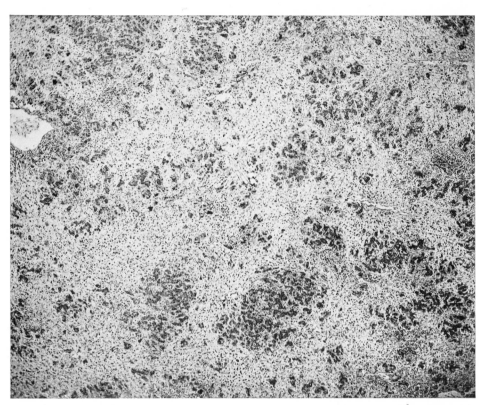

FIG. 38. Photomicrograph (low power) of the liver from a fatal case of infectious hepatitis in which death occurred on the ninth day of disease. Great destruction of parenchymal cells is evident. Grossly, the picture was that of acute yellow atrophy. (Paul, J. R., 1946, Infectious hepatitis. Bulletin New York Academy Medicine, 22, 204-216.)

months. Slight residual periportal infiltration may persist in some patients for several months longer. In the fulminant form of disease (Lucké and Mallory, 1946), in which death occurs within 10 days after onset, the liver is reduced in size, yellow or mottled in color, smooth and soft. Its parenchyma is destroyed uniformly and completely without any noteworthy evidence of regenerative hyperplasia (Fig. 38). An intense inflammatory response is present at tains numerous proliferated macrophages and erythrocytes so that the liver may resemble a spongy framework infiltrated with inflammatory cells and blood. In such cases, death may occur very early, within 3 or 4 days of onset, before jaundice appears. In the subacute form of disease in which death occurs 3 to 6 weeks after onset, the liver is frequently firm, reduced in size, and the cut surface may be granular. Destruction of parenchymal cells is neither complete nor uniform, and considerable evidence of regeneration is found.

Other lesions found at necropsy include phlegmonous inflammation and hemorrhage of the stomach and intestinal walls. The spleen is frequently enlarged and congested with follicular hyperplasia. Large edematous, mesenteric and peripheral lymph nodes are found. Ascites is common.

EXPERIMENTAL INFECTION; HOST RANGE

Numerous attempts (van Rooyen and Gordon, 1942) to produce infectious hepatitis by giving the virus to laboratory animals, including many rodents, many species of monkeys, and even chimpanzees (Havens and Ward, 1945), have failed. Various experimental attempts have been summarized by Colbert (1949). Transmission of virus to pigs (Andersen and Tulinius, 1938), birds (Herzberg, 1943; Lucké and Radcliffe, 1949), embryonated eggs (Siede and Meding, 1941), and rats (MacCallum and Miles, 1946) has been reported but not confirmed. More recently, Jordan and Mirick (1951) reported the isolation of an agent causing transmissible hepatitis in mice, following the injection of liver obtained from a fatal case of acute hepatitis. The spontaneous appearance of a filterable agent causing hepatitis has already been observed in supposedly healthy mice (Olitsky and Casals, 1945; Gledhill and Andrewes, 1951) and puppies (Rubarth, 1945). Nothing is known about a relationship between these agents and those producing viral hepatitis in man. Henle et al. (1950a) reported the propagation of IH virus in tissue culture and embryonated eggs. After several transfers, the virus was re-identified by suggestive but not conclusive tests in volunteers (Drake et al., 1950). This promising work is still in the experimental stage.

ETIOLOGY*

From experiments with human volunteers, it has been shown that the etiologic

_____
* German workers (Essen and Lembke, 1944) have reported the virus of infectious hepatitis as being a

agent passes through bacteria-tight filters and is transmissible in series to man; it is resistant to a temperature of 56° C. for at least 30 minutes; and withstands chlorination, viz., 1 part chlorine residual per million for 30 minutes (Neefe et al., 1945a). The virus is readily recovered from the blood and feces of patients in the acute,

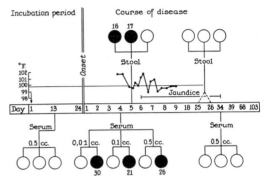

CHART 17. Illustration of results of administration to volunteers of serum and stool obtained during the midincubation period (13th day), acute (4th to 5th day), and convalescent phases (25th, 26th, 31st days), of experimentally induced infectious hepatitis in one patient (ZI). The small arrow on the left indicates the time of infection of patient (ZI). Rectal temperatures are recorded. Open circles indicate volunteers who were inoculated and failed to contract infectious hepatitis; black circles indicate volunteers who contracted infectious hepatitis. The figure adjacent to each black circle represents the length of incubation period in days. (Havens, W. P., Jr., 1946, Period of infectivity of patients with experimentally induced infectious hepatitis. Journal of Experimental Medicine, _83_, 251-258.)

preicteric or early icteric phases of disease, and may be transmitted to human volunteers by feeding or by parenteral inoculation of infectious materials. Several attempts to detect virus in the urine or

_____
polyhedral body with a diameter of the order of 180 mμ when visualized by means of the electron microscope. This report has not been confirmed, and it is the general belief that neither this virus nor any of those claimed to have been transferred to animals has been really identified as having reproduced the disease in human volunteers.

nasopharyngeal washings of patients at similar periods have yielded contradictory results (Findlay and Willcox, 1945). In general, they have been unsuccessful.

The period of infectivity of patients has been investigated (Havens, 1946a), but the number of experiments designed to determine when virus appears in the blood and feces and how long it remains there is, unfortunately, small. A single attempt to recover virus from the blood midway through the incubation period of one experimentally infected human volunteer was unsuccessful, but it has been found in the

embryonated eggs) may yield an antigen which is of value as a skin-testing agent. This work is still in the experimental stage.

At present, the absence of specific diagnostic tests for the identification of the various types of hepatitis makes it impossible to establish any definitive conclusions about immunity. The natural history of infectious hepatitis supports the concept of a widespread immunity in the general population, brought about by subclinical infection. The occasional high epidemic prevalence among unseasoned troops quartered in areas where the adult native population

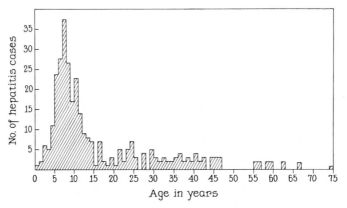

CHART 18. The age incidence of *hepatitis epidemica* in Germany prior to World War II. Data are from two outbreaks occurring in Hamburg and Wilhelmsberg, respectively. (von Bormann, F., 1940, Hepatitis Epidemica. Ergebn. d. inn. Med. u. Kinderh., *58*, 201.)

blood 3 days before the onset of the disease (Francis et al., 1946). Attempts to recover virus from the blood and feces 1 month after the onset of disease and also 3 weeks after disappearance of jaundice (Neefe et al., 1945b) have been unsuccessful (Chart 17). However, recently acquired evidence suggests that certain persons, with or without evidence of hepatic disease, may carry virus in the blood or feces (Capps and Stokes, 1951) for prolonged periods. Further discussion of this important subject is found in the section on serum hepatitis.

Preliminary reports (Henle et al., 1950b) indicate that there is reason to hope that IH virus growing in tissue culture (and

is relatively free from the disease would lead one to suspect that one or more attacks must confer some immunity. In support of this is also the age distribution of the disease in civilian populations, in which it is more common in children and young adults than it is in older age groups. With advancing years, there is a decreasing susceptibility in adults (Chart 18), and among U. S. troops the morbidity in men of 20 years of age was about twice as great as that in men of 40 (Paul and Gardner, 1950).

Neefe et al. (1946) and Gauld (1946), in the light of epidemiologic data, suggest that one attack of infectious hepatitis is followed by immunity. Moreover, the demonstration of the protective effect of normal human gamma globulin when administered during the incubation period of infectious hepatitis also suggests the presence of certain neutralizing substances in the blood of the normal human adult population, possibly as a result of a previous clinical or subclinical attack of the disease. Immunity has been demonstrated experimentally (Neefe et al., 1945c, 1946; Havens, 1946b) in human volunteers convalescent from hepatitis caused by two different strains of IH virus when challenged with the homologous strain from 6 to 9 months after their initial infection. Partial cross immunity was also demonstrated between these two strains of virus. However, specific immunity may not be solid; a history of second attacks of hepatitis is said to be obtainable in from 2 to 5 per cent of patients. Again, the lack of a specific diagnostic test makes it difficult to evaluate such evidence, for one cannot eliminate the possibility of infection due to SH virus or to other as yet unidentified and immunologically distinct strains of hepatitis virus.

DIAGNOSIS

In the absence of specific immunologic tests, diagnosis in the preicteric phase must be made on clinical and epidemiologic evidence. Early in the disease, percussion tenderness over the liver with posterior cervical adenopathy and splenomegaly may be of assistance. The measurement of retention of bromsulfalein is usually the first test of hepatic function to become abnormal, and this may occur as early as the second day of fever. The cephalin-cholesterol flocculation and the thymol-turbidity tests become positive somewhat later, and ordinarily bilirubin appears in the urine at the end of the preicteric phase before jaundice is apparent. The value of detection of bilirubinuria as a simple but reliable diagnostic aid at this time and also in nonicteric hepatitis has been emphasized by Swift et al. (1950a). Leukopenia with relative lymphocytosis is characteristic in the preicteric phase.

The sera of a very few patients with infectious hepatitis contain a heterogenetic antibody which agglutinates sheep erythrocytes and fixes complement when combined with an antigen made from human liver. This heterogenetic antibody may be distinguished from others in human serum primarily by its absorbability on bits of human liver or boiled guinea pig kidneys.

During the febrile preicteric phase, the diseases which may be confused are: acute bacillary dysentery, typhoid and paratyphoid fever, malaria, sandfly fever, dengue, influenza, infectious mononucleosis, and acute appendicitis. The subsequent course, the geographic location, the normal or reduced number of leukocytes, and the demonstration of specific etiologic agents or their antibodies make the distinction evident.

When jaundice is present, the following conditions may be considered: acute and subacute cholangitis, Weil's disease and yellow fever. Jaundice may also occasionally develop in a variety of acute and chronic infections, as in malaria, brucellosis, amebiasis, pneumococcic pneumonia, septicemias, syphilis, both congenital and acquired (secondary), and infectious mononucleosis. In addition to the jaundice associated with various infections, other types of jaundice to be distinguished include: (1) hemolytic, either congenital or acquired; (2) hepatocellular, resulting from toxicity of chemicals, notably the halogenated hydrocarbons; cirrhosis of the liver; primary or metastatic carcinoma of the liver; and (3) obstructive, due to obstruction of the biliary tract by calculus or neoplasm.

A diagnosis of chronic hepatitis depends on the demonstration of hepatic dysfunction or histologic alterations in the liver, with or without signs or symptoms. Although the wide variability in the duration of disease does not justify this diagnosis until at least six months have elapsed from the onset of acute hepatitis, the reappearance and the persistence of anorexia, easy fatigability and upper abdominal discomfort beyond this time suggest chronic hepatitis. The presence of enlargement and tenderness of the liver, jaundice and splenomegaly lends supportive evidence. In many instances, none of these symptoms and signs is present, and in such patients abnormality of the bromsulphalein-retention test is the most reliable evidence of chronic hepatic dysfunction. The cephalin-cholesterol-flocculation, thymol-turbidity and thymol-flocculation tests are frequently positive, and their degree of positivity is thought to be roughly proportional to the activity and the progression of the disease. Cholangiolar obstruction occurs at times, with severe jaundice and increased amounts of serum alkaline phosphatase and total cholesterol. Differential diagnosis from extrahepatic obstruction may be particularly difficult in such patients, and biopsy of the liver or even exploratory laparotomy may at times be indicated. In a certain number of patients who have had acute hepatitis, it is not easy to interpret persistent subjective complaints in the absence of objective evidence of hepatic disease. Attention has been called to the occurrence of anorexia, fatigue and abdominal discomfort long after the expected time of recovery when little or no evidence of hepatic dysfunction or histologic alterations in the liver may be found; the term posthepatitis syndrome has been applied to this condition (Sherlock and Walshe, 1946).

TREATMENT

Acute Hepatitis. Treatment of the disease is symptomatic, and the two most important therapeutic principles are the provision of adequate rest in bed and a well-balanced, palatable, nutritious diet. The use of cream, milk, butter and eggs (Hoagland et al., 1946) is recommended and makes it possible to increase the caloric intake early, rapidly to replace lost weight and to shorten the period of convalescence. The duration of rest in bed is controversial. Military experience during World War II indicated that early ambulation of physi-

cally depleted patients with this disease was not infrequently followed by relapse. Subsequent experience with Occupation troops who were in good physical condition before contracting the disease (Gardner et al., 1949; Swift et al., 1950b; Colbert, 1951) suggested that convalescence was not prolonged nor the rate of relapse increased if a less-rigid regimen of rest than usually advised was followed. However, until this controversial point is clarified, it is recommended that patients be allowed out of bed when clinical jaundice is gone and the bromsulphalein-retention test is normal; graduated activity should be instituted according to individual tolerance. In the average adult case with jaundice, the total serum bilirubin becomes normal in the sixth to the eighth week of disease, and the average period of hospitalization in military cases is 60 days.

Although preliminary reports (Colbert et al., 1951; Sborov, 1951) have indicated that the administration of ACTH to patients in the acute phase of viral hepatitis was followed by a sharp diminution in amount of serum bilirubin and a slight shortening of duration of disease, untoward effects, including "mooning" of the face, ascites, edema and hypertension, were frequently observed, and relapse following the cessation of too short a course of therapy was common (Evans, 1951). The significance of the alterations produced by ACTH is not clearly understood. The shortening of the course of disease is too slight and the danger of relapse too great to warrant its general use at the present time.

While none of the chemotherapeutic or antibiotic agents now known has any apparent beneficial effect on the average case of viral hepatitis (Shaffer et al., 1950a; Colbert et al., 1952), it has been reported that aureomycin (Farquhar et al., 1950; Shaffer et al., 1950b; Sborov and Sutherland, 1951), in amounts of 250 mg. every 6 hours by mouth, supplemented by 100 mg. every 6 hours intravenously, is of apparent value in patients seriously sick or in hepatic coma. In such patients, the intravenous administration of 1,000 to 2,000 ml. of a solution of 10 per cent dextrose and 25 gm. of salt-poor albumin is recommended daily during the acute phase of hepatic decompensation.

Chronic Hepatitis. In certain patients, functional hepatic disability may be the only manifestation of sequelae of acute hepatitis, and the clinical condition of the patient is frequently such as to be compatible with full activity. However, another group of patients with symptoms and signs

exact distribution and prevalence remain poorly defined. Outbreaks have been reported in widely separated parts of the world and it is probably endemic in many regions where its presence is unsuspected. In certain parts of the world there is a distinct seasonal trend, with a sudden increase in prevalence in the autumn, often building up to epidemic proportions during the early winter and declining in the spring. However, the epidemic season may reach a peak in late winter and extend well into the spring (Chart 19).

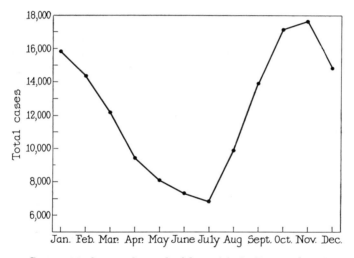

CHART 19. Seasonal trend of hepatitis in Denmark 1928-1947. (Havens, W. P., Jr., 1949, Viral hepatitis—progress and problems. Pa. Med. J., *52,* 1653-1657.)

of disease, including anorexia, epigastric discomfort (with or without jaundice), and enlarged, tender liver, may require rest in bed for prolonged periods with special attention to a well-balanced, nutritious diet. In those patients whose disease progresses to postnecrotic cirrhosis, the usual therapeutic regimen employed for persons with Laennec's cirrhosis is recommended but is frequently disappointing. The intravenous administration of salt-poor albumin appears to be of value in certain individual cases.

EPIDEMIOLOGY

It is probable that infectious hepatitis exists throughout the world, although its

Institutional and family outbreaks are traditional. In families, the usual sequence of events is that one member acquires the disease which is followed in 3 or 4 weeks by its appearance in one or more of the other members. Such a leisurely spread may also characterize institutional and military epidemics. However, sharp, explosive outbreaks may also occur. Within military units, the case rate as a result of a sharp epidemic can occasionally be as high as from 40 to 50 per cent of a command. High endemic rates may also be maintained in military groups (Paul and Gardner, 1950).

The exact ways in which infectious hepatitis normally spreads are not yet thoroughly known. Explosive water-borne (Neefe and Stokes, 1945), milk-borne (Murphy et al., 1946), and food-borne (Read et al., 1946) epidemics have been described. Gauld (1946) has indicated that epidemiologic evidence in most outbreaks points to some form of person-to-person spread. There is good experimental evidence favoring the intestinal-oral circuit as one of the natural routes of spread. This

from human excreta. It has been suspected that the prevalence of bacillary dysentery or salmonella infections may either predispose in some unknown way to the acquisition of hepatitis or that organisms of these diseases are prone to act as secondary invaders (Havens and Wenner, 1946). Gauld (1946) has emphasized the necessity of considering the possibility of respiratory spread, in that this is consistent with the

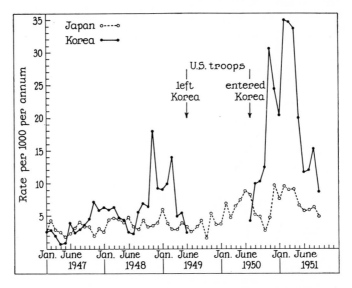

CHART 20. Incidence of viral hepatitis in U. S. personnel in Japan and Korea. (Preliminary rates furnished by the Medical Statistics Division, Office of The Surgeon General, Department of the Army, 21 November 1951. Air Force personnel are included through June 1949. Cases of viral hepatitis include serum hepatitis until May 1951, after which an effort was made to omit cases of serum hepatitis from the data; such cases constitute only a small percentage of the total.)

concept is based in part on investigative work quoted hereafter and, in part, on epidemiologic study of military populations in which a high prevalence of the disease has occurred when and where camp sanitation was poor and particularly during combat (Chart 20). The association of infectious hepatitis with intestinal diseases is recognized, and Kirk's (1945) study among New Zealand soldiers at Alamein in Egypt in 1942 led him to believe that the disease was spread there by flies carrying the infection

epidemic and seasonal pattern of infectious hepatitis. The experimental evidence for this is not well established since the few attempts to recover virus from the nasopharynx of patients in the active stage of the disease have been unsuccessful, with one possible exception (MacCallum and Bradley, 1944). The possibility of transmission by a biting insect also deserves consideration on the basis of the facts that virus is present in the blood during the acute phase of disease and may be transmitted by very small quantities (0.01 cc.) of infectious blood. However, possible vectors are not common in the late fall and early winter months in many areas where the disease is prevalent.

Its artificial spread as well as that of serum hepatitis through the use of contaminated blood or serum, and by the use of improperly sterilized syringes or needles as described by Droller (1945), is a point for consideration. The extreme viability of the icterogenic agent, the infectiousness of small quantities of blood, and the evidence just mentioned suggest that infectious hepatitis probably has been transmitted unintentionally more often than is realized.

Control Measures

Procedures which tend to interrupt the intestinal-oral route should be carried out in an attempt to control the spread of the disease. During any institutional or camp outbreak, attention should be directed toward the general sanitation of the site, fly abatement, sterilization of food receptacles, elimination of infected food handlers, and prevention of fecal contamination of food, water and milk supplies. The degree of chlorination effective against hepatitis virus has not yet been determined. Detection of healthy human carriers or subclinical cases is impossible at present because of the lack of suitable laboratory technics. Since it is as yet unknown how long virus remains in stools or blood, it is advisable to regard the stools as potentially infectious for at least one month after the onset of disease and to recommend that patients do not act as donors of blood except under the special conditions described in the section on serum hepatitis. Every possible effort should be made to keep food handlers free from infection. Particular effort should be made to clean properly and to sterilize with heat (boiling or autoclaving for 15 minutes) all needles and syringes which come in contact with the blood of such patients.

Normal human gamma globulin confers passive protection (Chart 21) if given during the incubation period; it is effective when given as late as 6 days before the onset of disease (Stokes and Neefe, 1945; Havens and Paul, 1945; Gellis et al., 1945). Doses of 0.06 to 0.12 cc. per pound of body weight, given intramuscularly, have been commonly used, although it has been shown recently that as little as 0.01 cc. per pound of body weight is effective. It has been estimated that passive protection lasts from 6 to 8 weeks. However, observations of groups of children inoculated with gamma globulin and subsequently heavily exposed to hepatitis virus over a period of several months suggest that a more permanent protection may occur. One possible explanation of this is that active immunization may be superimposed on passive protection under such conditions (Stokes et al., 1951). Passive immunization of this type is recommended for persons involved in certain family outbreaks and to interrupt the course of epidemics in institutions or camps.

SERUM HEPATITIS

Reference has been made to the fact that serum hepatitis (SH) and infectious hepatitis (IH) are members of the same group of diseases. At present, serum hepatitis may be described arbitrarily as a form of disease ordinarily produced by the parenteral inoculation of human blood or its products obtained from a person who, though not apparently ill, is carrying the causative filterable icterogenic agent in his blood. Many thousands of infections have been produced in persons who have received injections of human convalescent serum, vaccines containing human serum, plasma, and, rarely, whole blood. The course of disease is clinically indistinguishable from infectious hepatitis although there is some evidence to indicate that its onset is more apt to be insidious and accompanied by less fever (Turner et al., 1944). It may be more severe than the latter condition, particularly in debilitated patients.

It is probable that this type of hepatitis has existed for many years, but has been

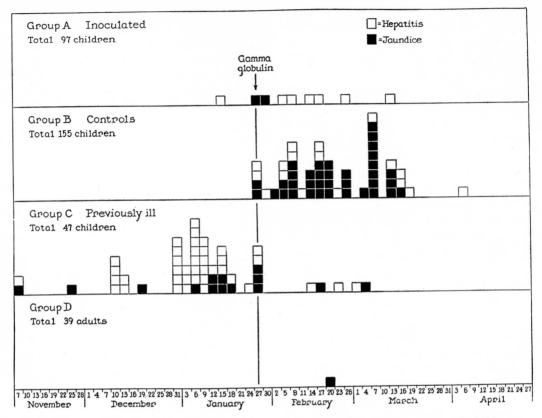

CHART 21. Rates at which infectious hepatitis developed in four groups of children during an epidemic of hepatitis at an asylum. Group A was inoculated with gamma globulin on January 27. Groups B, C and D did not receive gamma globulin. The open squares indicate cases without jaundice. The black squares indicate cases with jaundice. (Havens, W. P., Jr., and Paul, J. R., 1945, Prevention of infectious hepatitis with gamma globulin. Journal of the American Medical Association, *129,* 270-272.)

poorly defined. Thus, epidemics of jaundice following vaccination for smallpox in Germany (Lürman, 1885) in the 1880's were probably examples of this disease. Also, many of the cases of jaundice among syphilitic patients treated with arsenical drugs or bismuth, may fall into this category, for certain observers, notably Stokes et al. (1920) and Ruge (1927), suggested that the injury to the liver was caused by an infectious instead of a chemical agent. It is only within recent years, however, that the concept of the viral etiology of serum hepatitis has evolved, but credit for the first true recognition of the situation goes to a group of Swedish physicians (Flaum et al., 1926) who described an epidemic of jaun-

dice among patients attending a diabetic clinic. It is now apparent that patients with this form of hepatitis may be divided into two groups: (1) those who are infected by improperly sterilized syringes or needles employed in giving insulin, antisyphilitic therapy, penicillin, etc., or in withdrawing blood for various procedures such as observation of the erythrocyte-sedimentation rate or blood counts, or even during the procedure of tattooing; and (2) those who are infected by the administration of transfusions of blood or plasma, or contaminated human blood products such as convalescent serum, fibrin foam, thrombin, or vaccines containing human serum or plasma. In the years just prior to and during World War

II, many cases of serum hepatitis occurred in military personnel and in civilians following transfusions of plasma or vaccination with yellow fever vaccine which contained human serum (Fox et al., 1942). Subsequently, the widespread use of plasma and blood, particularly in depleted patients, has augmented the magnitude of this problem.

The geographic distribution of serum hepatitis is not known, but it appears to be widespread throughout the world, and there is good evidence to suggest that both forms of hepatitis, i.e., IH and SH, may be found together in time and place.

Clinically and pathologically, serum hepatitis and infectious hepatitis are almost indistinguishable after the onset of disease, and as in infectious hepatitis many cases of serum hepatitis never develop clinical evidence of jaundice. The same therapeutic principles apply to both conditions.

As in infectious hepatitis, the etiologic agent of serum hepatitis is believed to be a virus and is transmissible to man in series and evokes homologous immunity. The SH virus is filterable and resistant to 56° C. for from 30 to 60 minutes (Oliphant et al., 1943). It survives in the frozen state for several years, and in a desiccated state at room temperature for at least a year; it keeps well in serum containing merthiolate in concentration 1:2000, or in a 0.2 per cent concentration of tricresol (Neefe, 1946). It has been inactivated in serum by exposure to ultraviolet light for 45 minutes at 2537 Angström units (Oliphant and Hollaender, 1946; Blanchard et al., 1948).

Certain differences are apparent between these two forms of hepatitis and their etiologic agents (Table 20). The virus of serum hepatitis is present in the circulating blood during the long incubation period as well as in the active stage of the disease (Charts 22 and 23), (Havens, 1946c); indeed, it has been demonstrated (Neefe et al., 1944) in the blood 87 days prior to the onset of symptoms. It apparently produces disease only when inoculated parenterally

(one exception reported by MacCallum and Bauer, 1944), and symptoms appear insidiously after a long and variable incubation period of from 60 to 120 days or longer (Chart 24). The disease is not so contagious as infectious hepatitis; close contact infection has been suspected but is rare; and the

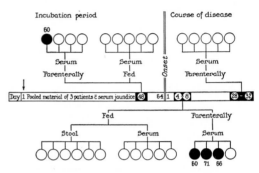

CHART 22. Illustration of results of administration to human volunteers of pools of serum and stool obtained three fourths through (48th day) the incubation period and during the acute (4th to 8th day) and convalescent (28th to 32nd day) phases of 3 patients with experimentally induced homologous serum jaundice. The small arrow on the left indicates the time of infection of the patients. Open circles indicate volunteers who were inoculated and failed to contract the disease; black circles indicate volunteers who contracted homologous serum jaundice. The figure adjacent to each black circle represents the length of incubation period in days. (Havens, W. P., Jr., 1946, Period of infectivity of patients with homologous serum jaundice and routes of infection in this disease. Journal of Experimental Medicine, *83*, 441-447.)

virus has not been demonstrated in the feces as it has in infectious hepatitis. This fact, in combination with the failure to produce disease in human volunteers by the oral administration of serum known to contain virus, suggests that the intestinal-oral route may not be of importance in its spread, differentiating it from infectious hepatitis. One must conclude, nevertheless, that the mechanism whereby serum hepatitis is acquired in nature is obscure. It might be satisfactory to regard serum hepatitis as a

TABLE 20. COMPARISON OF BEHAVIOR OF VIRUSES OF INFECTIOUS HEPATITIS AND
SERUM HEPATITIS IN EXPERIMENTALLY INFECTED HUMAN VOLUNTEERS*

VIRUS	INFECTIOUS HEPATITIS	SERUM HEPATITIS
1. Filterable	Seitz EK	Seitz EK
2. Resistance to heat	56° C. 30 minutes	56° C. 60 minutes
3. Susceptible host	Man	Man
4. Incubation period (Days) ...	15-34	56-134
5. Route of infection (Experimental)	Parenteral or oral inoculation	Parenteral inoculation
6. Virus in stool	Acute phase	Not demonstrated
7. Virus in serum	Acute phase	Incubation period and acute phase
8. Immunity		
a. Homologous	Present	Not tested
b. Heterologous	Not tested	None apparent

* (Havens, W. P., Jr., 1947, The etiology of infectious hepatitis. J. Am. Med. Assn., *134*, 653-655.)

clinical variant of infectious hepatitis were it not for the disturbing fact that immunologically the two viruses are distinct. Thus, studies on immunity in human volunteers corroborate the epidemiologic experience that patients who have had infectious hepatitis are susceptible to serum hepatitis and

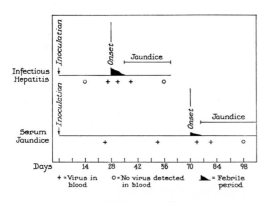

CHART 23. Schematic illustration of results of attempts to demonstrate virus in the blood of patients during the incubation period and course of disease of infectious hepatitis and homologous serum jaundice. Isolation of virus was determined by the reproduction of disease in human volunteers. (Neefe, J. R., et al., 1944; Paul, J. R., et al., 1945; Francis, T., Jr., et al., 1946; Havens, W. P., Jr., 1946a, b.)

vice versa (Havens, 1945b; Neefe et al., 1945b). Lastly, although every lot of normal human gamma globulin tested has been effective in preventing infectious hepatitis, a similar uniformity of protection against serum hepatitis by different lots of gamma globulin has not been found (Grossman et al., 1945; Duncan et al., 1947; Stokes, 1951). It is not known whether this variability in protection against SH virus indicates a failure of production or maintenance of sufficient neutralizing antibody or a number of different strains of virus with restricted geographic distribution.

PREVENTION AND CONTROL

It is difficult to devise measures for the control of this disease because of the lack of specific serologic tests, susceptible laboratory animals, and knowledge about the length of time that individuals carry virus. The use of a battery of tests of hepatic function to detect carriers of virus may reveal evidence of hepatic disease and, in retrospect, has furnished evidence that certain donors whose blood produced hepatitis had hepatic disease. However, the fact that asymptomatic donors, with normal hepatic function as determined by tests, have been proved to be carriers of virus makes this an unreliable method of detection.

The duration of the carrier state is unknown, although a small number of experiments with volunteers suggested that IH and SH viruses were not present in the blood when tested at varying times ranging from 1 to 12 months after the onset of disease. However, evidence is accumulating to suggest that the carrier state is well equilibrated under certain circumstances and exists more frequently than previously suspected. The prolonged period of viremia in experimentally infected volunteers who were asymptomatic and without laboratory evidence of hepatic dysfunction is in support of this concept as is the fact that, up to the present, those persons proved to be carriers have not had a history of preceding hepatitis or jaundice. Clinical observations (Stokes, 1951b) furnish supportive evidence in that SH virus was found on two occasions, two years apart, in the blood of a patient who was asymptomatic and with normal hepatic function as determined by tests. During this period, the patient was delivered of a baby which died of hepatitis. Another patient with so-called Laennec's cirrhosis has been proved to be a carrier of SH virus for 5 years. In a third case, it was observed (Havens, 1951) that two transfusions of blood, given to two different recipients 4 months apart, from a single donor produced hepatitis after a long incubation period in both recipients. One year after giving the last transfusion, this donor developed a clinically evident attack of hepatitis.

The resistance of IH and SH viruses to physical and chemical agents is such that there is no practicable way to treat all products of human blood to render them safe. In this regard, it should be emphasized that there is no knowledge as to whether such commonly employed disinfectants as alcohol, ether and zepharin are effective in destroying SH and IH viruses. Thus, the use of disinfectants on surgical and dental instruments should be considered in this light.

It is of interest that recent attempts to inactivate hepatitis virus in whole blood by the addition of nitrogen mustard were unsuccessful (Drake et al., 1951).

Although there is no single method of inactivating hepatitis virus which is applicable to human blood and all its components,

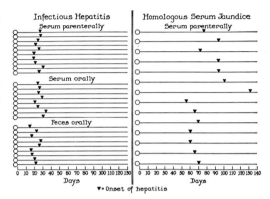

CHART 24. Comparison of the duration of incubation periods of human volunteers experimentally inoculated with a strain of infectious hepatitis virus and a strain of homologous serum jaundice virus. Each line represents the incubation period and course of disease of a single volunteer. Volunteers were inoculated at *0* days. These strains of hepatitis virus were previously described (Havens, W. P., Jr., et al., 1944; Paul, J. R., et al., 1945) as a part of experiments conducted by the Neurotropic Virus Disease Commission, U. S. Army.

methods of treatment of individual fractions have been devised which appear to be effective. Thus, heating human albumin at 60° C. for 10 hours inactivates the virus without influencing the therapeutic value of the albumin (Neefe, 1946). Although irradiation of plasma with ultraviolet light apparently inactivated hepatitis virus experimentally (Blanchard et al., 1948), more recent experience with it as a method of preparing this material for transfusion has not always been successful, and cases of hepatitis following the reception of irradiated plasma have been reported (James et al., 1950; Barnett et al., 1950; Rosenthal et al., 1950). Whether this indicates a difference in resistance of various strains of virus, an actual failure of the method, or a breakdown in the processing of individual lots of plasma is not clearly defined at present. Further investigation is needed of a recent report by Allen et al. (1950) indicating that plasma preserved in the liquid state at room temperature for prolonged periods apparently failed to produce hepatitis in any of the recipients.

Of particular importance in the use of products of human blood has been the fact that many thousands of injections of gamma globulin have been given prophylactically, particularly for measles, without the subsequent occurrence (with very rare exceptions) of hepatitis. There is no known reason that, in the process of fractionation of icterogenic plasma, hepatitis virus should not appear in all fractions; it has been assumed that it is neutralized in the gamma globulin by an excess of antibody. A recent report by Cockburn et al. (1951) is of interest in this regard since a single case of hepatitis followed the injection of gamma globulin prepared from a proved icterogenic pool of plasma. Whether this single case represented an example of artificial transmission, thereby incriminating gamma globulin, or was a spontaneously appearing case

of the naturally acquired disease is not known.

Because of the frequency of administration of human plasma and whole blood and the extreme infectivity of the virus (0.01 cc. of serum is infectious), the following precautions should be taken when human blood or its products are used. Patients with a history of jaundice should not act as donors of blood for transfusion. Pools of plasma should be irradiated with ultraviolet light. If irradiation is not practicable, pools of plasma should consist of material from only two donors. All needles and syringes should be rinsed and cleaned carefully prior to sterilization by boiling or autoclaving for 15 minutes before use on each patient. The need for the use of plasma, blood or convalescent human serum should be carefully considered because of the possibility of transmitting another disease to a patient already sick. Although the variability of protection against serum hepatitis by gamma globulin makes its use of questionable value, one may be justified in giving to certain patients 10 cc. of gamma globulin intramuscularly on two occasions, one month apart, after transfusions of blood or plasma are received.

REFERENCES

Allen, J. G., Sykes, C., Enerson, D. M., Moulder, P. V., Elghammer, R. M., Grossman, B. J., Mc-Keen, C. L., and Galluzzi, N. J., 1950, Homologous serum jaundice and its relation to methods of plasma storage. J. Am. Med. Assn., *144*, 1069-1074.

Andersen, T. T., and Tulinius, S., 1938, Etiology of hepatitis epidemica (epidemic jaundice). Acta Med. Scandinav., *95*, 497-509.

Barker, M. H., Capps, R. B., and Allen, F. W., 1945a, Acute infectious hepatitis in the Mediterranean Theater. J. Am. Med. Assn., *128*, 997-1003.

Barker, M. H., Capps, R. B., and Allen, F. W., 1945b, Chronic hepatitis in the Mediterranean Theater. A new clinical syndrome. J. Am. Med. Assn., *129*, 653-659.

Barnett, R. N., Fox, R. A., and Snavely, J. G., 1950, Hepatitis following the use of irradiated human plasma. J. Am. Med. Assn., *144*, 226-228.

Blanchard, M. C., Stokes, J., Jr., Hampil, B., Wade, G. R., and Spizizen, J., 1948, Methods of protection against homologous serum hepatitis. II. The inactivation of hepatitis virus SH with ultraviolet rays. J. Am. Med. Assn., *138*, 341-343.

Blumer, G., 1923, Infectious jaundice in the United States. J. Am. Med. Assn., *81*, 353-358.

Cameron, J. D. S., 1943, Infective hepatitis. Quart. J. Med., *12*, 139-155.

Capps, R. B., and Stokes, J., Jr., 1951, Personal communication.

Capps, R. B., Bennett, A. M., and Stokes, J., Jr., 1950, A prolonged outbreak of infectious hepatitis in nurses due to a group of small children serving as a reservoir of the virus. J. Clin. Investig., *29*, 802-803.

Cockayne, E. A., 1912, Catarrhal jaundice, sporadic and epidemic, and its relation to acute yellow atrophy of the liver. Quart. J. Med., *6*, 1-29.

Cockburn, W. C., Harrington, J. A., Zeitlin, R. A., Morris, D., and Camps, F. E., 1951, Homologous serum hepatitis and measles prophylaxis. Brit. Med. J., *2*, 6-12.

Colbert, J. W., Jr., 1949, Review of animal experimentation in infectious hepatitis and in serum hepatitis. Yale J. Biol. and Med., *21*, 335-343.

Colbert, J. W., Jr., 1951, Personal communication.

Colbert, J. W., Jr., Holland, J. F., Heissler, I., and

Knowlton, M., 1951, The use of ACTH in acute viral hepatitis. Proceedings of the Second Clinical ACTH Conference, Vol. I, Philadelphia, Blakiston Co., pp. 371-385.

Colbert, J. W., Jr., Bungards, L., and Knowlton, M., 1952, Aureomycin, chloromycetin and terramycin in the treatment of acute viral hepatitis. Proc. Soc. Exp. Biol. and Med. 79, 339-343.

Dible, J. H., McMichael, J., and Sherlock, S. P. V., 1943, Pathology of acute hepatitis: aspiration biopsy studies of epidemic, arsenotherapy and serum jaundice. Lancet, 2, 402-408.

Drake, M. E., Kitts, A. W., Blanchard, M. C., Farquhar, J. D., Stokes, J., Jr., and Henle, W., 1950, Studies on the agent of infectious hepatitis. II. The disease produced in human volunteers by the agent cultivated in tissue culture or embryonated hen's eggs. J. Exp. Med., 92, 283-297.

Drake, M. E., Stokes, J., Jr., Hampil, B., Pennell, R. B., and Spizizen, J., 1951, The effect of nitrogen mustard (methyl-bis beta chloroethyl amine hydrochloride) on the virus of serum hepatitis (S.H.) in whole blood. To be published.

Droller, H., 1945, An outbreak of hepatitis in a diabetic clinic. Brit. Med. J., 1, 623-625.

Duncan, G. G., Christian, H. A., Stokes, J. Jr., Rexer, W. F., Nicholson, J. T., and Edgar, A., 1947, An evaluation of immune serum globulin as a prophylactic agent against homologous serum hepatitis. Am. J. Med. Sci., 213, 53-57.

Essen, K. W., and Lembke, A., 1944, Zur Aetiologie der Hepatitis epidemica. Med. Ztschr., 1, 99-100.

Evans A. S., 1951, Personal communication.

Farquhar, J. D., Stokes, J., Jr., Whitlock, C. M., Jr., Bluemle, L. W., Jr., and Gambescia, J. M., 1950, Studies on the use of aureomycin in hepatic disease. III. A note on aureomycin therapy in hepatic coma. Am. J. Med. Sci., 220, 166-172.

Findlay, G. M., MacCallum, F. O., and Murgatroyd, F., 1939, Observations bearing on the aetiology of infective hepatitis (so-called epidemic catarrhal jaundice). Tr. Roy. Soc. Trop. Med. and Hyg., 32, 575-586.

Findlay, G. M., and Willcox, R. R., 1945, Transmission of infective hepatitis by faeces and urine. Lancet, 1, 212.

Flaum, A., Malmros, H., and Persson, E., 1926, Eine nosocomiale Ikterus-Epidemie. Acta Med. Scandinav., Suppl. 16.

Fox, J. P., Manso, C., Penna, H. A., and Pará, M., 1942, Observations on the occurrence of icterus in Brazil following vaccination against yellow fever. Am. J. Hyg., 36, 68-116.

Francis, T. Jr., Frisch, A. W., and Quilligan, J. J. Jr., 1946, Demonstration of infectious hepatitis virus in presymptomatic period after transfer by transfusion. Proc. Soc. Exp. Biol. and Med., 61, 276-280.

Gardner, H. T., Rovelstad, R. A., Moore, D. J., Streitfeld, F. A., and Knowlton, M., 1949, Hepatitis among American occupation troops in Germany: a follow-up study with particular reference to interim alcohol and physical activity. Ann. Int. Med., 34, 1009-1019.

Gauld, R. L., 1946, Epidemiological field studies of infectious hepatitis in the Mediterranean Theatre of Operations. I-VIII. Am. J. Hyg., 43, 248-313.

Gellis, S. S., Stokes, J. Jr., Brother, G. M., Hall, W. M., Gilmore, H. R., Beyer, E., and Morrissey, R. A., 1945, The use of human immune serum globulin (gamma globulin) in infectious (epidemic) hepatitis in the Mediterranean Theatre of Operations. 1. Studies on prophylaxis in two epidemics of infectious hepatitis. J. Am. Med. Assn., 128, 1062-1063.

Gledhill, A. W., and Andrewes, C. H., 1951, A hepatitis virus of mice. Brit. J. Exp. Path., 32, 559-568.

Grossman, E. B., Stewart, S. G., and Stokes, J. Jr., 1945, Post-transfusion hepatitis in battle casualties and a study of its prophylaxis by means of human immune serum globulin. J. Am. Med. Assn., 129, 991-994.

Havens, W. P. Jr., 1945a, Properties of the etiologic agent of infectious hepatitis. Proc. Soc. Exp. Biol. and Med., 58, 203-204.

Havens, W. P. Jr., 1945b, Experiment in cross immunity between infectious hepatitis and homologous serum jaundice. Proc. Soc. Exp. Biol. and Med., 59, 148-150.

Havens, W. P. Jr., 1946a, Period of infectivity of patients with experimentally induced infectious hepatitis. J. Exp. Med., 83, 251-258.

Havens, W. P. Jr., 1946b, Immunity in experimentally induced infectious hepatitis. J. Exp. Med., 84, 403-406.

Havens, W. P. Jr., 1946c, Period of infectivity of patients with homologous serum jaundice and routes of infection in this disease. J. Exp. Med., 83, 441-447.

Havens, W. P., Jr., 1951. Unpublished observation.

Havens, W. P., Jr., and Ginder, D. R., 1948, The sequelae of viral hepatitis. Stanford Med. Bull., 6, 311-318.

Havens, W. P. Jr., and Marck, R. E., 1946, The leukocyte response of patients with experimentally induced infectious hepatitis. Am. J. Med. Sci., 212, 129-138.

Havens, W. P. Jr., and Paul, J. R., 1945, Prevention of infectious hepatitis with gamma globulin. J. Am. Med. Assn., 129, 270-272.

Havens, W. P. Jr., and Ward, R., 1945, Failure to transmit infectious hepatitis to chimpanzees. Proc. Soc. Exp. Biol. and Med., 60, 102-104.

Havens, W. P. Jr., Ward, R., Drill, V. A., and Paul, J. R., 1944, Experimental production of hepatitis by feeding icterogenic materials. Proc. Soc. Exp. Biol. and Med., 57, 206-208.

Havens, W. P. Jr., and Wenner, H. A., 1946, Infectious hepatitis complicated by secondary invasion with salmonella. J. Clin. Investig., 25, 45-52.

Henle, G., Drake, M., Henle, W., and Stokes, J., Jr., 1950b, A skin test for infectious hepatitis. Proc. Soc. Exp. Biol. and Med., 73, 603-605.

Henle, W., Harris, S., Henle, G., Harris, T. N., Drake, M. E., Mangold, F., and Stokes, J., Jr., 1950a, Studies on the agent of infectious hepatitis. I. Propagation of the agent in tissue culture and in the embryonated hen's egg. J. Exp. Med., 92, 271-281.

Herzberg, K., 1943, Der Kanarienvogel als Versuchstier in der Hepatitis contagiosa-forschung. Klin. Wchnschr., *22*, 676-677.

Hoagland, C. L., Labby, D. H., Kunkel, H. G., and Shank, R. E., 1946, An analysis of the effect of fat in the diet on recovery in infectious hepatitis. Am. J. Pub. Health, *36*, 1287-1292.

James, G., Korns, R. F., and Wright, A. W., 1950, Homologous serum jaundice associated with use of irradiated plasma. A preliminary report. J. Am. Med. Assn., *144*, 228-229.

Jersild, M., 1945, Stigende hyppighed af hepatitis chronica. Saertryk af Ugeskrift for Lager, *107*, 819-826.

Jordan, J., and Mirick, G. S., 1951, Hepatitis in mice, of presumed viral origin (a preliminary report). Bull. Johns Hopkins Hosp., *89*, 326-331.

Kirk, R., 1945, Spread of infective hepatitis. Lancet, *1*, 80-81.

Klatskin, G., and Rappaport, E. M., 1947, Late residuals in presumably cured acute infectious hepatitis. Ann. Int. Med., *26*, 13-26.

Kunkel, H. G., and Labby, D. H., 1950, Chronic liver disease following infectious hepatitis. II. Cirrhosis of the liver. Ann. Int. Med., *32*, 433-450.

Kunkel, H. G., Labby, D. H., and Hoagland, C. L., 1947, Chronic liver disease following infectious hepatitis. I. Abnormal convalescence from initial attack. Ann. Int. Med., *27*, 209-219.

Lucké, B., and Mallory, T., 1946, The fulminant form of epidemic hepatitis. Am. J. Path., *22*, 867-945.

Lucké, B., and Radcliffe, H., 1949, Virus hepatitis of birds and its possible relation to epidemic hepatitis of man. Tr. Assn. Am. Physicians, *62*, 83-89.

Lürman, A., 1885, Eine Icterusepidemie. Berl. klin. Wchnschr., *22*, 20-23.

MacCallum, F. O., and Bauer, D. J., 1944, Homologous serum jaundice: transmission experiments with human volunteers. Lancet, *1*, 622-627.

MacCallum, F. O., and Bradley, W. H., 1944, Transmission of infective hepatitis to human volunteers. Lancet, *2*, 228.

MacCallum, F. O., and Miles, J. A. R., 1946, A transmissible disease in rats inoculated with material from cases of infective hepatitis. Lancet, *1*, 3-4.

Mallory, T. B., 1947, The pathology of epidemic hepatitis. J. Am. Med. Assn., *134*, 655-662.

Müller, T., 1947, Hepatitis epidemica mit hoher Letalität im Kanton Basel-Stadt im Jahre 1946. Schweiz. med. Wchnschr., *77*, 796-802.

Murphy, W. J., Petrie, L. M., and Work, S. D. Jr., 1946, Outbreak of infectious hepatitis, apparently milk-borne. Am. J. Pub. Health, *36*, 169-173.

Neefe, J. R., 1946, Recent advances in the knowledge of "virus hepatitis." Clin. North America, Philadelphia Number, November, pp. 1407-1443.

Neefe, J. R., Gellis, S. S., and Stokes, J. Jr., 1946, Homologous serum hepatitis and infectious (epidemic) hepatitis: studies in volunteers bearing on immunologic and other characteristics of the etiological agents. Am. J. Med., *1*, 3-22.

Neefe, J. R., and Stokes, J. Jr., 1945, An epidemic of infectious hepatitis apparently due to a water borne agent. J. Am. Med. Assn., *128*, 1063-1075.

Neefe, J. R., Stokes, J. Jr., Baty, J. B., and Reinhold, J. G., 1945a, Disinfection of water containing causa-

tive agent of infectious (epidemic) hepatitis. J. Am. Med. Assn., *128*, 1076-1080.

Neefe, J. R., Stokes, J. Jr., Garber, R. S., and Gellis, S. S., 1947, Studies on the relationship of the hepatitis virus to persistent symptoms, disability, and hepatic disturbance ("chronic hepatitis syndrome") following acute infectious hepatitis. J. Clin. Investig., *26*, 329-338.

Neefe, J. R., Stokes, J. Jr., and Reinhold, J. G., 1945b, Oral administration to volunteers of feces from patients with homologous serum hepatitis and infectious (epidemic) hepatitis. Am. J. Med. Sci., *210*, 29-32.

Neefe, J. R., Stokes, J. Jr., and Gellis, S. S., 1945c, Homologous serum hepatitis and infectious (epidemic) hepatitis. Experimental study of immunity and cross immunity in volunteers. A preliminary report. Am. J. Med. Sci., *210*, 561-575.

Neefe, J. R., Stokes, J. Jr., Reinhold, J. G., and Lukens, F. D. W., 1944, Hepatitis due to the injection of homologous blood products in human volunteers. J. Clin. Investig., *23*, 836-855.

Oliphant, J. W., Gilliam, A. G., and Larson, C. L., 1943, Jaundice following administration of human serum. Pub. Health Rep., *58*, 1233-1242.

Oliphant, J. W., and Hollaender, A., 1946, Homologous serum jaundice: experimental inactivation of etiologic agent in serum by ultraviolet irradiation. Pub. Health Rep., *61*, 598-602.

Olitsky, P. K., and Casals, J., 1945, Certain affections of the liver that arise spontaneously in so-called normal stock albino mice. Proc. Soc. Exp. Biol. and Med., *60*, 48-51.

Paul, J. R., and Gardner, H. T., 1950, Endemiologic aspects of hepatitis in U. S. troops in Germany, 1946-1950. Am. J. Med., *8*, 565-580.

Paul, J. R., Havens, W. P. Jr., Sabin, A. B., and Philip, C. B., 1945, Transmission experiments in serum jaundice and infectious hepatitis. J. Am. Med. Assn., *128*, 911-915.

Post, J., Gellis, S., and Lindenauer, H. J., 1950, Studies on the sequelae of acute infectious hepatitis. Ann. Int. Med., *33*, 1378-1397.

Quincke, A., 1903, Icterus in infectious diseases, *in* Nothnagel's Encyclopedia of Practical Medicine, Philadelphia, Saunders, Vol. 8, p. 500.

Read, M. R., Bancroft, H., Doull, J. A., and Parker, R. F., 1946, Infectious hepatitis—presumedly foodborne outbreak. Am. J. Pub. Health, *36*, 367-370.

Rich, A. R., 1930, The pathogenesis of the forms of jaundice. Bull. Johns Hopkins Hosp., *47*, 338-377.

Roholm, K., and Iversen, P., 1939, Leberveränderungen bei akuter epidemischer Hepatitis. Verhandl. deutsch. Ges. inn. Med., *51*, 359-361.

van Rooyen, C. E., and Gordon, I., 1942, Some experimental work on infective hepatitis in M. E. F. J. Royal Army Med. Corps, *79*, 213-225.

Rosenthal, N., Bassen, F. A., and Michael, S. R., 1950, Probable transmission of viral hepatitis by ultraviolet-irradiated plasma. Report of three cases. J. Am. Med. Assn., *144*, 224-226.

Rubarth, S., 1945, Bidrag till den patolog-anatomiska bilden och etiologin vid den s.k. toxiska leverdystrofin hos hund. Särtryck ur Skandinavisk Veterinartidskrift, pp. 356-361.

Ruge, H., 1927, Die akute Leberatrophie und ihre Beziehung zu Syphilis und Salvarsan nach den in der Marine von 1920-1925 beobachteten Fällen. Arch. Derm. u. Syph., *153*, 518-530.

Sborov, V. M., 1951, Discussion of: The use of ACTH in acute viral hepatitis by J. W. Colbert, Jr., et al. *in* Proceedings of the Second Clinical ACTH Conference, Vol. I, Philadelphia, Blakiston Co., pp. 381-384.

Sborov, V. M., and Sutherland, D. A., 1951, Fatty liver following aureomycin and terramycin therapy in chronic hepatic disease. Gastroenterol., *18*, 598-605.

Shaffer, J. M., Bluemle, L. W., Jr., Sborov, V. M., and Neefe, J. R., 1950b, Studies on the use of aureomycin in hepatic disease. IV. Aureomycin therapy in chronic liver disease (with a note on dermal sensitivity). Am. J. Med. Sci., *220*, 173-182.

Shaffer, J. M., Farquhar, J. D., Stokes, J., Jr., and Sborov, V. M., 1950a, Studies on the use of aureomycin in hepatic disease. I. Aureomycin therapy in acute viral hepatitis. Am. J. Med. Sci., *220*, 1-5.

Sherlock, S., 1948, Post-hepatitis cirrhosis. Lancet, *1*, 817-822.

Sherlock, S., and Walshe, V., 1946, The post-hepatitis syndrome. Lancet, *2*, 482-484.

Siede, W., and Meding, G., 1941, Zur Ätiologie der Hepatitis epidemica. Klin. Wchnschr., *20*, 1065-1067.

Stokes, J., Jr., 1951a, Personal communication.

Stokes, J., Jr., 1951b, Personal communication.

Stokes, J., Jr., Farquhar, J. A., Drake, M. E., Capps, R. B., Ward, C. S., Jr., and Kitts, A. W., 1951, Infectious hepatitis. Length of protection by immune serum globulin (gamma globulin) during epidemics. J. Am. Med. Assn., *147*, 714-719.

Stokes, J. Jr., and Neefe, J. R., 1945, The prevention and attenuation of infectious hepatitis by gamma globulin. J. Am. Med. Assn., *127*, 144-145.

Stokes, J. H., Ruedemann, R. Jr., and Lemon, W. S., 1920, Epidemic infectious jaundice and its relation to therapy of syphilis. Arch. Int. Med., *26*, 521-543.

Swift, W. E., Jr., Gardner, H. T., Moore, D. J., Streitfeld, F. H., and Havens, W. P., Jr., 1950b, Clinical course of viral hepatitis and the effect of exercise during convalescence. Am. J. Med. *8*, 614-622.

Swift, W. E., Jr., Miller, W. N., Streitfeld, F. H., and Knowlton, M., 1950a, An evaluation of two screening tests for the detection of early and sub-icteric viral hepatitis. Am. J. Med., *8*, 581-583.

Turner, R. H., Snavely, J. R., Grossman, E. B., Buchanan, R. N., and Foster, S. O., 1944, Some clinical studies of acute hepatitis occurring in soldiers after inoculation with yellow fever vaccine: with especial consideration of severe attacks. Ann. Int. Med., *20*, 193-218.

Voegt, H., 1942, Zur Aetiologie der Hepatitis epidemica. München med. Wchnschr., *89*, 76-79.

Watson, C. J., and Hoffbauer, F. W., 1946, The problem of prolonged hepatitis with particular reference to the cholangiolitic type and to the development of cholangiolitic cirrhosis of the liver. Ann. Int. Med., *25*, 195-227.

FRANK L. HORSFALL, Jr., m.d.

Hospital of The Rockefeller Institute for Medical Research

16

Common Cold

(Synonyms: Acute coryza, acute rhinitis)

INTRODUCTION

The common cold is now recognized as a disease entity with reasonably well-defined features. It is attributable to infection of the upper respiratory tract with a virus and is to be distinguished from other forms of rhinitis not primarily infective in origin, i.e., allergic or traumatic forms. The symptoms and signs indicate the presence of an acute but transient alteration in the physiology of the mucous membrane of the upper respiratory tract, particularly that lining the nose and the paranasal sinuses. Although all the etiologic factors are not yet fully understood, there is good evidence indicating that a cold is initiated by a virus, one or more. The disease occurs in man more frequently than all other ailments combined and leads to an enormous total morbidity each year. The incidence of colds is approximately from 2 to 4 attacks per person per year. Of themselves, colds are usually mild and generally do not linger for more than a few days. They often lead to secondary bacterial infections, especially of the paranasal sinuses and the middle ear, which may be protracted and occasionally are serious.

HISTORY

The condition was described in some of the earliest medical writings, and numerous papers concerning it have appeared in the past several decades. Kruse (1914) and Foster (1916) reported successful experimental transmission of colds with filtered materials in man. More than 10 independent reports have appeared confirming these findings, whereas in 5 other reports negative results in similar experiments were presented. Dochez et al. (1930) first reported successful transmission of the common cold to chimpanzees by means of filtrates. Cultivation of the virus in tissue-culture medium (Dochez et al., 1931) and on the chorioallantoic membrane of the chick embryo (Kneeland et al., 1936) has been described.

Three independent reports (Pollard and Caplovitz, 1947; Topping and Atlas, 1947; Ward and Proctor, 1950) described cultivation of the virus in the allantoic sac of the chick embryo. The extensive investigations carried out with large numbers of human volunteers at the Common Cold Research Unit, Salisbury, England, since 1946 (Andrewes, 1949, 1950) have reaffirmed the infective nature of the disease, the filterability of the inciting agent, and have added much additional information.

CLINICAL PICTURE

The incubation period appears to be relatively brief. In recent transmission experiments in man, it was generally 2 or 3 days in duration with a range of 1 to 6 days (An-

378

drewes, 1949). A feeling of roughness or soreness of the throat is often the first symptom. Commonly there is a sensation of irritation and fullness in the upper respiratory tract, particularly in the nasopharynx. Attacks of sneezing occur frequently. Nasal discharge, which may be copious, is almost invariably present. The discharge is usually thin and watery or serous but may be viscous or mucoid. Rarely does it become mucopurulent before the second or the third day. Nonproductive cough is present in about 30 per cent of patients. Headache, malaise, chilly sensations and some aching of the extremities are common. At times there is a slight increase in temperature, but this seldom exceeds 101° F. The nasal and the nasopharyngeal mucosa is swollen and injected; one or both nostrils may be partially or completely occluded. Postnasal discharge is uncommon during the first few days. The conjunctival vessels may be prominent, and the mucous membrane of the fauces and the posterior pharynx may be mildly injected. The upper anterior cervical lymph nodes may become slightly enlarged or tender. The olfactory sense is usually diminished and may be lost temporarily. Hearing may be impaired. Excoriations often develop at the nasal orifices. In some persons so-called cold sores commonly appear on the upper lip (see chapter on Herpes Simplex) in widely varying degrees. The course is variable both as to duration and severity. If complications do not develop, symptoms seldom persist longer than one week and may largely disappear in 3 or 4 days. Secondary bacterial infection of some area of the respiratory tract develops commonly; the paranasal sinuses, middle ears, tonsils, pharynx, larynx, trachea, bronchi or lungs may be invaded. Any of the potentially pathogenic micro-organisms in the upper respiratory tract may cause secondary infection.

PATHOLOGIC PICTURE

The mucous membrane of the upper respiratory tract, especially that of the nose,
is swollen, boggy and inflamed. The lymphoid follicles in the affected area are enlarged. There is a striking increase in secretion, both serous and mucous, from the nose. Frequently purulent exudate is present on the surface of the turbinates and walls of the nasopharynx. In the early stages the nasal secretions contain relatively few cells and bacteria; later in the course of the disease large numbers of cells and bacteria may be present. The chief alterations are confined to the mucous membrane; vascular engorgement and edema predominate; infiltration by lymphocytes and mononuclear cells occurs in mild degree as does desquamation of surface cells; necrosis is usually absent.

EXPERIMENTAL INFECTION; HOST RANGE

Bacteria-free filtrates of nasal secretions from patients with colds are capable of inciting colds in man and the chimpanzee (Olitsky and McCartney, 1923; Dochez et al., 1930). All other mammalian species tested appear to be insusceptible to infection with the virus (Andrewes, 1949). Successful cultivation of the agent in tissue-culture medium has been reported (Dochez et al., 1931; Powell and Clowes, 1931). In addition, the virus has been cultivated on the chorio-allantoic membrane of the chick embryo (Kneeland et al., 1936). Three independent groups of workers in the United States have reported that certain strains of the virus can be cultivated in series in the allantoic sac of the chick embryo (Pollard and Caplovitz, 1947; Topping and Atlas, 1947; Ward and Proctor, 1950). However, British workers have been unsuccessful in extensive attempts to cultivate their strains in the chick embryo (Andrewes, 1949, 1950). Experimentally induced colds, developing after the intranasal inoculation of bacteriologically sterile filtrates or chick-embryo-passage material, closely simulate natural colds and show, perhaps in slightly milder degree, all the features of the naturally acquired disease.

ETIOLOGY

Most workers accept the concept that the inciting agent of a cold is a virus. The comprehensive studies of Dochez and his co-workers (Dochez et al., 1930, 1931; Kneeland et al., 1936) left little doubt of the validity of this postulate. The recent elaborate investigations of the Common Cold Research Unit in England (Andrewes, 1949, 1950) have provided strong support for the hypothesis. The acquisition of detailed information about the virus has been impeded because of the lack of a susceptible laboratory animal and the consequent necessity for work with human volunteers. Whether there is but one kind of cold virus or a number, as in the case of influenza, is yet to be determined. That there may be differences between strains of the agent is suggested by the divergent results which have been obtained in England and in the United States in attempts to cultivate various strains in the chick embryo (Kneeland et al., 1936; Andrewes, 1949, 1950; Ward and Proctor, 1950). No satisfactory serologic procedure has been developed and, as a consequence, it has not been feasible to carry out antigenic analyses of various strains. Tests for immunity to reinfection in man or in the chimpanzee have not yet proved sufficiently satisfactory to permit a study of the immunologic relationship between different strains.

The virus is filterable through Berkefeld W candles and Seitz pads (Dochez et al., 1930). Recent studies with collodion membranes of graded porosity indicate that the virus may have dimensions of 40 to 50 mμ or less (Andrewes, 1949). The agent can be preserved by freezing and drying *in vacuo* and can be stored for some days under anaerobic conditions at 4° C. (Dochez et al., 1931; Kneeland et al., 1936). It can be maintained in an infective state for three to four months when frozen at −20° C. (Pollard et al., 1948) and for two years at −70° C. (Andrewes, 1949).

In volunteers, following intranasal instillation of secretions from natural colds, the incidence of experimental colds is about 55 per cent (Andrewes, 1950). The virus can be recovered from inoculated volunteers during the incubation period about 24 hours before symptoms appear as well as during the full-blown cold (Andrewes, 1950). How long the virus persists after a cold is not yet known, but it has been demonstrated in washings obtained as late as the seventh day. Whether the agent is present at times in the upper respiratory tract of normal persons is an open question. Because either pooled washings from normal persons or normal egg material may at times lead to a cold following inoculation of volunteers, this possibility has been considered (Andrewes, 1950).

Serum from persons convalescent from colds has the capacity to inactivate the virus, but it is not yet established that this is dependent upon the presence of specific antibodies (Andrewes, 1950). The results of tests for immunity to reinfection in chimpanzees suggest that resistance may develop and persist for 3 or 4 months. On the other hand, there is conflicting evidence regarding the development of immunity in man. The Commission on Acute Respiratory Diseases (1949) found no evidence of resistance to reinoculation with washings from one patient from 19 to 21 days after the first inoculation. However, Pollard and Caplovitz (1948) found volunteers to be refractory to reinoculation for at least 13 days. Andrewes (1950) concluded that susceptibility in volunteers is not correlated with the time elapsed after the last cold.

DIAGNOSIS

The diagnosis is dependent entirely upon clinical findings which in most cases are fairly typical; there is no laboratory test the results of which will positively support the diagnosis. Many conditions may cause clinical syndromes closely similar to, if not identical with, that of the common cold; among these are various forms of nasal allergy, bacterial infections of the upper respiratory tract, local irritations and a number of viral diseases, especially influenza, abortive measles, etc.

TREATMENT

No clearly effective method of treatment has been devised. Symptomatic therapy appears not to alter significantly the course of the condition, although it may give the patient some transient relief from the more distressing symptoms. It has been claimed recently that various antihistaminic drugs can be used as prophylactic or therapeutic agents. Numerous carefully controlled studies, both in naturally occurring and in induced colds, have failed entirely to affirm such claims (Feller et al., 1950; Hoagland et al., 1950; Cowan and Diehl, 1950; Shaw and Wightman, 1951).

EPIDEMIOLOGY

The disease occurs throughout the world, in every climate, and at any time. There appear to be seasonal variations in incidence. In the temperate zones the attack rate tends to rise during the fall and the spring seasons. In isolated Arctic communities the attack rate decreases markedly during the winter; the greater the degree of isolation, the lower is the incidence (Paul and Freese, 1933). Reestablishment of contact with other communities often leads to a striking increase in the number of colds. Whether this is attributable to the introduction of different strains of the causal agent or to a decline in resistance under conditions of isolation is not clear. It is thought that the virus is transmitted from one person to another under natural conditions; presumably by airborne droplets containing the agent. Attempts to induce contact infections under controlled conditions, however, have been surprisingly unrewarding (Andrewes, 1950). The idea that drafts and chilling tend to be associated with the development of colds seems firmly entrenched. Direct tests of the effects of chilling on susceptibility have failed to reveal any clear results (Andrewes, 1950).

CONTROL MEASURES

No effective control measure has been devised. Vaccines have not been shown to decrease susceptibility to the disease.

REFERENCES

Andrewes, C. H., 1949, The natural history of the common cold. Lancet, *1*, 71-75.

Andrewes, C. H., 1950, Adventures among viruses. III. The puzzle of the common cold. New England J. Med., *242*, 235-240.

Commission on Acute Respiratory Diseases, 1949, Experimental transmission of minor respiratory illness to human volunteers by filter-passing agents. II. Immunity on reinoculation with agents from the two types of minor respiratory illness and from primary atypical pneumonia. J. Clin. Investig., *26*, 974-982.

Cowan, D. W., and Diehl, H. S., 1950, Antihistaminic agents and ascorbic acid in the early treatment of the common cold. J. Am. Med. Assn., *143*, 421-424.

Dochez, A. R., Mills, K. C., and Kneeland, Y., Jr., 1931, Study of the virus of the common cold and its cultivation in tissue medium. Proc. Soc. Exp. Biol. and Med., *28*, 513-516.

Dochez, A. R., Shibley, G. S., and Mills, K. C., 1930, Studies in the common cold. IV. Experimental transmission of the common cold to anthropoid apes and human beings by means of a filterable agent. J. Exp. Med., *52*, 701-716.

Feller, A. E., Badger, G. F., Hodges, R. G., Jordan, W. S., Jr., Rammelkamp, C. H., Jr., and Dingle, J. H., 1950, The failure of antihistaminic drugs to prevent or cure the common cold and undifferentiated respiratory diseases. New England J. Med., *242*, 737-744.

Foster, G. B., Jr., 1916, The etiology of common colds. The probable role of a filterable virus as the causative factor: a preliminary note. J. Am. Med. Assn., *66*, 1180-1183.

Hoagland, R. J., Dietz, E. N., Myers, P. W., and Cosand, H. C., 1950, Antihistaminic drugs for colds. Evaluation based on a controlled study. J. Am. Med. Assn., *143*, 157-160.

Kneeland, Y., Jr., Mills, K. C., and Dochez, A. R., 1936, Cultivation of the virus of the common cold in the chorio-allantoic membrane of the chick embryo. Proc. Soc. Exp. Biol. and Med., *35*, 213-215.

Kruse, W., 1914, Die Erreger von Husten und Schnupfen. Münch. med. Wchnschr., *61*, 1547.

Olitsky, P. K., and McCartney, J. E., 1923, Studies on the nasopharyngeal secretions from patients with common colds. J. Exp. Med., *38*, 427-440.

Paul, J. H., and Freese, H. L., 1933, An epidemiological and bacteriological study of the "common cold" in an isolated Arctic community (Spitsbergen). Am. J. Hyg., *17*, 517-535.

Pollard, M., and Caplovitz, C. D., 1947, Experimental studies with the agent of the common cold. Science, *106*, 243-244.

Pollard, M., and Caplovitz, C. D., 1948, Immunological studies with common cold infection. Am. J. Hyg., *47*, 106-112.

Pollard, M., Dernehl, C. U., and Caplovitz, C. D., 1948, Survival of the virus of the common cold in specimens collected from naturally acquired cases of common cold. Am. J. Hyg., *47*, 103-105.

Powell, H. M., and Clowes, G. H. A., 1931, Cultivation of the virus of common cold and its inoculation in human subjects. Proc. Soc. Exp. Biol. and Med., *29*, 332-335.

Shaw, C. R., and Wightman, H. B., 1951, Further studies on the treatment of the common cold with antihistamine drugs. New York State J. Med., *51*, 387-388.

Topping, N. H., and Atlas, L. T., 1947, The common cold: a note regarding isolation of an agent. Science, *106*, 636-637.

Ward, T. G., and Proctor, D. F., 1950, Isolation of a common cold virus in chick embryos and the clinical manifestations it produces in human volunteers. Am. J. Hyg., *52*, 91-106.

FRANK L. HORSFALL, Jr., m.d.

Hospital of The Rockefeller Institute for Medical Research

17

Primary Atypical Pneumonia

(Synonyms: Acute pneumonitis, acute interstitial pneumonitis, atypical pneumonia, atypical bronchopneumonia, virus pneumonia)

INTRODUCTION

Primary atypical pneumonia is an acute, self-limited disease of man which is thought to be infectious. Whether the malady is to be considered as a syndrome definable merely in terms of clinical features or is a specific disease entity attributable to one or more infectious agents remains to be established. The chief manifestations of the disease appear to be the results of an infectious process in the respiratory tract; pneumonia which may vary widely in extent and severity is a constant characteristic. Various forms of bacterial pneumonia as well as pulmonary tuberculosis may present a similar clinical syndrome. In addition, certain viral or rickettsial diseases of established etiology may simulate primary atypical pneumonia very closely; these are psittacosis or ornithosis, Q fever and, in occasional instances, influenza. The chapters describing the latter diseases should be consulted.

HISTORY

Contemporary interest in this form of pneumonia arose from reports which appeared between 1930 and 1940. However, numerous reports of similar cases are to be found in various publications which appeared during the past five or six decades. Whether or not the disease is of recent origin, i.e., a so-called "new" disease, is a question which cannot be answered. The papers of Arrasmith (1930), Gallagher (1934), Bowen (1935), Allen (1936-37), Reimann (1938), Smiley et al. (1939), Reimann and Havens (1940), Kneeland and Smetana (1940), and Longcope (1940), as well as many others published later, have drawn attention to the disease and clearly described the clinical manifestations. Extensive reviews of the pertinent literature were published by Dingle and Finland (1942), MacLeod (1943), Owen (1944), Schmitz (1945), and Reimann (1947). The factors which probably were responsible for the relatively recent differentiation of this form of pneumonia from others, particularly the various bacterial pneumonias, are the following: the results of bacteriologic investigations on pneumonia; the results of viral studies on acute respiratory infections; the use of x-rays in the diagnosis of respiratory diseases; studies carried out on respiratory infections in schools, colleges and camps; and the use of antimicrobial chemotherapeutic agents in the treatment of acute respiratory diseases. During World War II the disease occurred commonly, especially among military personnel. Since 1946 the incidence of the ailment appears to have decreased considerably, but due to the difficulties in accurate diagnosis there is no adequate information as to the frequency of its occurrence in the civilian population.

Numerous intensive efforts to establish the etiology have been made. A number of infectious agents have been put forward as possible etiologic factors; most of these agents had properties suggesting that they were viruses. There is as yet no agreement among investigators regarding the identity or the number of infectious agents which may induce the disease.

In 1943 three different serologic reactions were found to occur during the disease; two of these reactions have become useful in laboratory procedures which aid in establishing the diagnosis. Positive cold-hemagglutination reactions (Peterson et al., 1943; Turner, 1943) and positive streptococcus MG agglutination reactions (Thomas et al., 1943b) can be demonstrated in approximately 50 per cent of cases in which the diagnosis is made on clinical grounds. In addition, a considerable proportion of patients may show positive complement-fixation reactions with a variety of non-specific antigens derived from animal tissues (Thomas et al., 1943a).

CLINICAL PICTURE

The incubation period appears to be between two and three weeks on the basis of instances of natural case-to-case transmission. In experimental transmission of the disease to man the incubation period ranged from 7 to 14 days (Commission on Acute Respiratory Diseases, 1946). The onset is usually gradual and ill-defined. The initial complaint is often lassitude, weakness, or fatigue. The symptoms which are present during the first few days are common to various acute respiratory infections and are not characteristic of any single disease entity. Often the presence of pneumonia is not suspected until roentgenograms of the chest are taken. The following signs and symptoms are the most common: fever, cough, sputum, headache, malaise and chilliness. Cough is almost invariably present; in its absence, the diagnosis is questionable.

Ultimately, the cough is productive of sputum which is either mucoid or muco-purulent. Early in the disease most patients do not appear very ill; fever is present but is usually not high; respirations are normal. The pulse rate is slow in relation to the fever; relative bradycardia occurs in about two thirds of cases and is of some diagnostic importance. Abnormal physical signs are not striking. Slight dullness or resistance to percussion over the affected lung area may be present. Harshness of the breath sounds or diminished breath sound transmission is common. Rales can be detected in most instances; during the early stages they are fine or subcrepitant, later they may become coarse and moist.

Roentgenograms almost invariably show more extensive pneumonia than the physical findings suggest. Pulmonary lesions show marked variation in density and in distribution. The consolidation usually appears most dense at the hilum and is progressively less dense nearer the periphery. The borders of the pneumonic area are irregular and ill-defined. X-ray shadows may appear diffuse, mottled, feathery, or, in rare instances, dense. The site is most frequently in the lower lobes, although any area in the lungs may be affected. In approximately 50 per cent of patients, pneumonia is present in only one lobe; in the remainder more than a single lobe is affected. In some instances pneumonia is migratory and may extend from one lobe to another. The duration of pneumonia demonstrable by x-rays varies widely. On the average, it is present for about two weeks with a range of a few days to 7 or 8 weeks. It is doubtful that a diagnosis can be made on x-ray evidence alone; the x-ray picture is not distinctive and is simulated closely by other forms of pulmonary disease.

The total leukocyte count is within the normal range in approximately two thirds of patients but may vary widely in certain cases. The differential leukocyte pattern is usually within normal limits. The erythrocyte sedimentation rate is almost always increased during the acute phase of illness and may remain elevated in convalescence. The urine is usually normal. Plasma α-amino acid and serum chloride levels, as well as chloride excretion, are within the normal range. The electrocardiogram is normal. Occasionally positive Wassermann or Kahn reactions may be obtained with acute phase serum. Cultures of the sputum show the presence of the usual array of bacterial species which are found in the upper respiratory tract of normal persons. Cultures of the blood show no bacterial growth.

The duration of fever and the degree to which the temperature is elevated vary widely. On the average, fever is present for about 10 days with a range of one day to 6 or 7 weeks. The temperature may vary from 99 to 106°F.; the average maximum temperature is approximately 103°F. Temperature charts show great individual variations; the most common temperature curve is of the moderately remittent variety. Fever usually falls by lysis. Resolution often begins at the time that the temperature comes to normal. However, complete resolution does not occur until the temperature has been normal for some days.

Complications are uncommon and are rarely of much significance. Pleuritis occurs rarely. Acute sinusitis, otitis media, dermatitis, stomatitis and gingivitis have been described. Hemolytic crises and anemia have been reported and apparently are associated with the presence of extremely high cold-hemagglutination titers. Thrombophlebitis or bronchiectasis may develop. In rare instances, the pneumonic lesion may fail to resolve completely, producing a persistent area of increased density demonstrable by x-rays.

PATHOLOGIC PICTURE

Relatively few patients in whom the diagnosis was well established have come to autopsy and, as a consequence, there is not much reliable information regarding the pathologic picture of the disease. It is doubtful that the pathologic alterations are distinctive or that they differentiate the disease from certain other forms of pneumonia, e.g., psittacosis, Q fever, etc. In varying degree there is evidence of a patchy, irregularly distributed pneumonia of the bronchopneumonic form. The pneumonic areas appear hemorrhagic, and there is an associated bronchitis and bronchiolitis. The pneumonic areas may be extensive and widespread or discrete, circumscribed and multiple. Various stages of consolidation are seen in a single lung, even in a single lobe. The lumina of the bronchi contain mucoid or mucopurulent exudate. The bronchial mucosa appears injected and inflamed. In some instances the consolidated areas are firm, grayish yellow and, on section, appear almost dry; in others, they are soft and friable, dark red or purple and, on section, bloody fluid may exude. Occasionally small amounts of straw-colored pleural fluid are present.

Microscopic examination of the affected lung areas shows evidence of multiple patches of pneumonia associated with bronchitis. The alveoli show thickening of their walls, dilatation of the septal capillaries, edema in varying degree, and infiltration of the interalveolar septa by lymphocytes, mononuclear cells, and erythrocytes. Polymorphonuclear cells are not prominent. The alveolar spaces, in most instances, are not completely filled either with edema fluid or with exudate. The paucity of abnormal physical signs may be attributable to the fact that air remains in many alveoli and, as a consequence, alterations in the transmission of sound through the lung, which account for the abnormal physical signs in lobar pneumonia, do not occur.

Pneumonic areas are most extensive in regions adjacent to bronchi and bronchioles. Peribronchial as well as perivascular cellular infiltrations, sometimes marked in extent, are usually present and the commoner cell types are lymphocytes and mononuclear cells. The bronchial mucosa is often well preserved, although areas of necrosis of the epithelium may be seen, especially in the bronchioles. The bronchial submucosa and rarely the deeper layers may show evidence of infiltration by polymorphonuclear cells. The bronchial lumina usually contain varying amounts of exudate in which polymorphonuclear cells are conspicuously prominent. Bacteria usually are not seen in the pneumonic areas. The presence of intracellular inclusion bodies, elementary bodies, or rickettsiae has not been demonstrated.

Pathologic alterations in organs other than the lung have not been impressive. In some cases an acute, follicular splenitis and swollen mesenteric lymph nodes have been described. In occasional instances, cerebral lesions associated with focal hemorrhages and perivascular cuffs of mononuclear cells have been noted.

EXPERIMENTAL INFECTION; HOST RANGE

Among the various infectious agents which have been implicated as possible primary incitants of the disease the following require comment. Stokes et al. (1939) reported the recovery of a filterable agent, infectious for mice, guinea pigs and ferrets, from 2 patients but the agent was lost before immunologic tests could be carried out. Weir and Horsfall (1940) reported the recovery of a virus, infectious for wild Jamaican mongoose (*Herpestes griseus*) and transmissible in series in chick embryos, from 4 patients and presented evidence to show that in 6 patients neutralizing antibodies against the agent developed during convalescence. Blake et al. (1942) recovered a filterable agent, infectious for cats and kittens, from cats ill at the same time as patients in a household epidemic and presented evidence suggesting that the infections in both species were similar. Eaton et al. (1942) reported the recovery of a filterable agent, infectious for cotton rats, from patients but failed in attempts to show that antibodies against it were produced. Horsfall et al. (1943) reported that a filterable agent, infectious for cotton rats, was present in the sputum of one patient and presented

evidence suggesting that antibodies against the agent developed during the disease in 6 patients. Eaton et al. (1944) reported the recovery from patients of a virus which is transmissible in series in chick embryos, and induces pneumonia following intranasal inoculation in cotton rats or hamsters. Evidence was presented to show that neutralizing antibodies against the virus are produced by patients during the illness (Eaton and Van Herick, 1947). The Commission on Acute Respiratory Disease (1946) reported that the disease could be experimentally induced in human beings following inoculation into the upper respiratory tract of pooled sputa and throat-washings obtained from patients. They showed also that bacteria-free filtrates of such pooled specimens were capable of inducing the disease in man and that the experimental infection could be transmitted in series a second time in volunteers.

Despite the results described in these various reports, confirmatory evidence obtained by independent workers has not yet appeared with respect to any of the agents mentioned. Attempts have been made to repeat, in appropriate animal species, several of the experimental procedures described but unequivocal results have not been obtained. Various kinds of specimens from many patients have been inoculated in numerous animal species by several routes and serial passages have been carried out without obtaining evidence for the presence of an infectious agent (Curnen et al., 1945; Commission on Acute Respiratory Diseases, 1945). The following animal species have been employed: mice, cotton rats, hooded rats, white rats, hamsters, guinea pigs, rabbits, mongoose, three species of monkeys, chick embryos, baby chicks, ferrets, rice birds, doves, puppies, dogs, kittens, and cats. Chimpanzees also have been inoculated without success.

The nonhemolytic streptococcus, designated streptococcus MG (Thomas et al., 1943b), which was isolated from the lungs of six fatal cases is not pathogenic for any of the common laboratory animals including monkeys, but does cause fatal infection of the chick embryo. The micro-organism is very resistant to sulfonamide action but is susceptible to the effect of penicillin both in vitro and in the chick embryo. It is also susceptible to the action of aureomycin.

ETIOLOGY

Despite many attempts to recover the infectious agent or agents, there is not yet complete agreement among investigators as to the nature and identity of the causal agent. Bacterial species of established pathogenicity for man appear not to play an etiologic role. Similarly, rickettsiae and viruses, known to be causally related to other diseases in human beings, appear not to be etiologically related to the illness. The condition is similar to certain forms of pneumonia which result from infection with viruses or rickettsiae of established identity, e.g., psittacosis (or ornithosis) virus, influenza A virus, influenza B virus, lymphocytic choriomeningitis virus, *Rickettsia burneti*, etc. However, conclusive and unequivocal evidence as to etiology is still lacking despite very thorough investigations by a number of competent workers.

The different results obtained in attempts to transmit the infectious agent or agents to laboratory animals are confusing and conflicting. It is possible that each of a variety of different infectious agents may be capable of inciting the disease, and that at different times and places one or another of these agents was recovered. It appears that no fewer than five seemingly different infectious agents, each of which may be a virus, have been implicated as possible etiologic factors (Stokes et al., 1939; Weir and Horsfall, 1940; Blake et al., 1942; Eaton et al., 1942; Horsfall et al., 1943; Eaton et al., 1944; and Commission on Acute Respiratory Diseases, 1946). However, none of the reports concerned with filterable infectious agents in relation to the disease has been confirmed by an independent report from another laboratory.

All the agents which have been claimed to be transmissible to laboratory animals possessed certain properties in common which made experiments with them difficult to carry out and the results even more difficult to interpret. Each agent was of very low pathogenicity, each produced evidence of infection in only a certain percentage of inoculated animals and each had a very limited host range. Moreover, all species of laboratory animals, excepting only the chick embryo, which appeared to be susceptible to infection by these agents are known to harbor one or more latent viruses which, in a number of instances, are themselves capable of inducing pneumonia in their natural hosts. The results of neutralization tests with sera from small numbers of patients (Weir and Horsfall, 1940; Blake et al., 1942; and Horsfall et al., 1943), as well as with sera from a large number of patients (Eaton and van Herick, 1947), were considered to indicate that neutralizing antibodies against each of the agents employed had developed during the illness. Convincing evidence for the development of such antibodies against a virus would provide strong evidence in favor of an etiologic relationship. However, in the light of the number and peculiarity of the serologic phenomena which are associated with the illness as well as the very low pathogenicity of the infectious agents described, which has necessitated the use of at most only a few 50 per cent infectious doses in the presence of much tissue material, it appears doubtful that entirely unassailable evidence for the development of antibodies against a virus has been obtained (Horsfall, 1949).

The results of experimental transmission of the disease in human volunteers (Commission on Acute Respiratory Diseases, 1946) appear to have been more decisive than results obtained in laboratory animals. Among 60 men who were inoculated with pooled specimens obtained from patients, 16 developed an illness which was thought to be primary atypical pneumonia, whereas 26 others developed a so-called minor respiratory illness without pneumonia. Among the 16 volunteers in whom the disease was apparently induced, 13 developed cold-hemagglutinins, and 2 also developed agglutinins against streptococcus MG. These workers concluded that the results of their studies indicate that the disease is at least initiated, if not caused, by a filter-passing agent, presumably a virus. In a later investigation (Commission on Acute Respiratory Diseases, 1947), an attempt was made to determine whether agents capable of inducing a minor respiratory illness in man were distinct from those which induce primary atypical pneumonia. A filtrate of respiratory secretions from one patient was inoculated in 21 men, each of whom had been inoculated earlier with a filtrate obtained from patients with a minor respiratory illness. Three volunteers developed primary atypical pneumonia, although 2 had experienced recent minor respiratory illnesses.

Thomas et al. (1945) raised the possibility that a nonhemolytic streptococcus, designated streptococcus MG, might be implicated in the pathogenesis of the disease. This micro-organism was isolated from the lungs of fatal cases of the disease, is a single serologic type of nonhemolytic streptococcus, and elaborates a capsular polysaccharide which is responsible for the type specific immunologic reactions obtained with it. Approximately 44 per cent of patients develop agglutinins against streptococcus MG. Present evidence indicates that the serologic reactions obtained with the micro-organism are caused by specific antibodies against it. Positive results were obtained with convalescent sera in agglutination tests with either the encapsulated streptococcus or nonencapsulated R variants; in precipitation tests with the capsular polysaccharide; and in capsular swelling tests with the micro-organism. In addition, positive skin reactions were obtained on intradermal injection of the capsular polysaccharide during convalescence (Thomas et al., 1945). Antibodies against streptococcus MG are distinct and different from

the serum components responsible for cold-hemagglutination and nonspecific complement fixation (Thomas et al., 1943a); they can be removed from serum by appropriate absorption without altering the other reactions. There appear to be two alternative explanations for the various serologic reactions which are obtained with streptococcus MG and antigens derived from it: (1) they may be attributable to the effects of secondary invasion by the micro-organism; (2) they may be the result of a so-called complex or double infection initiated by both streptococcus MG and some other infectious agent, presumably a virus.

DIAGNOSIS

To a large extent the diagnosis is one of exclusion and it is often necessary to accumulate considerable clinical, x-ray and laboratory data before the probability of error becomes small. The more common clinical features are the following: gradual onset, remittent fever which is seldom high, pulse rate which is slow relative to the fever, normal respiratory rate, cough, slight or absent physical signs of pneumonia, and definite x-ray evidence of pneumonia. Pertinent laboratory findings are the following: normal leukocyte count, the usual array of bacterial species in the upper respiratory tract, and a sterile blood culture. Two laboratory procedures are of aid in reaching a positive diagnosis: (1) cold-hemagglutination test, and (2) streptococcus MG agglutination test. Both are best carried out with serum specimens obtained at weekly intervals during the course of the disease. If either or both serologic tests are positive, and especially if a significant increase in either agglutination titer is demonstrable some weeks after onset, there is a high probability that the diagnosis is correct. If both tests are negative, it may be very difficult to establish a diagnosis.

Positive cold-hemagglutination reactions (Peterson et al., 1943; Turner, 1943) have been demonstrated with serum from 56 per cent of 801 patients (Horsfall, 1947). Both the frequency of positive reactions and the height of the titer which develops appear to be directly related to the severity or the duration of the disease. Cold-hemagglutination may be demonstrable with the serum of over 90 per cent of persons severely ill or in those with a prolonged illness, while the reaction may be positive in only about 20 per cent of mildly ill patients. The component responsible for this unusual reaction usually appears in the serum during the second week of the disease. Maximum titers are found usually during the third or the fourth week, and, thereafter, the titer gradually diminishes until eventually the component disappears. There is, as yet, no satisfactory explanation for the development of positive cold-hemagglutination reactions during the disease. The technic for carrying out the cold-hemagglutination test with human group O erythrocytes is described in the chapter on Serologic and Immunologic Technics.

Positive streptococcus MG agglutination reactions (Thomas et al., 1945) have been demonstrated with serum from 44 per cent of 669 patients with primary atypical pneumonia (Horsfall, 1947). In other diseases, an increase in the titer of agglutinins against streptococcus MG rarely occurs. Agglutinins may develop in over 75 per cent of patients with severe attacks of primary atypical pneumonia or those of long duration. During mild attacks or those of relatively short duration, agglutinins may develop in only about 20 per cent of the patients. Agglutinins against the bacterium usually appear during the second or the third week after onset, commonly reach maximum levels during the fourth or the fifth week and may decline somewhat during the seventh or the eighth week. There is a positive correlation between the frequency with which agglutinins against streptococcus MG develop and the severity of the disease, and also there is a similar correlation between the height of the titer and the duration of the illness (Curnen et al., 1945). The technic for carrying out

agglutination tests with streptococcus MG is described in the chapter on Serologic and Immunologic Technics.

A number of viral and rickettsial diseases may present similar or even identical clinical pictures. These diseases are the following: psittacosis (ornithosis), Q fever (*Rickettsia burneti* pneumonia), influenza A, influenza B and lymphocytic choriomeningitis. In children pneumonia associated with measles or whooping cough may present an analogous picture. Pneumococcal as well as other bacterial pneumonias may present clinical manifestations which are indistinguishable from those of primary atypical pneumonia. At times pulmonary tuberculosis, tularemia, coccidiomycosis, or toxoplasmosis may closely simulate the disease.

TREATMENT

Supportive and symptomatic treatment similar to that used in other forms of pneumonia may be helpful. None of the sulfonamide drugs, even in large doses, appears to exert a favorable influence. Similarly, penicillin in large dosages has not been found to be beneficial. Convalescent human serum has been tried but has not produced an obvious effect. Several reports have appeared regarding the effects of aureomycin on the course of primary atypical pneumonia. In some instances (Schoenbach and Bryer, 1949; Kneeland et al., 1949; Finland et al., 1949), it has been reported that the drug was beneficial and served to shorten the course of the disease. In other instances (Harvey et al., 1949; Hirsch et al., 1952), no evidence of a significant chemotherapeutic effect was obtained. In many cases, treatment was instituted about a week after onset following preliminary trial of penicillin, and in only a few instances were untreated control patients studied. In this connection, it should be pointed out that, on the average, fever persists for only about 10 days in patients treated symptomatically. On the basis of the available evidence, it appears doubtful that there are adequate grounds for regarding aureomycin as an effective chemotherapeutic agent in this disease.

EPIDEMIOLOGY

The disease is of widespread prevalence and, although it usually occurs in endemic form, small epidemics have been described. Epidemics have not been characterized by explosive outbreaks, and attack rates have not been high. Usually they have occurred among persons living under crowded or semicrowded conditions, e.g., in school dormitories, military camps, etc. The incidence in the general population is not known. Among armed force personnel during World War II the incidence was greater than that of all other forms of pneumonia and appeared to be directly related to the total incidence of respiratory disease; when colds and other undifferentiated respiratory infections were prevalent, the condition occurred more commonly (Commission on Acute Respiratory Diseases, 1944). The disease occurs in all seasons but is more common during cold weather. The disease occurs more commonly in the north temperate zone than elsewhere; it is not common in the tropics. Sex, age, color or race differences in incidence are not marked. The infection is not very contagious but apparently it can be directly transmitted from one person to another; usually, however, there is no evident contact between cases. The results of studies in human volunteers (Commission on Acute Respiratory Diseases, 1946) suggest that the infection may be transmitted by oral or nasal discharges of patients and that the portal of entry is the upper respiratory tract. There is no evidence that the infection is transmitted indirectly by food, water or insect vectors. Nothing is known of the duration of the period of communicability. There is very little evidence concerning relative susceptibility or resistance to infection. In transmission experiments in human volunteers the Commission on Acute Respiratory Disease (1946) found that the disease developed in approximately 25 per cent of men inoculated with material from patients. The degree and the duration of natural exposure to patients appear to be directly related to the frequency with which infection develops; among nurses, physicians and other hospital personnel the incidence has been considerably higher than among persons not closely associated with patients. Second attacks, separated by periods of well-being from the first attack, have been occasionally observed. It appears, therefore, that the disease is not always followed by the development of persistent immunity against reinfection.

CONTROL MEASURES

No procedure has been shown to affect significantly the incidence of the disease. No specific prophylactic measure is available. The isolation of patients may be helpful.

REFERENCES

Allen, W. H., 1936-37, Acute pneumonitis. Ann. Int. Med., *10*, 441-446.

Arrasmith, T. M., Jr., 1930, Influenzal pneumonia—a clinical report, with special reference to diagnosis. U. S. Nav. M. Bull., *28*, 769-783.

Blake, F. G., Howard, M. E., and Tatlock, H., 1942, Feline virus pneumonia and its possible relation to some cases of primary atypical pneumonia in man. Yale J. Biol. and Med., *15*, 139-166.

Bowen, A., 1935, Acute influenza pneumonitis. Am. J. Roentgenol., *34*, 168-174.

Commission on Acute Respiratory Diseases, 1944, Epidemiology of atypical pneumonia and acute respiratory disease at Fort Bragg, North Carolina. Am. J. Pub. Health, *34*, 335-346.

Commission on Acute Respiratory Diseases, 1945, The present status of the etiology of primary atypical pneumonia. Bull. N. Y. Acad. Med., *21*, 235-262.

Commission on Acute Respiratory Diseases, 1946, The transmission of primary atypical pneumonia to human volunteers. Bull. Johns Hopkins Hosp., *79*, 97-167.

Commission on Acute Respiratory Diseases, 1947, Experimental transmission of minor respiratory illness to human volunteers by filter-passing agents. II. Immunity on reinoculation with agents from the two types of minor respiratory illness and from primary atypical pneumonia. J. Clin. Investig., *26*, 974-982.

Curnen, E. C., Mirick, G. S., Ziegler, J. E., Jr.,

REFERENCES

Thomas, L., and Horsfall, F. L., Jr., 1945, Studies on primary atypical pneumonia. I. Clinical features and results of laboratory investigations. J. Clin. Investig., *24*, 209-226.

Dingle, J. H., and Finland, M., 1942, Virus pneumonias. II. Primary atypical pneumonias of unknown etiology. New England. J. Med., *227*, 378-385.

Eaton, M. D., Meiklejohn, G. Van Herick, W., and Talbot, J. C., 1942, An infectious agent from cases of atypical pneumonia apparently transmissible to cotton rats. Science, *96*, 518-519.

Eaton, M. D., Meiklejohn, G., and Van Herick, W., 1944, Studies on the etiology of primary atypical pneumonia. A filterable agent transmissible to cotton rats, hamsters and chick embryos. J. Exp. Med., *79*, 649-668.

Eaton, M. D., Meiklejohn, G., Van Herick, W., and and epidemiological studies on primary atypical pneumonia and related acute upper respiratory disease. Am. J. Hyg., *45*, 82-95.

Finland, M., Collins, H. S., and Wells, E. B., 1949, Aureomycin in the treatment of primary atypical pneumonia. New England J. Med., *240*, 241-246.

Gallagher, J. R., 1934, Bronchopneumonia in adolescence. Yale J. Biol. and Med., *7*, 23-40.

Harvey, J. C., Mirick, G. S., and Schaub, I. G., 1949, Clinical experience with aureomycin. J. Clin. Investig., *28*, 987-991.

Hirsch, J. G., Rammelkamp, C. H., Jr., and Dingle, J. H., 1952, Aureomycin treatment of primary atypical pneumonia. In press.

Horsfall, F. L., Jr., 1947, Primary atypical pneumonia. Ann. Int. Med., *27*, 275-281.

Horsfall, F. L., Jr., 1949, The diagnosis of primary atypical pneumonia *in* Diagnosis of Viral and Rickettsial Infections, Columbia University Press, New York, pp. 42-56.

Horsfall, F. L., Jr., Curnen, E. C., Mirick, G. S., Thomas, L., and Ziegler, J. E., Jr., 1943, A virus recovered from patients with primary atypical pneumonia. Science, *97*, 289-291.

Kneeland, Y., Jr., Rose, H. M., and Gibson, C. D., 1949, Aureomycin in the treatment of primary atypical pneumonia. Am. J. Med., *6*, 41-50.

Kneeland, Y., Jr., and Smetana, H. F., 1940, Current bronchopneumonia of unusual character and undetermined etiology. Bull. Johns Hopkins Hosp., *67*, 229-267.

Longcope, W. T., 1940, Bronchopneumonia of unknown etiology (variety X). A report of thirty-two cases with two deaths. Bull. Johns Hopkins Hosp., *67*, 268-305.

MacLeod, C. M., 1943, Primary atypical pneumonia. Med. Clin. N. America., *27*, 670-686.

Owen, C. A., 1944, Primary atypical pneumonia; analysis of 738 cases occurring during 1942 at Scott Field, Ill. Arch. Int. Med., *73*, 217-231.

Peterson, O. L., Ham, T.H., and Finland, M., 1943, Cold agglutinins (autohemagglutinins) in primary atypical pneumonias. Science, *97*, 167.

Reimann, H. A., 1938, An acute infection of the respiratory tract with atypical pneumonia, a disease entity probably caused by a filterable virus. J. Am. Med. Assn., *111*, 2377-2384.

Reimann, H. A., 1947, The viral pneumonias and pneumonias of probable viral origin. Medicine, *26*, 167-219.

Reimann, H. A., and Havens, W. P., 1940, An epidemic disease of the respiratory tract. Arch. Int. Med., *65*, 138-150.

Schmitz, R. C., 1945, Primary atypical pneumonia of unknown cause. Arch. Int. Med., *75*, 222-232.

Schoenbach, E. B., and Bryer, M. S., 1949, Treatment of primary atypical nonbacterial pneumonia with aureomycin. J. Am. Med. Assn., *139*, 275-280.

Smiley, D. F., Showacre, E. C., Lee, W. F., and Ferris, H. W., 1939, Acute interstitial pneumonitis: a new disease entity. J. Am. Med. Assn., *112*, 1901-1904.

Stokes, J., Jr., Kenney, A. S., and Shaw, D. R., 1939, New filterable agent associated with respiratory infections. Trans. and Studies College Physn., Philadelphia, *6*, 329-333.

Thomas, L., Curnen, E. C., Mirick, G. S., Ziegler, J. E., Jr., and Horsfall, F. L., Jr., 1943a, Complement fixation with dissimilar antigens in primary atypical pneumonia. Proc. Soc. Exp. Biol. and Med., *52*, 121-125.

Thomas, L., Mirick, G. S., Curnen, E. C., Ziegler, J. E., Jr., and Horsfall, F. L., Jr., 1943b, Serological reactions with an indifferent streptococcus in primary atypical pneumonia. Science, *98*, 566-568.

Thomas, L., Mirick, G. S., Curnen, E. C., Ziegler, J. E., Jr., and Horsfall, F. L., Jr., 1945, Studies on primary atypical pneumonia. II. Observations concerning the relationship of a non-hemolytic streptococcus to the disease. J. Clin. Investig., *24*, 227-240.

Turner, J. C., 1943, Development of cold-agglutinins in atypical pneumonia. Nature, *151*, 419-420.

Weir, J. M., and Horsfall, F. L., Jr., 1940, The recovery from patients with acute pneumonitis of a virus causing pneumonia in the mongoose. J. Exp. Med., *72*, 595-610.

FRANK L. HORSFALL, Jr., M.D.

Hospital of The Rockefeller Institute for Medical Research

18

Influenza

(SYNONYMS: *La grippe*, grip, febrile catarrh, catarrhal fever, acute nasopharyngitis, epidemic catarrh, epidemic influenza)

INTRODUCTION

Influenza is an acute, self-limited, infectious disease of man which is caused by a virus of the influenza group. The illness is characterized by symptoms which are predominantly constitutional, although the infection is limited to the respiratory tract. It tends to occur in epidemic forms. Two specific and distinct etiologic types of the disease are now recognized: one, termed influenza A, is caused by infection with influenza A virus; the other, termed influenza B, is caused by infection with influenza B virus. There are indications that a third specific etiologic type of the disease may come to be recognized; this would be designated influenza C in accordance with the nomenclature proposed previously (Horsfall et al., 1940b). The cause of pandemics of influenza has not been established.

HISTORY

The disease was recognized and described in ancient times. Numerous, extensive epidemics occurred during the past four centuries in various parts of the world. Great pandemics which affected persons in all inhabited areas of the globe have been recorded; of these, the greatest was the pandemic of 1918-1919 which, it is estimated, resulted in the death of some 20 million persons. Despite a number of prior claims

that the cause of influenza had been discovered, modern knowledge of the causal agents begins with the studies of Smith, Andrewes and Laidlaw (1933), who first recovered influenza A virus from throat-washings of patients and showed that neutralizing antibodies against the virus developed during convalescence from the disease. Their findings were confirmed and extended by numerous workers in various parts of the world. Smith and Stuart-Harris (1936) showed that, following passage in experimental animals, the virus retained its capacity to induce an attack of influenza in man. Similar results were obtained by other workers with human volunteers in various countries. It is now generally accepted that influenza A virus is the infectious agent primarily responsible for one etiologic type of influenza, i.e., influenza A. Francis (1940) and Magill (1940) independently recovered influenza B virus from throat-washings of patients and showed that specific antibodies against the virus developed during convalescence from the illness. Such patients, however, did not develop antibodies against influenza A virus. Similarly, patients with influenza A did not develop antibodies against influenza B virus. Their findings have been confirmed repeatedly and extended by various studies in a number of different countries. Francis et al.

(1944) showed that, following passage in experimental animals, influenza B virus retained its capacity to induce an attack of influenza in man. It is now generally conceded that influenza B virus is the infectious agent primarily responsible for the second etiologic type of influenza, i.e., influenza B.

Taylor (1949) first recovered what may be regarded as influenza C virus from the throat-washings of a patient and obtained evidence that specific antibodies against the virus developed during convalescence. Patients with this illness did not develop antibodies against either influenza A or influenza B virus. Moreover, patients with influenza A or influenza B did not produce antibodies against the new virus. These findings were confirmed and extended by Francis et al. (1950) who recovered a second strain of the same agent.

CLINICAL PICTURE

The incubation is short, usually one or two days. The onset is commonly abrupt. The first and most frequent symptoms are usually chills or chilliness, fever, anorexia, headache, malaise, lassitude and muscular pains or aches. Prostration in varying degrees usually develops. Nausea, occasionally associated with vomiting, may occur. Constitutional symptoms are more prominent than symptoms referable to the respiratory tract, although sneezing, nasal irritation and discharge as well as sensations of fullness or irritation in the nasopharynx, the larynx or the trachea often occur. Hoarseness may develop. Coughing is very common but usually is not productive of sputum. Substernal pain may occur. The pulse rate increases usually in proportion to the increase in temperature. The respiratory rate is normal or only slightly increased, and the physical signs are ordinarily neither definite nor striking. The skin, especially the face, may appear flushed. The conjunctivae are sometimes injected, and occasionally there is increased lacrimation. The nasal mucosa is usually somewhat injected and slightly or mildly swollen. Epistaxis may occur. The faucial pillars, the soft palate and the posterior pharyngeal wall may be mildly injected, and the lymphoid tissue may become prominent. There are no characteristic abnormal physical findings relative to the lower respiratory tract. Fine, moist rales may be heard over the lower lobes posteriorly, but, except during pandemics, signs of pulmonary consolidation occur only in rare instances. The course varies widely. Fever is commonly remittent and persists from 1 to 6 days, usually 2 or 3. The maximum temperature ranges from 100° to 105° F., regularly from 101° to 103° F. In general, the temperature is highest on the first day of disease. The leukocyte count is, on the average, within normal limits. However, leukopenia, usually only of moderate degree, may be found in patients with high fever and marked symptoms. The differential leukocyte pattern is generally normal. The erythrocyte sedimentation rate is increased. Cultures of the blood are sterile. The urine is usually normal, although slight albuminuria may occur. X-ray pictures of the chest show, in the great majority of patients, no evidence of pneumonia. Convalescence is usually uneventful and fairly rapid, although patients who have severe infections may show marked prostration, abnormal sweating or easy fatigability for some days after the temperature returns to normal. Complications are rare, except during a pandemic, and almost all patients with the common epidemic form of the disease recover completely. Influenza A may tend to cause somewhat more marked and slightly more definite symptoms than influenza B, but there are no clinical signs which serve to differentiate one infection from the other.

During the pandemic of 1918-1919, the disease was much more severe than it has been at any time since. Pneumonia developed in a large number of patients and probably was responsible for most of the deaths which occurred. Many patients first showed evidence of pneumonia from 2 to 4 days after the onset of the disease. In other patients signs of pneumonia did not develop until the acute phase of the initial infection had passed. In some instances fulminating infections, which ran an extremely rapid course, occurred and usually were fatal. Some patients died within a day or two after the onset of pneumonia, rarely in a few hours. In almost every instance, the occurrence of pneumonia was attributable to bacterial infection. A wide variety of bacterial species was associated with the pulmonary infections: most important were staphylococci, β hemolytic streptococci, *H. influenzae* and pneumococci. In numerous instances more than one bacterial species was isolated from the pneumonic lung. Infection of the pleura and empyema were commonly associated with β hemolytic streptococcal or pneumococcal pneumonia. Abscesses of the lung sometimes developed when staphylococci or β hemolytic streptococci were present. Bronchiectasis, chronic bronchitis and pulmonary fibrosis were common sequelae. It should be emphasized that during recent years, with the exception of a small number of cases of associated staphylococcal pneumonia, patients with either influenza A or influenza B have very rarely developed serious complications.

PATHOLOGIC PICTURE

Since the discovery of influenza A virus in 1933, there have appeared very few reports of pathologic studies on uncomplicated cases of influenza in man. Extensive and detailed studies were carried out during the pandemic of 1918-1919, but in almost every instance numerous bacteria were present in the lungs, and consequently the pathologic alterations may have been partly or largely attributable to the results of bacterial infection. Goodpasture (1919) described a pulmonary lesion which he considered to be peculiar to influenza and demonstrated its presence not only in pneumonic lesions associated with bacteria but also in the lungs of two fatal cases in which

no micro-organisms could be demonstrated. The lesion, which consisted of dilated alveolar ducts, with a hyaline membrane partially or completely covering their walls and those of adjacent alveoli, was described also by other workers and apparently was found with great constancy during the pandemic. Winternitz et al. (1920) found that lesions in the respiratory tract were responsible for the high mortality during the pandemic of 1918-1919. The lesions most frequently found, and those considered to be peculiar to the disease, were: acute tracheobronchitis associated with diffuse involvement of the pulmonary parenchyma; hyalinization of the epithelium of the air passages, and necrosis of the alveolar walls; dilatation of the terminal bronchioles; necrotizing and organizing bronchiolitis with lobar, lobular, peribronchial or interstitial pneumonia; proliferation of alveolar and bronchial epithelium. They concluded that the respiratory lesions were dependent primarily upon the damage produced by the true but unknown etiologic agent, and only secondarily upon invasion by bacteria.

Scadding (1937) described the lung changes which were found in patients who died during an epidemic which occurred in 1936-1937. Influenza A virus was recovered from 3 patients, and from the lung of 1 fatal case in which *Staphylococcus aureus* also was present in large numbers. There was tracheal and bronchial inflammation and marked epithelial desquamation with evidence of epithelial necrosis. The interstitial tissues showed some inflammatory reaction, and there was necrosis of the alveolar walls associated with hemorrhage. Extensive bronchopneumonia or interstitial pneumonia was also present. It was concluded that the difference between the findings in these cases and those studied during the pandemic was one of degree rather than kind. So far as is known, no reports have appeared of pathologic studies on biopsy material from patients with nonfatal, proven, influenza virus infection nor are there available reports of similar studies on patients who died of causes unrelated to the disease during an acute attack. Relatively little is known of the pathologic picture of uncomplicated influenza virus infection in man, but numerous, careful and detailed studies have been carried out with animals.

Francis and Stuart-Harris (1938) studied the nasal histology of influenza A virus infection in the ferret and showed that during the acute stage the respiratory epithelium of the nasal mucous membrane undergoes necrosis with desquamation of the superficial cells and exudation into the air passages. An inflammatory reaction occurs in the submucosa. Repair begins on the fourth day after infection, and from the sixth to the fourteenth day the respiratory area is covered successively by transitional, stratified squamous, and finally stratified columnar epithelium. By the twenty-first day the epithelium has been largely restored to normal, but repair in the submucosa and cartilage is still in progress. The respiratory mucosa is normal in structure a month after infection.

Brightman (1936) studied the pulmonary lesions in ferrets infected with influenza A virus. In animals of the first passage there are no pulmonary lesions, but they develop in the second or third passage and thereafter tend to occur regularly. The lesions are patchy or confluent areas of consolidation which are reddish-purple in color. Microscopically the lesions are chiefly peribronchial. The bronchial walls, peribronchial tissue and neighboring alveoli are infiltrated with large and small, round mononuclear cells. The alveolar capillaries are congested. In most areas the bronchial epithelium is intact, in others desquamated. The bronchial and bronchiolar lumina contain a small amount of exudate consisting of polymorphonuclear cells, erythrocytes, fibrin and cellular debris.

Straub (1937) found that in mice the primary lesion caused by infection with influenza A virus is necrobiosis and fibrinoid necrosis of the epithelium of the respiratory and terminal bronchioles, leading to complete epithelial desquamation. Secondarily,

there occur dilatation of the bronchioles and collapse of the alveoli, with edema and hyperemia. Polymorphonuclear exudation is not a typical feature. The healing process is characterized by widespread epithelial proliferation. In contrast to what occurs in man and in the ferret, the infection in the mouse is limited to the lower respiratory tract; the nasal mucosa remains normal.

In the chick embryo the lesions are influenced by a number of factors among which the following are important: the strain of virus employed; the age of the embryo; the route of inoculation; the duration of the infection. Most strains of influenza virus which have not been passed numerous times in the chick embryo fail to cause the development of characteristic lesions. Certain strains following multiple embryo passages acquire the capacity to cause the development of distinct focal lesions when inoculated on the chorioallantoic membrane and may induce fatal hemorrhagic infections of the embryo (Beveridge and Burnet, 1946). Following amniotic inoculation, the embryo lung may appear slightly swollen and paler than normal. Inoculation into the yolk sac does not cause the development of specific lesions. Most strains of virus cause only slight pathologic change in the chick embryo following allantoic inoculation. The allantoic fluid may become slightly turbid due to the presence of desquamated cells, but infected embryos may appear normal and may even be able to hatch. Strains which have been passed many times usually kill the embryo in from 2 to 4 days, but such lesions as are present are not characteristic of infection with influenza viruses.

EXPERIMENTAL INFECTION; HOST RANGE

Smith, Andrewes and Laidlaw (1933) first showed that ferrets are susceptible to infection with influenza viruses following intranasal inoculation. Subsequently they demonstrated that the infection can be transmitted by contact between uninfected and infected ferrets but that all methods of inoculation other than the intranasal are innocuous. Ferrets infected with influenza A virus often show fever and characteristic symptoms which begin from 1 to 3, occasionally not until 4 or 5, days following inoculation. The fever frequently is diphasic in character and is accompanied by symptoms such as sneezing, yawning, nasal discharge and obstruction which results from inflammation of the turbinates and paranasal sinuses. The fur may become ruffled or matted, the appetite is diminished or absent, and muscular weakness may develop. With numerous freshly recovered strains of influenza A virus, as with most strains of influenza B virus, the signs and symptoms of infection in the ferret are not sufficiently striking or definite to be diagnostic, and it is necessary to carry out serial passages or immunologic tests to identify the virus specifically. The virus remains localized in the tissues of the respiratory tract and apparently is incapable of multiplying in any other tissue in the ferret. The nasal mucosa and turbinates are rich sources of virus; likewise, following serial passage, the lung contains much virus, especially if pulmonary consolidation is present. Virus titer is highest in infected tissues of the respiratory tract from 2 to 5 days after inoculation; with some strains of influenza A virus, titers of 10^{-6} or more may be reached (Francis, 1939). Usually it is not possible to recover virus from infected ferret tissues later than the first week after inoculation, probably because of the rapid development of neutralizing antibodies in the blood. Following infection with most strains of virus, ferrets recover promptly and develop immunity to reinfection with the same or closely related strains. However, animals immune to infection with influenza A virus are not immune to influenza B virus and vice versa (Sugg and Magill, 1947). Specific immunity perists for 1 to 2 months and thereafter gradually diminishes; 6 to 12 months after infection most ferrets are susceptible to reinfection. Neutralizing antibodies against the virus appear in the blood of infected ferrets from 5 to 7 days after inoculation (Horsfall and Lennette, 1940), reach maximal titers in 2 or 3 weeks, and decline progressively after 2 months. Specific evidence of infection in the ferret is most readily obtained by carrying out serologic tests for the presence of antibodies against the virus 2 or 3 weeks following inoculation. Excepting only the chick embryo, the ferret is as susceptible to infection with influenza viruses as any other animal species. Despite their high degree of susceptibility, ferrets have the following disadvantages as experimental hosts: they are difficult to raise and handle; they are very susceptible to spontaneous infection with distemper viruses; they readily contract contact infection with influenza viruses and consequently should be kept under conditions of strict isolation.

Andrewes, Laidlaw and Smith (1934) as well as Francis (1934) showed that mice are susceptible to infection with influenza viruses. Mice lightly anesthetized with ether are inoculated by the intranasal route. Other routes of inoculation usually fail to induce infection. However, transthoracic injection directly into the lung has been successful (Andrewes, Laidlaw and Smith, 1934), large doses given intraperitoneally or intravenously can cause infection of the lung (Rickard and Francis, 1938), and, by means of serial intracerebral passage, certain strains have been caused to multiply in the brain (Stuart-Harris, 1939). Following intranasal inoculation, the virus multiplies in the lung and remains localized in the lower respiratory tract. Freshly recovered strains usually fail to cause lung lesions, but when serial lung passages are carried out, pneumonia commonly is induced; from 2 to 8 or more passages may be required before pulmonary consolidation develops.

It is possible but difficult and time-consuming to recover the virus directly in mice from human beings (Francis and Magill, 1937). Following serial lung passages, many strains cause fatal pneumonia in the mouse; dependent somewhat upon the strain employed and the amount of virus given, mice die from 3 days to 2 weeks after inoculation (Horsfall, 1939). Mice with definite pneumonia usually appear ill and eat less than normally; their fur is ruffled, and they may show cyanosis of the ears and tail; their breathing is labored, and they tend to huddle together. Mice which die of influenza virus pneumonia almost invariably have widespread lung lesions, the entire lung generally showing the presence of consolidation. Following intranasal inoculation the virus multiplies very rapidly in the lung of the mouse; with large doses, maximal titers are reached within 24 hours and remain constant until the death of the animals; with sublethal doses, somewhat lower maximal titers develop within 48 hours, remain constant during the first week and then progressively decline (Taylor, 1941). With certain strains of influenza A virus, titers of 10^{-6} or 10^{-7} are attained commonly whereas with strains of influenza B virus, titers higher than 10^{-4} or 10^{-5} are unusual. With some strains of influenza A virus, contact transmission from infected to normal mice has been obtained (Eaton, 1940). Mice which recover from pulmonary infection are immune for 2 or 3 months to reinfection with the same or closely related strains (Andrewes and Smith, 1937), but animals immune to reinfection with influenza A virus are not immune to influenza B virus and vice versa. Subcutaneous or intraperitoneal injection of virus, either active or inactivated by one of a variety of procedures, results in the development of immunity in mice.

Both the European hamster *(Cricetus cricetus)* and the Syrian hamster *(Cricetus auratus)* are susceptible on intranasal inoculation (Taylor, 1940) and may be employed for the direct recovery of virus from human beings. Freshly recovered strains cause no symptoms in hamsters but stimulate the production of specific antibodies. Following serial lung passages, fatal pneumonia may be induced in the hamster.

Hedgehogs, cotton rats, white rats, guinea pigs, mink, squirrels, chipmunks, swine and monkeys, all are more or less susceptible to inapparent infection upon intranasal inoculation.

Smith (1935) first successfully employed the chick embryo for the propagation of influenza viruses and showed that multiplication occurs in the chorio-allantoic membrane. In recent years the chick embryo has become increasingly important in investigations of influenza because of its uniform and extremely high susceptibility to infection, the concentration of virus which is present in the relatively cell-free, extra-embryonic fluids, and the capacity of such fluids to cause agglutination of chicken red blood cells. Chick embryos can be infected by almost any route of inoculation. For direct recovery of the virus from human beings, inoculation into the amniotic sac (Burnet, 1940) is most successful; following one or more passages in the embryo, inoculation into the allantoic sac (Nigg et al., 1940) usually leads to infection, as also does inoculation into the yolk sac or the embryo itself. When amniotic inoculation is employed for the direct recovery of influenza viruses from throat-washings, embryos from 13 to 14 days old are used as they are more susceptible than younger embryos (Beveridge and Burnet, 1946). Unfiltered throat-washings, to which chemotherapeutic agents (sulfonamides, penicillin, or both) have been added, give the highest proportion of successful recoveries of virus. Maximal virus titers are obtained in the amniotic fluid from 2 to 4 days after inoculation. The presence of virus in infected fluid is most readily demonstrated by the agglutination reaction with chicken erythrocytes (Hirst, 1941). Usually virus can be demonstrated in fluid from the first passage embryos, but occasionally not until a second passage has been carried out. Serial passage is fruitless if the second amniotic passage is negative and it may incur the risk of accidental virus infection of the embryo. Recovery of influenza viruses by inoculation into the amniotic sac appears to be the most sensitive of known methods (Hirst, 1945). Inoculation into the allantoic sac is technically much simpler than inoculation into the amniotic sac and most strains multiply readily in the allantoic sac after one or more passages by the amniotic route. For allantoic inoculation, embryos from 9 to 12, preferably 10, days old are employed. Maximal virus titers are obtained in the allantoic fluid in from 24 to 72 hours, depending somewhat upon the strain and the amount of virus inoculated. Material containing approximately 10 virus particles can initiate infection of the allantoic sac (Friedewald and Pickels, 1944). Most strains do not cause death of the embryo but those which have been passed many times may acquire the capacity to kill embryos in less than two days. Infected allantoic fluids almost invariably cause agglutination of chicken erythrocytes (Hirst, 1942a), and the concentration of virus is directly proportional to the hemagglutination titer. With strains of influenza A virus, infected allantoic fluids often give virus titers of 10^{-8} or 10^{-9}, whereas with strains of influenza B virus, titers higher than 10^{-7} or 10^{-8} are unusual. In the presence of chicken erythrocytes, infected allantoic fluids give hemagglutination titers ranging from less than 1:100 to more than 1:10,000, depending upon the concentration of red cells used and the technic employed. Details of the hemagglutination procedure are given in the chapter on Serologic and Immunologic Technics.

Inoculation into the yolk sac, because of the simplicity of the procedure, is useful for those not familiar with chick embryo technics. Embryos from 3 to 6 days old are employed, and 1.0 cc. or more of fluid may be injected. With freshly recovered strains, embryos usually do not die until from 4 to 8 days after inoculation; following prolonged serial passage virus strains may acquire the capacity to kill embryos in 1 or 2 days. To initiate infection in the yolk sac, considerably more virus is required in the inoculum than is necessary when the amniotic or allantoic route is employed. The presence of virus may be determined by the hemagglutination reaction as following inoculation by other routes. Although the chorio-allantoic membrane technic was the first successful procedure for the propagation of influenza viruses in the chick embryo and provided important information (Beveridge and Burnet, 1946), it is now little used.

Francis and Magill (1935) and Smith (1935) developed technics for the cultivation of influenza viruses in cultures of chick-embryo tissue. Minced embryo tissue suspended in Tyrode's solution (Li and Rivers' medium) is employed. After inoculation, cultures are incubated for 2 days. Maximal virus titers obtained in such cultures seldom are higher than 10^{-3} or 10^{-4}. Virus strains have been maintained in tissue-culture medium for long periods, in one instance for more than 700 transfers (Francis, 1947), and retained their pathogenicity for mice and ferrets. Minced embryo tissue on nutrient agar or in so-called roller tubes also supports virus multiplication, and titers are obtained which are comparable to those obtained following inoculation into the allantoic sac.

Intranasal inoculation of either type of virus leads to the development of the disease in man (Smorodintseff et al., 1937; Francis et al., 1944). However, subcutaneous or intramuscular injection of a fully active virus does not cause illness in human beings. In successful attempts to transmit the disease experimentally in human volunteers, relatively large amounts of virus were given. The experimentally induced illness tends to be somewhat milder than the natural disease but in other respects does not differ significantly.

Taylor (1951) studied infections of experimental animals induced with strain 1233 (influenza C virus). The agent is infectious for the chick embryo; multiplies readily after amniotic inoculation, but less extensively after allantoic inoculation. Infected amniotic fluid may give virus titers of 10^{-9} and hemagglutination titers of 1:10,000. After numerous passages in the allantoic sac, infected allantoic fluid may give virus titers of 10^{-7} and hemagglutination titers of 1:100 or more. Ferrets, hamsters and monkeys are susceptible on intranasal inoculation, but obvious signs of infection do not appear and gross lesions do not develop. Mice appear to be insusceptible.

ETIOLOGY

The causal agents of influenza are viruses of medium size. At the present time the group is divided into two distinct and immunologically unrelated serologic types termed influenza A virus and influenza B virus, respectively (Horsfall et al., 1940b). There are indications that a third serologic type, influenza C virus, has been identified (Taylor, 1949, 1951; Francis et al., 1950). Each of the two established types is represented by numerous different strains which are in many respects similar but may differ one from another as regards certain properties. Of chief importance is the fact that individual strains of influenza A virus or of influenza B virus may not be identical immunologically with other strains of the same serologic type (Magill and Francis, 1936; Gordon, 1942). Indeed, in occasional instances the immunologic differences between individual strains which belong to one type are so great as to cause considerable difficulty in the proper identification and classification of a strain. Such immunologic differences account for the confusing designation, A-prime (Salk and Suriano, 1949), which has been applied to many A strains recovered since 1947. Strains of influenza A virus do not possess, so far as is known, any antigenic components whatsoever in common with strains of influenza B virus; animals either actively or passively highly immune to A strains are fully susceptible to infection with B strains and vice versa; hyperimmune sera which contain, in very high titer, antibodies against A strains fail to give specific antiviral reactions in neutralization, hemagglutination-inhibition or complement-fixation tests with B strains and vice versa. With the exception of swine influenza virus which is immunologically related to, although different from, a number of strains of influenza A virus (Magill and Francis, 1938), no other virus has been shown to possess antigens in common with the influenza group. Influenza C virus (Taylor, 1949, 1951; Francis et al., 1950) appears not to possess antigenic components in common with either influenza A virus or influenza B virus.

Influenza A and B viruses possess in common the following properties: they are pathogenic for the same animal species, i.e., they have identical host ranges; they induce infections in susceptible hosts, the pathologic manifestations of which are indistinguishable; they multiply rapidly in the presence of susceptible cells; they are highly antigenic and rapidly induce the development of specific active immunity in susceptible mammalian hosts as well as rapidly stimulate the production of specific antibodies in both susceptible and resistant mammalian species; they show identical reactions with homologous antibodies in various serologic tests; they are resistant to the action of enzymes but are readily inactivated by radiation and a wide variety of chemical reagents; they combine with, agglutinate and dissociate from the erythrocytes of a number of animal species; they possess toxic properties; they produce reciprocal interference with heterologous strains; their infectivity is intimately associated with and apparently cannot be separated from spherical or nearly spherical particles which show no definite structural differentiation. Identification of strains of influenza A virus from strains of influenza B virus is entirely dependent upon immunologic procedures (Francis, 1940; Magill, 1940). However, there is evidence that the virus particles of certain B strains are slightly larger than those of certain A strains (Friedewald and Pickels, 1944;

Sharp et al., 1944). Should this difference in size between the two serologic types be found to be constant for various strains, it would constitute strong evidence for a fundamental structural difference in the two types.

Influenza A and influenza B viruses show a great capacity to undergo variation. With respect to the following properties, evidence of variation has been obtained: pathogenicity for various species of laboratory animals, particularly ferrets, mice (Andrewes et al., 1934), hamsters and chick embryos; capacity to agglutinate erythrocytes of various species, especially those of chickens and guinea pigs (Burnet et al., 1949); rate of elution from erythrocytes (Björkman and Horsfall, 1948); and antigenic constitution. Unusual variants pathogenic for the central nervous system of mice have been obtained from a few A strains (Stuart-Harris, 1939). Variation in antigenic structure has been observed frequently with either recently recovered or old laboratory strains; it is common when serial passage in the mouse lung is carried out (Hirst, 1947); it may occur also on prolonged chick-embryo or tissue-culture passage (Francis, 1947); and it can be obtained on partial neutralization with immune serum in the chick embryo (Archetti and Horsfall, 1950) and by passage at maximal infective dilution (Isaacs and Edney, 1950).

The influenza viruses are discrete particles of relatively uniform size and shape; they are spherical or nearly spherical with diameters of the order of 100 mμ. Recent values for the diameter of the hydrated virus particle of the PR8 strain of influenza A range from 80 to 100 mμ (Friedewald and Pickels, 1944; Lauffer and Stanley, 1944). Values for the diameter of the virus particle of the Lee strain of influenza B vary from 85 to 100 mμ (Friedewald and Pickels, 1944; Sharp et al., 1944). When A and B strains were compared under identical experimental conditions, it was found that the particles of B strains were somewhat larger than those of A strains (Friede-

wald and Pickels, 1944; Sharp et al., 1944); the difference is of the order of 10 per cent, a magnitude which is probably significant. The various biologic properties of the viruses, i.e., infectivity, antigenicity, hemagglutination capacity, and complement-fixing activity, are intimately associated with the particles (Friedewald and Pickels, 1944; Lauffer and Miller, 1944) and, with the exception of the soluble complement-fixing antigen, cannot be separated from them. Although highly purified preparations of the viruses have been prepared, it has not been possible to obtain virus entirely free of extraneous materials. As a consequence, the chemical constituents of the virus particle are not precisely known. Purified preparations contain protein, both ribonucleic and desoxyribonucleic acids, lipids, carbohydrates (i.e., polysaccharides composed of mannose, galactose and glucosamine units) and water (as much as 60 per cent by weight) (Knight, 1947). By means of both serologic and chemical studies, Knight (1946, 1947) showed that highly purified preparations contained, in appreciable concentration, antigens characteristic of the host from which the preparations were derived; preparations obtained from allantoic fluid contained antigens characteristic of normal allantoic fluid, while preparations obtained from mouse lungs contained antigens characteristic of normal mouse lungs. The hypothesis was advanced (Knight, 1946) that the virus particles themselves might contain a component characteristic of each kind of host from which the virus is obtained. Simpler explanations might be offered: the concentration of normal tissue antigen may merely reflect the degree to which the preparations are contaminated by host tissue; the virus particle may combine with and remain fixed to host tissue components as do certain other virus particles (Curnen and Horsfall, 1946).

Maximum stability for the biologic properties of the viruses is obtained between pH 6.5 and 7.9, depending somewhat upon the strain and the experimental conditions; loss of biologic properties occurs much more rapidly on the acid than on the alkaline side of optimum pH conditions (Miller, 1944). The isoelectric point for the PR8 strain is pH 5.3 (Miller et al., 1944). The density of the hydrated particles is about 1.1, the anhydrous specific volume is about 0.79, and the intrinsic viscosities of highly purified preparations range between 11.3 and 16.5 (Lauffer and Stanley, 1944). Infected allantoic fluid contains approximately 0.01 per cent virus or about 2×10^{10} virus particles per cc. (Friedewald and Pickels, 1944). Infectivity is lost following heating at 56° C. for a few minutes; irradiation with ultraviolet light, treatment with formaldehyde or numerous other reagents also cause loss of infectivity. The infectious titer of suspensions decreases in a few hours at room temperature but it is little affected by storage at 4° C. for a week; purified preparations properly buffered may be held at 4° C. for a month without showing any marked reduction in titer (Miller, 1944). Suspensions stored at −76° C. for more than 5 months show no diminution in infectious titer (Horsfall, 1939); if stored in sealed glass ampules, the virus can be kept indefinitely at this temperature.

Influenza viruses were the first, among a number of animal viruses, to be shown to possess the peculiar capacity to cause agglutination of red blood cells (Hirst, 1941). Hemagglutination is the result of the interaction of the virus particles themselves and erythrocytes: the first step is adsorption of virus by red blood cells; the second is the agglutination of red cell-virus aggregates; the third is the spontaneous dissociation of virus from red cells (Hirst, 1942c). Erythrocytes from at least 22 different animal species, including mammals, birds, reptiles and amphibians, are agglutinated by the viruses. Chicken red cells are most satisfactory, and the only mammalian cells which are useful are human and guinea pig erythrocytes (Clark and Nagler, 1943). With only one exception, all infective preparations of the viruses cause hemagglutination in a titer proportional to the infectivity titer (Hirst, 1942a); suspensions of infected ferret lung do not cause hemagglutination, no matter how much virus they contain. The exceptional finding with ferret lung virus is explained by the presence of a nonspecific inhibitor, since the addition of suspensions of the normal ferret lung to virus preparations with high hemagglutination titers abolishes the reaction. Between 10^4 and 10^5 virus particles are required to cause hemagglutination under standard conditions, consequently the hemagglutination titer is much lower than the infectivity titer. The ratio between the number of erythrocytes and virus particles at the titration endpoint is approximately 1 (Friedewald and Pickels, 1944).

Adsorption of virus by erythrocytes is rapid, and both the rate and degree of adsorption are functions of temperature and the concentration of red cells. With high concentrations of virus agglutination of red cells occurs in a few minutes; tests are usually read at 1 hour. The virus-erythrocyte combination undergoes spontaneous dissociation which, in a few hours, is complete. Red cells which have once combined with virus and then have been released are not capable of adsorbing either homologous or heterologous strains a second time and therefore do not show agglutination when mixed with fresh virus. However, the virus itself is apparently unaffected by the reaction, and, if fresh red cells are added, the cycle of adsorption and spontaneous dissociation can be repeated successively (Hirst, 1942c). The substance which reacts with the virus, i.e., the erythrocyte "receptor," is present in the stroma; it withstands high temperature and high pH; it is inactivated by sodium periodate, and by trypsin as well as by influenza virus itself; and it appears to be a mucoprotein (Hirst, 1948a). Burnet, McCrea and Stone (1946) showed that a filtrate of V. cholerae culture removes receptors from erythrocytes in a manner analogous to the action of the virus. Influenza virus inactivated by various gentle procedures, e.g., heating at 42° C., may retain the capacity to combine with and to elute from red cells. However, more vigorous procedures, e.g., heating at 56° C., often eliminate the ability to elute (Hirst, 1948b), while drastic procedures, e.g., heating at 65° C., cause loss of the hemagglutination property. Virus is also adsorbed and subsequently released spontaneously from the cells of the excised normal ferret lung. In almost all respects, the interaction between virus and the cells of the respiratory tract closely resembles that between virus and red cells (Hirst, 1943a). Hirst (1942c; 1943a) has drawn an analogy between the interaction of enzymes and substrates and the interaction between influenza viruses and erythrocytes and has suggested that a similar mechanism may be an essential preliminary event to the infection of susceptible cells in the living animal. The chapter on Hemagglutination should be consulted for more detailed information.

When influenza virus and immune serum against it are mixed and red cells are then added, hemagglutination does not occur. Immune serum can be diluted to an extent proportional to its virus-neutralization titer before its capacity to inhibit hemagglutination by a constant amount of virus is exceeded (Hirst, 1942a). This is the basis for the hemagglutination-inhibition test for antibodies against the virus which is described in the chapter on Serologic and Immunologic Technics. The hemagglutination-inhibition test with serum gives both qualitative and quantitative data relative to the presence of antibodies against the virus which correlate fairly well with data obtained by means of the virus-neutralization test. However, the antibodies responsible for hemagglutination-inhibition appear not to be identical with those responsible for neutralization of the agent (Walker and Horsfall, 1950). Normal serum and immune serum against other viruses usually inhibit hemagglutination caused by influenza viruses but do so only in relatively low titer

(Hirst, 1942a). Such inhibition is not attributable to antibodies against the virus but is due to the presence of nonspecific inhibitors of hemagglutination which appear to be mucoproteins (Hirst, 1948a). Similar inhibitors are present in a variety of tissues and body fluids (Burnet and Beveridge, 1945; Friedewald et al., 1947; Svedmyr, 1947). Such an inhibitory mucoprotein which is present in normal human urine has been obtained in a highly purified state and appears to be a single homogeneous substance (Tamm and Horsfall, 1952).

Interference is demonstrable between strains of influenza A virus in tissue culture (Andrewes, 1942) and between strains of the two serologic types in the chick embryo and the mouse (Ziegler and Horsfall, 1944). Infection of embryos with very small quantities of either serologic type of virus leads, in from 8 to 12 hours, to refractoriness to infection with the other serologic type. Similarly, the introduction of a very large amount of one type causes interference with the multiplication of the other type, injected simultaneously. The insusceptibility to infection by A strains which is induced by infection with B strains is not an absolute effect and may be overcome if the inoculum of the A strain is very large. Virus rendered completely noninfective by ultraviolet radiation is capable of causing interference in either the chick embryo or the mouse (Ziegler et al., 1944; Henle and Henle, 1944b). In the mouse, interference between A and B strains is not demonstrable 2 weeks following intranasal infection (unpublished experiments of the author); in the ferret, interference between the two serologic types is not demonstrable 1 week following intranasal infection (Sugg and Magill, 1947). Reciprocal interference between strains of influenza A and influenza B viruses in the chick embryo is as readily demonstrable with noninfective preparations as with active viruses; although when a noninfective virus is employed, large inocula are necessary to cause interference. A few hours after the establishment of infection in the chick embryo, additional multiplication of virus is inhibited by the injection of a large amount of noninfective virus. Preparations which show "auto-interference," i.e., interference caused by noninfectious virus particles in a single preparation, can be obtained by prolonged incubation in the chick embryo, prolonged storage at 4° C., heating, and ultraviolet radiation (Henle and Henle, 1944b). The capacity to produce interference is inactivated by ultraviolet radiation or by heat at a less rapid rate than is the property of infectiousness but at a more rapid rate than is the capacity to cause hemagglutination. Interference apparently is caused by the virus particle itself; the property cannot be separated from the virus and is specifically neutralized by the homologous type antiserum (Ziegler et al., 1944). The well-established facts that strains may be lost if serial passage is carried out with undiluted allantoic fluid and that higher virus titers are obtained when dilute inocula are employed may both be attributed to "auto-interference." It is thought (Henle, 1950) that interference is dependent upon the capacity of virus particles to react with susceptible cells and that when quantitative saturation of such cells by virus particles has been achieved, it is not possible to establish infection with the same or other virus strains, irrespective of their serologic type. Interference between human influenza viruses and the following other viruses has been demonstrated: swine influenza virus (Ziegler and Horsfall, 1944), yellow fever virus and West Nile virus (Lennette and Koprowski, 1946), Newcastle disease virus (Florman, 1948) and Western equine encephalomyelitis virus (Vilches and Hirst, 1947).

Both A and B virus strains cause so-called toxic reactions following intracerebral, intraperitoneal or intravenous injection in mice, rabbits, rats, guinea pigs and hamsters (Henle and Henle, 1946a, b). The toxic property cannot be separated from the infective property; toxic activity is not the result of virus multiplication. Intracerebral injection of virus preparations leads to tonic and clonic convulsions and death in tetanus, usually within 24 or 72 hours, destruction of the ependymal lining of the ventricles being the dominant finding. Toxic activity is directly correlated with virus concentration. Intraperitoneal or intravenous injection in mice may cause death in from 8 to 96 hours. The chief lesions are widespread necrosis of the liver and spleen, hemorrhages into the intestines, and pleural exudation. The toxic effect of influenza A virus preparations is neutralized by anti-influenza A virus but not by anti-influenza B virus serum, and vice versa. Moreover, vaccination of mice by either the subcutaneous or intraperitoneal route causes them to become specifically immune against the toxic effects of the same serologic type. The toxic property remains stable on storage at 4° C. for 2 or 3 months and is inactivated by heating, treatment with formaldehyde or irradiation with ultraviolet light at a rate slower than the infectivity. It is thought that the virus particle itself carries the toxic property (Henle and Henle, 1946b).

Influenza A virus can be recovered in a large proportion of instances from the upper respiratory tract of patients with influenza A. Similarly, influenza B virus is recoverable from a considerable percentage of patients with influenza B. Either type of virus may be obtained from throat-washings of appropriate patients by intranasal inoculation of ferrets (Smith, Andrewes and Laidlaw, 1933; Francis, 1940), intranasal inoculation and serial lung passage in mice (Francis and Magill, 1937; Francis, 1940), inoculation into the amniotic sac of the chick embryo (Burnet, 1940), intranasal inoculation of hamsters (Taylor, 1940), as well as by various other less satisfactory procedures. Inoculation into the amniotic sac is apparently the most sensitive and successful of present technics. The virus is present in the upper respiratory tract of patients from the first day of illness until the fifth, occasionally until the seventh, day after onset (Francis et al., 1937; Horsfall et al., 1940a). In fatal cases associated with secondary bacterial pneumonia, influenza A virus has been recovered occasionally from the lungs. In natural infections of human beings, as in experimental infections of ferrets, mice or hamsters, the virus remains strictly localized in the tissues of the respiratory tract; it is not present in the blood or in other organs. Throat-washings may contain a considerable quantity of virus, in some instances with influenza A virus as much as 10^7 chick embryo infectious doses per cc. (Hirst, personal communication). Undiluted secretions from the upper respiratory tract may contain even higher concentrations of virus and in the form of droplets expelled into the air readily account for the communicability of the infection and the rapidity of its spread among susceptible persons in proximity to patients.

Following an attack of influenza A, most patients develop a demonstrable antibody response against influenza A virus but do not develop antibodies against influenza B virus. Similarly, after influenza B there is in a large proportion of patients an unequivocal antibody response against influenza B virus, but not against influenza A virus. Antibody levels may be measured by a number of different technics: serum-neutralization tests against the virus in the ferret (Smith, Andrewes and Laidlaw, 1933); serum-neutralization tests against the virus in the mouse (Andrewes, Laidlaw and Smith, 1935); serum-complement-fixation tests in the presence of viral antigen (Smith, 1936); serum-inhibition-of-hemagglutination tests against the virus (Hirst, 1942a); serum-neutralization tests against the virus in the chick embryo (Hirst, 1942b). Because of its simplicity and the rapidity with which titrations of antibody levels can be carried out by means of the technic, the inhibition-of-hemagglutination test is now much more extensively used than any of the other serologic procedures. This test, when properly carried out, serves to measure the level of certain antibodies against the virus in

serum. The level of such antibodies parallels reasonably well that of neutralizing antibodies (Hirst, 1942a).

In the serum of patients an increased antibody level may be demonstrable as early as 7 days after onset of illness; maximal antibody levels usually are present 2 weeks after onset (Horsfall et al., 1940a), persist only for approximately a month and then gradually decline. Two months after infection, antibody levels are on the average only 5 times higher than during the acute phase of the disease; at 3 months they may be only 2 times higher, while after 8 or 12 months they drop almost, if not altogether, to preinfection levels (Francis et al., 1937; Horsfall, 1940). Most human beings of school age or older possess in their serum demonstrable antibodies against influenza viruses; among normal adults the incidence of neutralizing antibodies against influenza A virus may be as high as 55 per cent (Rickard et al., 1940) when 10^3 or more infectious doses of virus are used in neutralization tests, and over 80 per cent (Rickard et al., 1941) if smaller amounts of virus are employed; the incidence of hemagglutination-inhibiting antibodies is at least as high or higher (Hirst et al., 1942). Not only do most human beings possess specific antibodies against the viruses but also in many instances their sera show surprisingly high antibody levels. The serum of approximately 3 per cent of normal persons can neutralize more than 10^6 M.L.50 doses of influenza A virus; about 20 per cent can neutralize 10^5 to 10^6 such doses; over 55 per cent can neutralize 10^4 to 10^5 doses; over 75 per cent can neutralize 10^3 to 10^4 doses. Only approximately 20 per cent fail to neutralize 10^2 or less doses of virus (Rickard et al., 1941).

The frequency with which normal persons possess antibodies against influenza viruses in all probability reflects the frequency with which infection with the agents occurs and indicates that they are widely disseminated and commonly infect most persons at some time during life. Because most normal persons possess antibodies, it is necessary to determine with each patient the antibody level of serum obtained during the acute phase of the illness, preferably from the first to the third but not later than the fifth day after onset, and of serum obtained 2 to 4 weeks after onset if an increase in antibodies is to be demonstrated. A fourfold or greater increase in antibody titer is considered to be significant and, if the tests are carried out by those proficient in the technics, can be taken as evidence of a specific antibody response. In persons who have not recently received influenza virus vaccine, such a response is strong evidence of infection with the serologic type of virus which was employed in the tests.

In measuring antibody levels in serum, not only is the serologic type of virus of importance but also the strain of virus used may markedly affect the results. Antibody titers determined with one strain may be widely different from those determined with another strain of the same serologic type. Moreover, the increase in antibody level following an attack of the disease may be very marked and highly significant when one strain is employed and so small as not to be significant when another strain of the same serologic type is used (Magill and Sugg, 1944). This may complicate seriously the interpretation of the results of antibody titrations and also makes desirable the employment of two or more strains, independently, in serologic tests. It is probably best to use recently isolated strains and, if possible, strains obtained from patients in the epidemic under study. Not only are antibodies present in serum but they are present also in the nasal secretions of human beings (Francis, 1941-42). The concentration of antibodies in nasal secretions is related to, although somewhat lower than the serum antibody titer, and varies directly with the latter after an attack of the disease.

Quantitative factors are of great importance in serologic tests with influenza viruses and must be very carefully controlled if trustworthy results are to be obtained. This is as true of neutralization tests in the mouse or the chick embryo (Horsfall, 1939; Horsfall and Lennette, 1941; Walker and Horsfall, 1950) as of hemagglutination-inhibition tests (Hirst, 1942a; Salk, 1944; Whitman, 1947). In virus-neutralization tests, the quantity of virus employed and the reproducibility of the titration end point used are the factors which require most careful control. In hemagglutination-inhibition tests, the amount of virus, the concentration of red blood cells and the titration end point are the variables which should be most carefully controlled. The neutralization of virus by antibody, as judged by the results of tests in mice, is a reaction which appears not to follow multiple proportions. There is a linear relationship between the two variables, but this has an exponential form (Horsfall, 1939). As an approximation, a fivefold increase in the amount of antibody used results in a tenfold increase in the amount of virus neutralized and vice versa, i.e., the virus-neutralizing effectiveness of antibody appears to diminish progressively as the concentration of antibody decreases. It is evident that the neutralizing antibody titer of an immune serum is directly dependent upon, although not inversely proportional to, the quantity of virus used to measure it. It should be emphasized that the results of virus-neutralization tests, as carried out in the mouse, cannot be used as evidence for the mechanism of the interaction between virus and antibody; during the 10 or more days which elapse between inoculation of the mixture and the determination of the result, the animal host is not only capable of supporting the multiplication of virus but also possesses the capacity to produce antibody; neither host variable can be controlled adequately and either one may influence the result. In neutralization tests in the chick embryo a similar linear relationship has been demonstrated (Walker and Horsfall, 1950), but the deviation from multiple proportions is even more striking. Thus, a fivefold increase in the amount of antibody used results in a 2,000-fold increase in the amount of virus neutralized and vice versa. In this connection, it is of particular interest that the inhibition of viral hemagglutination by antibody does correspond to multiple proportions; the hemagglutination-inhibition titer of an immune serum is inversely proportional to the amount of virus used to determine it (Hirst, 1942a); a fivefold increase in the quantity of virus employed results in a fivefold decrease in the antibody titer. Moreover, a constant amount of antibody inhibits hemagglutination caused by a constant amount of virus regardless of the volume in which the reaction occurs, indicating that, in this respect at least, the virus-antibody reaction is similar to the better understood antigen-antibody reactions (Hirst, 1942a). It appears evident that the in-vitro hemagglutination-inhibition technic provides more exact information regarding the mechanism of virus-antibody reactions than does the much more complex in-vivo virus-neutralization technic.

Prior to the development of the hemagglutination-inhibition technic, the complement-fixation reaction was the only available in-vitro procedure for the measurement of antibody levels against the virus. Virus suspensions contain antigens which in the presence of antibody are capable of fixing complement (Smith, 1936). The larger part, but not all, of the complement-fixing antigen is separable from the virus particles (Hoyle and Fairbrother, 1937) and is very much smaller in size than the virus (Lennette and Horsfall, 1940). In many respects the antigen which is separable from the virus is analogous to the soluble antigens of other viruses. Soluble antigens freed of virus are immunologically specific for the serologic type from which they are derived but fail to reflect the immunologic differences between strains of one type (Lennette and Horsfall, 1941). In addition to the soluble antigen, there is a complement-fixing antigen which is intimately associated, if not identical, with the virus parti-

cles (Friedewald, 1943). This antigen, as distinct from the soluble antigen, shows in complement-fixation tests a high degree of strain specificity comparable to that obtained in neutralization or hemagglutination-inhibition tests. The serum of approximately 80 per cent of normal persons fails to give positive results in complement-fixation tests against the soluble antigen of influenza A virus (Rickard et al., 1940). Following an attack of influenza A, complement-fixing antibodies can be demonstrated with soluble antigen in serum from 80 to 90 per cent of the patients (Eaton and Rickard, 1941). On the average, such antibodies appear, reach maximal titers and decline at a rate which corresponds fairly well with that of the development and decline of neutralizing antibodies. The complement-fixation test with soluble antigen does not measure neutralizing or hemagglutination-inhibiting antibodies, but when virus particles are used as antigen the results are closely correlated with those obtained in inhibition tests (Wiener et al., 1946). It is possible that the soluble antigen represents merely fragments of or disintegrated virus particles; it can be released from intact virus particles by intense sonic vibration (Wiener et al., 1946). However, Hoyle (1948) as well as Henle and Henle (1949) have obtained results which led them to the view that the soluble antigen may be formed prior to the development of complete virus particles. The concept that influenza virus may multiply in stepwise fashion and may, under special circumstances, emerge as an incomplete virus, lacking the property of infectivity but possessing other features which serve to identify the agent, has been put forward by a number of workers (Gard and von Magnus, 1947; Hoyle, 1948; Henle and Henle, 1949; Schlesinger, 1950).

DIAGNOSIS

Because of the frequency with which the disease occurs, its tendency to appear in epidemic form and the fairly typical clinical picture which is commonly presented, diagnosis is usually not difficult. The common features are an abrupt onset, chills, fever, headache, muscular pains, prostration, cough and nasal symptoms in the absence of any very definite abnormal physical signs. Sporadic cases occur in the absence of epidemics and are difficult to diagnose clinically.

Infection with either serologic type of influenza virus may lead to a wide variety of different clinical pictures: subclinical or inapparent infections are common during epidemics. Mild infections with symptoms similar to those of the common cold also occur, whereas severe infections are rare but may be associated with pneumonia due to secondary bacterial infection. Influenza A is, in general, associated with somewhat more definite symptoms than influenza B, but there is no clinical evidence which serves to distinguish one infection from the other. An etiologic diagnosis can be made only by laboratory procedures, recovery and identification of the virus from the respiratory tract, demonstration of a specific and significant antibody response against the virus. Virus may be recovered most readily from throat-washings obtained during the acute phase of the disease by intra-amniotic inoculation of chick embryos; it may be identified by hemagglutination-inhibition tests with specific immune sera. An antibody response may be demonstrated most readily by determining the hemagglutination-inhibition titers of two serum specimens from each patient: one specimen should be obtained during the acute phase of the disease, i.e., less than 5 days after onset; the other specimen should be obtained during the second or third week after onset.

Numerous other infectious diseases may closely simulate influenza and should be distinguished from it. Among these are the following: the common cold, undifferentiated acute upper respiratory infections, primary atypical pneumonia, paranasal sinusitis, abortive measles, dengue, Rift Valley fever, lymphocytic choriomeningitis, and Venezuelan equine encephalomyelitis. Consult the chapters concerning these diseases.

TREATMENT

Symptomatic and supportive treatment identical to that employed in undifferentiated, acute, upper respiratory infections or in other illnesses with similar symptomatology gives some relief. The sulfonamide drugs do not give beneficial results or relief from symptoms. Because secondary bacterial infections occur only in rare instances, there is no real advantage in giving sulfonamides with the hope of preventing their development. Penicillin is not effective in treatment of the disease. Although there have been some claims that aureomycin was useful, a carefully controlled study (Thalmann et al., 1950) showed no significant effect from the drug in 69 patients with influenza A. There does not appear to be any reason to expect that chloramphenicol or terramycin would be effective chemotherapeutic agents in influenza. There is no rational basis for the use of immune serum once signs and symptoms of the disease have appeared. Similarly, there is no reason to think that the administration of influenza virus vaccine to patients with the illness would be beneficial in the least; it is probable that in numerous instances the injection of vaccine would tend to lead to increased symptoms.

EPIDEMIOLOGY

The disease occurs with considerable frequency and is world-wide in distribution. Most commonly it appears in epidemic form: numerous localized epidemics may occur in different geographic areas almost simultaneously; extensive epidemics may appear to spread over large areas. Sporadic cases, on the other hand, occur and may or may not lead to the development of secondary cases among contacts. Pandemics or very extensive intercontinental outbreaks have occurred rarely, and it should be pointed out that the causal agents of such outbreaks have not been established. In the temperate zones epidemics tend to develop during the winter months; in the north temperate zone they usually occur in the period from late November to the end of March. However, an epidemic may develop at any time of the year especially in the tropics where epidemics have occurred during the summer months. Outbreaks of influenza A of widely varying extent have occurred in one or another country almost every year since the virus was discovered in 1933.

Definite epidemics of influenza A, however, have shown some tendency to cyclic occurrence, and the interval between sizable epidemics has usually been 2 or, occasionally, 3 years. Outbreaks of influenza B have been less frequent and less extensive. Definite epidemics of the latter disease also have shown a tendency to cyclic occurrence: the interval between epidemics has varied from 4 to 5 years. Influenza A and B may occur simultaneously in the same geographic area, although this appears not to be common (Lennette et al., 1941). Concurrent infection with influenza A and B viruses has been observed (Kilbourne et al., 1951). There is evidence suggesting that influenza A and C may at times be associated (Francis et al., 1950). In the main, only one serologic type of virus is obtained from patients in a single outbreak and strains of a type recovered from the same epidemic tend to be immunologically closely related (Hirst, 1943b). Attack rates vary widely in different epidemics and may range from as low as 1 or 2 per cent to as high as 20 or 30 per cent. Under crowded living conditions where opportunities for contact are frequent, as in institutions, schools, camps, barracks or on shipboard, attack rates tend to be high. Conversely, among dispersed populations, as in rural communities, with fewer opportunities for contact, the attack rate tends to be low. The shape of the epidemic curve is also a function of the contact frequency. Under conditions of crowding, the epidemic peak may build up rapidly,

sometimes within a few days after the appearance of the first case, and then the epidemic may rapidly burn out so that the whole outbreak occupies a period of only 2 or 3 weeks (Francis, 1937; Horsfall et al., 1940a); among dispersed populations there may be no obvious peak of incidence, and small numbers of cases may continue to occur over a period of 2 or 3 months (Rickard et al., 1940).

Infection with influenza viruses is very common; most children over 5 years of age show evidence of past infection (Rickard et al., 1940); most adults possess neutralizing antibodies (Rickard et al., 1941) which is strong evidence of previous infection. Inapparent or subclinical infections may be as common as, or even more common than, manifest infections (Francis et al., 1937; Rickard et al., 1940) and probably serve to explain the high incidence of antibodies against the viruses as well as the prolonged maintenance of significant antibody levels by healthy persons. Persons of any age, race or color are about equally susceptible, as are both sexes (Francis, 1937). The infection is thought to be transmitted by means of droplets discharged from the upper respiratory tract of patients. The portal of entry of the virus is the upper respiratory tract. Unequivocal evidence for the existence of virus carriers among human beings or animals has not been obtained. The interepidemic reservoir of the viruses is not definitely known although it is suspected that sporadic infections may serve to maintain the viruses between epidemic periods (Burnet and Clark, 1942).

The type specific immunity which develops following an attack of either influenza A or influenza B does not persist indefinitely (Magill, 1941) and probably is not of significant degree after 6 or 8 months (Francis et al., 1944). An attack of influenza A does not induce immunity against influenza B and vice versa. The relatively transient immunity which results from infection with either type of virus may be a reflection of the fact that the infectious process is limited to the mucous membrane of the respiratory tract or to other unknown factors. Susceptibility to infection with either type of virus is to a degree inversely correlated with the serum antibody level against the homologous type (Francis et al., 1937; Rickard et al., 1941); the higher the antibody level, the less probable is infection. However, an attack may occur irrespective of a high antibody titer.

CONTROL MEASURES

Many groups of investigators have studied, in human beings, the efficacy of vaccines containing influenza viruses and numerous attempts have been made to determine their effectiveness as prophylactic agents against the disease. The first studies were those of Chenoweth et al. (1936) which were shortly followed by a number of others. Horsfall et al. (1941) as well as other workers showed that the subcutaneous injection of virus vaccine led to a significant reduction in the incidence of influenza A. During World War II the Commission on Influenza, Army Epidemiological Board, undertook extensive studies on vaccines against the disease. Members of the Commission on Influenza (1944) developed a concentrated virus vaccine which contained strains of both serologic types and showed that it was effective as a prophylactic agent. During epidemics of influenza A, the incidence of the disease was about 70 to 80 per cent lower in vaccinated persons than in those who were unvaccinated (Salk et al., 1945). During epidemics of influenza B, the attack rate was about 90 per cent lower in vaccinated than in unvaccinated persons (Francis et. al., 1946).

These results served to reaffirm the validity of earlier findings in experimental animals and showed that the parenteral injection of inactivated influenza virus in sufficient amount led in man to the development of a temporarily increased resistance to infection with the same or closely related strains. However, in 1947 new strains of influenza A virus, i.e., so-called A-prime strains (Salk and Suriano, 1949), appeared and were found to be considerably different from earlier strains with respect to antigenic constitution (Francis et al., 1947). Vaccines which had been prepared with strains recovered earlier proved ineffective during 1947 and failed to reduce the incidence of infections attributable to the new strains. The significance of antigenic variation of influenza viruses with respect to control of infection by means of vaccines came into sharp focus as a result of these experiences.

Available vaccines contain inactivated viruses derived from the allantoic fluid of infected chick embryos and purified in varying degree. Subcutaneous administration of vaccine stimulates the development of antibodies against the viruses contained in it and results in increased serum antibody levels (Hirst et al., 1942). Antibodies begin to appear approximately a week after the injection of the vaccine, reach maximal levels during the second week, remain constant for approximately a month and then gradually decline (Hirst et al., 1942). The degree of increased resistance to infection is to a considerable extent mirrored by the antibody curve: there is some evidence of protection 1 week after vaccination (Hirst et al., 1944); there is more evidence of protection thereafter for a month or two; following this period there is apparently progressively less protection (Members of the Commission on Influenza, 1944). There is as yet no agreement as to the duration of a significant degree of increased resistance following vaccination. Estimates vary between 2 and 12 months, but numerous workers doubt that vaccination leads to definitely reduced susceptibility for more than a few months. The response to vaccination varies widely among different persons. In general, the extent of the increase in antibody titer is inversely proportional to the antibody level at the time of vaccination (Hirst et al., 1942). Vaccinated persons can and do contract influenza, but, if the interval between vaccination and exposure is not too long, they are definitely less likely to develop the disease than are unvaccinated people. The currently used vaccine has certain disadvantages over and beyond the relatively short period during which it induces a degree of immunity. It contains a considerable concentration of virus material which, although inactivated, possesses toxic properties and, if given in sufficient quantity, may cause unpleasant symptoms in an appreciable percentage of persons, especially children. Moreover, it contains antigenic material of chick-embryo origin which may lead to sensitization or, rarely, to marked reactions in persons already hypersensitive to such material. The vaccine is prepared with only a few strains of each of the two serologic types of virus and consequently cannot be expected to give protection against all strains.

REFERENCES

Andrewes, C. H., 1942, Interference by one virus with the growth of another in tissue-culture. Brit. J. Exp. Path., *23*, 214-220.

Andrewes, C. H., Laidlaw, P. P., and Smith, W., 1934, The susceptibility of mice to the viruses of human and swine influenza. Lancet, *2*, 859-862.

Andrewes, C. H., Laidlaw, P. P., and Smith, W., 1935, Influenza: observations on the recovery of virus from man and on the antibody content of human sera. Brit. J. Exp. Path., *16*, 566-582.

Andrewes, C. H., and Smith, W., 1937, Influenza: further experiments on the active immunization of mice. Brit. J. Exp. Path., *18*, 43-55.

Archetti, I., and Horsfall, F. L., Jr., 1950, Persistent antigenic variation of influenza A viruses after incomplete neutralization *in ovo* with heterologous immune serum. J. Exp. Med., *92*, 441-462.

Beveridge, W. I. B., and Burnet, F. M., 1946, The cultivation of viruses and rickettsiae in the chick embryo. Medical Research Council, Special report series No. 256. London. His Majesty's Stationery Office. pp. 1-92.

Björkman, S. E., and Horsfall, F. L., Jr., 1948, The production of a persistent alteration in influenza virus by lanthanum or ultraviolet irradiation. J. Exp. Med., *88*, 445-461.

Brightman, I. J., 1936, Recovery of a filtrable virus from children with influenza. II. The experimental disease in ferrets. Am. J. Dis. Child., *52*, 78-91.

Burnet, F. M., 1940, Influenza virus infections of the chick embryo by the amniotic route. I. General character of the infections. Australian J. Exp. Biol. and Med. Sci., *18*, 353-360.

Burnet, F. M., and Beveridge, W. I. B., 1945, Studies on the Hirst haemagglutination reaction with influenza and Newcastle disease viruses. IV. The action of human tears on influenza virus. Australian J. Exp. Biol. and Med. Sci., *23*, 186-189.

Burnet, F. M., and Clark, E., 1942, Influenza. A survey of the last 50 years in the light of modern work on the virus of epidemic influenza. Monographs from the Walter and Eliza Hall Institute of Research in Pathology and Medicine, No. 4, 1-118, Melbourne, Macmillan.

Burnet, F. M., McCrea, J. F., and Stone, J. D., 1946, Modification of human red cells by virus action. I. The receptor gradient for virus action in human red cells. Brit. J. Exp. Path., *27*, 228-236.

Burnet, F. M., Stone, J. D., Isaacs, A., and Edney, M., 1949, The genetic character of O-D change in influenza A. Brit. J. Exp. Path., *30*, 419-425.

Chenoweth, A., Waltz, A. D., Stokes, J., Jr., and Gladen, R. G., 1936, Active immunization with the viruses of human and swine influenza. Amer. J. Dis. Child., *52*, 757-758.

Clark, E., and Nagler, F. P. O., 1943, Haem-agglutination by viruses. The range of susceptible cells with special reference to agglutination by vaccinia virus. Australian J. Exp. Biol. and Med. Sci., *21*, 103-106.

Curnen, E. C., and Horsfall, F. L., Jr., 1946, Studies on pneumonia virus of mice (PVM). III. Hemagglutination by the virus: the occurrence of combination between the virus and a tissue substance. J. Exp. Med., *83*, 105-132.

Eaton, M. D., 1940, Transmission of epidemic influenza virus in mice by contact. J. Bact., *39*, 229-241.

Eaton, M. D., and Rickard, E. R., 1941, Application of the complement-fixation test to the study of epidemic influenza. Am. J. Hyg., Sec. B., *33*, 23-35.

Florman, A. L., 1948, Some alterations in chicken erythrocytes which follow treatment with influenza and Newcastle disease virus. J. Bact., *55*, 183-196.

Francis, T., Jr., 1934, Transmission of influenza by a filterable virus. Science, *80*, 457-459.

Francis, T., Jr., 1937, Epidemiological studies in influenza. Am. J. Pub. Health, *27*, 211-225.

Francis, T., Jr., 1939, Quantitative relationships between the immunizing dose of epidemic influenza virus and the resultant immunity. J. Exp. Med., *69*, 283-300.

Francis, T., Jr., 1940, A new type of virus from epidemic influenza. Science, *92*, 405-408.

Francis, T., Jr., 1941-42, Factors conditioning resistance to epidemic influenza. Harvey Lectures, *37*, 69-99.

Francis, T., Jr., 1947, Apparent serological variation within a strain of influenza virus. Proc. Soc. Exp. Biol. and Med., *65*, 143-147.

Francis, T., Jr., and Magill, T. P., 1935, Cultivation of human influenza virus in an artificial medium. Science, *82*, 353-354.

Francis, T., Jr., and Magill, T. P., 1937, Direct transmission of human influenza virus to mice. Proc. Soc. Exp. Biol. and Med., *36*, 132-133.

Francis, T., Jr., Magill, T. P., Rickard, E. R., and

Beck, M. D., 1937, Etiological and serological studies in epidemic influenza. Am. J. Pub. Health, *27*, 1141-1160.

Francis, T., Jr., Pearson, H. E., Salk, J. E., and Brown, P. N., 1944, Immunity in human subjects artificially infected with influenza virus, type B. Am. J. Pub. Health, *34*, 317-334.

Francis, T., Jr., Quilligan, J. J. Jr., and Minuse, E., 1950, Identification of another epidemic respiratory disease. Science, *112*, 495-497.

Francis, T., Jr., Salk, J. E., and Brace, W. M., 1946, The protective effect of vaccination against epidemic influenza B. J. Am. Med. Assn., *131*, 275-278.

Francis, T., Jr., Salk, J. E., and Quilligan, J. J., Jr., 1947, Experience with vaccination against influenza in the spring of 1947. Am. J. Pub. Health, *37*, 1013-1016.

Francis, T., Jr., and Stuart-Harris, C. H., 1938, Studies on the nasal histology of epidemic influenza virus infection in the ferret. I. The development and repair of the nasal lesion. J. Exp. Med., *68*, 789-802.

Friedewald, W. F., 1943, The immunological response to influenza virus infection as measured by the complement fixation test. Relation of the complement-fixing antigen to the virus particle. J. Exp. Med., *78*, 347-366.

Friedewald, W. F., Miller, E. S., and Whatley, L. R., 1947, The nature of non-specific inhibition of virus hemagglutination. J. Exp. Med., *86*, 65-75.

Friedewald, W. F., and Pickels, E. G., 1944, Centrifugation and ultrafiltration studies on allantoic fluid preparations of influenza virus. J. Exp. Med., *79*, 301-317.

Gard, S., and von Magnus, P., 1947, Studies on interference in experimental influenza. II. Purification and centrifugation experiments. Ark. Kemi, Mineral. och Geol., 24B, No. 8.

Goodpasture, E. W., 1919, The significance of certain pulmonary lesions in relation to the etiology of influenza. Am. J. Med. Sci., *158*, 863-870.

Gordon, I., 1942, Demonstration of antigenic differences between different strains of influenza B. J. Immunol., *44*, 231-236.

Henle, W., 1950, Interference phenomena between animal viruses: a review. J. Immunol., *64*, 203-236.

Henle, W., and Henle, G., 1944a, Interference between inactive and active viruses of influenza. I. The incidental occurrence and artificial induction of the phenomenon. Am. J. Med. Sci., *207*, 705-717.

Henle, W., and Henle, G., 1944b, Interference between inactive and active viruses in influenza. II. Factors influencing the phenomenon. Am. J. Med. Sci., *207*, 717-733.

Henle, G., and Henle, W., 1946a, Studies on the toxicity of influenza viruses. I. The effect of intracerebral injection of influenza viruses. J. Exp. Med., *84*, 623-637.

Henle, W., and Henle, G., 1946b, Studies on the toxicity of influenza viruses. II. The effect of intra-abdominal and intravenous injection of influenza viruses. J. Exp. Med., *84*, 639-660.

Henle, W., and Henle, G., 1949, Studies on host-virus interactions in the chick embryo-influenza virus system. III. Development of infectivity, hemagglutination, and complement fixation activities during the first infectious cycle. J. Exp. Med., *90*, 23-37.

Hirst, G. K., 1941, The agglutination of red cells by allantoic fluid of chick embryos infected with influenza virus. Science. *94*, 22-23.

Hirst, G. K., 1942a, The quantitative determination of influenza virus and antibodies by means of red cell agglutination. J. Exp. Med., *75*, 49-64.

Hirst, G. K., 1942b, In vivo titrations of influenza virus and of neutralizing antibodies in chick embryos. J. Immunol., *45*, 285-292.

Hirst, G. K., 1942c, Adsorption of influenza hemagglutinins and virus by red blood cells. J. Exp. Med., *76*, 195-209.

Hirst, G. K., 1943a, Adsorption of influenza virus on cells of the respiratory tract. J. Exp. Med., *78*, 99-109.

Hirst, G. K., 1943b, Studies of antigenic differences among strains of influenza A by means of red cell agglutination. J. Exp. Med., *78*, 407-423.

Hirst, G. K., 1945, Direct isolation of influenza virus in chick embryos. Proc. Soc. Exp. Biol. and Med., *58*, 155-157.

Hirst, G. K., 1947, Studies on the mechanism of adaptation of influenza virus to mice. J. Exp. Med., *86*, 357-366.

Hirst, G. K., 1948a, The nature of the virus receptor of red cells. I. Evidence on the chemical nature of the virus receptors of red cells and of the existence of a closely analogous substance in normal serum. J. Exp. Med., *87*, 301-314.

Hirst, G. K., 1948b, The nature of the virus receptor of red cells. II. The effect of partial heat inactivation of influenza virus on the destruction of red cell receptors and the use of inactivated virus in the measurement of serum inhibitor. J. Exp. Med., *87*, 315-328.

Hirst, G. K., Rickard, E. R., Whitman, L., and Horsfall, F. L., Jr., 1942, Antibody response of human beings following vaccination with influenza viruses. J. Exp. Med., *75*, 495-511.

Hirst, G. K., Rickard, E. R., and Friedewald, W. F., 1944, Studies in human immunization against influenza. Duration of immunity induced by inactive virus. J. Exp. Med., *80*, 265-273.

Horsfall, F. L., Jr., 1939, Neutralization of epidemic influenza virus. The linear relationship between the quantity of serum and the quantity of virus neutralized. J. Exp. Med., *70*, 209-222.

Horsfall, F. L., Jr., 1940, Present status of knowledge concerning influenza. Am. J. Pub. Health, *30*, 1302-1310.

Horsfall, F. L., Jr., and Lennette, E. H., 1940, The synergism of human influenza and canine distemper viruses in ferrets. J. Exp. Med., *72*, 247-259.

Horsfall, F. L., Jr., and Lennette, E. H., 1941, Neutralization of influenza A virus by human serum. J. Exp. Med., *73*, 327-333.

Horsfall, F. L., Jr., Hahn, R. G., and Rickard, E. R., 1940a, Four recent influenza epidemics; an experimental study. J. Clin. Investig., *19*, 379-392.

Horsfall, F. L., Jr., Lennette, E. H., Rickard, E. R., Andrewes, C. H., Smith, W., and Stuart-Harris, C. H., 1940b, The nomenclature of influenza. Lancet, *2*, 413-414.

Horsfall, F. L., Jr., Lennette, E. H., Rickard, E. R., and Hirst, G. K., 1941, Studies on the efficacy of a complex vaccine against influenza A. Pub. Health Rep., 56, 1863-1875.

Hoyle, L., 1948, The growth cycle of influenza virus A. A study of the relations between virus, soluble antigen and host cell in fertile eggs inoculated with influenza virus. Brit. J. Exp. Path., 29, 390-399.

Hoyle, L., and Fairbrother, R. W., 1937, Antigenic structure of influenza viruses; the preparation of elementary body suspensions and the nature of the complement-fixing antigen. J. Hyg., 37, 512-520.

Isaacs, A., and Edney, M., 1950, Variation in laboratory stocks of influenza viruses: genetic aspects of the variations. Brit. J. Exp. Path., 31, 209-216.

Kilbourne, E. D., Anderson, H. C., and Horsfall, F. L., 1951, Concurrent infection with influenza A and B viruses in a single epidemic of influenza. J. Immunol., 67, 547-558.

Knight, C. A., 1946, Precipitin reactions of highly purified influenza viruses and related materials. J. Exp. Med., 83, 281-294.

Knight, C. A., 1947, The nucleic acid and carbohydrate of influenza virus. J. Exp. Med., 85, 99-116.

Lauffer, M. A., and Miller, G. L., 1944, The sedimentation rate of the biological activities of influenza A virus. J. Exp. Med., 80, 521-529.

Lauffer, M. A., and Stanley, W. M., 1944, Biophysical properties of preparations of PR8 influenza virus. J. Exp. Med., 80, 531-548.

Lennette, E. H., and Horsfall, F. L., Jr., 1940, Studies on epidemic influenza virus. The nature and properties of the complement-fixing antigen. J. Exp. Med., 72, 233-246.

Lennette, E. H., and Horsfall, F. L., Jr., 1941, Studies on influenza virus. The complement-fixing antigen of influenza A and swine influenza viruses. J. Exp. Med., 73, 581-599.

Lennette, E. H., and Koprowski, H., 1946, Interference between viruses in tissue culture. J. Exp. Med., 83, 195-219.

Lennette, E. H., Rickard, E. R., Hirst, G. K., and Horsfall, F. L., Jr., 1941, The diverse etiology of epidemic influenza. Pub. Health Rep., 56, 1777-1788.

Magill, T. P., 1940, A virus from cases of influenza-like upper-respiratory infection. Proc. Soc. Exp. Biol. and Med., 45, 162-164.

Magill, T. P., 1941, Repeated attacks of influenza. Proc. Soc. Exp. Biol. and Med., 46, 316-318.

Magill, T. P., and Francis, T., Jr., 1936, Antigenic differences in strains of human influenza virus. Proc. Soc. Exp. Biol. and Med., 35, 463-466.

Magill, T. P., and Francis, T., Jr., 1938, Antigenic differences in strains of epidemic influenza virus: I. Cross-neutralization tests in mice. Brit. J. Exp. Path., 19, 273-284.

Magill, T. P., and Sugg, J. Y., 1944, The significance of antigenic differences among strains of the "A group" of influenza viruses. J. Exp. Med., 80, 1-7.

Members of the Commission on Influenza, Army Epidemiological Board, 1944, A clinical evaluation of vaccination against influenza. Preliminary report. J. Am. Med. Assn., 124, 982-985.

Miller, G. L., 1944, Influence of pH and of certain other conditions on the stability of the infectivity and red cell agglutinating activity of influenza virus. J. Exp. Med., 80, 507-520.

Miller, G. L., Lauffer, M. A., and Stanley, W. M., 1944, Electrophoretic studies on PR8 influenza virus. J. Exp. Med., 80, 549-559.

Nigg, C., Crowley, J. H., and Wilson, D. E., 1940, On the use of chick embryo cultures of influenza virus in complement fixation tests. Science, 91, 603-604.

Rickard, E. R., and Francis, T., Jr., 1938, The demonstration of lesions and virus in the lungs of mice receiving large intraperitoneal inoculations of epidemic influenza virus. J. Exp. Med., 67, 953-972.

Rickard, E. R., Horsfall, F. L., Jr., Hirst, G. K., and Lennette, E. H., 1941, The correlation between neutralizing antibodies in serum against influenza viruses and susceptibility to influenza in man. Pub. Health Rep., 56, 1819-1834.

Rickard, E. R., Lennette, E. H., and Horsfall, F. L., Jr., 1940, A comprehensive study of influenza in a rural community. Pub. Health Rep., 55, 2146-2167.

Salk, J. E., 1944, A simplified procedure for titrating hemagglutinating capacity of influenza-virus and the corresponding antibody. J. Immunol., 49, 87-98.

Salk, J. E., Menke, W. J., Jr., and Francis, T., Jr., 1945, A clinical, epidemiological and immunological evaluation of vaccination against epidemic influenza. Am. J. Hyg., 42, 57-93.

Salk, J. E., and Suriano, P. C., 1949, Importance of antigenic composition of influenza virus vaccine in protecting against the natural disease. Am. J. Pub. Health, 39, 345-355.

Scadding, J. G., 1937, Lung changes in influenza. Quart. J. Med., 6, 425-465.

Schlesinger, R. W., 1950, Incomplete growth cycle of influenza virus in mouse brain. Proc. Soc. Exp. Biol. and Med., 74, 541-548.

Sharp, D. G., Taylor, A. R., McLean, I. W., Jr., Beard, D., Beard, J. W., Feller, A. E., and Dingle, J. H., 1944, Isolation and characterization of influenza virus B (Lee strain). J. Immunol., 48, 129-153.

Smith, W., 1935, Cultivation of the virus of influenza. Brit. J. Exp. Path., 16, 508-512.

Smith, W., 1936, The complement-fixation reaction in influenza. Lancet, 2, 1256-1259.

Smith, W., Andrewes, C. H., and Laidlaw, P. P., 1933, A virus obtained from influenza patients. Lancet, 2, 66-68.

Smith, W., and Stuart-Harris, C. H., 1936, Influenza infection of man from the ferret. Lancet, 2, 121-123.

Smorodintseff, A. A., Tushinsky, M. D., Drobyshevskaya, A. I., Korovin, A. A., and Osetroff, A. I., 1937, Investigations on volunteers infected with the influenza virus. Am J. Med. Sci., 194, 159-170.

Straub, M., 1937, The microscopical changes in the lungs of mice infected with influenza virus. J. Path. and Bact., 45, 75-78.

Stuart-Harris, C. H., 1939, A neurotropic strain of human influenza virus. Lancet, 1, 497-499.

Sugg, J. Y., and Magill, T. P., 1947, Susceptibility of convalescent ferrets to reinfection with influenza virus in absence of specific antibodies. Proc. Soc. Exp. Biol. and Med., *65*, 233-235.

Svedmyr, A., 1947, Studies on a factor in normal allantoic fluid inhibiting influenza virus hemagglutination. Ark. Kemi, Mineral. och Geol., 24B, No. 11.

Tamm, I., and Horsfall, F. L., Jr., 1952, A mucoprotein derived from human urine which reacts with influenza, mumps, and Newcastle disease viruses. J. Exp. Med., *95*, 71-97.

Taylor, R. M., 1940, Detection of human influenza virus in throat washings by immunity response in Syrian Hamster (*Cricetus auratus*). Proc. Soc. Exp. Biol. and Med., *43*, 541-542.

Taylor, R. M., 1941, Experimental infection with influenza A virus in mice. The increase in intra-pulmonary virus after inoculation and the influence of various factors thereon. J. Exp. Med., *73*, 43-55.

Taylor, R. M., 1949, Studies on survival of influenza virus between epidemics and antigenic variants of the virus. Am. J. Pub. Health, *39*, 171-178.

Taylor, R. M., 1951, A further note on 1233 ("Influenza C") virus. Arch. f. d. ges. Virusforsch., *4*, 485-500.

Thalmann, W. G., Kempe, C. H., Worrall, J. A., and Meiklejohn, G., 1950, Aureomycin in the treatment of influenza: a controlled study. J. Am. Med. Assn., *144*, 1156-1157.

Vilches, A., and Hirst. G. K., 1947, Interference between neurotropic and other unrelated viruses. J. Immunol., *57*, 125-140.

Walker, D. L., and Horsfall, F. L., Jr., 1950, Lack of identity in neutralizing and hemagglutination-inhibiting antibodies against influenza viruses. J. Exp. Med., *91*, 65-86.

Whitman, L., 1947, Factors influencing the red cell agglutination-inhibitive reaction in influenza and their application to the diagnostic test. J. Immunol., *56*, 167-177.

Wiener, M., Henle, W., and Henle, G., 1946, Studies on the complement fixation antigens of influenza viruses Types A and B. J. Exp. Med., *83*, 259-279.

Winternitz, M. C., Wason, I. M., and McNamara, F. P., 1920, The Pathology of Influenza. New Haven, Yale University Press, pp. 1-61.

Ziegler, J. E., Jr., and Horsfall, F. L., Jr., 1944, Interference between the influenza viruses. I. The effect of active virus upon the multiplication of influenza viruses in the chick embryo. J. Exp. Med., *79*, 361-377.

Ziegler, J. E., Jr., Lavin, G. I., and Horsfall, F. L., Jr., 1944, Interference between the influenza viruses. II. The effect of virus rendered noninfective by ultraviolet radiation upon the multiplication of influenza viruses in the chick embryo. J. Exp. Med., *79*, 379-400.

JOSEPH E. SMADEL, M.D.

Army Medical Service Graduate School

19

Smallpox and Vaccinia

INTRODUCTION

Smallpox has been a pestilence afflicting man since antiquity. Jennerian prophylaxis, introduced a century and a half ago, provided a means for controlling the scourge. Nevertheless, epidemics of smallpox continue to occur throughout the world, and it is only by constant vigilance that these are checked. Smallpox and vaccinia are caused by two closely related but distinct viruses. The former affects man primarily, being maintained in nature by transmission from one human being to another without the aid of vectors or animal reservoirs. Vaccine virus, the agent of cowpox, is indigenous to cattle, causing a mild disease in its natural host and in man; it derives its medical significance from its capacity to immunize against smallpox. Variola and vaccinia have been important for so long a time and have been investigated so thoroughly that their literature is voluminous. In this chapter emphasis will be placed on the disease caused by variola virus and on the nature of the virus of vaccinia.

SMALLPOX

(SYNONYMS: Variola, *petite vérole*, *Blattern*)

HISTORY

One of the earliest accounts of smallpox concerns an epidemic in China in 1122 B.C. The disease was known in ancient India and is believed to have occurred from time immemorial among the Negroes of Central Africa. Numerous epidemics were described in the Middle East and in France during the first millennium of the Christian era, and wide dissemination resulted from the Crusades. Smallpox was introduced into the western hemisphere shortly after the first voyage of Columbus and rapidly spread through Central and South America. The African slave trade contributed to its continued prevalence in North America (Woody, 1932).

A subject of historic and epidemiologic interest is the variation in mortality rate in different epidemics of variola. The fatality rates in the famous outbreaks of history were generally high, often reaching or exceeding 30 per cent. Furthermore, in certain areas, notably India, the mortality has been high in recent times; thus, between 1926 and 1930, among the 979,738 cases reported in British India, the deaths per 100 patients were 42.3. In contrast, 381,890 cases of smallpox were reported in the United States during the years 1921 to 1930, and the fatality rate in this group was only 0.9 per cent (Hedrich, 1936). As a result of such findings, smallpox is generally classified as variola major and variola minor; a number of synonyms have been applied to the latter in various parts of the world, such as alastrim, Cuban itch, amaas, Kaffir-pox and milk-pox. While differences in mortality rate such as those mentioned above are dependent upon many factors, it is the consensus that the severe and mild types of smallpox exist as stable entities.

CLINICAL PICTURE

The classical picture of smallpox observed during epidemics is so constant and so readily recognized that it will be discussed only briefly. Cases of smallpox which do not conform to the textbook picture are of particular importance, since the lack of their recognition results in failure to apply control measures which are effective in stopping the spread of the disease.

The typical picture of smallpox is as follows: 12 days after exposure to variola virus, a patient develops chills, prostration, headache, severe backache, vomiting, and fever of about 103° F. These prodromata continue for 3 or 4 days during which time a fleeting rash of indefinite type may be detected; at the end of this period, the eruption appears and the temperature falls close to the normal range. The rash begins as a discrete papular eruption on the face, but rapidly appears on the extremities and trunk; later it may become confluent in many areas. It involves the palms and soles as well as the buccal and pharyngeal mucosa. Fewer lesions appear on the trunk than on the extremities; thus, the distribution is centrifugal. After several days the papules become vesicular, and by about the tenth day after onset of fever they are pustular. A photograph of a patient with the typical pustular eruption of smallpox is reproduced in Figure 39. The pustules begin to dry and generally are crusted over by the end of the second week, the scabs dropping off about the end of the third week. Practically all of the lesions in one area simultaneously undergo transition from the papular to vesicular and thence to the pustular stage. With the onset of the pustular stage, fever generally returns and persists for several days at a level of 101°-102° F. A mild leukopenia often occurs

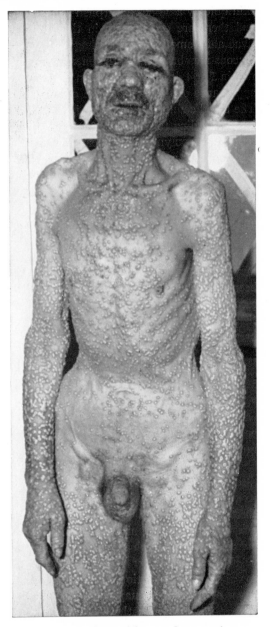

FIG. 39. Patient with pustular eruption of smallpox.

during the preeruptive stage while a moderate leukocytosis appears with pustulation.

A fulminating, purpuric type of smallpox which may not be recognized as a variolous infection is characterized below. On the second or the third day of fever a diffuse, hyperemic rash appears, beginning as small punctate hemorrhages in the skin. The skin quickly assumes a purplish appearance and there are ecchymoses in the conjunctivae and sometimes hemorrhages from the mucous membranes. Death generally results within 3 or 4 days after onset and before the appearance of the typical rash of smallpox. The blood count in these cases is characterized, according to Ikeda (1925), by a sharp reduction in polymorphonuclear cells, thrombocytopenia, and marked lymphocytosis; thus, the picture may resemble leukemia. In another type of hemorrhagic smallpox, bleeding may be delayed until the rash has appeared, in which case hemorrhage may occur into or between the lesions. Death usually occurs quickly in this type also, but may be delayed until the pustular stage has been reached. It is of interest that an unrecognized case of hemorrhagic smallpox of this latter type was responsible for the outbreak in New York City in 1947 (Greenberg, 1947).

The term varioloid is used to designate a mild type of variola which occurs in partially immune persons who have been vaccinated successfully a number of years previously. The prodromal symptoms are rarely severe; the rash is discrete and may be scanty. The lesions usually proceed through their appointed course of development at a more rapid rate than in the classical disease, and no secondary rise in temperature accompanies pustulation. During an epidemic, such cases may easily be overlooked, but they serve as means of spreading the infection. Extremely mild forms of the disease may occur without the appearance of pocks; these are usually encountered in recently vaccinated persons. The diagnosis of *variola sine exanthem* has generally been made on epidemiologic evidence (Conybeare, 1939), but with laboratory technics now available it should be possible to establish unequivocally the etiology of such cases by isolation of virus or demonstration of rise in specific antibodies during convalescence.

Pyogenic infections of various types are the most common complications which arise in smallpox. Terminal bronchopneumonia of greater or lesser extent occurs in practically all fatal cases. Bacteremia is frequent in patients who succumb. Thus, Councilman and co-workers (1904) obtained blood cultures at 11 autopsies and recovered a streptococcus from 9, a pneumococcus from one, and a staphylococcus from one; Ikeda (1925) found hemolytic streptococci in 8 of 9 postmortem cultures and an indifferent streptococcus in the remaining one.

Variations in the mortality in different epidemics of smallpox and in the several types of smallpox in a given outbreak are well illustrated in the report of Sweitzer and Ikeda (1927). These authors observed that variola minor was relatively common in Minnesota from 1913 to 1923, when there were 35,152 cases and 108 deaths. An outbreak of variola major occurred in Minneapolis in 1924-25 with 1,430 cases and 365 deaths. During the epidemic 581 patients were treated in one hospital and 246, or 42 per cent, died. This group was subdivided as follows: 10 unclassified type, no deaths; 225 discrete type, 14 deaths; 151 confluent type, 68 deaths; 144 hemorrhagic type, 113 deaths; 51 purpuric type, 51 deaths.

PATHOLOGIC PICTURE

Death from smallpox generally occurs about the end of the second week of illness, but in the purpuric type it may take place early in the first week. Little has been added to the knowledge of the pathology of variola since the careful studies of Councilman, Magrath and Brinckerhoff (1904) who examined materials collected during an epidemic in Boston. These workers grouped the pathologic changes under three headings: (A) those fundamentally specific and peculiar to the disease; (B) changes analogous to those present in many of the infectious diseases but in degree characteristic of smallpox; and (C) those caused by secondary factors such as bacteria. Their summary of the patho-logic anatomy of variola is quoted below.

A. The specific lesion.

1. The specific lesion of variola is a focal degeneration of stratified epithelium, vacuolar in character, and accompanied by serous exudation and the formation of a reticulum.

2. The fully developed product of these processes is a characteristic multilocular pock, or pustule.

3. The occurrence of these lesions is sharply limited to the stratified epithelium of the skin and of the mucous membranes of the soft palate, the pharynx, and the esophagus. . . .

6. The typical lesion is best seen in the skin. It begins with degeneration of the cells of the lower layers of the epidermis, accom-panied by exudation, at first serous, later more or less cellular, the products of which are contained within the spaces of a reticulum formed by the degenerated cells. The exudate increases in amount and the spaces of the reticulum enlarge until its fibers finally rup-ture, and the lesion becomes a filled-out pustule. This development may take place wholly within the epidermis, and the fluid contents of the pock be separated from the corium by comparatively intact cells; or the corium may form the bottom of the pustule, in which case there is usually necrosis of the papillary border.

7. The subsidence and the repair of the lesion are accomplished by the removal of the fluid portion of the exudate by absorption and by drying, and by the regeneration of the epidermis, in the course of which the residual mass of degenerated epithelial cells, leuco-cytes, and debris, enclosed between two layers of horny epidermis, the old and the newly-formed, is exfoliated. The complete evolution of the lesion occupies about two weeks. . . .

10. Contained within these lesions of the skin and the mucous membrane and determin-ing their specificity and occurring chiefly in the cells of the rete mucosum is the parasite* peculiar to variola; in its younger or cytoplasmic form it is present in the proto-plasm of the epithelial cells of early lesions and of such of the older lesions as are extend-ing; in its intranuclear form it is for the most part in lesions more advanced. No parasites have been found in any lesions of the skin in which repair was well advanced. . . .

B. Associated lesions of indeterminate specificity.

1. Proliferation within the hematopoietic organs is constant and well-marked, and gives rise in the spleen, the lymph nodes, and the bone marrow to the formation of mononuclear, basophilic cells, and in the lymph nodes and the marrow to phagocytic endothelial cells. The former pass into the blood in large numbers. This process is present to some degree in other infectious diseases, but is here so prominent as to be well-nigh characteristic.

2. Cellular infiltration with the mononu-clear basophilic elements above mentioned, focal and interstitial in distribution, occurs constantly in the testicle, and usually in the kidney, in the liver, and in the adrenal glands. In the testicle this infiltration, by pressure and by thrombosis, causes anemic focal necrosis, lesions which seem to be specific of the disease.

3. Degeneration, focal in character, ap-parently not anemic, but due to the action of toxines, and leading to necrosis, at times with hemorrhage, and accompanied by focal forma-tion of phagocytic cells, is present in the blood-forming cells of the bone marrow, and constitutes a lesion almost pathognomonic, but devoid of parasites. Diffuse degeneration, toxic in character, is present in the liver, the kidney, the adrenal gland, and the testicle; in the liver cloudy swelling is more marked than it is in any other acute infectious disease.

Otherwise, the degeneration is not to be dis-tinguished from that due to bacterial infec-tion. . . .

5. The paucity of polynuclear leucocytes, alike in the specific lesions, in the focal de-generations, and in the bone marrow, is a con-dition so constant and so pronounced as to render it a striking peculiarity of the disease.

Although Councilman and his co-workers described in detail the pulmonary lesions in their cases, they did not mention them in their summary quoted above. In view of the modern interest in pulmonary lesions associated with viral infections, certain of their statements bearing on this point are added.

---

* These authors were influenced by the work of Guarnieri (1892) who described the cytoplasmic inclu-sions of variola and regarded them as protozoan para-sites to which he gave the name *Cytoryctes variolae*. Councilman, Magrath and Brinckerhoff, who were the first to observe the intranuclear inclusions in variola, thought that these represented another stage in the development of the parasite. The modern con-cept that the viruses of variola and vaccinia are not protozoan parasites but elementary bodies with a diameter of about 200 mμ, is discussed elsewhere in the chapter.

The most common lesion found in the lungs, and one which is very rarely absent, is bronchitis, usually combined with more or less extensive broncho-pneumonia. This was found microscopically in cases in which there was no macroscopic evidence of it. . . . The exudate in the lungs contained great numbers of polynuclear leucocytes. . . . Interstitial lesions consisting of focal infiltration of the tissue around the bronchi and around the blood vessels of the lung were found in a number of cases. These did not seem to have any relation with the purely exudative lesions. The cells found in these interstitial foci were the large basophilic cells and a small number of phagocytic cells.

The cytoplasmic and intranuclear inclusions found in tissues infected with variola virus are of sufficient interest to warrant a brief description. The cytoplasmic inclusions, generally designated Guarnieri (1892) bodies, are large circular or oval structures having a diameter up to 10 μ. They are found in human and animal tissues infected with either variola or vaccinia virus and are homogeneous acidophilic masses lying in the cytoplasm close to the nucleus. There may be one or more in a cell and each one is usually surrounded by a clear unstained zone. Although they may occur in almost any type of tissue under experimental conditions, in smallpox of man they are found almost exclusively in lesions of skin and mucous membrane. Councilman and co-workers (1904) found inclusions in their human materials up to the tenth day of the disease, i.e., six days after the appearance of rash, at a time when the lesions were vesicular or becoming pustular. They were not able to find inclusions after the thirteenth day of the disease. Thus, the majority of patients dying from smallpox do not provide suitable material for studies of this type. Guarnieri bodies are found most readily in cells of the rete mucosum at the edge of an extending vesicle or in the early lesions of purpuric smallpox. Opinions have differed as to the exact nature of Guarnieri bodies. Himmelweit (1938) studied the development of these structures in situ by direct microscopic examination of chorio-allantoic membranes infected with vaccinia and concluded that they consist of a collection of elementary bodies contained in a matrix; this general concept is concurred in by most investigators who have worked recently with vaccine virus (Bland and Robinow, 1939; Eisenberg-Merling, 1940) and by Downie and Dumbell (1947a) who studied variola virus.

The intranuclear inclusions of variola are found in the lesions of man and monkeys (Magrath and Brinckerhoff, 1904) but have not been clearly observed in infected chorio-allantoic membranes (Buddingh, 1938; Downie and Dumbell, 1947a). These inclusions do not occur in the lesions of vaccinia. Torres (1935-36) points out minor differences in the tinctorial and morphologic properties of intranuclear structures in variola major and alastrim. The intranuclear inclusions of variola are single or multiple, round or oval, acidophilic structures which are separated from the thickened nuclear membrane by an unstained halo. They are rarely, if ever, found in a cell which contains a Guarnieri body. Little work has been done on the intranuclear inclusions of variola in recent years and their relation to the infective particle of the virus is unknown. Although characteristic for the variolous lesion, they may be independent of the viral agent itself; it may be noted that intranuclear inclusions can be found in lesions produced by nonviral materials (Olitsky and Harford, 1937).

EXPERIMENTAL INFECTION; HOST RANGE

Variolation has been practiced since long before the Christian era. Thus, the agent of smallpox was the first virus to be employed in planned transmission experiments. Blaxall (1930a) states:

The Chinese applied powdered old crusts to the nostrils; the Brahmins in India used preserved crusts and inoculated the skin, generally of the arm or forehead; the Persians ingested prepared crusts. In Europe the practice mostly in vogue was to take fluid from pocks as exhibited in a mild case and to apply this to the skin scarified by needle or lancet, or after the application of blisters. As experience grew, greater care was exercised in the selection of the material used, and it became customary to take clear fluid only from vesicles in the early stage.

Following variolation by the European method, the lesion at the site of inoculation goes through a stage of development similar to the primary reaction in vaccinia (see section on Control Measures for a detailed description of this). About the eleventh day after inoculation, a pock eruption appears with up to several hundred lesions distributed over the body. These go through the usual stages and generally heal without scar formation. Thus, the result of variolation is a local lesion followed by systemic disease similar in many respects to varioloid.

A disease resembling varioloid in man is induced in a number of species of anthropoids inoculated with variola virus. The histopathology of the experimental disease is similar to that of smallpox in man (Magrath and Brinckerhoff, 1904; Brinckerhoff and Tyzzer, 1906). The monkey appears to be the only animal able to contract variola under natural conditions. An epidemic of smallpox in Brazil is reported to have been associated with an epizootic among Mycetes and Cebus monkeys in the area; the bodies of sick and dead animals were covered with variolous pustules (Blaxall, 1930a).

A number of animal species is slightly susceptible to infection with variola virus. Difficulties have arisen, because certain of these, notably the rabbit and calf, are highly susceptible to vaccine virus, and vaccinia has usually been studied in laboratories engaged in work on variola. As a result, many reports of so-called primary isolations of variola virus in animals and the subsequent transformation of it to vaccine virus during passage are now discounted (Horgan, 1938; Nelson, 1943).

Rabbits inoculated on the scarified cornea with lymph from smallpox pustules develop a keratitis with some frequency; this is the basis for Paul's test which has been employed as a diagnostic procedure. The intracutaneous injection of variolous material induces a local reaction in normal rabbits; McKinnon and Defries (1928) considered this helpful in the laboratory diagnosis of smallpox. Although the inoculation of smallpox material into the skin of the rabbit is now rarely employed as a direct diagnostic method, it is useful in differentiating between variola and vaccinia viruses which have been grown on the chorio-allantoic membranes of embryonated eggs. It is difficult, if not impossible, to propagate variola virus by serial passage in the rabbit, whereas vaccine virus multiplies readily in this host.

The agent of smallpox grows well on the chorio-allantoic membrane of embryonated eggs producing pocklike lesions rich in virus (Torres and Teixeira, 1935; Lazarus, Eddie and Meyer, 1937). Buddingh (1938) studied the pathologic reaction in this host and recommended that the chorio-allantois be used for the diagnostic isolation of the virus. Lesions which develop on infected membranes differ in no significant way from those induced by vaccinia. Nelson (1943) and Downie and Dumbell (1947a) noted differences in the lesions caused by their strains of variola and vaccinia viruses, but different strains of vaccine virus can produce distinguishable types of lesions on the chorio-allantois (Buddingh, 1936). The titer of virus in passage membranes is of the order of 10^{-7} when tested on the chorio-allantois. The virus may be maintained by serial transfer in the yolk sac where the infectivity reaches 10^{-6}. While certain strains of variola rarely kill inoculated embryos (Nelson, 1943), the author's experience with a number of recently isolated strains has been that death regularly occurs on the third or fourth day following inoculation of the chorio-allantois or the yolk sac.

ETIOLOGY

The nature of variola virus has not been elucidated so clearly as has that of the closely related agent of vaccinia. Only in the last decade has a highly satisfactory laboratory host for propagating variola become available; the increasing use of the chorio-allantois of the embryonated egg for growing the virus may be expected to provide suitable material for studies which will supply the needed knowledge.

Fluid from variola lesions contains numerous elementary bodies, which are small, spherical structures having a diameter of about 200 mμ. These were first described in 1887 by Buist (Gordon, 1937) who believed that they represented the contagium of variola and vaccinia. Paschen (1906) redescribed these structures which are sometimes referred to as Paschen bodies. It is now generally assumed that the elementary body of variola represents the virus. This assumption is based largely on the accumulated results obtained during the past 20 years in studies of the closely related virus of vaccinia; the elementary body of vaccinia is the virus. Elementary bodies are stained by certain of the aniline dyes; the method of Paschen is generally used (van Rooyen and Illingworth, 1944). The silver technic of Morosow (1926) has also been employed for staining the virus particles in smears of human material and of infected chorio-allantoic membranes (Buddingh, 1938).

Variola virus is quite stable. It can be dried under relatively unfavorable conditions and still retain its viability. This stability is of great assistance in diagnostic studies, since a specimen of the virus for examination can be shipped without refrigeration. This property is also important in the spread of smallpox. Thus, Downie and Dumbell (1947b) found that desquamated crusts which were stored in a stoppered bottle for a year at room temperature contained viable virus. Such stability probably accounts for their observation that dust collected from a patient's room contained active virus and may explain the outbreaks of smallpox among laundry workers who handled contaminated bed clothes (Stallybrass, 1931). Variola virus remains viable for long periods of time when stored at —70° C. and —20° C., or in 50 per cent glycerol, or when dried either by simple methods or by lyophilization. The infectivity of variolous crusts suspended in saline solution is destroyed by heating at 55° C. for a half hour (Gordon, 1925).

Immunologic and serologic studies indicate an extremely close relationship between variola and vaccinia viruses. The classical observation of Jenner (1798) that infection with vaccinia protects man against variola serves as a bulwark in preventive medicine. The presence of common antigens and antibodies, demonstrable by in-vitro and in-vivo technics, in variola and vaccinia has been the basis for numerous communications. A number of the more recent of these are discussed in the section dealing with the etiology of vaccinia; others are reviewed by Gordon (1925), Blaxall (1930a), and van Rooyen and Rhodes (1948).

DIAGNOSIS

Diagnosis of smallpox during an epidemic is relatively simple. On the other hand, too much emphasis cannot be laid on the importance of the early recognition of the first case which appears in a community, because not infrequently it is missed. Findings during the initial stage of smallpox may suggest influenza or the prodromal phase of many infectious diseases. The eruption of varioloid may be confused with that of varicella. It will be recalled, however, that in the latter disease lesions of different age are found near each other in the same area of skin. In addition, the cutaneous lesions in varicella are more plentiful on the trunk than on the extremities. Severe hemorrhagic forms of smallpox may resemble septicemia, particularly that occurring during a meningococcal infection. Much emphasis has been placed in recent years on laboratory procedures which aid in the diagnosis of smallpox. These are important, but it should be remembered that the diagnosis of smallpox on clinical evidence is generally possible and that the institution of preventive measures should be begun as soon as the diagnosis is considered, without waiting for results of laboratory tests.

Laboratory diagnostic procedures for smallpox are of two general types: (1) direct demonstration by serologic technics of the virus or its specific antigens in materials from the cutaneous lesions, and (2) isolation and identification of the virus from such materials. Methods of the first type enable a worker to report results within a short time after receipt of a specimen, whereas those of the second type may not be expected to give interpretable data for three or four days.

Details of the various types of laboratory tests for the diagnosis of smallpox are given in an article by Parker (1948). The presence of complement-fixing antigen, specific for variola-vaccinia, in materials from skin lesions has been demonstrated by several groups of workers (Gordon, 1925; Parker and Muckenfuss, 1932; Craigie and Wishart, 1936a; Downie, 1946). This type of complement-fixation test has been found satisfactory for diagnostic purposes, and is recommended as the procedure of choice for quick results. The finding of specific complement-fixing antigen in the blood of a severely ill patient in the preeruptive stage (MacCallum, McPherson and Johnstone, 1950) is of considerable interest from the point of view of a potential diagnostic procedure applicable in early cases; the subject is worth further investigation. Isolation of variola virus on the chorio-allantoic membrane of an embryonated hen's egg is considered a suitable diagnostic procedure by Buddingh (1938), who pointed out

that this agent, as well as that of vaccinia, produces pocks on the membrane, whereas materials from patients with varicella do not. Buddingh's findings have been confirmed by Irons et al. (1941) and Downie and Dumbell (1947a).

The diagnostic isolation method employed at the Army Medical Service Graduate School is summarized below:

The surfaces of several vesicular or pustular lesions are cleaned with an ether-soaked pledget of cotton, and the tops are opened

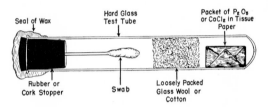

FIG. 40. Mailing tube to be used for transportation of vesicular fluid for isolation of smallpox virus. One gram of phosphorus pentoxide is wrapped carefully but loosely in one layer of tissue paper and placed in the bottom of a 16 x 150 mm. tube. It is essential to avoid contaminating the inside of the tube with the desiccant, since virus on the swab would be destroyed by contact with the drying agent. A loose plug of glass wool is inserted to hold the desiccant in place. The swab stick is stuck in the cork in a manner so that the swab itself does not touch the sides of the tube. The tube is sealed by immersing the stopper in melted paraffin. Calcium chloride may be used if P_2O_5 is not available.

with a sharp sterile instrument. Material from the lesions is collected on a sterile swab, which is placed in a special dehydrating tube for shipment. A diagram of this specimen tube is presented in Figure 40. The tube is shipped by air mail and on arrival the swab is washed with 2.0 cc. of saline solution containing 100 units of penicillin per cc. 0.1 cc. amounts of the solution are inoculated on the dropped chorio-allantoic membranes of 10-day embryonated eggs. After 3 days, the eggs are examined and material is taken from those showing lesions. A portion of this is reserved for passage to eggs and animals. A 10 per cent suspension of the infected membranes is pre-

CASES OF SMALLPOX REPORTED IN THE UNITED STATES 1921 TO 1944

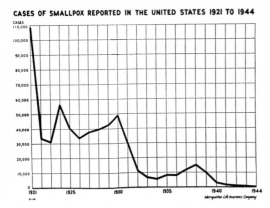

CHART 25. Cases of smallpox reported in the United States, 1921-1944. (Dublin, L. I., 1945, The conquest of smallpox. Statistical Bulletin Metropolitan Life Insurance Company, *29*, 8.)

pared and clarified by centrifugation in a horizontal machine at 2,000 r.p.m. for 10 minutes. The supernatant fluid is employed as antigen in a complement-fixation test with rabbit antivaccinal serum. Serial dilutions of the antigen and appropriate dilutions of rabbit antivaccinal serum known to contain two units of S antibody or L antibody are mixed, after which two units of complement are placed in the tubes and the mixtures are incubated at 37° C. for 2½ hours. The readings are made in the usual manner after addition of the hemolytic system and further incubation. Such preparations of antigen from first passage membranes infected with variolous material have complement-fixation titers of $\frac{1}{16}$ to $\frac{1}{128}$. A positive result at this stage permits the report of isolation of a virus of the variola-vaccinia group. Such a diagnosis is usually sufficient for the physician or health officer. The identification of the exact type of virus is made by determination of its pathogenicity for rabbits or mice.

Nelson (1943) found that his two strains of variola virus grown on the chorioallantois were nonpathogenic for rabbit skin. Thus, differentiation of his strains from the virus of vaccinia could be accomplished in the first inoculated rabbit. In the writer's experience, 10^{-3} or 10^{-4} dilutions of emulsions of membranes infected with recently isolated strains of variola virus induce lesions upon intra-

cutaneous inoculation of a rabbit which are indistinguishable from those caused by vaccine virus; however, passage of material from such lesions in a rabbit to a second rabbit induces no cutaneous response, a fact which immediately differentiates it from vaccine virus. The fact that mice injected intracerebrally with suspensions of variolous membranes die within a few days but passage mice do not succumb also aids in strain differentiation.

By inoculation of blood onto the chorioallantoic membrane of embryonated eggs (Downie, McCarthy and MacDonald, 1950; MacCallum, McPherson and Johnstone, 1950), viremia is demonstrable frequently during the first few days of fever, and for longer periods in severely ill patients. Thus, another diagnostic approach is available for selected cases. Virus is rarely present in the nose and the throat during the pre-eruptive stage but is found in some specimens taken several days after appearance of the eruption (MacCallum et al., 1950).

Until recently, demonstration of antibodies in a patient's serum was not employed often as a diagnostic measure because positive results came too late to be of importance to an individual or a community. Collier, Smit and Heerde (1950) have shown that specific antibodies which react with the viral hemagglutinins appear in the serum of patients with variola during the first few days of the pre-eruptive febrile illness. These increase rapidly, generally reaching titers of 1 in 2,000 by the end of the first week; they increase to 1 in 4,000 during the next few weeks and then slowly decline. As a result of observations on 800 Javanese patients with smallpox, they concluded that the procedure was helpful in the early diagnosis of the disease, especially in its differentiation from varicella. The occurrence in nonvaccinated persons of a moderately high titer of antihemagglutinins in a single specimen of serum taken at, or shortly after, the time of appearance of the eruption should permit a tentative diagnosis, but it would be preferable to demonstrate a rise in antibodies in several successive daily specimens.

TREATMENT

No specific therapy for variola is available. The most common complications of the disease are secondary bacterial infections; for these the use of the sulfonamide drugs, penicillin, or the newer antibiotics is indicated. Several workers (Wilkinson, 1942; Vengsarkar, Poonen and Walavalkar, 1942; Cottrell and Knights, 1943; Foulis, 1945; Anderson et al., 1951) have reported on the efficacy of the antibacterial drugs in variola, but carefully controlled observations were not made.

EPIDEMIOLOGY

Smallpox is transmitted from man to man by contact with a patient or his immediate surroundings. Lesions of the skin and mucous membranes are rich in virus and a patient thoroughly contaminates the area which he occupies. The stability of variola virus is such that on ordinary materials it retains its activity for some time. Thus, transmission of smallpox by contaminated bed clothes (Stallybrass, 1931) and by dust from a patient's room (Downie and Dumbell, 1947b) has been reported.

Blaxall (1930a) has emphasized the respiratory route of infection. Downie (1951) and MacCallum and his associates (1950) concur in this and consider the following as one hypothesis to account for the usual subsequent course of events. Inspired virus is disseminated from the respiratory tract via local lymph tissues and the blood stream to the viscera where it multiplies during the incubation period. With the release of virus from such sites, fever begins, and an appreciable viremia results in implantation of the pathogen at places in the skin, the mucous membranes and the viscera where focal lesions subsequently appear. Such patients would first become contagious when the lesions in the oral cavity break down and release virus, i.e., several days after the appearance of the rash. Recognizing that such a hypothesis would not explain the fact that some patients are capable of transmitting the disease during the pre-eruptive stage and the first days of the rash, MacCallum suggests that these persons develop a primary lesion in the respiratory mucosa which serves as an early source for external dissemination of the agent as well as for viremia. From the public health point of view one must regard a variola patient as potentially infectious during all stages of the illness until the scabs have exfoliated. Furthermore, the virus persists so long that the handling of a patient's body after death is a matter of considerable danger.

Smallpox occurs most frequently during the winter and is found in all regions and climates. Human beings are universally susceptible unless they possess immunity from previous infection or from vaccination. The annual numbers of cases of smallpox in the United States from 1921 to 1944 are presented graphically in Chart 25. During the years 1944 to 1951 the numbers of cases were 378, 334, 337, 173, 56, 56, 42 and 13, respectively.

The mortality rate in the United States during this period has remained low. Between 1921 and 1930 the fatality rate was 0.9 per cent (Hedrich, 1936). The greatest number of deaths in recent years was the 24 which occurred in 1946; five were reported in 1947 and in 1948 while only two were reported during 1949. The remarkable reduction in incidence of smallpox during the past three decades is a tribute to the vigorous application of control measures. However, one wonders why this success has been accomplished only recently, since the principles employed have been well known for many years. During World War II, 115 cases of smallpox with 24 deaths occurred in the United States Army.* During the winter of 1945 and 1946, however, 121 cases of smallpox developed among American troops in Korea and Japan and 25 of the patients

---

* Data supplied by the Preventive Medicine Division, Office of The Surgeon General.

died (Bull. U. S. Army Med. Dept., 1946). The British Army in the Middle East had 100 cases and 14 deaths (Illingworth and Oliver, 1944). When such episodes occur, the first assumption generally made is that the vaccine virus being used to immunize troops does not protect against a highly virulent local strain of variola virus. Such an assumption may be valid in certain instances, since strains of vaccine virus do differ in their immunizing capacity. However, Horgan and Haseeb (1945) consider these differences unimportant in the field control of smallpox. Moreover, it may be noted that, when the troops in the Far East were carefully revaccinated in 1945 and 1946 with potent vaccine virus shipped under proper conditions, smallpox in the military population was immediately controlled even though it continued in the native population.

Control Measures

The measures for control of smallpox which are recommended by the American Public Health Association (1950) and approved by the Public Health Service, the Army, the Navy and the Air Force, as well as numerous agencies of foreign governments, are as follows:

Methods of control:

A. Preventive measures:

1. General vaccination in early infancy, revaccination of children on entering school, and of entire population when the disease appears in a severe form.

2. Preservation of smallpox vaccine below freezing up to the hour of vaccination. This includes shipment between cakes of dry ice.

3. In order to avoid possible complications or secondary and subsequent infections at the site of vaccination, it is important that the vaccination insertion be as small and superficial as practicable, not over one-eighth inch in any direction, and that the site be kept dry and cool. The use of shields or dressings immediately after vaccination is to be condemned. The multiple pressure method is recommended. Primary vaccination at as early an age as possible is desirable with care to avoid vaccinating infants who have eczema, or allowing persons with eczema to come in contact with recently vaccinated persons. The time of vaccination should be adjusted to avoid skin lesions elsewhere on the body, and in older children to avoid the warmer months. Particular care should be used in primary vaccinations in persons beyond the age of infancy; leg vaccinations should be avoided. Previous immunity is not shown by the result of a vaccination unless a fully potent vaccine was used which had been kept continuously below freezing from the time of manufacture until the hour of use. If a firm indurated area develops at the site of revaccination within 3 days immediately following the use of a fully potent vaccine, immunity to smallpox can be reliably assumed. If no clear cut reaction occurs the person must be considered to be susceptible to smallpox and vaccination be repeated.

B. The infected individual, contacts, and environment:

1. Recognition of the disease and reporting: Clinical symptoms. The rapidly fatal or fulminating type and the very mild type may escape diagnosis until secondary cases appear. Isolation of the virus from vesicular and pustular fluid and the use of such materials as antigen in complement fixation tests is of value in establishing diagnosis in atypical cases, but administrative action must always be taken promptly when a diagnosis is based on clinical signs and symptoms of a case.

2. Isolation: Hospital isolation in screened wards until the period of infectivity is past.

3. Concurrent disinfection: All articles associated with the sick to be sterilized by high pressure steam; alternatively by boiling or by an equally effective method before removal from the sick room.

4. Terminal disinfection: Thorough cleaning and disinfection of premises.

5. Quarantine: Of all contacts until vaccinated with a vaccine of full potency and daily medical observation of these contacts until height of reaction is passed, if vaccination was performed within 24 hours of first exposure and the strain of smallpox was of the variola minor type; otherwise for 16 days from last exposure. Smallpox vaccine is of full potency if it gives at least 50 percent of vaccinoid reactions in persons revaccinated more than 10 years after their last successful vaccination. The reaction at the vaccination site should be carefully observed and recorded at least twice on the 3rd and 9th days after vaccination to determine whether the maximum diameter of redness was under 3 days (early reaction), over 7 days (vaccinia), or inter-

mediate between these two (vaccinoid). (In Great Britain contacts are kept under observation for 16 days after last exposure, even though vaccinated on the first day after exposure.)

6. Immunization: Vaccination. Only dermal vaccination is recommended. Vaccination by the multiple pressure method near the insertion of the deltoid muscle is recommended.

7. Investigation of source of infection: The immediate prior case should be sought assiduously, and cases of reported chickenpox associated in time or place carefully reviewed for error of diagnosis. Active cases of the disease without constitutional symptoms must be sought, also persons recently in contact with cases, and exposed vaccinated persons who may have developed unrecognized forms of the disease and thus be serving as sources of infection.

C. Epidemic measures:

1. Immediate and intense administrative publicity efforts and provision of service facilities to have the largest possible number of the community involved ask for or accept vaccination.

2. Rigorous enforcement of quarantine of all contacts until protected by successful vaccination.

3. Hospital care of all patients and suspects until no longer communicable.

4. Widespread education of the public by a frank statement of the situation from day to day with emphasis upon the primary obligation of every member of the community to be vaccinated at once in his own interest and for the sake of his family and neighbors.

D. International measures:

1. Notification: Each government should immediately notify the adjacent governments and at the same time WHO and the nearest WHO Regional Epidemiological Information Station, of the existence of an epidemic of smallpox. Every notification should be accompanied, or very promptly followed by the necessary detailed information. Subsequent communications should be sent regularly to WHO.

2. Measures on departure of vessels and aircraft (from an infected area): Prevention of the embarkation of persons showing symptoms of smallpox and of persons in such relations with the sick as to render themselves liable to transmit the infection; medical inspection of passengers and crew; inspection of personal effects, which should be accepted only if in a reasonable state of cleanliness;

disinfection of old garments and rags in the case of ships.

3. Measures on arrival of vessels and aircraft: Smallpox infected vessels or aircraft should be subjected to the following measures: medical inspection; immediate landing and isolation of patients; vaccination of other persons suspected of having been exposed to infection, if they are not sufficiently protected by recent vaccination or by a previous attack of smallpox. Such persons may also be subjected to observation or surveillance for a period not exceeding 14 days, reckoned from the date of arrival of the ship or aircraft; disinfection of personal effects, linen, and all other infected articles, disinfection of the parts of the ships or aircraft which have been occupied by the sick.

4. Vaccination: "Recent vaccination" should be taken as meaning evidence of successful vaccination not more than 3 years or less than 14 days previously, or evidence of an immune reaction.

5. Merchandise and Baggage: Body linen, wearing apparel, and bedding which have been in recent use, as well as rags may be subjected to disinfection.

6. Land traffic: The sanitary measures to be applied to land traffic should not exceed those laid down for air or sea traffic.

Smallpox vaccine is prepared from material collected from vaccinal lesions on the skin of calves; the virus in it is active or infectious. Methods of preparation and standardization of such calf-lymph virus, as well as the proper way of handling the material from the time it is manufactured until used for vaccination of human beings against smallpox, are carefully controlled. Regulations in force in the United States regarding these matters have been set forth in detail by the National Institute of Health (1946); those in force in the United Kingdom have been described by Blaxall (1930a).

There are three general types of reaction displayed by human beings inoculated with smallpox vaccine, namely, primary take, vaccinoid reaction or accelerated take, and immediate reaction (previously called the immune reaction). Plate 3 accurately portrays in color these reactions at different times after vaccination. A primary reaction or take represents an infection with cowpox virus in an individual who has had no previous infection with an agent of the variola-vaccinia group. In this type of reaction, an inflammatory lesion develops at the site of vaccination after an incubation period of several days and progresses through the stages of vesiculation, pustulation and scab formation. At the height of the cutaneous reaction lymphadenitis may develop in the nodes draining the area, and fever of several degrees may occur. A true exanthem, or generalized vaccinia, such as that induced regularly by variolation, occurs only rarely after vaccination. This is most likely to take place in children with skin diseases. Therefore, children with skin lesions, particularly eczema, should not be vaccinated unless definitely exposed to smallpox.

An immediate reaction following vaccination represents an allergic response to vaccinal materials; this appears rapidly, quickly goes through its cycle, and subsides without being accompanied by a constitutional reaction. It should be emphasized that an immediate reaction can be obtained with inactive virus as well as with infectious material (Hooker, 1929; Craigie and Wishart, 1933; Benenson, 1950). Although inactive virus will induce an immediate reaction in a person already immune to smallpox, it will not protect a susceptible individual against the disease. Too often in military medicine and in large scale vaccination programs in civilians, proper observation of the response of each person is not made. As a result, the vaccinator is apt to judge the potency of the lymph used on the basis of the early response or immediate reaction of a few individuals. If the vaccinator assumes that all of the people received potent vaccine because of an immediate response in a few, he may be misled about the current state of resistance to smallpox of the whole group; he might have used an inactive virus. It should also be emphasized that improper administration of active virus or the administration of in-

active virus may result in no cutaneous response. This is not an evidence of immunity; it is "no reaction" and should be recorded as such; any person showing no reaction should be revaccinated.

A vaccinoid reaction following Jennerian prophylaxis represents a modified infection in a partially immune person. It is more rapid in onset and less severe than a primary reaction but appears later and is more intense than an immediate response. A vaccinoid reaction is only obtained when active virus is administered in the proper manner. Therefore, the occurrence of vaccinoid reactions in members of a group being immunized indicates that potent lymph was used.

The vaccination of 5,000,000 persons in New York City during one month in 1947 provided an opportunity to estimate the complications which result from such a mass procedure (Greenberg, 1948). Forty-five cases and four deaths were attributed to postinfectious encephalitis. It is impossible to be certain how many of the 45 patients with disease of the central nervous system actually suffered from postvaccinal encephalitis. The typical histopathology of postinfectious encephalitis was encountered at necropsy in none of the four patients who died. At any rate, the incidence of postinfectious encephalitis was not greater than 1 per 110,000 vaccinations and probably was appreciably less than this. Forty-five persons suffered generalized vaccinia; 38 of these had a pre-existing dermatosis, and 28 of them were accidentally infected by contact with vaccinated persons. Two members of the last group, babies under one year of age, died. The only other serious complication among the 5,000,000 was one death which resulted from an infection beginning at the site of inoculation.

Smallpox has been so successfully controlled that the public and the medical profession have become complacent and neglectful of vaccination. This is forcefully emphasized by the occurrence of 23 cases of variola and 11 deaths among the staff members of two British hospitals which were called upon to care for the contacts of two persons who arrived in Britain from the Middle East and subsequently developed mild atypical smallpox (Laidlaw and Horne, 1950; Cramb, 1951). Moreover, incidental observations made during the mass-vaccination program in New York in 1947, which was undertaken after smallpox was introduced into the city, suggested that only about one third of the general population was immune to vaccinia virus (Greenberg, 1948). It should be clearly understood that a sufficient number of reasonably well-vaccinated members of a community offer appreciable protection to the nonvaccinated members and to those with waning vaccinal immunity, since they block the spread of the disease in the same manner as a firebreak stops the progress of a forest fire. In order to ensure immunity for each individual, there is no substitute for frequent revaccination. Therefore, the Military Services require revaccination of all personnel at yearly intervals if stationed overseas and at intervals of three years if stationed on the North American continent.

The standard smallpox vaccine is glycerolated calf lymph, and the multiple pressure method is the standard way of administration. However, in various parts of the world animals other than calves are used to prepare vaccine. Glycerolated vaccine is notoriously unstable. Regulations of the National Institute of Health require that the virus be stored at temperatures below minus 10° C. by the manufacturer and permit its use during a period of 3 months after being shipped from the place where it was prepared provided that it remains refrigerated at ordinary icebox temperature. More stable preparations are needed, especially in the tropics where refrigeration during storage and transportation is difficult to obtain. Otten, Collier and Meyer (1950) have prepared dried buffalo lymph and used it for several decades with great success in Indonesia; approximately 40,000,000 persons were vaccinated with such material from 1946 to 1950. Furthermore, many workers have grown vaccine virus for Jennerian prophylaxis in tissue cultures or in embryonated eggs; these methods provide bacteriologically sterile material which may be lyophilized and still be of acceptable potency. Three general types of culture virus have been used: the lyophilized, tissue-culture virus of Rivers and Ward (1935); the glycerolated virus from the infected chorioallantois of an embryonated hen's egg prepared by Goodpasture, Buddingh, Richardson and Anderson (1935); and the lyophilized, plasma-clot-culture virus of Plotz (1939). The intradermal inoculation of certain of the culture viruses is recommended by some workers. Some tissue-culture strains are known to become relatively avirulent during propagation, and vaccination with them does not elicit so good an immunity as might be desired (Rivers, Ward and Baird, 1939). In general, culture or egg-grown virus has not been widely accepted as a prophylactic vaccine against smallpox. However, the satisfactory experience in Texas (Cook, Crain and Irons, 1948) over a period of years with the field use of chick-embryo vaccine should assist in overcoming the prejudice against such materials.

VACCINIA

(Synonym: Cowpox)

History

The history of vaccinia is intimately associated with the subject of smallpox. Vaccine virus derives its medical importance from its capacity to induce immunity to variola, an observation originally made by Jenner (1798). The naturally occurring disease of cattle is of minor importance in veterinary medicine (Blaxall, 1930b).

Clinical Picture

Naturally acquired cowpox of man is an occupational disease limited to persons, particularly milkers, handling infected cattle. The disease is characterized by one or more nodules, vesicles or pustules on the hands. Constitutional symptoms are mild, and, if a generalized eruption appears, it is usually sparse and heals within a week without scarring (Davies, Janes and Downie, 1938). Vaccinal infections of the finger develop occasionally in partially immune laboratory workers who handle highly infectious material while suffering from minor cuts and abrasions. These represent immune or vaccinoid types of reaction, but because of the anatomic structure of the involved area they may behave like a felon of bacterial origin and may require surgical relief.

Pathologic Picture

Naturally acquired cowpox of man is a mild disease with a negligible mortality and the pathology has not been described. The pathologic changes encountered in calves and rabbits infected with vaccine virus are given in detail by Tyzzer (1904) and those found in various animal species infected by different routes with various strains of the agent are reviewed at length by van Rooyen and Rhodes (1948).

Experimental Infection; Host Range

Purposeful inoculation of man with cowpox virus, called vaccination, has been practiced since Jenner's classical observations (1798) on the immunity against smallpox induced by infection with this agent. The experimental disease thus obtained was discussed in considerable detail in the section on measures for the control of smallpox. Generalized vaccinia occasionally occurs following routine vaccination, and postvaccinal encephalitis develops very rarely. An enormous amount of work has been done on the latter complication (van Rooyen and Rhodes, 1948); the present consensus is that this form of encephalitis is identical with that which follows other viral infections and antirabies treatment and is not caused by the direct action of the virus of vaccinia.

There are several enzootic pock diseases of animals which are more or less similar to cowpox. Thus, horses, camels, goats, sheep, pigs, rabbits and mice have their own pock diseases (Findlay, 1936; Fenner, 1949). Discussion in this chapter, however, will be centered around strains of vaccine virus used for investigative work or for the production of vaccine for immunization of human beings against smallpox. These strains differ in certain respects one from another, and may differ from native cowpox virus (Downie, 1939).

Most laboratory animals are susceptible to infection with the virus of vaccinia. The hosts most frequently used in studies on this agent are rabbits and embryonated eggs, but mice, monkeys and guinea pigs are occasionally useful. The virus produces infection when inoculated by a variety of routes and is capable of multiplying in tissues of ectodermal, mesodermal and endodermal origin. Vaccine virus has the capacity of becoming adapted to growth in almost all types of cell. As a result there exist many well-defined strains of the virus which characteristically grow best in certain tissues. The seed strains of virus used on calves for preparing smallpox vaccine are thoroughly adapted to growth on the scarified skin and these are sometimes designated "dermal vaccine." The C. L. (Connaught Laboratory) strain grown on the skin of rabbits has been extensively used for obtaining highly purified preparations of elementary bodies of vaccinia (Craigie, 1932) which in turn have been employed in studies on the nature of the virus (Smadel and Hoagland, 1942). There are the testicular and neural strains of vaccine virus (Noguchi, 1918; Levaditi et al., 1921), which were derived from dermal strains by serial passage in rabbits by the testicular and cerebral route, respectively. They differ from dermal strains in their disease-producing potentialities not only in the rabbit but also on the chorio-allantoic membrane of an embryonated egg (Buddingh, 1938). Changes in virulence of dermal strains associated with continuous growth in tissue culture have been demonstrated (Rivers and Ward, 1935). Thus, a wide variety of lesions can be produced in experimental animals by strains of vaccine virus which are antigenically and immunologically indistinguishable but which elicit under appropriate conditions cutaneous lesions, meningo-encephalitis, orchitis, pneumonia, or keratitis (van Rooyen and Rhodes, 1948).

ETIOLOGY

Smadel and Hoagland (1942) stated that vaccine virus has been studied so diligently and successfully during the past decade that it then stood as the best-defined member of the group of animal viruses. Today vaccine virus still remains one of the best-defined animal virus, but certain others, e.g., influenza virus, are now almost as well characterized. Elementary bodies of vaccinia are spherical particles having a diameter of about 225 mμ and are just discernible by ordinary microscopy. These structures were described by Buist in 1887 (Gordon, 1937) and by Paschen (1906), both of whom considered them related to the infectious agent. Neither report was widely accepted at the time of its appearance, nor would the evidence presented be regarded today as conclusively demonstrating a relationship between the particles described and the infectious agent. However, information has accumulated which now indicates the soundness of the original hypothesis of these early workers.

Highly purified preparations of vaccine virus are prerequisite to studies dealing with the nature of the agent. Since the virus of vaccinia, like all other viral and rickettsial agents, is an obligate, intracellular parasite, starting materials rich in the agent contain much nonviral, cellular debris. Methods for eliminating the nonviral material were developed gradually over a period of years (MacCallum and Oppenheimer, 1922; Ledingham, 1931) and culminating in the technic of Craigie (1932) which is summarized in Chapter 3. In brief, it consists of infecting myriads of epidermal cells of a rabbit and collecting the contents of the infected cells without appreciable contamination by materials from normal cells. The dermal pulp obtained in this manner is subjected to a series of washings and differential centrifugations, and eventually yields a suspension consisting almost entirely of elementary bodies; from each rabbit, about 40 cc. of final suspension are obtained, which has an infective titer of 10^{-9} to 10^{-10} when tested intracutaneously in rabbits and contains from 1 to 2 mg. of virus by dry weight. Preparations of washed elementary bodies of vaccinia have also been obtained from suspensions of infected chorio-allantoic membranes subjected to differential centrifugation and tryptic digestion (Smadel and Wall, 1937); but these do not possess the state of purity attained in the suspensions from dermal pulp.

Early attempts to associate elementary bodies with infectivity were essentially qualitative in character. Even as late as 1932, the important observations of Eagles and Ledingham, which dealt with the correlation of elementary bodies with infectivity of virus filtrates, resulted from all-or-none experiments. Following the development of methods for obtaining highly purified suspensions of virus and for estimating accurately the infectivity of virus suspensions, quantitative correlation of elementary bodies and infective units was undertaken.

Parker (1938) applied statistical analysis to results obtained by a highly accurate method for titrating the infectivity of a suspension of virus on a rabbit's skin, and concluded that under appropriate conditions a single infective particle produces a lesion. Such deductions concerning a single infective particle need no assumption regarding the structural nature of that particle; they are equally valid regardless of whether the virus is as small as a molecule of albumin or as large as a bacterium. Elementary bodies of vaccinia can be readily seen by ordinary dark-field microscopy.

Using a special counting chamber and dark-field illumination, Parker and Rivers (1936b) estimated the number of elementary bodies in a suspension and then determined its infective titer. Although they found a direct correlation between the values obtained by these two procedures, the authors concluded that their data did not justify a statement regarding the number of elementary bodies in a single infective unit. A somewhat different approach to the question was used by Smadel, Rivers and Pickels (1939) who calculated the weight of a single, dehydrated elementary body and found it to be 5.34×10^{-15} grams. They then determined the number of infective units in a series of preparations of washed elementary bodies, and, after drying the preparations and determining their weights, calculated the number of elementary bodies which would be required to give such weights. The ratios of elementary bodies to infective units were calculated for seven consecutive preparations; these varied between 2.1:1 and 9.2:1, with an average of 4.2:1. There are several factors inherent in this method of experimental approach which would tend to make the ratios greater than unity, for example, the presence in a preparation of inactive virus particles, aggregates of particles, and nonviral material. In view of these variables, the fact that the ratio of elementary bodies to infective units approached unity is considered good evidence for believing that under proper conditions a single active elementary body represents a single infective unit of vaccine virus. Hence, the elementary body is the virus.

Electron microscopy has contributed much to the understanding of the morphologic structure of the virus of vaccinia. Green, Anderson and Smadel (1942) observed that elementary bodies had six rectangular surfaces so arranged that their three-dimensional shape was more bricklike than cuboidal. Evidence of some sort of internal structure in elementary bodies, similar to that seen in bacteria and ricket-

tsiae, was also obtained. The virus particles regularly contained a centrally-located, spherical area having increased density to penetration by the electronic beam which was surrounded by four smaller areas of similar density. An electron micrograph depicting elementary bodies of vaccine virus is presented in the frontispiece. Sharp, Taylor, Hook and Beard (1946) interpreted their electron micrographs of gold-shadowed elementary bodies as indicating these structures to be more cylindrical than bricklike. An elementary body is surrounded by a membranelike structure, since treatment with dilute alkali results in swelling of the particle which is followed by the appearance of breaks in its surface through which a protoplasmlike substance can be seen, in occasional micrographs, in the act of streaming out (Green et al., 1942). The dimensions of elementary bodies estimated by electron microscopy are slightly less than those calculated from ultracentrifugation data. This is to be expected, since dehydrated particles are examined in the ultramicroscope, while hydrated ones are studied in the analytical centrifuge.

Wyckoff's (1951) excellent electronmicrographs of infected chorio-allantoic membranes show large clusters of typical elementary bodies forming the Guarnieri body in the cytoplasm of epithelial cells. In addition, they show small groups of elementary bodies lying scattered throughout the cytoplasm of other infected cells.

Several methods have been employed for estimating the size of vaccine virus. Buist, using ordinary microscopy in 1887 (Gordon, 1937), concluded that its diameter was about 150 mμ. Experiments conducted by workers during the period between 1930 and 1940 provided through ultrafiltration and ultracentrifugation values (van Rooyen and Rhodes, 1948) in the range from 125 to 252 mμ, which are in fairly close agreement considering the technical difficulties involved. The writer prefers the figure 236 mμ (Pickels and Smadel, 1938) which was calculated with the aid of the sedimentation constant of the primary sedimenting boundary of a suspension of elementary bodies in dilute buffer solution, namely, 4910 Svedberg units.

The density of elementary bodies has been estimated by determining the sedimentation rate of the particles in solutions of different specific gravities. When particles are unaffected by the suspending medium, their sedimentation rate decreases proportionately to increases in density of the menstruum, until ultimately no sedimentation occurs at the point where the density of the particles and medium are equal. Smadel, Pickels and Shedlovsky (1938) observed that elementary bodies, suspended in sucrose solution having a specific gravity of 1.25, moved neither up nor down in an analytical centrifuge, and concluded that in this medium the virus had a density equal to that of the sugar solution. However, experiments in which solutions of varying concentrations of urea, glycerol, or sucrose were used as suspending media provided data which could best be accounted for by assuming that the virus particles responded to osmotic influences in a manner more or less similar to that of erythrocytes. Therefore, they regarded the value of 1.25 as representing the density of a dehydrated elementary body and estimated the density of the virus particle in distilled water, or very dilute buffer solution, as being 1.16. Subsequently, Lépine, Levaditi and Giuntini (1942) compared the sedimentation rates of elementary bodies in NaCl solutions prepared with ordinary water and with heavy water (D_2O), respectively, and estimated that the density of the hydrated virus particle is 1.28. McFarlane, Macfarlane, Amies and Eagles (1939) applied direct pyknometric measurements to dried elementary bodies and obtained a value of 1.26. Thus, the density of vaccine virus varies somewhat under different conditions of hydration and when suspended in solutions of different ionic and osmotic properties; it lies somewhere between that of bacteria, 1.10, and proteins, 1.33. Changes

in the density of elementary bodies which were noted in solutions of urea, glycerol and sucrose may not necessarily prove that the surface of a virus particle acts as a semipermeable membrane. The virus might respond similarly if it were a gellike structure without a superficial membrane as postulated by McFarlane and co-workers (1939).

Data on the nature and constituents of the surface of an elementary body have been obtained by immunologic and physical methods. The virus particles are agglutinated by antibodies against LS and NP antigens, substances that will be described later; therefore, the LS protein and the NP nucleoprotein constitute part of the surface mosaic. Evidence that these antigens make up an appreciable portion of the surface area is supplied by the observation that the mobility of elementary bodies in an electrophoretic apparatus is close to that of LS and NP (Shedlovsky and Smadel, 1940). Indeed, a mixture of elementary bodies and collodion particles coated with heated LS antigen migrates as a single boundary in an electrical field, whereas a mixture of virus and collodion particles coated with rabbit-serum proteins yields two distinct boundaries which move at different speeds (Smadel, Pickels, Shedlovsky and Rivers, 1940). The role of lipids in the surface structure remains to be determined; cholesterol can be removed without affecting the electrophoretic mobility, but procedures which extract neutral fat and phospholipid are sufficiently drastic to make it difficult to perform such studies on elementary bodies. Chu (1948a) concluded that the hemagglutinin of vaccinia "is distinct from, and apparently unassociated with the elementary bodies"; hence, this interesting substance presumably is absent from the surface of the virus particle.

Elementary bodies of vaccinia contain the following chemical constituents in the percentages listed: carbon, 33.7; nitrogen, 15.3; phosphorus, 0.57; copper, 0.05; total lipids, 5.7, consisting of cholesterol, 1.4, phospholipid, 2.2, and neutral fat, 2.2 ; reducing sugars, 2.8 ; and thymonucleic acid, 5.6 (Hoagland, Smadel and Rivers, 1940 ; Hoagland, Lavin, Smadel and Rivers, 1940 ; Hoagland, Ward, Smadel and Rivers, 1941a). Only cholesterol among the substances mentioned appears not to be an integral part of the virus ; it can be removed by extraction with ether without reducing the infectivity of a preparation. Practically all of the phosphorus and the reducing sugars are contained in the thymonucleic acid fraction. The copper in the virus is

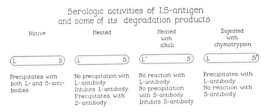

CHART 26. Graphic representation of LS antigen of vaccinia. (Smadel, J. E., and Hoagland, C. L., 1942, Elementary bodies of vaccinia. Bacteriological Reviews, *6*, 79-110.)

firmly bound to some constituent, presumably protein. No iron is demonstrable in elementary bodies.

A number of biologically active substances have been found in appreciable quantities in preparations of elementary bodies; these include phosphatase, catalase, ribonuclease (Macfarlane and Salaman, 1938 ; Macfarlane and Dolby, 1940), lipase, biotin and flavin (Hoagland, Ward, Smadel and Rivers, 1940 ; 1941b ; 1942). Proof that these are integral constituents of the virus and not contaminating substances derived from cells in which the virus was grown has not been brought forward in most instances. The capacity of the virus particles to adsorb certain of the enzymes on the surfaces and to hold them firmly through repeated washings has been demonstrated. Evidence for the presence of biotin and flavin in the virus itself is more convincing than that for the enzymes.

Close immunologic relationship between vaccinia and variola was well established long before the agents of the diseases were classified as viruses and before the subject of immunology was recognized. Jenner's observations (1798), in which man served as the experimental host, proved that infection with vaccinia protected against variola. Sacco (1801, cited by Blaxall, 1930a) showed that variolation performed during the first five days after vaccination elicited only a local pustule and that after the eleventh day it did not induce even a local lesion. Conversely, vaccination performed during the prodromal stage of smallpox gives a take but does not do so when performed after the eruption has been present for several days. Monkeys convalescent from vaccinia are resistant to variola and vice versa, but numerous workers have believed that variola protected less well against vaccinia than did vaccinia against variola (Brinckerhoff and Tyzzer, 1906 ; Gordon, 1925 ; Blaxall, 1930a ; da Cunha and Teixeira, 1934). Antibodies which appear in the sera of animals or human beings infected with either the virus of vaccinia or that of variola are capable of neutralizing the heterologous virus. In studies of this type, Schneider (1923) inoculated a rabbit's cornea with a mixture of human variola serum and vaccine virus (at the present time the skin of the rabbit would probably be used instead of the cornea) ; for the reciprocal cross, Bohls and Irons (1942) used antivaccinal rabbit serum, variola virus and the chorio-allantoic membrane of an embryonated hen's egg. Downie and McCarthy (1950) concluded that the minor antigenic differences among the viruses of variola, vaccinia, cowpox and ectromelia, which could be demonstrated by neutralization technics, were no greater than those observed among some strains of influenza A virus. Chapter 3 contains a discussion of different types of neutralization tests and some of their applications in vaccinia. It is of historical interest that in 1877 Raynaud demonstrated passive immunity to vaccinia by means of convalescent serum, and that the first neutralization test with any viral agent was performed in 1892 by Sternberg who used vaccinal immune serum to inactivate vaccine virus.

The in-vitro serologic reactions obtained with vaccinal materials were studied early in the 20th century, both flocculation (Tanaka, 1902) and complement fixation (Jobling, 1906) being employed. The field remained chaotic until 1925 when Gordon established these reactions on a firm basis. Craigie (1932) recognized the existence of a soluble antigen in tissue suspensions rich in virus. This noninfectious substance is readily separated from the elementary bodies by filtration through a Seitz pad or by high-speed centrifugation, and is demonstrable by precipitation or complement-fixation technics. Craigie and Wishart (1936b) subsequently found that the soluble substance contained a heat labile (L) and a heat stable (S) factor which occurred in close combination (LS) in solution, and that it constituted part of the surface of an elementary body. Craigie and Wishart (1936c) described a simple method of isoelectric precipitation for concentrating and partially purifying LS antigen. Modifications of this method yielded pure LS antigen which possessed the properties of a protein molecule with a molecular weight of 240,000 (Shedlovsky and Smadel, 1942). LS antigen is specific for the variola-vaccinia viruses; samples of it are serologically indistinguishable regardless of whether they are obtained from human crusts or chorio-allantoic membranes infected with variola virus, or from tissues of calves, rabbits, guinea pigs, or embryonated eggs infected with the virus of vaccinia (Smadel and Hoagland, 1942).

The LS protein is of considerable immunologic interest even though it is incapable of inducing either immunity or neutralizing antibody against the virus. The LS antigen provides the first example of a single native protein molecule capable of eliciting two distinct antibodies. Furthermore, both the L and S parts of the molecule can be de-graded independently by appropriate treatment (Smadel and Rivers, 1942; Shedlovsky and Smadel, 1942; Smadel, Hoagland and Shedlovsky, 1943). The results of a series of degradations of LS and the serologic means used for their detection are summarized in Chart 26. The native LS protein precipitates with either L or S antibody. Each serologically active part of the antigen, when subjected to the first stage of degradation, combines with its antibody but does not form a visible precipitate; this antigen-antibody reaction is demonstrable by an inhibition technic, that is, the combined antibody fails to react with native antigen added to the mixture. Completely degraded antigen does not react with antibody as shown by the results of precipitation and inhibition tests. Demonstration of different degradation products of LS protein, which in precipitation tests appear to represent either pure L or pure S substance, clarified confusion regarding relationship of these two precipitinogens.

The NP antigen represents another immunologically specific constituent of the virus of vaccinia (Smadel, Rivers and Hoagland, 1942). It is obtained from elementary bodies by extraction with dilute alkali and constitutes at least half of the substance of a virus particle. The antigen is a nucleoprotein containing 6 per cent thymonucleic acid. It is insoluble in the pH range between 4.5 and 7.5, but dissolves at pH 8.0; precipitin and complement-fixation tests are most conveniently carried out in solutions buffered at pH 8.0 to 8.5. Antibodies which react with the NP antigen are found in the sera of several species of animals following hyperimmunization with active vaccine virus. Furthermore, injection of noninfectious alkaline extracts of elementary bodies, which contain about 90 per cent NP antigen, elicits specific precipitins in rabbits, but the sera from such animals do not neutralize the virus nor are the animals resistant to infection. Further evidence for the specificity of the NP antibody and the neutralizing substance of vaccinia is brought out by absorption tests; removal of the NP antibody does not materially affect the neutralizing capacity of a serum. Neutralizing antibodies can be absorbed from antivaccinal sera by appropriate material, i.e., active elementary bodies (Salaman, 1937). The NP antigen has not been searched for in the elementary body of variola and antivariola sera have not been tested for their capacity to react with this antigen.

LS and NP antigens make up an appreciable portion of the surface of an elementary body, and elementary bodies are agglutinated by L, S, and NP antibodies. Hyperimmune sera apparently contain another agglutinating antibody which has been designated as X agglutinin (Craigie and Wishart, 1936b,c; Smadel, Rivers and Hoagland, 1942). The exact nature of the X agglutinin and its relation to other antibodies of vaccinia which are demonstrable either in vivo or in vitro remain to be · determined.

The hemagglutinin of vaccinia (Nagler, 1942) is closely related immunologically to that of variola (North, 1944) and ectromelia (Burnet and Stone, 1946). It is distinct from the elementary body and the LS protein molecule, being associated with particles of a diameter of 65 mμ and a density of 1.1 (Chu, 1948a, b). Chu regarded his observations on the size and the density of the agglutinin, its stability on boiling, and its ready aggregation and absorption as compatible with Burnet's suggestion (1946) that it is a lipoprotein. Vaccinal hemagglutinins occur in various tissues and hosts in which the virus multiplies (Chu, 1948a) and specific inhibitory antibodies develop in vaccinated animals and man (Nagler, 1942). Absorption tests show that these antibodies are unrelated to L, S, or neutralizing antibodies (Chu, 1948a). Thus, the hemagglutinin seems to be a specific vaccinal material with physical and antigenic properties different from those of the elementary body or the soluble antigen of vaccinia.

The antigenic fraction in the active virus of vaccinia which is responsible for eliciting resistance to infection and neutralizing antibody is unknown. It is evident from the preceding paragraphs that the noninfectious antigens which have been separated from the elementary bodies are incapable of producing these phenomena. Repeated attempts to induce an immune state or appreciable quantities of neutralizing antibody with virus inactivated by heat, phenol, formalin, or alcohol have generally been fruitless (Bland, 1932; Parker and Rivers, 1936a; Donnally and Weil, 1940; McClean, 1945). In those instances where slight beneficial effects were obtained, the amounts of virus required were relatively enormous; thus, the immunization of man with inactive vaccine virus remains an impracticable procedure.

The state of nutrition and hormone balance of an animal affects the growth of vaccine virus and the lesions it induces. The size of a cutaneous vaccinal lesion in rabbits is reduced by malnutrition (Sprunt, 1942a) and by local edema of tissues (Taylor and Sprunt, 1943). Similarly, the susceptibility of rabbits is reduced by administration of estrogenic hormones (Sprunt and McDearman, 1940), and methionine and choline (Sprunt, 1942b).

A wide variety of substances is capable of altering to some extent the growth of vaccine virus in tissue culture. Of particular interest are the findings of Thompson and his associates (1947; 1949a, b) who showed that the addition of certain substituted amino acids, analogues of purine and pyrimidine bases, and haloacylamides had some inhibitory effect on multiplication of the virus while sulfadiazine did not. Penicillin, 10 units per cc., has no effect on the growth of virus in tissue cultures, and 500 units of the substance was not virucidal in infected embryonated eggs (Parker and Diefendorf, 1944); however, appreciable invitro inactivation of virus results from incubation of it with relatively large amounts of commercial penicillin (Gohar and,

Bashatli, 1946; Groupé and Rake, 1947). In search for fundamental knowledge and a satisfactory chemotherapeutic agent, many substances have been tested on vaccine virus with negative results. These are listed in the papers referred to above and in that of Andrewes, King and van den Ende (1943).

The virus of vaccinia is one of the more stable viral agents. It can be stored for long periods of time in glycerol when properly refrigerated, or for years in the frozen state at $-10°$ C. or lower temperatures, without appreciable reduction in activity (Blaxall, 1930a). Lyophilized vaccine virus has been used for Jennerian prophylaxis (Rivers and Ward, 1935). The loss in infectivity which results from lyophilization is relatively slight when compared with that which accompanies lyophilization of many other viruses or bacteria; for example, in one lot of virus the elementary body-infective unit ratio was 3.7:1 before drying and 241:1 after drying (Hoagland, Smadel and Rivers, 1940). Improvements in methods now permit lyophilization of vaccine virus with even smaller losses in infectivity. The virus is readily inactivated by ultraviolet light, x-ray radiation, photodynamic action of a number of dyes in the presence of ordinary light, and a number of antiseptics (van Rooyen and Rhodes, 1948).

Observations of Lea and Salaman (1942) on inactivation of elementary bodies of vaccinia by radiation are of fundamental interest in their contribution toward an understanding of the nature of the virus. These workers concluded that the virus possessed genes and that these were not present in a compact mass but were either distributed throughout the particle or confined to a nucleus of a diameter of at least half that of the particle. The internal structure of the virus particle as revealed by electron microscopy and the presence of a nucleoprotein (NP antigen) which makes up about half of the mass of the elementary body may be regarded as not inconsistent with the idea of Lea and Salaman; at least

they provide structural and biochemical data of the type which would be required in such a hypothesis.

Briody and Stannard (1951) followed the development of vaccine virus in the chorioallantois by means of frequent titrations of infective and hemagglutinin activity. These observations indicated that inoculated virus rapidly became undetectable but that it reappeared and increased in a stepwise fashion at intervals of eight hours. Hemagglutinin became detectable only after several such 8-hour growth cycles had elapsed but was assumed to have been present earlier in amounts too minute to detect. For a more extensive discussion of the phenomena of the one-step growth curve and its possible implications in the mode of multiplication of viruses, the chapters dealing with bacteriophage and influenza virus may be consulted. Vaccine virus should be a particularly good model for the study of virus multiplication, since it should be possible to correlate the morphologic findings, as elucidated by electronmicroscopy, with those obtained by serologic and infectivity studies.

DIAGNOSIS

Diagnosis of naturally acquired cowpox in man or of induced vaccinia is usually simple on the basis of the history and the cutaneous lesions. Laboratory procedures outlined in the section on diagnosis of variola are applicable to vaccinia.

TREATMENT

Treatment is symptomatic.

EPIDEMIOLOGY

Cowpox is a contact infection acquired during the handling of infected cattle.

CONTROL MEASURES

No control measures are indicated in regard to the natural disease. Persons who propose to work with vaccinia should be vaccinated or revaccinated prior to initiation of the work.

REFERENCES

American Public Health Association, 1950, Smallpox, *in* The Control of Communicable Diseases, ed. 7. New York, Am. Pub. Health Assn., pp. 120-122.

Anderson, T., Foulis, M. A., Grist, N. R., and Landsman, J. B., 1951, Clinical and laboratory observations in a smallpox outbreak. Lancet, *1*, 1248-1252.

Andrewes, C. H., King, H., and van den Ende, M., 1943, Chemotherapeutic experiments with the viruses of influenza A, lymphogranuloma venereum and vaccinia. J. Path. and Bact., *55*, 173-181.

Benenson, A. S., 1950, Immediate (so-called "immune") reaction to smallpox vaccination. J. Am. Med. Assn., *143*, 1238-1240.

Bland, J. O. W., 1932, Immunisation with inactive vaccinia virus. J. Hyg., *32*, 55-66.

Bland, J. O. W., and Robinow, C. F., 1939, The inclusion bodies of vaccinia and their relationship to the elementary bodies studied in cultures of the rabbit's cornea. J. Path. and Bact., *48*, 381-403.

Blaxall, F. R., 1930a, Smallpox, *in* A System of Bacteriology in Relation to Medicine, London, His Majesty's Stationery Office, Vol. 7, pp. 84-132.

Blaxall, F. R., 1930b, Animal Pock Diseases, *in* A System of Bacteriology in Relation to Medicine, London, His Majesty's Stationery Office, Vol. 7, pp. 140-156.

Bohls, S. W., and Irons, J. V., 1942, Chorio-allantoic membrane infection as a diagnostic test for smallpox. Am. J. Pub. Health, *32*, 300-306.

Brinckerhoff, W. R., and Tyzzer, E. E., 1906, Studies upon experimental variola and vaccinia in Quadrumana. J. Med. Res., *14*, 213-359.

Briody, B. A., and Stannard, C., 1951, Studies on vaccine virus. I. The development of hemagglutinating and infective particles in the chorioallantois of the chick embryo. J. Immunol., *67*, 403-411.

Buddingh, G. J., 1936, Comparison of the behavior of a neurotesticular and a dermal strain of vaccine virus in the chorio-allantoic membrane of the chick embryo. Am. J. Path., *12*, 511-524.

Buddingh, G. J., 1938, Infection of the chorio-allantois of the chick embryo as a diagnostic test for variola. Am. J. Hyg., *28*, 130-137.

Bulletin of U. S. Army Medical Department, 1946, Smallpox in Japan and Korea. Bull. U. S. Army Med. Dept., *6*, 101-102.

Burnet, F. M., 1946, Vaccinia haemagglutinin. Nature, *158*, 119-120.

Burnet, F. M., and Stone, J. D., 1946, The haemagglutinins of vaccinia and ectromelia viruses. Australian J. Exp. Biol. and Med. Sci., *24*, 1-8.

Chu, C. M., 1948a, Studies on vaccinia haemagglutinin. I. Some physico-chemical properties. J. Hyg., *46*, 42-48.

Chu, C. M., 1948b, Studies on vaccinia haemagglutinin. II. Some immunological properties. J. Hyg., *46*, 49-59.

Collier, W. A., Smit, A. M., and v. Heerde, A. F., 1950, Der Nachweis von Antihamagglutininen bei Variola Patienten als diagnostiches Hilfmittel. Zeits. f. Hyg. u. Infektionskr., *131*, 555-567.

Conybeare, E. T., 1939, Illness occurring in contacts with confluent smallpox. Lancet, *1*, 813-815.

Cook, E. B. M., Crain, P. N., and Irons, J. V., 1948, A report on the field use of chick membrane smallpox vaccine in Texas. Pub. Health Lab., *6*, 50-56.

Cottrell, J. D., and Knights, H. T., 1943, Notes on cases of smallpox treated with sulphanilamide. J. Roy. Army Med. Corps, *81*, 7-15.

Councilman, W. T., Magrath, G. B., and Brinckerhoff, W. R., 1904, The pathological anatomy and histology of variola. J. Med. Res., *11*, 12-135.

Craigie, J., 1932, The nature of the vaccinia flocculation reaction, and observations on the elementary bodies of vaccinia. Brit. J. Exp. Path., *13*, 259-268.

Craigie, J., and Wishart, F. O., 1933, Skin sensitivity to the elementary bodies of vaccinia. Canad. Pub. Health J., *24*, 72-78.

Craigie, J., and Wishart, F. O., 1936a, The complement-fixation reaction in variola. Canad. Pub. Health J., *27*, 371-379.

Craigie, J., and Wishart, F. O., 1936b, Studies on the soluble precipitable substances of vaccinia. I. The dissociation *in vitro* of soluble precipitable substances from elementary bodies of vaccinia. J. Exp. Med., *64*, 803-818.

Craigie, J., and Wishart, F. O., 1936c, Studies on the soluble precipitable substances of vaccinia. II. The soluble precipitable substances of dermal filtrate. J. Exp. Med., *64*, 819-830.

Cramb, R., 1951, Smallpox outbreak in Brighton, 1950-51. Pub. Health, *64*, 123-128.

da Cunha, A. M., and Teixeira, J., 1934, Notes sur l'alastrim. Relations d'immunité entre l'alastrim et la vaccine. Compt. rend. Soc. biol., *116*, 61-62.

Davies, J. H. T., Janes, L. R., and Downie, A. W., 1938, Cowpox infection in farmworkers. Lancet, *2*, 1534-1538.

Donnally, H. H., and Weil, A. J., 1940, Formolized vaccine virus. Results of its use with children who had never been vaccinated previously. J. Pediat., *17*, 639-646.

Downie, A. W., 1939, The immunological relationship of the virus of spontaneous cowpox to vaccinia virus. Brit. J. Exp. Path., *20*, 158-176.

Downie, A. W., 1946, The laboratory diagnosis of smallpox. Month. Bull. Min. Health and Emerg. Pub. Health Lab. Serv., *5*, 114-116.

Downie, A. W., and Dumbell, K. R., 1947a, The isolation and cultivation of variola virus on the chorio-allantois of chick embryos. J. Path. and Bact., *59*, 189-198.

Downie, A. W., and Dumbell, K. R., 1947b, Survival of variola virus in dried exudate and crusts from smallpox patients. Lancet, *1*, 550-553.

Downie, A. W., and McCarthy, K., 1950, The viruses of variola, vaccinia, cowpox and ectromelia. Neutralization tests on the chorio-allantois with unabsorbed and absorbed immune sera. Brit. J. Exp. Path., *31*, 789-796.

Downie, A. W., McCarthy, K., and MacDonald, A., 1950, Viraemia in smallpox. Lancet, *2*, 513-514.

Downie, A. W., 1951, Infection and immunity in smallpox. Lancet, *1*, 419-422.

Eagles, G. H., and Ledingham, J. C. G., 1932, Vaccinia and the Paschen body: infection experiments with centrifugalized virus filtrates. Lancet, *1*, 823-826.

Eisenberg-Merling, K. B., 1940, Observations on living vaccinia virus in the corneal cells of the rabbit. J. Path. and Bact., *50*, 279-286.

Fenner, F., 1949, Mouse-pox (infectious ectromelia of mice): A review. J. Immunol., *63*, 341-374.

Findlay, G. M., 1936, Variation in animal viruses. A review. J. Roy. Micro. Soc., *56*, 213-299.

Foulis, M. A., 1945, Confluent smallpox treated with penicillin. Brit. Med. J., *1*, 910-911.

Gohar, M. A., and Bashatli, A., 1946, The effect of penicillin on the vaccinia virus. J. Trop. Med. and Hyg., *49*, 115-116.

Goodpasture, E. W., Buddingh, G. J., Richardson, L., and Anderson, K., 1935, The preparation of anti-smallpox vaccine by culture of the virus in the chorio-allantoic membrane of chick embryos, and its use in human immunization. Am. J. Hyg., *21*, 319-360.

Gordon, M. H., 1925, Studies of the viruses of vaccinia and variola. Med. Res. Council, Special Report Series No. 98, London, His Majesty's Stationery Office.

Gordon, M., 1937, Virus bodies. John Buist and the elementary bodies of vaccinia. Edinburgh Med. J., *44*, 65-71.

Green, R. H., Anderson, T. F., and Smadel, J. E., 1942, Morphological structure of the virus of vaccinia. J. Exp. Med., *75*, 651-656.

Greenberg, M., 1947, Combined staff clinics—smallpox. Am. J. Med., *3*, 355-370.

Greenberg, M., 1948, Complications of vaccination against smallpox. Am. J. Dis. Child., *76*, 492-502.

Groupé, V., and Rake, G., 1947, Studies on the chemotherapy of the pox viruses. I. The effect of commercial penicillin and other selected substances on canary pox virus. J. Immunol., *57*, 17-29.

Guarnieri, G., 1892, Ricerche sulla patogenesi ed etiologia dell' infezione vaccinica e vaiolosa. Arch. per le sci. med., *16*, 403-424.

Hedrich, A. W., 1936, Changes in the incidence and fatality of smallpox in recent decades. Pub. Health Rep., *51*, 363-392.

Himmelweit, F., 1938, Observations on living vaccinia and ectromelia viruses by high power microscopy. Brit. J. Exp. Path., *19*, 108-123.

Hoagland, C. L., Smadel, J. E., and Rivers, T. M., 1940, Constituents of elementary bodies of vaccinia. I. Certain basic analyses and observations on lipid components of the virus. J. Exp. Med., *71*, 737-750.

Hoagland, C. L., Lavin, G. I., Smadel, J. E., and Rivers, T. M., 1940, Constituents of elementary bodies of vaccinia. II. Properties of nucleic acid obtained from vaccine virus. J. Exp. Med., *72*, 139-147.

Hoagland, C. L., Ward, S. M., Smadel, J. E., and Rivers, T. M., 1940, Biotin in elementary bodies of vaccinia. Proc. Soc. Exp. Biol. and Med., *45*, 669-671.

Hoagland, C. L., Ward, S. M., Smadel, J. E., and Rivers, T. M., 1941a, Constituents of elementary bodies of vaccinia. IV. Demonstration of copper in the purified virus. J. Exp. Med., *74*, 69-80.

Hoagland, C. L., Ward, S. M., Smadel, J. E., and Rivers, T. M., 1941b, Constituents of elementary bodies of vaccinia. V. A. flavin associated with the purified virus. J. Exp. Med., *74*, 133-144.

Hoagland, C. L., Ward, S. M., Smadel, J. E., and Rivers, T. M., 1942, Constituents of elementary bodies of vaccinia. VI. Studies on the nature of the enzymes associated with the purified virus. J. Exp. Med., *76*, 163-173.

Hooker, S. B., 1929, A skin test for susceptibility to smallpox; human endermal reactions to killed vaccine virus. J. Infect. Dis., *45*, 255-262.

Horgan, E. S., 1938, The experimental transformation of variola to vaccinia. J. Hyg., *38*, 702-715.

Horgan, E. S., and Haseeb, M. A., 1945, Vaccinia virus; immunological unity of different strains. Lancet, *2*, 170-171.

Ikeda, K., 1925, The blood in purpuric smallpox; clinical review of forty-eight cases. J. Am. Med. Assn., *84*, 1807-1813.

Illingworth, R. S., and Oliver, W. A., 1944, Smallpox in the Middle East: Lessons from 100 cases. Lancet, *2*, 681-685.

Irons, J. V., Bohls, S. W., Cook, E. B. M., and Murphy, J. N., Jr., 1941, The chick membrane as a differential culture medium with suspected cases of smallpox and varicella. Am. J. Hyg., *33*, Sect. B., 50-55.

Jenner E., 1798, An inquiry into the causes and effects of the variolae vaccinae, a disease discovered in some of the western counties of England, particularly Gloucestershire, and known by the name of the cow pox. Reprinted by Cassell and Company, Limited, 1896. Available in Pamphlet Vol. 4232, Army Medical Library, Washington. D. C.

Jobling, J. W., 1906, The occurrence of specific immunity principles in the blood of vaccinated calves. J. Exp. Med., *8*, 707-712.

Laidlaw, S. I. A., and Horne, W. A., 1950, Smallpox outbreak in Glasgow, 1950. Med. Offr., *83*, 187-192.

Lazarus, A. S., Eddie, B., and Meyer, K. F., 1937, Propagation of variola virus in the developing egg. Proc. Soc. Exp. Biol. and Med., *36*, 7-8.

Lea, D. E., and Salaman, M. H., 1942, The inactivation of vaccinia virus by radiations. Brit. J. Exp. Path., *23*, 27-37.

Ledingham, J. C. G., 1931, The aetiological importance of the elementary bodies in vaccinia and fowlpox. Lancet, *2*, 525-526.

Lépine, P., Levaditi, J. C., and Giuntini, J., 1942, Détermination par ultracentrifugations comparatives de la densité du virus vaccinal. Ann. Inst. Pasteur, *68*, 432-435.

Levaditi, C., Harvier, P., and Nicolau, S., 1921, Affinités neurotropes du virus de la vaccine. Compt. rend. Soc. biol., *85*, 345-347.

MacCallum, F. O., McPherson, C. A., and Johnstone, D. F., 1950, Laboratory investigation of smallpox patients with particular reference to infectivity in the early stages. Lancet, *2*, 514-517.

MacCallum, W. G., and Oppenheimer, E. H., 1922, Differential centrifugation. A method for the study of filtrable viruses, as applied to vaccinia. J. Am. Med. Assn., *78*, 410-411.

Macfarlane, M. G., and Salaman, M. H., 1938, The enzymic activity of vaccinial elementary bodies. Brit. J. Exp. Path., *19*, 184-191.

Macfarlane, M. G., and Dolby, D. E., 1940, The enzymic activity of vaccinial elementary bodies. Brit. J. Exp. Path., *21*, 219-227.

Magrath, G. B., and Brinckerhoff, W. R., 1904, On the occurrence of *Cytoryctes variolae*, Guarnieri. in the skin of the monkey inoculated with variola virus. J. Med. Res., *11*, 173-179.

McClean, D., 1945, The antigenicity of vaccinia virus inactivated with alcohol. J. Path. and Bact., *57*, 261-265.

McFarlane, A. S., Macfarlane, M. G., Amies, C. R., and Eagles, G. H., 1939, A physical and chemical examination of vaccinia virus. Brit. J. Exp. Path., *20*, 485-501.

McKinnon, N. E., and Defries, R. D., 1928, The reaction in the skin of the normal rabbit following intradermal injection of material from smallpox lesions: the specificity of this reaction and its application as a diagnostic test. Am. J. Hyg., *8*, 93-106.

Morosow, M. A., 1926, Die Färbung der Paschenschen Körperchen durch Versilberung. Zentralbl. f. Bakt., l. Abt., Orig., *100*, 385-387.

Nagler, F. P. O., 1942, Application of Hirst's phenomenon to the titration of vaccinia virus and vaccinia immune serum. Med. J. Australia, *1*, 281-283.

National Institute of Health, 1946, Minimum requirements: smallpox vaccine. Bethesda, Maryland, National Institute of Health, 2nd revision.

Nelson, J. B., 1943, The stability of variola virus propagated in embryonated eggs. J. Exp. Med., *78*, 231-239.

Noguchi, H., 1918, Further studies on the properties of pure vaccine virus cultivated *in vivo*. J. Exp. Med., *27*, 425-442.

North, E. A., 1944, A study of the immunological reactions of the variola and vaccinia viruses grown in the developing egg. Australian J. Exp. Biol. and Med. Sci., *22*, 105-109.

Olitsky, P. K., and Harford, C. G., 1937, Intranuclear inclusion bodies in the tissue reactions produced by injections of certain foreign substances. Am. J. Path., *13*, 729-748.

Otten, L., Collier, W. A., and Meyer, F. H., 1950, Dry lymph vaccine. Publication 27, Organization for Scientific Research in Indonesia, Djakarta, pp. 1-32.

Parker, R. F., 1938, Statistical studies of the nature of the infectious unit of vaccine virus. J. Exp. Med., *67*, 725-738.

Parker, R. F., 1948, Variola and vaccinia, *in* Diagnostic Procedures for Virus and Rickettsial Diseases. New York, Amer. Pub. Health Assoc.

Parker, R. F., and Muckenfuss, R. S., 1932, Complement-fixation in variola and vaccinia. Proc. Soc. Exp. Biol. and Med., *29*, 483-485.

Parker, R. F., and Rivers, T. M., 1936a, Immunological and chemical investigations of vaccine virus. III. Response of rabbits to inactive elementary bodies of vaccinia and to virus-free extracts of vaccine virus. J. Exp. Med., *63*, 69-94.

Parker, R. F., and Rivers, T. M., 1936b, Immunological and chemical investigations of vaccine virus. IV. Statistical studies of elementary bodies in relation to infection and agglutination. J. Exp. Med., *64*, 439-452.

Parker, R. F., and Diefendorf, H. W., 1944, Effect of penicillin on certain viruses. Proc. Soc. Exp. Biol. and Med., *57*, 351-354.

Paschen, E., 1906, Was wissen wir über den Vakzineerreger? Münch. med. Wchnschr., *53*, 2391-2393.

Pickels, E. G., and Smadel, J. E., 1938, Ultracentrifugation studies on the elementary bodies of vaccine virus. I. General methods and determination of particle size. J. Exp. Med., *68*, 583-606.

Plotz, H., 1939, Smallpox immunization by the scarification method with cultured vaccine virus (abstract). Rept. of Proc., Third International Congress for Microbiology, New York, Internat. Assn. Microbiol., pp. 358-359.

Raynaud, M., 1877, Étude expérimentale sur le rôle du sang dans la transmission de l'immunité vaccinale. Compt. rend. Acad. sci., *84*, 453-456.

Rivers, T. M., and Ward, S. M., 1935, Jennerian prophylaxis by means of intradermal injections of culture vaccine virus. J. Exp. Med., *62*, 549-560.

Rivers, T. M., Ward, S. M., and Baird, R. D., 1939, Amount and duration of immunity induced by intradermal inoculation of cultured vaccine virus. J. Exp. Med., *69*, 857-866.

van Rooyen, C. E., and Rhodes, A. J., 1948, The variola-vaccinia virus. Chapters 26-35 *in* Virus Diseases of Man, New York, Thos. Nelson and Sons, pp. 282-429.

van Rooyen, C. E., and Illingworth, R. S., 1944, A laboratory test for diagnosis of smallpox. Brit. Med. J., *2*, 526-529.

Salaman, M. H., 1937, The combining properties of vaccinia virus with the antibodies demonstrable in anti-vaccinial serum. Brit. J. Exp. Path., *18*, 245-258.

Schneider, H., 1923, Ueber den Nachweis virulizider Antikörper im Blute von Pockenkranken und Pockenrekonvaleszenten. Ztschr. f. Immunitätsforsch., *38*, 271-291.

Sharp, D. G., Taylor, A. R., Hook, A. E., and Beard, J. W., 1946, Rabbit papilloma and vaccinia viruses and T$_2$ bacteriophage of *E. coli* in "shadow" electron micrographs. Proc. Soc. Exp. Biol. and Med., *61*, 259-265.

Shedlovsky, T., and Smadel, J. E., 1940, Electrophoretic studies on elementary bodies of vaccinia. J. Exp. Med., *72*, 511-521.

Shedlovsky, T., and Smadel, J. E., 1942, The LS-antigen of vaccinia. II. Isolation of a single substance containing both L- and S- activity. J. Exp. Med., *75*, 165-178.

Smadel, J. E., and Wall, M. J., 1937, Elementary bodies of vaccinia from infected chorio-allantoic membranes of developing chick embryos. J. Exp. Med., *66*, 325-336.

Smadel, J. E., Pickels, E. G., and Shedlovsky, T., 1938, Ultracentrifugation studies on the elementary bodies of vaccine virus. II. The influence of sucrose, glycerol, and urea solutions on the physical nature of vaccine virus. J. Exp. Med., *68*, 607-627.

Smadel, J. E., Rivers, T. M., and Pickels, E. G., 1939, Estimation of the purity of preparations of elementary bodies of vaccinia. J. Exp. Med., *70*, 379-385.

Smadel, J. E., Pickels, E. G., Shedlovsky, T., and Rivers, T. M., 1940, Observations on mixtures of elementary bodies of vaccinia and coated collodion particles by means of ultracentrifugation and electrophoresis. J. Exp. Med., *72*, 523-529.

Smadel, J. E., and Hoagland, C. L., 1942, Elementary bodies of vaccinia. Bact. Reviews, *6*, 79-110.

Smadel, J. E., and Rivers, T. M., 1942, The LS-antigen of vaccinia. I. Inhibition of L- and S- antibodies by substances in treated vaccine dermal filtrate. J. Exp. Med., *75*, 151-164.

Smadel, J. E., Rivers, T. M., and Hoagland, C. L., 1942, Nucleoprotein antigen of vaccine virus. I. A new antigen obtained from elementary bodies of vaccinia. Arch. Path., *34*, 275-285.

Smadel, J. E., Hoagland, C. L., and Shedlovsky, T., 1943, The LS-antigen of vaccinia. IV. Chemical analysis of LS and the effect of chymotrypsin on LS. J. Exp. Med., *77*, 165-171.

Sprunt, D. H., 1942a, The effect of undernourishment on the susceptibility of the rabbit to infection with vaccinia. J. Exp. Med., *75*, 297-304.

Sprunt, D. H., 1942b, Inhibiting effect of methionine, choline and betaine on rabbit's susceptibility to infection with vaccinia. Proc. Soc. Exp. Biol. and Med., *51*, 226-227.

Sprunt, D. H., and McDearman, S., 1940, Studies on the relationship of sex hormones to infection. III. A quantitative study of the increased resistance to vaccinial infection produced by the estrogenic hormone and pseudopregnancy. J. Immunol., *38*, 81-95.

Stallybrass, C. O., 1931, The principles of epidemiology and the process of infection. London, Routledge, p. 329.

Sternberg, G. M., 1892, Practical results of bacteriological researches. Trans. Assn. Am. Phys., *7*, 68-86.

Sweitzer, S. E., and Ikeda, K., 1927, Variola; a clinical study of the Minneapolis epidemic of 1924-1925. Arch Derm. Syph., *15*, 19-29.

Tanaka, K., 1902, Über die Untersuchung des Pockenerregers. Zentralbl. f. Bakt., 1. Abt., Orig., *32*, 726-728.

Taylor, H. M., and Sprunt, D. H., 1943, Increased resistance to viral infection as a result of increased fluid in tissues. J. Exp. Med., *78*, 91-97.

Thompson, R. L., 1947, The effect of metabolites, metabolite antagonists and enzyme-inhibitors on the growth of the vaccinia virus in Maitland type of tissue cultures. J. Immunol., *55*, 345-352.

Thompson, R. L., Wilkin, M. L., Hitchings, G. H., Elion, G. B., Falco, E. A., and Russell, P. B., 1949a, The effects of antagonists on the multiplication of vaccinia virus *in vitro*. Science, *110*, 454.

Thompson, R. L., Wilkin, M. L., Hitchings, G. H., and Russell, P. B., 1949b, The virostatic and virucidal action of a-haloacylamides on vaccinia virus *in vitro*. Proc. Soc. Exp. Biol. and Med., *72*, 169-171.

Torres, C. M., 1935-36, Further studies on the pathology of alastrim and their significance in the variola-alastrim problem. Proc. Roy. Soc. Med., *29*, 1525-1540.

Torres, C. M., and Teixeira, J. de C., 1935, Culture du virus de l'alastrim sur les membranes de l'embryon de poulet. Compt. rend. Soc. biol., *118*, 1023-1024.

Tyzzer, E. E., 1904, The etiology and pathology of vaccinia. J. Med. Res., *11*, 180-229.

Vengsarkar, S. G., Poonen, T. U., and Walavalkar, S. A., 1942, Effects of sulphanilamide on smallpox. J. Indian Med. Assn., *11*, 361-365.

Wilkinson, P. B., 1942, Sulphanilamide in treatment of smallpox; review of 103 cases. Lancet, *2*, 67-69.

Woody, S. S., 1932, Variola, *in* F. Tice, Practice of Medicine, Hagerstown, Maryland, Prior, Vol. 3, pp. 187-213.

Wyckoff, R. W. G., 1951, The virus of vaccinia in chick embryo membrane. Proc. Nat. Acad. Sci., *37*, 565-569.

K. F. MEYER, M.D.

The George Williams Hooper Foundation for Medical Research,
University of California

20

Psittacosis-Lymphogranuloma Group

The infective agents of psittacosis of birds and man, lymphogranuloma venereum of man, murine and feline pneumonitis, opossum meningopneumonitis, calf enteritis and ewe abortion have been tentatively placed in a group that appears to be intermediate between the rickettsiae and viruses. It is premature to follow the taxonomy proposed by Moshkovsky (1945), who suggested the family name of *Chlamydozoaceae* and the genus *Miyagawanella* for the group.

Study of primary pneumonia in human beings not incurred by known bacteria has in recent years led to the discovery of viral agents indistinguishable from those causing psittacosis. Simultaneously, additional psittacosislike viruses have been isolated from apparently healthy or diseased mammals. Active agents comprising this group have been given the following names: meningopneumonitis virus (Francis and Magill, 1938); spontaneous mouse pneumonitis virus (Gönnert, 1941; Nigg and Eaton, 1944); Australian mouse pneumonitis virus (de Burgh et al., 1945); feline pneumonitis virus (Baker, 1944); S. F. (San Francisco) human pneumonitis virus (Eaton, Beck and Pearson, 1941); Illinois pneumonitis virus (Zichis and Shaughnessy, 1945); Louisiana pneumonitis virus (Larson and Olson, 1946); opossum virus A (Roca-García, 1949); calf enteritis virus (York and Baker, 1951) and virus of enzootic abortion of sheep (Stamp et al., 1950; McEwen, Stamp and Littlejohn, 1951; Barwell and Bishop, 1951). Since the type relation of agents long ago isolated from psittacine birds, pigeons, fulmars, willets and ducks has not yet been definitely established, it is not surprising that the position of these comparatively new mammalian viruses as well as the nonavian viruses isolated from human patients is still under discussion. Facts acquired in recent years, however, emphasize that viral agents of the group are infective coccoid elementary bodies tinctorially demonstrable with basic dyes and readily seen under an ordinary microscope. Morphologically, this group of viruses is characterized by the formation of intracellular castaneda-positive inclusion bodies first recognized as an integral part of the life cycle of the psittacosis and later of the lymphogranuloma agent. The infective bodies usually have a diameter of 300 to 450 mμ and are held back partially or completely by ordinary filters; they are readily propagated in the yolk sac of an embryonated hen's egg and in tissue cultures. All members of the group infect mice by the intranasal route, and some are infective by the intraperitoneal or intracerebral route. On the basis of complement-fixation tests they are antigenically related; neutralization tests may indicate sharp antigenic dif-

440

ferences. Neutralization tests of viral infectivity (Hilleman, 1945) and viral toxicity (Manire and Meyer, 1950) differentiated the antigenic relationship of certain avian and mammalian strains. Distinction on the basis of reputed susceptibility to sulfonamide drugs if of questionable value. Only the large, castaneda-positive viruses are susceptible to the chemotherapeutic action of aureomycin, terramycin, chloramphenicol and penicillin.

PSITTACOSIS

(SYNONYMS: Ornithosis, parrot fever, *psittacose, Papageienkrankheit*)

INTRODUCTION

Psittacosis, though an avian infection, is communicable to man. It may be a severe illness with a high mortality or a mild ambulatory or subclinical infection; it affects all ages and both sexes. Its cause is an elementary-body virus which develops in reticulo-endothelial cells.

HISTORY

From a relatively obscure disease which was first recognized in Switzerland, then in France and Germany, human psittacosis became a malady of world-wide interest in 1929-1930 when it appeared in twelve different countries and involved from 750 to 800 persons (Meyer, 1942). Careful inquiries by Roubakine (1930) and by Barros (1940) indicate that South American parrots were the main source of the infection. The discovery of latent domestic psittacosis in parakeets, pigeons, doves, chickens, ducks, seagulls and other birds by Meyer and Eddie (1933, 1947, 1951) has well established the independence of infective sources from imported exotic birds. Levinthal (1930), Coles (1930) and Lillie (1930) simultaneously discovered the minute spherical bodies within reticulo-endothelial cells, and Bedson and Bland (1932) and Bland and Canti (1935) conclusively proved the etiologic relationship of the elementary

bodies to infection. Propagation of the virus in embryonated eggs (Burnet and Rountree, 1935; Lazarus and Meyer, 1939) and in tissue culture (Yanamura and Meyer, 1941) furnished suitable antigens for serologic studies. Demonstration of the viral agent in the sputum of psittacosis patients (Rivers and Berry, 1935) advanced diagnostic procedures. A neutralization test enabled Hilleman (1945) to differentiate the antigenic relationship of certain avian and mammalian strains. Recent observations on the high person-to-person communicability of psittacosislike agents give credence to the hypothesis that nonavian, and possibly human strains, play a role in the ecology of psittacosis (Eaton et al., 1941; Meiklejohn et al., 1944; Olson and Treuting, 1944; Zichis and Shaughnessy, 1945; Yeatman and McEwin, 1945; de Gara and Furth, 1948).

CLINICAL PICTURE

The incubation time varies from 7 to 14 days, with a mean of 10 days. In many clinical descriptions the strikingly uniform manifestations of psittacosis, so often confused with influenza, atypical pneumonia and typhoid fever, repeat themselves with remarkable regularity. The onset may be sudden, with chilly sensations, fever, anorexia, sore throat, malaise, photophobia and severe headache, or the beginning may be gradual and insidious. The temperature at the onset is usually from 100° to 102° F. and gradually rises. During the second week, in severe cases, it maintains itself at a high level with slight morning remissions, or it may fall to normal on the seventh or eighth day in mild cases. Termination by crisis is rare. Nose bleed occurs in 25 per cent of the cases.

A slight, irritating, dry cough during the first few days persists or increases in intensity; however, despite extensive lung involvement, cough may be insignificant or absent throughout the entire illness. Sputum, always scanty, is sometimes entirely absent; at first mucoid, it may later become mucopurulent. In rare instances, when secondary infection is present, the sputum is blood tinged. Abnormal signs over the lungs are scanty, and the earliest demonstrable ones may be confined to an area of dullness, on percussion, at the base of either lung. Crepitations may be heard as early as the fifth day. The real extent of pneumonitis is usually not evident until roentgenologic examination has been made, which reveals patchy areas of consolidation over one or both lungs. Pleural reaction is generally slight or absent. Physical signs begin to disappear by the third week, but x-ray examinations disclose a slow resolution. The rate and depth of respirations are not increased except in fatal cases, in which a rate as high as 60 has been observed. The relative slowness of the pulse is characteristic, but in nearly all fatal cases the pulse becomes rapid and weak. Cyanosis and low blood pressure may be marked; collapse at some time during the illness is common. Thrombophlebitis may occur and cause death through pulmonary emboli. Insomnia, disorientation, apathy, mental depression and even delirium may occur in all except mild cases. Nausea and vomiting are common, and either constipation or diarrhea may be present. The spleen is palpable in very few patients. Albuminuria of varying degrees is not infrequent, and transient glycosuria has been reported. "Rose spot" rashes have been noted by Horder and Gow (1930). The leukocyte count is either normal or subnormal; a definite leukopenia is present in only 25 per cent of the patients. Leukocytosis occurs late in the disease or in early convalescence. Relapses are by no means uncommon.

Pathologic Picture

The changes observed at necropsy are those of a viremia with destructive inflammation in the lungs (Lillie, 1933; Binford and Hauser, 1944; de Gara and Furth, 1948). The consolidated areas are readily palpable and sharply demarcated from normal lung tissue. They are gray, gray-red or plum-colored lesions. The pleura may be smooth or exhibit petechiae and fresh fibrin deposits. A small amount of seromucoid fluid may be present in the trachea and bronchi, but in the majority of cases they are empty and the mucosa is not swollen. When the psittacotic process is complicated by secondary, bacterial invasion, the mucosa is swollen and the bronchi are filled with purulent exudate. Microscopic examination discloses that the areas, which, at first glance, appear to be completely consolidated, have undergone unevenly distributed lobular changes. Alveoli containing air or serum are dispersed throughout the consolidated portion of the lung. In fully developed lesions, the alveolar spaces contain an abundance of fibrin and many lymphocytes, macrophages and desquamated alveolar epithelial cells. Many cells in the alveolar exudate and in the lymph sinuses of the hilar lymph nodes show active phagocytosis and intracytoplasmic elementary bodies. The relative absence of polymorphonuclear leukocytes in the exudate and the minor change in the large bronchioles and bronchi give the pneumonia in psittacosis a characteristic pattern. It is doubtless not absolutely specific, since in proved cases the lesions are similar to those seen in interstitial pneumonia associated with other viral agents. However, Binford and Hauser (1944) were able to find definite differences between the microscopic lung lesions of psittacosis and those of Q fever or other virus pneumonias.

In the slightly enlarged and congested liver, the characteristic microscopic lesions are due to focal necrosis. Kupffer cells contain elementary bodies. The spleen may be enlarged and may contain relatively small follicles and engorged sinuses filled with phagocytic cells. Cloudy swelling and hypertrophy of the muscle are the principal changes in the heart. Varying degrees of degeneration involve the parenchyma of the kidneys. Hemorrhages and capillary thrombi have been observed in the adrenals of patients infected by the highly toxic

Louisiana virus. Congestion and edema of the brain and spinal cord are not infrequent. Although Sprunt and Berry (1936) found no evidence of changes in the neurons, they noted proliferative and degenerative changes in the capillary endothelium and hemorrhages which they attributed to toxic factors secondary to the presence of pneumonia.

EXPERIMENTAL INFECTION; HOST RANGE

Mice, depending on the strain of virus used, may be infected by the intranasal, intraperitoneal, intracerebral, intravenous or subcutaneous routes or by feeding. The duration of the illness depends upon the amount, virulence and toxin-producing ability of the virus. Death ensues in from 3 to 30 days with an average of 8 to 10 days; occasionally, some mice recover. In animals infected by the subcutaneous route or by feeding, the course is always protracted. Latent infections persisting for 10 to 12 months have been observed (Meyer and Eddie, 1933; Bedson, 1938). At necropsy two to four days after intraperitoneal inoculation, the spleen and liver appear normal and the abdominal viscera are covered by a thin, sticky exudate consisting of endothelial cells and leukocytes usually packed with viral bodies. There are no lung lesions. At necropsy five to ten days after intraperitoneal inoculation, the abdominal cavity is filled with a stringy, turbid, fibrinous exudate, rich in viral bodies; the enlarged liver and spleen are coated with a thick layer of fibrin, which is easily peeled off. Marginal necroses varying in size and number are present in the liver. Psittacosis virus administered intranasally produces widespread consolidations of the lung. Discrete foci of pneumonia are manifested as limiting infective dilutions of virus are approached; these areas are gray, almost translucent, 1 to 3 mm. in diameter (Hornus, 1940; Rudd and Burnet, 1941; de Gara and Furth, 1948). Virus injected intracerebrally causes irritability, ataxia, convulsive seizures and death within 3 to 6 days. The meninges are moist and deeply injected. Microscopically, the meningo-encephalitis is characterized by an exudate of polymorphonuclear and mononuclear cells, which extends along the blood vessels into the brain.

Most strains of psittacosis virus are reported to have little effect on guinea pigs when inoculated intraperitoneally, except for a prolonged febrile reaction. However, strains recently isolated in Louisiana (Olson and Larson, 1945; Fite, Larson and Olson, 1946) and California from human beings and the egret strain are highly virulent for guinea pigs, irrespective of the route of inoculation. Some strains of psittacosis virus produce fatal meningo-encephalitis in rabbits infected by the intracerebral route. Occasionally, extensive pneumonic consolidations are produced by intratracheal injections of virus (Rivers and Berry, 1931a). Infection of the rabbit eye has produced a violent reaction (Evans and Moore, 1950). Pocket gophers (*Thomomys bottae bottae*) are susceptible to subcutaneous infection. Wild and white laboratory rats and deer mice (*Peromyscus sp.*) are not very susceptible to intraperitoneal infection. Syrian hamsters (*Cricetus auratus*), cotton rats (*Sigmodon hispidus hispidus*) and squirrels (*Citellus beecheyi*) may be successfully infected by the intranasal or intracranial route. *Macacus rhesus* monkeys may be infected by the intratracheal or intracerebral route (Rivers and Schwentker, 1934). Intraperitoneal inoculation of the Louisiana virus produced no ill effects and no gross lesions in rodents sacrificed on the twenty-second day after injection (Olson and Larson, 1945).

Parakeets or love birds (*Melopsittacus undulatus*) from aviaries proved free from psittacosis are susceptible to intramuscular, intranasal and intracerebral infection. Immature birds readily contract an infection by exposure to sick birds which shed the virus in droppings. When death occurs during the acute stage, gross pathologic findings are a semipurulent coating over the air sac and the inner lining of the sternum, exudate in the pericardial sac, a large liver occasionally studded with areas of necrosis or infarction surrounded by hemorrhagic zones, a large spleen sometimes spotted with necrotic areas, and large, soft kidneys; only rarely are lesions demonstrable in the lungs. At least 31 species of the parrot family act as spontaneous hosts to psittacosis. Java ricebirds (*Munia oryzivora*), canaries (*Serinus canaria*), and various finches (*Poephila, Cyanospiza*) and sparrows (*Zonotrichia*) of the order *Passeriformes* contract psittacosis when exposed to infected parrots or parakeets. The domestic fowl (*Gallus gallus*) is occasionally spontaneously infected (Meyer and Eddie, 1942; Karrer, Eddie and Meyer, 1950). They are susceptible to psittacosis virus by injection or by exposure; many develop latent infections and few succumb (Meyer, 1948). Pigeons (*Columba livia*) (Coles, 1940; Meyer, Eddie and Yanamura, 1942b; Smadel, Wall and Gregg, 1943; Labzoffsky, 1947; Davis, 1950) and doves (*Streplopelia risoria*) are readily infected by intramuscular and intracerebral routes. Intramuscular injections of virus are commonly fatal to doves, while intracerebral injection is required to accomplish the same result in pigeons. Parrot or parakeet psittacosis viruses rarely produce fatal meningo-encephalitis in pigeons, while intracranial inoculation of viruses isolated from pigeons and chickens regularly produces fatal meningitis even in birds with complement-fixing antibodies in their sera (Meyer, Eddie and Yanamura, 1942a). Ducks (*Anas platyrhynchos*) are readily infected by the intramuscular route with pigeon and duck viruses (Meyer and Eddie, 1947). Occasionally, the disease ends fatally; if the fowl recovers, the virus may persist in the liver and spleen for several weeks or as long as 50 days. Fulmars or petrels (*Fulmar glacialis*) (Haagen and Mauer, 1938), American herring gulls (*Larus argentatus smithsonianus*) (Meyer and Eddie, 1947), willets (*Catotrophus semipalmatus*), bleeding-heart doves (*Galli columbia cruenta*) and snowy

egrets (*Egretta candissima*) are spontaneously infected.

ETIOLOGY

The elementary bodies of psittacosis, singly or in pairs, undergo a developmental cycle in the cytoplasm of host cells (Bedson and Bland, 1932; Levinthal, 1930; Bland and Canti, 1935). In tissue cultures or in yolk-sac cells they enlarge rapidly and become embedded in a homogeneous ground substance or matrix. These initial bodies at first divide into elements of comparable size, but as multiplication progresses the elements of division become smaller and smaller until the final elementary-body stage is reached. Intracellular development progresses as follows (Yanamura and Meyer, 1941; Weiss, 1949): One or more elementary bodies, which are red when tinged according to Macchiavello's method, or black-purple when stained with Castaneda's method, invade a cell and incite the formation of a common matrix. Later, the virus particles are dispersed at opposite ends of a cell, and each group is surrounded by a separate matrix, thus inducing double or triple foci of infection within a cell. These large forms measure 2 to 12 μ in diameter and correspond to the plaques of Bland and Canti, and to the inclusion bodies of Levinthal. The matrix of these homogeneous inclusion bodies is blue-green when stained according to Macchiavello's method, and, since it is not densely colored, the virus particles themselves are readily recognized. Within 18 to 24 hours after infection this first phase of development is completed. The virus particles then begin to multiply profusely, and decrease in size to form typical elementary bodies. As the matrix becomes less dense, tinctorial differences become apparent; the larger virus particles stain blue and the smaller forms, red. Electron micrographs suggest that a capsular substance may be responsible for the varying tinctorial reactions. In living preparations, the initial particles, which are immobile in the originally rigid homogeneous inclusion bodies, increase in motility until finally in the flexible virus colony the elementary bodies undergo rapid oscillatory movement. This change more or less coincides with the conversion from blue to red staining reactions. The inclusion body is always surrounded by a definite membrane which persists when in a multiple infection of the cytoplasm one or two colonies coalesce; a free dispersal of the elements of a colony through the cytoplasm is rarely observed. By the forty-eighth hour the matrix of the inclusion body presents evidences of liquefaction and the elementary bodies have become so numerous that they may fill the entire cytoplasm of the cell. Death and rupture of the host cell release myriads of elementary bodies, which are then capable of repeating the cycle in new cells. Levinthal's (1935) observation that in damaged cells the virus multiplies without a definite matrix formation is readily demonstrated in tissue cultures, in which the embryonic cells are merely surviving. The initial bodies in the plaques are always larger than the parent organisms and must be low in virulence, since they find it difficult to enter new cells. That these cytoplasmic plaques or inclusion bodies are true virus colonies made up of elementary bodies is conclusively established. Only the exact nature of the matrix remains uncertain. Although findings in tissue cultures strongly indicate that it may be a product of the cytoplasm, Findlay (1938b) suggested that it may be a secretory product of the elementary bodies.

Elementary bodies of psittacosis are usually retained by Berkefeld V, W and N and Chamberland L3 filter candles and Seitz EK filter pads. Collodion membranes with an average pore size of 0.6 μ give filtrates having as much virus as the original material. The largest elementary bodies observed in photomicrographs measure 380 mμ, and the smallest 280 mμ (Lazarus and Meyer, 1939), while according to Kurotchkin et al. (1947) in electron micrographs the mean diameter of the spherical elements is 455 ± 78 mμ. Centrifugation for from six to eight hours at 15,000 r.p.m. deposits the major portion of the virus. Exposure to 56° C. for 30 minutes does not completely inactivate the virus; it is readily inactivated at 60° C. for ten minutes. Crude, heavy suspensions in broth may remain infectious at +4° C. for several weeks, but preparations of elementary bodies in buffered saline are noninfectious 29 days after storage. Frozen at −70° C., the virus remains active for over 2 years. When preserved in 50 per cent glycerol in buffered saline with a pH 7.6 and held at +4° C., heavy suspensions retain their activity for from 10 to 20 days. Sputum and human lung specimens rapidly lose potency in glycerol. Formalin (0.1 per cent) and phenol (0.5 per cent) inactivate psittacosis virus in 24 to 36 hours, while 10 per cent ether at room temperature is destructive within 30 minutes.

Psittacosis virus is readily grown in tissue cultures of the Maitland, Li-Rivers and Zinsser-FitzPatrick types (Yanamura and Meyer, 1941). More recently, the roller-tube-tissue technic has come into use (Morgan and Wiseman, 1946). Successful propagation of the virus in the chick embryo infected by the chorio-allantoic, amniotic, allantoic and yolk-sac methods provides highly infective suspensions needed in serologic and immunologic studies (Beveridge and Burnet, 1946).

Yolk sacs heavily infected with certain human, avian and mammalian viruses of the psittacosis-lymphogranuloma group when shaken with amniotic or allantoic fluid are toxic to mice on intravenous or intraperitoneal injection (Rake and Jones, 1942, 1944; Hamre and Rake, 1944; Manire and Meyer, 1950). Certain viruses kill 50 per cent of the mice within the first 16 hours after injection; later deaths, presumably due to infection, begin 24 hours after the intravenous inoculation. The two-phase death curves are characteristic for the Louisiana, Illinois, and meningopneumonitis viruses. The primary toxicity of these viruses, although bound to virus particles, is not affected by aureomycin treatment of test mice. The toxicity of psittacosis viruses isolated from birds or patients, who gave histories of bird contact, is low and bound to the virus particles; therefore, no time lapse between toxic and infectious deaths in mice is observed.

Bedson (1936) found that the psittacosis virus contains at least two antigens, one a heat-labile antigen destroyed by temperatures above 60° C., the other able to withstand boiling or even autoclaving at 135° C. The labile antigen is also destroyed by phenol, acids and papain. The heat-stable antigen is resistant to proteolytic enzymes but is readily destroyed by potassium periodate in low concentrations. This behavior suggests that it is a carbohydrate (Barwell, 1948). During infection, antibodies against both antigens are produced. Although the relation of antibodies against the heat-stable antigen to immunity against infection is not known, they constitute a reliable index of infection. The heat-stable antigen in all probability is common to the entire lymphogranuloma-psittacosis group. The toxin-neutralization technic with antiserum produced in the rooster by hyperimmunization has arranged 27 strains thus far tested into six separate and distinct antigenic groups represented by (1) the Louisiana virus, (2) the feline pneumonitis agent of Baker, (3) the San Francisco pneumonitis agent, (4) the meningopneumonitis virus of Francis and Magill, (5) four pigeon ornithosis agents of Meyer and Eddie and (6) 14 strains isolated from a wide variety of avian and human sources. Nothing definite is known about the antigens which give rise to antibodies responsible for the high species-specific protection against different members of the lymphogranuloma-psittacosis group (Hilleman, 1945). Cross-protection tests indicate that strains of avian origin have a broader antigenic pattern than those of mammalian origin (Wagner, Golub and Andrew, 1949).

Individuals recovering from an attack of psittacosis are generally believed to be re-sistant to reinfection. However, Rasmussen-Ejde (1938) reported on two women who contracted the fulmar disease a second time, and Meyer (1939-1940) and Wenckebach (1936) presented data on proved second attacks. Apparently, immunity is not absolute, and the residual virus held in certain tissues is not always in innocuous equilibrium. A viral agent endowed with the ability to persist in the tissues occasionally produces a carrier stage after recovery, and a patient who continues to shed virus in the sputum eight years after a severe psittacosis infection was recently discovered by Meyer and Eddie (1951a).

Early reports on immunity (Rivers, Berry and Rhoads, 1930; Bedson, 1933) emphasized that neutralizing antibodies were not demonstrated in sera of convalescent patients. Later, by using a very delicate technic, Rivers and Schwentker (1934) found that monkeys recovered from psittacotic pneumonitis or vaccinated with active virus possessed small amounts of neutralizing antibodies in their sera, and that some human beings who gave a history of psittacosis possessed demonstrable neutralizing antibodies. In the hands of Hilleman (1945) and St. John and Gordon (1947) the neutralization of viral activity by antiserum prepared in chickens proved valuable in identifying some members of the psittacosis-lymphogranuloma group. Certain pneumonitis strains of human origin, those of feline origin, the majority of those of murine origin and those isolated from calves are antigenically distinct entities. The ultimate aim—to type psittacosis viruses isolated from human sputum or lung tissue and thus determine the source of infection—cannot be achieved with certainty with this technic. The protective effect of the antisera on experimental infections has likewise been demonstrated. Bedson (1936) has shown that the serum of human psittacosis patients reacts specifically by fixing complement when brought in contact with infectious mouse spleen. Parrots and parakeets (Meyer and Eddie, 1939a,b) recovered from psittacosis develop antibodies that fix complement in the presence of psittacosis and lymphogranuloma antigens, while sera from pigeons (Eddie and Francis, 1942; Davis, 1950) and occasionally human sera may react only in the presence of psittacosis antigens. During active immunization with active or inactive virus, specific complement-fixing antibodies are demonstrable in sera of mice, guinea pigs, rabbits and monkeys. Specific antibodies in the serum of human beings infected with psittacosis and lymphogranuloma venereum viruses are revealed by removing the group antibody by absorption with steamed virus (Bedson et al., 1950). The indirect complement-fixation test (Karrer, Eddie and Meyer, 1950), the hemagglutination and conglutinating-complement-absorption tests are employed in the study of infection with psittacosis viruses in avian populations (Hilleman, Haig and Helmold, 1951).

Hyperimmune serum of guinea pigs, rabbits, monkeys and chickens agglutinates elementary bodies in titers as high as 1:320 (Lazarus and Meyer, 1939; Hilleman, 1945; Labzoffsky, 1946).

Specific intradermal reactions in patients with psittacosis are obtained by the use of skin-test antigens consisting of dilute hydrochloric acid extracts of suspensions of psittacosis virus (Barwell, 1949; Bedson et al., 1949).

DIAGNOSIS

A history of association with birds always suggests a diagnosis of psittacosis in patients with pneumonitis; but some cases of "influenza" or "atypical pneumonia" with no definite history of avian exposure have lately been diagnosed as psittacosis. During the acute and convalescent phases of suspected psittacosis, every effort should be made to isolate the virus by inoculation of citrated blood or sputum into mice (Rivers and Berry, 1935). Virus has been found in the blood of human psittacosis patients taken during the first two weeks of an attack, in throat-washings, in vomitus, and in sputum up to and including the

twenty-sixth day of the disease. At necropsy, efforts should be made to obtain the virus from lungs and spleen. Of 364 clinically and serologically proved cases of psittacosis, the nature of the infection was confirmed in 62 through the isolation of virus (Meyer and Eddie, 1951b).

The demonstration of complement-fixing antibodies is being used with increasing success to establish that a given acute illness in man is caused by a member of the psittacosis-lymphogranuloma group (Meyer and Eddie, 1939b; Smadel, 1943). Although at present it is impossible to make a precise differentiation between human psittacosis and lymphogranuloma venereum, serologic tests are the clinician's only rapid diagnostic tool (Meyer, 1942; Smadel, Wertman and Reagan, 1943). Cold agglutinins as a rule are not demonstrable in the blood of psittacosis patients. Complement-fixing antibodies may appear in the serum of untreated patients from four to eight days after the onset of symptoms. Under vigorous chemotherapy appearance of these antibodies may be delayed for 20 to 40 days. Additional serum specimens must be examined and any rise in titer noted; if the titer rises within the next four or five days, a tentative diagnosis of psittacosis may be rendered. A serum titer of 1:16 or greater when obtained from a patient with clinical manifestations suggestive of psittacosis may be considered positive. Precautions are necessary in interpreting the test. Serum from a patient infected with the virus of lymphogranuloma venereum reacts strongly with psittacosis antigen. The sera of patients with acute lymphogranuloma infections occasionally yield significantly high complement-fixation titers in the presence of psittacosis virus; these fade during convalescence. This is in contrast to psittacosis infections, in which titers rise during convalescence and persist for many months; in carriers, they may remain stable for years. Confusing anamnestic co-reactions may be encountered in slaughter-house workers who have acute Q fever or brucellosis (Meyer and Eddie, 1951b). Individuals constantly exposed to psittacosis virus, such as aviary owners, pet-shop employees, pigeon breeders, as a rule show complement-fixing antibodies in their sera in titers varying from 1:8 to 1:32 (Meyer, 1942).

TREATMENT

Chemotherapy. Drug therapy has scored noteworthy successes against the infections caused by large viruses comprising the psittacosis-lymphogranuloma group. Sulfonamides were first used for the successful treatment of human lymphogranuloma venereum (Gjurić, 1938; Wilson, 1948), and experiments on mice and guinea pigs infected with this virus fully confirmed the clinical observations (Levaditi, 1938). Though symptoms cease, the virus can still be obtained from infected tissues for at least a year after treatment. The mode of action of sulfonamides, as well as the sulfones, is very similar to that on bacteria; it is virustatic, not virucidal. In tissue cultures, as in mice, sulfonamides inhibit growth of the lymphogranuloma virus, and this growth inhibition is antagonized by p-aminobenzoic acid or procaine. In fact, the compound accelerates the growth of the virus. By contrast, the growth of typhus rickettsiae is not inhibited by sulfonamides, but is inhibited by p-aminobenzoic acid. Both organisms grow together in tissue culture; by addition of the appropriate drug, the growth of one organism can be stimulated, that of the other inhibited (Takemori, 1949). Psittacosis virus is very rarely sensitive to sulfonamides, either in mice (Rudd and Burnet, 1941; Hurst, Peters and Melvin, 1950) or in man (Meiklejohn et al., 1944; Levinson, Gibbs and Beardwood, 1944), and therefore sulfonamides are of little therapeutic value in this disease. The well-known parakeet strain 6BC and the mouse pneumonitis virus are sensitive to sulfadiazine or sulfapyridine, and p-aminobenzoic acid antagonizes the protective action in mice (Mudrow and Bock, 1943; Golub, 1948; Morgan, 1948). Pteroylglutamic acid is actively antago-

nistic for increasingly large doses of sulfadiazine, suggesting that, as in the case of certain bacteria which synthesize pteroylglutamic acid, the primary action of sulfadiazine on the 6BC psittacosis virus is directed against the incorporation of p-aminobenzoic acid into pteroylglutamic acid (Morgan, 1948).

The large viruses of the psittacosis-lymphogranuloma group are susceptible to certain antibiotics. Inhibition of their growth by penicillin was first observed (Andrewes, King and van den Ende, 1943; Levaditi and Vaisman, 1944), and then the curative effect of the drug was established in mice, pigeons, ricebirds and human beings (Heilman and Herrel, 1944a,b; Bedson and May, 1945; Meyer and Eddie, 1947; Turgasen, 1944; Wolins, 1948; Goggio, 1949). The virus is not eliminated from mice and birds successfully treated with penicillin during an acute attack, and they become immune carriers of the agent (Hurst, Peters and Melvin, 1950; Quan, Meyer and Eddie, 1950). Through microscopic studies on the effect of penicillin on the agents of feline and murine pneumonitis in the yolk sac of chick embryos it was learned that this antibiotic prevented division of the virus particle. Under the influence of penicillin, an abnormal growth, evidenced by irregularly shaped, vacuolated plaques, continues to injure host cells (Weiss, 1950b). In sharp contrast, under identical experimental conditions, aureomycin is a more powerful inhibitor of activity of the large viruses. This antibiotic prevents initial-body division and almost completely suppresses growth of the virus. The dwarfed small plaques which may eventually develop from initial bodies have little or no injurious effect on the invaded host cells (Gogolak and Weiss, 1950). The superior inhibitory effect of aureomycin is reflected in the reports on its curative action against psittacosis and lymphogranuloma venereum in mice (Wagner, 1949; Levaditi and Vaisman, 1949). Despite its activity, many treated mice have become carriers

(Hurst, Peters and Melvin, 1950). Early accounts of aureomycin treatment of lymphogranuloma venereum in man have been enthusiastic (Wright et al., 1948; Prigot et al., 1949), but in recent reports the lack of impressive clinical improvement is stressed (Robinson, Zheutlin and Trice, 1950; Schamberg, Carrozzino and Boger, 1951). In contrast, the favorable results of treatment of a number of patients with psittacosis have been placed on record (Brainerd et al., 1949; Woodward, 1949; Green, 1950; Schalm, de Vos and Dekking, 1950). In fact, early treatment of these acute infections may, in accordance with the experimental observations, throttle virus multiplication to such an extent that the development of complement-fixing antibodies is frequently delayed. Streptomycin shows little activity in the treatment of infections caused by the psittacosis-lymphogranuloma viruses. There is general agreement that chloramphenicol is less active than aureomycin or terramycin (Wells and Finland, 1949; Hurst, Peters and Melvin, 1950; Kneeland and Price, 1950).

EPIDEMIOLOGY

The observations of the past 15 years fully attest to the wide distribution of psittacosis among birds. Of great significance was the discovery that visibly healthy birds harbor the virus and as shedders distribute the infective agent. Evidence collected by Burnet in Australia (1935; 1939) and by Parodi and Silvetti (1946) strongly supports the belief that the infection is common among wild parrots, parakeets and conures, perhaps as a population regulator. Mortality rates among imported birds (Meyer and Eddie, 1939a; Dunnahoo and Hampton, 1945) and in zoological gardens (Troup, Adam and Bedson, 1939; Tomlinson, 1941) are high either because the birds had not been immunized by nest infections or because relapses were brought about by low temperature, crowding in insanitary cages and improper feeding. Enzootic psittacosis is constantly present in parakeet aviaries and pigeon and duck breeding establishments (Meyer, 1948). The disease has a world-wide distribution in man (Meyer and Eddie, 1951a; Lépine and Sautter, 1951). In the early years, 317 cases were attributed to the handling of parrots and parakeets. Since 1940 it has been discovered that pigeons, ducks, chickens and possibly turkeys and pheasants disseminate the virus, and over 200 infections in the United States have been linked with these birds (Meyer and Eddie, 1951). It is now evident that the epidemiologist must carefully investigate every known avian and mammalian source before inquiring into the possibility of human spreaders of the virus. In the past, single cases escaped detection, and old reports deal principally with house epidemics which established the pattern, now so well known, of the psittacosis epidemic. The great epidemics of the past occurred during the winter months. This seasonal peak is probably due to prolonged exposure of persons to infected avian pets in closed rooms of a winter household. It is well to remember, however, that severe psittacosis on the Faroe Islands and among pigeon fanciers the world over is not uncommon in midsummer and early fall and that more recent observations indicate that psittacosis can be contracted throughout the year (Meyer, 1942). People of middle age or older are the ones usually attacked. Although the disposition to contract psittacosis is not confined to the older age groups, children rarely react in a clinically recognizable manner. That the younger age groups are susceptible was proved when psittacosis virus was isolated from the lung of a 14-year-old boy who handled birds (Meyer and Eddie, 1947). The disease has a greater incidence among women than men. In California the ratio is 60:31; in Germany, 33:19 (Pfaffenberg, 1936) and 17:8 (Haagen and Mauer, 1938). This heavier distribution among women may be ascribed in part to the fact that many engage in parakeet breeding as a livelihood, or that as lovers of pets they more frequently come in contact with birds. Approximately 40 clinical infections are recognized annually in the United States.

That occupational psittacosis is quite common in persons engaged in handling psittacine birds, pigeons and ducks has not been fully accepted, though published records amply attest to its existence (Meyer, 1942). The ways by which psittacosis virus is transmitted from birds to man, in order of importance, are: (1) by indirect transmission by air, (2) through handling sick or dead birds, or having contact with feathers, excreta or nasal discharge of sick or latently infected birds, and (3) through bite wounds (Laubscher et al., 1945). The ease with which inhalation of virus induces pneumonic lesions in susceptible mammals points directly to the respiratory tract as the principal portal of entry for the virus. Forty-four laboratory-acquired psittacosis infections in scientific personnel and animal caretakers fully attest to the extreme contagiousness of the disease which demands utmost caution in the handling of the diverse specimens suspected of carrying the virus (Sulkin and Pike, 1951).

Over the years, data have continued to mount on the frequency of spread of infection from person to person. At least 23 instances involving 30 nurses are known in which contact with sick birds was definitely excluded. Greatly disconcerting are the transmissions which occur in hospitals; in an epidemic in Buenos Aires, reported by Loizaga and Averbach (1945), 26 cases with 13 deaths were observed. Eaton, Beck and Pearson (1941) reported that a man transmitted psittacosis virus to 3 nurses. The 1943 epidemic of a severe pneumonitis in the bayou region of Louisiana, with a toll of 8 deaths in 19 recognized infections among nursing attendants, emphasizes the importance of direct contact in human-to-human transmission of psittacosis (Treuting and Olson, 1944). The unusual history of a patient known to be a psittacosis carrier for 8 years without transmitting the disease fails to indicate that chronic psittacosis in man is contagious (Meyer and Eddie, 1951c).

The case-fatality rate for the pandemic years 1929 and 1930, 18 per cent, declined with the recognition of mild infections to about 11 per cent. Then with the introduction of penicillin it dropped further; in a series of 228 cases studied between 1940 and 1946 there were only 21 fatal infections, a fatality rate of 9.3 per cent (Meyer and Eddie, 1947). Improved chemotherapy with aureomycin and terramycin lowered the case fatality in 92 cases to only 2 deaths (Meyer and Eddie, 1951a). Most of the deaths occurred in people from 40 to 60 years old.

Control Measures

Psittacosis is a minor public health problem and requires no elaborate administrative apparatus (Meyer and Eddie, 1951a). However, effective educational campaigns must continuously warn the public and physicians to appreciate the danger from contact with apparently healthy birds.

Immunization of human volunteers against psittacosis has been carried out with dilutions of active virus given subcutaneously (Rivers and Schwentker, 1934). The injection of antigens prepared from phenol-killed, ether-extracted, yolk-sac suspensions (Wagner et al., 1946), if administered repeatedly in large amounts, likewise stimulates the production of antibodies in man. How effective such measures are in the control of the disease in man is not known.

LYMPHOGRANULOMA VENEREUM

(Synonyms: Climatic bubo, tropical bubo, venereal bubo, fourth venereal disease, sixth venereal disease, lymphogranuloma inguinale, granulomatous lymphomatosis, poradenitis, lymphopathia venereum, esthiomene, *maladie de Nicolas et Favre*).

Introduction

Lymphogranuloma venereum is a protean disease usually transmitted by venereal contact, and manifested by both constitutional symptoms and acute and chronic tissue changes in the inguinal and rectoanal regions. It is caused by a virus which is similar to that producing psittacosis.

HISTORY

Although John Hunter described inguinal buboes in the male, it was reserved for Wallace accurately to describe them and their accompanying constitutional symptoms. Desruelles gave an excellent account of two cases of vulvar hypertrophy following the involvement of the inguinal lymph nodes. Hugier is credited with introducing the name esthiomene for the characteristic induration and discoloration which involves the affected parts. Multiple abscesses in inguinal adenitis were originally observed by Velpeau; it was Nélaton and Tanton and Pigeon, who declared them to be the nontuberculous manifestations of an unknown disease (Koteen, 1945). Suppurative inguinal adenitis, described by Blanc, Godding, Scheube and others (Brumpt, 1935) between 1896 and 1912 as climatic bubo, was attributed to plague, malaria, or fatigue, until Rost in 1912 advanced the hypothesis that it was probably of venereal origin. The term *strumösen Bubonen* was introduced by Klotz (1890), who first observed and described the disease in the United States and who also was the first to note the presence of penile lesions. Durand, Nicolas and Favre (1913) brought the heterogeneous manifestations of strumous buboes into one disease entity, which they called subacute inguinal lymphogranulomatosis. They asserted that it was transmitted sexually and conclusively differentiated it from syphilis and tuberculosis. But erroneously they believed that its close resemblance to the picture of Hodgkin's disease sanctioned the designation lymphogranuloma inguinale. Phylactos, a pupil of Favre, called it the fourth venereal disease, but emphasized that its characteristics were identical with those of climatic bubo.

For a time, there appeared to be no correlation between lymphogranuloma venereum and the seemingly independent genital diseases observed by gynecologists and surgeons for many years, viz., the troublesome ulceration and elephantiasis of the female pudenda which had been known for nearly a hundred years and the inflammatory strictures of the rectum. Though often associated with venereal disease, the origin of lymphogranuloma venereum was clarified only with the advent of the Frei test (Frei, 1925). Hellerström and Wassén (1930) succeeded in producing a bacteria-free meningitis in rhesus monkeys by intracerebral inoculation of pus derived from a bubo. Their work was continued by Levaditi et al. (1932) and Findlay (1933), who proved that many of these diverse diseases independently recognized and described in the past were caused by the same virus.

With the introduction of the mouse as a suitable laboratory animal for study of the disease and the demonstration of virucidal antibodies by Levaditi et al. (1932), lymphogranuloma venereum began to be investigated as a virus infection. Gamma (1924) described large bodies in the cytoplasm of cells from infected lymph nodes; the nature of these bodies still is uncertain. The small granules reported by Gay Prieto (1927-28) and the granulocorpuscles of Miyagawa et al. (1935) were recognized by Findlay et al. (1938a,b) and by Rake and Jones (1942) as elementary bodies derived from larger initial bodies in an interesting developmental cycle. Rake, McKee and Shaffer (1940) propagated the virus in the yolk sac of the embryonated chicken egg. The complement-fixation test and an improved skin-test antigen soon followed (Bedson et al., 1949).

CLINICAL PICTURE

The symptomatology can best be grasped when the pathogenesis of the infection is understood. The disease process usually includes the following stages: (1) invasion by the viral agent, usually symptomless; (2) primary stage, genital or anorectal lesion;

(3) invasion of lymphatic nodes; (4) late sequelae due to fibrotic changes in or around lymph nodes (Coutts, 1950).

Only a few days may elapse between exposure to infection and the appearance of the primary lesion. If the primary lesion escapes notice, it may be from several weeks to two months before other lesions become obvious. Sézary and Drain (1935) reported that the primary lesion was recognized in only 39 of 73 cases. In one clinic, only 14 of 60 patients acknowledged a primary lesion, while in another only 4 were seen in 130 early cases. The initial lesion appears as a vesicle, known as the herpetiform lesion of Cole (1933), and then bursts, leaving a shallow, grayish ulcer or lymphogranulomatous chancre. The clean-cut edges of the lesion, surrounded by a narrow band of reddened skin, are not indurated. It is usually painless and heals rapidly without leaving a scar. These evanescent lesions appear on the glans and prepuce of the penis, the posterior aspect of the labia, the vaginal walls, or the cervix. That the initial lesions may also be found within the urethra or in the region of the anus is well known. Axillary lesions have developed in surgeons accidentally infected in the course of surgical removal of infected lymph nodes. Orderlies have become contaminated while cleaning patients. Patients with painless, blisterlike lesions and considerable local swelling on the tip of the tongue, followed by enlarged glands in the neck have been reported; these lesions developed from 10 days to three weeks after the practice of cunnilingus. Cases of meningo-encephalitis caused by the agent of lymphogranuloma have been reported by Sabin and Aring (1942). Lymphogranulomatous infections of the eye in the form of conjunctivitis with oculoglandular syndromes, although rare, are being recognized with increasing frequency (Oliphant et al., 1942).

The secondary stage with enlargement of the regional lymph nodes usually occurs from 7 to 14 days after appearance of the initial lesion. Pain in the groin, followed by palpable and visible enlargement of the nodes, may be the only symptoms. In the male, the buboes involve the inguinal region, and at first are noticeable only as discrete, slightly tender, movable lymph nodes. Later they become adherent to the underlying tissues and form a large, single, tender inflammatory mass. In the majority of patients seen in the temperate zone, the adenitis is unilateral, while in the tropics it is frequently bilateral. It may heal spontaneously, but in about 40 to 60 per cent the nodes suppurate. When the primary lesion is intra-urethral or anorectal, the infection spreads to the pelvic nodes. The lymph drainage of the vagina favors involvement of the intrapelvic-perianal and deep pelvic nodes in the female.

The tertiary stage presents itself, early or late in the course of the disease, in well-defined syndromes or in isolated or associated manifestations in different organs or systems. The more easily recognized are esthiomene, urethrogenitoperineal syndrome, elephantiasis of the penis and the scrotum, rectal stenosis and plastic induration of the penis. The esthiomene frequently mentioned in the literature is a nondestructive elephantiasis in the preputium, the clitoris or the labia minora. It sometimes extends to the labia majora and other soft parts of the vulva and anus. Left untreated, the rectal type may lead to vaginorectal and vaginovesical fistulae, secondary infections, and death from sepsis and exhaustion. The effect of these processes on pregnancy appears to be minimal. Rectal strictures formerly attributed to injuries, syphilis or other causes are now recognized as sequels to lymphogranuloma infections. The specific proctitis usually arises from a spread of the infection from the perirectal tissues through the rectal wall; in the majority of cases it produces a stricture if left untreated. In the early stages of the proctitis the patients have little or no pain. Complete obstruction is uncommon, but the chronic process is frequently complicated by perirectal and perianal abscesses and fistulae. The adenitis is accompanied by constitutional symptoms consisting of chills, sweats, fever, prostration, loss of weight, anorexia, nausea, vomiting, pains in the chest and muscles, stiffness of the neck, headache, epistaxis, and bronchitis. Scarlatiniform rashes and those resembling erythema multiforme have been reported. Acute systemic invasion by the virus may bring about enlargement of all lymphatic nodes, the spleen and the liver. The virus is frequently disseminated throughout the body during the early stages of the disease; it has been recovered from the circulating blood, the spinal fluid and from material obtained by puncture of the spleen during the period when buboes are present. Accidental laboratory infections (Harrop, Rake and Shaffer, 1941) attest that the disease may have minimal symptoms: mild fever, fleeting muscular pains, and malaise. Moderate secondary anemia and leukopenia are common early in the disease. When the nodes suppurate there is often leukocytosis with relatively slight mononucleosis. The erythrocyte sedimentation rate is usually increased, and hyperproteinemia due to an increase in serum globulin has been reported. Transitory positive Wassermann reactions have been observed. A fatal termination is very rare, but may occur in patients with rectal strictures and other complications (Jaffé, 1948).

PATHOLOGIC PICTURE

There are no characteristic tissue changes in the lymphogranulomatous chancre; the cellular infiltration surrounding the ulcer consists mostly of plasma cells and histiocytes containing inclusion bodies. The reaction in the lymph nodes is a chronic, prolonged process in which necrosis and suppuration are conspicuous. Microscopically, the tissue response prevailing in perineal and genital tissues is the same as that in inguinal and pelvic lymph nodes. At times the lesions have some of the characteristics of those seen in tuberculosis and syphilis. However, Chapman and Hayden (1937) state that an experienced patholo-

gist can distinguish the lesions of lymphogranuloma from those of tuberculosis and syphilis. The inflammatory process consists of a great outpouring of mononuclear elements, especially plasma cells, a few neutrophiles and eosinophiles, and proliferation of the macrophages with giant-cell formation. Epithelioid transformation of the macrophages gives rise to peculiar tubercle-like nodules, which undergo necrosis. There is, in addition, a marked proliferation of fibrous tissue which, as the lesions heal, contracts, producing the rectal and anal strictures. The tendency toward keloid formation in the Negro may be responsible for the extent and frequency of stricture in this race. The cone or dumb-bell shaped, basophilic gamma bodies and the clusters and chains of the smaller azurophilic elementary bodies first described by Gay Prieto (1927-28) and Miyagawa et al. (1935) have been demonstrated in cells of human lesions (Coutts et al., 1942).

EXPERIMENTAL INFECTION; HOST RANGE

The first experimental transmission of the disease is credited to Hellerström (1929), who infected a man by the intraurethral route. Using monkey-passage material, Wassén (1935) infected Frei-negative patients suffering from general paralysis or dementia praecox; the lesions produced were typical of lymphogranuloma.

It was the successful transmission of the virus to the monkey and the mouse which greatly accelerated knowledge of the disease, its etiologic agent and methods of diagnosis. The span of the host range is still not completely known. The most highly susceptible animals are the monkey and mouse; less susceptible are the guinea pig (Grace and Suskind, 1940), rabbit, squirrel, marmot, harvest mouse (*Microtus agrestis*), rat, cat, dog and sheep. Results have been erratic in experimental infection of the less susceptible animals. Not considering individual differences in susceptibility, it is the age of the rat, guinea pig and rabbit which decides the outcome of experimental infections. Fowl, pigeons, ricebirds and para-keets fail to react to intracerebral injections of highly infectious passage virus.

To produce models of the human disease, monkeys have been infected by the intra-peritoneal, intrapreputial, intracutaneous, intrapulmonary and intra-ocular routes, and in the tissues of the intestine, rectum and lymph nodes. Typical inflammatory reac-tions developed locally, and the virus was readily demonstrable in the enlarged re-gional lymph nodes. Neither the intravenous nor the intraneural mode of injection will establish an infection.

Levaditi et al. (1932) injected mice intra-cerebrally with monkey-passage virus, while Findlay (1933) and Levaditi et al. (1949) initiated infections with human material. Of 26 strains transmitted to mice, only two were highly virulent; others lost their in-fectiousness on passage (Findlay, 1938a). The two virulent strains produced symp-toms of meningitis in 2 to 4 days. Many strains, when injected intracerebrally, in-duce, after an incubation time of 7 to 14 days, muscular in-co-ordination, paresis and weakness, with a mortality rate varying from 12 to 39 per cent (Wassén, 1935). In such mice, the histologic findings are those of a leptomeningitis, and impression prep-arations from the meninges furnish excel-lent material for the study of the large and small viral elements. Intranasal administra-tion of virus incites a pneumonic process which may be fatal between the fourth and sixth days; it is characterized by desquama-tive alveolitis, nodular inflammation around the capillaries and lymphatics, and the for-mation of virus bodies (Schoen, 1940; Shaffer et al., 1940). When the virus is in-jected intraperitoneally, it localizes in the brain if starch is injected intracerebrally. It may be successfully passaged through the testes of mice.

ETIOLOGY

The infective agent of lymphogranuloma venereum is a filterable, microscopically visible elementary body, which passes through its developmental cycle in the cytoplasm of reticulo-endothelial cells. Ele-mentary bodies may be demonstrated in cells from human lesions, and they are transferable to experimental animals. They are agglutinated by specific antisera and serve as specific antigens in complement-fixation tests and skin tests (Frei test).

Small bodies which sometimes appeared within monocytes of lymphogranuloma ab-scesses were described by Gay Prieto (1927-28) and by Findlay (1933). Subsequently, Miyagawa et al. (1935) named these bodies granulocorpuscles and estimated their diam-eter as being 0.3 μ. Coles (1936) and Nauck and Malamos (1937) demonstrated in Giemsa-stained films elementary bodies resembling those found in psittacosis and vaccinia. These elementary bodies were constantly present in the lesions, in tissue cultures and in infectious filtrates. All recent studies have furnished supportive evidence that when suitably stained, the virus of lymphogranuloma is visible under an ordi-nary microscope. Findlay, Mackenzie and MacCallum (1938) established the exist-ence of a developmental cycle in host cells. Gey and Bang (1939), who grew the lym-phogranuloma virus in tissue cultures of fibroblasts, observed that on the seventh day the cells were occupied by large vesicles filled with bodies in active Brownian move-ment. They saw no initial bodies and sug-gested that the vesicles might represent a cellular reaction to the invading viral agent. Coutts et al. (1942) described and illus-trated micro-inclusion and macro-inclusion bodies, which they demonstrated in 96 per cent of the smears prepared from lympho-granulomatous lymph nodes. The diverse observations have been correlated in an ex-cellent study by Rake and Jones (1942), who investigated the morphologic cycle of the lymphogranuloma agent in the yolk sac of the chick embryo. Using smears and sec-tions stained by the methods of Giemsa, Castaneda, Macchiavello and Noble, these workers showed that the morphology, de-velopmental forms and staining characteristics of the lymphogranuloma agent are practically indistinguishable from those of the etiologic agent of psittacosis.

The filterability of the agent is not constant. By the use of gradocol membranes according to the method of Elford, the diameter of the viral body has been estimated as being from 120 to 180 mμ. Electron micrographs of the elementary bodies propagated in the yolk sacs of developing chick embryos revealed a mean diameter of 438±47 mμ (Kurotchkin et al., 1947). At 37° C. the virus remains active from two to four days, while at 56° C. it loses the power to infect within 10 minutes. To keep the virus alive for a year or longer, it is best held at —30° to —70° C. in the frozen state. Ultraviolet radiation renders it noninfective within 30 minutes. In 50 per cent neutral glycerol, the activity is retained only for 7 to 14 days. Formalin (0.1 per cent) and phenol (0.5 per cent) inactivate the agent in 24 to 48 hours. Ten per cent ether at room temperature inactivates the virus in yolk-sac suspensions within 30 minutes.

The lymphogranuloma virus has been cultivated in media of the Maitland type, by the Miyagawa method, by the roller-tube tissue-culture technic, and by the Zinsser-FitzPatrick method modified according to Yanamura and Meyer. The agent is readily propagated in embryonated hens' eggs. The method of yolk-sac inoculation, used by Rake et al. (1940), is particularly valuable, as it yields highly infective (LD50 10⁻⁸) suspensions especially useful in morphologic and immunologic studies.

Rake and Jones (1944) reported isolating a toxic substance which is associated with the virus. The endotoxinlike factor is readily demonstrable in heavily infected yolk sacs of moribund embryos. It kills young mice rapidly after intravenous injection; if the activity is high and the dilutions are made in the allantoic and amniotic fluids, it occasionally kills after intraperitoneal injection. The toxin is labile and is readily inactivated at room temperature and by chemicals. It produces hemorrhages in the lung and gives specific complement-fixation reactions in the presence of serum from lymphogranuloma venereum patients. There is a heat-stable antigen which is apparently common to all the viruses of the lymphogranuloma-psittacosis group. Nigg, Hilleman and Bowser (1946), while attempting to enhance the antigenicity of virus in yolk-sac suspensions, noted that by adding phenol and boiling, the reactivity of the yolk-sac suspensions in complement-fixation tests was greatly intensified. Its heat-stability at boiling, dissociation by phenol and solubility in ether suggest that the complement-fixing antigen is probably a protein-polysaccharide-lipid complex. Treatment of partially purified yolk-sac suspensions of lymphogranuloma venereum virus with dilute hydrochloric acid yields an acid extract which causes intradermal reactions only in patients with lymphogranuloma venereum (Bedson et al., 1949; Barwell, 1949).

Koteen (1945) has stated that an attack of lymphogranuloma venereum probably induces a lasting immunity. It is known that an infected person is fully refractory to a cutaneous or intradermal reinfection with material proved to contain the virus; a local reaction similar to that induced by inactive virus (Frei reaction) develops at the site of insertion, but neither the skin nor the regional lymph nodes show signs of infection. Whether or not the immunity survives the disappearance of the virus from the host has not been determined. The prolonged coexistence of infection and immunity is characteristic of the lymphogranuloma-psittacosis viral agents. Consequently, clinical relapses have been reported and may be anticipated. However, recent studies have shown that in completely recovered experimental animals, a fairly large percentage becomes immune to intranasal or intracerebral reinfection (Beck, Eaton and O'Donnell, 1944). There is also evidence that the injection of inactivated preparations of the lymphogranuloma-psittacosis agents leads to the development of immune bodies and resistance to moderate infections. There are no records of human immunization against lymphogranuloma venereum by means of vaccines.

Reports are contradictory regarding the production of neutralizing antibodies to lymphogranuloma venereum virus. Negative results are attributable to the use of faulty technics, such as too short incubation of virus-serum mixtures or the use of serum dilutions in the presence of concentrated viral suspensions. Hyperimmunization of chickens (Hilleman, 1945) with yolk-sac suspensions invariably produces potent neutralizing antisera which possess protective, neutralizing, agglutinative and complement-fixation-inhibiting properties. A serum prepared against the lymphogranuloma venereum virus, however, neither neutralizes nor protects against an infection with any other member of the lymphogranuloma-psittacosis group. The sera of guinea pigs, rabbits, mice and rats immunized with the lymphogranuloma virus give strong complement-fixation reactions with the homologous antigen, and frequently an equally marked reaction will occur with heterologous antigens prepared from other members of the lymphogranuloma-psittacosis group (Eaton, Martin and Beck, 1942). The complement-fixation test indicates a broad antigenic similarity between the members of the group; however, unexplained differences in complement-fixation titers are on record in the literature (Eddie and Francis, 1942; Eaton, Martin and Beck, 1942; Smadel, Wertman and Reagan, 1943). The effective antigen is the heat-stable component common to viruses of the psittacosis-lymphogranuloma group. Absorption with steamed virus of serum from patients with lymphogranuloma venereum removes not only its ability to react with steamed homologous virus, but also the heat-labile and heat-stable antigens of a heterologous virus, but it will continue to react with unheated virus (Bedson et al., 1949).

DIAGNOSIS

Lymphogranuloma venereum must be differentiated from chancroid, bubo due to pyogenic lesions of the lower extremities, tuberculosis of the inguinal lymph nodes, gonorrhea, syphilis, granuloma inguinale, balanitis, plague, tularemia, carcinoma and tuberculosis of the rectum, and ulcerative colitis. Films of pus or biopsy material are examined for elementary bodies by means of the Macchiavello stain. Suspected material should be inoculated into the yolk sac of an embryonated hen's egg; intracerebral inoculation in mice is preferred, however, for diagnosis can be made in mice from 5 to 14 days earlier than in the chick embryo. Furthermore, the rodents are fairly resistant to infection by bacteria occasionally contaminating specimens of bubo pus or biopsy material. Identification of the virus is based upon its morphology, the fact that it is more liable to cause disease by the intracerebral than by the intraperitoneal route, and its susceptibility to sulfonamides. Toxin and neutralization tests of Hilleman, although reliable, are laborious and expensive. The virus, regularly present in pus from buboes, is being isolated with increasing frequency from tertiary lesions, but only occasionally from primary lesions. Thus far, it has been found only once in the human blood (Beeson, Wall and Heyman, 1946). The agent has been demonstrated in the spinal fluid in meningeal infections and in the stool of patients with proctitis. Unfortunately, biopsy is not commonly used for the diagnosis of lymphogranuloma venereum. Changes in chancres and lymph nodes are characteristic enough to distinguish it quite accurately from similar lesions of other known venereal diseases (Smith and Custer, 1948).

The skin test used in lymphogranuloma diagnosis, known as the Frei test, consists of the intradermal injection of 0.1 cc. of antigen and 0.1 cc. of control material. The test is read 48 and 96 hours after injection, and, if positive, the central induration of the papule caused by the antigen measures 6x6 mm. or more, while that caused by the control material measures 5x5 mm. or less. Originally, the Frei antigen was prepared by diluting pus from the bubo of a known human case of lymphogranuloma with five times its volume of sterile saline solution. Then, it was sterilized by heating at 60° C. for 2 hours on one day, and for 1 hour on the next. The antigens, which were prepared from infected mouse brains, were not satisfactory because of frequent nonspecific reactions. Rake, McKee and Shaffer (1940) reported on the preparation of an antigen from the yolk sacs of chick embryos moribund or recently dead from infection with the virus of lymphogranuloma venereum. Control material is prepared from the normal yolk sac of 10-day chick embryos. The skin-test material is known commercially as "lygranum." Positive reactions to yolk-sac antigens remain readily visible and palpable for 10 days and longer, and repeated testing apparently does not intensify the cutaneous sensitization.

The Frei test usually becomes positive 7 to 40 days after the onset of the adenitis. The rare negative Frei results in definite cases are usually due to such factors as the menses, septicemia, fever, tuberculosis, and coexistent early syphilis or early chancroid. The Frei test should be repeated if a patient is in the early stage of the infection. Connor and his associates (1937) have reported the results of studies on 1,265 patients; of these, 243 gave persistently positive reactions, and all but 17 of the 243 gave a history typical of infection or showed clinical manifestations. D'Aunoy and von Haam (1936) obtained results in 500 infected patients that were 98.1 per cent correct. The specificity of the Frei test is now considered to be of a high order (Reymann, 1951). The serologic reaction with lygranum may be positive in cases of viral pneumonia (Shaffer and Rake, 1947), and cutaneous reactions with psittacosis virus antigens may be positive in cases of lymphogranuloma venereum (Pollard and Witka, 1947). Acid extracts of lymphogranuloma venereum virus appear to give specific reactions when injected intradermally (Bedson et al., 1949). The Frei test probably remains positive for the life of the patient, but recent observations indicate that after immediate sulfonamide therapy it may be negative (Koteen, 1945).

With the obtainment of potent antigens by propagation of the virus in the yolk sac of the embryonated hen's egg (Rake, McKee and Shaffer, 1940) or in the lungs of mice (Shaffer, Rake and McKee, 1940), the use of the complement-fixation test for diagnostic purposes has assumed increasing importance. In the carefully executed examinations of Grace and Rake (1943), sera from patients with inguinal adenitis reacted in titers ranging from 1:6 to 1:480, with a mean of 1:98; sera from patients with proctitis were 96.8 per cent positive. The titer limits of both groups of patients were 1:6 to 1:920, with a mean of 1:213. Sera from symptomless patients gave an average titer of 1:32; of sera from 133 such patients, 97.7 per cent reacted positively to the complement-fixation test, while only 81.2 per cent gave a positive Frei test. A Wassermann or Kahn test should always be done as a control on the specimen of serum used for this work. Experience has taught that titers of 1:32 or over in the complement-fixation test made with steamed lymphogranuloma venereum virus and sera from patients, in whom the clinical findings are compatible with a diagnosis of lymphogranuloma venereum, suggest active infection with the lymphogranuloma venereum virus provided the patients are not in the early stages of syphilis (Knott et al., 1943; Bowser and Nigg, 1946; Bedson et al., 1949; Wetherbee et al., 1951). A single positive complement-fixation reaction as a rule is not a sufficient basis for a serologic diagnosis; tests should be repeated in order to find out whether the titer is rising (Reyn, 1951). It may serve as a useful instrument for screening population groups and for gauging the incidence of lymphogranuloma venereum; it has special epidemiologic significance since it can be performed concomitantly with a serologic examination for syphilis (Beeson and Miller, 1944). Occasionally, antibodies may be detected in sera of patients a month after infections, and sometimes prior to the appearance of a positive Frei reaction. The reaction probably remains positive as long as virus is still present in the host. The complement-fixation test is unsatisfactory as an index of the therapeutic effect of drugs (Robinson, Zheutlin and Trice, 1951). As a precaution against erroneous diagnosis, it must be remembered that the sera of patients recovered from psittacosis may give positive complement-fixation reactions with lymphogranuloma antigens. The ability of the serum of lymphogranuloma venereum patients to react with the psittacosis antigen may be removed by absorption of the group antibody with steamed lymphogranuloma virus. This somewhat laborious procedure leaves the major part of the antibody intact; the absorbed serum gives a specific complement-fixation reaction with unheated lymphogranuloma venereum virus, but not with the psittacosis virus (Bedson et al., 1949).

TREATMENT

Sulfonamides, in combination with fuadin, were introduced by Gjurić (1938) for the treatment of inguinal lymphogranuloma. The use of the drugs was later extended with good results to anorectal and genito-rectal cases. Grace (1944) achieved impressive effects with sulfanilamide and sulfa-thiazole; he preferred the latter. The sulfon-amide compounds are more effective in the treatment of early stages of lymphogranu-loma venereum than of the late complica-tions, such as elephantiasis, ulcerative processes and multiple draining sinuses. Conjunctivitis and iritis due to lympho-granuloma venereum virus readily yield to treatment with the sulfonamides. The seri-ous side effects have placed an obstacle in the way of their prolonged use. Patients may be clinically cured in spite of the per-sistence of the virus in the body. Penicillin has proved ineffective in treating the dis-ease in human beings. The encouraging results with aureomycin were brought out by Wright and his co-workers (1948) through studies of comparative therapeutic activity of various drugs against experi-mental infections in mice and in the chick embryo. Aureomycin and terramycin proved highly effective, while chloramphenicol is only indifferently active in the mouse in-fected intracerebrally or intraperitoneally (Levaditi and Vaisman, 1949; Hurst, Peters and Melvin, 1950). The enthusiastic reports concerning the high therapeutic value of aureomycin in human beings during the early stages of lymphogranuloma venereum have not been substantiated in recent re-ports. Clinical improvement is not impres-sive; failures in the early cases with buboes are not infrequent (Wammock et al., 1950; Robinson, Zheutlin and Trice, 1950). Aureo-mycin is as effective as sulfonamides but is too expensive for general use (Schamberg, Carrozzino and Boger, 1951). Aureomycin and terramycin may prove of value in the late manifestations such as proctitis and rectal stricture (Wammock et al., 1950).

EPIDEMIOLOGY

Lymphogranuloma venereum has a world-wide distribution, but since it is reportable in only a few places, there is no evidence concerning its prevalence. The deficiency is not imputable to administrative procedure alone; the disease has been poorly reported because satisfactory means for establish-ing a correct diagnosis have not been avail-able. The prevalence in tropical countries, and in the Mediterranean, southern and eastern ports is less a matter of climate than of unfortunate social conditions which go uncontrolled. In the United States, there is no scarcity of cases in clinics and hospitals. The disease is reportable in only 4 states: Alabama, California, Illinois and Washing-ton. The greatest number of cases occurs in areas east of the Mississippi (Koteen, 1945). The incidence at the New York Hospital in 1940 had reached 8 per 10,000 admissions. In San Francisco, of 34,766 admissions to the municipal venereal disease clinic, 1.9 per cent gave strong serologic reactions indic-ative of lymphogranuloma infection. The large reservoir of infection among Negroes, as shown by 25 to 40 per cent positive Frei tests or complement-fixation reactions in surveys in certain areas of the United States, represents a major public health problem (Luger, 1950). This high incidence in the colored race is not indicative of any racial predisposition.

CONTROL MEASURES

Modern plans for combating syphilis and gonorrhea, emphasizing, as they do, case finding and medical care and control of infected persons, are equally applicable to lymphogranuloma venereum. Little can be gained in the execution of such a program, however, until cases are made reportable. Adequate diagnostic facilities, including the complement-fixation test, must be made available through local health departments. Since serologic examinations are less expensive and more readily carried out, the complement-fixation test should be used in the routine examination of sexually promiscuous persons. The city health department should provide, free of charge, drugs for treatment. Early, intensive treatment of clinical and subclinical infections should be assigned to private physicians or special clinics. Public education as to the nature and extent of lymphogranuloma, and the providing of opportunities through which physicians may be kept informed of modern developments in its diagnosis and treatment, are important steps in any lymphogranuloma control program.

REFERENCES

Andrewes, C. H., King, H., and van den Ende, M., 1943, Chemotherapeutic experiments with the viruses of influenza A, lymphogranuloma venereum and vaccinia. J. Path. and Bact., 55, 173-181.

Baker, J. A., 1944, Virus causing pneumonia in cats and producing elementary bodies. J. Exp. Med., 79, 159-172.

Barros, E., 1940, La psittacose durante el decennio 1929-1939. Buenos Aires, Buffarini.

Barwell, C. F., 1948, Antigenic components of Psittacosis virus. Nature, 162, 460-461.

Barwell, C. F., 1949, Extraction of a specific antigen from the virus of lymphogranuloma venereum. Nature, 164, 1013.

Barwell, C. F., and Bishop, L. W. J., 1951, Virus of enzootic abortion in ewes: antigenic relationship with viruses of the psittacosis group. Nature, 167, 998.

Beck, M. D., Eaton, M. D., and O'Donnell, R., 1944, Further laboratory studies on the classification of psittacosis-like agents. J. Exp. Med., 79, 65-77.

Bedson, S. P., 1933, Immunological studies with the virus of psittacosis. Brit. J. Exp. Path., 14, 162-170.

Bedson, S. P., 1936, Observations bearing on the antigenic composition of psittacosis virus. Brit. J. Exp. Path., 17, 109-121.

Bedson, S. P., 1938, Study of experimental immunity to the virus of psittacosis in the mouse, with special reference to persistence of infection. Brit. J. Exp. Path., 19, 353-360.

Bedson, S. P., and Bland, J. O. W., 1932, Morphological study of psittacosis virus, with description of a developmental cycle. Brit. J. Exp. Path., 13, 461-466.

Bedson, S. P., and May, H. B., 1945, Penicillin in experimental psittacosis of mice. Lancet, 2, 394-396.

Bedson, S. P., Barwell, C. F., King, E. J., and Bishop, L. W. J., 1949, The laboratory diagnosis of lymphogranuloma venereum. J. Clin. Path., 2, 241-249.

Beeson, P. B., and Miller, E. S., 1944, Epidemiological study of lymphogranuloma venereum, employing the complement-fixation test. Am. J. Pub. Health, 34, 1076-1082.

Beeson, P. B., Wall, M. J., and Heyman, A., 1946, Isolation of virus of lymphogranuloma venereum from blood and spinal fluid of a human being. Proc. Soc. Exp. Biol. and Med., 62, 306-307.

Beveridge, W. I. B., and Burnet, F. M., 1946, The cultivation of viruses and rickettsiae in the chick embryo. Medical Research Council Special Report Series No. 256, London.

Binford, C. H., and Hauser, G. H., 1944, An epidemic of a severe pneumonitis in the bayou region of Louisiana. III. Pathological observations. Report of autopsy on two cases with brief comparative note on psittacosis and Q fever. Pub. Health Rep., 59, 1363-1373.

Bland, J. O. W., and Canti, R. G., 1935, Growth and development of psittacosis virus in tissue cultures. J. Path. and Bact., 40, 231-241.

Bowser, B. M., and Nigg, C., 1946, Studies on lymphogranuloma venereum complement-fixing antigens. II. Serological studies with boiled phenolized antigens. J. Immunol., 53, 269-275.

Brainerd, H., Lennette, E. H., Meiklejohn, G., Bruyn, H. B., Jr., and Clark, W. H., 1949, The clinical evaluation of aureomycin. J. Clin. Investig. 28, 992-1005.

Brumpt, E., 1935, La lymphogranulomatose inguinale doit être nommée bubo climatique. Bull. Acad. de méd., 113, 162-165.

de Burgh, P., Jackson, A. V., and Williams, S. E., 1945, Spontaneous infection of laboratory mice with a psittacosis-like organism. Australian J. Exp. Biol. and Med. Sci., 23, 107-110.

Burnet, F. M., 1935, Enzootic psittacosis amongst wild Australian parrots. J. Hyg., *35*, 412-420.

Burnet, F. M., 1939, Note on occurrence of fatal psittacosis in parrots living in the wild state. Med. J. Australia, *1*, 545-546.

Burnet, F. M., and Rountree, P. M., 1935, Psittacosis in the developing egg. J. Path. and Bact., *40*, 471-481.

Chapman, E. M., and Hayden, E. P., 1937, Lympho-granuloma inguinale; clinical study of thirty cases of sixth venereal disease in natives of New England. New England J. Med., *217*, 45-57.

Cole, H. N., 1933, Lymphogranuloma inguinale, fourth venereal disease; its relation to stricture of the rectum. J. Am. Med. Assn., *101*, 1069-1076.

Coles, A. C., 1930, Micro-organisms in psittacosis. Lancet, *1*, 1011-1012.

Coles, A. C., 1936, Virus bodies in lymphogranuloma inguinale. Edinburgh Med. J., *43*, 528-530.

Coles, J. D. W. A., 1940, Psittacosis in domestic pigeons. Onderstepoort J. Vet. Sci. and Animal Industry, *15*, 141-148.

Connor, W. H., Levin, E. A., and Ecker, E. E., 1937, Observations on the Frei test. J. Infect. Dis., *60*, 62-63.

Coutts, W. E., 1950, Lymphogranuloma venereum. A general review. Bull. World Health Organ., *2*, 545-562.

Coutts, W. E., Martini, J., Brieva, I., Lerner, J., and Said, A., 1942, Visible forms and possible life cycle of lymphogranuloma venereum virus. J. Trop. Med. and Hyg., *45*, 137-143.

D'Aunoy, R., and von Haam, E., 1936, Diagnostic value of Frei reaction in lymphogranuloma inguinale. Am. J. Clin. Path., *6*, 529-545.

Davis, D. J., 1950, Psittacosis infections in feral pigeons. J. Am. Vet. Med. Assn., *116*, 220-223.

Durand, Nicolas, J., and Favre, 1913, Lymphogranulomatose inguinale subaiguë d'origine génitale probable, peut-être vénérienne. Bull. et mém. Soc. méd. des hôp., *35*, 274-288.

Dunnahoo, G. L., and Hampton, B. C., 1945, Psittacosis. Occurrence in the United States and report of 97 per cent mortality in a shipment of psittacine birds while under quarantine. Pub. Health Rep., *60*, 354-357.

Eaton, M. D., Beck, M. D., and Pearson, H. E., 1941, Virus from cases of atypical pneumonia; relation to viruses of meningopneumonitis and psittacosis. J. Exp. Med., *73*, 641-654.

Eaton, M. D., Martin, W. P., and Beck, M. D., 1942, The antigenic relationship of the viruses of meningopneumonitis and lymphogranuloma venereum. J. Exp. Med., *75*, 21-23.

Eddie, B., and Francis, T., Jr., 1942, Occurrence of psittacosis-like infection in domestic and game birds of Michigan. Proc. Soc. Exp. Biol. and Med., *50*, 291-295.

Evans, C. A., and Moore, G. E., 1950, The effects of viruses on intraocular tissues. II. Infections with the viruses of herpes simplex, feline agranulocytosis and ornithosis. J. Infect. Dis., *87*, 1-9.

Findlay, G. M., 1933, Experiments on the transmission of the virus of climatic bubo (lymphogranuloma inguinale) to animals. Trans. Roy. Soc. Trop. Med. and Hyg., *27*, 35-66.

Findlay, G. M., 1938a, Climatic bubo or lymphogranuloma inguinale—experimental investigation. Trans. Roy. Soc. Trop. Med. and Hyg., *31*, 587-598.

Findlay, G. M., 1938b, B. Inclusion bodies and their relationship to viruses, in R. Doerr and C. Hallauer, Handbuch d. Virusforschung, Wien, Springer, pp. 292-368.

Findlay, G. M., Mackenzie, R. D., and MacCallum, F. O., 1938, A morphological study of the virus of lymphogranuloma inguinale (climatic bubo). Trans. Roy. Soc. Trop. Med. and Hyg., *32*, 183-188.

Fite, G. L., Larson, C. L., and Olson, B. J., 1946, An epidemic of a severe pneumonitis in the bayou region of Louisiana. VII. Histopathology in laboratory animals. Pub. Health Rep., *61*, 1100-1115.

Fleming, A., (ed.) 1946, Penicillin; its practical application. Philadelphia, Blakiston, p. 289.

Francis, T., Jr., and Magill, T. P., 1938, An unidentified virus producing acute meningitis and pneumonitis in experimental animals. J. Exp. Med., *68*, 147-160.

Frei, W., 1925, Eine neue Hautreaktion bei "Lymphogranuloma inguinale." Klin. Wchnschr., *4*, 2148-2149.

Gamma, C., 1924, Sur l'étiologie de la lymphogranulomatose inguinale subaiguë. Presse méd., *32*, 404-405.

de Gara, P. F., and Furth, J., 1948, Pneumonia produced by a meningopneumotropic virus. Report of a fatal case, with observations on the interrelationship of psittacosis-like viruses. Arch. Path., *45*, 474-493.

Gay Prieto, J. A., 1927-28, Contribución al estudio de la linfogranulomatosis inguinal subaguda: úlcera venérea adenógena de Nicolás y Favre. Act. Dermosifiliogr., Madrid, *20*, 122-174.

Gey, G. O., and Bang, F. B., 1939, Experimental studies on the cultural behavior and the infectivity of lymphopathia venerea virus maintained in tissue culture. Bull. Johns Hopkins Hosp., *65*, 393-417.

Gjurić, N. J., 1938, Neue Wege in der Behandlung des Lymphogranuloma inguinale. München. med. Wchnschr., *85*, 335-337.

Gönnert, R., 1941, Die Bronchopneumonie, eine neue Viruskrankheit der Maus. Zentralbl. f. Bakt., Abt. I, Orig., *147*, 161-174.

Goggio, A. F., 1949, Human psittacosis cured by penicillin therapy. California Med., *70*, 167-170.

Gogolak, F. M., and Weiss, E., 1950, The effect of antibiotics on agents of the psittacosis-lymphogranuloma group. II. The effect of aureomycin. J. Infect. Dis., *87*, 264-274.

Grace, A. W., 1944, Lymphogranuloma venereum. In. Clinical Tropical Medicine. New York, Hoeber, pp. 499-508.

Grace, A. W., and Rake, G., 1943, Complement fixation test for lymphogranuloma venereum; results obtained with its use. Arch. Dermat. and Syph., *48*, 619-625.

Grace, A. W., and Suskind, F. H., 1940, The transmission of lymphogranuloma venereum to the guinea pig. Am. J. Path., *16*, 169-188.

Green, T. W., 1950, Aureomycin therapy of human psittacosis. J. Am. Med. Assn., *144*, 237-238.

Haagen, E., and Mauer, G., 1938, Ueber eine auf den Menschen übertragbare Viruskrankheit bei Sturmvögeln und ihre Beziehung zur Psittakose. Zentralbl. f. Bakt., Abt. I, Orig., *143*, 81-88.

von Haam, E., and Hartwell, R., 1937, Pulmonary lesions in animals produced by virus of lymphogranuloma inguinale. J. Trop. Med. and Hyg., *40*, 214-216.

Hamre, D., and Rake, G., 1944, Feline pneumonitis (Baker), a new member of the lymphogranuloma-psittacosis group of agents. J. Infect. Dis., *74*, 206-211.

Hamre, D., Rake, H., and Rake, G., 1947, Morphological and other characteristics of the agent of feline pneumonitis grown in the allantoic cavity of the chick embryo. J. Exp. Med., *86*, 1-6.

Harrop, G. A.. Rake, G. W., and Shaffer, M. F., 1941, New clinical conceptions of lymphogranuloma venereum. Trans. Assn. Am. Physicians, *56*, 101-105.

Heilman, F. R., and Herrell, W. E., 1944a, Penicillin in the treatment of experimental ornithosis. Proc. Staff Meet., Mayo Clin., *19*, 57-65.

Heilman, F. R., and Herrell, W. E., 1944b, Penicillin in the treatment of experimental psittacosis. Proc. Staff Meet., Mayo Clin., *19*, 204-207.

Hellerström, S. C., 1929, A contribution to the knowledge of lymphogranuloma inguinale. Acta dermat.-venereol. Supp. I, 5-224. (224 pp.)

Hellerström, S., and Wassén, E., 1930, Meningoenzephalitische Veränderungen bei Affen nach intracerebraler Impfung mit Lymphogranuloma inguinale. Compt. rend. 8e cong. internat. de dermat. et syph., 1147-1151.

Herzberg, K., 1942, Mikroskopische Darstellung des filtrierbaren Mäusepneumonieerregers "Greifswald." Zentralbl. f. Bakt., Abt. I, Orig., *149*, 386-389.

Hilleman, M. R., 1945, Immunological studies on the psittacosis-lymphogranuloma group of viral agents. J. Infect. Dis., *76*, 96-114.

Hilleman, M. R., and Nigg, C., 1946, Studies on lymphogranuloma venereum complement-fixing antigens. III. The solubility in ether of an active fraction. J. Immunol., *53*, 201-208.

Hilleman, M. R., Haig, D. A., and Helmold, R. J., 1951, The indirect complement fixation, hemagglutination and conglutinating complement absorption tests for viruses of the psittacosis-lymphogranuloma venereum group. J. Immunol., *66*, 115-130.

Hoge, V. M., 1934, Psittacosis in the United States; incidence, scientific aspects and administrative control measures. Pub. Health Rep., *49*, 451-462.

Horder, T., and Gow, A. E., 1930, Psittacosis. Record of nine cases, with special reference to morbid anatomy in two of them. Lancet, *1*, 442-445.

Hornus, G. J. P., 1940, Psittacose pulmonaire expérimentale de la souris blanche. Ann. Inst. Pasteur, *64*, 97-116.

Hurst, E. W., Peters, J. M., and Melvin, P., 1950, The therapy of experimental psittacosis and lymphogranuloma venereum (inguinale). I. The comparative efficacy of penicillin, chloramphenicol, aureomycin, and terramycin. Brit. J. Pharmacol., *5*, 611-624.

Hutchison, R., Rowlands, R. A., and Simpson, S. L., 1930, A study of psittacosis. Brit. Med. J., *1*, 633-646.

Jaffé, R., 1948, Beitrag zur pathologischen Anatomie und zur Pathogenese der Rectitis poradaenica (Lymphogranulomatosis inguinalis oder Nicolas-Favresche Krankheit). Arch. f. d. Ges. Virusforsch., *4*, 63-74.

Jones, H., Rake, G., and Stearns, B., 1945, Studies on lymphogranuloma venereum. III. The action of the sulfonamides on the agent of lymphogranuloma venereum. J. Infect. Dis., *76*, 55-69.

Karrer, H., Meyer, K. F., and Eddie, B., 1950, The complement fixation inhibition test and its application to the diagnosis of ornithosis in chickens and in ducks. II. Confirmation of the specificity and epidemiological application of the test. J. Infect. Dis., *87*, 24-36.

Klotz, H. G., 1890, Über die Entwickelung der sogenannten strumösen Bubonen un die Indicationen für die frühzeitige Exstirpation derselben. Berl. klin. Wchnschr., *27*, 132-134.

Kneeland, Y., Jr., and Price, K. M., 1950, Treatment with chloramphenicol, aureomycin, and terramycin of the pneumonia of mice caused by feline pneumonitis virus. J. Immunol., *65*, 653-660.

Knott, L. W., Bernstein, L. H. T., Eagle, H., Billings, T. E., Zobel, R. L., and Clark, E. G., 1943, The differential diagnosis of lymphogranuloma venereum and chancroid by laboratory and skin tests. Am. J. Syph., Gonor. and Ven. Dis., *27*, 657-685.

Koteen, H., 1945, Lymphogranuloma venereum. Medicine, *24*, 1-69.

Kurotchkin, T. J., Libby, R. L., Gagnon, E., and Cox, H. R., 1947, Size and morphology of the elementary bodies of the psittacosis-lymphogranuloma group of viruses. J. Immunol., *55*, 283-287.

Labzoffsky, N. A., 1946, Rapid agglutination test as a possible aid in the laboratory diagnosis of ornithosis. J. Infect. Dis., *79*, 96-100.

Labzoffsky, N. A., 1947, Ornithosis among "wild" pigeons in Ontario. Canad. J. Pub. Health, *38*, 187-192.

Larson, C. L., and Olson, B. J., 1946, An epidemic of a severe pneumonitis in the bayou region of Louisiana. VI. A comparative study of the viruses of lymphogranuloma venereum, psittacosis and Louisiana pneumonitis. Pub. Health Rep., *61*, 69-78.

Laubscher, J. H., Wentzien, A. J., and Jordan, C. F., 1945, Psittacosis in Iowa; report of case. J. Iowa Med. Soc., *35*, 44-46.

Lazarus, A. S., and Meyer, K. F., 1939, The virus of psittacosis. I. Propagation and developmental cycle in egg membrane, purification and concentration. J. Bact., *38*, 121-151.

Lépine, P., and Sautter, V., 1951, Sur l'infection des pigeons parisiens par le virus de l'ornithose. Bull. Acad. nat. méd., *135*, 332-338.

Levaditi, C., 1938, L'activité thérapeutique des dérivés benzéniques sulfurés dans les maladies provoquées par les ultravirus. Compt. rend. Soc. de biol., *127*, 958-960.

Levaditi, C., and Vaisman, A., 1944, Action théra-

peutique de la pénicilline dans la syphilis clinique-
ment inapparente et la maladie de Nicolas-Favre
chez la souris. Bull. Acad. de méd., *128*, 699-701.

Levaditi, C., and Vaisman, A., 1945, Effet curatif de
la pénicilline dans la maladie de Nicolas-Favre de
la souris. Bull. Acad. de méd., *129*, 253-255.

Levaditi, C., and Vaisman, A., 1949, Action de la
chloromycétine (chloramphénicol) et de l'auréo-
mycine sur le virus lymphogranulomateux (maladie
de Nicolas-Favre). Compt. rend. Acad. sc., *229*,
1274-1276.

Levaditi, C., Ravaut, P., Lépine, P., and Schoen, R.,
1932, Étude étiologique et pathogénique de la
maladie de Nicolas et Favre (lymphogranulomatose
inguinale subaiguë, ulcère vénérien adénogène,
poradénolymphite). Ann. Inst. Pasteur, *48*, 27-88.

Levaditi, J. C., Lépine, P., Vinzent, P., and Reinie, L.,
1949, Transmission directe de l'homme à la souris
d'une souche de virus de la maladie de Nicolas et
Favre *(lymphogranuloma venereum)*. Ann. Inst.
Pasteur, *76*, 369-371.

Levinson, D. C., Gibbs, J., and Beardwood, J. T., Jr.,
1944, Ornithosis as a cause of sporadic atypical
pneumonia. J. Am. Med. Assn., *126*, 1079-1084.

Levinthal, W., 1930, Die Ätiologie der Psittakosis.
Klin. Wchnschr., *9*, 654.

Levinthal, W., 1935, Recent observations on psittacosis. Lancet, *1*, 1207-1210.

Lillie, R. D., 1930, Psittacosis: Rickettsia-like inclusions in man and in experimental animals. Pub.
Health Rep., *45*, 773-778.

Lillie, R. D., 1933, I. The pathology of psittacosis in
man; II. The pathology of psittacosis in animals
and the distribution of *Rickettsia psittaci* in the
tissues of man and animals. National Inst. of
Health Bull. No. 161, Washington, D. C., 1-66.

Loizaga, N. S., and Averbach, S., 1945, Sobre una
epidemia de psitacosis. Predominio del contagio in-
terhumano. Revista de medic. y Ciencias Afines, *7*,
297-310; 379-390; 461-474; 543-560.

Luger, N. M., and Cheatham, E. B., 1950, The incidence of lymphogranuloma venereum as determined
by the quantitative complement-fixation test. Am.
J. Syph., *34*, 351-355.

MacCallum, F. O., and Findlay, G. M., 1938, Chemotherapeutic experiments on the virus of lymphogranuloma inguinale in the mouse. Lancet, *2*, 136-
138.

McEwen, A. D., Stamp, J. T., and Littlejohn, A. I.,
1951, Enzootic abortion in ewes. II. Immunization
and infection experiments. Vet. Rec., *63*, 197-201.

Meiklejohn, G., Beck, M. D., and Eaton, M. D., 1944,
Atypical pneumonia caused by psittacosis-like
viruses. J. Clin. Investig., *23*, 167-175.

Meiklejohn, G., Wagner, J. C., and Beveridge, G. W.,
1946, Studies on the chemotherapy of viruses in the
psittacosis-lymphogranuloma group. I. Effect of
penicillin and sulfadiazine on ten strains in chick
embryos. J. Immunol., *54*, 1-8.

Meyer, K. F., 1939-1940, The host-parasite relationship in the heterogeneous infection chains. The
Harvey Lectures, Series 35, 91-134.

Meyer, K. F., 1942, The ecology of psittacosis and
ornithosis. Medicine, *21*, 175-206.

Meyer, K. F., 1943, Psittacosis and ornithosis, *in*

Biester, H. E., and Devries, L., Diseases of Poultry.
Ames, Iowa, Iowa State College Press, pp. 433-
464.

Meyer, K. F., and Eddie, B., 1933, Latent psittacosis
infections in shell parrakeets. Proc. Soc. Exp. Biol.
and Med., *30*, 484-488.

Meyer, K. F., and Eddie, B., 1934, Psittacosis in the
native Australian budgerigars. Proc. Soc. Exp. Biol.
and Med., *31*, 917-920.

Meyer, K. F., and Eddie, B., 1939a, Psittacosis in
importations of psittacine birds from the South
American and Australian continent. J. Infect. Dis.,
65, 234-241.

Meyer, K. F., and Eddie, B., 1939b, The value of the
complement fixation test in the diagnosis of psittacosis. J. Infect. Dis., *65*, 225-233.

Meyer, K. F., and Eddie, B., 1942, Spontaneous ornithosis (psittacosis) in chickens the cause of a
human infection. Proc. Soc. Exp. Biol. and Med.,
49, 522-525.

Meyer, K. F., and Eddie, B., 1947, The knowledge
of human virus infections of animal origin. J. Am.
Med. Assn., *133*, 822-828.

Meyer, K. F., and Eddie, B., 1951a, A review of psittacosis for the years 1948 to 1950. Bull. Hyg.,
26, 1-8.

Meyer, K. F., and Eddie, B., 1951b, Human carrier
of the psittacosis virus. J. Infect. Dis., *88*, 109-125.

Meyer, K. F., and Eddie, B., 1951c, Unpublished data.

Meyer, K. F., Eddie, B., and Yanamura, H., 1942a,
Active immunization to the *Microbacterium multiforme psittacosis* in parrakeets and ricebirds. J. Immunol., *44*, 211-217.

Meyer, K. F., Eddie, B., and Yanamura, H. Y., 1942b,
Ornithosis (psittacosis) in pigeons and its relation
to human pneumonitis. Proc. Soc. Exp. Biol. and
Med., *49*, 609-615.

Miyagawa, Y., Mitamura, T., Yaoi, H., Ishii, N., and
Okanishi, J., 1935, Studies on virus of lympho-
granuloma inguinale Nicolas, Favre and Durand.
Jap. J. Exp. Med., *13*, 331-339; 723-750.

Morgan, H. R., 1948, Studies on the relationship of
pteroylglutamic acid to the growth of psittacosis
virus (strain 6BC). J. Exp. Med., *88*, 285-294.

Morgan, H. R., and Wiseman, R. W., 1946, Growth
of psittacosis virus in roller tube tissue culture;
use in a vaccine. J. Infect. Dis., *79*, 131-133.

Moshkovsky, S. D., 1945, The cytotropic agents of infections and the positions of the rickettsiae in the
system of chlamydozoa (in Russian). Uspekhi
Souremennoi Biologii, *19*, 1-44.

Mudrow, L., and Bock, M., 1943, Der Antagonismus
von Sulfonamiden und Para-Aminobenzoesäure bei
experimentellen Spirochäten-, Spirillen und Virusinfektionen. Ztschr. f. Immunitätsforsch., *104*, 463-
473.

Nauck, E. G., and Malamos, B., 1937, Über Erreger-
befunde bei Lymphogranuloma inguinale. Arch. f.
Schiffs- u. Tropen-Hyg., *41*, 537-552.

Nigg, C., and Eaton, M. D., 1944, Isolation from
normal mice of a pneumotropic virus which forms
elementary bodies. J. Exp. Med., *79*, 497-510.

Nigg, C., Hilleman, M. R., and Bowser, B. M., 1946,
Studies on lymphogranuloma venereum comple-

ment-fixing antigens. I. Enhancement by phenol or boiling. J. Immunol., *53*, 259-268.

Oliphant, J. W., Powell, W. F., and Perrin, T. L., 1942, Sulfadiazine in lymphogranuloma venereum ophthalmitis. J. Am. Med. Assn., *118*, 973-974.

Olson, B. J., and Larson, C. L., 1944, An epidemic of severe pneumonitis in the bayou region of Louisiana. IV. Preliminary note on etiology. Pub. Health Rep., *59*, 1373-1374.

Olson, B. J., and Larson, C. L., 1945, An epidemic of a severe pneumonitis in the bayou region of Louisiana. V. Etiology. Pub. Health Rep., *60*, 1488-1503.

Olson, B. J., and Treuting, W. L., 1944, An epidemic of a severe pneumonitis in the bayou region of Louisiana. I. Epidemiological study. Pub. Health Rep., *59*, 1299-1311.

Parodi, A. S., and Silvetti, L. M., 1946, La psitacosis en los psitacidos silvestres (*Myiopsitta monacha*, Bodde) de la República Argentina. Prensa med. argentina, *33*, 529-530.

Peterson, E., Spalding, O. B., and Wildman, O., 1930, Psittacosis; a clinical and roentgenologic study of seven cases with post mortem observations in one case. J. Am. Med. Assn., *95*, 171-179.

Pfaffenberg, R., 1936, Die Psittacosis (Papageienkrankheit) in den Jahren 1931-1935. Epidemiologie, Forschungsergebnisse, Bekämpfung. Ergebn. d. Hyg., Bakt., Immunitätsforsch. u. Therap., *18*, 251-331.

Pollard, M., and Witka, T. M., 1947, The antigenic relationship of lymphogranuloma venereum and psittacosis by skin test in humans. Texas Rep. Biol. and Med., *5*, 288-293.

Prigot, A., Wright, L. T., Logan, M. A., and deLuca, F. R., 1949, Anorectogenital lymphogranuloma venereum and granuloma inguinale treated with aureomycin. New York State J. Med., *49*, 1911-1917.

Quan, S. F., Meyer, K. F., and Eddie, B., 1950, Attempts to cure parakeet psittacosis carriers with aureomycin and penicillin. J. Infect. Dis., *86*, 132-135.

Rake, G., and Jones, H. P., 1942, Studies on lymphogranuloma venereum. I. Development of the agent in the yolk sac of the chicken embryo. J. Exp. Med., *75*, 323-338.

Rake, G., and Jones, H. P., 1944, Studies on lymphogranuloma venereum. II. The association of specific toxins with agents of the lymphogranuloma-psittacosis group. J. Exp. Med., *79*, 463-486.

Rake, G., McKee, C. M., and Shaffer, M. F., 1940, Agent of lymphogranuloma venereum in the yolk sac of the developing chick embryo. Proc. Soc. Exp. Biol. and Med., *43*, 332-334.

Rasmussen-Ejde, R. K., 1938, Ueber eine durch Sturmvögel übertragbare Lungenerkrankung auf den Färöern. Zentralbl. f. Bakt., Abt. I, Orig., *143*, 89-93.

Reymann, F., 1951, Specificity of skin tests in lymphogranuloma venereum and chancroid. Acta dermato-venereol., *31*, 257-261.

Reyn, A., 1951, Complement-fixation with Lygranum antigen. Acta dermato-venereol., *31*, 262-266.

Rivers, T. M., and Berry, G. P., 1931a, Psittacosis.

III. Experimentally induced infections in rabbits and guinea pigs. J. Exp. Med., *54*, 119-128.

Rivers, T. M., and Berry, G. P., 1931b, Psittacosis. IV. Experimentally induced infections in monkeys. J. Exp. Med., *54*, 129-144.

Rivers, T. M., and Berry, G. P., 1935, Diagnosis of psittacosis in man by means of injections of sputum into white mice. J. Exp. Med., *61*, 205-212.

Rivers, T. M., Berry, G. P., and Rhoads, C. P., 1930, Psittacosis; observations concerning the experimental disease in parrots, mice, rabbits, guinea pigs and monkeys. J. Am. Med. Assn., *95*, 579-583.

Rivers, T. M., Berry, G. P., and Sprunt, D. H., 1931, Psittacosis. I. Experimentally induced infections in parrots. J. Exp. Med., *54*, 91-103.

Rivers, T. M., and Schwentker, F. F., 1934, Vaccination of monkeys and laboratory workers against psittacosis. J. Exp. Med., *60*, 211-238.

Robinson, R. C. V., Zheutlin, H. E. C., and Trice, E. R., 1950, Treatment of lymphogranuloma venereum with aureomycin. Am. J. Syph., *34*, 67-70.

Roca-García, M., 1949, Viruses of the lymphogranuloma-psittacosis group isolated from opossums in Colombia, opossum virus. A. J. Infect. Dis., *85*, 275-289.

Rost, G., 1912, Klimatische Bubonen. Arch. f. Schiffs- u. Tropen-Hyg., *16*, 677-693.

Roubakine, A., 1930, General review on psittacosis. League of Nations Monthly Epidemiological Report, *9*, 141-175.

Rudd, G. V., and Burnet, F. M., 1941, Intranasal infection of mice with the virus of psittacosis. Australian J. Exp. Biol. and Med. Sci., *19*, 33-38.

Sabin, A. B., and Aring, C. D., 1942, Meningoencephalitis in man caused by the virus of lymphogranuloma venereum. J. Am. Med. Assn., *120*, 1376-1381.

St. John, E., and Gordon, F. B., 1947, Studies on the immunological relationships of the psittacosis-lymphogranuloma venereum group of viruses. J. Infect. Dis., *80*, 297-306.

Schalm, L., de Vos, J. F., and Dekking, F., 1950, Een kleine, door kooivogels veroorzaakte epidemie van psittacosis. Nederl. Tjidschr. f. geneesk., *94*, 1769-1776.

Schamberg, I. L., Carrozzino, O. M., and Boger, W. P., 1951, Treatment of early lymphogranuloma venereum with aureomycin. Am. J. Syph., *35*, 370-377.

Schoen, R., 1940, La pneumopathie lymphogranulomateuse expérimentale des souris blanches; transmission de l'infection par voie nasale. Ann. Inst. Pasteur, *65*, 336-355.

Sézary, A., and Drain, M., 1935, La fréquence et les formes cliniques du chancre lymphogranulomateux (maladie de Nicolas-Favre). Bull. Soc. frse. de dermat. et syph., *42*, 757-760.

Shaffer, M. F., and Rake, G., 1947, Studies on lymphogranuloma venereum: evaluation of the complement fixation test with Lygranum. J. Lab. and Clin. Med., *32*, 1060-1086.

Shaffer, M. F., Rake, G., and McKee, C. M., 1940, Agent of lymphogranuloma venereum in the lungs of mice. Proc. Soc. Exp. Biol. and Med., *44*, 408-410.

Smadel, J. E., 1943, Atypical pneumonia and psittacosis. J. Clin. Investig., *22*, 57-65.

Smadel, J. E., Wall, M. J., and Gregg, A., 1943, An outbreak of psittacosis in pigeons, involving the production of inclusion bodies, and transfer of the disease to man. J. Exp. Med., *78*, 189-204.

Smadel, J. E., Wertman, K., and Reagan, R. L., 1943, Yolk sac complement fixation antigen for use in psittacosis-lymphogranuloma venereum group of diseases. Proc. Soc. Exp. Biol. and Med., *54*, 70-74.

Smith, E. B., and Custer, R. P., 1948, The histopathology of lymphogranuloma venereum. Tr. and Stud. Coll. Physicians, Phila., *16*, 91.

Sprunt, D. H., and Berry, G. P., 1936, Psittacosis; review of literature on lesions of central nervous system with report of case. J. Infect. Dis., *58*, 129-133.

Stamp, J. T., McEwen, A. D., Watt, J. A. A., and Nisbet, D. I., 1950, Enzootic abortion in ewes. I. Transmission of the disease. Vet. Rec., *62*, 251-254.

Stannus, H. S., 1933. A sixth venereal disease. London, Baillière, Tindall & Cox.

Sulkin, S. E., and Pike, R. M., 1951, Survey of laboratory-acquired infections. Am. J. Pub. Health, *41*, 769-781.

Takemori, N., 1948, Culture du virus lymphogranulomateux sur milieu gélosé de Zinsser. Étude comparative avec la culture des rickettsies. Kitasato Arch. Exp. Med., *21*, 261-266.

Tomlinson, T. H., Jr., 1941, An outbreak of psittacosis at the National Zoological Park, Washington, D. C., Pub. Health Rep., *56*, 1073-1081.

Treuting, W. L., and Olson, B. J., 1944, An epidemic of a severe pneumonitis in the bayou region of Louisiana. II. Clinical features of the disease. Pub. Health Rep., *59*, 1331-1350.

Troup, A. G., Adam, R., and Bedson, S. P., 1939, An outbreak of psittacosis at the London Zoological Gardens. Brit. Med. J., *1*, 51-55.

Turgasen, F. E., 1944, Human ornithosis treated with penicillin. J. Am. Med. Assn., *126*, 1150-1151.

Wagner, J. C., Golub, O. J., and Andrew, V. W., 1949, Cross immunity studies between virus strains in the psittacosis-lymphogranuloma venereum group. J. Infect. Dis., *84*, 41-46.

Wagner, J. C., Meiklejohn, G., Kingsland, L. C., and Hickish, H. W., 1946, Psittacosis vaccines prepared from chick embryo tissues. J. Immunol., *54*, 35-46.

Wall, M. J., 1946, Isolation of the virus of lymphogranuloma venereum from twenty-eight patients; relative value of the use of chick embryos and mice. J. Immunol., *54*, 59-64.

Wammock, V. S., Greenblatt, R. B., Dienst, R. B., Chen, C., and West, R. M., 1950, Aureomycin in the treatment of granuloma inguinale and lymphogranuloma venereum. J. Investig. Dermatol., *14*, 427-434.

Wassén, E., 1935, Studies of lymphogranuloma inguinale from etiological and immunological points of view. Acta path. et microbiol. Scandinav., Supp. XXIII, 1-181.

Weiss, E., 1949, The extracellular development of agents of the psittacosis-lymphogranuloma group. (Chlamydozoaceae). J. Infect. Dis., *84*, 125-149.

Wells, E. B., and Finland, M., 1949, Comparative effect of aureomycin and chloromycetin on psittacosis infection in chick embryos. Proc. Soc. Exp. Biol. and Med., *72*, 365-368.

Wenckebach, G. K., 1936, Wiedererkrankung an Psittacosis. Med. Klin., *32*, 1594-1595.

Wetherbee, D. G., Hilfer, R. J., Maspero, B., and Kuhns, D. M., 1951, The complement-fixation test in the diagnosis of lymphogranuloma venereum. Am. J. Clin. Path., *21*, 521-529.

Wilson, W. W., 1948, The venereal granulomas: a comparative study of these diseases in Florida. South. M. J., *41*, 412-419.

Wiseman, R. W., Meiklejohn, G., Lackman, D. B., Wagner, J. C., and Beveridge, G. W., 1946, Studies on the chemotherapy of viruses in the psittacosis-lymphogranuloma group; II. Effect of penicillin and sulfadiazine on several strains in mice. J. Immunol., *54*, 9-16.

Wolins, W., 1948, Ornithosis (psittacosis). A review, with a report of eight cases resulting from contact with the domestic Pekin duck. Am. J. Med. Sci., *216*, 551-564.

Woodward, T. E., 1949, Chloromycetin and aureomycin: therapeutic results. Ann. Int. Med., *31*, 53-82.

Wright, L. T., Sanders, M., Logan, M. A., Prigot, A., and Hill, L. M., 1948, The treatment of lymphogranuloma venereum and granuloma inguinale in humans with aureomycin. Ann. New York Acad. Sc., *51*, 318-330.

Yanamura, H. Y., and Meyer, K. F., 1941, Studies on the virus of psittacosis cultivated in vitro. J. Infect. Dis., *68*, 1-15.

Yanamura, H. Y., and Meyer, K. F., 1942, Active immunity to the *Microbacterium multiforme psittacosis* in the mouse. J. Immunol., *44*, 195-209.

Yeatman, C., and McEwin, J., 1945, Infections with psittacosis in Adelaide. Med. J. Australia, *2*, 109-114.

York, C. J., and Baker, J. A., 1951, A new member of the psittacosis-lymphogranuloma group of viruses that causes infection in calves. J. Exp. Med., *93*, 587-604.

Zichis, J., and Shaughnessy, H. J., 1945, Isolation of an apparently new virus from two fatal pneumonia cases. Science, *102*, 301-302.

PHILLIPS THYGESON, M.D.

University of California Medical School

21

Trachoma and Inclusion Conjunctivitis

Trachoma and inclusion conjunctivitis are closely related virus infections of the external eye. They differ chiefly in the following respects. Whereas trachoma involves the cornea and forms pannus, has little or no tendency to spontaneous cure, and inevitably produces conjunctival and corneal cicatrization, inclusion conjunctivitis never affects the cornea significantly and always heals spontaneously without cicatricial changes of any kind.

In spite of these important differences the diseases have often been confused clinically and their similarities, both clinical and etiologic, have induced research workers to study them simultaneously; hence their consideration in the same chapter in the present volume.

TRACHOMA

(Synonym: Granular conjunctivitis)

History

Trachoma is a disease of antiquity, references to it appearing in the earliest records of mankind. Egyptian papyri, such as the Ebers papyrus, mention its complications and treatment, and Hippocrates appears to have been well acquainted with it. During the Crusades and in the course of Napoleon's campaign in Egypt the disease was of major military importance, and troops returning to Europe from the Middle East disseminated it widely. Of all ocular affections trachoma has always been the one of greatest world-wide military, economic, and social consequence. Unfortunately, it retains that pre-eminence to this day in spite of intensive campaigns in many countries to reduce its incidence.

The highest incidence is reached in Egypt and the Middle East where more than 90 per cent of the population is affected, but the infection is widespread in all the countries bordering the Mediterranean, in Russia, and throughout the Orient. In the United States it is still prevalent among the Indians and among the mountain whites along the so-called "Daniel Boone Trail" although the incidence in both groups is rapidly decreasing.

In 1907, Halberstaedter and Prowazek described the cytoplasmic inclusion bodies characteristic of the disease, and in 1912 Nicolle, Blaisot and Cuénod reported the first positive filtration experiments which they performed with modified Berkefeld V filters. The work of other investigators has shown the virus to be of large particle size and a member of the psittacosis-lymphogranuloma venereum group of viruses. Trachoma virus studies have been greatly handicapped, however, by the failure to obtain cultivation in tissue culture and by the fact that the only susceptible animals (monkeys, baboons, and apes) fail to develop an infection certainly identifiable as trachoma. The recognition by Loe (1938) and others that the disease was susceptible

465

to sulfonamide therapy marked a turning-point in its history.

CLINICAL PICTURE

The incubation period of trachoma, as determined from experimental human inoculations, is from five to seven days. The onset may be insidious or fulminating, depending apparently upon the amount of inoculum. Mild onset is observed most commonly in children, particularly in the heavily infected countries such as Morocco, Tunisia, and Egypt. In such cases there may be no external signs of the infection, except perhaps a slight ptosis of the lids, but when the upper lids are everted a follicular hypertrophy of the upper tarsal conjunctiva is displayed. The acute onset is characterized by acute conjunctival inflammation with dense infiltration and papillary hypertrophy. There is superficial inflammation of the cornea, particularly of the upper limbus region, and not infrequently swelling of the lids and mild preauricular adenopathy. The exudate may be abundant and mucopurulent in character. The acute stage tends to last for several weeks and is then followed by subacute and chronic stages in which the exudate becomes scanty and the symptoms minimal.

Regardless of whether the onset is insidious or acute, the disease tends to progress in much the same way over a period of months to conjunctival and corneal cicatrization. In the late stages, deformity of the eyelids with cicatricial entropion may occur and vision may be markedly reduced by cicatrization from pannus and recurrent ulcers. In unusually severe cases, tear-function may be lost and the complications of keratitis sicca added to the picture. Secondary bacterial infection complicates more than 50 per cent of cases in this country and a much higher percentage in the Middle East and Orient. After apparent healing there is often a recurrence or reinfection. There has been nothing to indicate that any immunity develops.

PATHOLOGIC PICTURE

The earliest recognizable pathologic manifestation of trachoma is the development of the characteristic cytoplasmic inclusion bodies in the conjunctival and corneal epithelial cells (Wilson, 1937). This is followed by subepithelial infiltration with small round cells, plasma cells predominating, and by the development of lymphoid follicles. Subepithelial infiltration of the cornea is followed by blood vessel invasion in the form of pannus. Advanced stages are characterized by cell necrosis, and finally by cicatrization. All the pathologic changes in trachoma affect the upper half of the conjunctival sac and cornea more prominently than the lower.

Although the subepithelial infiltration is mononuclear in type, the exudate is composed chiefly of polymorphonuclear cells. This is particularly true in the acute stages of the disease and is in no way dependent upon secondary bacterial infection. In contradistinction, the exudates of conjunctival infections with typical viruses, such as epidemic keratoconjunctivitis virus and herpes simplex virus, are characteristically mononuclear.

The inclusion bodies occur in numbers varying in proportion to the clinical severity of the disease and are most numerous in scrapings from the upper tarsal and upper limbus regions, i.e., from the areas of maximum disease intensity. They are most numerous in the superficial layers of the epithelium, are rarely seen in the basal layers, and never occur in the cells of the follicles or in the subepithelial layers.

EXPERIMENTAL INFECTION; HOST RANGE

The only experimental animals found to be susceptible to trachoma virus are, in the order of their susceptibility, apes, baboons, and monkeys. Unfortunately, none of these animals develops pathologic changes characteristic of human trachoma, i.e., pannus and cicatrization. The experimental disease they do develop, moreover, is self-limited and appears only as a follicular conjunctivitis which cannot be differentiated with certainty from the follicular conjunctivitis produced by inclusion conjunctivitis virus, or even from the spontaneous folliculosis with which monkeys, baboons, and apes are frequently affected (Wilson, 1930; Bland, 1945). The inclusion bodies characteristic of trachoma have been found in the experimental disease in apes but never in the experimental disease in monkeys or baboons. This paucity of inclusions is believed to be due to the mildness of the experimental disease in which there are neither inflammatory signs nor exudate. That the disease is actually trachoma, however, has been established by Nicolle, Blaisot and Cuénod (1912), and by Bland (1944), who succeeded in transferring the experimental disease from its animal hosts to human volunteers who in turn developed typical trachoma.

Experimental infection in human beings has been accomplished on numerous occasions and has usually had an acute onset and abundant inclusions.

ETIOLOGY

The cause of trachoma is a virus of large particle size belonging to the psittacosis-lymphogranuloma venereum group of viruses. It appears in the conjunctival and corneal epithelium and in the exudate in the form of elementary bodies (Fig. 41A) which, when stained according to Giemsa's method, measure about 0.25 micron in diameter. The elementary bodies occur free in the exudate and intracellularly as agglomerations known as inclusion bodies. Mature inclusion bodies are made up almost entirely of elementary bodies. Larger forms of the virus, the so-called "initial bodies" (Lindner, 1910a) are seen commonly in young inclusion bodies (Fig. 41B) and occasionally free in the exudate. They are coccobacillary and bipolar staining, show division forms, and vary in size up to 1.5 microns in length.

The inclusion body is a virus colony in which the elementary and initial bodies are embedded in a carbohydrate matrix composed principally of glycogen (Figs. 41C, 41D, 41E and 41F) (Rice, 1936). The evolution of the inclusion body in the susceptible cell requires about 48 hours. Multiple infection of cells is common (Fig. 41G). The existence of a toxin is suggested by the following facts: (1) toxins have been demonstrated for other members of the psittacosis-lymphogranuloma venereum group (Rake and Jones, 1944); (2) in the experiment of Mitsui, Tanaka, and Yamashita (1951), repeated instillations of a virus-free ultrafiltrate of trachoma material produced follicular hypertrophy of the conjunctiva of a volunteer; and (3) important subepithelial changes occur in trachoma even though the virus appears to be limited strictly to the epithelial layer. In this connection, it is noteworthy that attempts to infect the subepithelial layers of the conjunctiva by injecting trachoma virus through the skin of the lids failed but that subsequent direct inoculation of the conjunctiva in the same subjects succeeded (Michail and Vancea, 1932).

The virus is rapidly inactivated by drying, by alternate freezing and thawing, and by incubator temperature (37°C.). Its thermal death point is 45°C. maintained for 15 minutes (Julianelle, 1938). At refrigerator temperature or in 50 per cent glycerol it can be preserved for as long as a week. Sulfanilamide has no virucidal effect in vitro (Julianelle and Smith, 1942). Attempts to cultivate the virus in tissue culture have been generally unsuccessful, even when human conjunctival and corneal epithelium have been employed. Trachomatous conjunctival epithelium rapidly loses its infectivity for baboons when cultivated in tissue culture (Thygeson, 1939). Claims for cultivation in the chick embryo, however, have been made by Macchiavello (1944), Poleff (1949), and Stewart and Badir (1950). Group antibodies for the psittacosis-lymphogranuloma venereum group of viruses have been demonstrated in sera from trachoma patients (Rake, Shaffer and Thygeson, 1942), but no evidence has been advanced to suggest that they are concerned in the clinical course of the disease or in developing immunity to it. Monkeys and baboons that have recovered from experimental trachoma show no immunity to reinfection and the second infection runs the same clinical course as the first.

The virus filters with difficulty and only through the coarse grades of filter, such as the Berkefeld V candle and gradocol membranes of 0.6 micron A.P.D. or above. If an active filtrate is to be obtained, the elementary bodies must pass the filter. This was demonstrated in the experiment of Thygeson, Proctor and Richards (1935) in which a human volunteer was inoculated successfully with a gradocol filtrate (0.6 micron A.P.D.). The original material, consisting of ground epithelial scrapings from trachomatous Indian children, contained abundant inclusions. Elementary bodies were demonstrated in the bacteria-free filtrate on centrifugation and inclusion bodies were numerous in the experimental disease at onset.

DIAGNOSIS

The diagnosis of trachoma can usually be made on the basis of the following clinical signs: (1) follicle formation, most prominent on the upper tarsal region, (2) trachomatous pannus, which can be recognized in its incipience early in the disease on slit-lamp examination of the upper limbus region, and (3) conjunctival cicatrization.

Laboratory diagnosis is based on the finding of the cytoplasmic inclusion bodies and on cytologic changes in expressed follicular material. Although the inclusions are morphologically identical with those of inclusion conjunctivitis, in trachoma they are much more numerous on the upper tarsal conjunctiva than on the lower and in inclusion conjunctivitis the situation is reversed (Braley, 1940). In expressed follicular material from trachoma, necrotic changes not found in other follicular diseases of the conjunctiva are to be seen in the form of cell debris, pale-staining cells, and numerous

---

FIG. 41 (A). Free elementary bodies in the exudate from a case of severe trachoma. Giemsa stain × 1500.

(B) Young inclusion bodies made up of large swollen forms, the so-called initial bodies of Lindner. Giemsa stain × 1500.

(C) Mature inclusion body in which the cytoplasm of the epithelial cell has been entirely replaced by elementary bodies. Giemsa stain × 1500.

(D) Epithelial cell (shown in C) previously stained by Lugol's solution to show the carbohydrate matrix which takes a reddish-brown coloration with iodine.

(E) An inclusion body showing both elementary and initial bodies. Giemsa stain × 1500.

(F) Epithelial cell (shown in E) previously stained with Lugol's solution to show the carbohydrate matrix. The iodine has been partially removed to bring out the honeycomblike arrangement of the matrix in which the elementary and initial bodies, not affected by the iodine, are embedded. × 1500.

(G) Multiple inclusion bodies in a single epithelial cell. Giemsa stain × 1500.

(H) Elementary bodies in exudate from inclusion conjunctivitis in a newborn infant. Giemsa stain × 1200.

(I) Inclusion body in a conjunctival epithelial cell from inclusion conjunctivitis. Giemsa stain × 1500.

(J) Free elementary and initial bodies in the exudate from a severe case of inclusion conjunctivitis. Giemsa stain × 1400.

(K) Inclusion body in cervical epithelium from the mother of a baby with inclusion conjunctivitis. Giemsa stain × 1200.

(L) Free elementary bodies in cervical secretion from a woman whose child developed inclusion conjunctivitis. Giemsa stain × 1750.

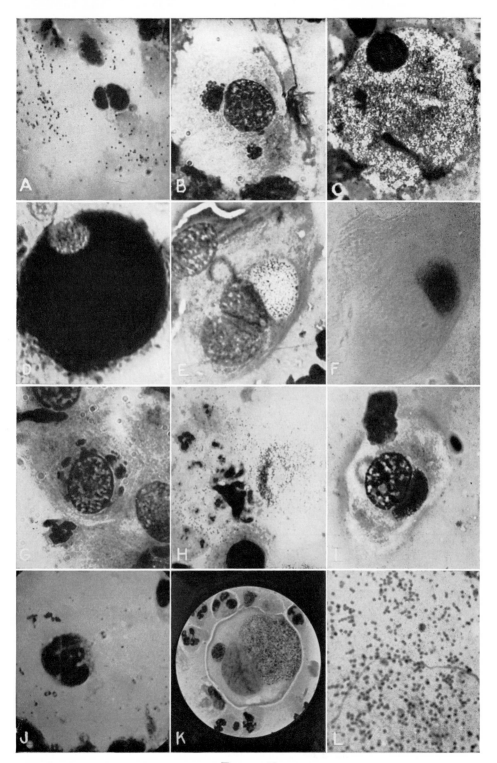

FIGURE 41

macrophages loaded with cell fragments (Thygeson, 1946).

TREATMENT

Prior to the introduction of sulfonamide therapy in 1938, trachoma was treated by a combination of medical and surgical means. Medical treatment consisted in the control of secondary infection by antiseptic drops. and in the application to the conjunctiva of caustics, such as copper sulphate, silver nitrate, quinine bisulphate, etc. Surgical treatment consisted in the correction of cicatricial deformities, such as entropion and trichiasis, and in the removal of diseased conjunctiva by tarsectomy. The inadequacy of these measures is indicated by the fact that few patients tolerated treatment sufficiently long to obtain relief and that the few cures obtained took from one to many years of continuous medical care.

Under sulfonamide therapy the prognosis of trachoma has changed entirely. In early cases cures can now be expected in a matter of weeks. As in the related virus disease. lymphogranuloma venereum, low dosages and relatively prolonged treatment times (2 to 4 weeks) are required. In the cicatricial stages sulfonamide therapy has proven less satisfactory and surgical intervention for the relief of cicatricial complications is sometimes necessary. Prognosis is poorest in those cases in which tear-function has been lost.

The broad-spectrum antibiotics, aureomycin, Chloromycetin (chloramphenicol), and terramycin, have all shown antitrachomatous activity (Mitsui et al., 1951; Bietti, 1951). When used orally, their effect has been comparable with that of the sulfonamides, but when used topically they appear to be more efficacious than topically administered sulfonamides.

EPIDEMIOLOGY

In the countries of the Middle East, such as Egypt, trachoma is commonly acquired in the first year of life, usually from the mother. In areas in which periodic epidemics of the acute ophthalmias occur, it is often transmitted simultaneously with the bacterial infections (Wilson, 1930). In countries in which the disease is only endemic, as in the United States for example, spread occurs only when there is constant exposure to infection under conditions of poor hygiene such as obtain among the mountain folk of West Virginia, Kentucky, and Tennessee. On the basis of the virus content of epithelial scrapings, it is believed that acute cases are highly infectious and chronic cases only slightly so. In sporadic cases occurring in adults it is often impossible to trace the source of infection, but it is believed that eye-to-eye transmission by means of fingers or fomites is possible and that the fly may play an important rôle (Wilson, 1930). So far no evidence to indicate the existence of a subclinical infection or carrier state has been advanced.

CONTROL MEASURES

The control of trachoma in the countries in which it is pandemic devolves chiefly upon the control of the acute ophthalmias (Wilson, 1945). This is now theoretically possible by means of chemotherapy but on practical grounds is limited by lack of funds, the countries in which trachoma is widespread being the ones most economically depressed. Since trachoma is a disease of filth and poor personal hygiene, all measures leading to improvement in the economic condition of the population exert a prophylactic effect. In the United States, the experience of the Indian Service in its attempts to control the disease has illuminated the dramatic effect of the change in therapeutic method. Prior to the introduction of the sulfonamides in 1938, the extensive antitrachoma campaign conducted in the Indian schools was showing only partial success; as a result of the sulfonamide therapy instituted at that time the incidence of the disease has been strikingly reduced (Forster and McGibony, 1944). In the white population of the United States control consists in the recognition and treatment of the disease, particularly in isolated communities. To this end stationary and mobile trachoma clinics have been instituted in the states of Arkansas, Illinois, Missouri, and Virginia.

INCLUSION CONJUNCTIVITIS

(SYNONYMS: Inclusion blennorrhea, paratrachoma, swimming-pool conjunctivitis)

HISTORY

A benign form of conjunctivitis in the new-born, unassociated with pathogenic bacteria, was described by Morax as early as 1903. Shortly after Halberstaedter and Prowazek discovered cytoplasmic inclusion bodies in trachoma in 1907, Stargardt (1909), and then Schmeichler (1909), noted identical inclusions in ophthalmia neonatorum. In 1911, Lindner reported that he had found inclusions in all but a very few cases of ophthalmia neonatorum of nonbacterial origin, and that he had been able to transmit the disease to the conjunctiva of the baboon and to recover identical inclusion bodies from the experimental disease. He defined the clinical characteristics of the disease and named it *Einschlussblennorrhöe*, or inclusion blennorrhea. In 1910, Wolfrum described two successful inoculations of human beings with inclusion blennorrhea exudate.

Searching for the origin of this disease of the newborn, Halberstaedter and Prowazek (1909) found typical inclusions in scrapings from the genito-urinary tract of mothers of diseased infants and postulated the existence of an inclusion disease of the male and female genito-urinary tracts. This theory was supported by the work of Lindner (1910b) and Heymann (1910), who found inclusions in several cases of urethritis in the male. Later, Fritsch, Hofstätter, and Lindner (1910) produced a conjunctival infection in a baboon with urethral exudate from nongonorrheal urethritis containing inclusions.

The first filtration experiments were made in 1914. Botteri (1912) induced infection in the eye of a baboon with a Berkefeld V filtrate, and Gebb (1914) confirmed his work by obtaining infection in a human subject with a similar filtrate. Subsequent filtration studies by Thygeson (1934), Tilden and Gifford (1936), and Julianelle et al. (1938) showed that the virus was filterable with relative ease through coarse Berkefeld candles and gradocol membranes.

Unfortunately, some confusion arose as to the relationship of the disease to trachoma and to the conjunctivitis with inclusions seen in adults, particularly in bathers in certain swimming pools. Some authors claimed the identity of this adult disease with trachoma but such a conclusion was untenable in view of the self-limited nature of the inclusion disease and its failure to produce pannus or cicatrization. Morax (1933) differentiated it sharply from trachoma and offered evidence, later confirmed by Thygeson (1934) and by Julianelle (1937), to show that the infant and adult types of conjunctivitis with inclusions, in spite of certain differences between them, were manifestations of a single disease.

Thygeson and Mengert (1936) found that in mothers of babies with inclusion blennorrhea the genito-urinary disease was limited to the external os of the cervix and to an area of transitional epithelium identical histologically with the epithelium of the conjunctiva. They reported that the infection produced no clinical symptoms in the mothers but that in the fathers it was only occasionally subclinical, usually appearing as a mild, nonspecific urethritis of several months' duration. Knowledge of the genito-urinary aspects of the disease was extended by Thygeson and Stone (1942a) who found the ocular infection to be an occupational disease of obstetricians and gynecologists. They suggested that the genito-urinary disease, although of little clinical significance, was probably widespread throughout the population. Thygeson (1941) reported that inclusion conjunctivitis responded rapidly to sulfonamide therapy, and later with Stone (1942b) showed that topical applications of the sulfonamides were invariably successful in the treatment of the disease in the newborn. Aureomycin and terramycin have recently been shown to be equally efficacious.

CLINICAL PICTURE

The incubation period of inclusion conjunctivitis varies from a minimum of five days to a maximum of twelve. In the newborn the onset is acute, a purulent conjunctivitis developing rapidly with intense infiltration of the conjunctiva, particularly of the lower lid. In very severe cases transient pseudomembranes are noted and clinical differentiation from gonorrheal ophthalmia may be difficult. After an acute stage, lasting from ten days to two weeks, the disease gradually loses its intensity over a period of months. The discharge may cease in as short a time as two months, but the conjunctiva rarely if ever returns to normal in less than three months and may show infiltration for as long as a year. Unlike trachoma, however, inclusion conjunctivitis never develops pannus or significant conjunctival cicatrization. It is always self-limited, and persistent chronic infections are unknown.

The clinical appearance of the disease in the adult differs, often rather strikingly, from that in the newborn baby. Typically it presents the picture of an acute follicular conjunctivitis with scanty discharge and preauricular adenopathy; the follicular hypertrophy, unlike that of trachoma, is much more marked in the conjunctiva of the lower lid than in that of the upper. Occasionally, however, a severe infection may appear as a papillary conjunctivitis with moderately abundant exudate. In this form the adult disease more closely resembles the disease in the newborn but has never been known to have the fulminating character so often seen in the latter. The adult disease tends to persist over a longer period of time, sometimes for more than a year. All reported cases, however, have eventually resolved spontaneously without residual conjunctival or corneal changes.

PATHOLOGIC PICTURE

Examination of biopsy material from the disease in the newborn infant at onset shows an infiltration of the conjunctiva with small round cells, resulting in a many-fold increase in the thickness of the conjunctiva. The epithelium is infiltrated with polymorphonuclear cells and contains numerous basophilic cytoplasmic inclusion bodies morphologically identical with those of trachoma. The presence of these inclusion bodies is the first recognizable pathologic sign of the disease; they have been demonstrated during the incubation period of experimental human infections. Biopsy material taken late in the course of the infection may show lymphoid follicles, a feature entirely lacking in the early stages.

In the adult the typical pathologic picture is a follicular hypertrophy of the conjunctiva associated with an infiltration of small round cells. The follicles have the same histologic structure as those of trachoma but none of their necrotic aspects. Polymorphonuclear leukocytes predominate in conjunctival scrapings collected during the acute phase, but as the disease becomes chronic there is an admixture of mononuclear cells.

EXPERIMENTAL INFECTION; HOST RANGE

Like trachoma virus, inclusion conjunctivitis virus is infective only for monkeys, baboons, apes, and human beings; baboons and apes are more susceptible than monkeys. Baboons inoculated with exudate develop an acute follicular conjunctivitis identical clinically with the adult human disease, but the clinical picture of inclusion blennorrhea in the newborn has never been reproduced in animals. Experimental inclusion conjunctivitis in lower animals is somewhat more intense than is experimental trachoma; it is of shorter duration, and its inclusions are relatively easy to demonstrate. Otherwise the two experimental diseases are indistinguishable. Because of the relatively intense character of experimental inclusion conjunctivitis, spontaneous folliculosis does not cause as much confusion as it does in connection with experimental trachoma. The cervix of the female baboon has been experimentally infected with inclusion conjunctivitis virus (Braley, 1939), but all attempts to induce experimental urethritis in the male baboon have been unsuccessful.

ETIOLOGY

The cause of inclusion conjunctivitis is a virus of large particle size belonging to the psittacosis-lymphogranuloma venereum group of viruses. It passes Berkefeld V candles and its diameter, as determined by filtration through gradocol membranes, lies between 0.15 and 0.39 micron (Thygeson, 1934). It is destroyed rapidly by drying but can be preserved for several days in 50 per cent glycerol or at refrigerator temperatures. All attempts to propagate it in chick embryo or in human conjunctival tissue culture have failed. Group antibodies for the psittacosis-lymphogranuloma venereum group of viruses have been demonstrated in sera from patients with inclusion conjunctivitis (Rake, Shaffer and Thygeson, 1942).

Infectious units of inclusion conjunctivitis virus are elementary bodies, which, when stained according to Giemsa's method, have a diameter of about 0.25 micron. Masses of them can be seen in cells in the form of inclusion bodies (Fig. 41H) or they occur free in the exudate in acute cases (Fig. 41I). In addition to the elementary bodies, larger forms, first described by Lindner (1910a) and known as initial bodies, are seen in young inclusions and occasionally free in the exudate (Fig. 41J). They appear to be the forms produced in the first few divisions of the virus within the cytoplasm of susceptible cells. In the inclusion body the virus appears as masses of elementary and initial bodies embedded in a carbohydrate matrix identical with that described for trachoma virus by Rice (Thygeson, 1938). The inclusion bodies are limited strictly to the superficial layers of the epithelium (Braley, 1938). This applies also to the genito-urinary infection in the female (Fig. 41K). The existence of a toxin has been postulated to explain the subepithelial changes which occur. The virus is not affected by sulfonamides in vitro, but the disease is rapidly cured by sulfonamide therapy. Morphologic observations indicate that the sulfonamide probably acts by preventing development of the virus in vivo rather than by killing it. Cortisone used topically increases the susceptibility of the conjunctival and corneal cells to the virus and tends to reactivate quiescent cases.

Lindner suggested that trachoma virus and inclusion conjunctivitis virus were originally identical, that inclusion conjunctivitis virus, as a result of its sojourn on the mucous membranes of the genito-urinary tract through countless generations, eventually lost its ability to produce pannus and cicatrization, and that the two viruses bear a relationship to each other similar to that exhibited by the viruses of vaccinia and variola. Up to the present time no data to support this hypothesis have been submitted, however. Moreover, Allen (1944) reported that inclusion conjunctivitis virus has not taken on any of the characteristics of trachoma virus after serial conjunctival transfer on 40 human subjects. In this connection, Braley (1939) made the interesting observation that trachoma virus could produce infection of the cervix of the female baboon.

DIAGNOSIS

The clinical diagnosis of inclusion conjunctivitis in the infant is facilitated by its delayed onset (5 to 12 days) and by the characteristic conjunctival thickening and coxcomblike appearance of the lower fornix. Clinical diagnosis, however, must be confirmed by the finding of inclusion bodies.

Since trachoma never develops in newborn infants in the first week or two of life, the demonstration of inclusions is pathognomonic of inclusion conjunctivitis in the infant.

In the adult an acute follicular conjunctivitis with mild preauricular adenopathy always suggests inclusion conjunctivitis. The absence of corneal changes is the clinical basis for differentiation from trachoma, but differentiation from other forms of acute follicular conjunctivitis cannot always be made clinically. For the latter purpose laboratory diagnosis based on the finding of cytoplasmic inclusions is conclusive, except, of course, with respect to trachoma from which supplementary differentiation on clinical or cytologic grounds must be made. As noted above, the expressed follicular material from trachoma shows necrotic changes never seen in follicular material from inclusion conjunctivitis.

Group antibodies for the psittacosis-lymphogranuloma venereum group of viruses, which have been reported, have no diagnostic significance in inclusion conjunctivitis.

Inclusion blennorrhea is the most important type of nongonococcal ophthalmia neonatorum and clinical laboratories in all hospitals should be capable of diagnosing it, particularly in view of the serious social consequences which may result from confusing it with gonococcal ophthalmia. It is important that epithelial scrapings be taken instead of the exudate films used for determining bacterial infections.

Treatment

Prior to the introduction of sulfonamides, no form of therapy had had any effect on inclusion conjunctivitis. Sulfonamide therapy, however, is highly successful and may effect a clinical cure in as short a time as five days. Topical sulfonamide therapy, usually employed six times daily over a period of ten days in the form of 5 per cent sulfathiazole or sulfadiazine ointment, has been uniformly successful in the new-born infant and irregularly successful in adults. The lesser efficacy of topical therapy in adults is believed to be due to the dilution of the ointment by the tears, a negligible factor in newborn infants who have low tear-function in the first few weeks of life. Oral administration of the sulfonamides has been invariably successful in adult cases, however, and relapses are almost unknown. No instance of a sulfonamide-resistant virus strain has as yet been reported. Secondary bacterial infection is not a problem.

Penicillin has not been effective in the treatment of inclusion conjunctivitis (Thygeson, 1947).

Epidemiology

Eye-to-eye transmission of inclusion conjunctivitis is extremely rare and no epidemics have been shown conclusively to be traceable to ocular infection. The epidemiology is believed to parallel that of gonorrheal ophthalmia as seen in the United States and European countries. The genito-urinary disease, like gonorrhea, serves as a reservoir from which infection of newborn eyes occurs during childbirth and from which sporadic adult infections develop as a result of accidental transfer of the genito-urinary exudate to the eye. The eye disease would in all probability cease to exist if it were not for the genito-urinary reservoir of virus. Doctors and nurses dealing with newborn infants and gynecologic conditions have been accidentally infected with inclusion conjunctivitis (Thygeson and Stone, 1942a), just as they have been accidentally infected with gonorrheal ophthalmia. Swimming-pool infection was a problem before chlorination was introduced, the virus being transmitted through the water from the genito-urinary tract to the eye; cases are still being reported from small lakes and unchlorinated pools. Figure 41L shows the extraordinary number of virus elementary bodies which have been found on occasion in scrapings from the cervix and indicates what an abundant source of contamination the genito-urinary tract can be.

CONTROL MEASURES

Control measures parallel those applicable to the control of gonorrheal ophthalmia, except that the Credé silver-nitrate prophylaxis does not prevent inclusion blennorrhea. The intracellular habitat of the virus no doubt serves to protect it from the action of the caustic. Penicillin used as a substitute for silver nitrate has been no more effective. Control of swimming-pool infection would seem to depend upon proper chlorination. In a survey of university swimming pools, all properly chlorinated, Thygeson and Stone (1942a) found no instance of infection. This was in sharp contrast to the number of cases studied which were known to have been contracted in unchlorinated pools.

Simple precautions regarding the cleanliness of hands are sufficient to prevent transfer of the infection from a patient with the ocular disease to attendants. In nurseries. however, careful isolation should be enforced to prevent transfer from infant to infant.

CLASSIFICATION

Although the viruses of trachoma and inclusion conjunctivitis possess the essential properties of viruses, i.e., filterability, inclusion body formation, and obligate cell parasitism, they are set apart from the typical large viruses, such as those of vaccinia and fowl-pox, by a number of distinguishing properties. These include their susceptibility to chemotherapy, the basophilic character of their inclusion bodies, and their intracellular cycle of morphologic variation.

The similarity of the viruses of trachoma and inclusion conjunctivitis to psittacosis virus was noted by Thygeson in 1934, and several other atypical viruses with basophilic inclusions and intracellular cycles of morphologic variation have been identified since then. With the essential properties of viruses, but differing from typical viruses in the properties enumerated above, these organisms constitute a transitional group midway between the typical large viruses and the rickettsiae. In this connection it is interesting to note that Coles (1941), working on conjunctivitis of oxen, sheep, and goats from which he recovered rickettsialike organisms, called attention to their morphologic variation and pointed out that a typical rickettsia such as *Rickettsia ruminantium* showed the elementary-initial-body type of morphologic variation and was even sulfonamide-sensitive.

Some authors (Busacca, 1933) have recommended, on the basis of staining characteristics and morphology, that the agents of trachoma and inclusion conjunctivitis be classified with the rickettsiae. Since one of the essential features of rickettsiae is the existence of an arthropod host, however, and there are no arthropod hosts for trachoma or inclusion conjunctivitis, or in any of the other diseases whose causative agents belong in this group, such a classification would seem to be unjustified. Furthermore, the agent of trachoma, unlike most rickettsiae, is not susceptible to therapy with para-aminobenzoic acid (Bietti, 1951). It has indeed become increasingly apparent that the group should be set apart from both the typical viruses and the rickettsiae. To this end, a number of proposals for definitive terminology have been advanced, all of them giving credit to Prowazek in one way or another for his original observations on trachoma virus which was the first member of the group to be described. The suggestion having priority is that of Moshkovsky (1945) who proposed the family name of *Chlamydozoaceae* for the group and the names *Chlamydozoon trachomatis* and *Chlamydozoon oculogenitale* for the viruses of trachoma and inclusion conjunctivitis respectively. "Chlamydozoa" or "mantlebody" was the term employed by Halberstaedter and Prowazek in their original description of the agent of trachoma.

REFERENCES

Allen, J. H., 1944, Inclusion blennorrhea. Am. J. Ophth., *27*, 833-846.

Bietti, G. B., 1951, Memorandum on results obtained in treatment of trachoma by various antibiotics and by chemotherapy. WHO, doc. WHO/Trachoma/17, Sept. 20. To be published.

Bland, J. O. W., 1944, Spontaneous folliculosis of the conjunctiva in grivet and vervet monkeys. J. Path. and Bact., *56*, 161-171.

Bland, J. O. W., 1945, The aetiology of trachoma. Brit. J. Ophth., *29*, 407-420.

Botteri, A., 1912, Klinische, experimentelle und mikroskopische Studien über Trachom, Einschlussblennorrhöe und Frühjahrskatarrh. Klin. Monatsbl. f. Augenh., *50*, 653-690.

Braley, A. E., 1938, Inclusion blennorrhea: a study of the pathologic changes in the conjunctiva and cervix. Am. J. Ophth., *21*, 1203-1207.

Braley, A. E., 1939, Relation between the virus of trachoma and the virus of inclusion blennorrhea. Arch. Ophth., *22*, 393-398.

Braley, A. E., 1940, Intracellular bodies of the conjunctival epithelial cells. Arch. Ophth., *24*, 681-689.

Busacca, A., 1933, Sulla presenza di germi simuli a rickettsie nei tissuti trachomatosi. Abstr., Klin. Monatsbl. f. Augenh., *91*, 278.

Coles, J. D. W. A., 1941, A rickettsia-like organism of the conjunctival epithelium of pigs. Arch. Ophth., *25*, 101-112.

Forster, W. G., and McGibony, J. R., 1944, Trachoma. Am. J. Ophth., *27*, 1107-1117.

Fritsch, H., Hofstätter, A., and Lindner, K., 1910, Experimentelle Studien zur Trachomfrage. Arch. f. Ophth., *76*, 547-558.

Gebb, H., 1914, Experimentelle Untersuchungen über die Beziehungen zwischen Einschlussblennorrhöe und Trachom. Ztschr. f. Augenh., *31*, 475-485.

Halberstaedter, L., and von Prowazek, S., 1907, Über Zelleinschlüsse parasitärer Natur beim Trachom. Arb. k. Gsndhtsamte, *26*, 44-47.

Halberstaedter, L., and von Prowazek, S., 1909, Ueber Chlamydozoenbefunde bei Blennorrhea neonatorum non gonorrhoica. Berl. klin. Wchnschr., *46*, 1839-1840.

Heymann, B., 1910, Ueber die Fundorte der Prowazekchen Körperchen. Berl. klin. Wchnschr., *47*, 663-666.

Julianelle, L. A., 1937, Relation of inclusion blennorrhea to swimming-bath conjunctivitis as determined by an accidental transmission. Proc. Soc. Exp. Biol. and Med., *36*, 617-619.

Julianelle, L. A., 1938, The Etiology of Trachoma. New York, Commonwealth Fund, p. 176.

Julianelle, L. A., Harrison, R. W., and Lange, A. C., 1938, Studies on inclusion blennorrhea: III. Experimental considerations of the etiology. Am. J. Ophth., *21*, 1230-1241.

Julianelle, L. A., and Smith, J. E., 1942, Studies on the infectivity of trachoma: XI. The effect of sulfanilamide on the virus. Am. J. Ophth., *25*, 317-321.

Lindner, K., 1910a, Die freie Initialform der Prowazekschen Einschlüsse. Arch. f. Ophth., *76*, 559-567.

Lindner, K., 1910b, Zur Aetiologie du gonokokkenfreien Urethritis. Wien klin. Wchnschr., *23*, 283-284.

Lindner, K., 1911, Gonoblennorrhöe, Einschlussblennorrhöe, und Trachom. Arch. f. Ophth., *78*, 345-380.

Loe, F., 1938, Sulfanilamide treatment of trachoma: preliminary report. J. Am. Med. Assn., *111*, 1371-1372.

Macchiavello, A., 1944, El virus del tracoma y su cultivo en el saco vitelino del hueva de gallina. Rev. Ecuator. de Hig. y Med. Trop., *1*, 211-243.

Michail, D., and Vancea, P., 1932, Quelques faits expérimentaux dans le trachome. Rev. internat. du Trachome, *9*, 33-36.

Mitsui, Y., 1951, Use of the new antibiotics in the treatment of trachoma. WHO, doc. WHO/Trachoma/16, Sept. 12.

Mitsui, Y., and Tanaka, C., 1951, Terramycin, aureomycin, and chloramphenicol in the treatment of trachoma. Antibiotics and Chemotherapy, *1*, 146-157.

Mitsui, Y., Tanaka, C., and Yamashita, K., 1951, Soluble toxin-like substance of trachoma virus. WHO, doc. WHO/Trachoma/21, Oct. 22. To be published.

Morax, V., 1903, Sur l'étiologie des ophtalmies du nouveau-né et la déclaration obligatoire. Ann d'ocul., *129*, 346-363.

Morax, V., 1933, Les conjonctivites folliculaires. Bull. et mém. Sco. frse. d'ophth., *46*, 5-142.

Moshkovsky, S. D., 1945, The cytotropic agents of infections and the positions of rickettsiae in the system of chlamydozoa (in Russian). Uspekhi Souremennoi Biologii, *19*, 1-44.

Nicolle, C., Blaisot, L., and Cuénod, A., 1912, Le magot animal réactif du trachome. Filtrabilité du virus. Pouvoir infectant des larmes. L'immunité dans le trachome. Compt. rend. Acad. sci., *155*, 241-243.

Poleff, L., 1949, Culture des corps du trachome à la lumière des acquisitions nouvelles. Rev. internat. du Trachome, *26*, 175-176.

Rake, G., Shaffer, M. F., and Thygeson, P., 1942, Relationship of agents of trachoma and inclusion conjunctivitis to those of lymphogranuloma-psittacosis group. Proc. Soc. Exp. Biol. and Med., *49*, 545-547.

Rake, G., and Jones, H. P., 1944, Studies on lymphogranuloma venereum: II. The association of specific toxins with agents of the lymphogranuloma-psittacosis group. J. Exp. Med., *79*, 463-486.

Rice, C. E., 1936, The carbohydrate matrix of the epithelial-cell inclusion in trachoma. Am. J. Ophth., *19*, 1-8.

Schmeichler, L., 1909, Ueber Chlamydozoenbefunde bei nicht gonorrhoischer Blennorrhöe der Neugeborenen. Berl. klin. Wchnschr., *46*, 2057-2058.

Stargardt, K., 1909, Über Epithelzellveränderungen beim Trachom und andern Conjunctivalerkrankungen. Arch. f. Ophth., *69*, 525-542.

Stewart, F. H., and Badir, G., 1950, Experiments on

the cultivation of trachoma virus in the chick embryo. J. Path. Bact., 62, 457-460.

Thygeson, P., 1934, The etiology of inclusion blennorrhea. Am. J. Ophth., 17, 1019-1035.

Thygeson, P., 1938, The matrix of the epithelial cell inclusion body of trachoma. Am. J. Path., 14, 455-462.

Thygeson, P., 1939, Cultivation of trachomatous conjunctival epithelium in vitro. Arch. Ophth., 21, 229-234.

Thygeson, P., 1941, Treatment of inclusion conjunctivitis with sulfanilamide. Arch. Ophth., 25, 217-226.

Thygeson, P., 1946, The cytology of conjunctival exudates. Am. J. Ophth., 29, 1499-1511.

Thygeson, P., 1947, Unpublished observations.

Thygeson, P., and Mengert, W. F., 1936, The virus of inclusion conjunctivitis. Arch. Ophth., 15, 377-409.

Thygeson, P., Proctor, F. I., and Richards, P., 1935, Etiologic significance of the elementary body in trachoma. Am. J. Ophth., 18, 811-813.

Thygeson, P., and Stone, W., Jr., 1942a, Epidemiology of inclusion conjunctivitis. Arch. Ophth., 27, 91-119.

Thygeson, P., and Stone, W., Jr., 1942b, The treatment of inclusion conjunctivitis with sulfathiazole ointment. J. Am. Med. Assn., 119, 407-408.

Tilden, E. B., and Gifford, S. R., 1936, Filtration experiments with the virus of inclusion blennorrhea. Arch. Ophth., 16, 51-54.

Wilson, R. P., 1930, Folliculosis of the conjunctiva in animals. 4th Ann. Rep. Mem. Ophth. Lab. (1929), Giza, Cairo, p. 63.

Wilson, R. P., 1937, "Inclusion bodies." 11th Ann. Rep. Mem. Ophth. Lab. (1936), Giza, Cairo, p. 117.

Wilson, R. P., 1945, A statement on the economic importance of the acute ophthalmias of Egypt, with recommendations for their control. 14th Ann. Rep. Mem. Ophth. Lab. (1939-44), Giza, Cairo, p. 38-48.

Wolfrum, M., 1910, Beiträge zur Trachomforschung. Klin. Monatsbl. f. Augenh., 48, Beilageheft, 154-174.

GEOFFREY RAKE, M.B., B.S.

The Squibb Institute for Medical Research

22

Measles

(SYNONYMS: Morbilli, rubeola,* *rougéole, Masern*)

INTRODUCTION

Measles is one of the important exanthemata. The morbidity rate in young children is very high and by adult age almost everyone has had the disease. It is characterized by a prodromal period with increasing fever, catarrhal symptoms, and enanthem in the mouth (Koplik's spots) followed by a typical rash whose onset portends disappearance of the fever. Nowadays the prognosis is good in the uncomplicated disease and, with modern chemotherapy, even in complications other than encephalitis.

HISTORY

Measles was certainly recognized as an independent disease by the English physician Sydenham in the 17th century but the Arabian, Rhazes, in the 9th century had distinguished it from smallpox of which he thought it a mild form. Epidemics of varying severity have occurred in all inhabited parts of the world, striking with particular severity at certain periods as in the black measles of the 18th century (1763-1768) in London, in virgin soil as in the Faroe Islands (Panum 1846), or when accompanied by bacterial trailers as in the U. S. Army camps during the first world war

* Rubeola unfortunately is used as a synonym for both measles and rubella.

(Cole and MacCallum, 1918). Home in 1758 reported attempts at transmission of the disease by placing cotton soaked with fresh blood from patients, in the acute phase of the disease, in incisions in the skin of individuals with no previous history. Measles apparently resulted within seven days in 7 of the 15 volunteers. Unequivocal success in transmission of measles was accomplished by Hektoen (1905) who injected two individuals subcutaneously with blood taken from patients 24 and 30 hours after the appearance of the rash. Typical measles appeared after incubation periods of from 11 to 13 days. Anderson and Goldberger (1911a) first demonstrated significant and successful transmission of measles to an animal, namely, the macaque monkey. Plotz (1938) described the first convincing cultivation of the virus in tissue culture, and Rake and Shaffer (1939) were able to accomplish the same result in embryonated chicken eggs. The prevention of the disease by inoculation of human serum containing neutralizing antibodies was first described by Nicolle and Conseil (1918).

CLINICAL PICTURE

The incubation period of the natural disease up to the appearance of the exanthem (rash) is from 12 to 19 days, usually exactly 14 days. Deliberate human inoculation of amounts of virus probably larger than those transmitted naturally may result in shorter incubation periods, i.e., 10 to 13 days until the appearance of the rash. The emergence of rash is preceded, however, by 1 to 5 days of prodromal symptoms and incubation periods as short as 7 days, until the onset of such symptoms, are recorded in the natural disease.

The prodromal symptoms are for the most part catarrhal. Onset may be sudden with a chill. There are sneezing, running nose, redness of eyes, cough and fever. Faint or scattered prodromal rash may occur but the characteristic diagnostic lesions are the Koplik or buccal spots (Koplik, 1896). These appear in 90 to 95 per cent of all cases from 4 to 1 days before onset of rash. They are usually bilateral and occur at the level of the premolars and around the papilla of the parotid duct; not infrequently they appear on the mucous membrane of the lower lip. They have a white or bluish-white center set on an erythematous base, and are best seen by daylight.

The fever and cough become steadily worse until the appearance of the rash. This appears first on the forehead and behind the ears. From there it spreads over face, neck, trunk and limbs. It consists of macular or maculopapular lesions, often becoming confluent and blotchy. It disappears on pressure. One to 2 days are required for its complete development and after this the fever falls coincident with the gradual disappearance of rash. The rash leaves behind it a brownish staining which is followed later by branny desquamation. Photophobia and leukopenia are usually found at the height of the disease.

Virus is present in the blood and in the nasopharyngeal secretions probably during the whole of the prodromal period and up to 24 or 30 hours following the appearance of rash.

Complications are not infrequent. The most usual are otitis media with perforation of the drum, and bronchopneumonia. The former is always due to secondary bacterial infection. The latter is also due in most instances to complicating bacterial infection with streptococci, pneumococci or *H. influenzae,* and it is in these cases that the highest mortality occurred before the development of the modern methods of chemotherapy. Encephalomyelitis is today the most severe sequela. This is fortunately rare (usually about 1 in 10,000 cases), but the incidence may be higher in certain epidemics. Symptoms of involvement of the central nervous system appear usually some days after appearance of the rash, perhaps after this has faded. The temperature rises again and the patient becomes drowsy or has convulsions. Protein and cells increase in the spinal fluid. The mortality is approximately 10 per cent, but as many as 65 per cent of survivors show permanent mental or physical impairment (Ford 1928). Appendicitis is a definite though rare complication and seems to be due to specific alterations in the mucosa (see below).

PATHOLOGIC PICTURE

The catarrhal inflammation of the mucous membranes is not typical. The lymphoid tissue, as for example that in the appendix, is often hyperplastic and characteristic multinucleated giant cells are found in such tissue in lymph nodes, tonsils, adenoids, spleen and appendix. The cells measure up to 100 μ across and contain as many as 100 nuclei (Warthin, 1931; Finkeldey, 1931). Their origin appears to be from lymphocytes, but whether by amitotic division or by fusion is not clear. The Koplik spots consist of focal exudations of serum and endothelial cells which form vesicles. These are followed by focal necrosis (Ewing, 1909). The rash starts around the superficial vessels of the corium with exudation of serum and proliferation of endothelial cells. This exudate spreads into the epidermis, both focally and diffusely, leading to vacuolation and necrosis of the epithelial cells and vesicle formation. Later the epithelium and exuded endothelial cells are desquamated. Extravasation of red cells is rare (Mallory and Medlar, 1920). No convincing evidence of an inclusion body characteristic for measles has been presented; many bodies implicated as specific are not true inclusions. In cases of encephalomyelitis the central nervous system shows, in the gross, congestion and petechial hemorrhages. Microscopically, early cases show perivascular hemorrhage and lymphocytic infiltration. Later demyelination of greater or lesser extent appears in brain and cord. The demyelinated areas may show some infiltrations with leukocytes and monocytes, and secondary gliosis.

EXPERIMENTAL INFECTION; HOST RANGE

Measles can be transmitted to monkeys as was first indicated by Josias (1898) and established by Anderson and Goldberger (1911a). Species found susceptible include *Macacus rhesus* (*Macaca mulatta*) and *M. cynomolgus* (Anderson and Goldberger, 1911b); *M. sinicus* (Nicolle and Conseil, 1911); and *M. fuscatus* (Kawamura, 1922). Monkeys can be infected by subcutaneous, intradermal, intramuscular, intravenous, intracerebral, intraperitoneal (Anderson and Goldberger, 1911b), and intratracheal (Blake and Trask, 1921a) routes, when human blood or catarrhal secretions are used; also by contact, although this has proved very difficult to reproduce (Goldberger and Anderson, 1911a) and by inhalation (Rake and Shaffer, 1940). The incubation period in monkeys varies with the dose of virus and may be from 3 to 22 days, with a usual period of 9 or 10 days (Blake and Trask, 1921a; Shaffer, Rake, Stokes and O'Neil, 1941). Various symptoms occur, the most common of which is an exanthem of greater or lesser extent. Enanthemata occur in approximately 46 per cent of *M. mulatta;* conjunctivitis or other catarrhal signs in 30 to 50 per cent; fever in approximately 30 per cent and neutrophilopenia in 90 per cent (Blake and Trask, 1921a; Shaffer, Rake, Stokes and O'Neil, 1941). Although in a severe infection in a monkey all above symptoms may occur, in most instances only two or three will be present and their intensity varies markedly. In rare instances, in monkeys receiving combined subcutaneous and intranasal inoculations, mild symptoms suggestive of involvement of the central nervous system have been observed (Rake and Shaffer, 1940). Virus is present in the buccal mucosa and secretions (Goldberger and Anderson, 1911a; Blake and Trask, 1921a), and in the blood (Lucas and Prizer, 1912). Study of exanthem or enanthem shows a picture essentially similar to that in man (Blake and Trask, 1921b). There is no convincing evidence that the virus of measles produces any disease, or multiplies, in any experimental mammal other than monkeys.

ETIOLOGY

The virus in blood or nasopharyngeal washings passes through Berkefeld N or Seitz EK filters (Goldberger and Anderson, 1911b; Blake and Trask, 1921a; Wenckebach and Kunert, 1937; Rake and Shaffer, 1940). It can be preserved at —72°C. or —35°C. for periods up to four weeks, and for several days at 0°C. At room temperature infectivity is retained for at least 34 hours. It may be dried in vacuo from the frozen state and following such drying will remain active for at least 15 weeks. At temperatures around —72°C. it resists a pH of 6 for 60 hours, but lower pH ranges rapidly inactivate it. It withstands 10 per cent anesthetic ether for 40 minutes at room temperature. Many claims of successful cultivation of the virus of measles have been made. See reviews by Rake, Shaffer and Jones (1941) on studies with tissue culture, and Shaffer, Rake, Stokes and O'Neil (1941) on studies with chicken embryos. In many cases the agents cultivated would seem not to be those responsible for measles. In the author's opinion probably the first successful cultivation in tissue culture was that of Plotz (1938) and in the chicken embryo that of Rake and Shaffer (1939). The tissue culture used (Plotz, 1938) consisted of minced 10-day chick embryo in Tyrode's solution, monkey serum and chicken plasma. Successful propagation for ten passages was demonstrated by monkey inoculation with production of mild disease and subsequent solid immunity to challenge inoculation with known positive human blood. In the chicken embryo the virus has been cultivated by inoculation into the amniotic or allantoic cavities (Rake, 1943) but mostly on the chorio-allantois by the Burnet technic. The virus produces no characteristic lesion on the membrane. Egg-passage virus from the early passages is capable of producing a slightly modified disease in man, while later passages have resulted in a greatly modified disease with slight symptoms or signs, or nothing at all. In monkeys even the earliest passages usually produce a mild disease, as does material from human cases (Shaffer, Rake, Stokes and O'Neil, 1941). Successful production of disease with cultured virus results in increased resistance to natural infection or to challenge inoculation with virus in human material (Maris, Rake, Stokes, Shaffer and O'Neil, 1943). How long such increased resistance may last is not known. There is evidence that a too greatly modified disease will not result in prolonged increased immunity, a result similar to that seen with serum modification of the natural disease (see below).

DIAGNOSIS

During an epidemic the diagnosis is easy. The Koplik spots in the mouth, rather than the rash, are diagnostic of sporadic cases or cases at the commencement of an epidemic. In some instances, perhaps 5 per cent, Koplik spots may be absent and then the differentiation from rubella becomes extremely difficult. The latter disease tends to be milder with only slight catarrhal symptoms. Moreover, in rubella early and marked adenitis is the rule. The severer forms of

catarrhal laryngitis preceding the rash of measles must be distinguished from that of early smallpox, from rubella and from scarlet fever. The latter shows characteristic circumoral pallor and a rash which is never punctate on the face. Serum or drug rashes may be morbilliform in character; as may the rash accompanying infectious mononucleosis.

TREATMENT

In the uncomplicated form, treatment is largely symptomatic. Bed rest and light diet are indicated together with subdued light because of the conjunctivitis and photophobia. A sedative may be required for the cough. Secondary bacterial infections can be successfully combated with sulfonamides, penicillin and other antibiotics or, in case of gram-negative organisms such as *H. influenzae,* streptomycin.

Specific therapy consists in the use of serum antibodies. Several forms of antibody preparations have been used including serum from convalescents (Nicolle and Conseil, 1918), adult serum (Rietschel, 1921), or placental preparations (McKhann and Chu, 1933), all of which depend for their efficacy on the fact that most adults have suffered from measles and that pools of adult blood will therefore contain specific globulin antibodies. Lately, plasma globulin concentrates, especially Fraction II which consists of all the gamma and considerable beta globulin, have been used (Cohn, Oncley, Strong, Hughes and Armstrong, 1944). Before the advent of the globulin concentrates, therapy has been administered mostly during the incubation period to prevent or modify the disease in children known to have been exposed. Prevention is advisable in the case of very young or sick children and is obtained by use of a large dose sufficiently early after exposure, i.e., in children three years or younger 5 cc. of convalescent or 10 cc. of adult serum within six days after exposure. For older children the age is multiplied by

2 for convalescent serum or by 4 for adult serum to obtain the dose in cubic centimeters. Attenuation of the disease can be obtained by use of a dose of serum or other preparation properly adjusted to the size of the child and the probable length of time since exposure. For attenuation the same amounts as for prevention may be used if given later than six days after exposure, or half the amount may be given within the first six days, preferably on the third day. In the case of globulin concentrates, 0.5 cc. given to children under 6 years within seven days of exposure results in complete protection of about 50 per cent of them and modified disease in the others. If ideal dosage is attained the disease is modified to a degree in which no real malaise is suffered but complete protection is achieved. Stillerman, Marks and Thalhimer (1944) have drawn attention to the frequency with which very mild symptoms are noted on careful examination, following doses assumed to be preventive. Without careful follow up, such symptoms would be, and often are, entirely overlooked, but too large a dose with no symptoms or markedly modified ones will not result in lasting protection. The failure of markedly modified experimental disease to produce immunity has been commented on under etiology.

Now that highly concentrated preparations of immune globulin are available, with antibody titers from 15 to 35 times as high as in the original plasma pool, attempts are being made to use these therapeutically by intramuscular injection, particularly in the prodromal stages of the established disease (Stokes, Maris and Gellis, 1944). The results are suggestive but not too clear. Apart from encephalitis, the prognosis of the disease is good.

EPIDEMIOLOGY

Measles, smallpox and chickenpox are the most infective of the exanthemata. Measles is particularly infective during the catarrhal, prodromal stage when the virus can undoubtedly be spread over considerable distances within closed spaces. Articles freshly contaminated with catarrhal secretions can carry the disease, so apparently can third parties acting as passive carriers although unequivocal examples of this are rare (Leake, 1951). Infectivity wanes rapidly after the appearance of the rash. Measles is endemic in all large communities. Major epidemics appear at about three-year intervals. Only approximately 1 per cent of susceptible individuals fail to contract measles on their first close contact with the disease. By the age of 20 approximately 85 per cent of persons in civilized countries have had the disease, and when it has been introduced into isolated communities it rarely spares any but those who have experienced a previous epidemic. Second attacks are unusual but not unknown, and certain very unusual individuals appear never to acquire an immunity and suffer repeated typical attacks.

CONTROL MEASURES

Early reporting of cases of measles is important. When the disease is recognized in a community any known susceptible child suffering from a catarrhal infection is suspect, particularly if there is history of exposure. Koplik spots should be watched for especially. Isolation, and disinfection of articles soiled with catarrhal secretions, should be carried out from the first appearance of the prodromal symptoms until four or five days after the appearance of the rash, a period of some nine days in all. Quarantine of children during epidemics in large communities is of little value. Quarantine of exposed individuals for 14 days may be practiced in the case of scattered communities, at least to the extent of forbidding such individuals to attend schools or public gatherings. Segregation of infants, young children or those sick from other diseases should be carried out wherever possible.

REFERENCES

Anderson, J. F., and Goldberger, J., 1911a, Experimental measles in the monkey. A preliminary note. Pub. Health Rep., 26, 847-848.

Anderson, J. F., and Goldberger, J., 1911b, The period of infectivity of the blood in measles. J. Am. Med. Assn., 57, 113-114.

Blake, F. G., and Trask, J. D., 1921a, Studies on measles. I. Susceptibility of monkeys to the virus of measles. J. Exp. Med., 33, 385-412.

Blake, F. G., and Trask, J. D., 1921b, Studies on measles. II. Symptomatology and pathology in monkeys experimentally infected. J. Exp. Med., 33, 413-422.

Cohn, E. J., Oncley, J. L., Strong, L. E., Hughes, W. L., Jr., and Armstrong, S. H., Jr., 1944, Chemical, clinical, and immunological studies on the products of human plasma fractionation. 1. The characterization of the protein fractions of human plasma. J. Clin. Investig., 23, 417-432.

Cole, R., and MacCallum, W. G., 1918, Pneumonia at a base hospital. J. Am. Med. Assn., 70, 1146-1156.

Ewing, J., 1909, The epithelial cell changes in measles. J. Infect. Dis., 6, 1-16.

Finkeldey, W., 1931, Über Riesenzellbefunde in den Gaumenmandeln, zugleich ein Beitrag zur Histopathologie der Mandelveränderungen im Maserninkubationsstadium. Virchow's Arch., 281, 323-329.

Ford, F. R., 1928, The nervous complications of measles. Bull. Johns Hopkins Hosp., 43, 140-184.

Goldberger, J., and Anderson, J. F., 1911a, An experimental demonstration of the presence of the virus of measles in the mixed buccal and nasal secretions. J. Am. Med. Assn., 57, 476-478.

Goldberger, J., and Anderson, J. F., 1911b, The nature of the virus of measles. J. Am. Med. Assn., 57, 971-972.

Hektoen, L., 1905, Experimental measles. J. Infect. Dis., 2, 238-255.

Home, F., 1759, Medical facts and experiments. London, A. Millar, p. 253.

Josias, A., 1898, Recherches expérimentales sur la transmissibilité de la rougéole aux animaux. Méd. moderne, Paris, 9, 153-154.

Kawamura, R., 1922, Studies on measles. Japan Med. World, 2, 31-35.

Koplik, H., 1896, The diagnosis of the invasion of measles from a study of the exanthema as it appears on the buccal mucous membrane. Arch. Pediat., 13, 918-922.

Leake, J. P., 1951, Personal communication.

Lucas, W. P., and Prizer, E. L., 1912, An experimental study of measles in monkeys. J. Med. Res., 26, 181-194.

McKhann, C. F., and Chu, F. T., 1933, Use of placental extract in prevention and modification of measles. Am. J. Dis. Child., 45, 475-479.

Mallory, F. B., and Medlar, E. M., 1920, The skin lesion in measles. J. Med. Res., 41, 327-348.

Maris, E. P., Rake, G., Stokes, J., Jr., Shaffer, M. F., and O'Neil, G. C., 1943, Studies on measles. V. The results of chance and planned exposure to unmodified measles virus in children previously inoculated with egg-passage measles virus. J. Pediat., 22, 17-29.

Nicolle, C., and Conseil, E., 1911, Reproduction expérimental de la rougéole chez le Bonnet chinois. Virulence du sang des malades 24 heures avant le début de l'éruption. Compt. rend. Acad. sci., 153. 1522-1524.

Nicolle, C., and Conseil, E., 1918, Pouvoir préventif du sérum d'un malade convalescent de rougéole. Bull. et mém. Soc. méd. des hôp. de Paris, 42, 336-338.

Panum, P. L., 1846, Observations made during the epidemic of measles on the Faroe Islands in the year 1846. New York, Delta Omega Society, 1940.

Plotz, H., 1938, Culture "in vitro" du virus de la rougéole. Bull. Acad. méd. Paris, 119, 598-601.

Rake, G., 1943, Experimental investigation of measles. J. Ped., 23, 376-380.

Rake, G., and Shaffer, M. F., 1939, Propagation of the agent of measles in the fertile hen's egg. Nature, 144, 672-673.

Rake, G., and Shaffer, M. F., 1940, Studies on measles. I. The use of the chorio-allantois of the developing chicken embryo. J. Immunol., 38, 177-200.

Rake, G., Shaffer, M. F., and Jones, H. P., 1941, Studies on measles. III. The use of tissue culture in propagation of measles virus. J. Infect. Dis., 69, 65-69.

Rietschel, P., 1921, Zur Masernprophylaxe nach Degkwitz. Ztschr. f. Kinderheilk., 29, 127-132.

Shaffer, M. F., Rake, G., Stokes, J., Jr., and O'Neil, G. C., 1941, Studies on measles. II. Experimental disease in man and monkey. J. Immunol., 41, 241-257.

Stillerman, M., Marks, H. H., and Thalhimer, W., 1944, Prophylaxis of measles with convalescent serum. Am. J. Dis. Child., 67, 1-14.

Stokes, J., Jr., Maris, E. P., and Gellis, S. S., 1944, Chemical, clinical, and immunological studies on the products of human plasma fractionation. XI. The use of concentrated normal human serum gamma globulin (human immune serum globulin) in the prophylaxis and treatment of measles. J. Clin. Investig., 23, 531-540.

Warthin, A. S., 1931, Occurrence of numerous large giant cells in the tonsils and pharyngeal mucosa in the prodromal stage of measles. Arch. Path., 11, 864-874.

Wenckebach, G. K., and Kunert, H., 1937, Die Züchtung des Masernvirus. Deutsche med. Wchnschr., 63, 1006-1008.

GEOFFREY RAKE, M.B., B.S.

The Squibb Institute for Medical Research

23

Rubella

(SYNONYMS: German measles, rubeola,*
epidemic roseola, *Rötheln* or *Röteln, rubéole*)

INTRODUCTION

Rubella is a mild exanthem in childhood. Recent work has shown the serious effects on the fetus following the occurrence of the disease during pregnancy, but in the mother herself the disease, if somewhat severer than occurs in childhood, is not serious. Apart from effects in unborn children, the prognosis is always excellent.

HISTORY

Although rubella has undoubtedly existed for many centuries, confusion of it with other exanthemata has obscured its true identity until comparatively recently. Wagner (1829) first separated it from measles and scarlet fever as a distinct entity, but his observations were largely ignored for the next 50 years. Confusion between rubella and measles still exists, and probably the most important observation from the stand of differential diagnosis was that of Koplik (1896) on the characteristic enanthem of measles which today bears his name. Until recently rubella has been considered a mild and unimportant disease. This view has been altered by the brilliant observations of Gregg (1941), since amply confirmed, on the serious effect

* Rubeola unfortunately is used as a synonym for both measles and rubella.

of the disease in pregnant females on the fetus in utero.

CLINICAL PICTURE

The symptoms are usually mild, particularly in children. After an incubation period of from 14 to 23 days, usually 18, there may be a short prodromal period with mild catarrhal symptoms and malaise, but no fever. The rash then appears, starting on the face and head and spreading to neck and trunk. It reaches its full development usually within 24 hours. In early stages it resembles the rash of measles, consisting of round, pink, slightly raised macules which may be discrete or confluent. Such confluent rash in its later stages may resemble scarlet fever, but usually it is morbilliform. Rarely the rash is papular. The exanthem lasts only two or three days and may characteristically appear on new areas after it has faded in those first affected. Slight branny desquamation is sometimes seen. Koplik spots (see measles) are absent; but a fine red enanthem may occur on the soft palate, and the tonsils may be enlarged. Fever is slight and may last for the duration of the rash. The lymphadenitis is characteristic and affects particularly the cervical and occipital nodes. These may be tender. Such swelling persists for two or three weeks. According to Habel (1942), virus is present in blood and nasopharyngeal secretions during the first 30 hours after the appearance of the rash. Complications are rare but those seen, such as encephalitis, neuritis and arthritis, appear to be more frequent in adults than in children. There is no tendency to secondary infection.

Gregg (1941) first showed the serious effect on the child of rubella in the mother during pregnancy, particularly during the early postconceptual months. He drew particular attention to cataract and cardiac malformations. Later studies in Australia, the United States, England and Europe have confirmed the essentials of Gregg's observations. There is some evidence that such malformations are more frequent following severe attacks in the mother but, as has already been pointed out, rubella is a more severe disease in adults, at least as it occurs today. Attention should be drawn in particular to three large surveys in Australia (Gregg et al., 1945; Swan et al., 1946; Swan, 1949). From these it appears that rubella in the first four months of pregnancy results in serious congenital malformations so often, ranging from 83 per cent in the first month to 61 per cent in the fourth month (Swan, 1949), that abortion in such cases warrants consideration. American statistics (Ingalls and Gordon, 1947; Ober, Horton and Feemster, 1947) now available suggest a defect rate of about 50 per cent for rubella in the first three months of pregnancy. This figure is much lower than that given by the Australian groups. It should be emphasized, however, that the American statistics are collected at an earlier date after birth than are the Australian, and many of the commoner abnormalities, particularly the deafness, would not be included. Infection in the later months carries with it less liability. Although of less frequent occurrence than other abnormalities, abortion, miscarriage or stillbirth may fallow maternal rubella during the first 3 or 4 months of pregnancy.

The Australian studies have made it clear that of all the congenital defects microcephaly (70 per cent) and deafness with secondary mutism (75 per cent) are the most frequent, with cardiac malformations (63 per cent) and eye defects, particularly cataract (66 per cent), following closely behind. Dental abnormalities appeared in 45 per cent of the children; in two thirds of the instances they were of major character.

PATHOLOGIC PICTURE

Although the lymph nodes are swollen and some authors note enlargement of the spleen, no characteristic changes have been described. Hess (1914) states that lymphocytosis at or preceding the time of appearance of rash is characteristic.

Pathologic changes have been studied in congenitally affected children born of mothers infected with rubella during pregnancy. From the extent of the malformations it is clear that all three germ layers are affected, but least of all the entoderm. Gregg (1941) noted that all three necropsies in his series showed patent ductus arteriosus, and one of them showed patent foramen ovale. Swan (1944) found patencies of both in all his three necropsies, and no signs of endarteritis obliterans could be found in the ducti. The children were usually undernourished with signs pointing to some involvement of all cells. Affected eyes were small (microphthalmia) and the lens showed massive central or nuclear necrosis with distortion of the peripheral lens fibers. Carruthers (1945) examined the ears in one case with deafness and found absence of differentiation of primitive cells to form the organ of Corti.

EXPERIMENTAL INFECTION; HOST RANGE

The disease has been transmitted to children by the inoculation of filtered nasal washings (Hiro and Tasaka, 1938). Six of 16 developed typical rubella and two others *rubella sine eruptione* after an incubation period of 5 to 17 days. Hess (1914) inoculated four rhesus monkeys with blood taken from human cases within 24 hours of the appearance of rash. One animal showed a sharp febrile response on the nineteenth day but nothing else. Habel (1942) has reported the successful transmission of the disease to *M. mulatta* (rhesus monkeys). Nasal washings or defibrinated blood were used, being collected usually within 12 hours of the appearance of the rash. The animals, following subcutaneous, intraperitoneal, intranasal or intravenous inoculation of filtered or unfiltered material, showed mild disease in 13 out of 16 attempts. The incubation period was from seven to nine days. Pyrexia was slight. Some leukopenia occurred. The exanthem, which was not always present, consisted of sparse pink macules chiefly on the trunk. There was no enanthem. Habel transferred the disease from monkey to monkey in one series for five passages. Challenge inoculations of monkeys, within one to three months after the original infection, were inconclusive. At least two of five animals were reinfected. No cross immunity between measles and rubella was found. Cultivation in the chicken embryo is discussed under etiology. Attempts to transmit the disease to other animals have failed.

Anderson (1949) infected volunteers with a spray of freshly prepared throat-washings taken from patients with rubella during the first 24 hours of rash. The incubation period to the appearance of rash in these volunteers was 13 to 20 days; lymphadenopathy in some instances preceded the rash as long as 6 days. Some subclinical infections apparently were produced. The inoculation disease spread to exposed contacts but not during the incubation period. Krugman and Ward (1951) infected volunteers by blood and nasopharyngeal washings taken from patients 13 hours after appearance of the rash; incubation periods ranged from 12 to 16 days regardless of whether inoculations were made by the intramuscular or intranasal route. Contact infection by exposure to the inoculation disease also succeeded.

Rubella without rash apparently occurred in two inoculated volunteers. Krugman and Ward (1951) were unable to infect 17 cynomolgus monkeys.

ETIOLOGY

Hiro and Tasaka (1938) reported successful transfer of the disease to children by the use of nasal washings filtered through Berkefeld W or Seitz EK filters. Habel (1942, 1947) also used filtered nasal washings for successful transfer of rubella, showing that the material passed through Berkefeld N filters. Apart from filterability, pointing to a virus, little is known about the causative agent. Anderson (1949) demonstrated that the virus would pass a filter with pore-diameters of 800 mμ. It was viable in throat-washings after storage for 90 days at $-70°$ C. Krugman and Ward (1952) found that virus was viable after storage for 9 months in a dry-ice chest. Rubella does behave in many ways like a viral disease. Habel (1942) has made serial passages on the chorio-allantois of the chicken embryo. No lesions developed on the membrane, but successful transmission of rubella to the monkey was noted after five such passages. Neither Anderson (1949) nor Krugman and Ward (1952) could demonstrate any multiplication of the virus in chick embryos.

DIAGNOSIS

Rubella must be distinguished from measles, exanthem subitum and infectious mononucleosis (glandular fever). Differential diagnosis from the first is best established by the absence of Koplik spots but the milder course of rubella, the enlarged cervical nodes and the different distribution of the rash are useful features. Exanthem subitum starts abruptly with fever, and rash is unusual before defervescence; the disease is even milder than rubella and is usually confined to infants and very small children. The rash which may occur in infectious mononucleosis is protean in type but may mimic any of the common exanthemata. In this disease, however, there is an increase, up to 75 or 85 per cent, of lymphoblastic mononuclear cells in the blood and a rise in the titer of heterophile antibodies. Rashes due to drugs may resemble rubella, and such a cause for the exanthem must be excluded.

TREATMENT

The treatment of rubella is largely symptomatic, and in many cases the disease is so mild that no treatment, even bed rest, is required. Some of our ideas have changed, however, with the demonstration of the serious and frequent damage to the unborn child if rubella occurs during pregnancy. If a pregnant woman is exposed to rubella, trial may be made of the use of immune globulin in one form or another (see Measles). Results with serum used as a prophylactic or modifying agent in rubella are contradictory. Barenberg and his colleagues (1942) present presumptive evidence of its suppressive action, and McLorinan (1950) gives evidence suggesting that 4 ml. of the gamma-globulin fraction of serum from patients convalescent from rubella, administered not later than the eighth day after contact, will prevent the disease in the majority of susceptible contacts.

EPIDEMIOLOGY

Rubella occurs in epidemics with a maximum incidence in winter and spring months. The incubation period is from two to three weeks, usually 18 days. An attack usually, but not always, produces a permanent immunity. The disease is transmitted, as is measles, by contact with discharges from the nasopharynx of the patient either directly or from freshly soiled articles, especially during the prodromal period and for perhaps 48 hours thereafter. That contagiousness is less than in measles is indicated by the higher attack rate for rubella amongst adults.

CONTROL MEASURES

Before the serious results of an attack during pregnancy were recognized control measures were of little importance. It is now clear, however, that girls should have rubella, when possible, before the childbearing period. If a pregnant woman has not had rubella, or even if she has (because of possible faulty diagnosis of the first attack or because of possible second attack), every attempt should be made to isolate her from the disease if it is known to be occurring in the vicinity in endemic or epidemic form. If despite precautions, she is exposed, prophylaxis with immune globulin should be attempted for lack of anything else. A definitive study of the usefulness of immune globulin in this connection is urgently needed.

REFERENCES

Anderson, S. G., 1949, Experimental rubella in human volunteers. J. Immunol., 62, 29-40.

Barenberg, L. H., Levy, W., Greenstein, N. M., and Greenberg, B., 1942, Prophylactic use of human serum against contagion in a pediatric ward. Am. J. Dis. Child., 63, 1101-1109.

Carruthers, D. G., 1945, Congenital deaf-mutism as a sequela of a rubella-like maternal infection during pregnancy. Med. J. Austral., I, 315-320.

Gregg, N. M., 1941, Congenital cataract following German measles in the mother. Trans. Ophthal. Scc. Austral. (B.M.A.), 3, 35-46.

Gregg, N. McA., Beavis, W. R., Heseltine, M., Machin, A. E., Vickery, D., and Meyers, E., 1945, The occurrence of congenital defects in children following maternal rubella during pregnancy. Med. J. Austral., 2, 122-126.

Habel, K., 1942, Transmission of rubella to *Macacus mulatta* monkeys. Pub. Health Rep., 57, 1126-1139.

Habel, K., 1947, Personal communication.

Hess, A. F., 1914, German measles (rubella): an experimental study. Arch. Int. Med., 13, 913-916.

Hiro, Y., and Tasaka, S., 1938, Die Röteln sind eine Viruskrankheit. Monatschft. f. Kinderheilk., 76, 328-332.

Ingalls, T. H., and Gordon, J. E., 1947, The epidemiologic implications of developmental arrests. Am. J. Med. Sci., 214, 322-328.

Koplik, H., 1896, The diagnosis of the invasion of measles from a study of the exanthem as it appears on the buccal mucous membrane. Arch. Pediat., 13, 918-922.

Krugman, S., and Ward, R., 1952, Rubella without

rash: a phenomenon observed during studies on immunization. To be published.

McLorinan, H., 1950, Diagnosis and prophylaxis of rubella. Med. J. Australia, *2*, 390-392.

Ober, R. E., Horton, R. J. M., and Feemster, R. F., 1947, Congenital defects in a year of epidemic rubella. Am. J. Pub. Health, *37*, 1328-1333.

Swan, C., 1944, A study of three infants dying from congenital defects following maternal rubella in the early stages of pregnancy. J. Path. and Bact., *56*, 289-295.

Swan, C., Tostevin, A. L., and Black, G. H. B., 1946, Final observations on congenital defects in infants following infectious diseases during pregnancy, with special reference to rubella. Med. J. Austral., *2*, 889-908.

Swan, C., 1949, Rubella in pregnancy as an etiological factor in congenital malformation, stillbirth, miscarriage and abortion. J. Obstet. and Gyn., *56*, 341-363 and 591-605.

Wagner, 1829, Die Rötheln als fur sich bestehende Krankheit. Litt. Ann. der ges. Heilkunde, *13*, 420-428.

GEOFFREY RAKE, m.b., b.s.

The Squibb Institute for Medical Research

24

Exanthem Subitum

(SYNONYMS: Roseola subitum, roseola infantilis, roseola infantum, pseudo-rubella, exanthem criticum, sixth disease, rose rash of infants)

INTRODUCTION

Exanthem subitum is an acute illness with sudden onset, confined almost entirely to infants and young children. It is mildly contagious and may occur in limited outbreaks or in epidemic form in institutions. It is characterized by fever, from three to five days, which terminates on or shortly before the appearance of a transient fine rash on neck, trunk and upper extremities. The prognosis is excellent.

HISTORY

The disease, although probably known for over a century, was first described as a distinct entity by Zahorsky (1910) in the United States. This report was immediately followed by reports of the disease from many parts of the world. It had hitherto been overlooked due to confusion of it with other exanthemata.

CLINICAL PICTURE

Most of the cases occur in children under 4 years. Twelve months is a particularly susceptible age. Cutts (1938) has described a typical case in a 31-year-old woman. Both sexes are equally affected. The onset is sudden and the rise in temperature, sometimes to 105° or 106° F., may be complicated with convulsions. Fever lasts from three to five days, is of intermittent or remittent type and disappears by crisis.

The child is irritable. In some cases the onset of rash may precede the disappearance of fever, but in most cases it follows such disappearance by a few hours to one day. The rash is typically macular and fine but may be maculopapular. It appears first on the trunk, later on the neck and upper extremities. It tends to be most prominent over the thighs and the buttocks where each macule may be surrounded by a pale halo. Sparse rash may occur on the face, which, however, is often spared except behind the ears. The rash fades rapidly, desquamation is rare and pigmentation does not occur. Clemens (1945) has described an enanthem of erythematous specks and streaks on the soft palate. Typical cases without the rash (*roseola sine eruptione*) occur. Diarrhea is often present. The disease may recur after apparent complete recovery. Occasionally neurologic symptoms may be seen. These are usually of the mild type termed "meningismus." Leukopenia and relative or even absolute lymphocytosis are characteristic and are most marked around the third day of fever. Such lymphocytosis may be accompanied by slight enlargement of the lymph nodes. Monocytes may also be increased to as high as 17 per cent.

ETIOLOGY

The causative agent is still not definitely known. All attempts at cultivation of bacteria from the blood at various stages of the disease have been negative. Recently, Kempe and his colleagues (1950) have been able to transmit the disease from one infant to another by the intravenous injection of serum collected on the third but not on the first day of the febrile period. The positive serum was shown to be free from bacteria. The induced disease, which appeared after an incubation period of 9 days, was typical. The disease was also apparently transmitted to monkeys, both from the donor and from the recipient by means of serum or throat-washings taken on the third day of fever. The monkeys developed fever and leukopenia, but neither exanthem nor enanthem. The incubation period in the monkey was 4 or 5 days. The febrile disease was passed to other monkeys by the use of serum taken on the second day of fever and inoculated, either untreated or after filtration through a Seitz EK filter. The febrile disease produced an immunity in monkeys for at least a 9-day period.

DIAGNOSIS

Exanthem subitum must be distinguished from measles, rubella, scarlet fever and dengue. From the first it may be distinguished by the mildness or absence of coryzal symptoms, absence of Koplik spots, and distribution of the rash. The critical termination of fever on or before the appearance of the rash is a distinguishing feature from all the above exanthemata, as is the low degree of apparent contagiousness. From rubella it is also distinguished by the sudden onset and the slight degree of enlargement of lymph nodes. Scarlet

fever shows marked angina, a different blood picture and a type and course of rash entirely different with its typical circumoral pallor, its residual staining and its marked and coarse desquamation. From dengue, exanthem subitum is distinguished by the lack of a second rise of temperature and the absence of intense pains in bones, joints and muscles. Distinction of the rash of exanthem subitum from that produced by certain drugs may be difficult and history of administration of sulfonamides or other drugs should be sought.

TREATMENT

The treatment is entirely symptomatic. Sulfonamides are without effect. The prognosis is excellent in all cases.

EPIDEMIOLOGY

The maximum incidence of the disease is in the spring and fall. The incubation period appears to be about ten days with a range of 7 to 17 days (Cushing, 1927). As pointed out above, the disease can assume mildly epidemic form. Usually, however, it does not spread even within a family group of young children and many authors have flatly denied that it is contagious. In view of the occurrence of the disease without rash and the transient nature of the rash in many cases, it seems to the author that the mild contagiousness is, in part at least, only apparent and results from a high proportion of subclinical or unrecognized infections, particularly in older children.

No special methods of control are indicated.

REFERENCES

Clemens, H. H., 1945, Exanthem subitum (roseola infantum). J. Pediat., *26*, 66-77.

Cushing, H. B., 1927, An epidemic of roseola infantum. Canad. Med. Assn. J., *17*, 905-906.

Cutts, M., 1938, Exanthem subitum; report of a case. Ann. Int. Med., *11*, 1752-1753.

Kempe, C. H., Shaw, E. B., Jackson, J. R., and Silver, H. K., 1950, Studies on the etiology of exanthem subitum (roseola infantum). J. Ped., *37*, 561-568.

Zahorsky, J., 1910, Roseola infantilis. Pediatrics, *22*, 60-64.

T. F. McNAIR SCOTT, M.D.

The Children's Hospital of Philadelphia
(Department of Pediatrics, School of Medicine, University of Pennsylvania)

25

Diseases Caused by the Virus of Herpes Simplex

INTRODUCTION

The virus of herpes simplex is one of the commonest infectious agents of man. The clinical conditions known to be due to this agent can be classified under diseases (1) of the skin, (2) of the mucous membranes, (3) of the eye, (4) of the central nervous system, and (5) miscellaneous.

The following factors are common to all these diseases: (1) tissues preferentially attacked are those of the embryonic ectodermal layers; (2) visible manifestations are characterized by vesicle formation in the epithelial layers; (3) lesions are histologically characterized by intranuclear inclusion bodies; and (4) the virus can be isolated with relative ease from infected tissues.

HISTORY

Löwenstein (1919) was the first to publish evidence that a virus from human herpetic keratitis and from herpes simplex would produce specific lesions on the cornea of a rabbit. He credited Grüter with priority for similar unpublished experiments in 1912 and 1913. Grüter (1920) described the successful transmission of the disease from an experimentally infected rabbit back to the normal cornea of a blind man. In 1920, it was found that herpes virus could cause encephalitis in rabbits (Doerr

1920), and, in the same year, an active agent with the characteristics of herpes virus was isolated from a patient who had died of von Economo's encephalitis (Levaditi and Harvier, 1920). This gave rise to the idea that herpes virus might be a less virulent variant of the "virus of encephalitis" (Levaditi, 1922). However, with increased experience the conclusion has been reached that herpes virus is not the cause of this type of epidemic encephalitis, its occasional isolation being the result of a coincidental latent infection.

Andrewes and Carmichael (1930) observed that a large proportion of normal adults had in their blood neutralizing antibodies against herpes virus, and that recurrent herpes occurred in those with neutralizing antibodies, while those without were free. Since these findings appeared to be contrary to the usual pattern of infectious disease, and since herpes did not seem to spread from patient to patient but seemed to be provoked by some nonspecific stimulus, such as fever, Doerr (1938) suggested "that herpes is not an infectious agent which is maintained by a chain of infection but that it is endogenously generated in the human organism."

Some of the difficulties outlined above have been resolved since the discovery by

Dodd and co-workers (1938) that herpes virus could be routinely isolated from the mouths of infants suffering from a common form of stomatitis, and by Burnet and Williams (1939) that such infants also developed neutralizing antibodies during convalescence from the stomatitis. In other words, the first contact of certain persons with herpes virus results in a typical infectious disease; from this, it is clear that the virus behaves essentially like other infectious agents.

CLINICAL PICTURE

Before considering the individual clinical entities that are attributable to herpes virus, it is important to emphasize one basic principle common to all of them. There are two types of clinical herpetic disease regardless of site infected, which must be clearly differentiated: (1) primary infections with the virus, occurring in persons without neutralizing antibodies in their blood stream; (2) recurrent attacks, occurring in persons with such neutralizing antibodies. In a primary attack, the local lesion is usually accompanied by a systemic illness that is often severe and sometimes fatal; whereas the patient with a recurrent attack, however severe the local lesion may be, is as a rule singularly free from systemic symptoms. Although clinical manifestations of primary infection are usually severe when they occur, the comparative infrequency of such illnesses cannot account for the 70 to 90 per cent of adults who demonstrate by the presence of circulating antibodies against the virus that they have had a previous infection. There must, therefore, be numerous subclinical infections. Recovered individuals, whether from a manifest or subclinical infection, become carriers of the virus and are apt, following nonspecific stimuli, such as fever, menstruation, or emotional upsets, to have recurrent manifestations of herpetic infection. Virus can be isolated from all the sites of clinical disease. In addition, the virus has been isolated from apparently unrelated diseases, such as atypical pneumonia (Morgan and Finland, 1949) for which there is no adequate explanation.

HERPES SIMPLEX

[SYNONYMS: Herpes labialis, facialis, febrilis (Becker and Obermayer, 1947)]

This is so universally recognized and described as to merit but brief description here. The lesions are heralded by a subjective feeling of irritation or burning pain in the area of skin involved. Reddish papules then appear which quickly vesiculate and become grouped, thin-walled vesicles on an erythematous base. These rupture, become scabbed, and eventually heal, usually without leaving a scar. They tend to recur in the same area. Although they may occur anywhere on the skin, there is a predilection for mucocutaneous junctions. *Herpes progenitalis* of the male is usually manifested by a recurrent cluster of small erosions (eroded vesicles) on the glans penis or corona, sometimes associated with a group of typical herpetic vesicles on the shaft. Primary clinical infection in the male is very rare. Slavin (1951) described it, in a boy with stomatitis, as a cluster of tiny vesicles surrounding a reddened meatal orifice accompanied by a watery discharge and dysuria. Herpetic infection of the genitalia of females may be primary or recurrent. The primary disease is manifested by the appearance of superficial lesions on the labia majora, minora and lower vaginal mucous membrane. The lesions are tender and covered by a grayish-yellow membrane. Patients suffer discomfort for a week or longer. The recurrent disease may show similar erosions or clustered vesicles (Slavin and Gavette, 1946).

ECZEMA HERPETICUM (Lynch 1945)

(SYNONYMS: Kaposi's varicelliform eruption, Juliusberg's pustulosis vacciniformis acuta)

In 1887, Kaposi described a varicelliform eruption complicating infantile eczema of which he did not know the cause; he suggested the descriptive name "eczema herpetiforme." His clinical description (Kaposi, 1895) remains good today:

A very alarming complication of eczema infantum . . . is an acute outbreak of numerous vesicles, partly scattered and partly arranged in groups. The vesicles are as large as a lentil, filled with clear serum, and the majority are umbilicated. They look like varicella vesicles but undoubtedly do not belong in this class. . . . The patients have high fever,—40° C. or more—and are very restless. The vesicles develop very acutely (sometimes overnight), in large numbers and often continue to appear in successive crops, for three or four days, or even a week. Those which appear first undergo desiccation, rupture and expose the corium or they become encrusted and fall off. The largest number of the varicella-like vesicles are found upon the already eczematous skin but smaller groups appear on the previously intact skin of the neighborhood. . . . The outcome of the peculiar affection is in the majority of cases favorable.

Seidenberg (1941) first isolated herpes simplex virus from the skin lesions of two such patients. Several American workers substantiated these findings and demonstrated that in the majority of patients the skin disease is a primary herpetic infection accompanied by a severe systemic illness which is sometimes fatal. The patients, on recovery, develop neutralizing antibodies. Occasionally, the clinical picture occurs in patients with circulating antibodies as a manifestation of recurrent herpes, in which case the systemic manifestations are much less severe (Boake, Dudgeon and Burnet, 1951). In primary infections, there is a frequent history of contact with a manifest case of herpes simplex. The pathogenesis of this disease is a matter of speculation. The close association with atopic eczema may implicate the virus-potentiating activity of histamine (Good and Campbell, 1945) or the wide expanse of denuded skin so common in these patients may merely provide a good nidus for exogenous infection with the virus or since a viremia occurs early in primary infection

(Ruchman and Dodd, 1950) this may represent a "locus minoris resistentiae" in which the virus localizes. The disease (Fig. 42) must be differentiated from eczema vaccinatum.

TRAUMATIC HERPES

Inoculation of herpes virus occasionally occurs through traumatic breaks (burns, abrasions) in the normal skin of a susceptible child and results in a characteristic illness. About 2 or 3 days after the original trauma, the skin lesion becomes erythematous, and vesicles appear. The child develops fever, and within the next few days a vesicular eruption may extend up the limb, assuming a distribution that simulates herpes zoster. The regional lymph nodes are enlarged and tender. The illness may last from 10 days to 3 weeks before all lesions have disappeared. Other manifestations of herpes, such as stomatitis, may occur during the course of the illness. Following recovery, herpes may recur at the site of original injury. Occasionally large bullae take the place of vesicles and recur as such at the site of trauma (Findlay and MacCallum, 1940).

ACUTE HERPETIC GINGIVOSTOMATITIS

(SYNONYMS: 'Acute infectious gingivostomatitis, aphthous stomatitis, catarrhal stomatitis, ulcerative stomatitis, Vincent's stomatitis)

This is a common disease of young children, chiefly between the ages of 18 months and six years; it may occur in adults. Until Dodd, Johnston and Buddingh (1938) isolated the virus of herpes simplex from the saliva of almost 100 per cent of patients with the malady and Burnet and Williams (1939) demonstrated the rise of antibodies against herpes virus in such patients following recovery, its etiology was unknown. This is probably the most common clinical picture caused by a primary infection with herpes virus. The chief clinical characteristics (Scott, Steigman and Convey, 1941) are as follows.

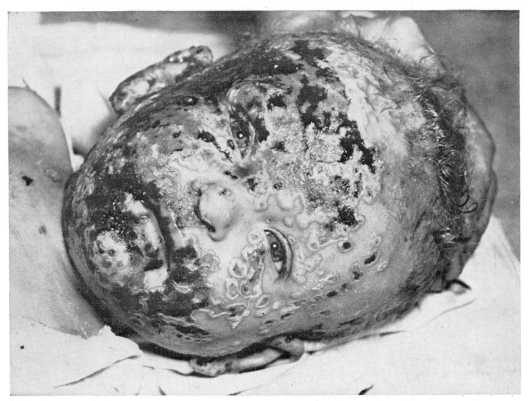

FIG. 42. Eczema herpeticum showing grouped umbilicated vesicles. (Ruchman, I., Welsh, A. L., and Dodd, K., 1947, Kaposi's varicelliform eruption: isolation of virus of herpes simplex from cutaneous lesions of 3 adults and 1 infant. Archives of Dermatology and Syphilology, *56,* 848.)

There are fever, irritability, red swollen gums, a vesicular eruption on the mucous membranes of the mouth, oral fetor, and local lymphadenopathy. In about a third of the cases, the onset is insidious, the child being ill for two or three days before a sore mouth develops; in the remainder, there is early refusal to eat or actual complaint of sore mouth. A constitutional reaction is always present but varies in severity; a high fever, from 104 to 105° F., is not uncommon. Lesions in the mouth are essentially vesicular, although it is rare to see true vesicles except in very early cases. The typical lesion is a grayish-yellow plaque representing a modified vesicle with a thickened roof. These vary in size and number and later lose their covering to become shallow ulcers. No portion of the oral lining is immune, although the tongue and cheeks are most commonly involved (Plate 4, *top*). In some patients the tonsillar region is affected early. Under these circumstances the lesions must be distinguished from those of herpangina due to Coxsackie virus (see chapter on Coxsackie Group) and bacterial tonsillitis. The unilateral tonsillar ulcers of Vincent's angina, which is not herpetic (Steigman and Scott, 1947), can easily be differentiated. One of the most common findings is a characteristic involvement of the gums, which varies from a thin red line along the dental margin to extreme redness and swelling of the gums (Plate 4, *bottom*). In the rare infant, infected before the eruption of teeth, the gums escape involvement. Submaxillary lymphadenopathy of varying degree is extremely common. The disease is self-limiting in about two weeks. With anti-biotic control of bacterial infection the usual clinical course is from 7 to 10 days. Pain tends to disappear before the lesions heal. Scarring is absent or very slight. Swelling of the gums and lymphadenopathy, among the first signs to appear, usually persist for many days after the ulcers heal. The nasal mucosa is rarely the site of primary infection (Ruchman and Dodd, 1950).

RECURRENT STOMATITIS

It is possible that herpetic stomatitis recurs but this must be extremely rare. The suggested reason for the usual nonrecurrence is that all the infected cells of the mucous membrane have been shed during primary attack so that the virus has been eliminated from the area. Good evidence has been presented (Blank et al., 1950; Dodd and Ruchman, 1950) that recurrent aphthous ulcers are not usually herpetic. A history of recurrent stomatitis of any sort should weigh against the diagnosis of herpes.

CONJUNCTIVITIS AND KERATO-CONJUNCTIVITIS

The eye is one of the common sites of herpetic infection. Keratoconjunctivitis is more common than conjunctivitis, but the latter may occur (Granström, 1937) and give rise to the following pictures.

The palpebral conjunctiva is intensely congested and swollen with little, if any, purulent discharge; the preauricular node may or may not be palpable and tender. The palpebral conjunctiva at times is covered with a thin, grayish, tough, easily detachable membrane; associated with this type of lesion, there may be no preauricular-node enlargement, or a fully developed Parinaud's syndrome (unilateral conjunctivitis, usually membranous; swollen, painful preauricular node; fever) may be present. One of the characteristics of a keratoconjunctivitis is the protean nature of the corneal lesion. It may take the form of superficial punctate keratitis, marginal keratitis, multiple corneal erosions, dendritic ulcer, or disciform keratitis. For a clinical description of these states, reference should be made to standard ophthalmic textbooks (Duke-Elder, 1938). The clinical characteristics which should arouse suspicion of an herpetic etiology in any inflammatory condition of the eye are as follows: (1) the frequency with which it follows pyrexia; (2) relapses or recurrences; (3) slight, if any, purulent discharge; (4) herpetic vesicles on the lids; (5) bacteriologic sterility of the conjunctiva; (6) rapid and complete healing as a rule (Hamilton, 1943); (7) hypesthesia of the eye; (8) a visible and slightly tender preauricular node (Thygeson, 1947). The majority of the described cases are of the recurrent type, but primary keratoconjunctivitis has been described by Gallardo (1943).

HERPETIC MENINGO-ENCEPHALITIS

Originally, the majority of the proved cases of this type of herpetic infection were fatal, and the diagnosis was established by isolation of virus and typical histology in the brain. Recently, Afzelius-Alm (1951) has established this virus as one of the causes of nonfatal meningo-encephalitis. Diagnosis in such cases is made by the isolation of the virus from the spinal fluid and/or the demonstration of the development of specific antibodies following the illness. The clinical picture in recovered patients is quite variable, resembling uncomplicated aseptic meningitis (Armstrong, 1943) or showing various encephalitic signs, such as somnolence, dizziness, aphasia and ocular palsies. Common symptoms are headache, fever and vomiting. The cerebrospinal fluid usually, but not always, shows a pleocytosis, mostly lymphocytes. Fever falls by lysis from the fifth to the eleventh day, and recovery appears to be complete, although sometimes delayed. Other signs of herpes may appear, such as vesicles on the skin or the mucous membranes. The fatal illnesses have shown early development of intracranial pressure and the protean manifestations of encephalitis, such as stupor, paresis of muscle groups, sensory changes and convulsions. Death has occurred between the eighth and twelfth days (Whitman, Wall and Warren, 1946). The blood leukocyte count varies.

MISCELLANEOUS

A primary attack may be atypical due to predominance of systemic illness or unusual local lesions. One adult was diagnosed as having smallpox (Kipping and Downie, 1948) because atypical skin lesions accompanied a severe systemic illness. Kilbourne and Horsfall (1951) described two adults with symptoms suggestive of infectious mononucleosis. An infant born of a mother with herpetic stomatitis died on the twelfth day with generalized involvement of the skin, brain and liver (Quilligan and Wilson, 1951).

PATHOLOGIC PICTURE

Details of the pathologic picture vary with the type of infected tissue. In general the characteristic change induced by the virus is the intranuclear inclusion body first described by Lipschütz (1921). It has been shown by various workers, most completely by Crouse et al. (1950), that the development of the inclusion body is a dynamic occurrence, beginning with the appearance of one or more areas of Feulgen-positive material between strands of condensed chromatin. These coalesce to form a Feulgen-positive homogeneous body, staining bluish in H. and E. preparations, which fills the nucleus and compresses the chromatin to the margin. Later this body becomes shrunken, loses its nucleoprotein, thus becoming Feulgen- and toluidine blue-negative, and lies as a pink (in H. and E. preparations) body separated by a halo from the marginated chromatin. This is now the classical Type A inclusion body of Cowdry (1934).

Pathologic changes in the skin and the mucous membranes are characterized by vesicle formation. In the latter the vesicle is modified by early maceration and leakage of fluid. These changes take place in the stratum mucosum, resulting in proliferation, and intracellular and intercellular edema, leading to formation of a vesicle in the prickle-cell layer (Scott et al., 1950). The skin vesicles with their thinned-out roof-cells are tense with fluid (Plate 5, *top*), which contains exfoliated epithelial cells, characteristic multinucleated giant cells, leukocytes and fibrin. Each giant-cell nucleus contains an inclusion body. These giant cells are of diagnostic aid and can be recognized in a smear from a fresh vesicle. The infected epithelium at the edge of the vesicle can be distinguished from the normal skin by the presence of proliferation, "ballooning degeneration" and intranuclear inclusions (Plate 5, *bottom*). The mucosal lesion resembles the skin lesion except for the relative absence of fluid, greater amount of fibrin and edematous thickening of the roof-cells. The corium of both skin and mucous membrane shows pronounced capillary dilatation and infiltration of inflammatory cells but no necrosis, which accounts for the usual absence of scarring.

The pathologic changes in the nervous system occur mostly in the cortex with progressively less involvement of the central white matter and basilar structures. Grossly there are focal areas of dusky discoloration, studded with petechiae, which are swollen and friable. Histologically, there is widespread mononuclear infiltration of the leptomeninges. The lesions in the cortex are characterized by intense degeneration and mild inflammation. The appearance suggests encephalomalacia due to circulatory disturbance. Fat-laden phagocytes flood the field, and the capillaries show endothelial hyperplasia. Neuronophagia occurs. At the margins of necrotic areas, hypertrophied microglial cells and mild astrocytosis are seen. There is perivascular cuffing with mononuclear cells. Inclusion bodies can be demonstrated, preferably with phloxine-methylene blue stain, in oligo-

PLATE 4

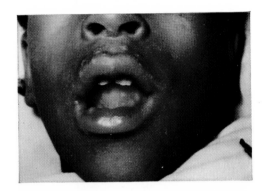

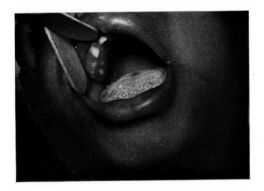

(*Top*) Herpetic gingivostomatitis, showing sublingual ulcers and herpes labialis.

(*Bottom*) Herpetic gingivostomatitis, showing characteristic red gums, buccal ulcer and white furred tongue. (Photographs by Dr. Harvey Blank)

PLATE 5

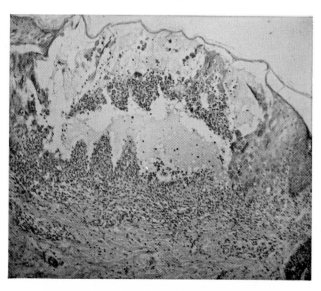

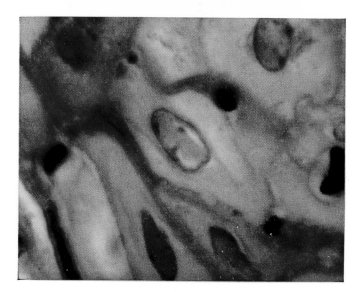

(*Top*) Cutaneous lesion from eczema herpeticum, showing deep epidermal vesicle bordered with ballooning cells.
H and E. × 75.

(*Bottom*) Cells from border of herpetic vesicle, showing
ballooning degeneration and one intranuclear inclusion body.
H and E. × 1500. (Photographs by Dr. R. M. Allen)

dendria and less frequently in nerve cells (Wolf, 1950).

EXPERIMENTAL INFECTION; HOST RANGE

The natural host of the virus is man; it can be transmitted, however, to the following experimental hosts: rabbit, guinea pig, mouse, hamster, rat, cotton rat, and the chorio-allantoic membrane of the embryonated egg. The agent can be introduced into experimental hosts by the corneal, the intracerebral, the intraperitoneal or the intradermal route.

Under anesthesia, the cornea of the rabbit is scarified in such a way that the lines of injury lie at right angles to each other and penetrate the epithelial layer. The infected material is rubbed over the scarified area. Depending on the virulence of the strain of virus used, a keratoconjunctivitis develops between 12 hours and seven days after inoculation. The conjunctiva becomes injected and the cornea cloudy through the development of small vesicles along the scratch marks. A conjunctival exudate appears, at first watery and then, within 24 hours, purulent. However, such an exudate is bacteriologically sterile and on smear contains a large number of mononuclear cells although polymorphonuclear cells usually predominate. The nictitating membrane becomes red and swollen. Gradually, over the course of a week or more, the acute reaction clears up leaving a varying degree of residual corneal opacity. If the cornea is examined histologically within 24 hours of the onset of signs, the characteristic picture of proliferated epithelial cells, which later slough, on each side of the scratch marks can be seen. It is in these cells that inclusion bodies should be looked for. The substantia propria shows marked inflammatory changes. Early exudate or portions of the nictitating membranes can be used for passage.

A small portion of infected fluid or tissue emulsion, 0.03 to 0.25 cc., depending on the size of the animal, is inoculated into the brain. Reactions differ somewhat with various hosts but, in general, an encephalitis results after a varying incubation period. This may manifest itself by fever, tremors, lethargy, weakness or paralysis of muscle groups, convulsions, and death. Any one of these symptoms may be predominant, and recovery may take place. It should be pointed out that an entirely comparable encephalitis may occur in rabbits after corneal inoculation with certain neurotropic strains of the herpes virus. The pathologic picture of brains in experimental encephalitis reveals type A inclusion bodies as in the human brains just described. Kilbourne and Horsfall (1951) have shown that newborn mice are very susceptible and die on the fifth or sixth day after intraperitoneal inoculation.

The intradermal route is not satisfactory except for dermotropic strains. From 0.05 to 0.1 cc. of virus emulsion is injected into the plucked skin of the flank of a rabbit or guinea pig. About two days after the injection, red papular lesions develop which may vesiculate and then subside after two or three days. The virus may be inoculated into the foot pads of guinea pigs, which become inflamed and swollen on the second day; the reaction gradually subsides within a few days.

In the embryonated egg the chorio-allantoic membrane is used for inoculation. After 48 to 72 hours' incubation at 96° F. the virus is harvested by removing the infected membrane. This is then examined under a good light in a Petri dish, the bottom of which is painted with black enamel on the outside. Characteristic findings depend on the amount of virus present and its state of "egg adaptation." At a suitable dilution of virus the membrane shows a number of small, raised, white plaques. These tend to have an oval or even a tailed form and appear very superficial. Central necrosis and a mesodermal "halo" of accumulated inflammatory cells occur in old lesions, but these are not conspicuous. This is in contrast to the marked necrosis and "halo" occurring on the larger, round, deeper, plaques of vaccinia (Beveridge and Burnet, 1946). Specific lesions must be distinguished from those caused by nonspecific irritation among which are areas of thickening and irregular opacities along the blood vessels. In the first eggs used for primary isolation the plaques may be difficult to distinguish, and, in some cases, the membranes may be thickened and edematous. At least three passages may be needed before characteristic lesions are seen. Histologic examination at 20 hours after infection reveals many small plaques of proliferated cells, 90 per cent of which contain homogeneous blue-staining inclusions filling the nuclei. During the ensuing 72 hours the following changes occur: the epithelial cells slough, remaining inclusions become shrunken, the mesoderm shows an inflammatory reaction and some inclusion bodies and, finally, the entoderm becomes thickened by cell proliferation (Crouse et al., 1950).

ETIOLOGY

The diameter of the virus determined by filtration through gradocol membranes is 100 to 150 millimicra (Elford, Perdrau and Smith, 1933). When suspended in broth it passes through a Berkefeld V filter but not through N and W candles. Centrifugation at 11,000 r.p.m. for one hour at 4° C. in an angle high-speed centrifuge (Sorvall) sediments about 98 per cent of allantoic fluid virus. Under the electron microscope the virus particles appear to be spherical with early changes in the center, resulting in indented and doughnut-shaped forms. The bodies are readily seen in early vesicles but are virtually absent in those more than 48 hours old (Coriell et al., 1950). The virus in portions of infected animal brain can be preserved for 12 months in 50 per cent glycerol at −20° C. in sealed ampules. Egg-adapted virus can be preserved in unground chorio-allantoic membrane in 50 per cent glycerol for several weeks and for at least 6 months in ground membranes suspended in skim-milk or egg-yolk at −20° C. (Speck et al., 1951). Buffered saline solution, 10 per cent serum-saline solution or 0.5 per cent gelatine-saline solution is preferred to unmodified physiologic salt solution for routine handling of the virus. As early as the fourth or the fifth day after a primary infection complement-fixing and neutralizing antibodies develop, reaching their height before the fourteenth day. In many patients, this titer is apparently maintained for life.

DIAGNOSIS

Diagnosis of infection with herpes simplex virus can be made by recognition of the different disease entities produced by the virus, grouped vesicles and recurrences being especially characteristic; demonstration of the virus in lesions; demonstration, in a primary infection, of an increase during convalescence in the amount of specific antibody; and demonstration of typical cells by smear or histologic section.

Infection with herpes simplex virus must be distinguished from that caused by five other viruses. Eczema vaccinatum may be clinically indistinguishable from eczema herpeticum. However, the causative viruses can be distinguished immunologically and serologically; also histologically since vaccine virus produces cytoplasmic inclusion bodies. Epidemic keratoconjunctivitis is clinically indistinguishable from an infection of the eye due to herpes virus (Maumenee et al., 1945). However, the status of the causative agent of this disease is currently in doubt (Ruchman, 1951). "B virus," which is immunologically related to herpes virus, produces an ascending myelitis, usually following a monkey bite, unlike the meningo-encephalitis produced by herpes virus (Sabin and Wright, 1934). Stomatitis, with or without diarrhea of the newborn (Buddingh and Dodd, 1944), occurs in infants so young that they are almost never susceptible to herpetic infection. Also, although its virus produces a keratoconjunctivitis in rabbits, the picture is different from that produced by herpes virus, and no inclusion bodies have been observed. Herpangina (caused by a Coxsackie virus) is a febrile disease characterized by ulcers on the faucial pillars and the pharynx. The lesions rarely spread to other areas of the buccal mucosa. As opposed to herpes, it is strikingly epidemic in character (Huebner, 1951).

TREATMENT

Clinical manifestations of herpes virus infections are usually self-limited; there is no good evidence of effective specific therapy. Symptomatic treatment, however, is of great importance in the successful management of patients suffering from them. Adequate measures must be taken to combat dehydration induced by high fever (eczema herpeticum) or inability to drink (herpetic stomatitis). Measures to prevent secondary bacterial infections, especially with Vincent's organisms in the oral lesions, by the use of suitable antibiotics or chemotherapy should be undertaken early in the disease. Blood or plasma transfusions may be indicated as supportive measures. For ordinary skin vesicles, Zephiran chloride 1:1000 (alkyl dimethylammonium chloride), or any other antiseptic drying agent may be used. In widespread lesions, such as eczema herpeticum, saline soaks may be necessary to remove and prevent scabs. For mucous membrane lesions, Zephiran 1:1000 is probably the most useful application, since in this concentration it is harmless to tissues and is both bactericidal and virucidal. The use of ice-cold fluids or semi-solids, and applications of a local anesthetic, such as Butyn 2 per cent, to oral lesions may help in maintaining adequate food and fluid intake. Roentgenotherapy has been widely employed for palliation of superficial lesions, although the results are often disappointing. When the cornea is ulcerated, every effort should be made to prevent secondary bacterial infection, since permanent scarring may result from a combined infection, while it is rare in herpetic infection alone. Ophthalmologists advocate skillful cauterization of an ulcer with strong iodine or curettage to get rid of infected cells. The use of smallpox vaccination for the treatment of recurrent herpes has been widely used in this country during the last 10 years. Reports of its efficacy are conflicting; some patients apparently obtain relief, while others relapse during a course of vaccination. If tried, vaccination should be performed every 1 or 2 weeks, depending on the type of take, for 8 to 10 inoculations. Frequent recurrences unassociated with the usual trigger mechanisms are probably an indication for psychotherapy (Blank and Brody, 1950). Reports of beneficial effects of x-ray and smallpox vaccination very likely depend on the enthusiasm of the physician in a highly suggestible group of patients. Vaccination with inactivated herpes virus has been shown to be of no value.

EPIDEMIOLOGY

Until the formulation of the present concept of herpetic infections, it was difficult to understand why herpes labialis usually did not appear to spread to contacts and yet was so widespread. It is now possible to explain some of the discrepancies.

Recent studies have demonstrated the following points of epidemiologic importance: (1) there are two groups in the population, one with circulating antiherpetic antibodies, and one without; (2) the proportion of the former (immune) group varies with the socioeconomic level, being high (up to 93 per cent) in the lower income brackets, and much lower (37 per cent) in the high income brackets; (3) the proportion of the susceptible group is high in childhood, after the age of six months, and decreases with age regardless of income; (4) a newborn infant of an immune mother has circulating antibodies which probably account for the almost complete absence of herpetic infection under six months of age; (5) the spread of herpes among contacts of a patient with an attack of manifest herpes, e.g., herpes labialis, varies with the susceptibility of the contacts. Herpes spreads with ease as a primary infection among a susceptible group, either subclinically or with clinical manifestations, while no spread occurs in immune contacts. The skin test (Nagler, 1946) has not proved to be a useful epidemiologic tool because, in children below puberty, a relationship between a positive test and circulating antibodies does not seem to hold (Scott et al., 1951).

It is not known exactly how this ubiquitous infection is disseminated among the population. If spread by air-borne-droplet infection, it is hard to understand how any adult, regardless of socioeconomic level, could escape. If, however, the disease is spread by contact, the increased crowding and decreased hygiene found among the lower income groups would tend to make passage of the virus from person to person easier in this segment of the population. It is thought that the more sensitive mucous membranes of the infant and child may be a factor in the increased incidence of stomatitis in this age group. However, an alternative explanation may be that, in ordinary families, the young and susceptible child has closer physical contact with other members of the household (especially the adults who may be carriers), than at any period of life until the time of marital cohabitation. It is perfectly possible for a susceptible adult to contract a primary gingivostomatitis from intimate exposure

to the disease in the family (Rogers et al., 1949). Genital herpes can also be contracted by a susceptible adult from an infected partner.

Whatever the method of spread, it is a very successful one, from the point of view of the parasite. While some of its hosts have clinical symptoms, in many the only evidence of infection is the presence of circulating antibodies. Once individuals have recovered from a primary infection, whether clinical or subclinical, they carry the virus in a latent state. Such people provide the reservoir from which the virus spreads to new susceptibles. Since the virus has been demonstrated in the saliva of apparently healthy people, a manifest lesion is not essential as a source of infection. Infectious saliva is found more frequently among healthy children of 1 to 3 years than among healthy adults (Buddingh, 1951).

The incubation period is uncertain but in some cases it appears to be as short as two or three days.

CONTROL MEASURES

There are no specific control measures apart from generally accepted standards of hygiene. Susceptible persons should avoid contact with clinical manifestations of herpetic infection. It is particularly important for persons suffering from atopic eczema to avoid exposure. For the susceptible adult, sexual contact in some form probably provides the greatest risk of infection.

REFERENCES

Afzelius-Alm, L., 1951, Aseptic encephalo-meningitides in Gothenburg, 1932-1948. Clinical and experimental investigation with special reference to the viruses of herpes, influenza, mumps and lymphocytic choriomeningitis. Göterborg, 1951.

Andrewes, C. H., and Carmichael, E. A., 1930, A note on the presence of antibodies to herpes virus in post-encephalitic and other human sera. Lancet, *1*, 857-858.

Armstrong, C., 1943, Herpes simplex virus recovered from the spinal fluid of a suspected case of lymphocytic choriomeningitis, Pub. Health Rep., *58*, 16-21.

Becker S. W., and Obermayer, M. E., 1947, Herpes simplex *in* Becker and Obermayer, Modern Dermatology and Syphilology, ed. 2. Philadelphia, Lippincott, pp. 539-542.

Beveridge, W. I. B., and Burnet, F. M., 1946, The cultivation of viruses and rickettsiae in the chick embryo. Medical Research Council, Special Report Series No. 258. London, His Majesty's Stationery Office, p. 39.

Blank, H., and Brody, M. W., 1950, Recurrent herpes simplex. A psychiatric and laboratory study. Psychosomatic Medicine, *12*, 254-260.

Blank, H., Burgoon, C. F., Coriell, L. L., and Scott, T. F. M., 1950, Recurrent aphthous ulcers. Am. Med. Assn., *142*, 125-126.

Boake, W. C., Dudgeon, J. A., and Burnet, Sir MacFarlane, 1951, Recurrent Kaposi's varicelliform eruption in an adult. Lancet, *1*, 383-390.

Buddingh, G. J., and Dodd, K., 1944, Stomatitis and diarrhea of infants caused by a hitherto unrecognized virus. J. Pediat., *25*, 105-113.

Buddingh, G. J., 1951, Personal communication.

Burnet, F. M., and Williams, S. W., 1939, Herpes simplex: a new point of view. Med. J. Australia, *1*, 637-642.

Coriell, L. L., Rake, G., Blank, H., and Scott, T. F. M., 1950, Electron microscopy of herpes simplex. J. Bact., *59*, 61-68.

Cowdry, E. V., 1934, The problem of intranuclear inclusions in virus diseases. Arch. Path., *18*, 527-542.

Crouse, H. V., Coriell, L. L., Blank, H., and Scott, T. F. M., 1950, Cytochemical studies on the intranuclear inclusion of herpes simplex. J. Immunol., *65*, 119-128.

Dodd, K., Johnston, L. M., and Buddingh, G. J., 1938, Herpetic stomatitis. J. Ped., *12*, 95-102.

Dodd, K., and Ruchman, I., 1950, Herpes simplex virus not the etiologic agent of recurrent stomatitis. Pediatrics, *5*, 883-887.

Doerr, R., 1920, Sitzungsberichte Gesellschaft der Schweizerischen Augenärtzte Diskussion. Klin. Monatsbl. Augenheilkh., *65*, 104.

Doerr, R., 1938, Herpes febrilis, *in* Doerr, R., and Hallauer, C., Handbuch d. Virusforschung, Wien, Springer, Vol. 1, pp. 41-45.

Duke-Elder, Sir W. S., 1938, Textbook of Ophthalmology. London, Kimpton, Vol. 2, pp. 1894 et seq.

Elford, W. J., Perdrau, J. R., and Smith, W., 1933, The filtration of herpes virus through graded collodion membranes. J. Path. and Bact., *36*, 49-54.

Findlay, G. M., and MacCallum, F. O., 1940, Recurrent traumatic herpes. Lancet, *1*, 259-261.

Gallardo, E., 1943, Primary herpes simplex keratitis. Clinical and experimental study. Arch. Ophthalmol., *30*, 217-220.

Good, R. A., and Campbell, B., 1945, Potentiating effect of anaphylactic and histamine shock upon herpes simplex virus infection in rabbits. Proc. Soc. Exp. Biol. and Med., *59*, 305-306.

Granström, K. O., 1937, A contribution to the knowledge of the importance of herpes infections in corneal and conjunctival affections, especially in membranous conjunctivitis. Acta. Ophthal., *15*, 361-369.

Grüter, W., 1920, Experimentelle und klinische Untersuchungen über den sogenannten Herpes corneae. Ber. versam. deut. Ophth. Ges. *42*, 162-166.

Hamilton, J. B., 1943, Notes on forms of keratitis presumably due to the virus of herpes simplex. Brit. J. Ophthal., *27*, 80-87.

Huebner, R. J., Cole, R. M., Beeman, E. A., Bell, J. A., and Peers, J. H., 1951, Herpangina. Etiological studies of a specific infectious disease. J. Am. Med. Assn., *145*, 628-633.

Kaposi, M., 1895, Pathology and Treatment of Diseases of the Skin. New York, Wood, pp. 346-347.

Kilbourne, E. D., and Horsfall, F. L., Jr., 1951, Studies of herpes simplex virus in newborn mice. J. Immunol., *67*, 321-329.

Kilbourne, E. D., and Horsfall, F. L., Jr., 1951, Primary herpes simplex infection of the adult. With a note on the relation of herpes simplex virus to recurrent aphthous stomatitis. Arch. Int. Med., *88*, 495-502.

Kipping, R. H., and Downie, A. W., 1948, Gener-alized infection with the virus of herpes simplex. Brit. Med. J., *1*, 247-249.

Levaditi, C., 1922, Ectodermoses neurotropes: poliomyélite, encéphalite, herpes. Étude clinique, epidémiologique, histopathologique et expérimentale. Paris, Masson.

Levaditi, C., and Harvier, P., 1920, Le virus de l'encéphalite léthargique. Compt, rend. Soc. biol., *83*, 354-355.

Lipschütz, B., 1921, Untersuchungen über die Ätiologie der Krankheiten des Herpes Gruppe (Herpes Zoster, Herpes Genitalis, Herpes Febrilis). Arch. Dermat. u. Syph. *136*, 428-482.

Löwenstein, A., 1919, Aetiologische Untersuchungen über den fieberhaften Herpes. Münch. med. Wchnschr., *66*, 769-770.

Lynch, F. W., 1945, Kaposi's varicelliform eruption: Extensive herpes simplex as a complication of eczema. Arch. Derm. and Syph., *51*, 129-137.

Maumenee, A. E., Hayes, G. S., and Hartman, T. L., 1945, Isolation and identification of the causative agent in epidemic keratoconjunctivitis (superficial punctate keratitis) and herpetic keratoconjunctivitis. Am. J. Ophthal., *28*, 823-839.

Morgan, H. R., and Findland, M., 1949, Isolation of herpes virus from a case of atypical pneumonia and erythema multiforme exudativum with study of four additional cases. Am. J. Med. Sci., *217*, 92-95.

Nagler, F. P. O., 1946, A herpes skin test reagent from amniotic fluid. Australian J. Exp. Biol. and Med. Sci., *24*, 103-105.

Quilligan, J. J., and Wilson, J. L., 1951, Fatal herpes simplex infection in a newborn infant. J. Clin. and Lab. Med., *38*, 742-746.

Rogers, A. M., Coriell, L. L., Blank, H., and Scott, T. F. M., 1949, Acute herpetic gingivostomatitis in the adult. New England J. Med., *241*, 330-333.

Ruchman, I., 1951, Relationship between epidemic keratoconjunctivitis and St. Louis encephalitis viruses. Proc. Soc. Exp. Biol. and Med., *77*, 120-125.

Ruchman, I., and Dodd, K., 1950, Recovery of herpes simplex from the blood of a patient with herpetic rhinitis. J. Lab. and Clin. Med., *35*, 434-439.

Ruchman, I., Welsh, A. L., and Dodd, K., 1947, Kaposi's varicelliform eruption. Isolation of the virus of herpes simplex from the skin lesions of three adults and one infant. Arch. Derm. and Syph. *56*, 846-863.

Sabin, A. B., and Wright, A. M., 1934, Acute ascending myelitis following a monkey bite, with the isolation of a virus capable of reproducing the disease. J. Exp. Med., *59*, 115-136.

Scott, T. F. M., Blank, H., Coriell, L. L., and Crouse H., 1950, Pathology and pathogenesis of the cutaneous lesions of variola, vaccinia, herpes simplex, herpes zoster, and varicella *in* The Pathogenesis and Pathology of Viral Diseases. Editor, J. G. Kidd, Columbia University Press, New York, pp. 74-98.

Scott, T. F. M., Schipper, M., and Coriell, L. L., 1951, Unpublished observations.

Scott, T. F. M., Steigman, A. J., and Convey, J., 1941, Acute infectious gingivostomatitis. Etiology, epidemiology, and clinical picture of a common disorder caused by the virus of herpes simplex. J. Am. Med. Assn., *117*, 999-1005.

Seidenberg, S., 1941, "Zur Aetiologie der Pustulosis vacciniformis acuta." Schweiz. Ztschr. f. Path. u. Bakt., *4*, 398-401.

Slavin, H. B., 1951, The clinical ramifications of infections caused by the virus of herpes simplex. Med. Clin. North America, *35*, 563-569.

Slavin, H. B., and Gavette, E., 1946, Primary herpetic vulvovaginitis. Proc. Soc. Exp. Biol. and Med., *63*, 343-345.

Speck, R. S., Jawetz, E., and Coleman, V. R., 1951, Studies on herpes simplex virus. I. The stability and preservation of egg-adapted herpes simplex virus. J. Bact., *61*, 253-258.

Steigman, A. J., and Scott, T. F. M., 1947, Evidence that virus of herpes simplex does not cause Vincent's angina of the tonsil. Proc. Soc. Exp. Biol. and Med., *64*, 244-245.

Thygeson, P., 1947, Clinical signs of diagnostic importance in conjunctivitis. J. Am. Med. Assn., *133*, 437-441.

Whitman, L., Wall, M. J., and Warren, J., 1946, Herpes simplex encephalitis. A report of two fatal cases. J. Am. Med. Assn., *131*, 1408-1411.

Wolfe, A., 1950, The pathology of some viral encephalitides *in* The Pathogenesis and Pathology of Viral Diseases. Editor, J. G. Kidd. Columbia University Press, New York, pp. 194-213.

THOMAS M. RIVERS, M.D.

Hospital of The Rockefeller Institute for Medical Research

26

Epidemic Keratoconjunctivitis

(SYNONYMS: Shipyard conjunctivitis, epidemic infectious conjunctivitis, superficial punctate keratitis, keratitis maculosa, keratitis nummularis)

INTRODUCTION

Epidemic keratoconjunctivitis is characterized by nonpurulent inflammation of the conjunctivae, preauricular lymphadenitis and superficial punctate corneal opacities, and is caused by a virus.

HISTORY

The disease was first noted by Fuchs (1889), and during the past 45 years epidemics have occurred in India, the Far East, Central Europe, and the United States. In the latter country, the first epidemics were noted on the Pacific coast (Hobson, 1938) and in Hawaii (Holmes, 1941). Wright (1930) reported the transmission of the disease to 5 of 13 volunteers by means of conjunctival scrapings filtered through a Kitasato candle, an unglazed porcelain filter used in working with small quantities of material. The results of this work, as well as those of other experiments which pointed to a viral causation of the malady, were inconclusive. Sanders (1942) and Sanders and Alexander (1943) conducted systematic investigations of the etiology of the disease and isolated a virus from conjunctival scrapings obtained from two patients. At first the virus was propagated in tissue cultures and later in mice by means of intracerebral inoculations.

CLINICAL PICTURE

The natural incubation period is unknown. The onset is sudden, with redness and chemosis of the conjunctiva and edema of the periorbital tissues. There is generally only a thin serous or seromucoid exudate or none at all. In addition, there may be headache, malaise and low fever. At the onset the disease is ordinarily unilateral, but from three to seven days later, in about half of the patients, the other eye becomes involved. Within two or four days after onset the homolateral preauricular lymph node usually enlarges and becomes tender. Small, round, superficial opacities of the cornea are noted within 4 to 14 days after onset of the disease, and in severe cases they may coalesce. The disease endures for two to four weeks, and complete recovery takes place in most individuals; in 1 to 10 per cent of the patients, depending on the epidemic, keratitis with impairment of vision may persist. In view of the fact that neutralizing antibody has been found in persons who offer no history of an attack of the malady, it would appear that clinically inapparent infection with the virus can occur.

PATHOLOGIC PICTURE

An examination by means of a slit-lamp of a fully developed ocular reaction reveals

503

states varying from slight injection of the conjunctiva to marked chemosis and small hemorrhages of the conjunctiva and corneal opacities which are either in Bowman's membrane or in the superficial part of the cornea. The opacities may coalesce but usually do not stain with fluorescin (Maumenee, Hayes and Hartman, 1945). A transient iritis occasionally occurs. The conjunctival secretion contains no microorganisms as a rule during the first week; but after this time secondary invaders may be found. Mononuclear cells predominate in smears prepared from conjunctival scrapings collected before the onset of secondary infection.

EXPERIMENTAL INFECTION; HOST RANGE

Adult mice given the virus by the intracerebral or intranasal route develop, after two to seven days lethargy, tonic and clonic convulsions, and spastic paralysis; death ensues within 24 hours after onset of illness. Unweaned Swiss mice can be infected by the intraperitoneal route. Virus in a dilution of 10^{-5} or 10^{-6} produces disease after intracerebral injection. The lesions induced are limited to the CNS and are those of a nonpurulent meningo-encephalitis. Rabbits show irregularly a keratitis after inoculation of the virus on the cornea, and in the corneal epithelium can be found intranuclear inclusion bodies (Maumenee et al., 1945). Intracerebral inoculation of the virus into rabbits produces an encephalitis within eight days; this rapidly terminates in death. Guinea pigs and albino rats are wholly resistant. A human being voluntarily receiving virus in the conjunctival sac developed a mild but characteristic attack of keratoconjunctivitis; this patient had for the first time neutralizing antibody in his serum one month after onset of the experimentally induced disease.

ETIOLOGY

The diameter of the virus determined by filtration through gradocol membranes is from 25 to 50 millimicrons. It passes through Berkefeld V, N and W candles, and Seitz filters. It can be preserved in 50 per cent glycerol and by being kept frozen at $-70°$ C. It is inactivated by methylene blue in the presence of light. The virus can be propagated in minced chick-embryo tissue cultures and in the developing chick embryo. Neutralizing antibody against the virus has been detected in serum obtained from patients four to ten weeks after the onset of the disease (Korns et al., 1944). According to Maumenee et al. (1945), the virus of keratoconjunctivitis is immunologically related to the agent causing herpes simplex. Furthermore, it would appear that herpes simplex virus can induce a keratoconjunctivitis in human beings which is almost identical with that brought about by the active agent of epidemic keratoconjunctivitis (Maumenee et al., 1945). "In spite of the similarity in the clinical picture and the cross immunologic reactions of the two viruses, they are thought to be separate entities but are probably of the same genus" (Maumenee et al., 1945). Ruchman (1951) has reported that there is a close relationship between the viruses of epidemic keratoconjunctivitis and St. Louis encephalitis. Cheever (1951) has confirmed Ruchman's observations and stressed the importance of careful studies of current outbreaks of epidemic keratoconjunctivitis to assess the significance of the findings.

DIAGNOSIS

Diagnosis of the disease as it occurs in epidemics is not difficult, but as a sporadic disease its recognition is not easy. It must be differentiated from herpetic keratoconjunctivitis. If possible, the virus should be isolated and identified. The distinct features of the malady are (1) presence of homolateral enlarged preauricular gland; (2) nonpurulent conjunctival secretions free from ordinary bacteria; (3) corneal opacities; and (4) presence of specific neutralizing antibody in serum obtained during convalescence when it was absent in serum collected during the acute or early stages of the malady.

TREATMENT

Intravenous use and instillation into the conjunctival sac of human convalescent serum have been suggested as an effective treatment (Braley and Sanders, 1943). Efficacy of this form of therapy has not as yet been generally proved (Maumenee et al., 1945).

EPIDEMIOLOGY

The disease was first thought to be more prevalent among workers in shipyards, but soon it was found to occur in many kinds of industrial plants. Since most cases arise in workers in such plants, males are more often attacked than females. Sanders et al. (1943) have shown that the disease may be spread in physicians' offices and in ophthalmic dispensaries where proper aseptic technics are not used.

CONTROL MEASURES

Rigid asepsis should be used in the medical divisions of factories and institutions in order to prevent the spread of infection by hands and instruments of attendants or in drugs used for treatment. Isolation of patients with the disease has been advised.

REFERENCES

Braley, A. E., and Sanders, M., 1943, Treatment of epidemic keratoconjunctivitis; preliminary report of 10 cases. J. Am. Med. Assn., *121*, 999-1000.

Cheever, F. S., 1951, A possible relationship between viruses of St. Louis encephalitis and epidemic keratoconjunctivitis. Proc. Soc. Exp. Biol. and Med., *77*, 125-129.

Fuchs, E., 1889, Keratitis punctata superficialis. Wien. klin. Wchnschr., *2*, 837-841.

Hobson, L. C., 1938, Acute epidemic superficial punctate keratitis. Am. J. Ophthal., *21*, 1153-1155.

Holmes, W. J., 1941, Epidemic infectious conjunctivitis. Hawaii Med. J., *1*, Nov., 11-12. (Each number paged separately.)

Korns, R. F., Sanders, M., and Alexander, R. C., 1944, Epidemic keratoconjunctivitis: correlation of epidemiologic data and results of serum virus neutralization tests. Am. J. Pub. Health, *34*, 567-571.

Maumenee, A. E., Hayes, G. S., and Hartman, T. L., 1945, Isolation and identification of the causative agent in epidemic keratoconjunctivitis (superficial punctate keratitis) and herpetic keratoconjunctivitis. Am. J. Ophthal., *28*, 823-839.

Ruchman, I., 1951, Relationship between epidemic keratoconjunctivitis and St. Louis encephalitis viruses. Proc. Soc. Exp. Biol. and Med., *77*, 120-125.

Sanders, M., 1942, Epidemic keratoconjunctivitis (Shipyard conjunctivitis). Arch. Ophthal., *28*, 581-586.

Sanders, M., and Alexander, R. C., 1943, Epidemic keratoconjunctivitis. I. Isolation and identification of a filterable virus. J. Exp. Med., *77*, 71-96.

Sanders, M., Gulliver, F. D., Forchheimer, L. L., and Alexander, R. C., 1943, Epidemic keratoconjunctivitis: clinical and experimental study of an outbreak in New York City. Further observations on the specific relationship between a virus and the disease. J. Am. Med. Assn., *121*, 250-255.

Wright, R. E., 1930, Superficial punctate keratitis Brit. J. Ophthal., *14*, 257-291; 595-601.

JOSEPH STOKES, Jr., M.D.

The Children's Hospital of Philadelphia
(Department of Pediatrics, School of Medicine, University of Pennsylvania)

27

Varicella-Herpes Zoster Group

(SYNONYM FOR VARICELLA: Chickenpox. SYNONYMS
FOR HERPES ZOSTER: Zona, shingles, zoster)

INTRODUCTION

Varicella, a mild communicable disease, is characterized by fever and an itching, vesicular eruption of the skin and mucous membranes, individual lesions of which are surrounded by erythema. It is caused by a virus similar to that which induces herpes zoster.

Herpes zoster, a severely painful and incapacitating infectious disease confined chiefly to adults, is characterized by inflammation of dorsal-root ganglia or extramedullary ganglia of cranial nerves accompanied by crops of vesicles, identical with those of varicella, in areas supplied by affected sensory nerves. It is caused by a virus similar to that which induces varicella.

These diseases are discussed in the same chapter to emphasize their similarities and differences. Their greatest similarities lie in the nature of their viral agents, their vesicular eruptions and intranuclear inclusion bodies, while their greatest differences are found in age incidence, epidemiology, clinical picture, and changes in the central nervous system.

HISTORY

Herpes zoster was described very early in medical literature and was known to the Greeks as zona. Von Bärensprung (1862a, b; 1863) first recorded observations relating the area of skin involved by eruption to its corresponding dorsal-root ganglion. In 1884, Landouzy (Levaditi, 1926) on clinical grounds, suggested its infectious nature. Head and Campbell (1900) furnished a classical description of the neuropathology, while Lipschütz (1921) described the histopathologic changes in the vesicles. In 1888, von Bokay (1909) suggested its possible relation to varicella and later recorded many cases in point; Kundratitz (1925) inoculated human subjects and apparently obtained some successful "takes."

Varicella was not described as a clinical entity until the era of Sydenham; it was confused with variola until the 19th century. Steiner (1875) experimentally demonstrated it to be infectious. Paschen (1917) described elementary bodies in the vesicular fluid and suggested a virus as the etiologic agent.

CLINICAL PICTURE OF HERPES ZOSTER

The incubation period of the disease has been difficult to establish, but is placed at from 7 to 14 days, which is somewhat shorter than that of varicella. It is usually

506

initiated by a severe pain, fever, malaise, and often exquisite tenderness along the dorsal nerve roots and their corresponding skin areas. The pain may be generalized over the area supplied by the nerve or may be sharply localized to the point of nerve exit close to the spine or to the midaxilla where the nerve divides into a deep and a superficial branch.

It may be secondary to an insult to a susceptible dorsal nerve root, such as that caused by arsenic, tuberculosis, tumor, leukemia, or it may appear without apparent cause. At times abortive zoster occurs in which only an erythematous patch appears over the area involved without vesiculation. For primary and secondary zoster, the local vesicular lesions are identical, but a somewhat more severe general reaction and higher fever usually occur in the former. It is rarely bilateral. Early in the disease, the lymph node draining the involved area is usually large and tender. A crop of papules, rapidly becoming vesicles, appears within 3 or 4 days after onset over the skin supplied by affected nerves and may continue to appear occasionally for 2 or 3 weeks. There are also occasionally aberrant vesicles which may be so numerous at times that they simulate the eruption of varicella. Vesicles may become pustular if secondarily infected with bacteria. As crusts form, pain and tenderness usually disappear. Extensive involvement of a ganglion may affect motor roots or it may extend to anterior horn cells, resulting in temporary or permanent paralysis. The dorsal roots of the trunk are most frequently involved, while next in frequency are the areas supplied by the second to the fourth cervical ganglia, i.e., the shoulders, the arms and the neck. Finally, the lower extremities and the perineal area, in that order, are least frequently affected. Inflammation of the maxillary division of the trigeminal nerve will produce lesions in the uvula and the tonsillar area, while similar lesions in the anterior part of the tongue, the mouth floor and the buccal mucosa result from involve-

ment of the mandibular division. Zoster ophthalmicus follows involvement of the ophthalmic division which may be particularly serious with resulting scleritis, keratitis and iridocyclitis; ulcers of the cornea and the conjunctiva may occur. Vesicles on the pharynx, the tongue, the uvula and the larynx may be extremely painful; laryngeal and faucial paralysis are not infrequent. In approximately 50 per cent of cephalic cases of zoster, paralysis occurs. When the geniculate ganglion is involved, pain in the auditory canal is followed by a vesicular eruption on the pinna and in the external canal. Facial paralysis frequently results, which on rare occasions is permanent. Rare involvement of the otic ganglion results in deep pain of the fauces on the affected side, combined with a few vesicles in this area and on the uvula. There is usually a mild lymphocytosis in the spinal fluid, unless the number of cells is markedly increased by meningo-encephalitis which is an occasional complication. Persistent neuralgia following convalescence in older subjects is common.

CLINICAL PICTURE OF VARICELLA

The incubation period is usually from 14 to 16 days; occasionally, it may be as long as 21 days. Approximately 24 hours after the onset of fever, crops of papules, followed or accompanied by vesicles with surrounding erythema, appear on the face and trunk, spreading usually to the mouth and pharynx and extremities. In chickenpox, the lesions are usually most abundant over the trunk, while the face and extremities suffer the most damage from smallpox. Occasionally, the generalized eruption will be accompanied by a localized eruption characteristic of zoster. The eruption occurs simultaneously with the fever, and its duration is proportional to the height and persistence of the latter. Successive crops of lesions appear, furnishing all the characteristic stages of papules, vesicles and crusts at the same time over the affected areas. There is a general lymphadenopathy, which is particularly noticeable in the suboccipital and the posterior cervical regions when vesicles occur in the scalp. The vesicles, which are indistinguishable from those of zoster, frequently become pustular and the crusts are often removed by scratching because of itching. Impetigo, furuncles, septicemia and glomerulonephritis may complicate the picture. Vesicles on the laryngeal mucosa, about the eyes and genitalia and in the hair present difficult problems. The encephalitis, which occasionally complicates varicella, is symptomatically similar to that accompanying herpes zoster but is less common and less severe than that occurring in measles. Occasionally, neuritis of the cranial nerves or myelitis may occur. Even temporary blindness may complicate the picture. Small, depressed, white scars may result from severe varicella or a secondary infection of vesicles with pathogenic bacteria. No significant changes occur in the number and character of the blood cells.

PATHOLOGIC PICTURE

In contrast to the vesicle of variola which exhibits a reticular degeneration of the prickle-cells, the vesicles of varicella and herpes zoster are obviously the result of a ballooning of the cells with very little reticulation. In the early stages, nuclei of infected cells contain the spheroidal and eosinophilic inclusion bodies described by Lipschütz in zoster and by Tyzzer (1906) in varicella. In the process of nuclear degeneration, these bodies apparently enter the cytoplasm so that they may be seen simultaneously in nuclei and cytoplasm. While in early stages of the development of lesions some proliferation of the epidermis occurs, the corium remains practically unaltered. Later, amitoses of the prickle-cells with formation of sickle-shaped, multinuclear cells, the ballooning of cells with their subsequent disintegration, and the entrance of tissue fluids result in the typical vesicle. In some large vesicles, the corium may form the base, and in such cases all layers of the skin may be involved and scarring may result. See

Plate 6 for cellular changes induced by virus of varicella.

There are several reports (Johnson, 1940) of young infants having died of varicella. A complete postmortem examination was made on one by Johnson (1940) who found characteristic lesions in the esophagus, pancreas, liver, renal pelvis, ureters, bladder and adrenal glands. Cellular changes, including intranuclear inclusions, in the visceral lesions were similar to those seen in the skin.

Zoster virus, in addition to skin lesions, produces a characteristic inflammatory reaction in the posterior nerve roots and ganglia. Rarely, the inflammation spreads to the anterior horns, resulting in temporary or permanent paralysis. In the posterior root, there is infiltration of small round cells and red blood cells, necrosis of nerve cells and fibers, and an inflammatory reaction of the ganglion sheath. It has been shown (Ebert, 1949) that zoster can cause destruction of sensory nerve fibers from the corium. The corresponding fibers of the spinal cord undergo degeneration. In severe cases, scarring is found in the involved ganglionic area, with loss of cells and nerve fibers and thickening of the ganglion sheath, while in milder cases little or no permanent damage occurs. The dorsal ganglia more often involved, as shown by Head and Campbell (1900), are those that receive fibers from the viscera through the white ramus of the sympathetic branches.

EXPERIMENTAL INFECTION; HOST RANGE

Despite experiments by Eckstein (1933), the results of which indicate that monkeys may be infected by the viruses of zoster and varicella, there is no conclusive evidence that any host other than man is susceptible to either of the active agents. Intranuclear inclusion bodies were found in the tubular cells of monkey testes by Rivers (1926) five or six days after intratesticular injection of varicella virus in young vervets and green monkeys. Typical varicella le-

PLATE 6

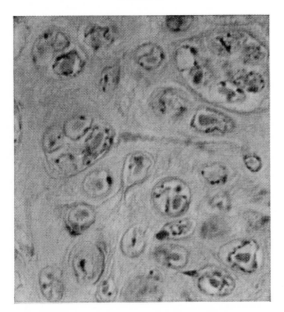

Cellular changes in human epidermis induced by the virus of varicella. Note several amitotic giant cells and numerous acidophilic intranuclear inclusions. Eosin-methylene blue. × 900. (Dr. H. N. Johnson, Laboratories of the Division of Medicine and Public Health of The Rockefeller Foundation; photograph by R. F. Carter)

sions in the skin were not produced. Steiner (1875) produced varicella in children by inoculating them experimentally with fluid from varicella vesicles. This work has been fully confirmed by others. Zoster vesicular fluid apparently also has induced varicella in experimental human subjects as well as local vesicles more characteristic of zoster. According to Taniguchi et al. (1932; 1935), chick-embryo-tissue cultures, egg membranes, and the lungs and testes of rabbits may be infected by varicella virus; furthermore, it was stated that membrane-passage virus was inoculated into susceptible children with the production of typical varicella. These experiments require confirmation because of the strong possibility that vaccinia rather than varicella virus was the active agent used. Evidence of propagation of zoster virus in human skin grafted on the chorio-allantois of chick embryos was obtained by Goodpasture and Anderson (1944) and Blank, Coriell and Scott (1948), although the chick-embryo tissues themselves appeared to be nonsusceptible. The lesions obtained resembled those of the natural disease with intranuclear inclusions in affected epithelial cells.

ETIOLOGY

Both viruses are apparently of similar size, having diameters variously estimated at from 210 to 250 millimicra. Electron micrographs (Rake et al., 1948; Nagler and Rake, 1948) showed that viral bodies from vesicles of varicella and herpes zoster are, as a rule, brick-shaped and identical in appearance and size. By means of the electron microscope it was also demonstrated that zoster viral particles agglutinated in the presence of serum collected from patients convalescent either from zoster or from varicella. Vesicles 12 hours old contain numerous viral particles, while those 24 hours old yield very few.

The accumulation of data on the similarities of the two diseases since von Bokay's original observations has indicated the following problems in their antigenic relation.

Varicella in children more often induces zoster in exposed adults than it does in exposed children.

Zoster, whether in children or adults, rather frequently has been observed as the apparent source of varicella in children (almost never in adults), initiating at times large epidemics of this disease. The number of such recorded incidents is too great to be explained satisfactorily on the basis of chance alone. Inconclusive evidence has been published (The School Epidemics Committee, 1938) that epidemics of varicella initiated by a case of zoster have had a lower incidence of infection than those initiated by a case of varicella.

Varicella and zoster not infrequently occur at the same time in the same child. Obviously, such an occurrence may be an unusual manifestation of varicella virus or vice versa.

Certain careful studies, such as those made by The School Epidemics Committee (1938) of Great Britain in a large number of boarding schools, have shown that varicella and zoster occur during the same terms more frequently than is likely to be due to chance, and apparently are not seasonal.

Despite certain contradictory evidence, zoster apparently occurs frequently in children and adults who previously have had varicella, thus indicating a lack of complete resistance to the zoster virus as a result of previous experience with the virus of varicella.

Zoster and varicella usually produce lasting immunity to their own viruses.

Zoster vesicular fluid has been used experimentally to inoculate children intradermally with some success in the production of varicella (Kundratitz, 1925). This has been confirmed (Bruusgard, 1932) by a second human passage which resulted in a contact infection.

In at least two isolated island communities, zoster has been observed, whereas no cases of varicella have ever been recorded.

Laboratory studies (Rivers, 1927; Rivers and Eldridge, 1929a, b; Amies, 1934), for example, neutralization and agglutination tests, have not established conclusively the antigenic relation of the viruses.

A working hypothesis for the student to relate the above apparently contradictory observations may be useful, if only to provoke thought or alternative hypotheses. Such an hypothesis could consider the varicella virus as infecting the general population almost universally at an early age. A generalized infection with the virus with a relatively long incubation period may permit the development of permanent resistance. However, in certain cases, the varicella virus may have neurotropic properties, as indicated by the simultaneous development at times of zoster and varicella, and it may remain within the nerve cells of a few individuals in a manner similar to the symbiosis exhibited by herpes simplex virus and ectodermal cells. In adult life, exposure to cold, pressure on a nerve, or a fresh massive dose of varicella virus (in epidemic parotitis, heavy exposure of a resistant individual may at times disturb the parotid without generalized symptoms) may cause a localized virus activity along posterior root fibres with subsequent development of zoster vesicles. Zoster virus produces varicella with greater difficulty and less frequency than does varicella virus. This may be explained by the ease of spread of virus from varicella lesions in the mouth and the throat, whereas the virus in zoster skin lesions is well covered and without a ready means of transport. The absence of varicella and the presence of zoster in isolated communities may possibly represent the activity of an endemic neurotropic varicella virus (zoster virus) with which the population has been universally infected, but which becomes apparent in relatively few.

There are other ways of explaining this antigenic puzzle. Obviously, one of these is to consider the viruses of zoster and varicella as distinct entities, possessing certain antigenic constituents in common.

DIAGNOSIS

The lesions of herpes simplex may at times be confined to a nerve distribution in the skin, in which case inoculation of vesicular fluid on the scarified cornea of a rabbit appears to be the only sound method of differentiation, inasmuch as herpes simplex virus will infect the rabbit, whereas zoster virus will not. Otherwise, little difficulty should be experienced in differentiating zoster from herpes simplex. Varicella and herpes zoster are frequently indistinguishable. The severe constitutional reaction caused by variola, together with uniformity of development of the eruption in all areas of the skin at the same time and the somewhat larger number of vesicles on the extremities, as compared to the trunk, serve to distinguish this disease from varicella.

TREATMENT

The vesicles of herpes zoster and varicella require similar care to prevent secondary infection, and similar treatment of secondary infections when they occur. Oral or parenteral administration of sulfonamides or penicillin, and the local application of tyrothricin are useful when the invading bacteria are sensitive to these therapeutic agents. Cleanliness of the skin, care of the hands, cutting and cleaning finger nails, and local treatment for relief of irritation and itching and for the prevention of secondary bacterial infections, are important measures. In addition, herpes zoster lesions may require sedative ointments, such as 1 per cent cocaine in lanolin. Deep x-ray therapy may also prove effective when used early in the disease. For late neuralgia, section of sensory roots may be necessary.

EPIDEMIOLOGY

While varicella usually occurs in epidemics, zoster is usually a sporadic disease. The two diseases differ widely in age incidence; varicella occurs infrequently after 20 years, while zoster is rarely seen before

20 years. Varicella attacks the sexes equally, while zoster has a slightly higher incidence in males, which may be accounted for by the more frequent exposure of older males to severe climatic conditions. Contact infections occur rarely in zoster, while varicella spreads more readily than most infectious diseases, perhaps more readily than measles. Much of the dissemination of varicella is through the air. It may result from the inhalation of small amounts of air by a susceptible person in any enclosed space containing an infectious individual. Accurate data are not available on the length of time during which the lesions of zoster and varicella remain infectious. Both diseases occur more frequently in the winter and spring. Frequency of the recurrence of varicella epidemics depends upon the density of susceptibles; the recurrence rate is lower in rural than in urban populations, acting in this respect in a manner similar to that of measles.

CONTROL MEASURES

No control measures are available for herpes zoster as it occurs in sporadic form. Convalescent serum is apparently of little, if any, value for protection against varicella, and of no value in its treatment. Transplacental immunity apparently is not present in the newborn. There is available no method of active immunization. Under school or institutional conditions, partial disinfection of the air by means of ultraviolet light has limited the epidemic spread of varicella. Glycol vapors for such purposes have not been sufficiently developed for general use. As a rule, isolation and quarantine are useless, inasmuch as the spread of varicella apparently occurs most readily before the disease is clinically manifest. The crusts appear to be infectious while still moist, but dry crusts apparently have lost their infectivity. Thus, if isolation is warranted, seven days should be sufficient.

REFERENCES

Amies, C. R., 1933, Elementary bodies of varicella and their agglutination in pure suspension by serum of chicken-pox patients. Lancet, 1, 1015-1017.

Amies, C. R., 1934, Elementary bodies of zoster and their serological relationship to those of varicella. Brit. J. Exp. Path., 15, 314-20.

von Bärensprung, F. G. F., 1862a, Fernere Beiträge zur Kenntniss des Zoster. Ann. Charité-Krankenhauses, 10, 1 Hft., 37-54.

von Bärensprung, F. G. F., 1862b, Neue Beobachtungen über Herpes. Ann. Charité-Krankenhauses, 10, 1 Hft., 123-143.

von Bärensprung, F. G. F., 1863, Beiträge zur Kenntniss des Zoster. Dritte Folge. Ann. Charité-Krankenhauses, 11, 2. Hft., 96-116.

von Bokay, J., 1909, Ueber den ätiologischen Zusamenhang der Varizellen mit gewissen Fällen von Herpes zoster. Wien. klin. Wchnschr., 22, 1323-1326.

Blank, H., Coriell, L. L., and Scott, T. F. M., 1948, Human skin grafted upon the chorioallantois of the chick embryo for virus cultivation. Proc. Soc. Exp. Biol. and Med., 69, 341-345.

Bruusgard, E., 1932, Mutual relation between zoster and varicella. Brit. J. Derm. and Syph., 44, 1-24.

Cantor, S. J., 1921, Herpes and varicella. Brit. Med. J., 2, 508.

Ebert, M. H., 1949, Histologic changes in sensory nerves of the skin in herpes zoster. Arch. Derm. and Syph., 60, 641-648.

Eckstein, A., 1933, Klinische und experimentelle Untersuchungen zur Frage der Varicellenencephalitis. Ztschr. f. d. ges. Neurol. u. Psychiat., 149, 176-190.

Goodpasture, E. W., and Anderson, K., 1944, Infection of human skin, grafted on the chorioallantois of chick embryo, with the virus of herpes zoster Am. J. Path., 20, 447-455.

Head, H., and Campbell, A. W., 1900, The pathology of herpes zoster and its bearing on sensory localization. Brain, 23, 353-523.

Johnson, H. N., 1940, Visceral lesions associated with varicella. Arch. Path., 30, 292-307.

Kundratitz, K., 1925, Experimentelle Übertragungen von Herpes zoster auf Menschen und die Beziehungen von Herpes zoster zu Varicellen. Ztschr. f. Kinderheilk., 39, 379-387.

Levaditi, C., 1926, L'Herpès et le zona. Paris, Masson.

Lipschütz, B., 1921, Untersuchungen über die Ätiologie der Krankheiten der Herpesgruppe (Herpes zoster, Herpes genitalis, Herpes febrilis). Arch. Dermatol. u. Syph., Orig., 136, 428-482.

Nagler, F. P. O., and Rake, G., 1948, Use of electron microscope in diagnosis of variola, vaccinia, and varicella. J. Bact., 55, 45-51.

Paschen, E., 1917, Vergleichende Untersuchungen von Varizellen, Variola, Scharlach, Masern und Röteln. Deutch. med. Wchnschr., 43, 746-747.

Rake, G., Blank, H., Coriell, L. L., Nagler, F. P. O., and Scott, T. F. M., 1948, The relationship of varicella and herpes zoster: electron-microscope studies. J. Bact., *56, 293-303*.

Rivers, T. M., 1926, Nuclear inclusions in testicles of monkeys injected with tissue of human varicella lesions. J. Exp. Med., *43, 275-287*.

Rivers, T. M., 1927, Varicella in monkeys. Nuclear inclusions produced by varicella virus in testicles of monkeys. J. Exp. Med., *45, 961-968*.

Rivers, T. M., and Eldridge, L. A., Jr., 1929a, Relation of varicella to herpes zoster. I. Statistical observations. J. Exp. Med., *49, 899-906*.

Rivers, T. M., and Eldridge, L. A., Jr., 1929b, Relation of varicella to herpes zoster. II. Clinical and experimental observations. J. Exp. Med., *49, 907-917*.

Steiner, 1875, Zur Inokulation der Varicellen. Wien. med. Wchnschr., *25, 306-307*.

Taniguchi, T., Hosokawa, M., Kuga, S., Nakamura, F., and Matsumoto, S., 1932, On the virus of chickenpox. Japanese J. Exp. Med., *10, 599-605*.

Taniguchi, T., Kogita, Y., Hosokawa, M., and Kuga, S., 1935, A cultivation of the vaccinia and varicella viruses in the chorio-allantoic membrane of the chick embryo; with special references to the preparation of the bacteria-free vaccine and prophylactic inoculation against varicella. Japanese J. Exp. Med., *13, 19-30*.

The School Epidemics Committee, 1938, Epidemics in schools. Medical Research Council Special Report Series no. *227, 181-184*.

Tyzzer, E. E., 1906, The histology of the skin lesions in varicella. Philippine J. Sci., *1, 349-372*.

Woolley, E. J. S., 1946, Herpes zoster in an isolated community. Brit. Med. J., *1, 392*.

JOHN F. ENDERS, PH.D.

Children's Hospital, Boston

28

Mumps

(SYNONYM: Epidemic parotitis)

INTRODUCTION

Mumps is an acute, self-limiting contagious disease with a high morbidity and a very low mortality. The most constant feature is an enlargement of the parotid gland, but involvement of other organs is not uncommon.

HISTORY

Mumps is one of the first diseases which were recognized as clinical entities. In the fifth century B.C. (Adams, 1891), its most common manifestations were clearly recorded by Hippocrates who described it as a mild epidemic sickness characterized by nonsuppurative swellings near the ears and occasionally accompanied by painful enlargement of the testes. In modern times, Hamilton (1790) was among the first to stress orchitis as a frequent manifestation of the infection. He also noted certain patients suffering from parotitis who showed symptoms referable to the central nervous system. It was not until the beginning of the twentieth century, however, that clinically apparent and inapparent meningoencephalitis were generally recognized as complications. Thereafter it also became evident that other organs, e.g., the ovary and the pancreas, might be injured by the infectious agent (Wesselhoeft, 1941). During the first decades of the present century con-

siderable effort was expended in attempts to determine the etiologic agent. Various reports appeared incriminating a variety of bacteria as well as a spirochete, but it was not until 1934 that the causative agent was definitely proved to be a filterable virus (Johnson and Goodpasture, 1934).

CLINICAL PICTURE

Eighteen to 21 days usually elapse between exposure and the development of symptoms; in exceptional cases the period of incubation may be 12 days, or less, or as long as 35 days. Infection of the salivary glands is manifested by a varying degree of enlargement. The parotids are those most constantly involved. Often, the swelling is unilateral; or one gland may become enlarged and after from one to five days the other may show an increase in size. Enlargement of the submaxillary and sublingual glands is not uncommon and is best determined by palpation. Edematous infiltration of the tissues surrounding the salivary glands is a frequent event and in certain cases may be very marked. Occasionally, presternal edema may be present, a clinical sign that has been recognized only in recent years. Swelling of a gland usually reaches a maximum within 48 hours and most often persists for seven to ten days. Occasionally, some enlargement of the structure can be discerned after the lapse of several weeks. In the earlier stages a restricted area of redness may be observed immediately about the orifices of the ducts of Stensen and Wharton. Fever of moderate degree may be present 12 to 24 hours before swelling is observed and usually persists from one to three days. In certain cases it may be absent.

The following is a list of most of the other organs which have been mentioned in the literature as exhibiting signs of involvement: testis, epididymis, prostate, ovary, pancreas, spleen, thyroid, kidneys, labyrinth, eye, thymus, heart (myocardium), vulvovaginal glands, mammary glands (male and female), and nervous system (as manifested by symptoms of encephalitis, encephalomyelitis, neuritis of the facial, trigeminal, and optic nerves). In general, it must be emphasized that certain of these structures may be affected not only before or after the parotitis as well as synchronously with it, but even when there is no indication of inflammation of the salivary glands. Furthermore, it should be noted that the frequency with which certain of these organs are attacked has varied widely among several groups that have been studied. Most commonly the testes or the central nervous system is involved. Orchitis occurs on the average once in every five cases of parotitis, although wide variations from this mean may be expected in different outbreaks. In spite of this incidence, sterility resulting from mumps orchitis is rare. This is due in part to the fact that only about one sixth or less of the cases are bilateral and that atrophy of all glandular tissue may not ensue, even in the severe cases (Werner, 1950). An even greater variation in the frequency of meningo-encephalitis, ranging from 0.5 to 10 per cent of the cases of parotitis, has been reported by various observers. Epididymitis, prostatitis, ovaritis, and pancreatitis of marked intensity are more rarely noted. On the basis, however, of recent studies that reveal a regular elevation in the blood amylase, it is possible that some degree of pancreatic involvement may be common (Zelman, 1944; Applebaum, 1944).

The total white blood cell count is variable in different patients, at times being either moderately elevated or depressed and at others within normal limits. The differential count often shows an absolute or relative increase in lymphocytes from the first to the fourteenth day of the illness, but this phenomenon is by no means invariable. Obviously, blood leukocyte counts are of little aid in diagnosis. In contrast to the blood, the white cell count of the spinal fluid is of great significance in the diagnosis of the general syndrome of aseptic lymphocytic meningo-encephalitis, of which mumps virus is one of the known etiologic agents. In mumps encephalitis the number of white cells of the fluid is increased. The total count may range from 8 to 10 cells (normal) to more than 2,000 per c.mm. In a series of 11 cases recently studied, the mean count was 434 (Kane and Enders, 1945). In a majority of cases, the proportion of lymphocytes is from 90 to 100 per cent (Kilham, 1949). When interpreting the significance of an increased white count in the spinal fluid, it should be borne in mind that in a variable number of cases of simple parotitis presenting no signs of involvement of the nervous system, a moderate or marked increase in lymphocytes may occur. This indication of a latent encephalitis has been construed by certain internists as evidence for regarding mumps as a primary invasion of the central nervous system; this point of view is debatable.

Although long suspected on the basis of epidemiologic data, it is only recently that evidence has been obtained which indicates that infection with the virus of mumps may be so innocuous that symptoms do not occur or at least are so mild as to escape observation (Maris, Enders, Stokes and Kane, 1946). Thus, specific complement-fixing antibody has been found in the blood of approximately a half of the tested adults who denied having had mumps. Even in groups of children which have been studied, the number of inapparent infections based on this criterion is considerable, at times approaching that of the adults. The available experimental observations indicate that this antibody arises only in response to an infection with the virus or after its inoculation in an inactive state. A more direct indication for the occurrence of inapparent infections is provided by the findings of Henle, Henle, Wendell and Rosenberg, 1948, who isolated the agent between the fourteenth and the fifteenth days after exposure from the saliva of 6 of 8 volunteers infected experimentally with mumps virus but who failed to develop any clinical signs of infection.

PATHOLOGIC PICTURE

From the diagnostic point of view, pathologic changes induced by the virus are not usually of assistance. In general, the injury is not extensive, with the exception of that occurring in the testis in severe orchitis. The limited observations on material from infected parotid glands indicate that the reaction consists of a serofibrinous exudate with leukocytes in the connective tissue. The cells of the ducts show evidence of degeneration, and necrotic debris and polymorphonuclear cells are found in their lumina (Dopter and Repaci, 1909; Weller and Craig, 1949). Characteristic inclusion bodies have not been described. In the testis, there are considerable destruction of the epithelium of the seminiferous tubules, marked congestion, and punctate hemorrhages. Edema and serofibrinous exudation are present in the interstitial tissues (Smith, 1912; Manca, 1932; Gall, 1947). In the pancreas, evidence of congestion, interstitial edema, slight degeneration of the islets, and fat necrosis have been observed. The changes induced by the virus in the central nervous system are uncertain, since in the few cases which have terminated fatally the evidence for the mumps virus as the cause of death is not conclusive.

EXPERIMENTAL INFECTION; HOST RANGE

In addition to man, the only other animals known to be susceptible at the present time are the chick embryo (Habel, 1945; Levens and Enders, 1945) and certain species of monkeys; the latter include the rhesus (*Macaca mulatta*), the cynomolgus (*Macaca irus*), the pig-tailed (*Macaca nemestrinus*), and the moor (*Macaca maurus*) (Swan and Mawson, 1943). The virus has been isolated by inoculating the amniotic cavity or the yolk sac of the chick embryo; sulfadiazine and penicillin were used to eliminate bacterial contaminants in the saliva (Beveridge, Lind and Anderson, 1946). After several passages the virus becomes well adapted to this host, and can be recovered from most of its tissues and fluids after an incubation period of three or four days or longer. Tests for the presence of virus may be made by employing either the hemagglutination reaction, chicken or human erythrocytes being used, or the complement-fixation reaction. Typical parotitis characterized by parotid enlargement, facial edema, and pathologic changes closely resembling those found in the affected parotid of man can be produced in monkeys only by inoculating the material containing the virus via Stensen's duct directly into the gland. When this procedure is followed, the virus may be demonstrated in saliva obtained from patients within 48 hours after the appearance of the swelling. Serial passages in monkeys can be effected by injection of a suspension of the parotid gland removed 4 to 7 days following inoculation of the virus.

ETIOLOGY

Johnson and Goodpasture (1934) showed that the etiologic agent passes readily through Berkefeld V and N filters. More recently, preliminary observations (Enders et al., unpublished results), in which graded collodion membranes were employed as filters, indicate that the diameter of the infective particle in allantoic fluid of the chick embryo is probably in the range of 90 to 135 mμ. Others have subsequently recorded somewhat higher values based on electron-micrographic measurements, e.g. 179 ± 28 mμ (mean value). Considerable variation in particle size, however, was revealed in the micrographs (Weil, Beard, Sharp and Beard, 1948; Dawson and Elford, 1949). The infectivity of the virus for the chick embryo is destroyed by heating for 20 minutes at temperatures between 55° and 60° C. Under these conditions, the hemagglutinin is also inactivated. In contrast, complement-fixing antigen is relatively thermostable, withstanding a temperature of 80° C. for 20 minutes. The substance giving allergic skin tests in hypersensitive individuals can be heated at 65° C. for 20 minutes without loss of activity. The conditions for its inactivation have not yet been determined. Infectivity is well retained on storage at low temperatures. Mumps virus hemolysin (Morgan, Enders and Wagley, 1948) is inactivated almost completely at 50° C. The virus has been found to be active after at least 10 months at a temperature of approximately —70° C. At approximately 4° C., infectivity persists for at least two months. The other activities of the virus mentioned above, with the exception of its hemolytic property, likewise have been found to be stable under these conditions. At room temperature infectivity is lost within 4 days, but the other properties are retained for a longer period. Small amounts of formalin or short exposure to ultraviolet light brings about loss of infectivity. Thus, this property is lost within 12 hours after the addition of 0.1 per cent formalin and after 0.28 second of intense ultraviolet radiation. The hemagglutinative and complement-fixing properties as well as the allergic factor of the virus are much more resistant to treatment with low concentrations of formalin.

The virus of mumps has the property of causing agglutination of red cells of certain species (Levens and Enders, 1945), causing the lysis of erythrocytes (Morgan, Enders and Wagley, 1948), and bringing about fixation of complement in the presence of specific antibody (Enders and Cohen, 1942), and eliciting a delayed allergic reaction in the skin of human beings who have been previously infected (Enders, 1943). The infective, hemagglutinative and hemolytic properties are closely associated. There appear to be two components capable of fixing complement, which may be separated either by adsorption on red cells (Enders, unpublished data) or by differential centrifugation (Henle, Henle and Harris, 1947; Henle, Harris and Henle, 1948). Antibodies which neutralize infectivity, inhibit hemagglutination, and fix complement appear in the blood serum after infection with the virus. The relationship of the allergenic factor to the other antigenic properties has not been determined, but like the immediate reaction to vaccinia virus, a positive reaction to it has been shown to be correlated in most instances with an immune state (Enders and co-workers, 1946a; Henle, Henle, Burgoon, Bashe and Stokes, 1951a).

Mumps, in nearly all instances, confers a durable immunity, as is indicated by the low rate of second attacks. This rate is usually cited as about 4 per cent, but it is likely that the figure is too high, since it is probable that erroneous diagnoses either of the first or of the second illness have often been recorded. Contrary to common belief, when a single parotid is attacked the immunity which ensues would appear on the basis of the available experimental data to be as solid and persistent as when both glands are involved. Infection of any organ, even in the absence of parotitis, probably induces the same high order of resistance. Finally, as already noted, there is evidence, which shows that clinically inapparent infections, as revealed by the complement-fixation test (Maris and co-workers, 1946) and the skin test for hypersensitivity (Enders and co-workers, 1946a), confer immunity as effectively as does an overt attack. That the active immunity induced by infection can be passively transferred from mother to offspring via the placenta is strongly suggested by the fact that mumps in children under six or even nine months of age is very rare. Furthermore, recent experiments have shown that the complement-fixing antibody when present in the mother is also demonstrable in the cord blood. For a review of immunity of mumps see the paper of Enders (1946).

DIAGNOSIS

Mumps parotitis can usually be diagnosed with fair accuracy, particularly under epidemic conditions, on the basis of clinical criteria alone. The diagnosis of sporadic cases is at times difficult, since a variety of other agents may produce an enlargement of the parotid. Thus, it is sometimes necessary to differentiate mumps from suppurative parotitis, enlargements due to foreign bodies in the salivary ducts, neoplasms, Mikulicz's disease, uveoparotid fever, and other rare conditions. In cases where salivary gland involvement is minimal or absent and in which the virus has attacked other organs, it is frequently impossible to make a conclusive diagnosis on the basis of clinical findings alone. This is especially true in aseptic lymphocytic meningoencephalitis—a syndrome caused by several viruses and other agents as yet unknown. It is, however, possible to obtain serologic evidence of any type of infection caused by mumps virus. This can be accomplished (1) by demonstrating the appearance of or increase in antibody capable of fixing complement in the presence of mumps antigen (Enders and co-workers, 1945), and (2) by the demonstration of the appearance or increase of a specific factor, antihemagglutinin (Levens and Enders, 1945; Robbins, Kilham, Levens and Enders, 1949), in the blood serum which inhibits the agglutination of chicken or human erythrocytes by mumps antigen. These procedures have now been fairly extensively studied as diagnostic tools. Because of its greater simplicity, the test for antihemagglutinin is to be recom-

mended as routine. Antigens for the complement-fixation test may be obtained in the form of a suspension of tissue from an infected parotid gland (monkey) or the infected allantoic fluid of the embryonated egg. Only materials from infected eggs are satisfactory as antigens in hemagglutinin-inhibition tests.

As with most serologic tests, a definite diagnosis can usually be made only when a significant rise in antibody titer is demonstrated by examining two specimens of serum taken at appropriate intervals following the onset of the disease. Complement-fixing antibody against mumps virus develops rapidly in most patients so that by one week after the first clinical signs this substance has emerged in a majority. By the end of the third week, in all cases which have been studied, antibody has been demonstrated. In many persons the antibody may persist in the circulating blood for years, although in a concentration (1:6 to 1:192 final dilution of serum) lower than that reached during convalescence (greater than 1:192 final dilution of serum). In cases where the first specimen of serum has not been obtained sufficiently early to permit the demonstration of a rise in titer, the finding of titers exceeding 1:192 can be interpreted as suggestive of a recent infection. By testing a single specimen of serum taken shortly after onset of symptoms for complement-fixing antibodies against the "S" and the "V" antigens, an early presumptive diagnosis can sometimes be made; since, as Henle, Harris and Henle (1948) have shown, early in the disease the level of antibody reacting with "S" antigen is frequently higher than that of antibody reacting with "V" antigen. The antihemagglutinin compared with complement-fixing antibody tends to persist for a longer time at a higher titer. It should be noted that the skin test is of little or no value in diagnosis, since dermal hypersensitivity in most patients develops several weeks following the onset of mumps. Indeed, it is best not to do a skin test for diagnosis, because production of complement-fixing antibody may be initiated or stimulated by this procedure in persons who are not suffering from the disease.

Since all strains of mumps virus so far examined appear to belong to a single antigenic type, the demonstration of mumps antibody by any of the technics mentioned above may be taken, with considerable assurance, as evidence of previous infection with this agent. One should bear in mind, however, that following infection with mumps virus many persons develop antibodies which react with Newcastle disease virus of fowls (NDV). This phenomenon probably depends upon the sharing of a similar or identical antigenic component by the two species of viruses (Kilham, Jungherr and Luginbuhl, 1949).

TREATMENT

The treatment of simple parotitis is symptomatic. In severe orchitis, recourse is sometimes had to surgical procedures for reducing the pressure caused by edema. In encephalitis, if the headache is severe, lumbar drainage may afford marked relief. There are no particular procedures employed in the treatment of the other so-called complications of mumps (Wesselhoeft, 1941). Specific therapy, consisting of the administration of various materials derived from human blood, has been attempted in the case of orchitis and meningitis. Most of the efforts have centered upon the prevention and treatment of orchitis; the materials have been administered before the onset of orchitis but after swelling of the parotid had appeared as well as during the acute stage of orchitic inflammation. They have consisted of whole blood from recent convalescents, convalescent serum, and concentrates of globulin either from pooled normal adult plasma or from pooled convalescent sera. Results obtained in a limited number of patients in which the treatment of established orchitis or meningitis has been attempted have been equivocal, and indeed it might be anticipated that a pro-

cedure of this sort would not prove efficacious once the virus had caused cellular injury. On the other hand, there are limited data suggesting that concentrated convalescent gamma globulin is of some value in preventing the development of orchitis if given after the onset of parotitis. Concentrated normal gamma globulin, however, has proved to be of no value under these circumstances (Gellis and co-workers, 1945).

Diethylstilbestrol has lately been employed in the prophylaxis and the treatment of mumps orchitis (Savran, 1946; Hoyne, Diamond and Christian, 1949); final evaluation of the drug must await results of further clinical studies.

EPIDEMIOLOGY

Mumps is not confined to any area or climate but is world-wide in its distribution. In settled populations, it occurs as an endemic disease throughout the entire year. Periodically, however, an increase in the incidence is recorded, usually during the winter and early spring months. Although there is a seasonal increase at this time, which may or may not reach epidemic proportions, it is especially marked at intervals of about seven or eight years when severe epidemics may be observed. Both sexes are equally susceptible. Although predominantly a disease of childhood, adults who have escaped infection as children are often attacked. Although among the commonest of infections, a positive history of mumps is obtained less frequently among adults than is the case with certain other diseases of childhood, such as measles (mumps about 60 per cent; measles, about 90 per cent). The frequency of inapparent infections in mumps and their rarity in measles would appear to account largely for the difference noted. The only known reservoir of infection is man. Transmission of the virus apparently takes place through direct contact, air-suspended droplets, or fomites contaminated with saliva. The period that a patient may be able to spread the disease has not been exactly determined, but there is a certain amount of evidence which indicates that it probably extends from 24 to 48 hours before to at least 6 days after salivary gland enlargement is noted. Practically nothing is known about the infectivity of patients in whom involvement of the salivary glands cannot be distinguished, although recently some unpublished evidence has been obtained which indicates that infection has been spread from cases of meningo-encephalitis without parotitis to contacts who afterwards developed uncomplicated mumps. For reviews of the epidemiology of mumps see the papers by Gordon and Heeren (1940) and Gordon and Kilham (1949).

CONTROL MEASURES

Attempts have been made to prevent the development of mumps (1) by passive immunization through the use of certain of the products mentioned for specific therapy and (2) by active immunization through the injection of inactivated or attenuated mumps virus. Most observers, who have used unconcentrated serum derived from those recently convalescent, have believed that it is of value as a temporary prophylactic measure, provided it is administered in doses of from 5 to 20 cc. within the first few days following exposure. There is general agreement that any passive immunity so conferred is of short duration, i.e., probably two or three weeks. A critical analysis, however, of the available data leaves some doubt as to whether the procedure is sufficiently dependable to be of value. Experimental studies which have been carried out recently would suggest that some of these data have been interpreted too optimistically, since, as unpublished data of Janeway and Enders show, very large doses of convalescent serum (200 cc.) have failed to prevent the disease and the concentration of virus-neutralizing antibody in convalescent sera appears to be relatively low as compared with that found in certain other virus diseases.

During the last few years work has been undertaken on the development of a practicable method of inducing active immunity. The immunizing effect in monkeys and in human beings of virus, in emulsions of infected parotid glands from monkeys, inactivated by formalin has been studied. Any resistance so induced was challenged by inoculation of virulent virus; the vaccine prevented the development of typical infection in from 50 to 60 per cent of those who received it. Although falling short of an ideal prophylactic agent, formalinized virus has thus been shown capable of preventing mumps in certain persons under very severe conditions of exposure (Stokes and co-workers, 1946). Following the development of the technic for cultivating the virus in embryonated eggs, a further step toward a practicable vaccine was taken, since this made available unlimited quantities of material containing the virus. Egg virus inactivated by ether or ultraviolet light has been shown capable of protecting monkeys against experimental infection (Habel, 1946). Experiments on the protective effect of such vaccines in man have shown that the frequency of mumps among control groups exposed to the disease was 3 times that among the vaccinated (Habel, 1951a, 1951b). Since the groups included 2,825 individuals among whom 336 cases of mumps were observed, these results appear to leave little doubt of the prophylactic value of inactivated virus as vaccine provided exposure occurs within 4 to 6 weeks after it is administered.

In addition to investigations on the use of inactivated virus as a vaccine, preliminary studies on the effect of administering virus attenuated by repeated passage through the embryonated egg have been reported. It has been shown that after such treatment the virus loses its ability to produce typical parotitis in the monkey and, with rare exceptions, in man also. Such attenuated but active material renders the monkey solidly immune to reinfection with highly virulent virus and, on the basis of limited data, human beings as well (Enders and co-workers, 1946b; Henle, Stokes, Burgoon, Bashe, Burgoon and Henle 1951b). In the work just mentioned, the attenuated virus was not inoculated parenterally but introduced either via Stensen's duct or sprayed into the oral cavity. On the basis of general knowledge of immunity in virus diseases, it would be anticipated that the resistance established by such attenuated virus would be more effective and more durable than that resulting from vaccination with inactivated material. For detailed treatment of the various aspects of specific prophylaxis, the following references may be consulted: Wesselhoeft (1940); Enders (1946); Gellis and co-workers (1945);

Lyday (1941); Stokes and co-workers (1946); Enders and co-workers (1946a); Gordon and Kilham (1949).

The available data indicate that a patient may transfer the infection to a susceptible person during a period which extends approximately from 6 days before to 9 days after onset of symptoms (Henle, Henle, Wendell and Rosenberg, 1948; Gordon and Kilham, 1949). Although some workers may not entirely approve of it, the standard method of control as now recommended consists in the isolation of a patient until all swelling of affected glands has subsided. Recent advances in the knowledge of the duration of infectivity may lead to a modification of this recommendation.

REFERENCES

Adams, Francis, 1891, The Genuine Works of Hippocrates. New York, Wood, Vol. 1, p. 294.

Applebaum, I. L., 1944, Serum amylase in mumps. Ann. Int. Med., 21, 35-43.

Beveridge, W. I. B., Lind, P. E., and Anderson, S. G., 1946, Mumps 1. Isolation and cultivation of the virus in the chick embryo. Australian J. Exp. Biol. and Med. Sci., 24, 15-19.

Dawson, I. M., and Elford, W. J., The investigation of influenza and related viruses in the electron microscope, by a new technique. J. Gen. Microbiol., 3, 298-311.

Dopter and Repaci, G., 1909, Contribution à l'étude anatomo-pathologique des oreillons. Arch. méd. exp., 21, 533-545.

Enders, J. F., 1943, Observations on immunity in mumps. Ann. Int. Med., 18, 1015-1019.

Enders, J. F., 1946, Mumps: techniques of laboratory diagnosis, tests for susceptibility and experiments on specific prophylaxis. J. Ped., 29, 129-142.

Enders, J. F., and Cohen, S., 1942, Detection of antibody by complement fixation in sera of man and monkey convalescent from mumps. Proc. Soc. Exp. Biol. and Med., 50, 180-184.

Enders, J. F., Kane, L. W., Cohen, S., and Levens, J. H., 1945, Immunity in mumps. I. Experiments with monkeys (Macacus mulatta). The development of complement-fixing antibody following infection and experiments on immunization by means of inactivated virus and convalescent human serum. J. Exp. Med., 81, 93-117.

Enders, J. F., Kane, L. W., Maris, E. P., and Stokes, J., Jr., 1946a, Immunity in mumps. V. The correlation of the presence of dermal hypersensitivity and resistance to mumps. J. Exp. Med., 84, 341-364.

Enders, J. F., Levens, J. H., Stokes, J., Jr., Maris, E. P., and Berenberg, W., 1946b, Attenuation of

virulence with retention of antigenicity of mumps virus after passage in the embryonated egg. J. Immunol., 54, 283-291.

Gall, E. A., 1947, The histopathology of acute mumps orchitis. Am. J. Path., 23, 637-651.

Gellis, S. S., McGuinness, A. C., and Peters, M., 1945, A study on the prevention of mumps orchitis by gamma globulin. Am. J. Med. Sci., 210, 661-664.

Gordon, J. E., and Heeren, R. H., 1940, The epidemiology of mumps. Am. J. Med. Sci., 200, 412-428.

Gordon, J. E., and Kilham, L., 1949, Ten years in the epidemiology of mumps. Am. J. Med. Sci., 218, 338-359.

Habel, K., 1945, Cultivation of mumps virus in the developing chick embryo and its application to studies of immunity to mumps in man. Pub. Health Rep., 60, 201-212.

Habel, K., 1946, Preparation of mumps vaccines and immunization of monkeys against experimental mumps infection. Pub. Health Rep., 61, 1655-1664.

Habel, K., 1951a, Vaccination of human beings against mumps: vaccine administered at the start of an epidemic. I. Incidence and severity of mumps in vaccinated and control groups. Am. J. Hyg., 54, 295-311.

Habel, K., 1951b, Vaccination of human beings against mumps: vaccine administered at the start of an epidemic. II. Effect of vaccination upon the epidemic. Am. J. Hyg., 54, 312-318.

Hamilton, R., 1790, An account of a distemper, by the common people in England vulgarly called the mumps. Trans. Royal Soc. Edinb., 2, 59-72.

Henle, G., Henle, W., and Harris, S., 1947, The serological differentiation of mumps complement fixation antigens. Proc. Soc. Exp. Biol. and Med., 64, 290-295.

Henle, G., Harris, S., and Henle, W. 1948, The reactivity of various human sera with mumps complement fixation antigens. J. Exp. Med., *88*, 133-147.

Henle, G., Henle, W., Wendell, K. K., and Rosenberg, P., 1948, Isolation of mumps virus from human beings with induced apparent or inapparent infections. J. Exp. Med., *88*, 223-232.

Henle, G., Henle, W., Burgoon, J. S., Bashe, W. J., and Stokes, J. Jr., 1951, Studies on the prevention of mumps. I. The determination of susceptibility. J. Immunol., *66*, 535-549.

Henle, G., Stokes, J. Jr., Burgoon, J. S., Bashe, W. J., Burgoon, C. F., and Henle, W., 1951, Studies on the prevention of mumps. IV. The effect of oral spraying of attenuated active virus. J. Immunol., *66*, 579-594.

Hoyne, A. L., Diamond, J. H., and Christian, J. R., 1949, Diethylstilbesterol in mumps orchitis. J. Am. Med. Assn., *140*, 662-665.

Johnson, C. D., and Goodpasture, E. W., 1934, An investigation of the etiology of mumps. J. Exp. Med., *59*, 1-20.

Kane, L. W., and Enders, J. F., 1945, Immunity in mumps. III. The complement fixation test as an aid in the diagnosis of mumps meningoencephalitis. J. Exp. Med., *81*, 137-150.

Kilham, L., 1949, Mumps meningoencephalitis with and without parotitis. Am. J. Dis. Child., *78*, 324-333.

Levens, J. H., and Enders, J. F., 1945, The hemoagglutinative properties of amniotic fluid from embryonated eggs infected with mumps virus. Science, *102*, 117-120.

Lyday, J. H., 1941, An evaluation of convalescent serum in the prevention of mumps. J. Ped., *18*, 473-475.

Manca, C., 1932, Über die Mumpsorchitis. Virchows Arch. fur path. Anat., *285*, 426-442.

Maris, E. P., Enders, J. F., Stokes, J., Jr., and Kane, L. W., 1946, Immunity in mumps. IV. The correlation of the presence of complement-fixing antibody and resistance to mumps in human beings. J. Exp. Med., *84*, 323-339.

Morgan, H. R., Enders, J. F., and Wagley, P. F., 1948, A hemolysin associated with the mumps virus. J. Exp. Med., *88*, 503-514.

Robbins, F. C., Kilham, L., Levens, J. H. and Enders, J. F., 1949, An evaluation of the test for antihemagglutinins in the diagnosis of infections by the mumps virus. J. Immunol., *61*, 235-242.

Savran, J., 1946, Diethylstilbestrol in the prevention of orchitis following mumps. Rhode Island Med. J., *29*, 662.

Smith, G. G., 1912, Two cases of orchitis due to mumps treated by operation. Boston Med. and Surg. Journal, *167*, 323-325.

Stokes, J., Jr., Enders, J. F., Maris, E. P., and Kane, L. W., 1946, Immunity in mumps. VI. Experiments on the vaccination of human beings with formolized mumps virus. J. Exp. Med., *84*, 407-428.

Swan, C., and Mawson, J., 1943, Experimental mumps: transmission of the disease to monkeys: attempts to propagate the virus in developing hens' eggs. Med. J. Australia, *1*, 411-416.

Weil, M. L., Beard, D., Sharp, D. G., and Beard, J. W., 1948, Purification, pH stability and culture of the mumps virus. J. Immunol., *60*, 561-582.

Weller, T. H., and Craig, J. M., 1949, The isolation of mumps virus at autopsy. Am. J. Path., *25*, 1105-1115.

Werner, C. A., 1950, Mumps orchitis and testicular atrophy. I. Occurrence. Ann. Int. Med., *32*, 1066-1074.

Wesselhoeft, C., 1940, Mumps: its glandular and neurologic manifestations, *in* Gordon, J. E., Mueller, J. H., Zinsser, H. et al., Virus and Rickettsial Diseases. Cambridge, Harvard University Press, pp. 309-348.

Wesselhoeft, C., 1941, Mumps, *in* Oxford Loose-Leaf Medicine, p. 1065, New York, Oxford University Press, pp. 489-497(*36*).

Zelman, S., 1944, Blood diastase in mumps and mumps pancreatitis, Am. J. Med. Sci., *207*, 461-464.

THOMAS M. RIVERS, M.D.

Hospital of The Rockefeller Institute for Medical Research

29

Infectious Mononucleosis

(SYNONYMS: Glandular fever, *Drüsenfieber,* monocytic angina, angina with lymphatic reaction, acute benign lymphoblastosis, acute mononucleosis)

INTRODUCTION

Infectious mononucleosis usually attacks children and young adults and is characterized by fever, angina, enlarged lymph nodes and spleen, a pathognomonic blood picture, and the presence of a heterophile antibody in the serum. The etiology is not definitely known, although a virus is suspected. It should be distinguished from acute infectious lymphocytosis of children (Smith, 1944), the etiology of which is also unknown.

HISTORY

Pfeiffer (1889) described a disease that he called glandular fever. In the United States, such a disease was first reported by West (1896) in eastern Ohio. Sprunt and Evans (1920) used the name infectious mononucleosis for cases similar to those seen by Pfeiffer and regarded the disease as infectious. Epidemics or sporadic cases of glandular fever, monocytic angina, angina with lymphatic reaction, or infectious mononucleosis have been described as occurring in many parts of the world. It is now believed that all these designations refer to the same malady, even though different signs or symptoms may dominate the clinical picture at various times. Paul and Bunnell (1932), by establishing the fact that a heterophile antibody is present in the serum of patients with the disease, have made possible an important diagnostic test which has aided considerably in the proper classification of various clinical types.

CLINICAL PICTURE

The incubation period is estimated to be from four to ten days. The onset may be acute or insidious with loss of appetite, constipation, irritability or somnolence, and fatigue. Then occur fever, nausea or vomiting in younger children, epistaxis, headache, chills and sweating. Early the lymph nodes, especially the anterocervical and postcervical, become enlarged and tender; the spleen is usually palpable. Angina, as a rule more pronounced in older patients, may occur early and presents a picture varying from a mild hyperemia to an ulcerating, pseudomembranous, diphtherialike inflammation. Certain patients exhibit conjunctivitis, cutaneous rash, hepatitis, and rarely nephritis. Scheer (1930) reported that clinically inapparent infections may be encountered during an epidemic. The fever and acute symptoms subside usually within one to three weeks, but often enlargement of the lymph nodes and spleen and an abnormal blood picture may persist for several months. Relapses are common, but complete recovery eventually is the rule.

There is involvement of the CNS of certain patients which becomes manifest during the second week of illness as a meningitis, encephalitis, neuronitis or meningo-encephalitis. In order of occurrence, the signs and symptoms most frequently noted are headache, nuchal rigidity, positive Kernig, lethargy, muscle twitching, dizziness, dysarthria, positive Babinski, facial paralysis, nausea and photophobia. The cerebrospinal fluid shows a lymphocytic pleocytosis and/or increased amount of protein. Patients having this syndrome usually recover completely (Slade, 1946). According to Bernstein and Wolff (1950), acceptable reports on 34 patients with infectious mononucleosis, who had involvement of the CNS, have been recorded. They estimate that involvement of the CNS occurs in less than 1 per cent of those suffering from this malady, and state that recovery is complete in 85 per cent of those with such an involvement in periods ranging from a few days to several months. The investigators were unable to find heterophile antibody in the spinal fluid of their patient.

In the active phase of the disease, the total white blood cell count may range from 10,000 to 80,000. Polymorphonuclear leukocytes are reduced sometimes to as few as 2,000 per c.mm. Monocytes and large lymphocytes are increased in number and often are somewhat abnormal in appearance. It must be remembered that in about 50 per cent of the cases a leukopenia may be observed very early in the course of the disease.

PATHOLOGIC PICTURE

Excised glands show hyperplasia of the lymphatic tissue, and at times there is also proliferation of the reticular and endothelial cells. Deaths are rare. Allen and Kellner (1947) reported the necropsy findings in a patient who "died 2 to 4 weeks after the acute illness as a result of an accident"; they consisted of focal cellular infiltrations in the kidneys, liver, lungs, heart, adrenals, testes, and brain. Such lesions account for the variety of clinical manifestations observed in patients.

EXPERIMENTAL INFECTION; HOST RANGE

Experimental infection, except for suggestive studies in man and monkeys (*v. infra*, Etiology) has not as yet been achieved.

ETIOLOGY

At one time, *Listerella monocytogenes* was believed to have a causal relation to infectious mononucleosis, but no definite confirmatory evidence has been obtained. Van den Berghe and Liessens (1939) induced a monocytic leukocytosis and heterophile antibody in a monkey by means of intramuscular inoculation of blood from a patient with infectious mononucleosis. Serum of this animal, filtered through a Seitz pad, produced a similar condition in another monkey. In later tests, an active agent propagated in tissue culture for ten generations produced mononuclear leukocytosis in monkeys. Sohier et al. (1940) also induced, by means of blood from a patient at the height of the malady, a mononuclear cell increase and slight fever in a rhesus monkey. However, blood from this monkey brought about the presence of heterophile antibody in a young adult person. Wising (1942) reported the induction of enlarged lymph glands and a slight monocytosis in *Macacus* and *Cercopithecus* monkeys by means of intracerebral, intraperitoneal or subcutaneous injections of emulsified lymph nodes from patients. Five successful monkey passages by means of excised lymph glands were achieved, and the titer of heterophile antibody in the serum of the animals rose to 1:128. Wising (1942) also transfused five human volunteers with blood from patients acutely ill with infectious mononucleosis; only one came down with the disease. On the other hand, Bang (1943), Julianelle et al. (1944) and others failed to transmit the malady to man, monkeys and other laboratory animals, including embryonated eggs. Moreover, in this connection it must be kept in mind that it is possible to transfer passively heterophile antibody when large amounts of blood are used as inocula (Bang, 1943). A virus may be the cause of the disease, but more experimental work is needed to establish the fact.

DIAGNOSIS

The diagnosis of infectious mononucleosis is made in the presence of fever, generalized lymphatic hyperplasia, characteristic blood picture, and the presence of a heterophile antibody in the serum. The latter is revealed by an increased titer of agglutinins for sheep erythrocytes (Paul and Bunnell, 1932). This test is positive in from 50 to 80 per cent of the cases; a negative result is, therefore, not always indicative of the absence of the malady. The test is performed with serum inactivated at 56° C. for 15 minutes to which is added a 2 per cent suspension of washed sheep red blood cells in saline solution. The mixture is kept in a waterbath at 37° C. for an hour and overnight in a refrigerator. A positive reaction is one in which serum diluted 1:80 or more agglutinates sheep red blood corpuscles. It must be remembered that normal human serum diluted 1:60 may cause agglutination. Moreover, the heterophile antibody in normal human serum rises after injection of horse serum. Therefore, in order to avoid errors, it is wise before testing a serum to absorb conflicting substances from it by means of guinea pig kidney and with boiled beef red blood cells; for it has been shown that the heterophile antibody in normal human serum is adsorbed completely by guinea pig kidney and that the heterophile antibody produced following the injection of horse serum is adsorbed by guinea pig kidney and by boiled beef red blood cells, while the heterophile antibody found in the serum of patients with infectious mononucleosis is absorbed only by boiled beef erythrocytes (Stuart et al., 1936; Davidsohn, 1937).

TREATMENT

There is no specific treatment; sulfonamides and penicillin are ineffective.

EPIDEMIOLOGY

In view of the fact that infectious mononucleosis is frequently a mild disease, many cases are probably overlooked. Epidemics occur especially in children between the ages of two and ten years; the malady is rare in infants under 6 months of age. Epidemics often flare up in orphanages, schools and colleges, and were observed in the United States Army during World War II. The disease is said to be contagious, but transmission through human contact is difficult (Lemierre, 1944) and is assumed to succeed only when the contact is close (Scheer, 1930). It has also been postulated that the malady is spread by droplet infection, through the mucosa of the alimentary or genital tracts, or through the skin (Lemierre, 1944). No control measures are known.

REFERENCES

Allen, F. H., Jr., and Kellner, A., 1947, Infectious mononucleosis. An autopsy report. Am. J. Path., 23, 463-478.

Bang, J., 1943, Experiments with the transmission of infectious mononucleosis to man. Acta med. Scand., 113, 304-310.

van den Berghe, L., and Liessens, P., 1939, Transmission de la mononucléose infectieuse humaine (fièvre ganglionnaire de Pfeiffer) au Macacus rhesus et passages successifs d'un virus filtrant. Compt. rend. Soc. biol., 130, 279-283.

Bernstein, T. C., and Wolff, H. G., 1950, Involvement of the nervous system in infectious mononucleosis. Ann. Inter. Med., 33, 1120-1136.

Davidsohn, I., 1937, Serologic diagnosis of infectious mononucleosis. J. Am. Med. Assn., 108, 289-295.

Julianelle, L. A., Bierbaum, O. S., and Moore, C. V., 1944, Studies on infectious mononucleosis, Ann. Int. Med., *20*, 281-292.

Lemierre, A., 1944, Mononucléose infectieuse, *in* Lemierre, Bowin, Levaditi, Mollaret, Lépine et Gastinel, Conférences d'actualité sur les ultravirus. Paris, Maloine, pp. 1-13.

Paul, J. R., and Bunnell, W. W., 1932, The presence of heterophile antibodies in infectious mononucleosis. Am. J. Med. Sci., *183*, 90-104.

Pfeiffer, E., 1889, Drüsenfieber. Jahrb. f. Kinderh., *29*, 257-264.

Scheer, K., 1930, Eine epidemie des Pfeifferschen Drüsenfiebers. Monats. f. Kinderh., *48*, 59-69.

Slade, J. deR., 1946, Involvement of the central nervous system in infectious mononucleosis. New England J. Med., *234*, 753-757.

Smith, C. H., 1944, Acute infectious lymphocytosis: a specific infection. Report of 4 cases showing its communicability. J. Am. Med. Assn., *125*, 342-349.

Sohier, R., Lépine, P., and Sautter, V., 1940, Recherches sur la transmission expérimentale de la mononucléose infectieuse au singe et à l'homme. Ann. Inst. Pasteur, *65*, 50-62.

Sprunt, T. P., and Evans, F. A., 1920, Mononuclear leucocytosis in reaction to acute infections ("infectious mononucleosis"). Bull. Johns Hopkins Hosp., *31*, 410-417.

Stuart, C. A., Welch, H., Cunningham, J., and Burgess, A. M., 1936, Infectious mononucleosis: Further studies. Arch. Int. Med., *58*, 512-522.

West, J. P., 1896, An epidemic of glandular fever. Arch. Pediat., *13*, 889-900.

Wising, P. J., 1942, A study of infectious mononucleosis (Pfeiffer's disease) from the etiological point of view. Acta med. Scand., Suppl., 133, 1-102.

HERALD R. COX, sc.d.

Lederle Laboratories Division, American Cyanamid Company

30

Colorado Tick Fever

(Synonyms: Mountain fever, tick fever, mountain tick fever,
nonexanthematous tick fever, American mountain fever)

INTRODUCTION

Colorado tick fever is a nonexanthematous disease of man, characterized by a short course and intermittent fever, and is caused by a tick-borne virus.

HISTORY

This disease undoubtedly was mentioned over a hundred years ago in medical reports of army doctors stationed at the various camps and forts in the Rocky Mountain region. Toomey (1931) reviewed these early reports and proposed the name *American mountain tick fever* for the disease. However, Becker (1930) was the first to report the condition as a separate clinical entity, to describe the disease clearly, and to suggest the name it now bears, *Colorado tick fever*. Topping, Cullyford and Davis (1940), while conducting a clinical and epidemiologic study of the disease, were unable to establish the causative agent in guinea pigs, monkeys, rats, mice, rabbits, and chick embryos, but concluded that it apparently is associated with the bite of the wood tick *Dermacentor andersoni*, as previously postulated by Becker (1930). Florio and his colleagues (1944) transmitted the disease serially in man and hamsters by parenteral injection of blood or serum and showed that the virus passes collodion-membrane filters. Koprowski and

Cox (1946, 1947a, 1947b) adapted the virus to the mouse and developing chick embryo and prepared an experimental vaccine.

CLINICAL PICTURE

The disease has a sharp and clearly defined onset and it is not unusual for a patient to be able to establish the exact time of onset. It usually starts with chilly sensations and aching of the entire body. Headache, deep ocular pain and lumbar backache are the prominent symptoms; anorexia, nausea, vomiting, photophobia, muscle pains, and hyperesthesia of the skin may be a part of the syndrome. With the onset of symptoms, the temperature rises rapidly and is sustained at from 102° to 104° F. for about 48 hours. There is a concurrent increase in the pulse rate. A period of remission then occurs, lasting two or three days during which a patient is symptom-free except for slight weakness. At the end of this period there is usually a recrudescence, and the second bout is similar to the first but may last a day or so longer. In typical cases the white blood cell count falls to 2,000 or 3,000 cells per cubic millimeter (Florio and Stewart, 1947), the lowest count usually being found during relapse. This is the usual pattern, but occasionally single and triple bouts have been reported. Following the recrudescence, patients not infrequently complain of great weakness and the convalescent period seems unusually long considering the relatively short duration of fever. Physical examination reveals only a slight injection of the throat and conjunctivae; complications and deaths have never been reported.

PATHOLOGIC PICTURE

Nothing is known of the pathologic picture in man. In hamsters the only constant and significant lesions are found in the spleen (Black, Florio and Stewart, 1947). Spleens from infected animals when stained with hematoxylin and eosin show alterations in the cellular type and arrangement of the follicular lymphoid tissue, with variations in the extent, but not in the type, of reaction. There is an apparent reduction in the number of lymphoid cells in the central portion of the follicle, with the appearance throughout the follicle of large pale-staining mononuclear cells, mingled with polymorphonuclear leukocytes and erythrocytes. The periphery of the follicle shows a partial or complete disappearance of the normally well-defined margin, which is replaced by a ragged border of mononuclear cells, with occasional polymorphonuclear leukocytes and erythrocytes. With Giemsa stain both eosinophilic and basophilic intracytoplasmic inclusions are seen in the large mononuclear cells.

EXPERIMENTAL INFECTION; HOST RANGE

In the early passages, hamsters inoculated intraperitoneally with infectious blood remained normal in appearance, but starting with the twelfth passage they began to die, and thereafter a mortality rate of from 25 to 50 per cent was common. Successive passage of the virus by parenteral injection of blood or serum through a series of six human volunteers did not increase or decrease the virulence of the virus for hamsters, although the incubation period in man was usually three days instead of four

to six (Florio, Mugrage and Stewart, 1946). Dilute brown agouti mice or albino mice inoculated intracerebrally with mouse-adapted virus first show signs of illness on the third or fourth day; they develop paralysis of the legs, soon become prostrate and die generally on the fifth to seventh day. Mice 8 days of age are fully as susceptible to intraperitoneal infection as 28-day-old mice are to infection induced by intracerebral inoculation. Resistance to virus inoculated intraperitoneally begins to be evident in 14-day-old mice. Infectious mouse-brain tissue is lethal for mice by the intracerebral route in 10^{-5} and 10^{-6} dilutions. Following intracerebral inoculation, mice, cotton rats, hamsters and opossums have virus in their blood, but sheep and rabbits do not; the mice and hamsters alone die of viral infection by this route (Koprowski and Cox, 1947a). The virus may be propagated in chick embryos when the yolk-sac method is used. The virus, which is found chiefly in the central nervous system of the chick embryo, reaches its maximum titer in four or five days. CNS tissue of chick embryos is lethal for mice by the intracerebral route in $10^{-3.5}$ and 10^{-4} dilutions. Chick-embryo-propagated virus retains its virulence for mice and hamsters receiving it by the intracerebral route.

Oliphant and Tibbs (1950), using either blood serum or emulsified blood-clot from human beings suspected of having the disease and residing in Colorado, Wyoming, Oregon or Utah, reported primary isolation of 10 strains of Colorado tick fever virus by intraperitoneal inoculation of albino Swiss mice 3 to 5 days old. In 5 instances, signs of illness were seen in the first-passage mice at intervals varying from 5 to 8 days following inoculation. Isolation of the other 5 strains required blind-passage technic in which harvested brain tissue was transferred by intraperitoneal injection on the fifth day. All 10 strains were immunologically similar to the Florio strain adapted to mice by Koprowski and Cox (1946).

Great difficulties were experienced in adapting the established virus strains to Swiss mice 16 days old or older, but this was accomplished by using 16- to 17- and 17- to 18-day-old mice in successive passages.

ETIOLOGY

The virus readily passes Berkefeld N and W candles and single Seitz EK pads. Through the use of graded collodion membranes, the diameter of the hamster-adapted virus was estimated by Florio, Stewart and Mugrage (1946) to be 10 mμ, while Koprowski and Cox (1947a) found the diameter of the mouse-brain-adapted virus to be from 35 to 50 mμ. The virus is remarkably stable, surviving for at least three and a half years either in the ice compartment of an ordinary refrigerator or in a commercial deep-freeze unit. It is also readily preserved by freezing and drying. It is inactivated when heated at 60° C. for 30 minutes.

By means of cross-immunity tests in human volunteers, Florio, Hammon et al. (1946) and Pollard et al. (1946) showed that the viruses of dengue and Colorado tick fever are not related. Neutralization tests carried out in mice (Koprowski and Cox, 1946; 1947a), or complement-fixation tests (De Boer et al., 1947), indicate that the virus of Colorado tick fever is different from the viruses of Russian spring-summer encephalitis, louping-ill, Venezuelan equine encephalitis, western equine encephalitis, eastern equine encephalitis, Japanese B encephalitis, St. Louis encephalitis, lymphocytic choriomeningitis, rabies, yellow fever and dengue fever, and also from the rickettsiae of murine (endemic) typhus, Rocky Mountain spotted fever, and American Q fever.

The virus introduced parenterally in minimal amounts elicits an immune response in mice which withstand subsequent intracerebral challenge with massive doses of mouse-brain virus (Koprowski and Cox, 1947b).

There are no reports of persons having the disease a second time. Florio and his colleagues (1944) inoculated three human volunteers with a different strain of Colorado tick fever virus 9 to 12 months after the original experimental infection. They did not develop the disease, thus indicating that the disease confers immunity. In addition, several volunteers who had lived in endemic areas for many years were found to be resistant to experimental infection.

DIAGNOSIS

History of exposure to ticks, the saddleback temperature curve, the symptomatology and leukopenia suggest a diagnosis of Colorado tick fever. Neither acute phase nor convalescent sera show any significant Weil-Felix reaction in the presence of Proteus OX-19, OX-2, or OX-K. Specific diagnostic complement-fixing antigens for Colorado tick fever have been prepared from infected mouse brains. The antigens prepared by benzene extraction, following lyophilization, give no false positive reactions in the presence of positive-syphilitic sera (De Boer et al., 1947). Close correlation is obtained in the complement-fixation and mouse-neutralization tests with human convalescent sera. The complement-fixing and neutralizing antibodies apparently appear in the blood of human beings on about the 9th to 14th day after diagnosis of illness and may remain demonstrable as long as 34 months.

TREATMENT

Treatment is symptomatic.

EPIDEMIOLOGY

The disease is at present known to occur in Oregon (Becker, 1930), Utah, Idaho and Wyoming (Topping, Cullyford and Davis, 1940). In Colorado, cases are reported in greater numbers than in the surrounding states, probably because local interest was stimulated by the work of Becker (1930), Topping, Cullyford and Davis (1940), and

Florio, Stewart and Mugrage (1944, 1946). Patients invariably give a history of having been in a tick-infested area four or five days previous to the onset of illness and in most instances have found a tick or ticks attached to their bodies. At present the known geographic distribution of Colorado tick fever is limited to the habitat of the wood tick, *Dermacentor andersoni.* The majority of the cases occur in the older age groups and, as would be expected, particularly in males since these persons through vocational pursuits are more exposed to tick bites. Florio, Miller and Mugrage (1950a) demonstrated that *D. andersoni* is infected in nature. Nine strains of virus were isolated by inoculating hamsters with ground suspensions of ticks that were collected from three different areas near Denver, Colorado. They also reported that the virus is transovarially transmitted by the adult female *D. andersoni.* They demonstrated transmitted virus in the larval, nymphal and subsequent adult life-cycle stages, although no virus was detected in the eggs of the originally infected adults. The same authors (1950b) also reported the isolation of three strains of Colorado tick fever virus from dog ticks, *Dermacentor variabilis,* collected on Long Island, N. Y.; hamsters were used for this work. Thus far no human cases have been reported from this area. Eklund (personal communication), using the suckling-mice technic of Oliphant and Tibbs (1950), apparently has isolated many additional strains of virus from naturally infected *D. andersoni* collected in the Bitter Root Valley of western Montana as well as one strain from a human being residing in the same area. Neutralizing antibodies were not present in an early blood specimen of this patient but appeared in high titer during convalescence.

CONTROL MEASURES

The prevention of Colorado tick fever depends primarily upon the avoidance of tick-infested areas and the early removal of ticks that become attached to the body. If this is not possible, it is recommended that suitable clothing (high boots, leggings, or socks worn outside the trouser legs) be worn so that ticks will find it more difficult to become attached. Koprowski and Cox (1947b) reported on the vaccination of four human volunteers with active, chick-embryo-adapted virus. Reactions to the inoculation consisted of slight swelling and tenderness of the lymph nodes adjacent to the site of inoculation, which appeared on the sixth or seventh day after injection and subsided within 24 to 48 hours. One individual showed circulating virus on the sixth and eighth days after inoculation, and two others on the sixth day, while one failed to show circulating virus. All four volunteers developed specific neutralizing antibodies.

Twenty additional volunteers, 17 males and 3 females ranging in age from 21 to 60 years, were vaccinated with active, chick-embryo-adapted virus representing material from the thirty-seventh and the seventy-fourth passage in this host (Koprowski, Cox, Miller and Florio, 1950). Three of the 20 individuals probably were immune prior to vaccination and these showed no clinical reaction to the vaccine. The remaining 17 became more or less ill from 6 to 7 days following vaccination, and 16 had enlarged, tender axillary lymph glands near the site of injection. Twelve had a mild attack of illness which lasted from 2 to 5 days and resembled Colorado tick fever, except that there was only a single febrile response, and the onset and the disappearance of symptoms were more gradual than is usually seen in the natural disease. All vaccinated individuals, including the three presumably immune, developed neutralizing antibodies. The latter subjects showed a comparatively earlier and greater serologic response. Five of the inoculated persons were subsequently challenged with a living, human strain of Colorado tick fever virus and apparently were immune.

REFERENCES

Becker, F. E., 1930, Tick-borne infections in Colorado. I. The diagnosis and management of infections transmitted by the wood tick. Colorado Med., *27*, 36-44.

Black, W. C., Florio, L., and Stewart, M. O., 1947, A histologic study of the reaction in the hamster spleen produced by the virus of Colorado tick fever. Am. J. Path., *23*, 217-224.

De Boer, C. J., Kunz, L. J., Koprowski, H., and Cox, H. R., 1947, Specific complement-fixing diagnostic antigens for Colorado tick fever. Proc. Soc. Exp. Biol. and Med., *64*, 202-208.

Eklund, C. M., 1951, Personal communication. Rocky Mountain laboratory, U. S. Public Health Service, Hamilton, Montana.

Florio, L., Stewart, M. O., and Mugrage, E. R., 1944, The experimental transmission of Colorado tick fever. J. Exp. Med., *80*, 165-188.

Florio, L., Hammon, W. McD., Laurent, A., and Stewart, M. O., 1946, Colorado tick fever and dengue. An experimental immunological and clinical comparison. J. Exp. Med., *83*, 295-301.

Florio, L., Mugrage, E. R., and Stewart, M. O., 1946, Colorado tick fever. Ann. Int. Med., *25*, 466-472.

Florio, L., Stewart, M. O., and Mugrage, E. R., 1946, The etiology of Colorado tick fever. J. Exp. Med., *83*, 1-10.

Florio, L., Miller, M. S., and Mugrage, E. R., 1950a, Colorado tick fever. Isolation of the virus from *Dermacentor andersoni* in nature and a laboratory study of the transmission of the virus in the tick. Jour. Immunol., *64*, 257-263.

Florio, L., Miller, M. S., and Mugrage, E. R., 1950b, Colorado tick fever. Isolations of virus from *Dermacentor variabilis* obtained from Long Island, New York, with immunological comparisons between eastern and western strains. Jour. Immunol., *64*, 265-272.

Koprowski, H., and Cox, H. R., 1946, Adaptation of Colorado tick fever virus to mouse and developing chick embryo. Proc. Soc. Exp. Biol. and Med., *62*, 320-322.

Koprowski, H., and Cox, H. R., 1947a, Colorado tick fever. I. Studies on mouse brain adapted virus. J. Immunol., *57*, 239-253.

Koprowski, H., and Cox, H. R., 1947b, Colorado tick fever. II. Studies on chick embryo adapted virus. J. Immunol., *57*, 255-262.

Koprowski, H., Cox, H. R., Miller, M. S., and Florio, L., 1950, Response of man to egg-adapted Colorado tick fever virus. Proc. Soc. Exp. Biol. and Med., *74*, 126-131.

Oliphant, J. W., and Tibbs, R. O., 1950, Colorado tick fever. Isolation of virus strains by inoculation of suckling mice. Pub. Health Rep. *65*, 521-522.

Pollard, M., Livesay, H. R., Wilson, D. J., and Woodland, J. C., 1946, Immunological studies of dengue fever and Colorado tick fever. Proc. Soc. Exp. Biol. and Med., *61*, 396-398.

Toomey, N., 1931, Mountain fever and spotted fever of the Rocky Mountains—clinical studies. Ann. Int. Med., *5*, 585-600.

Topping, N. H., Cullyford, J. S., and Davis, G. E., 1940, Colorado tick fever. Pub. Health Rep., *55*, 2224-2237.

MAX THEILER, m.r.c.s. (Eng.), l.r.c.p. (Lond.)

Laboratories of the Division of Medicine and Public Health,
The Rockefeller Foundation, New York City

31

Yellow Fever

(Synonyms: *Fièvre jaune, fiebre*
amarilla, febre amarela, Gelbfieber)

INTRODUCTION

Yellow fever in man is an acute infection caused by a virus. In severe cases, it is characterized by an incubation period of from three to six days, fever, a pulse rate relatively slow in proportion to the temperature, albuminuria, jaundice, and a tendency to hemorrhage, particularly from the mucosa of the stomach and gums. In severity, the disease varies from an almost symptomless infection to a severe, rapidly fatal one, death occurring usually within ten days of onset. There are no sequelae. Recovery leaves a life-long immunity. Man acquires the infection by the bite of an infected mosquito. The disease occurs in two main epidemiologic varieties. In the first, the virus is transmitted from man to man by certain species of mosquito belonging to the genus *Aëdes* of domestic or semidomestic nature. The classic urban yellow fever belongs to this variety, the virus cycle being man—*Aëdes aegypti*—man. In the second variety, in the course of a virus cycle involving wild animals, particularly monkeys and forest-loving mosquitoes, man is only secondarily infected. Yellow fever is now present in large areas of continental South America and Africa.

HISTORY

It is not known whether the original home of yellow fever was in Africa or in America. The first epidemic that can be definitely identified as yellow fever occurred in Yucatan in 1648 (Carter, 1931); accounts of previous epidemics are too vague for identification, but there can be little doubt that at this time the disease was already very widespread. During the seventeenth, eighteenth and nineteenth centuries, the disease was widely distributed throughout the Caribbean islands and the adjoining coastal regions of North, Central, and South America. From this large focus, it was at times transported to more northerly-located cities. Thus, Baltimore, Philadelphia, and New York at times suffered severe epidemics, which were always confined to the warmer months of the year, disappearing entirely with the onset of cold weather and leaving the cities free until reinfected from outside. During this time, yellow fever was essentially a disease of the trade routes of the Atlantic. Epidemics were common on sailing vessels where *A. aegypti* bred in water vats, and this means of transportation was undoubtedly the method of dissemination. On several occasions, yellow fever was

531

taken into the Iberian peninsula where severe epidemics occurred. From infected coastal towns, yellow fever was introduced into the heart of North and South America by traffic on the Mississippi and the Amazon.

Some evidence of the severity of yellow fever may be obtained from the figures quoted by Reed et al. (1911). It was estimated that there must have been at least 500,000 cases of the disease in the United States during the period between 1793 and 1900. The great epidemic in Spain in 1800 caused 60,000 deaths. In Rio de Janeiro, yellow fever was responsible for 23,000 deaths between 1851 and 1883. Yellow fever was first reported in Cuba in 1649 and was almost continuously present until 1900, causing 35,900 deaths in Havana during the period between 1853 and 1900. During the brief occupation of Cuba by the American forces during the Spanish-American War, 1,575 cases of yellow fever with 231 deaths occurred in the American army; because of this the Yellow Fever Commission was appointed, with Major Walter Reed in charge. Modern knowledge of the etiology and epidemiology of yellow fever stems from the findings of this commission, which clearly demonstrated that the agent responsible for yellow fever passed through bacteria-tight filters and was present in the blood of a patient during the first three days of fever, and that the mosquito *Aëdes aegypti* was capable of transmitting the disease by bite, provided a period of 12 days was allowed to lapse after an infective feeding. Acting on this information, Gorgas, by applying antimosquito measures, was able to eradicate yellow fever from Havana.

Following the application of anti-aegypti measures, it was noticed that yellow fever showed a tendency to disappear from neighboring small towns and villages. This led to the development by Carter of the "key center" theory, according to which, two factors are necessary to maintain yellow fever in a community; first, a large population of susceptible human beings, and second, a constant supply of the mosquito. As considerable evidence was available that an attack of yellow fever produced a life-long immunity, it was obvious that the requisite number of susceptible persons could occur only where an adequate immigration of people from yellow-fever-free countries took place or in large cities where the newborn supplied this factor. On the basis of this theory, the possible key centers were surveyed, and a campaign was set on foot with the object of eradicating yellow fever from the Americas. One of the major key centers was Guayaquil. Following the eradication of yellow fever from this city the disease disappeared from the entire Pacific coast of South America. At the time when it looked as though this campaign was about to be crowned with success a sudden and unexplained epidemic of yellow fever occurred in Rio de Janeiro in 1928.

Stokes, Bauer and Hudson (1928), investigating yellow fever in Africa, showed that the rhesus monkey is susceptible to the virus. By the use of this experimental animal, it was shown that monkeys indigenous to Africa or South America are susceptible to yellow fever and that mosquitoes, other than *Aëdes aegypti*, under experimental conditions can transmit the virus. These observations first opened up the possibilities of an epidemiology of yellow fever not confined to the cycle, man—*aegypti*—man. This possibility was emphasized by the finding of cases of yellow fever in South America in areas where *Aëdes aegypti* does not exist, and led to the discovery of the epidemiologic entity now known as jungle yellow fever. It has been clearly established that yellow fever virus is maintained in the jungle in South America and Africa in the absence of both man and *A. aegypti* and that under such conditions man becomes infected only by close contact with the jungle.

The discovery (Theiler, 1930), that white mice are susceptible to an intracerebral inoculation of yellow fever virus, even though the experimental disease in this host does not show the clinical and pathologic pictures of the human malady, led to the development of various protection tests which have proved of value in the study of the epidemiology and distribution of the disease. The observation that serial passage of the virus in the brains of mice produces a loss of virulence for monkeys led to one method of human vaccination which is still extensively used. A more profound modification of the virus was produced by its prolonged maintenance in tissue culture. This led to the development of the 17D strain of virus, which is likewise still in use for human vaccination.

CLINICAL PICTURE

The most exact information available concerning the incubation period is that obtained as a result of the infection of human volunteers (Reed et al., 1911). Of 22 cases produced by the bite of from 1 to 15 infected *Aëdes aegypti* mosquitoes, the mean incubation period was 3 days and 17 hours. The extremes were two hours less than 3 days, and two hours more than 6 days. This coincides with the findings of Carter (Reed et al., 1911) who observed an average incubation period of slightly less than four days in 12 individuals who, after being in an uninfected environment, were exposed for a short time in an infected one and then returned to the first environment. It may therefore be concluded that during an epidemic outbreak of urban yellow fever the incubation period is seldom more than six days. The incubation period of yellow fever, acquired from accidental contamination of the skin by yellow fever virus, may, however, be ten days.

There are usually no prodromata; a patient with a typical infection becomes ill suddenly. The clinical course of a severe case is usually divided into the stages of active congestion and stasis with the following signs and symptoms.

The onset is usually acute and marked by fever, rigor, headache, and backache. The temperature rises rapidly to reach its maxi-

mum on the first or second day. The initial temperature is continuous and seldom exceeds 103.5° F. The period of active congestion lasts three or four days, when the temperature drops. The stage of stasis then sets in and the temperature rises again but seldom reaches its previous maximum. The two stages may coalesce without any drop in temperature to mark the transition. During the stage of congestion the patient is intensely ill and restless; nausea and vomiting are common. The face is flushed, lips swollen, and eyes injected. The tongue is bright red. A tendency to bleeding may be apparent early. During the stage of stasis the whole aspect changes. The active congestion fades, to be replaced by a venous stasis. The face is no longer swollen, and a dusky pallor replaces the bright red of the first stage. The gums become swollen and spongy and bleed spontaneously or on light pressure. Nausea and vomiting are common. The vomited matter usually contains some altered blood; this is the "black vomit." The tendency to hemorrhage is marked; ecchymoses may develop; melaena is common. The pulse rate is markedly slow in relation to the temperature; this is known as Faget's sign and develops during the first stage and becomes progressively more marked during the second stage. The blood pressure is low. Prostration may occur and is usually out of proportion to the clinical picture. Albuminuria usually appears toward the end of the period of congestion, but becomes very marked during the period of stasis. Oliguria or anuria may develop. Jaundice appears during the second stage, and is seldom very marked; it may indeed be absent. It is more marked as a rule in cases in which the malady is prolonged and in convalescence. Most deaths occur on the sixth or seventh day, and seldom later than ten days after onset. Complications are not frequent. Recovery is rapid and complete.

The severity of the disease varies from an extremely mild to a fulminating infection. It is probable that many immunizing infections are without symptoms. Diagnosis can then be made only by serologic tests. However, a study of yellow fever accidentally contracted in the laboratory (Berry and Kitchen, 1931) demonstrated that mild cases show many of the characteristic signs and symptoms of the severe ones. In all but a few cases, the saddleback type of temperature curve is apparent. The pulse reaction is typical; the peculiar relationship of a slowing heartbeat to a constant or increasing temperature is almost invariable. Albuminuria, such a marked feature in severe cases, may be entirely absent in mild ones. An important sign in yellow fever infection is the change observed in the white blood cell count. There is a steady fall in the number of leukocytes beginning with the onset of the disease. The leukopenia is at its maximum on the fifth or sixth day and is chiefly due to a decrease in the number of neutrophiles. Lymphopenia is usual and may be marked (Berry and Kitchen, 1931). The most marked pathologic changes in yellow fever are observed in the liver and kidney. In the most severe cases there is an almost complete destruction of the parenchymatous cells of the liver, and consequently one would expect the metabolic changes associated with extensive liver destruction. Wakeman and Morrell (1930) found in terminal stages of yellow fever in monkeys that urea formation diminished while amino acid nitrogen of both blood and urine rose rapidly. These disturbances of deaminization of urea formation are preceded by hypoglycemia. No definite impairment of kidney function was observed, except a terminal anuria. These authors failed to find any important changes in the uric acid of blood and urine except in the terminal stages of the experimental disease. Findlay and Hindle (1930) found significant increases of blood guanidine in infected monkeys. Definite small increases of guanidine were found in a patient with a laboratory infection (Berry and Kitchen, 1931).

Most authorities agree that in the Negro, yellow fever is milder than in other races. However, severe epidemics among Negroes with a number of deaths, such as that which occurred in the Nuba Mountains in Africa, have been reported (Kirk, 1941). Opinions differ as to whether the disease in children is as severe as in adults. It is very difficult to evaluate the overall mortality of yellow fever. This is usually high in cases in which black vomit and jaundice occur. However, experience has shown that for every case diagnosed, there are usually a great many undiagnosed mild infections as shown by the development of specific neutralizing antibodies. Taking into account missed cases, the mortality is probably seldom greater than 5 per cent.

PATHOLOGIC PICTURE

The outstanding macroscopic findings in yellow fever are signs of degeneration in the liver, kidney and heart, accompanied by hemorrhages and jaundice. The cadaver usually has a livid appearance due to venous congestion. Since the blood in fatal yellow fever remains fluid for a long time, it collects in the dependent portions of the body. Jaundice is always present, seldom well marked. The liver is of normal size or slightly enlarged, somewhat yellow in color, and fatty on section; when drained of blood, it has a boxwood color. The tense and swollen kidneys are likewise fatty and yellow; the cortex is not clearly demarcated from the medulla. Evidence of hemorrhage is usually found; the most frequent site is in the mucosa at the pyloric end of the stomach, where erosions and punctate hemorrhages are present. In very few cases is there a complete absence of altered blood in the stomach contents.

On microscopic examination, the most characteristic lesions are found in the liver (da Rocha Lima, 1912). The liver cells undergo cloudy and fatty degeneration and a distinctive type of necrosis (Plate 7, *top*). The necrotic cells are mainly confined to the midzone, although in severe cases the necrosis may involve almost the entire lobule. In such cases, however, there will always be found a few normal-appearing

PLATE 7

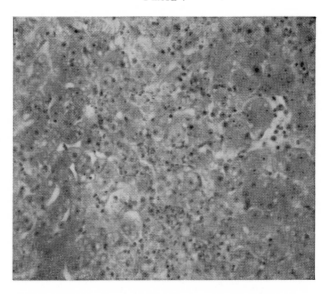

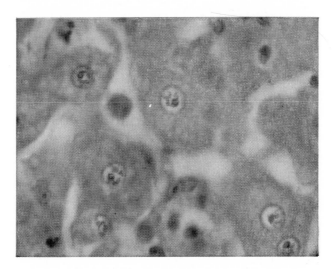

(*Top*) Section of the liver of a rhesus monkey that had died of experimentally induced yellow fever. Note midzonal necrosis. Phloxine-methylene blue stain. $\times$ 200.

(*Bottom*) Higher magnification of the plate above, illustrating intranuclear inclusions in parenchymatous cells of liver. Phloxine-methylene blue stain. $\times$ 900. (Photographs by R. F. Carter)

cells about the central vein and about the periphery of the lobule. Furthermore, all cells in the midzonal section may not be destroyed, resulting in a spotty distribution of the necrotic areas. The necrosis is hyaline in type and may be confined to part of the cytoplasm, but usually the whole cell is involved. Such necrotic, hyaline cells are known as Councilman bodies. The Kupffer cells are enlarged and may be granular in appearance. The sinusoids in the necrotic areas are engorged. Actual hemorrhage in the liver is rare. In spite of extensive necrosis, the architecture remains intact. During recovery the parenchymatous cells are replaced, leading to a complete restoration of the liver without residual signs of infection such as cirrhosis.

The lesions observed in the kidney are not distinctive. As in the liver, there is a complete absence of inflammatory reaction. Cloudy and fatty degeneration of the entire kidney tubule, often more marked in the convoluted portion, is usually present. The spleen is usually hyperemic, but this is unaccompanied by a leukocytic infiltration (Klotz and Belt, 1930). The most distinctive feature is found in the malpighian corpuscles. At first there is a mononucleosis consisting of undifferentiated cells derived from the reticular tissue which persists throughout the entire course of the disease. There is a striking loss of lymphocytes. False germinal centers are formed. Degeneration is marked throughout the entire organ, which, characterized by cells with vesicular nuclei and waxy-appearing cytoplasm, may lead to actual necrosis, particularly noticeable in the false germinal centers. Parallel changes are observed in the lymph nodes. Degenerative changes are present throughout the heart.

Lesions observed in rhesus monkeys are essentially the same as those in man, namely, degenerative lesions in the liver (Plate 7, *top*), kidney, spleen, and lymph nodes. In monkeys that have died of yellow fever following inoculation of unmodified virus, there are no lesions of encephalitis.

The encephalitis produced by the neurotropic virus presents no distinctive features, being manifested by necrosis of ganglion cells and perivascular infiltration with round cells. Similar changes are found in the central nervous system of infected mice.

Yellow fever virus infection may produce inclusion bodies, which are intranuclear, acidophilic, variable in size, granular in appearance and irregular in outline (Plate 7, *bottom*). As a rule they partially surround the nucleolus. The chromatin of the nucleus becomes marginated. These bodies are only occasionally seen in livers of human beings with yellow fever (Cowdry and Kitchen, 1930). The inclusions are found in the nuclei of parenchymatous cells of the liver of infected monkeys and in cells of the brain and spinal cord of infected mice.

It is apparent that the lesions described above provide an almost complete explanation of the signs and symptoms of yellow fever. Damage of the liver causes hemorrhage and changes in metabolism; albuminuria is due to degenerative changes in the kidney, brachycardia and low blood pressure to involvement of the heart; lymphopenia results from involvement of the lymphoid tissue of the spleen and lymph glands. Unfortunately, no studies have been made on the bone marrow of man or monkey dead of yellow fever. The marked leukopenia suggests that the myelogenic centers may be affected.

Support for most of the above statements has been obtained by a study of the mode of spread and the sites of multiplication of yellow fever virus in rhesus monkeys. It has been shown that, following an intradermal inoculation, virus spreads immediately to the local lymph glands where multiplication occurs. After several days, it enters the blood stream and infects the liver, spleen, kidneys, bone marrow, and lymph nodes. If a monkey survives, virus can still be demonstrated in the lymph nodes, spleen, and bone marrow for several days after the blood has become virus-free. There is a clear distinction of the organs involved, depending on the virulence of the virus. With highly virulent strains, such as the Asibi, the highest titer of virus is found in the liver. On the other hand, the almost avirulent 17D strain can be demonstrated only in spleen, lymph nodes, and bone marrow. Strains of virus intermediate between these two, for example, the mouse-adapted French neurotropic strain, follow more closely the pattern of the Asibi; however, the titers of virus obtained in the liver and blood are not so high (Theiler, 1951).

Yellow fever in monkeys, and presumably in man, is basically an infection of the hemapoietic system and only secondarily involves other organs. Almost all lesions can be explained on the basis of infection by and multiplication of the virus. Death occurs probably as a direct result of damage done by the virus in the liver and kidney. It is an interesting observation that from man dead of yellow fever the virus has only once been isolated. It appears that yellow fever is a self-limited infection, which if severe enough, will lead to death, even at a time when the defense mechanism has overcome the virus.

EXPERIMENTAL INFECTION; HOST RANGE

Yellow fever virus shows marked tissue affinities. Unmodified virus is pantropic, showing affinity for all three embryonal layers. By viscerotropism is meant affinity of the virus for abdominal viscera, particularly the liver, and the rhesus monkey is the experimental animal largely used for demonstrating it. All yellow fever viruses exhibit some neurotropism; the common albino mouse is the animal of choice for demonstrating it. By various experimental means both of these attributes can be modified.

Various strains of yellow fever virus differ in their affinities. Thus, some strains are highly pathogenic for the viscera of rhesus monkeys, almost invariably producing a fatal infection, with death due to an acute necrosis of liver cells. In such infections the virus invades the blood stream where it is present in high concentration. Other strains when inoculated by extraneural routes have little capacity to destroy visceral cells, rarely producing death from liver necrosis; the only manifestation of infection may be the presence of virus in the blood. When a highly viscerotropic strain is inoculated into the brain of a rhesus monkey, death occurs as a result of liver damage and not encephalitis. The essential neurotropism of such a strain can, however, be shown if, at the time virus is inoculated intracerebrally, the liver is protected by an injection of specific, immune serum. A monkey so inoculated will develop fatal encephalitis. The virus can be transmitted in series in this manner, always producing encephalitis. After a number of such passages, the virus loses some of its viscerotropism so that, when inoculated intracerebrally without the concomitant injection of immune serum, a monkey dies of encephalitis (Penna, 1936).

The modification of yellow fever virus is most readily accomplished by serial intracerebral passages in mice (Theiler, 1930). This procedure leads to two predictable results. First, the incubation period and the course of the disease in the mice becomes shorter; and second, the pathogenicity for monkeys by parenteral inoculation is diminished. *Pari passu* with this loss of viscerotropism there is an enhancement of neurotropism. All yellow fever viruses so far studied, if serially passaged in mouse brains, acquire the ability of producing a fatal encephalitis in rhesus monkeys. This ability is most readily shown by intracerebral inoculation, although from 5 to 10 per cent of monkeys inoculated subcutaneously may die of encephalitis. The survivors acquire a solid immunity to a subsequent infection with highly viscerotropic virus. That the mouse-adapted virus has not entirely lost its viscerotropic affinity can readily be shown by the demonstration of circulating virus. In fatal encephalitis, produced either by intracerebral or by parenteral inoculation, the virus is widespread in the peripheral nervous system. At the time of death it can be recovered from the brain, spinal cord, retina, peripheral nerves, salivary glands, and adrenal glands, but not from the blood, cerebrospinal fluid or liver. Neutralizing antibodies are present at the time of death.

A further loss of virulence has been produced by prolonged cultivation in tissue culture (Lloyd, Theiler and Ricci, 1936). One of the variants, known as the 17D strain, is used extensively for human vaccination (Theiler and Smith, 1937a) and has lost to a considerable extent both its viscerotropic and neurotropic affinities (Theiler and Smith, 1937b). On subcutaneous inoculation of it into rhesus monkeys, a mild systemic infection occurs which can be demonstrated by the presence of minimal amounts of virus in the circulation; on intracerebral inoculation, it produces an encephalitis which is fatal in only about 5 per cent of animals.

In addition to the rhesus monkey, it has been found that all South American and African species of monkey so far tested are susceptible to the virus of yellow fever. In most instances, the infection is comparatively mild, and accompanied only by a temporary invasion of the blood stream and the development of specific antibodies. However, the invasion of the blood is sufficient for mosquitoes to be readily infected by feeding on them, as a rule, thus indicating the possibility of these animals acting as hosts for the preservation of the virus in nature.

Adult mice are very susceptible to the virus after intracerebral, less after intranasal, and seldom after intraperitoneal inoculation. Immature mice, however, are highly susceptible to the virus administered parenterally. In both adult and infant mice, at the time of death, the virus can be demonstrated only in nervous tissue and in the adrenal gland, an organ which is developmentally a part of the nervous system. With age, mice rapidly acquire a resistance to virus inoculated peripherally (Bugher, 1941). This resistance is quite apparent at nine days of age. Mice younger than this are just as susceptible to neurotropic and viscerotropic strains of virus inoculated subcutaneously as adult mice are to similar strains given intracerebrally. The susceptibility of infant mice to peripheral inoculation has been used to determine the infectivity of mosquitoes in transmission experiments. Not all strains of mice are equally susceptible to yellow fever (Sawyer and Lloyd, 1931); of the strains available to these authors, the Swiss strain proved the most suitable.

Findlay and Clarke (1934a, b) found that the common European hedgehog is susceptible to the virus of yellow fever. Not only do these animals die after an inoculation of virulent viscerotropic strains, but they also succumb to infection after subcutaneous inoculation of the modified neurotropic French strain, which in these animals still has the capacity of producing liver necrosis.

The rabbit and the rat are completely resistant to the virus. The guinea pig is, as a rule, susceptible to virus given intracerebrally, developing a fatal encephalitis. Different strains of guinea pig vary in their response to parenteral inoculation of virus. Some are highly susceptible, developing a symptomless, systemic infection, as demonstrated by the presence of virus in the circulation; others appear to be completely resistant (Theiler, 1951).

In the search for possible hosts of jungle yellow fever, the susceptibility of numerous wild animals has been studied (Bugher, 1951). To date, birds, cold-blooded animals, and mammals belonging to the orders of *Carnivora* and *Chiroptera*, and most rodents have been shown to be resistant to virus inoculated parenterally. In most of these groups, very few species have been studied and, as a rule, only adults. Animals which have been found susceptible include the peccary, several species of edentates (anteaters, armadillos, and sloths), a few rodents, and all the marsupials. Most of these animals are only moderately susceptible, as minimal amounts of circulating virus are present.

The classic urban type of yellow fever is transmitted by *Aëdes aegypti*. The experiments of Reed et al. (1911) showed that *Aëdes aegypti* becomes infected by biting a patient during the first three days of the disease and that an interval of approximately 12 days must elapse before it can transmit infection by bite. Subsequent work has shown that, under experimental conditions, this extrinsic incubation period can be as short as four days and as long as three weeks if the mosquitoes are kept at 37° C. or 20° C., respectively (Davis, 1932). A mosquito once infected remains infective for life. There is no evidence that the virus can pass to the next generation through the egg. The mosquito harbors the infection without any ill effect.

Evidence is conclusive that yellow fever virus actually multiplies in the mosquito (Whitman, 1937). Following an infective blood-meal the virus in the mosquito diminishes, reaching a minimum during the first week. It then increases rapidly until quantities far greater than the amount ingested can be demonstrated. This may occur following ingestion of very small quantities of virus. Very little is known concerning the relative efficiency of various mosquitoes, shown to be capable of transmitting the virus, to act as intermediate hosts. Moreover, it is not known whether the *Aëdes aegypti* mosquito is equally efficient as a vector in its many homes throughout the world. Finally, it is not known whether or not all strains of yellow fever virus are equally capable of infecting susceptible mosquitoes. From the human experiments of Reed et al. (1911), one is warranted in concluding that under the conditions of their work, the *aegypti* mosquitoes used by them became infected readily, as they had no difficulty in transmitting the disease by the bite of from 1 to 15 mosquitoes. Virus

may multiply in species of mosquitoes incapable of transmitting it by bite.

For a time, it was thought that yellow fever virus as it exists in the mosquito is not filterable. The explanation for this is that, when infected mosquitoes are ground in saline solution, the virus is inactivated by the salt; but, when a diluent containing normal serum is used, the virus is readily filterable.

The optimum conditions under which mosquitoes become infected is not known. Bates and Roca-García (1945) had difficulty at first in experimentally infecting *Haemagogus* mosquitoes, although numerous infected mosquitoes of this species, capable of producing infection in experimental animals by bites, had been caught in nature. Finally, it was discovered that laboratory-fed mosquitoes, if kept at 30° C., are able to transmit the infection readily by bite. In these experiments, not only was the extrinsic incubation period shortened by the higher temperature, but the percentage of mosquitoes becoming infected was increased. Whitman and Antunes (1938) showed that mosquito larvae can be infected by immersion in virus preparations; male and female adults, which are derived from these larvae, are infected and the females are capable of transmitting the disease by biting.

Of African mosquitoes, in addition to *Aëdes aegypti*, the following have been shown experimentally capable of transmitting the virus by bite: *Aëdes luteocephalus*, *A. stokesi*, *A. vittatus*, *A. africanus*, *A. simpsoni*, *A. taylori*, *A. metallicus*, *Eretmopodites chrysogaster*, *Taeniorhynchus africanus* and *Culex thalassius*. South American mosquitoes capable of acting as experimental hosts are: *Aëdes scapularis*, *A. fluviatilis*, *A. leucocelaenus*, *Trichoprosopon frontiosus*, and various members of the genus *Haemagogus*. Species identified as *Haemagogus capricornii*, *H. spegazzinii*, *H. splendens*, *H. uriartei*, and *H. equinus* have been shown capable of transmitting the virus.

However, very few of these mosquitoes have actually been incriminated in the epidemiology of yellow fever. In South America, yellow fever virus has been isolated on numerous occasions from wild-caught species of *Haemagogus* and several times from *Aëdes leucocelaenus*. In Africa, *Aëdes simpsoni*, *A. africanus*, and *A. aegypti* have been found infected in nature.

Mosquitoes are the only bloodsucking arthropods which have been definitely shown to play a part in the epidemiology of yellow fever. Miscellaneous experiments have been made with a great variety of other arthropods, such as ticks, mites, fleas, lice, triatomas and bloodsucking flies. None of these, however, was found capable of transmitting the disease (Whitman, 1951).

ETIOLOGY

Early investigations of the properties of yellow fever virus were made by means of human volunteers, who were used by the American Army Commission under Walter Reed in Havana in 1901 (Reed et al., 1911). Work was therefore extremely limited, but it was possible to show that the virus passed through filters which retained bacteria. When experimental animals became available, it was shown that the etiologic agent of yellow fever is one of the small viruses. It readily passes through Seitz as well as all grades of Berkefeld and Chamberland filters. By the use of collodion membranes of graded porosity (gradocol membranes), its diameter has been estimated to be from 17 to 25 mμ. The particle size of neurotropic and viscerotropic strains appear to be identical. By ultracentrifugation, Pickels and Bauer (1940), on the assumption that the virus particle is spherical, estimated its diameter to be between 12 and 19 mμ.

The virus of yellow fever is extremely labile; it is readily inactivated by heat and the usual antiseptics. It can be preserved in 50 per cent glycerol for several months. Frozen infected material retains its activity for a long time. The best method for the preservation of yellow fever virus is through desiccation while in the frozen state, and storage in a refrigerator; under such conditions the virus may remain viable for many years. Storage of frozen material in a dry-ice container is convenient and satisfactory provided that the ampules are sealed. Unless this precaution is taken, carbon dioxide readily dissolves in the material and the virus becomes inactivated. Dilution in physiologic salt solution quickly inactivates the virus (Bauer and Mahaffy, 1930). The deleterious action of the salt can be prevented by incorporating from 5 to 10 per cent normal serum in the diluent. In all experiments with yellow fever virus, a diluent containing normal serum should be used.

Neurotropic yellow fever virus can be readily cultivated in a Maitland-type of tissue culture. However, it was found difficult to adapt an unmodified pantropic strain to tissue culture; the first success was obtained by Lloyd, Theiler and Ricci (1936), who were able to grow the Asibi strain in a medium containing minced mouse-embryo tissue. After some passages, successful cultivation was obtained in a medium containing minced chick embryo. In studies to determine whether or not the amount of nervous tissue in the medium had an influence on the neurotropic affinity of the virus, several parallel series of cultures were established containing varying amounts of nervous tissue. Thus, in one series, only chick-embryo brain was used; in another, whole chick; and finally in a third, minced chick embryos from which the brain and spinal cord had been removed. In the last series, containing minimal amounts of nervous tissue, a marked modification of both the viscerotropic and neurotropic affinities occurred. This is the 17D strain, now extensively used for vaccination.

The method of establishing the unmodified Asibi strain in tissue cultures was not successful with other strains of yellow fever virus. It was found, however, that if the tissue component consisted of minced mouse-embryo brain, other strains could be cultivated (Smith and Theiler, 1937). After the maintenance of the viruses in this medium, successful multiplication was obtained in chick-embryo-tissue media containing varying amounts of nervous tissue. The prolonged cultivation of these strains in media containing minimal amounts of nervous tissue did not lead to the marked change noted under similar conditions with the Asibi strain. This, as well as other observations, is conclusive evidence that the loss of neurotropism noted in the 17D strain was not due to the use of a medium containing minimal amounts of nervous tissue. The results of extensive experiments on the modification of virulence of yellow fever virus when cultivated in tissue culture indicate that all strains lose a considerable amount of their viscerotropic affinity, but as a rule the neurotropism remains unaltered. There is no explanation for the marked loss of neurotropism noted in the 17D series of cultures.

Yellow fever virus can be maintained in the developing chick embryo. Pantropic, unmodified strains are established with difficulty, but strains which have been maintained in tissue culture or by serial passage in mouse brains are readily established. The chick embryo is used as a routine for the production of vaccine from the 17D strain. Penna and Moussatché (1939) studied the effect of serial passage in the chick embryo on a pantropic strain. After a few passages in tissue culture, they established the Asibi strain in chick embryos and noted not only that the viscerotropism of the cultivated strain decreased but that the neurotropism for monkeys was markedly diminished. They were thus able to produce a strain like the 17D. It is noteworthy that in Penna and Moussatché's experiments the marked attenuation occurred in an environment containing large amounts of nervous tissue, for it is known that in the developing chick embryo, the brain is one of the main sites of virus multiplication.

Yellow fever virus multiplies when inoculated into the testes of mice (Smith, 1938) and serial propagation can be maintained. Intratesticular injection of virus causes no generalized infection, and only slight local lesions are discernible. No modification of the pathogenicity of a virulent strain was demonstrated after forty passages.

Yellow fever virus infection gives rise to specific protective antibodies. These can be readily demonstrated by means of various protection tests, the one most extensively used being the intraperitoneal protection test of Sawyer and Lloyd (1931). Mixtures of the sera to be tested and virus suspension are inoculated intraperitoneally into groups of adult mice. At the same time sterile 2.0 per cent starch solution in saline is injected into the brain. The quantities of virus and serum are such that in the 0.6 cc. inoculum there is 0.4 cc. serum and 0.2 cc. of a 20 per cent suspension of infective mouse brain. As a rule, six mice are used to test each serum. If all or all but one of the mice in a group live, the serum is considered protective. On the other hand, if all or all but one die, the serum is negative. Intermediate mortality rates are inconclusive. This test has been extensively used in a world survey of immunity to yellow fever and is extremely specific (Sawyer and Whitman, 1936; Sawyer, Bauer and Whitman, 1937; Soper, 1937; Mahaffy, Smithburn and Hughes, 1946). The main drawbacks of the intraperitoneal protection test are the difficulty of standardization and the relatively large quantities of serum required. The latter is important when it is desired to test the sera of small experimental animals. Furthermore, the test is so severe that sera containing minimal amounts of antibodies are likely to give negative results.

Various modifications of the intraperitoneal test are in use. Thus, Whitman (1943) was able to render the test more delicate and to omit the starch inoculation by using young mice 21 days of age. At this age mice are still susceptible to a relatively large amount of virus inoculated parenterally, without the simultaneous damage of the brain. By the use of this test, some sera, which are negative by the routine intraperitoneal test of Sawyer and Lloyd, are shown to be positive. These delicate tests are particularly valuable in studies where the immune response to the virus may be minimal such as that occurring in some individuals following vaccination with the 17D virus, or in some species of animals in which antibody response to the virus is mild.

The intracerebral protection test (Theiler, 1933; Bugher, 1940) consists of mixing the sera to be tested with a suspension of standardized virus of known concentration and injecting the mixtures intracerebrally into mice. The standard virus used consists of filtered infective mouse brain, desiccated while frozen in measured amounts and stored at a low temperature. Several preliminary titrations of the virus preparation make it possible to dilute it so that when mixed with the serum and inoculated in 0.03 cc. amounts, each mouse receives 100 M.L.D. To determine the end point in virus titrations, the method used is that of Reed and Muench (1938), giving the theoretical dilution that will kill half the number of inoculated mice.

The complement-fixation reaction has been extensively studied in yellow fever (Davis, 1931; Lennette and Perlowagora, 1943). Antigens capable of fixing complement are found in liver and serum of infected monkeys and in the brains of infected mice. The antigen can be demonstrated only in the serum of severely ill monkeys; this probably applies also to human infections.

The complement-fixing and protective antibodies are not identical. In man and in experimentally infected monkeys, protective antibodies are demonstrable before complement-fixing antibodies. Furthermore, in very mild infections, such as that produced by the 17D vaccine, complement-fixing antibodies are rarely demonstrable (Lennette and Perlowagora, 1943). Complement-fixing antibodies disappear compar-atively rapidly; consequently, survey for their presence in a population affords information only of severe yellow fever in the immediate past. On the other hand, protective antibodies persist for a long time, if not throughout life, and a survey for them gives an accurate index of the total exposure of a population to yellow fever. An antigen that is probably the same as the one causing fixation of complement has been demonstrated by Hughes (1933) by means of a precipitation test. Evidence supplied by both these tests indicates that the antigen concerned is not the virus; Hughes has suggested that it is produced by the action of virus on tissues.

DIAGNOSIS

During an epidemic, a diagnosis of yellow fever can often be made on clinical grounds, if the patient shows classic signs and symptoms. However, very mild or atypical cases occur in which a diagnosis on clinical grounds usually is impossible. Three laboratory procedures are available to establish a diagnosis: (1) isolation of the virus, (2) demonstration of the development of specific antibodies during the course of the disease, and (3) pathologic examination of the liver in fatal cases.

For the isolation of virus, serum obtained from a patient is inoculated intracerebrally into mice. Virus has been isolated from patients by this means up to the fifth day of the disease. Mice, after a variable incubation period which depends on the concentration of virus in the blood as well as its virulence, develop signs of encephalitis. Inasmuch as the signs of disease in the mouse are not specific for yellow fever, the agent thus isolated from a patient must be identified by various means. The commonest method is to determine whether or not the isolated virus is neutralizable by specific yellow fever immune serum. This specificity test is usually performed by making serial dilutions of the isolated virus. Then to a quantity of each virus dilution, an equal amount of immune serum is added. To another series of tubes containing the virus dilutions, normal serum is added. The mixtures, with or without incubation for an hour at 37° C., are inoculated into the brains of mice. If the mice inoculated with the immune serum-virus mixtures live, the agent is that of yellow fever.

In attempts to isolate yellow fever virus from man, it must be borne in mind that some strains of the agent act in a paradoxical manner. Thus, none of a group of mice inoculated with undiluted serum will become infected, whereas the same serum diluted 10- or 100-fold will cause encephalitis in the inoculated animals. Therefore, serum to be tested should be inoculated undiluted and in several dilutions into groups of mice. By passage in mouse brains, this peculiarity is lost rapidly.

Monkeys can also be used for the isolation of yellow fever virus. It must be borne in mind, however, that strains of yellow fever may not be lethal for all species of monkey; consequently, an inoculated animal subsequently is tested for circulating virus at regular intervals by the inoculation of its serum into mice. The virus isolated in the mice is then identified in the manner described above. Finally, in the case of survival, the serum of the monkey is tested for specific antibodies. Rhesus monkeys have been used most extensively for the isolation of yellow fever viruses. However, as all species of monkey so far studied have been found susceptible to the virus, any available monkey can be used, provided that it is known not to have been infected previously by yellow fever. In laboratories where experiments are conducted in monkeys, it is comparatively common for cross infections to occur. In efforts to isolate yellow fever virus by the use of monkeys, it is consequently of prime importance to take all precautions that animals have the minimum opportunity of becoming accidentally infected.

As facilities for animal inoculation are usually not available, a diagnosis can often be established by the examination of two specimens of serum in the protection test. The first is obtained as soon as possible after the onset of the disease and the second during convalescence. If the first specimen is without antibodies, whereas specific antibodies are present in the second, the person was infected with yellow fever. As antibodies in yellow fever are very rapidly produced, it may happen that both specimens protect the mice. In order to make a diagnosis in such cases, both specimens must be titrated for their neutralizing capacity. Should the second specimen neutralize yellow fever virus in a higher dilution than the first, this is very good evidence that the disease was yellow fever. If both specimens have the same titer, the disease under study is probably not yellow fever; the presence of antibodies being due to a yellow fever infection in the past.

The diagnosis of fatal yellow fever by the examination of the liver plays a very important part in those countries where the disease is endemic. In certain countries, notably Brazil, where yellow fever occurs over an enormous area, the systematic study of liver sections of persons who have died of an acute febrile disease of less than ten days' duration, is a very important function of the Yellow Fever Service (Rickard, 1937). The viscerotome, a simple instrument by which small portions of liver can be obtained from a cadaver, is used. This instrument can be employed by a lay person. The portions of liver thus obtained are fixed in formalin solution, embedded in paraffin, and stained with hematoxylin and eosin. Diagnosis is based on the presence of typical lesions.

TREATMENT

There is no specific treatment. Complete rest in bed and careful nursing are essential for even the mildest cases. Solid food should be withheld. Fluids should be forced; Vichy water is recommended. Orange juice is valuable in combating hypoglycemia and supplying extra alkali. If persistent vomiting occurs, saline solution may be given by epidermoclysis, and glucose by intravenous injection. Cracked ice by mouth may relieve vomiting. If this fails, codeine sulphate by hypodermic injection or cocaine hydrochloride by mouth should be given. High temperature may be relieved by tepid water sponges. To relieve the headache, ice caps may be used; it may, however, be necessary to give an analgesic such as codeine sulphate. In view of the tendency to constipation, a laxative should be given early in the disease, and thereafter daily enemas should be administered.

EPIDEMIOLOGY

Following the development of the protection test and its application to the study of the world-wide distribution of immunity to yellow fever, several important facts were established. It was shown that yellow fever as it occurred years ago in Cuba, New Orleans, and Panama was immunologically the same as that which is encountered at the present time. The identity of the disease in Africa and America has been clearly established. The presence of immunity to yellow fever was shown to be confined to the American and African continents. However, an analysis of the age distribution of protective antibodies indicated that yellow fever is now no longer present in places where it had formerly been prevalent. Thus, no evidence was found of any immunity to yellow fever in persons born in Cuba or New Orleans since the last reported epidemics in these places during the first few years of this century. Extensive investigations indicate that the disease has completely disappeared from the Caribbean islands and from North America and most of Central America, north of the Panama Canal.

In Africa and in South America the zone of immunity to yellow fever was found to be unexpectedly large. The limits of the area in which antibodies to yellow fever were found in children, and hence areas where the infection has been present in recent years, comprise the bulk of the tropical zones in the two continents. In South America this endemic zone consists of the major portion of the Amazon and Orinoco basins, in addition to the greater part of Colombia, the Republic of Panama, and the Guianas (Soper, 1937). In this enormous region, Aëdes aegypti is not universally present so that, clearly, in many places the infection was transmitted in the absence of this vector. In Africa, previous to the modern era of research, yellow fever had only been reported along the west coast in a comparatively narrow zone, extending from Dakar to the mouth of the Congo. Actually, yellow fever occurs in an area extending from the Atlantic to the Indian Ocean. The northern boundary is the Sahara from Dakar to the Eritrean coast on the Red Sea. The southern boundary has not yet been clearly demarcated, but extends into Northern Rhodesia.

Two main epidemiologic entities are distinguished, based on the habits of the vector: the classic urban aegypti-transmitted infection and jungle yellow fever, a disease essentially of wild animals and transmitted to man only secondarily.

Aëdes aegypti is confined to the tropics, with extensions both north and south into subtropical regions. This mosquito, like other species belonging to the subgenus Stegomyia, is an old world species and was probably introduced into the western hemisphere during antiquity. The female Aëdes aegypti prefers to oviposit in water in artificial containers. It is thus essentially a domestic mosquito breeding in or in the immediate vicinity of houses. This domesticity seems to be more marked in America than in Africa, where it has been captured in small numbers even in primeval forest. It is probable that Aëdes aegypti, like the other species of the subgenus Stegomyia, was originally a tree-hole breeder. Although this species is present in the tropical zones of the entire world, aegypti-transmitted yellow fever has only been reported in the Americas, Africa, and Europe. Northward or southward extension of the disease outside the tropics has occurred only during the warm season of the year when climatic conditions were favorable for the mosquito; with the advent of winter epidemics ceased.

Being transmitted by *Aëdes aegypti,* a domestic mosquito, urban yellow fever is a household disease affecting all ages and both sexes equally. The virus cycle, man—mosquito—man, necessitates an abundance of both the vertebrate and invertebrate hosts for its maintenance in a community. It follows, therefore, that it is only in large centers of population with a constant influx of susceptibles that this form of yellow fever can persist for any length of time. In an aegypti-transmitted epidemic the natural course of events leads to a gradual diminution of the number of susceptibles due to immunization or death. Consequently, as the epidemic progresses, more mosquitoes are necessary to maintain the virus cycle. Although centers of population with an adequate number of susceptible people are usually large towns, this is not necessarily so. An area containing numerous small collections of people with frequent communication between them may remain infected for a long time. The infection in such areas wanders from place to place. This condition is present in large parts of tropical Africa, and at one time prevailed in Yucatan and in the northeastern portion of Brazil. In the last region, owing to the extreme scarcity of water during the dry season, every house had its own water storage. So scarce was water at times that people visiting neighboring villages and farm houses would carry their own drinking water with them. In this manner *Aëdes aegypti* was widely spread throughout the rural area, and when yellow fever was eradicated from the towns and villages, it still managed to maintain itself in the comparatively sparsely populated rural area. Here, therefore, was the phenomenon of rural yellow fever transmitted by *Aëdes aegypti.*

The disappearance of yellow fever following the initiation of antimosquito measures was so striking that public health authorities became convinced that the man—aegypti—man cycle was the only one. As the war against *Aëdes aegypti* progressed, yellow fever apparently disappeared from large areas, and the authorities were justified in their opinions. Indeed, by the use of the protection test, it has been shown that yellow fever is now no longer present in the Caribbean islands or in Central America north of the Panama Canal. The last case reported from the United States occurred in New Orleans in 1905, and the last epidemic north of the Canal occurred in 1924 in Salvador, although examination by means of the protection test of sera of children born since then indicated that yellow fever persisted for a short time after that epidemic.

However, in spite of success attending the anti-aegypti campaigns, observations were made that did not fit into the accepted theory. Thus, yellow fever was reported repeatedly from the emerald mines of Muzo in Colombia. Competent investigators came to the conclusion that the disease in Muzo could not be yellow fever, and this conclusion was largely based on the absence of *Aëdes aegypti* from the region. Renewed interest in Muzo occurred following aegypti-transmitted epidemics of yellow fever in the nearby towns of Bucaramanga and Socorro. These towns are very isolated, and it was a mystery how the infection was introduced. By the use of the protection test, it was shown that immunity to yellow fever was very prevalent in rural, aegypti-free districts including the Muzo region (Kerr and Patiño Camargo, 1933). Conclusive evidence that yellow fever can occur in rural areas in the absence of *Aëdes aegypti* was furnished by the isolation of yellow fever virus during an epidemic which occurred in the Valle do Chanaan, Brazil, in 1932 (Soper, Penna, Cardoso, Serafim, Frobisher and Pinheiro, 1933). Extensive surveys of immunity to yellow fever clearly demonstrated that the disease was widely distributed in South America in many places where *Aëdes aegypti* does not exist.

The epidemiologic entity, jungle yellow fever, occurs in South America either in epidemic or endemic form. In the endemic form the disease is almost constantly present and human cases occur year after year. The factors concerned in determining human infection in an endemic region have been studied by Soper (1938), Taylor and da Cunha (1946), and Laemmert et al. (1946). Cases of jungle yellow fever are confined almost entirely to adult males. This is due to the fact that, as a rule, only the adult male enters the forest to work, clear the jungle, hunt, etc. The infection acquired in the jungle is not transmitted as a rule to the women and children as the common domestic mosquito *Aëdes aegypti* is absent. The intimate relationship between the incidence of jungle yellow fever and contact with forest is an adequate explanation of the peculiar sex and age distribution of immunity in a population exposed to the disease, which is quite different from that seen in aegypti-transmitted infections.

Numerous observations in various parts of South America have shown that species of mosquito belonging to the genus *Haemagogus* play an important role in the epidemiology of jungle yellow fever. On numerous occasions yellow fever virus has been isolated from *Haemagogus* mosquitoes. Man is only secondarily infected in a virus cycle in the jungle. As yet, the virus cycle or cycles have not been entirely established. It is known, however, that various species of monkey play an important role. Thus, in almost all regions where cases of jungle yellow fever have occurred, a considerable proportion of the monkeys show neutralizing antibodies to yellow fever virus. Furthermore, in the study of endemic jungle yellow fever in the Ilhéus region, yellow fever virus was isolated on four separate occasions from marmosets (Laemmert et al., 1946). Extensive investigations in this region failed to produce evidence that any other vertebrate was involved, and *Haemagogus spegazzinii* appeared to be the only vector.

Although it is reasonably certain that primates and *Haemagogus* mosquitoes play an important role in the maintenance of the jungle yellow fever virus in nature, there still are many unexplained observations. Thus, in the Muzo region, which is a true endemic area, monkeys are either rare or absent. Bugher et al. (1944) have presented evidence that in such areas species of marsupials may act as vertebrate hosts. With certain species of marsupials, yellow fever virus infection can be maintained experimentally by means of mosquitoes. The commonest species, the opossum (*Didelphis marsupialis*), is not very susceptible to the virus. Bugher et al. (1944), however, have presented evidence that in jungle yellow fever areas this species shows a high incidence of neutralizing antibodies. Essentially similar results were obtained by Whitman (1943) in Brazil. Thirty-two per cent of sera from wild-caught *Didelphis* from an area recently overrun by the disease were shown to have neutralizing antibodies, whereas none of the sera from the same species caught in a yellow-fever-free area was positive. These observations afford good evidence that the *Didelphis* had been infected in nature, but do not necessarily mean that these animals acted as a link in the virus cycle.

In addition to endemic jungle yellow fever, there is the epidemic type. The epidemic form has a tendency to spread farther each year. The most extensive epidemic studied was that of 1933-1938 (Soper, 1938). Presumably originating in the Amazon basin, it spread southeastward through Brazil. The spread lasted several years. During the colder portions of the year, the infection apparently disappeared, to recommence with the advent of the next summer. The first cases in the new season were often hundreds of miles ahead of the last cases of the previous season. This wave spread diagonally throughout Brazil, reaching the Atlantic coast at Rio de Janeiro and then spreading northwards along the coast to die out naturally. It was during this epidemic wave that the genus *Haemagogus* was first shown to play some part in the epidemiology of the disease. The factors involved in the epidemic spread of the disease are entirely unknown.

Somewhat similar conditions are found in Africa. *Aëdes aegypti* is more widely distributed in Africa than in South America, and thus it is difficult to make a clear distinction between the two epidemiologic types of the disease. However, conclusive evidence has been obtained that primates act as vertebrate hosts of the virus. The most likely invertebrate host in the forest is *Aëdes africanus,* which is most active at twilight and at night and prefers the upper foliage. As in Brazil, man plays no part in the maintenance of the virus in the jungle. The habitat of *Aëdes africanus* makes it extremely unlikely that it infects man in the forest. The sequence of events seems to be as follows:

Certain species of monkey have the habit of raiding human plantations. In the edge of the forest and in the plantations another mosquito, *Aëdes simpsoni*, occurs, which is a plant-axil breeder. Presumably, this mosquito becomes infected from monkeys and then transmits the disease to man. Under experimental conditions both *Aëdes africanus* and *Aëdes simpsoni* are efficient vectors of the disease. Yellow fever virus has been isolated from *A. simpsoni* caught in a region where cases of yellow fever were occurring (Smithburn and Haddow, 1949) and from *Aëdes africanus* caught in the uninhabited forest (Smithburn, Haddow and Lumsden, 1949). It is an interesting fact that, although *Aëdes aegypti* may be present in the jungle, it does not occur in sufficient numbers to be considered as a possible vector. The incidence of immunity to yellow fever in man in the Bwamba region of Uganda, where the above observations were made, is higher near forested regions than in the grassland portion of the country.

The classic urban, aegypti-borne yellow fever is comparatively common in Africa This is the type which has been frequently observed in West Africa. Extensive epidemics of rural yellow fever also occur. This type may or may not be transmitted by *Aëdes aegypti.* The most extensive epidemic of this type, and one of the most severe described in recent years, is that which occurred in the Nuba Mountains in the Anglo-Egyptian Sudan in 1940 (Kirk, 1941). Over 15,000 cases were recorded, with more than 1,500 deaths. A survey for immunity to yellow fever after the epidemic indicated that approximately 40,000 cases must have occurred. *Aëdes aegypti,* although present, was, on epidemiologic grounds, not the principal vector. *Aëdes vittatus, Aëdes taylori,* and *Aëdes metallicus,* all known to be efficient vectors under experimental conditions, were present in the region, and one of them was probably the main vector in the epidemic.

CONTROL MEASURES

Prior to the development of methods of vaccination, anti-aegypti measures were the only ones available for the control of yellow fever. Their efficacy was clearly established by Gorgas and others immediately following the demonstration that *Aëdes aegypti* acted as a vector. Following the successes in Havana, New Orleans, Panama, and Guayaquil, the methods became firmly established. In certain countries, notably Brazil, extensive campaigns against *Aëdes aegypti* have been undertaken. The measures employed are at first confined to the control of breeding. This is achieved by a weekly search for larvae in and in the immediate vicinity of every house. Inspectors have authority to pour oil into any container found to harbor *Aëdes aegypti* larvae. This procedure has a twofold effect. First, the oil kills the larvae, and secondly, the householder is impelled to clean the container. The difficulty of cleaning receptacles after oil has been poured into them induces the householder to do everything possible to prevent mosquito breeding. Such weekly inspection and eradication of all breeding places are adequate to reduce the number of adult mosquitoes below a level where transmission is possible. This procedure, however, is not sufficient to eradicate the mosquito entirely, because hidden breeding foci are not discovered during routine inspections. In order to find these, specially trained inspectors are employed. Their function is to make captures of adult mosquitoes in every house. Should adults of *Aëdes aegypti* be captured, this is proof that breeding is going on. By a survey of all the neighboring houses, a hidden focus of breeding is usually discovered in that house in which the largest number of adult mosquitoes is found. By these means it is possible to find every breeding focus in a town and consequently to eradicate *Aëdes aegypti*. From an administrative point of view, it has been found cheaper to eradicate *Aëdes aegypti* than to keep the mosquito population below a critical level. The latter necessitates a permanent inspection force to prevent the re-establishment of a large mosquito population. Following eradication, reinfestation does not readily occur, and a skeleton force is sufficient to verify the continued absence of the mosquito, particularly if similar anti-aegypti measures are employed in nearby towns. In Brazil, anti-aegypti measures have been employed so extensively that for several years no cases of yellow fever have been reported as being aegypti-borne. In fact, the species has been eradicated from entire states.

In Africa the situation in regard to the control of *Aëdes aegypti* is not so favorable as in other areas. In the first place, *Aëdes aegypti* is far more widely distributed. Secondly, this species does not seem to be so domestic as in the Americas. In fact, specimens have been captured in primeval forest. Furthermore, in tropical Africa, there are very few large centers of population; natives live as a rule in small villages. In large towns, the installation of a piped-water supply is one of the most efficacious methods of aegypti control.

The development of the newer insecticides has proved of great value to the sanitarian interested in yellow fever control. Thus, DDT would appear to be almost ideal for the control of *Aëdes aegypti*; applied as a residual spray to the walls of all houses or to the outside and inside of household water containers at infrequent intervals, it will reduce the number of mosquitoes so significantly that the procedure alone is a very effective and inexpensive method of control. The extensive use of a DDT spray is probably the method of choice in combating a severe aegypti-borne epidemic of yellow fever. Marked reduction of adult mosquitoes should occur immediately, whereas experience has shown that anti-larval measures require approximately six weeks to reduce the mosquito population below the critical level (Antunes, 1948).

Two strains of attenuated yellow fever virus are currently in use for human vaccination. These are known as the French neurotropic and the 17D strains. The French neurotropic virus is extensively used by the French in their West and Central African colonies (Peltier et al., 1940). The original French strain of yellow fever virus was isolated from a Syrian in Dakar in 1929. This is the strain which was first shown to be pathogenic for mice by intracerebral inoculation. By serial passage, this virus became more pathogenic for these rodents, but lost entirely its capacity for producing fatal visceral yellow fever in rhesus monkeys. The method of vaccination as employed by the French consists in the use of this mouse-adapted virus.

Other investigators, largely as a result of animal experiments, considered this strain too virulent for human use. Consequently, a method of vaccination was evolved in which the subcutaneous inoculation of the French neurotropic virus was preceded by an injection of human yellow fever immune serum (Sawyer, Kitchen and Lloyd, 1932). The method proved to be effective but cumbersome and impracticable for large-scale immunization. Efforts were consequently made to produce a strain more modified than the French neurotropic. This was achieved by prolonged cultivation of yellow fever virus in tissue culture. Meanwhile, the production of hyperimmune animal sera considerably facilitated the method of vaccination. Of the hyperimmune sera, the most practicable proved to be that prepared in monkeys. By the use of such sera the quantity needed per man was reduced from 30 to 40 cc., which was required when human immune serum was used, to 1.0 to 4.0 cc.

Finally, the degree of change in the virus, essential for its safe use in a vaccine without simultaneous injection of immune serum, was accidentally obtained in one of the tissue-culture experiments. For the production of vaccine, developing chick embryos are inoculated. After four days' incubation at 37° C. the embryos are harvested and reduced to a pulp, either in a ball mill or a Waring Blendor. The infected chick-embryo juice, after the addition of some sterile distilled water, is then measured into ampules and desiccated while in the frozen state. Before sealing, the ampules are filled with dry nitrogen gas. Vaccine is stored in a refrigerator. For use, the vaccine is reconstituted in the requisite amount of sterile salt solution, and 0.5 cc. is injected subcutaneously. As the virus in the vaccine is active, only one inoculation is necessary. Experiments have shown that very minute quantities of active virus are capable of producing immunity in man (Fox, Kossobudzki and da Cunha, 1943); the minimum inoculum for successful vaccination has been set at 500 M.L.D. (for mice). The reactions following vaccination usually are remarkably mild. In approximately 5 per cent of persons there is a reaction on about the seventh day (Smith, Penna and Paoliello, 1938); this consists of malaise, headache, backache, and a slight elevation of temperature, and, usually lasting about a day, it is seldom severe enough to interfere with a person's daily routine. Immunity, as determined by the demonstration of specific neutralizing antibodies, is manifest by the seventh to the ninth day after vaccination. The titer of antibodies in persons vacci-

nated with 17D virus is, as a rule, low. In fact, as evaluated by the standard protection test, there are always approximately 5 or 10 per cent of people whose sera must, according to the criteria of the test, be considered negative. By the use of more delicate tests, however, it can be shown that these are not truly negative, but contain specific neutralizing antibodies, though in minimal amounts. The duration of immunity following vaccination has not been determined. It is known, however, that the number of persons showing antibodies is not significantly decreased after six years (Dick and Smithburn, 1949). There is some evidence that the immune response in children is less than in adults.

Though vaccination with the 17D strain has been used extensively for a number of years and the reactions, as a rule, have been extremely mild, several untoward episodes have occurred. The first was the observation that some lots of vaccine failed to produce an antibody response in a considerable proportion of vaccinated people. The most probable explanation of this is that the virus had undergone further change in tissue culture, resulting in some loss of potency. The substitution of an earlier passage virus as seed for the manufacture of vaccine eliminated this difficulty. The second untoward episode consisted of a few cases of encephalitis, all of which followed the use of one lot of vaccine (Fox, Lennette, Manso and Souza Aguiar, 1942). No explanation is apparent for this enhanced neurotropism. However, the occurrence of these changes in virulence in both directions led to the standardization of the manufacture of vaccine. This consists essentially of using a large seed-lot of virus. All vaccines prepared over a long period of time are consequently made from the same seed. Since adopting this method, no changes of virulence of the virus have been reported. The third, and by far the most serious complication following yellow fever vaccination, was postvaccinal jaundice. There is no doubt but that this was due to the use of supposedly normal human serum, which, nevertheless, contained the icterogenic virus, in the vaccine at the time of manufacture. Since the omission of serum from the vaccine, this complication has not occurred.

The method of vaccination used at present by the French consists of applying the vaccine suspended in a solution of gum arabic to the scarified skin (Peltier et al., 1940). The vaccine is issued in the form of dried mouse brain infected with the French neurotropic strain of virus. Suspension of the vaccine in gum arabic is made immediately before vaccination. Often dried vaccinia virus is mixed with the gum at the same time, and the individuals are thus vaccinated against two diseases simultaneously, viz., yellow fever and smallpox. The development of specific antibodies to yellow fever following the French method of vaccination is better than that following the use of 17D. However, the number of reactions is greater, being approximately 15 per cent. Serious reactions are rare. This method of vaccination has been extensively used in the African colonies. The ease of administration and the cheapness of manufacture is of great importance. The great majority of individuals vaccinated by the French method have been Negroes. It is the consensus that, as a rule, the Negro reacts less severely to yellow fever virus than do white people. However, it is noteworthy that the number of severe reactions are far less than the results of experiments on monkeys would have led one to expect.

The most conclusive evidence that vaccination is an effective prophylactic measure is supplied by the fact that, since the introduction of vaccination, no accidental cases of yellow fever have occurred in laboratory workers. Prior to the development of a vaccine, these infections were extremely common and in several cases even fatal. Of similar nature is the observation that workers, investigating jungle yellow fever and using themselves as mosquito bait, on numerous occasions have isolated virus from *Haemagogus* mosquitoes caught in this manner. All such workers had been vaccinated and did not contract yellow fever. Observations such as this are good evidence that vaccination is highly efficacious; furthermore, they also indicate that the 5 to 10 per cent of people who respond to vaccination by the production of only minimal amounts of antibodies are protected.

To date, the results of mass vaccination have been satisfactory. In areas in Colombia where jungle yellow fever is prevalent and where efforts were made to vaccinate the entire population, fatal cases of yellow fever continued to occur. But it is noteworthy that all these cases were in the small portion of the population which had not been vaccinated. Vaccination is the only method available for the protection of persons exposed to the risk of jungle yellow fever. However, it is extremely doubtful that even mass vaccination of people would have any effect on the prevalence and extent of the virus in the jungle, that is in the mosquito and animal hosts. In rural areas mass vaccination is the only feasible method of protecting the population. In Africa, where anti-aegypti measures are to a large extent impracticable, mass vaccination is of particular value. This is in fact the policy of the French government which has embarked on a plan of vaccinating every person in their colonies every four years wherever yellow fever is present. The ease of manufacture and administration of their vaccine makes such a plan feasible.

REFERENCES

Antunes, W. S., 1948, Field control in yellow fever. Proc. Internat. Cong. Trop. Med. and Malaria, *1*, 498-505.

Bates, M., and Roca-García, M., 1945, Laboratory studies of the Saimiri-Haemagogus cycle of jungle yellow fever. Am. J. Trop. Med., *25*, 203-216.

Bauer, J. H., and Mahaffy, A. F., 1930, Studies on the filtrability of yellow fever virus. Am. J. Hyg., 12, 175-195.

Berry, G. P., and Kitchen, S. F., 1931, Yellow fever accidentally contracted in the laboratory. A study of seven cases. Am. J. Trop. Med., 11, 365-434.

Bugher, J. C., 1940, The demonstration of yellow fever antibodies in animal sera by the intracerebral protection test in mice. Am. J. Trop. Med., 20, 809-841.

Bugher, J. C., 1941, The use of baby mice in yellow fever studies. Am. J. Trop. Med., 21, 299-307.

Bugher, J. C., 1951, The Mammalian Host in Yellow Fever, in Yellow Fever, edited by George K. Strode. McGraw-Hill Book Company, Inc.

Bugher, J. C., Boshell-Manrique, J., Roca-Garcia, M., and Osorno-Mesa, E., 1944, Epidemiology of jungle yellow fever in eastern Colombia. Am. J. Hyg., 39, 16-51.

Carter, H. R., 1931, Yellow Fever, an Epidemiological and Historical Study of its Place of Origin. Baltimore, Williams & Wilkins.

Cowdry, E. V., and Kitchen, S. F., 1930, Intranuclear inclusions in yellow fever. Am. J. Hyg., 11, 227-299.

Davis, G. E., 1931, Complement fixation in yellow fever in monkey and in man. Am. J. Hyg., 13, 79-128.

Davis, N. C., 1932, The effect of various temperatures in modifying the extrinsic period of the yellow fever virus in Aedes aegypti. Am. J. Hyg., 16, 163-176.

Dick, G. W. A., and Smithburn, K. C., 1949, Immunity to yellow fever six years after vaccination. Am. J. Trop. Med., 29, 57-61.

Findlay, G. M., and Clarke, L. P., 1934a, The susceptibility of the hedgehog to yellow fever. I. The Viscerotropic virus. Tr. Roy. Soc. Trop. Med. and Hyg., 28, 193-200.

Findlay, G. M., and Clarke, L. P., 1934b, The susceptibility of the hedgehog to yellow fever. II. The neurotropic virus. Tr. Roy. Soc. Trop. Med. and Hyg., 28, 335-345.

Findlay, G. M., and Hindle, E., 1930, Guanidine-like substances in the blood in experimental yellow fever. Lancet, 2, 678-679.

Fox, J. P., Lennette, E. H., Manso, C., and Souza Aquiar, J. R., 1942, Encephalitis in man following vaccination with 17D yellow fever virus. Am. J. Hyg., 36, 117-142.

Fox, J. P., Kossobudzki, S. L., and da Cunha, J. F., 1943, Field studies on the immune response to 17D yellow fever virus. Relation to virus substrain, dose and route of inoculation. Am. J. Hyg., 38, 113-138.

Hughes, T. P., 1933, A precipitin reaction in yellow fever. J. Immunol., 25, 275-294.

Kerr, J. A., and Patiño Camargo, L., 1933, Investigaciones sobre fiebre amarilla en Muzo y Santander. Revista de Higiene, Bogota, 2, 63-83.

Kirk, R., 1941, An epidemic of yellow fever in the Nuba Mountains, Anglo-Egyptian Sudan. Ann. Trop. Med. and Parasit., 35, 67-112.

Klotz, O., and Belt, T. H., 1930, The pathology of the spleen in yellow fever. Am. J. Path., 6, 655-662.

Laemmert, H. W., de Castro Ferreira, L., and Taylor, R. M., 1946, An epidemiological study of jungle yellow fever in an endemic area in Brazil. Part II. Investigations of vertebrate hosts and arthropod vectors. Am. J. Trop. Med., 26, Supp. 23-69.

Lennette, E. H., and Perlowagora, A., 1943, The complement fixation test in the diagnosis of yellow fever. Use of infectious mouse brain as antigen. Am. J. Trop. Med., 23, 481-504.

Lloyd, W., Theiler, M., and Ricci, N. I., 1936, Modification of the virulence of yellow fever virus by cultivation in tissues in vitro. Tr. Roy. Soc. Trop. Med. and Hyg., 29, 481-529.

Mahaffy, A. F., Smithburn, K. C., and Hughes, T. P., 1946, The distribution of immunity to yellow fever in Central and East Africa. Tr. Roy. Soc. Trop. Med. and Hyg., 40, 57-82.

Peltier, M., Durieux, C., Jonchère, H., and Arquié, E., 1940, Vaccination mixte contre la fièvre jaune et la variole sur des populations indigène du Sénégal. Ann. Inst. Pasteur, 65, 146-169.

Penna, H. A., 1936, The production of encephalitis in Macacus rhesus with viscerotropic yellow fever virus. Am. J. Trop. Med., 16, 331-339.

Penna, H. A., and Moussatché, H., 1939, Modificação do virus de febre amarella por passagens em serie no embryao de gallinha em desenvolvimento. Brasil-med., 53, 903-905.

Pickels, E. G., and Bauer, J. H., 1940, Ultracentrifugation studies of yellow fever virus. J. Exp. Med., 71, 703-717.

Reed, W., Carroll, J., Agramonte, A., and Lazear, J. W., 1911, Yellow Fever: A compilation of various publications, U. S. 61st Cong., 3d sess. Senate, Doc. no. 822, Washington.

Reed, L. J., and Muench, H., 1938, A simple method of estimating fifty per cent endpoints. Am. J. Hyg., 27, 493-497.

Rickard, E. R., 1937, The organization of the viscerotome service of the Brazilian cooperative yellow fever service. Am. J. Trop. Med., 17, 163-190.

da Rocha Lima, H., 1912, Zur pathologischen Anatomie des Gelfiebers. Verhandl. d. deutsch. path. Gesellsch., 15, 163-181.

Sawyer, W. A., Bauer, J. H., and Whitman, L., 1937, The distribution of yellow fever immunity in North America, Central America, the West Indies, Europe, Asia and Australia, with special reference to the specificity of the protection test. Am. J. Trop. Med., 17, 137-161.

Sawyer, W. A., Kitchen, S. F., and Lloyd, W., 1932, Vaccination against yellow fever with immune serum and virus fixed for mice. J. Exp. Med., 55, 945-969.

Sawyer, W. A., and Lloyd, W., 1931, The use of mice in tests of immunity against yellow fever. J. Exp. Med., 54, 533-555.

Sawyer, W. A., and Whitman, L., 1936, The yellow fever immunity survey of North, East, and South Africa. Tr. Roy. Soc. Trop. Med. and Hyg., 29, 397-412.

Smith, H. H., 1938, The propagation of yellow fever virus in mouse testicle. Am. J. Trop. Med., 18, 77-84.

Smith, H. H., Penna, H. A., and Paoliello, A., 1938, Yellow fever vaccination with cultured virus (17D) without immune serum. Am. J. Trop. Med., *18,* 437-468.

Smith, H. H., and Theiler, M., 1937, The adaptation of unmodified strains of yellow fever virus to cultivation *in vitro.* J. Exp. Med., *65,* 801-808.

Smithburn, K. C., Haddow, A. J., and Lumsden, W. H. R., 1949, An outbreak of sylvan yellow fever in Uganda with *Aëdes (Stegomyia) africanus* Theobald as principal vector and insect host of virus. Ann. Trop. Med., *43,* 74-89.

Soper, F. L., 1937, The geographical distribution of immunity to yellow fever in man in South America. Am. J. Trop. Med., *17,* 457-511.

Soper, F. L., 1938, Yellow Fever: The present situation (October, 1938) with special reference to South America. Tr. Roy. Soc. Trop. Med. and Hyg., *32,* 297-332.

Soper, F. L., Penna, H., Cardoso, E., Serafim, J., Jr., Frobisher, M., Jr., and Pinheiro, J., 1933, Yellow fever without *Aëdes aegypti.* Study of a rural epidemic in the Valle do Chanaan, Espirito Santo, Brazil, 1932. Am. J. Hyg., *18,* 555-587.

Stokes, A., Bauer, J. H., and Hudson, N. P., 1928, Experimental transmission of yellow fever to laboratory animals. Am. J. Trop. Med., *8,* 103-164.

Taylor, R. M., and Fonseca da Cunha, J., 1946, An epidemiological study of jungle yellow fever in an endemic area in Brazil. Part I. Epidemiology of human infections. Am. J. Trop. Med., *26,* Suppl. 1-21.

Theiler, M., 1930, Studies on the action of yellow fever virus in mice. Ann. Trop. Med. and Parasit., *24,* 249-272.

Theiler, M., 1933, A yellow fever protection test in mice by intracerebral injection. Ann. Trop. Med. and Parasit., *27,* 57-77.

Theiler, M., 1951, The Virus, *in* Yellow Fever, edited by George K. Strode. McGraw-Hill Book Company, Inc.

Theiler, M., and Smith, H. H., 1937a, The use of yellow fever virus modified by *in vitro* cultivation for human immunization. J. Exp. Med., *65,* 787-800.

Theiler, M., and Smith, H. H., 1937b, The effect of prolonged cultivation *in vitro* upon the pathogenicity of yellow fever virus. J. Exp. Med., *65,* 767-786.

Wakeman, A. M., and Morrell, C. A., 1930, Chemistry and metabolism in experimental yellow fever in *Macacus rhesus* monkeys. II. Nitrogen metabolism. Arch. Int. Med., *46,* 382-401.

Whitman, L., 1937, The multiplication of the virus of yellow fever in *Aëdes aegypti.* J. Exp. Med., *66,* 133-143.

Whitman, L., 1943, A modified intraperitoneal protection test for yellow fever based on the greater susceptibility of immature white mice to the extraneural injection of yellow fever virus. Am. J. Trop. Med., *23,* 17-36.

Whitman, L., 1951, The Arthropod Vectors, *in* Yellow Fever, edited by George K. Strode. McGraw-Hill Book Company, Inc.

Whitman, L., and Antunes, P. C. A., 1938, Studies on *Aëdes aegypti* infected in the larval stage with the virus of yellow fever. Proc. Soc. Exp. Biol. and Med., *37,* 664-666.

MAX THEILER, M.R.C.S. (ENG.), L.R.C.P. (LOND.)

Laboratories of the Division of Medicine and Public Health,
The Rockefeller Foundation, New York City

32

Rift Valley Fever

(SYNONYM: Enzootic hepatitis)

INTRODUCTION

Rift valley fever is an acute disease of sheep and other lower animals and is caused by a specific virus. In man the disease is characterized by a short incubation period, acute onset, fever of several days' duration, prostration, pain in the extremities and joints, abdominal discomfort, and leukopenia. The mortality rate is low, and the immunity following recovery is lasting. Man is usually secondarily infected during the course of an epizootic in domesticated animals. The natural disease has been reported only from Africa.

HISTORY

During an extensive epizootic of a hitherto undescribed disease in sheep in the Rift Valley in East Africa in 1930, Daubney, Hudson and Garnham (1931) isolated a virus. Workers associated with these investigations contracted a short but severe febrile disease and a similar clinical picture was common among the herders of the infected flocks. The natural disease in sheep was ill-defined, consisting of listlessness, disinclination for food, and prostration. The mortality was high in newborn lambs, death being due to acute liver necrosis; pregnant ewes aborted. The removal of infected herds to the highlands led to cessation of epizootics. Daubney, Hudson and

Garnham (1931) showed that inoculation of a human volunteer with a filtrate of infected sheep tissue produced a disease similar to that observed in the herders. In the experimental human disease, virus was recovered from blood by inoculating it into lambs, and development of specific neutralizing antibodies in the patient was demonstrated. Epidemiologic evidence pointed to a bloodsucking arthropod, perhaps a night-biting mosquito, as a vector. Studies for the presence of specific antibodies in man have shown that the infection is rather widespread in East and Central Africa. Accidental laboratory infection is common (Smithburn, Mahaffy, et al., 1949).

CLINICAL PICTURE

The incubation period is five or six days. Onset is usually abrupt with malaise, chilly sensation, and headache. The symptoms increase rapidly and the temperature rises to 102° or 104° F., associated at times with chills. Pain in the extremities and joints may be extreme. There is usually a feeling of discomfort in the epigastrium; definite tenderness or even abdominal pain may be present. Nausea and vomiting are sometimes present. The face is flushed and the conjunctivae injected; photophobia is common. The temperature curve is, as a rule, of the saddleback type, thus resembling

552

that of dengue and yellow fever. The disease usually lasts only a few days. Convalescence is rapid, and recovery complete. A fatal outcome is rare. One of the most characteristic features is a marked leukopenia, which is due chiefly to a diminution of the polymorphonuclear leukocytes. The urine, as a rule, is normal. Of the numerous laboratory infections that have occurred, only one was fatal, due to the development of venous thrombosis 45 days after the onset of the disease (Schwentker and Rivers, 1934).

PATHOLOGIC PICTURE

Human material not being available for study, knowledge of the pathologic picture of Rift Valley fever has been obtained by investigation of material from lower animals. In sheep and other animals the most marked changes are observed in the liver (Daubney, Hudson and Garnham, 1931); focal necrosis, evenly distributed throughout the organ, and pinpoint hemorrhages are present. In acute fulminating infections in lambs, the necrosis may be very extensive destroying almost all the parenchymatous cells. The architecture is destroyed, and there is an accumulation of phagocytic cells, chiefly polymorphonuclear leukocytes. The necrosis begins as a hyaline degeneration in a portion of the cell, rapidly extending to involve the whole cell; this process usually commences in the midzone of a lobule. At first the degenerating cells are isolated and resemble a similar type of cell seen in livers infected with yellow fever virus and known as the Councilman bodies. Characteristic of the infection is the presence of intranuclear inclusion bodies. Chromatin of the nucleus becomes marginated and acidophilic material appears in the nucleoplasm. These inclusions are more homogeneous than those seen in yellow fever. The pathologic changes observed in other organs are not distinctive. There is a tubular nephrosis; in the spleen and lymph nodes toxic degeneration is present,

and petechial hemorrhages are common in all the viscera. Hemorrhagic enteritis has been described.

EXPERIMENTAL INFECTION; HOST RANGE

All monkeys tested to date have been found susceptible, South American primates more so than African. African monkeys inoculated with the virus usually remain afebrile, but have circulating virus for a few days. South American monkeys respond with a febrile reaction. Sheep, goats, and cattle are readily infected (Findlay, 1932). Animals which have been shown to be susceptible are the mouse, ferret, hamster, white rat, various species of wild European and African rodents, and possibly the rabbit. Animals not susceptible are the horse, pig, guinea pig, chicken, canary and pigeon. Mice are particularly susceptible to the virus, death occurring usually within two or three days after inoculation. These animals are susceptible to the virus given by all routes of inoculation; intracerebral inoculation produces a disease in all respects like that produced by subcutaneous inoculation. Mackenzie and Findlay (1936) and Mackenzie, Findlay and Stern (1936) produced a neurotropic strain by inoculating mice intracerebrally immediately after an intraperitoneal injection of immune serum. By serial passage in such passively immunized animals, the virus lost to a considerable extent its viscerotropic affinities, so that it no longer produced death due to liver lesions when inoculated subcutaneously. Inoculated intracerebrally, this modified virus produced a fatal meningo-encephalitis in mice and monkeys. Smithburn (1949), by serial passage in mice, produced a modified strain of Rift Valley fever virus with marked reduction in its hepatotropic affinities. The subcutaneous inoculation of this neurotropic Rift Valley fever virus into newborn lambs or older sheep resulted in the development of immunity, although the virus was not demonstrable in the circulating blood and did not cause any objective signs of infection. That no attenuation occurs for man by the prolonged passage in mice is shown by the accidental infection of a worker with virus which had undergone at least 300 passages in these animals (Sabin and Blumberg, 1947).

ETIOLOGY

The virus is filterable through Berkefeld filters V, N, and W candles, and through Chamberland bougies even up to L3 size. Its size as determined by filtration through gradacol membranes is 23 to 35 mμ. In blood, the thermal death point is 56° C. for 40 minutes. It is inactivated within 40 minutes by methylene blue in the presence of light. Rift Valley fever virus retains its activity in glycerol for at least 8 months when stored at 4° C. It may be readily preserved by lyophilization. The virus has been cultivated in a tissue-culture medium consisting of minced chick embryo in Tyrode's solution. It can be readily propagated in the developing chick embryo. Complement-fixing and neutralizing antibodies are developed in both man and animals following recovery from the infection.

DIAGNOSIS

Presumptive diagnosis of Rift Valley fever is made in individuals suffering from a denguelike fever following contact with the virus in the laboratory or with naturally infected animals. A positive diagnosis is made by isolation of virus from blood; this is most readily achieved by the inoculation of mice. The virus isolated in this way is identified by typical lesions produced in the liver and by being neutralized by a Rift Valley fever immune serum. Virus is present in the blood of human beings during the first three days of the disease. In convalescence, the diagnosis can be made by demonstrating the development of specific neutralizing antibodies. For this purpose, the serum to be tested is mixed with an equal quantity of a virus preparation known to be lethal for mice, and 0.2 cc. of the mixture is inoculated intraperitoneally into mice. Control mice are inoculated with a mixture containing normal serum and virus. If serum being tested is free from protective antibodies, the inoculated mice die within two or three days. Survival of the mice indicates that the serum contains specific protective antibodies. Neutralizing antibodies have been demonstrated as early as four days after onset and as long as 12 years after recovery (Sabin and Blumberg, 1947).

TREATMENT

This is entirely symptomatic, as there is no specific treatment.

EPIDEMIOLOGY

The naturally acquired disease has only been reported from Africa. Evidence has been obtained that the infection, first described from Kenya, is fairly widespread in Africa, including Uganda, Anglo-Egyptian Sudan, French Sudan, French Equatorial Africa and the Union of South Africa. The disease is not contagious. Infected animals can be kept in contact with normal ones without cross infection taking place. Daubney, Hudson and Garnham (1931) have shown that, in an infected region, sheep can be protected by screening at night. From this, it may be concluded that the disease is transmitted by a bloodsucking insect active at night. The cessation of an epidemic in a herd removed to the highlands is likewise evidence in favor of insect transmission. Smithburn, Haddow and Gillett (1948), during their studies of the jungle vector of yellow fever in Uganda, isolated Rift Valley fever virus from six different lots of mosquitoes caught in the uninhabited Semliki Forest. The mosquitoes involved, included several species of the genus *Eretmapodites* and three of genus *Aëdes*. By transmission experiments (Smithburn, Haddow and Lumsden, 1949), it was shown that *Eretmapodites chrysogaster* can act as a vector of the virus. It is apparent that very little definitive information is available concerning the epidemiology of the disease. It is probable that domestic animals are infected by some bloodsucking arthropod. Man as a rule seems to become secondarily infected during the course of an epizootic. The finding of the virus in wild-caught mosquitoes of the Semliki Forest is highly suggestive of some virus cycle in wild animals.

How human beings are infected in the laboratory is also unknown.

CONTROL MEASURES

Due to the numerous accidental laboratory infections, extreme precautions should be taken by all those working with the virus. There is no specific means of prevention at present. Arthropod abatement or eradication is perhaps indicated.

REFERENCES

Daubney, R., Hudson, J. R., and Garnham, P. C., 1931, Enzootic hepatitis or Rift Valley fever. An undescribed virus disease of sheep, cattle and man from East Africa. J. Path. and Bact., 34, 545-579.

Findlay, G. M., 1932, Rift Valley fever or enzootic hepatitis. Tr. Roy. Soc. Trop. Med. and Hyg., 25, 229-265.

Mackenzie, R. D., and Findlay, G. M., 1936, The production of a neurotropic strain of Rift Valley fever virus. Lancet, 1, 140-141.

Mackenzie, R. D., Findlay, G. M., and Stern, R. O., 1936, Studies on neurotropic Rift Valley fever virus: the susceptibility of rodents. Brit. J. Exp. Path., 17, 352-361.

Sabin, A. B., and Blumberg, R. W., 1947, Human infection with Rift Valley fever virus and immunity twelve years after single attack. Proc. Soc. Exp. Biol. and Med., 64, 385-389.

Schwentker, F. F., and Rivers, T. M., 1934, Rift Valley fever in man. Report of a fatal laboratory infection complicated by thrombophlebitis. J. Exp. Med., 59, 305-313.

Smithburn, K. C., 1949, Rift Valley fever: the neurotropic adaptation of the virus and the experimental use of this modified virus as a vaccine. Brit. J. Exp. Path., 30, 1-16.

Smithburn, K. C., Haddow, A. J., and Gillett, J. D., 1948, Rift Valley fever. Isolation of the virus from wild mosquitoes. Brit. J. Exp. Path., 29, 107-121.

Smithburn, K. C., Haddow, A. J., and Lumsden, W. H. R., 1949, Rift Valley fever: transmission of the virus by mosquitoes. Brit. J. Exp. Path., 30, 35-47.

Smithburn, K. C., Mahaffy, A. F., Haddow, A. J., Kitchen, S. F., and Smith, J. F., 1949, Rift Valley fever: accidental infections among laboratory workers. J. Immunol., 62, 213-227.

ALBERT B. SABIN, M.D.

*The Children's Hospital Research Foundation, University of Cincinnati
College of Medicine*

33

Dengue

(SYNONYMS: Break-bone fever, dandy fever, *denguero,* bouquet
fever, giraffe fever, polka fever, five-day fever, seven-day fever)

INTRODUCTION

Dengue is an infectious, mosquito-transmitted disease of virus etiology, characterized by fever, pain in various parts of the body, prostration, rash, lymphadenopathy and leukopenia.

HISTORY

David Bylon is credited with the first description of an epidemic of this disease, which he called "joint fever," in Batavia, Java, in 1779 (Pepper, 1941). In 1780, Benjamin Rush described an epidemic in Philadelphia, Pennsylvania, under the name of "bilious remitting fever." During the 19th century, innumerable reports appeared of epidemics in subtropical and tropical regions throughout the world, and the name dengue was accepted for standard usage by the Royal College of Physicians of London in 1869 (Doerr, 1930). Some of the largest epidemics in history have occurred in the United States, Australia, Greece and Japan since 1920. Chandler and Rice (1923) estimated that between 500,000 and 600,000 cases occurred in Texas during the 1922 epidemic and Siler (1935) stated that it was estimated that between one and two million people had dengue in the southern states that were affected at that time. The

Queensland-New South Wales epidemic of 1925-1926 attacked approximately 560,000 persons (McCallum and Dwyer, 1927), and another epidemic occurred during 1942 (Lumley and Taylor, 1943). During the 1927-1928 epidemic in Greece, the total number of cases probably exceeded a million, and Copanaris (1928) reported that 80 to 90 per cent of the populations of Athens and Piraeus had dengue in 1928. During the years of 1942 to 1945, the main ports of Japan had large, yearly epidemics of dengue with an estimated number of cases of from one to two million, the city of Osaka alone having one third to one half of its population attacked in 1944 (Sabin, 1952a). Although only 84,090 cases of dengue were officially reported during the war years in U. S. Army personnel, the total number of cases was undoubtedly much larger.

Bancroft (1906) published the first evidence of the fact that *Aedes aegypti* mosquitoes are vectors of the disease which was conclusively established by Cleland, Bradley and McDonald (1916, 1919), Siler, Hall and Hitchens (1926), and Simmons, St. John and Reynolds (1931); the latter authors also proved that *Aedes albopictus* is a true vector. Ashburn and Craig (1907) provided the first evidence that the etilogic

556

agent of dengue is filterable and ultra-microscopic. The demonstration that dengue virus can produce inapparent infection in certain species of monkeys (Blanc, Caminopetros, Dumas and Saenz, 1929; Simmons, St. John and Reynolds, 1931), led to (Sabin, 1944), the adaptation of the virus to mice and its subsequent mutation permitting the development of an effective vaccine against dengue, and the development of a neutralization test in mice (Sabin and Schlesinger, 1945) leading to new

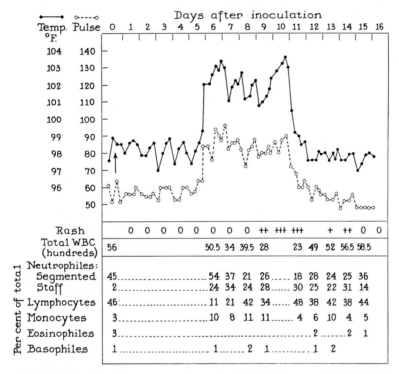

CHART 27. Graphic representation of temperature and pulse rate of a human volunteer inoculated experimentally with the Hawaiian strain of dengue virus by means of the bites of eight infected *Aedes aegypti* mosquitoes; arrow indicates day on which the patient was bitten. Time of appearance of rash is also indicated, as well as total and differential blood counts.

the accumulation of evidence indicating that certain monkeys may be infected in nature, that the infection can be transmitted by mosquitoes from monkey to monkey as well as from monkey to man, and that monkeys may constitute one of the links in the chain of events which perpetuate the virus in nature (Simmons, St. John and Reynolds, 1931). During World War II, extensive studies resulted in the demonstration of the very small size and other important properties of the virus including the existence of multiple immunologic types studies on specific diagnosis, antigenic pattern of the various types of virus and their role in different epidemics in different parts of the world.

CLINICAL PICTURE

The clinical manifestations presented are those which have been seen in natural cases of the disease and in several hundred human volunteers. The usual incubation period is from five to eight days, although it may vary from 2.5 to 15 days, depending on the amount of virus introduced. Prodromal symptoms of headache, backache, fatigue, stiffness, anorexia, chilliness, malaise and occasionally rash may make their appearance 6 to 12 hours before the first rise in temperature. In perhaps 50 per cent of the patients the onset is sudden with a sharp rise in temperature associated with severe headache, pain behind the eyes, backache, pain in the muscles and joints, chilliness and rarely a shaking chill. In typical cases, the fever (Chart 27) persists for five or six days and usually terminates by crisis. The temperature rarely exceeds 105° F., only occasionally returns to normal during the middle of the febrile period to give rise to the saddleback or diphasic type of curve, and quite frequently reaches its highest level during the last 24 hours of the febrile period. Salicylates affect the fever in dengue and may give rise to very bizarre, spiking temperature curves. The pulse rate (Chart 27) may at first rise proportionately to the temperature, but after the first day or two there is usually a relative bradycardia; an absolute bradycardia may occur during convalescence. Anorexia and constipation are common during the entire illness. Epigastric discomfort and colicky pain with abnormal tenderness may be seen. Altered taste sensations constitute a very common symptom early in the disease. The patient may become so weak and dizzy that he collapses when he tries to get out of bed. Photophobia, drenching sweats, sore throat, cough, epistaxis, dysuria, hyperesthesia of the skin, pain in the groin and testicles, delirium are some of the other manifestations occasionally encountered. A flushed appearance of the face, neck and chest, and a punctiform rash, especially over points of friction as at the back of the elbows and front of the knees, may be seen early in the disease. The bulbar and the palpebral conjunctivae may be injected; the eyes are tender to pressure and painful on movement. Lymph nodes are frequently enlarged, but rarely the spleen. Although there may occasionally be sufficient edema about the fingers to interfere with closure of the

hand, large joints present no abnormalities even when there is a great deal of subjective pain. Nuchal rigidity is absent even when the patient complains of a stiff neck.

The rash may be maculopapular or scarlatiniform, commonly appears on the third to fifth day and rarely lasts more than three or four days. It is usually first seen on the chest, trunk and abdomen, and spreads to the extremities and face. The incidence of this rash varies in different epidemics and also in the experimental disease caused by different strains of virus. Although itching, especially of the palms and soles, is very common, desquammation occurs only rarely. Another type of eruption, occurring on the last day of fever or shortly after defervescence and consisting of very small petechiae over the dorsum of the feet and legs, occasionally in the axillae, over the dorsum of the wrists, hands and fingers, and on the buccal mucosa and hard and soft palates, has been observed in the majority of human volunteers inoculated with the Hawaiian strain of virus (Sabin, 1944) and in 20 per cent of the cases among American Naval personnel on a South Pacific island (Stewart, 1944). This petechial eruption, unlike the earlier maculopapular or scarlatiniform rash, does not blanch on pressure and fades after one to three days, leaving a transitory brownish discoloration.

Changes in the leukocytes (Chart 27) are not characteristic for dengue, being found in certain other diseases associated with leukopenia. During the first 24 hours the total number of white cells may be normal, but the lymphocytes show an absolute and relative decrease, while the number of neutrophiles is increased by the appearance of immature forms. As the disease progresses, the total number of leukocytes drops, sometimes to as low as 1,500 cells per c.mm. The drop is due to a marked diminution in the neutrophiles. The lymphocytes begin to increase in number as the neutrophiles diminish, and toward the end of the febrile period and early in convalescence frequently constitute the major portion of the circulating leukocytes. The blood picture, as a rule, returns to normal within a week after defervescence. The urine is normal in most cases. The cerebrospinal fluid has been found to be normal in large numbers of patients with dengue, and reports to the contrary cannot be accepted without evidence for the correctness of the diagnosis.

The description given above applies to typical cases, but there is evidence, viz., recovery of virus from patients, that mild febrile illness of from one to three days' duration without rash may be dengue (Sabin, 1944). Experimental studies on human volunteers have shown that reinfection with a different immunologic type of virus two to three months after a primary attack may give rise to malaise and slight fever for less than 24 hours, and mosquitoes feeding on such patients acquire the capacity to transmit the infection; furthermore, as the group immunity wears off, infection with a heterologous type of virus has been found frequently to cause febrile illnesses of two and three days' duration without rash (Sabin, 1944). Since more than one immunologic type of virus has been recovered from the same region at the same time (Sabin, 1944), reinfection with heterologous types of virus may be one of the causes for many of the atypical forms of the disease encountered during certain epidemics.

Convalescence from severe attacks may take several weeks and is characterized by marked asthenia. Occasionally, during convalescence a disturbance of vision due to accommodative weakness or paralysis of the ciliary muscle may occur and persist for from one to four weeks. Although there is doubt as to whether dengue can be a primary cause of death, it has been so reported during some of the large epidemics in Australia and Greece, and McCallum and Dwyer (1927) have estimated the case fatality rate to be 3 per 10,000.

PATHOLOGIC PICTURE

Goldsmid (1917), Photakis (1929), Catsaris (1931) and Melissinos (1937) have reported on fatal cases of what they believed to be uncomplicated dengue, and described degenerative changes in the liver, kidneys, heart or brain, and hemorrhagic manifestations of varying extent in the endocardium, pericardium, pleura, peritoneum, mucosa of the stomach and intestines, muscles, skin and central nervous system. Local skin lesions caused by the intracutaneous injection of dengue virus, the maculopapular eruption and petechial eruption in human volunteers were studied by biopsy (Sabin, 1945). The epithelium was not involved and no inclusion bodies were found. The chief abnormality occurred in and about small blood vessels and consisted of endothelial swelling, perivascular edema and infiltration with mononuclear cells. In the petechial lesions extensive extravasation of blood, without appreciable inflammatory reaction, was observed.

EXPERIMENTAL INFECTION; HOST RANGE

Intracutaneous injection of 0.1 cc. to 0.2 cc. of human serum containing ten or more minimal human infective doses (M.I.D.) of dengue virus, is followed after an interval of from three to five days by local edema and erythema, 1 to 4 cm. in diameter, and this lesion has been shown to be due to local multiplication of the virus (Sabin, 1944). Serum obtained from experimentally infected persons within 24 hours after the first rise of temperature was found to contain a million human M.I.D. of virus per cc. (Sabin, 1944). Ten M.I.D. injected intracutaneously produced as severe an infection as did 1 million M.I.D. Amounts of virus in the range of one M.I.D. produced: (1) typical attacks of dengue; (2) mild, short attacks without rash followed by complete immunity; or (3) no evidence of infection except a partial immunity. Undiluted infectious serum rubbed on scarified skin produced unmodified dengue. Nasal instillation of 1 million or 100,000 M.I.D. resulted in a very mild disease in some human volunteers, while others suffered from a typical, unmodified attack. Nasal instillation of 10,000 M.I.D. produced neither disease nor immunity. Instillation of 200,000 M.I.D. into the conjunctival sac produced typical dengue in one volunteer, while 10,000 M.I.D. produced neither disease nor immunity in another (Sabin, 1945). A laboratory worker developed dengue 9 days after human serum containing unmodified dengue virus was accidentally squirted in his eye (Melnick et al., 1948).

Inapparent infection with dengue virus occurs in the following species of monkeys: *Cynomolgus fascicularis* and *Cercopithecus callitrichus* (Blanc et al., 1929), *Macacus fuscatus* and *Macacus philippinensis* (Simmons et al., 1931), and *Macacus rhesus* (Findlay, 1932; Sabin and Theiler, 1944). Focal infiltrative lesions of the type seen in nonparalytic poliomyelitis have been found in the spinal cord of rhesus monkeys sacrificed 6 weeks after intracerebral injection of human dengue virus; neutralizing and complement-fixing antibodies appeared in these monkeys from 14 to 21 days after inoculation and persisted for many months (Sabin, 1950). An essentially inapparent infection has been produced in chimpanzees (Paul et al., 1948) with development of neutralizing and complement-fixing antibodies which persisted for at least 10 months (Sabin, 1950). Dogs, young hogs, rabbits, guinea pigs, white mice, white rats, hamsters and cotton rats inoculated with human dengue blood have shown no signs of infection. Tests for inapparent infection in dogs, rabbits (Blanc and Caminopetros, 1930), young hogs (Siler, Hall and Hitchens, 1926), and guinea pigs (Simmons et al., 1931; Sabin, 1944) have been negative. Suckling or older mice, which rarely develop clinical manifestations of infection following intracerebral injection of human serum containing dengue virus, are, nevertheless, resistant to infection by the highly virulent mouse-adapted virus during the first days after receiving the former, as a result of interference, and during subsequent months, as a result of active immunity (Sabin, 1950; 1952a).

Several strains of dengue virus have now been adapted to mice (Sabin and Schlesinger, 1945; Hotta and Kimura in Japan reported by Sabin, 1952a) and maintained in serial passage by the intracerebral route. In the early passages a small and varying proportion of the inoculated mice show clinical evidence of the infection after incubation periods which vary from 5 to 35 days. The mice exhibit motor weakness, flaccid paralysis of one or more extremities with or without signs of encephalitis. The intracerebral titer may be no more than 10^{-1} to 10^{-2} after the first 10 to 15 passages and 10^{-4} to 10^{-5} after the first forty passages; during the course of further passages in 2- to 3-week-old mice, the titer rose to a level of 10^{-5} to 10^{-6} with corresponding shortening of the incubation period. The titer of virus depends upon the age of the mice in whose brains it is propagated. If the mice are from 1 to 7 days old at the time of inoculation, their brains yield virus suspensions with intracerebral titers of 10^{-7} to 10^{-8} upon titration in approximately 3-week-old mice. However, even after many serial passages in newborn mice, the titer reverts to 10^{-5} to 10^{-6} after a single passage in 14-day-old mice (Sabin, 1950). The use of newborn mice for routine passage led not only to the development of a potent complement-fixing antigen (Sabin and Young, 1948) but also to more satisfactory tests for neutralizing antibody (Sabin, 1950). Histologic examination of the brain and spinal cord of affected mice indicates that the primary attack is on the neurons. By the use of virus that has had only 40 to 50 intracerebral passages, it has not been possible to infect 14-day-old mice by the intraperitoneal route. In the early passages, only young mice were found suitable for intracerebral titrations, but after thorough adaptation of the virus old mice could also be used. The mouse-adapted dengue viruses tested thus far are not pathogenic for rabbits, guinea pigs, young cotton rats and hamsters.

In rhesus monkeys, the intracerebral injection of 10^5 to 10^7 mouse LD_{50} of mouse-adapted dengue virus regularly produces a febrile illness occasionally followed by typical flaccid paralysis of the extremities. A fatal paralytic disease, which clinically and pathologically is not readily distinguishable from experimental poliomyelitis, occurs more frequently with virus of greater potency derived from newborn mice. Neutralizing and complement-fixing antibodies develop in all rhesus monkeys inoculated with mouse-adapted dengue virus, but the C-F antibodies are of lower titer and disappear more rapidly than in monkeys inoculated with human virus (Sabin, 1950).

Adaptation of the virus to mice resulted in a change in its pathogenic properties for man. Beginning with the seventh passage of the Hawaiian strain in mice, the virus had lost its capacity to produce in human beings severe illness and protracted fever characteristic of the natural disease, but retained the capacity to produce a rash and solid immunity to unmodified virus. Blood taken from such persons at the time the rash first appears and inoculated into susceptible human volunteers causes only the modified disease. Furthermore, *Aedes aegypti* mosquitoes feeding on people inoculated with the tenth-mouse-passage virus acquired the capacity to transmit the infection but only in the modified form. Extensive tests carried out on people inoculated with the fifteenth-mouse-passage virus indicated that several lots of *Aedes aegypti* mosquitoes, which had fed daily on the experimental subjects for a period of 14 days after inoculation, were unable to transmit the infection even after prolonged extrinsic incubation periods. At a time when the intracerebral titer in mice was only 10^{-2}, the centrifuged, physiologic-salt-solution extract from a single mouse brain contained at least 10,000 human immunizing doses. Thirty-three human volunteers inoculated with varying quantities of the mouse-adapted dengue virus were subsequently found to be completely immune to unmodified virus transmitted either by infected mosquitoes or by the inoculation of large doses of highly infectious human serum.

ETIOLOGY

The diameter of the virus, as determined by filtration of highly infectious human serum through gradocol membranes, was found to be from 17 to 25 millimicrons (Sabin, 1944), but it may be somewhat smaller since the filtrate through the limiting (50 mμ) membrane produced partial immunity although it failed to produce obvious infection. The virus can be sedimented from human serum by centrifugation at 24,000 r.p.m. for 90 minutes in an eight-inch rotor of a vacuum ultracentrifuge. Examination with the electron microscope of preparations, purified by differential centrifugation, from highly infectious human dengue serum revealed dumbbell-shaped structures (700 mμ x 20-40 mμ) which were not found in preparations from normal human serum, but the relationship of these structures to dengue virus has not been established (Sabin, Schlesinger and Stanley, 1945). The virus, in the form of human serum, has been preserved in the frozen state at $-70°$ C. and in the lyophilized state at about $5°$ C. for at least 5 years (Sabin, 1950). Human blood has been found to be infectious after storage in an ordinary refrigerator for several weeks. The virus in human serum or in mosquito suspensions is inactivated by ultraviolet light or by 0.05 per cent formalin, but when so inactivated it failed to produce immunity. Although successful cultivation of dengue virus on the chorio-allantoic membrane of the developing chick has been claimed, the claims have either not been substantiated by human tests (Shortt et al., 1936), or the human tests which were carried out yielded no conclusive evidence that the cultured material was dengue virus (Kimura et al., 1944). Numerous attempts to propagate a variety of strains of the unmodified virus in embryonated eggs inoculated by various routes, or in tissue cultures containing minced chick embryo, minced mouse embryo, or human leukocytes yielded negative results as judged by tests for virus in susceptible human beings (Sabin and Schlesinger, 1944). However, after 16 or 18 intracerebral passages in mice, it proved possible to propagate the virus in embryonated eggs when five-day embryos were used for inoculation and a period of from eight to ten days at 35° C. for incubation (Schlesinger and Sabin, 1945). The best sustained multiplication in embryonated eggs was achieved by using the one hundred and first mouse passage of the Hawaiian strain in 5-day-old embryos incubated for 7 days after inoculation (Schlesinger, 1950). After a number of egg passages, incubation for 5 days was sufficient to achieve maximum titers. The greatest multiplication occurred in the nervous system of the chick embryo and titers of approximately 10^{-5} were the rule, even after 88 egg passages (Schlesinger, 1951). This is about 1/100 to 1/1,000 the amount of virus which develops in the brains of newborn mice.

The existence of at least two immunologic types of dengue virus was established by (1) active cross-immunity tests in human volunteers, (2) dermal neutralization tests with convalescent sera in human volunteers, (3) neutralization tests in mice with convalescent sera from human beings and rhesus monkeys, and (4) complement-fixation tests with convalescent sera of human beings and rhesus monkeys. Human volunteers reinoculated with the same strain of virus proved to be completely immune 18 months after a single experimental infection. Since the volunteers lived in nondengue areas, there can be no question of reinforcement of immunity by intercurrent, inapparent infection. The results of reinoculation with a heterologous immunologic type depended on the interval after the original attack. During the first one to two months there was active immunity to heterologous as well as to homologous strains. That this effect is most likely due to a common antigen and not to nonspecific resistance resulting from a preceding febrile illness was confirmed by the fact that phlebotomus fever convalescents exhibited no such immunity to dengue virus. From 2 to 9 months after the initial attack, reinfection with a heterologous type, as a rule, resulted in a modified form of the disease which was of shorter duration, less severe and without rash. By this method of comparison 4 of 7 human strains, i.e., the Hawaiian and New Guinea "A" strains, and two strains from India belonged to one immunologic type (Type 1), while the other 3, New Guinea "B," "C" and "D" belonged to another (Type 2) (Sabin, 1944; 1950).

Neutralization of mouse-adapted dengue virus by intracerebral tests in mice has been found to be a function of two factors: (1) specific antibody which is heat-stable (56° C. for 30 min.) and (2) a nonspecific, complementlike, heat-labile, accessory substance which produces the maximum inactivation of the sensitized virus after incubation in vitro for 2 hours at 37° C. Thus, when dengue virus with a low mouse intracerebral titer (10^{-3} to 10^{-4}) was used, no neutralization was demonstrable, either when heated serum was used with incubation of the serum-virus mixtures or when fresh or frozen serum was used without incubation of the serum-virus mixtures. When both fresh or frozen serum and incubation of the serum-virus mixtures were employed, the neutralization indices of convalescent sera varied with the mouse intracerebral potency of the virus used; indices of 100 to 300 were the rule with viruses having titers of 10^{-3} to 10^{-4}, as compared with 10,000 to 100,000 with virus having an intracerebral titer of about 10^{-7}. With virus of higher potency, the heated dengue antiserum can by itself yield neutralization indices of 100 to 500. However, when an accessory factor is supplied to such a mixture in the form of fresh or frozen, "normal" (i.e., no effect on dengue virus per se), undiluted human or guinea pig serum (by preparing the virus dilutions in such serum), the neutralization index becomes 50,000 (Sabin, 1950).

Neutralization tests can now be performed with two immunologically distinct types of dengue virus of high intracerebral potency in mice—the Hawaiian strain representing Type 1 and the New Guinea "C" strain representing Type 2. The New Guinea "C" strain used for this purpose was adapted by Dr. Gordon Meiklejohn by passage in newborn mice. Tests carried out by Sabin showed that sera obtained from human beings and rhesus monkeys after inoculation with the human New Guinea "B," "C" and "D" strains, which completely failed to neutralize the Hawaiian mouse-adapted virus, yielded high neutralization indices (10,000 or more) with this New Guinea "C" virus. On the other hand, human and rhesus Hawaiian convalescent sera with homologous neutralization indices of 20,000 or more yielded neutralization indices of 100 to 200 with this New Guinea "C" mouse-adapted virus. The data obtained thus far suggest that while the major neutralizing antibody is type-specific, there is also a group-specific antibody which yields lower titers and occurs in some individuals but not in others. This is particularly true of sera from human beings and rhesus monkeys infected with the Type 2 dengue viruses; the majority fail to neutralize the Type 1 (Hawaiian) virus, while occasional individuals may yield titers of 50 to 500 (Sabin, 1950). Neutralizing antibodies for the Hawaiian type of virus have been found as early as 7 days after onset of fever and for at least 4 years (the longest period tested thus far) after a single experimental infection in human beings in nondengue areas (Sabin, 1950).

A complement-fixing (C-F) antigen, consisting of a benzene-extracted preparation made from the brains of newborn mice infected with the Hawaiian virus, has yielded specific results with sera of human beings and rhesus monkeys infected with both immunologic types of dengue virus. In human volunteers infected with the heterologous New Guinea strains, the C-F titers at 2 months were in the range of 1:4 to 1:16 as compared with titers of 1:64 to 1:256 among those infected with the Hawaii type viruses. Seven volunteers infected with Hawaiian virus were still positive, with titers ranging from 1:2 to 1:128, at 3 and 4 years after a single infection, while those infected with the Type 2 New Guinea strains no longer had C-F antibody for the heterologous Hawaiian antigen at 6 months. Rhesus monkeys inoculated with the Type 2 New Guinea human strains exhibited the highest titers (as high as 1:256) of C-F antibody for the heterologous Hawaiian antigen at 3 to 4 weeks, even though they had no heterologous neutralizing antibody. In monkeys also the group-specific C-F antibody disappeared rapidly—in some animals as early as 6 weeks after inoculation—in contrast with the long persistence of the type-specific antibody. Infection with the mouse-adapted dengue viruses gave rise to C-F antibody of low titer, which disappeared as early as 6 weeks, in rhesus monkeys, and to no C-F antibody at all in human beings. Human volunteers, vaccinated with living mouse-adapted Hawaiian dengue virus, developed neutralizing antibodies and resistance to infection with unmodified virus, but no C-F antibodies (Sabin and Young, 1948; Sabin, 1950).

A definite antigenic relationship between the dengue viruses and those of yellow fever, Japanese B encephalitis and West Nile fever has been demonstrated by the complement-fixation test. Rhesus monkeys receiving a single intracerebral injection of either Type 1 or Type 2 human dengue viruses develop no neutralizing antibodies for the yellow fever virus (17-D strain), but at 3 to 4 weeks all develop C-F antibodies with titers ranging from 1:8 to 1:32 for the yellow fever antigen and 1:128 for the Type 1 dengue antigen. The same rhesus monkeys also develop C-F antibodies for the West Nile and Japanese B viruses with titers ranging from 1 : 16 to 1 : 64, but not for the St. Louis, western equine or Rift Valley fever viruses. An occasional monkey also developed neutralizing antibodies for the Japanese B or West Nile viruses with neutralization indices as high as 500. American volunteers, never out of the U.S.A., also exhibited C-F antibodies for the Japanese B, West Nile and yellow fever viruses after experimental infection with human dengue virus either by the bite of *Aedes aegypti* mosquitoes or injection of human serum. These group relationships were demonstrable not only with antidengue sera but also with potent hyperimmune sera against the other viruses. Thus, a Japanese B hyperimmune mouse serum exhibited the following C-F titers: 1 : 256 for Japanese B, 1 : 128 for West Nile, 1 : 2 for St. Louis, 1 : 32 for yellow fever, 1 : 4 for dengue, and nothing for western equine or Rift Valley fever antigens. Hyperimmune yellow fever antisera with homologous C-F titers of 1 : 32 to 1 : 128 had C-F titers of 1 : 4 to 1 : 32 with West Nile and Japanese B antigens, but only 6 of 12 such sera had C-F antibody for dengue antigen with titers of 1 : 4 to 1 : 16. These group relationships by the C-F test were demonstrable only with the most potent, 20 per cent, benzene-extracted, brain antigens, suggesting that the common antigenic groups were present in much lower concentration than the type-specific antigenic component (Sabin, 1949 ; 1950).

Recently, additional evidence has been obtained to indicate that the viruses of dengue, yellow fever, West Nile fever, Japanese B and St. Louis encephalitis may constitute a distinct, generically related group. Thus, a strain of mice has been discovered which exhibits an inherited resistance to this entire group of viruses, but not to other viruses, such as those of western equine encephalitis, herpes, poliomyelitis, rabies, TO mouse encephalomyelitis, lymphocytic choriomeningitis and Rift Valley fever

(Sabin, 1952b). Similarly, a nonantibody, antiviral factor has been found in human milk which neutralizes all members of the dengue-yellow fever-West Nile-Japanese B-St. Louis group of viruses, but not the western equine, herpes or poliomyelitis viruses (Sabin and Fieldsteel, 1952).

This group relationship between the dengue and other viruses is not associated with any significant, active cross immunity. Human volunteers, immunized with the 17-D strain of yellow fever were not resistant to small amounts of dengue virus, although an interference phenomenon was observed when the interval between administration of these 2 viruses was 7 days or less (Sabin, 1950 ; 1952a). An interference phenomenon between dengue and yellow fever has also been demonstrated in rhesus monkeys and to a certain extent in *Aedes aegypti* mosquitoes (Sabin and Theiler, 1944). There is also no cross immunity between dengue and phlebotomus fever (Sabin, 1944 ; 1952a) or Rift Valley fever (Findlay, 1932).

DIAGNOSIS

Dengue should be suspected when a disease, having the characteristics mentioned, occurs in persons living in or having recently arrived from areas where specific mosquito vectors are prevalent. Diagnosis is difficult in sporadic, atypical and primary cases, but is relatively easy during an epidemic. To obtain strains of virus, blood should be collected, preferably within 24 or 48 hours after onset, and if it cannot be used or frozen immediately in a box containing solid CO_2, the serum should be stored in an ordinary refrigerator for not more than two weeks. If the laborious procedure of adaptation to mice is attempted, suckling mice, not older than 3 days, of known susceptibility to dengue should be used, and the serum should be inoculated diluted 1 : 100, as well as undiluted. However, to obtain a strain of virus it may be necessary to inoculate human volunteers. A strain of dengue virus can be considered as having been recovered from human beings when the characteristic features of the disease have been reproduced by it in man after an appropriate incubation period and when transmission of it by *Aedes aegypti* mosquitoes, following a suitable extrinsic incubation period, has been accomplished. Such a virus must be considered as belonging to the dengue group, until proved otherwise, even when cross-immunity tests with known strains of dengue virus are negative. A virus recovered by adaptation to mice can be identified by its limited host range, neutralization by sera containing only specific dengue antibodies obtained from rhesus monkeys or by hyperimmunization of rabbits. The following may also be regarded as a presumptive test for the presence of dengue virus in the blood. Inoculate a group of suckling or mature mice with a patient's fresh serum, and one month later test them for immunity with 100 LD_{50} of the known mouse-adapted strains of dengue virus of high potency. For control, another group of mice may be inoculated with the patient's serum heated at 56° C. and similarly challenged one month later.

In order to prove by serologic methods that a given infection was caused by dengue virus it is necessary to demonstrate that antibodies were either absent or present in low concentration during the acute phase of the illness and developed or increased in amount during convalescence. It must be remembered that the large amount of virus in the serum collected during the first 24 hours after onset has been shown to exert a protective effect against the mouse-adapted virus which is due to an interference phenomenon and not to neutralizing antibodies (Schlesinger and Sabin, 1946). However, while incubation for two hours at 37° C. is necessary for the optimum demonstration of dengue neutralizing antibody by intracerebral tests in mice, no incubation is necessary for the demonstration of the interference phenomenon.

The complement-fixation test would appear to be the serologic test of choice with acute and convalescent serum specimens, because it is group-specific and more rapidly performed. Neither the C-F nor the neutralization tests have as yet been used during an outbreak of the disease, and the experience gained with sera of experimentally infected human volunteers is the only available guide at present. These tests will have to be adjusted and interpreted with care in regions where the viruses of West Nile fever, yellow fever, and Japanese B encephalitis are also prevalent.

TREATMENT

There is no specific therapy.

EPIDEMIOLOGY

The most important facts in the epidemiology of the disease are that the virus is transmitted only by certain species of *Aedes* mosquitoes, and that human beings, certain species of monkeys in some regions, and mosquitoes constitute the cycle of infection by which the virus is perpetuated in nature. *Aedes aegypti* Linn., *Aedes albopictus* (Skuse) and *Aedes scutellaris* Walk., the variety also known as *Aedes hebrideus* (Mackerras, 1946) are the only proved vectors of the virus. Although circumstances obtaining on Espiritu Santo, New Hebrides during the epidemic of 1942-1943 (Daggy, 1944) and in certain parts of New Guinea (Mackerras, 1946) strongly pointed to *Aedes hebrideus* as a vector under natural conditions, the opinion has been expressed that "the island form of *Aedes hebrideus* found in the New Hebrides does not appear to be a vector of dengue in nature under normal conditions" (Perry, 1948). *Armigeres obturbans* has been claimed as a vector (Koizumi et al., 1917), but, because the experiments were carried out in Formosa at a time when dengue was occurring, judgment is suspended. *Culex fatigans (quinquefasciatus)* has been shown to be incapable of acting as a true vector, and recent studies in the United States (Sabin and Jahnes, 1944) have shown that the following mosquitoes did not transmit the infection under conditions which permitted *Aedes aegypti* to act as an effective vector: *Aedes vexans, Aedes solicitans, Aedes taeniorhynchus, Aedes cantator, Anopheles punctipennis, Anoph. quadrimaculatus* and *Culex pipiens. Aedes aegypti* mosquitoes can acquire the infection from patients 6 to 18 hours before and for at least three days after the onset (Siler et al., 1926). A minimum extrinsic incubation period of eight days, more usually 11 to 14 days, is required after an infective blood meal before the mosquitoes can transmit the infection, and under suitable conditions of temperature they can function as effective vectors for the rest of their lives which may vary from one to three months or more. Blanc and Caminopetros (1930) have shown that *Aedes aegypti* may remain infective for at least 174 days. Very small numbers of mosquitoes suffice to transmit the infection, the experimental disease having been produced by the bite of one (Simmons et al., 1931) or two mosquitoes (Siler et al., 1926). Results of experiments (Siler et al., 1931) indicate that the virus is not carried from infected mosquitoes to succeeding generations through the eggs, nor has it been possible to obtain infected mosquitoes by leaving larvae in human serum containing 1,000,000 M.I.D. of virus per cc. (Sabin, 1944). It is clear, therefore, that the disease is most likely to persist in those areas where the conditions are favorable for the survival of mosquitoes throughout the year, and for this reason Rogers and Megaw (1942) suggested that countries near the equator are probably the permanent reservoir of dengue. The newborn human population in these equatorial regions may be enough to keep the cycle of infection going from year to year. Although *Aedes aegypti* is strictly domestic in its habits, *Aedes albopictus* can exist in the bush or jungle

and by keeping the infection going among susceptible monkeys (Simmons et al., 1931) can give rise to a type of jungle dengue which may be as important in the epidemiology of human dengue as jungle yellow fever is in the epidemiology of human yellow fever. The circumstances surrounding the occurrence of dengue in Panama have suggested the possibility that the Hemagogus mosquitoes, which are important in jungle yellow fever, might also play a role in jungle dengue, although the capacity of these mosquitoes to transmit dengue has not yet been tested (Sabin, 1946; 1952a).

CONTROL MEASURES

To prevent the recurrence of epidemics, it is necessary to maintain a constant vigil against the breeding of *Aedes aegypti* mosquitoes. In regions like Hawaii where, in addition to *Aedes aegypti, Aedes albopictus* mosquitoes multiply unchecked outside of cities, the control of mosquito breeding presents an especially difficult problem (Usinger, 1944). It takes fewer mosquitoes to keep a dengue epidemic going than are required for the continued dissemination of yellow fever (Hanson, 1936). Antimosquito measures on airplanes and ships contribute to prevention but they cannot keep out a person who may be in the incubation period of dengue. In the face of an epidemic, individual measures directed against mosquito breeding in all sorts of containers in the immediate vicinity of homes, offices and factories, as well as the judicious use of DDT residual spray inside these buildings must receive the greatest attention, while mass spraying from airplanes may be useful in the attack on *Aedes albopictus* breeding in the outskirts of the human community. Dengue vaccine has ben found to be stable, safe and effective in studies on human volunteers (Sabin and Schlesinger, 1945), and it is possible that it may prove to be useful in the control of epidemics and for troops or those who have to move from nondengue areas into endemic zones.

REFERENCES

Ashburn, P. M., and Craig, C. F., 1907, Experimental investigations regarding the etiology of dengue fever. J. Infect. Dis., *4*, 440-475.

Bancroft, T. L., 1906, On the etiology of dengue fever. Australasian Med. Gaz., *25*, 17-18.

Blanc. G., Caminopetros, J., Dumas, J., and Saenz, A., 1929, Recherches expérimentales sur la sensibilité des singes inférieurs au virus de la dengue. Compt. rend. Acad. sci., *188*, 468-470.

Blanc, G., and Caminopetros, J., 1930, Recherches expérimentales sur la dengue. Ann. Inst. Pasteur, *44*, 367-436.

Catsaras, J., 1931, Pathologisch-anatomische Beobachtungen zum Denguefieber. Arch. f. Schiffs- u. Tropen-Hyg., *35*, 278-286.

Chandler, A. C., and Rice, L., 1923, Observations on the etiology of dengue fever. Am. J. Trop. Med., *3*, 233-262.

Cleland, J. B., Bradley, B., and McDonald, W., 1916, On the transmission of Australian dengue by the mosquito Stegomyia fasciata. Med. J. Australia, *2*, 179-184; 200-205.

Cleland, J. B., Bradley, B., and MacDonald, W., 1919, Further experiments in the etiology of dengue fever. J. Hyg., *18*, 217-254.

Copanaris, P., 1928, L'épidémie de dengue en Grèce au cours de l'été 1928. Bull. off. internat. hyg. publ., *20*, 1590-1601.

Daggy, R. H., 1944, *Aedes scutellaris hebrideus;* probable vector of dengue in the New Hebrides. War Med., *5*, 292-293.

Doerr, R., 1930, Pappatacifieber und Dengue, *in* Kolle u. Wassermann, Handbuch der pathogenen Mikroorganismen. Jena, Fischer, Vol. 8, pp. 500-546.

Findlay, G. M., 1932, The relation between dengue and Rift Valley fever. Trans. Roy. Soc. Trop. Med. Hyg., *26*, 157-160.

Goldsmid. J. A., 1917, Fatal haemorrhagic dengue. Med. J. Australia, *1*, 7-9.

Hanson, H., 1936, Some observations on dengue. Am. J. Trop. Med., *16*, 371-375.

Kimura, R., Higashi, N., and Akazawa, H., 1944, Über die Züchtung des Denguevirus auf der Chorioallantoismembran von Hühnereiern. Japanese J. Med. Sci., VI. Bact. and Parasitol., *2*, 241-246.

Koizumi, T., Yamaguchi, K., and Tonomura, K., 1917, An epidemiological study of dengue fever. J. Med. Assn. Formosa (nos. 176-177); Abstr. in Trop. Dis. Bull., 1918, *12*, 77.

Lumley, G. F., and Taylor, F. H., 1943, Dengue, Service Publication No. 3, School of Public Health and Tropical Medicine (University of Sydney), Department of Health, Commonwealth of Australia. 171 pp. (Excellent review of all work on dengue up until 1943.)

Mackerras, I. M., 1946, Transmission of dengue fever by *Aedes* (Stegomyia) *scutellaris*, Walk. in New Guinea. Trans. Roy. Soc. Trop. Med. Hyg., *40*, 295-312.

McCallum, F., and Dwyer, J. P., 1927, Dengue as a cause of death. Med. J. Australia, *1*, 10-15.

Melissinos, J., 1937, Pathologisch-anatomische Untersuchungen bei Denguefieber. Arch. f. Schiffs- u. Tropen-Hyg., *41*, 321-331.

Melnick, J. L., Curnen, E. C., and Sabin, A. B., 1948, Accidental laboratory infection with human dengue virus. Proc. Soc. Exp. Biol. and Med., *68*, 198-200.

Paul, J. R., Melnick, J. L., and Sabin, A. B., 1948, Experimental attempts to transmit phlebotomus (sandfly, pappataci and dengue fevers to chimpanzees. Proc. Soc. Exp. Biol. and Med., *68*, 193-198.

Pepper, O. H. P., 1941, A note on David Bylon and dengue. Ann. Med. History, *3*, 363-368.

Perry, W. J., 1948, The dengue vector on New Caledonia, the New Hebrides, and the Solomon Islands. Am. J. Trop. Med., *28*, 253-259.

Photakis, B. A., 1929, Die klinischen Äusserungen des "Denguefiebers" im Lichte der Obduktionsbefunde. Arch. f. Schiffs- u. Tropen-Hyg., *33*, 333-335.

Rogers, L., and Megaw, J. W. D., 1942, Tropical Medicine, 4th Ed., 156.

Sabin, A. B., 1944, 1945, 1946, Unpublished studies on dengue reported to Office of Surgeon General, U. S. Army.

Sabin, A. B., 1949, Antigenic relationship of dengue and yellow fever viruses with those of West Nile and Japanese B encephalitis. Federation Proc., *8*, 410 (abstract).

Sabin, A. B., 1950, The dengue group of viruses and its family relationships. Bact. Rev., *14*, 225-232.

Sabin, A. B., 1952a, Research on dengue during World War II. Am. J. Trop. Med. and Hyg., *1*, 30-50.

Sabin, A. B., 1952b, Genetic, hormonal and age factors in natural resistance to certain viruses. Ann. N. Y. Acad. Sci. In press.

Sabin, A. B., and Fieldsteel, A. H., 1952, Studies to be published.

Sabin, A. B., and Jahnes, W. G., 1944, Capacity of various mosquitoes prevalent on the Atlantic coast of the U. S. A. to transmit dengue. Unpublished studies reported to Office of Surgeon General, U. S. Army.

Sabin, A. B., and Schlesinger, R. W., 1945, Production of immunity to dengue with virus modified by propagation in mice. Science, *101*, 640-642.

Sabin, A. B., and Schlesinger, R. W., 1944, 1945, 1946, Unpublished studies on dengue reported to Office of Surgeon General, U. S. Army.

Sabin, A. B., Schlesinger, R. W., and Stanley, W. M., 1945, Electron microscope studies on human dengue serum. (Unpublished observations.)

Sabin, A. B., and Theiler, M., 1944, Interference between the viruses of dengue and yellow fever. Unpublished studies reported to Office of Surgeon General, U. S. Army.

Sabin, A. B., and Young, I., 1948, A complement fixation test for dengue. Proc. Soc. Exp. Biol. and Med., *69*, 478-480.

Schlesinger, R. W., 1950, Propagation in chick embryos of the Hawaiian strain of dengue virus. I. Sustained serial passage in eggs after one hundred and one intracerebral passages in mice. Am. J. Hyg., *51*, 248-254.

Schlesinger, R. W., 1951, Propagation in chick embryos of dengue virus, Hawaiian strain. II. Findings in infected eggs. Proc. Soc. Exp. Biol. and Med., *76*, 817-823.

Schlesinger, R. W., and Sabin, A. B., 1945, Cultivation of mouse-adapted dengue virus in the chick embryo. Unpublished studies reported to Office of Surgeon General, U. S. Army.

Schlesinger, R. W., and Sabin, A. B., 1946, Interference phenomenon between unadapted, human and mouse-adapted dengue virus in mice. Unpublished studies reported to Office of Surgeon General, U. S. Army.

Shortt, H. E., Rao, R. S., and Swaminath, C. S., 1936, Cultivation of the viruses of sandfly fever and dengue fever on the chorio-allantoic membrane of the chick-embyro. Indian J. Med. Res., *23*, 865-870.

Siler, J. F., 1935, Dengue Fever, *in* E. B. McKinley, The Geography of Disease, Washington, D. C., George Washington University Press, pp. 402-408.

Siler, J. F., Hall, M. W., and Hitchens, A. P., 1926, Dengue: its history, epidemiology, mechanism of transmission, etiology, clinical manifestations, immunity and prevention, Philippine J. Sci., *29*, 1-304.

Simmons, J. S., St. John, J. H., and Reynolds, F. H. K., 1931, Experimental studies of dengue. Philippine J. Sci., *44*, 1-247. (Monograph 29 of the Bureau of Science, Manila.)

Stewart, F. H., 1944, Dengue: analysis of the clinical syndrome at a South Pacific advance base. U. S. Naval Med. Bull., *42*, 1233-1240.

Usinger, R. L., 1944, Entomological phases of the recent dengue epidemic in Honolulu. Pub. Health Rep., *59*, 423-430.

ALBERT B. SABIN, M.D.

The Children's Hospital Research Foundation, University of Cincinnati College of Medicine

34

Phlebotomus Fever

(SYNONYMS: Sandfly fever, pappataci fever, three-day fever)

INTRODUCTION

Phlebotomus fever is a self-limited, non-fatal, phlebotomus-transmitted illness of virus etiology, characterized by fever, severe headache, pain in the eyes, conjunctival injection, malaise and leukopenia. The term sandfly fever, popularly used among English speaking people, has not been accepted in international scientific literature because biting insects belonging to the genus *Culicoides,* and having no relation to the disease under discussion, are also called sandflies. Pappataci fever, the popular name for the disease in Italy and the Balkans, has also failed to find general acceptance. The name phlebotomus fever, first suggested by Newstead (1911) and stressing the most important fact about the disease, namely, its specific relationship to the insects of the genus *Phlebotomus,* has been used by many writers and seems to be the most appropriate for international usage.

HISTORY

Although Pick (1886) is generally credited with the first description of the disease as a clinical entity under the name of *Hundskrankheit* (dog disease—apparently because the conjunctival injection was so striking that the eyes resembled those of a bloodhound), Birt (1913) and Whittingham (1924) call attention to Sir William Burnett's account of Mediterranean fever during the Napoleonic wars in 1799, Pym's description of Bulam fever in Gibraltar in 1804, and the reports of other British military surgeons during the early nineteenth century on Malta summer febricula as accurate clinical descriptons of the disease. Taussig's (1905) epidemiologic observations in the Adriatic region provided support for the popular belief that there was a connection between the midges known as the pappataci flies (*Phlebotomus papatasi,* Scopoli) and the disease from which newly-arrived Austrian troops suffered each summer, and led to the classic experiments of the Austrian military commission consisting of Doerr, Franz and Taussig (1909). By appropriate tests on human volunteers living in areas free from the disease, the commission proved that the etiology was an ultramicroscopic, filterable agent present in the blood of patients on the first day of the fever, and that *Phlebotomus papatasi* was the vector. Being a constant problem to foreign troops stationed in endemic areas, the disease has been the subject of study by several British military commissions (Whittingham and Rook, 1923; Young, Richmond and Brendish, 1926; Shortt, Poole and Stephens, 1935) and during World War

II for the first time by American investigators (Sabin, Philip and Paul, 1944; Sabin, 1943-1948, 1951; Hertig and Fisher, 1945).

CLINICAL PICTURE

Since there is as yet no specific diagnostic test for the individual case of phlebotomus fever, observations on more than 100 cases have been seen; following intravenous inoculation, however, incubation periods of 42 to 44 hours are common. The onset of the disease is sudden in the majority of cases. In some there may be a prodromal period characterized by malaise, giddiness, constipation and abdominal distress. The following signs and symptoms may be en-

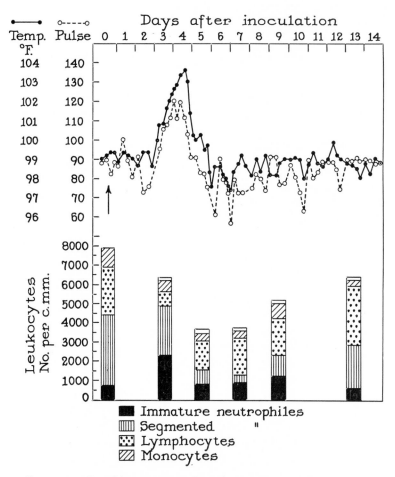

CHART 28. Graphic representation of temperature, pulse rate and blood picture of a human volunteer experimentally inoculated with the virus of phlebotomus fever; arrow indicates time of inoculation.

of the experimental disease in human beings produced with different strains of virus constitute the best basis for a description of the clinical manifestations of the malady. The incubation period of three or four days in the average case may vary from 2.5 to 6 days; exceptional incubation periods, one each of 50 hours, seven days and nine days, countered at the onset or sometime during the course of the disease; however, some of them are frequently absent in otherwise typical cases: frontal headache, burning sensation or pain in eyes, photophobia, backache, stiffness in neck and back, pains in joints and extremities, anorexia, nausea, vomiting, abdominal distress, alteration or loss of taste, constipation during the first few days and diarrhea during convalescence, sore throat, epistaxis, chills or chilliness, profuse sweating, giddiness and weakness, especially during convalescence.

The temperature usually reaches its peak, not over 104.5° F., within 24 or 48 hours after onset, and the febrile period in 85 per cent of the cases is two, three or four days (Chart 28). Fevers of less than one day's duration and of five to nine days' duration may occur. The pulse rate (Chart 28) is usually elevated in proportion to the fever on the first day of the disease, and thereafter returns to normal more rapidly than does the temperature. A bradycardia may be present at the end of the febrile period and during convalescence. Other physical findings are limited to an erythema of the face and exposed parts of the neck and chest, conjunctival injection which is occasionally limited to the exposed portion of the ocular conjunctiva (Pick's sign), tenderness of the eyeballs, and congestion of the fauces, soft palate and posterior pharyngeal wall. Rhinitis, tracheobronchitis, lymphadenopathy, and enlargement of the liver and spleen are not a part of the disease. Urticaria or erythema multiforme may occasionally be encountered, but a true rash as seen in dengue does not occur.

Changes in the leukocytes are no different from those seen in dengue, infectious hepatitis and certain other infections with leukopenia. The characteristic finding (Chart 28) on the first day of the fever is a total count within normal limits, a relative and absolute decrease in the lymphocytes accompanied by a relative and sometimes absolute increase in the neutrophiles which is due to an increase in immature cells. During the second or third day of fever, the number of lymphocytes begins to return to normal and for a few days thereafter may constitute from 40 to 65 per cent of the total count. At the same time, the number of neutrophiles begins to drop, and the immature cells increase to a point at which they usually outnumber the segmented cells. The greatest drop in the total number of leukocytes may not occur until the end of the febrile period or after defervescence, but the marked shift to the left in the neutrophiles and changes in the proportions of different types of cell at various stages of the disease are more important for diagnosis than is a single total leukocyte count. The urine is normal. The cephalin-cholesterol-flocculation and phosphatase tests for hepatic damage are negative. The cerebrospinal fluid is normal in experimental cases, and there is no evidence that the pleocytosis reported in some outbreaks (Fleming et al., 1947) can be caused by the virus of phlebotomus fever.

The duration of convalescence varies with the individual and the climate; marked uncontrollable, transitory mental depression is occasionally encountered. Recurrences of the fever and symptoms during convalescence from the naturally acquired disease have been reported by several investigators and have also been observed from five to seven days after the initial defervescence among 5 per cent of the experimentally inoculated volunteers (Sabin et al., 1944).

PATHOLOGIC PICTURE

There have been no fatalities among thousands of uncomplicated cases, and nothing is known of the pathologic changes produced by the virus.

EXPERIMENTAL INFECTION; HOST RANGE

Thus far, human beings constitute the only known vertebrate host for the virus. No evidence of pathogenicity has been obtained with virus of proved infectivity for human beings after inoculation in the following lower animals by the intracerebral, intracutaneous, subcutaneous, intratesticular, intranasal or intraperitoneal routes: young baboons (*Papio hamadryas*), grivet (*Cercopithecus griseoviridis*), vervet (*Cercopithecus aethiopis centralis*), red African hussar (*Cercopithecus patas*), *Macaca radiata* and *Macaca mulatta* (rhesus monkeys), young white mice, wild gray mice, cotton rats, Egyptian desert rats (jerboas), Syrian hamsters, guinea pigs and rabbits. The virus could not be demonstrated in the serum of rhesus monkeys three and four days after inoculation by subinoculation in human beings of proved susceptibility (Sabin et al., 1944). Six chimpanzees inoculated with human serum believed to contain the virus exhibited no clinical signs of infection. A slight febrile response in the 2 chimpanzees whose temperatures were being recorded could not be interpreted with certainty (Paul et al., 1948).

Virus has been recovered from the blood and serum of experimentally inoculated human beings during the 24 hours preceding and the 24 hours following the onset of fever, but not thereafter. The amount of virus in human serum, obtained even within a few hours after onset of fever, is relatively small; the maximum amount found thus far has been about 1,000 infective doses per cc. Furthermore, the amount of virus in the serum obtained from individual donors varied a great deal since in some instances even doses of 1 cc. did not produce disease (Sabin, 1944). Approximately 5 per cent of human adults, living in areas free of the disease, have been found refractory when the virus was inoculated by the intracutaneous or intravenous routes. In several simultaneous tests, doses of virus, which usually produced the disease by the intracutaneous or intravenous routes, failed to cause fever, symptoms or leukocyte changes in from 50 to 75 per cent of the individuals inoculated by the subcutaneous or intramuscular routes. That an inapparent infection may have been produced in the latter human subjects is suggested by the fact that they were subsequently immune to large doses of virus injected by the intracutaneous or intravenous routes. On the other hand, persons inoculated intracutaneously or intravenously with amounts of virus too small to produce disease were not, with one possible exception, immune to the virus upon reinoculation of large amounts. The virus of phlebotomus fever does not give rise to skin lesions at the site of intracutaneous injection and differs in this respect from dengue viruses.

ETIOLOGY

By passing infectious human serum through gradocol membranes it was found that filtrates from membranes with an average pore diameter (A.P.D.) of about 200 millimicrons or more regularly produced the disease in human volunteers, while filtrates from membranes with an A.P.D. of 100 millimicrons or less did not (Sabin et al., 1944; Sabin, 1945). From these findings it is estimated that the diameter of the virus is not greater than 40 or 60 millimicrons; it may be smaller, however, since the concentration of virus in the human serum used for filtration was relatively low. The often-quoted diameter of 160 millimicrons based on the finding (Shortt et al., 1938) that an agent producing lesions on the chorio-allantoic membrane of chick embryos passed a gradocol membrane having an A.P.D. of 480 millimicrons but not one with an A.P.D. of 380 millimicrons, is unacceptable, not only because it was erroneously calculated (according to Elford's formula it should have been 190-285 millimicrons) but also because there is no evidence that the virus of phlebotomus fever was being filtered. In frozen human serum, the virus has retained its infectivity for human beings for a period of at least four years by storage in a box containing solid CO_2 (Sabin, 1943-1948). The virus may also be preserved in an ordinary refrigerator after suitable lyophilization. Reproducible results have not yet been obtained on the inactivation of the virus by ultraviolet light; and the absence of disease upon reinoculation of potent virus in human volunteers who failed to develop the disease following inoculation with ultraviolet-irradiated human serum, although difficult to explain, should not be interpreted as indicating that inactive phlebotomus fever virus can give rise to immunity (Sabin et al., 1944; Sabin, 1951).

Cultivation of the virus on the chorio-allantoic membrane of chick embryos as evidenced by the development of plaques has been reported by Shortt et al. (1938) who later (1939) failed to reproduce the disease in human beings with such cultures. Others (Demina and Levitanskaja, 1940; Demina, 1941) have stated that material cultivated in chick embryos produced symptoms of typical phlebotomus fever in human beings, but the available reports do not indicate whether or not serial passage and immunity studies were carried out to prove that the symptoms were produced by the virus of phlebotomus fever. Results of more recent studies (Sabin et al., 1944; Sabin, 1943, 1944) indicated that the plaques on the chorio-allantoic membrane were nonspecific; furthermore, tests on human beings revealed that virus of known potency passaged in chick embryos in various ways or in mouse-embryo brain cultures produced neither disease nor immunity (Sabin, 1951).

Multiple attacks of the disease during the same season or in subsequent seasons have led many to doubt that an attack of the disease produces appreciable immunity. However, experiments on human volunteers residing in phlebotomus-free regions of the United States have shown that a solid immunity to reinfection with the same strain of virus is present as long as two years (longest period tested thus far) after a single experimental attack of the disease (Sabin, 1945). Three different strains of phlebotomus fever virus were obtained by human passage from natural cases occurring during 1943 and 1944 in troops stationed in the Mediterranean area (Sabin, 1943-1945). Two of these, one from the Middle East and one from Sicily, proved to be identical by cross-immunity tests

carried out one month, four months, and two years, respectively, after primary attacks. The third strain, recovered during an outbreak in Naples, possessed the characteristic properties of phlebotomus fever virus but was immunologically completely different from the other two. Human volunteers proved to be immune to reinfection with the homologous Naples virus, developed typical, unmodified attacks of the disease after inoculation of the Sicilian virus within two months of the first infection. Likewise, those who recovered from infection with the Sicilian virus suffered from unmodified attacks of the disease after inoculation with the Naples virus (Sabin, 1951). This complete lack of cross immunity is unlike the picture exhibited by the multiple immunologic types of dengue virus in which a group relationship is manifested by cross-immunity tests during the first one or two months after the initial attack and by modified forms of the disease at later periods. The Naples strain of virus, which is thus a completely distinct immunologic entity, has not yet been submitted to the ultimate test for a phlebotomus fever virus, namely, transmission by *Phlebotomus papatasi*. No immunologic relationship was demonstrable between the phlebotomus fever and dengue viruses. Only equivocal results have been obtained in attempts to demonstrate neutralizing antibodies in the serum of known, immune convalescents; the amount of antibody is probably small since the positive results have been obtained when large amounts of convalescent serum and small amounts of virus were used. Negative results were obtained in complement-fixation tests in which the antigens consisted of serum taken within 24 hours after onset, extracts of *Phlebotomus papatasi*, allantoic fluid or yolk sac of embryonated eggs inoculated with virus of known potency. Skin tests with fresh or heated infectious sera were negative, and hemagglutination tests with chicken, sheep and type-O human erythrocytes were also negative (Sabin et al., 1944; Sabin, 1943).

DIAGNOSIS

The diagnosis of phlebotomus fever is generally made on clinical and epidemiologic grounds. The disease is suspected when outbreaks of an illness with fever of short duration occur during the hot, dry season, especially among immigrants, tourists, or foreign troops in countries known to harbor *Phlebotomus papatasi*. Differentiation from outbreaks of dengue is aided by the shorter duration of fever and the absence of rash and lymphadenopathy in phlebotomus fever. Influenza is not common during the hot season and can be diagnosed by serologic reactions. In localities where malaria is also prevalent and when, because of the pressure of events, antimalarial therapy may be administered in the absence of a positive smear, thousands of cases of phlebotomus fever have been erroneously diagnosed as malaria (Birt, 1915; Sabin et al., 1944). Infectious hepatitis at the onset may simulate phlebotomus fever, but the subsequent appearance of jaundice or a positive cephalin-cholesterol test serves to differentiate the two conditions. In certain parts of Africa, yellow fever and Rift Valley fever may cause confusion, but their true identity can be established by recovery of the viruses of these diseases from patients and by neutralization tests.

TREATMENT

No specific therapy is available.

EPIDEMIOLOGY

According to present knowledge the disease is maintained in nature by passage from man to man through the medium of the intermediate host and vector, *Phlebotomus papatasi*. Secondary cases do not arise by contact in the absence of the vector. Although other species of *Phlebotomus*, e.g., *perniciosus* and *caucasicus*, have been found in areas where the disease has occurred, there is no experimental proof that they may act as vectors.

Phlebotomus papatasi is a sand-colored, hairy midge, 2 to 3 mm. long, somewhat less than 1 mm. thick, easily recognized by the position of its two wings which are elevated and spread to form a V. The body of the female appears distended and red for some hours after a blood meal, and black for several days thereafter. Only the female bites and usually does so during the night and early hours of the morning. The site of a bite may or may not be marked by a reddish, pinpoint spot, and before a person becomes sensitive to the insects there is neither pain nor irritation beyond that of the initial stab. However, from one to two weeks after the primary exposure to such bites, markedly inflamed, itching papules (2 to 3 mm. in diameter, pink or red, sometimes vesicular) usually appear at almost all of the sites originally bitten, and may persist for four or five days. Once sensitization is established, such papules appear soon after bites. The flies are most prevalent near the ground level, and, because of their small size and ability to squeeze through small apertures, ordinary screens and mosquito nets fail to exclude them. Their flight is conducted as a series of short hops, alighting on stones and other obstacles in their approach to a house, and then, instead of entering at once, they tend to alight on the outer walls where they continue to hop about with relatively long pauses between hops. After entering a house they continue to hop about on the walls and ceiling for some time before attempting to feed. These peculiar habits of phlebotomus flies render them especially vulnerable to the residual action of DDT (Hertig and Fisher, 1945). Breeding places of the insects are difficult to demonstrate, but typical sites are found in loose soil, organic debris beneath stones, cracks in masonry, embankments, rubble, and dark, protected spots containing sufficient moist organic matter (Whittingham and Rook, 1923a). The larvae are not aquatic and are killed by too much moisture. They thrive during hot, dry seasons, and under optimum conditions 4.5 to 6 weeks are required for the eggs to develop into winged insects. The life of the adult is relatively short in hot weather, and in the laboratory it lives no longer than two or three weeks. An extrinsic incubation period of seven to ten days after feeding on a patient is known to be sufficient for transmission, but not enough work has been done to be certain that a shorter period will not suffice.

The geographic distribution of the disease is regarded as being limited to the areas harboring *Phlebotomus papatasi* which include particularly those parts of Europe, Africa and Asia that lie between 20 and 45 degrees north latitude. The disease is definitely known to occur in Sicily, Italy as far north as the Po Valley, along the Adriatic coast of Yugoslavia, Greece, Malta, Crete, Cyprus, Egypt, Palestine, Syria, Iraq, Iran, the coast of Crimea, the Azov and Black Sea littoral, provinces of central Asia in the USSR, and the northwest and central provinces of India. The disease is not known to occur in the United States, although man-biting species of *Phlebotomus*, *P. diabolicus* in Texas and an undetermined species in the Okefenokee Swamp, Georgia (Johannsen, 1943), have been reported. Whether or not these and other man-biting species of *Phlebotomus* in the western hemisphere are capable of acting as vectors of phlebotomus fever virus is not known. *Aedes aegypti, Culex pipiens, Pulex irritans* (Sabin et al., 1944; Sabin, 1951) and bedbugs (Doerr et al., 1909) have been tested and found incapable of transmitting the infection.

Phlebotomus fever, unlike dengue, is not known to have invaded new territories. Large outbreaks have invariably occurred among troops or immigrants from countries free from the malady who had moved into endemic regions. Although the total number of cases of phlebotomus fever officially reported as hospital admissions in the U. S. Army during World War II was only 12,434, the actual number was undoubtedly much greater, thousands of cases having been reported as fever of unknown origin or as malaria (Sabin et al., 1944). Although the disease is practically never seen among the native adolescent or adult populations of endemic regions, it is obvious that all of them must have acquired the infection in infancy and childhood. While it is clear how new susceptible subjects become available each year to aid in the perpetuation of the virus, it is not clear what the reservoir of the virus is during the late autumn and winter months when the phlebotomus flies are absent. The virus quickly disappears from the blood of human beings, and there is no evidence that it may be carried by lower animals. Doerr and Russ (1909) first suggested the possibility that the virus may be transmitted from one generation of infected *Phlebotomus papatasi* to another. Whittingham (1924) reported that *Phlebotomus papatasi* reared in the laboratory in England produced the disease in human beings without previously feeding on infected persons; he believed, however, that the larvae might have acquired the virus by feeding on the dejecta or dead bodies of adult flies. Others (Young et al., 1926), noting that the flies did not die in their breeding grounds after oviposition and that the larvae showed no preference for feeding on the dead bodies of adult flies, maintained that infection of the insect probably occurred in their breeding grounds and suggested that the mites (*Trombidium hindustanicum* Hirst and *Raphignathus youngi* Hirst) which were found on about 4 per cent of adult phlebotomus flies might constitute the true reservoir of the virus. Moshkovsky et al. (1937), starting with the ova of thousands of flies which had been fed on patients, proved in a series of well-controlled experiments that certain of the adults raised from ova hatched away from their "parents" were capable of producing phlebotomus fever in human volunteers; that a virus caused the illness was established by serial passage in other human beings. The American commission (Sabin et al., 1944) was unable to produce the disease with offspring from flies of proved infectious capacity or from larvae which had ingested lyophilized virus, and concluded that transmission of the virus from one generation of flies to another is not a regular event. The question of how the virus overwinters and what its true reservoir may be, cannot be regarded as having been settled.

CONTROL MEASURES

Control measures are directed against the

vector. DDT residual spray is effective against *Phlebotomus papatasi* (Hertig and Fisher, 1945) and should be used to control the vector in living quarters and breeding sites within a radius of 100 to 200 meters, which is the usual flight range for flies breeding near human habitations. Regular use of dimethyl phthalate and other effective insect repellents after sundown and upon retiring has been found helpful in preventing the disease (Sabin et al., 1944; Philip et al., 1944). Prior to the advent of DDT, hospital epidemics (Cullinan and Whittaker, 1943) were not infrequent in certain types of military installations, and separate wards, located from 300 to 600 meters away from other buildings, were considered desirable for patients with this disease.

REFERENCES

Birt, C., 1913, Phlebotomus fever and dengue. Trans. Roy. Soc. Trop. Med. and Hyg., *6*, 243-262.

Birt, C., 1915, Phlebotomus fever (sandfly fever). Brit. Med. J., *2*, 168-169.

Cullinan, E. R., and Whittaker, S. R. F., 1943, Outbreak of sandfly fever in two general hospitals in the Middle East. Brit. Med. J., *2*, 543-545.

Demina, N. A., and Levitanskaja, P. B., 1940, Studies on pappataci fever. X. Attempts to cultivate the virus on the chorio-allantoic membrane of the chick embryo. Med. Parasit. and Parasit. Dis. (Moscow), *9*, 272-284 (Russian). Abstr. in Trop. Dis. Bull., 1943, *40*, 305.

Demina, N., 1941, Studies on pappataci fever. XI. Further investigations on the pappataci virus in culture. Med. Parasit. and Parasit. Dis. (Moscow), *10*, 271-283 (Russian). Abstr. in Trop. Dis. Bull., 1943, *40*, 305.

Doerr, R., Franz, K., and Taussig, S., 1909, Das Pappatacifieber. Leipzig und Wien, Deuticke.

Doerr, R., and Russ, V. K., 1909, Weitere Untersuchungen über das Pappatacifieber. Arch. f. Schiffs u. Tropen-Hyg., *13*, 693-706.

Fleming, J., Bignall, J. R., and Blades, A. N., 1947, Sandfly fever: review of 664 cases. Lancet, *1*, 443-445.

Hertig, M., and Fisher, R. A., 1945, Control of sandflies with DDT. Bull. U. S. Army Med. Dept., No. 88 (May), 97-101.

Johannsen, O. A., 1943, A noxious species of Phlebotomus in the Okefenokee Swamp, Georgia. Psyche, *50*, 112-113.

Moshkovsky, S. D., Diomina, N. A., Nossina, V. D., Pavlova, E. A., Livshitz, J. L., Pels, H. J., and Roubtzova, V. P., 1937, Pappataci fever. VIII. On

the transmission of the virus of pappataci fever in phlebotomi born from eggs laid by infected females. Med. Parasitol., *6*, 922-937 (in Russian).

Newstead, R., 1911, The papataci flies (Phlebotomus) of the Maltese Islands. Ann. Trop. Med. Parasitol., *5*, 139-186.

Paul, J. R., Melnick, J. L., and Sabin, A. B., 1948, Experimental attempts to transmit phlebotomus (sandfly, pappataci) and dengue fevers to chimpanzees. Proc. Soc. Exp. Biol. and Med., *68*, 193-198.

Philip, C. B., Paul, J. R., and Sabin, A. B., 1944, Dimethyl phthalate in control of phlebotomus (pappataci or sandfly) fever. War Medicine, *6*, 27-33.

Pick, A., 1886, Zur Pathologie und Therapie einer eigenthümlichen endemischen Krankheitsform. Wien. med. Wchnschr., *36*, 1141-1145; 1168-1171.

Sabin, A. B., 1943-1948, Unpublished studies on phlebotomus fever.

Sabin, A. B., 1951, Experimental studies on phlebotomus (pappataci, sandfly) fever during World War II. Arch. f. d. ges. Virusforschung, *4*, 367-410.

Sabin, A. B., Philip, C. B., and Paul, J. R., 1944, Phlebotomus (pappataci or sandfly) fever: a disease of military importance; summary of existing knowledge and preliminary report of original investigations. J. Am. Med. Assn., *125*, 603-606; 693-699.

Shortt, H. E., Poole, L. T., and Stephens, E. D., 1935, Note on some experiments with sandfly fever blood and serum. Indian J. Med. Res., *23*, 279-284.

Shortt, H. E., Pandit, C. G., and Rao, R. S., 1938, The virus of sandfly fever in culture and certain of its properties. Indian J. Med. Res., *26*, 229-239.

Shortt, H. E., Pandit, C. G., and Anderson, W. M. E., 1939, Studies on sandfly fever virus, Abstr. Communic. Third Internat. Congress Microbiol., p. 133.

Taussig, S., 1905, Die Hundskrankheit, endemischer Magankatarrh in der Herzegowina. Wien. klin. Wchnschr., *18,* 129-136; 163-169.

Whittingham, H. E., 1924, The etiology of phlebotomus fever. J. State Med., *32,* 461-469.

Whittingham, H. E., and Rook, A. F., 1923, The prevention of phlebotomus fever. Trans. Roy. Soc. Trop. Med. and Hyg., *17,* 290-330.

Whittingham, H. E., and Rook, A. F., 1923a, Observations on the life history and bionomics of *Phlebotomus papatasii.* Brit. Med. J., *2,* 1144-1151.

Young, T. C. McC., Richmond, A. E., and Brendish, G. R., 1926, Sandflies and sandfly fever in the Peshawar district. Indian J. Med. Res., *13,* 961-1021.

JOHN C. SNYDER, M.D.

Harvard University, School of Public Health

35

The Typhus Fevers

Several human infections are induced by micro-organisms called "rickettsiae" which have been tentatively placed in the family *Rickettsiaceae* (Pinkerton, 1936). These micro-organisms are intermediate in characteristics between bacteria and viruses. They are readily visible in microscopic preparations as pleomorphic cocco-bacillary forms, multiply only within certain cells of susceptible species, and are found in various arthropods in nature. On the basis of clinical features, epidemiologic aspects, serologic and immunologic characteristics, the rickettsial diseases of man are divided into the five groups listed below.

1. Typhus group (discussed in this chapter)
   a. Classic epidemic (louse-borne) typhus
   b. Brill's disease (recrudescent typhus)
   c. Murine (flea-borne) typhus
2. Spotted-fever group (Chapter 36)
3. Scrub typhus (Tsutsugamushi disease) (Chapter 37)
4. Q fever (Chapter 38)
5. Trench fever (Chapter 39)

CLASSIC EPIDEMIC TYPHUS (LOUSE-BORNE)

(SYNONYMS: Jail fever, camp fever, war fever, famine fever, ship fever, hospital fever, petechial fever, morbus hungaricus, *typhus historique, typhus exanthematique, dermotypho, tabardillo, typhus exantematico, Fleckfieber*)

INTRODUCTION

Typhus fever is an acute, infectious disease characterized by sustained high fever, severe headache, generalized macular or maculopapular rash, and termination by rapid lysis in 14 to 18 days. Case-fatality rate in epidemics is about 20 per cent. The etiologic agent was named *Rickettsia prowazeki* in honor of two investigators, Dr. Howard Taylor Ricketts, an American, and Dr. S. von Prowazek, an Austrian, who died of typhus fever in the course of their studies of its etiology (da Rocha-Lima, 1916).

HISTORY

Although typhus fever has probably afflicted mankind since ancient times, it has not been definitely identified in the numerous records of epidemics which occurred before the sixteenth century. Zinsser believed that the account of an illness in the Italian monastery near Salerno which occurred in 1083 may have referred to typhus fever (Zinsser, 1935). However, the description by Fracastorius (1546) is the earliest medical record which is sufficiently clear to identify typhus fever as a separate entity. The word typhus is derived from the Greek, *typhos*, meaning smoky or hazy. Although the term had been used by Hippocrates to depict a "confused state of intellect with a tendency to stupor," it was not actually applied to typhus fever until

1760 when Sauvages selected it to describe the mental state of patients suffering from the disease (Murchison, 1884). It should be emphasized that *typhus* and *typhoid* fevers were frequently confused by physicians until 1837 when W. W. Gerhard in Philadelphia called attention to the important clinical and pathologic differences between the two diseases (Gerhard, 1837). Confusion in terminology persists even now, since *typhoid fever* is called *typhus abdominalis* in some parts of Europe.

Typhus fever has always been intimately associated with wars, famines and human misfortunes of all kinds. Its effect on the outcome of battles has often been decisive. The earliest military chronicle implicating typhus is that which describes the siege of Granada in 1489; there were 17,000 deaths from typhus in the Spanish Army, almost six times the number killed in combat with the Moors (Villalba, quoted from Zinsser, 1935). Perhaps typhus was brought to Spain by the Spanish soldiers who had fought against the Turks in Cyprus. Soon thereafter the disease broke out in Italy where Fracastorius had occasion to study its characteristics. In 1528, the French Army besieging Naples was at the point of decisive victory over the forces of Charles V, a victory which would have had enormous effects on the subsequent developments in Europe. But then " . . . typhus made its political debut—by one of the most far-reaching and profoundly effective strokes of its entire career . . . " (Zinsser, 1935). With great rapidity it struck down 30,000 soldiers in the camps of the French and the remnants of the army were forced to withdraw.

The Balkan campaigns in the sixteenth century contributed greatly to the spread of typhus across Europe. Large forces were assembled from various parts of Germany, Italy and France for combat with the Turks, but many of the men were stricken by typhus before they reached the battlefields. The disease became known as the "morbus hungaricus" as it was disseminated throughout Europe by the soldiers returning from Hungary (Prinzing, 1916). The first account of a typhus epidemic in the New World is found in the writings of Padre Sabagun (Sinclair and Maxcy, 1925), who refers to the severe epidemic in the highlands of Mexico in 1576 and 1577 during which more than two million Indians died. Although the records suggest that typhus fever may have existed in the New World before the arrival of the Spanish explorers, it is not possible to decide this point on present evidence (Zinsser, 1935). Throughout the seventeenth century typhus continued its exploits in Europe, affecting civilians and soldiers alike in the military struggles of that era. During the Thirty Years' War, the Swedish army under Gustavus Adolphus was forced to withdraw from a projected campaign against Wallenstein at Nuremberg in 1632, because typhus, aided by scurvy, killed 18,000 soldiers. In the century and a half between the Thirty Years' War and the Napoleonic campaigns, typhus contributed almost continuously to the chronicles of epidemic disease. The disaster which befell Napoleon's army of half a million men in 1812 was in part the work of typhus. During the period from 1816 to 1819, a great epidemic of typhus is said to have caused at least 700,000 cases among the six million inhabitants of Ireland (Zinsser, 1935). Typhus tended to subside somewhat in the last half of the nineteenth century, but it reappeared again in World War I, striking Serbia severely in 1915. There were only 400 Serbian doctors and almost all of them contracted typhus; 126 of these doctors died. The mortality in the civilian population ranged from approximately 20 per cent during the rise and decline of the epidemic, to 60 and even 70 per cent at its height. In less than six months more than 150,000 Serbians died of typhus (Hunter, 1919; Strong et al., 1920). Between 1918 and 1922, typhus ravaged Russia; estimates place the number of cases as

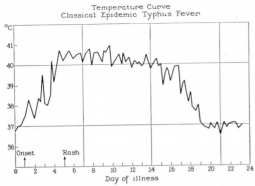

CHART 29. Temperature curve, classic
epidemic typhus fever.

high as thirty million in this period and
deaths as many as three million (Beeuwkes,
1926).

Between World War I and World War II
typhus was reported from China, Russia,
Poland, the Balkans, Iran, Egypt, Abys-
sinia, Algeria, Tunisia, Morocco, South
Africa, Mexico, Guatemala, Colombia,
Bolivia, and Chile. During World War II
some of these countries suffered sharp increases in the incidence of typhus, particularly French North Africa, Egypt, Iran,
Yugoslavia, Japan and Korea. Information
from Poland and Russia is incomplete.
Moreover, typhus appeared in epidemic
form in a few countries which ordinarily
are free from the disease, notably Spain,
Italy and Germany. Cases were reported
from England and France, but these were
repatriated persons who traveled to those
countries during the incubation period of
the disease. During World War II typhus
more than once threatened to complicate
military operations. The areas of North
Africa in which Allied forces made their
landings in late 1942 were suffering from
severe outbreaks of typhus. In October,
1943, the disease broke out in Naples just
as that badly overcrowded and heavily
bombed city was occupied by the Allied
forces (Bayne-Jones, 1948). In 1944, the
Yugoslavian army, engaged in bitter
struggle with the Germans, was severely
handicapped by the spread of typhus not
only in the civilian population but in the

army itself (Murray, 1945). As the Allied
armies crossed Germany in 1945, typhus
was encountered in many of the notorious
Nazi concentration camps. Although only
a very short interval elapsed between the
liberation of these camps and the arrival
of adequate forces to maintain discipline
and control from the sanitary point of view,
many of the louse-infested, typhus-infected
inmates escaped into the surrounding
countryside, scattering far and wide. Attempts to restrict the spread of typhus were
vastly handicapped by the floods of persons who had been transplanted into Germany from occupied countries; more than
a million of these "slave laborers" were
freed by the Allied armies and nearly all
crowded the roads seeking to return to
their own countries (Snyder, 1947).
Shortly after the cessation of hostilities in
the Far East, Japan and Korea underwent
a severe typhus epidemic of approximately
26,000 cases (Scoville, 1948).

The examples cited above are only a few
of the many recorded epidemics of typhus
fever, but they suffice to indicate that
classic typhus has been one of the major
epidemic diseases of all time. It is probable
that typhus fever has been exceeded only
by malaria as a cause of widespread human
suffering. (References which contain reviews of the literature: Hirsch, 1883;
Murchison, 1884; Strong et al., 1920; Wolbach, Todd and Palfrey, 1922; Otto and
Munter, 1930; Zinsser, 1935; Snyder,
1947.)

CLINICAL PICTURE

The incubation period usually is from
10 to 14 days; but it may be shorter if
the infecting dose is unusually large. Prodromal symptoms occur infrequently; if
present, they are headache, lassitude and
weakness, sometimes accompanied by slight
fever. Onset is usually abrupt and patients
are frequently able to state the exact hour
at which they noted the beginning of their
illness. The first symptoms are malaise,
chilly sensations, headache, weakness, gen-

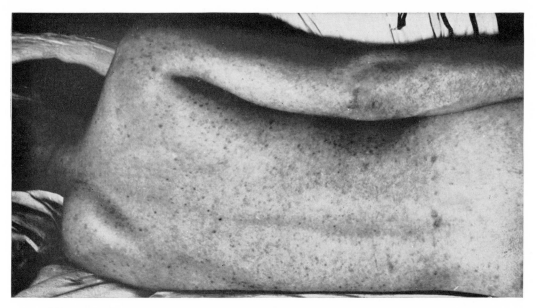

FIG. 43. Photograph of patient with typical rash of typhus fever, eleventh day of disease. (U.S.A. Typhus Commission.)

eralized aches and pains. During the first two or three days the temperature may fluctuate from normal to 39° C., but after the third day it attains a level of 39° to 41° C. where it remains until death or recovery of the patient (Chart 29).

There may be one or more shaking chills early in the first week. Headache increases in severity and may be generalized or most severe in the frontal region; it is one of the most constant features of typhus fever, and efforts to diminish its intensity usually fail. Patients tend to cough in the first week of disease without raising much, if any, sputum. Vomiting occurs infrequently with the onset of the disease and is rare after the third day, except when azotemia develops. Constipation is far commoner than is diarrhea. Patients may appear to be deaf, and they often complain of ringing in the ears or vertigo. Pains in the muscles of the back and legs may be very troublesome. The appearance of a generalized eruption, usually between the fourth and seventh days of the disease, is an important feature. Preceding the rash in some instances, there may be a transient blotchy erythema or a

marbled appearance of the skin, sometimes referred to as subcuticular mottling. The characteristic rash is first apparent on the trunk, spreading in the course of one or two days over the entire body except the face, palms and soles, which are involved only in gravely ill patients. Lesions have been recognized on the soft palate in rare instances. At first the skin lesions are macules or maculopapules about two to four millimeters in diameter, pinkish to bright red in color, with rather indefinite borders. Slight pressure causes them to fade completely. This eruption has been described as a "mulberry rash" (Fig. 43).

The rash may be absent throughout the disease in perhaps 10 per cent of light-skinned persons; lesions are even more difficult to detect in dark-skinned persons. In the first few days, the pulse rate may not be quite so high as the temperature would warrant, but toward the end of the first week and for the remainder of the disease the pulse rate is rapid in proportion to the temperature. The blood pressure is usually low, and there may be brief periods of severe hypotension. The respiratory rate is quite often increased out of proportion to any findings in the chest. Toward the end of the first week, patients exhibit varying degrees of photophobia and suffusion of the conjunctivae. The face is often flushed and sometimes assumes a dusky appearance. Some observers have commented on the presence of facial edema in certain patients. Delirium may appear, but it is more common to observe only mental dullness or slight stupor at this stage. The urine frequently is reduced in amount and the specific gravity is elevated. Sometimes there may be inability to void or incontinence of urine and feces, although these usually do not occur before the second or third week.

In the second week of illness, the skin lesions become darker in color, assuming a reddish to reddish-purple hue; pressure no longer causes them to fade. In mild cases the rash may last for two or three days and then disappear. In moderately or severely ill patients, the lesions are usually visible until the end of the febrile period. In many of the severe cases the rash becomes petechial or even frankly hemorrhagic. Confluence of the rash has been noted in very severely ill patients. In general, there is no residual evidence of the rash after recovery; in rare instances, however, brownish areas of pigmentation are visible for several months. If a patient dies, the rash ordinarily persists after death, particularly in dependent areas.

The second and third weeks of illness constitute the critical period. Increasing prostration develops and patients are unable to eat or drink without assistance. Mental dullness supervenes and patients seem to be quite deaf. The dullness may progress to stupor or coma. The stupor may be interrupted by brief episodes of delirium in which patients become active or even violent and then lapse back into apathy. They may mutter to themselves or carry on conversations with imaginary friends. In rare instances, stiffness of the neck may develop in sufficient degree to prompt the performance of a lumbar puncture; the spinal fluid may be under slightly increased pressure but otherwise is normal. Murchison in 1862 gave the following account of the clinical picture of typhus in the second week of the disease which is remarkable for its accuracy. His description is especially interesting not only because he studied the disease for many years, but also because he was one of the very few persons who suffered two severe attacks of classic typhus, a fact which qualified him to write authoritatively of the disease.

. . . the stupor and delirium alternate, the latter being most marked in the night-time. The prostration is extreme: the patient lies on his back, moaning, muttering incoherently, or still and motionless, with a tendency to sink to the bottom of the bed. He is quite unable to raise himself, or even to turn on his side, is with difficulty aroused, and is utterly indifferent to surrounding objects and persons. Tremors, subsultus, and picking of the bedclothes may be observed. The expression is stupid and vacant; the conjunctivae are injected, the eyelids for the most part closed, and the pupils often contracted. Deafness is not uncommon. If spoken to loudly, the patient opens his eyes and stares vacantly at those about him, and when told to put out his tongue he opens his mouth and leaves it open until desired to close it. These are all the signs of consciousness exhibited; and even they may be absent. But all this time the mind is far from inactive; the imagination conjures up the most frightful fancies, to which implicit belief is attached, and of which a distinct recollection may remain after recovery. The ideas often revolve on previous events of the patient's life. He believes himself persecuted and tormented by his attendants and dearest relatives; he compresses years into hours, and in a few hours imagines that he has lived a life-time. They who have passed through these mental sufferings can alone imagine their intensity. The teeth and lips are now covered with sordes; the tongue is hard and dry, dark brown or black, contracted into a ball, tremulous and protruded with difficulty or not at all. The abdomen is flaccid, or sometimes tympanitic; the bowels are still confined, or one or two slightly relaxed motions are passed daily in bed. The urine is more copious, but paler, and of low specific gravity, and is passed involuntarily, or retained so as to necessitate recourse to the catheter. The skin is cooler than before, and sometimes moist; the number of spots presenting a petechial character increases. The parts subjected to pressure and particularly the skin over the sacrum become red and tender, and are liable to slough. The pulse is frequent (112 to 140), small, weak, and undulating, often disclosed by roentgenograms than by physical examination. Respirations are usually rapid and somewhat shallow. The blood pressure continues to be lower than normal and may fall below 80/50 in severe cases. Although the myocardium is damaged, the syndrome of congestive heart

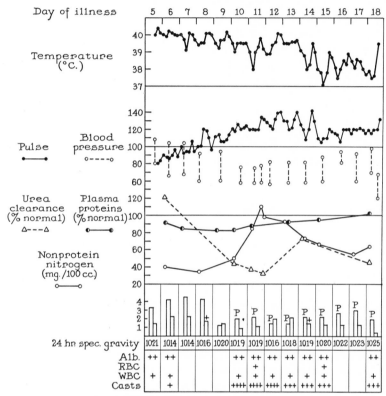

CHART 30. Graphic representation of clinical findings on a male patient, 46 years old, admitted on 5th day of disease, dying on 18th day. In space on chart directly above "specific gravity," data about fluid intake and output (liters/24 hrs.) are portrayed; P represents fluid given parenterally. (Yeomans, A., Snyder, J. C., Murray, E. S., Ecke, R. S., and Zarafonetis, C. J. D., 1945, Azotemia in typhus fever. Annals of Internal Medicine, *23,* 735.)

and not unfrequently [sic] intermittent, irregular, or scarcely perceptible; the cardiac impulse and systolic sound of the heart are diminished in intensity, or absent. (Murchison, 1884, pp. 122-123.)

To this account a few more details may be added to complete the picture of the critical period of the illness. Persistent cough with difficulty in expectoration may be accompanied by development of a patchy pulmonary consolidation, more failure does not appear in the acute stage of the disease. Gallop rhythm often develops in severely ill patients. The spleen becomes palpable in about half the cases. Renal insufficiency of varying degree is a common occurrence. Oliguria and elevated blood urea nitrogen are nearly always features of the clinical course of fatal cases of typhus fever (Yeomans et al., 1945). (Chart 30) Gangrene of the toes, feet, tips of fingers, ear lobes, nose, penis, scrotum or vulva may occur. Parotitis, otitis media and furunculosis are common complications which may appear toward the end of the second week of illness.

In fatal cases, the terminal period is usually characterized by profound stupor which changes to coma; some patients have other features characteristic of uremia. Cyanosis deepens and pulmonary consolidation develops to an extent readily detectable by physical examination. The blood pressure may fall to a very low level. Evidence of peripheral vascular collapse may be noted shortly before death. The skin becomes cold and moist with a livid appearance; the pulse becomes very faint or absent at the wrist, and death ensues. In some instances, the temperature may drop to subnormal values a few hours before death. Unless the fatal termination is due to secondary bacterial infection, death from typhus per se usually occurs between the ninth and eighteenth days of illness.

If a patient recovers, the fever generally subsides by rapid lysis in the third week of illness, the temperature becoming normal or subnormal within two or five days. The mental state improves strikingly when the temperature begins its descent. With the exception of infrequent cases of very severe encephalitis due to typhus itself, recovery of normal mental and physical capacities is remarkably rapid in convalescence. Full strength and activity are regained in two or three months. An astonishing feature of the disease is the absence of serious sequelae, despite the fact that the central nervous system, myocardium and kidneys are dangerously involved in the acute stage. (References which give detailed descriptions of the clinical course of typhus: Murchison, 1884; Wolbach, Todd and Palfrey, 1922; van den Ende et al., 1946; Yeomans, 1947, 1948.)

The hemoglobin and red blood cell count decrease during the course of typhus, particularly in the second and third weeks of illness when the red count may fall to 3.5 million cells per cubic millimeter with a corresponding reduction in hemoglobin values. Return to normal levels usually is rapid. In the first week of illness, the white blood cell count tends to be somewhat reduced; values range from 8,000 to 2,000 cells per cubic millimeter. Differential counts are interesting chiefly because of the constant absence of eosinophiles during the febrile period. In the second and third weeks of illness, the white blood cell count may be normal or slightly elevated. In the presence of secondary bacterial complications, the leukocyte count may be considerably above normal. Practically all patients have albumin in the urine in varying amounts while fever is present. There is a tendency for the specific gravity of the urine to be high during the first week, possibly because of dehydration. In the second and third weeks of the disease, severely ill patients may excrete only small amounts of urine of relatively low specific gravity. Diuresis has been observed at the beginning of the convalescent period in some patients. Red blood cells may occur in the urine in varying numbers, but gross hematuria is a very rare finding. Granular casts, however, may be numerous, particularly when patients have nitrogen retention. The nonprotein nitrogen and urea nitrogen of the blood are increased in about half the cases. The rise begins in the second week of illness, and often follows a drop of blood pressure, although not invariably. Values between 100 and 200 mg. per cent for the blood nonprotein nitrogen have been observed with survival of the patient, but usually such levels presage fatal outcome. A reduction in renal plasma flow may be responsible for the kidney damage. The appearance of renal insufficiency as indicated by azotemia is one of the earliest laboratory findings of serious prognostic import; azotemia precedes death almost without exception. Changes in serum proteins are observed toward the end of the first week of illness; serum albumin is reduced and serum globulin is increased, leading to a reversal of the albumin-globulin ratio. Serum chlorides are usually reduced below 95 milliequivalents per liter, and values as low as 85 may be encountered; the chlorides in the urine are concomitantly reduced. Carbon dioxide the lung field, often more extensive than the physical signs of pulmonary involvement would indicate. Transient abnormalities in the electrocardiogram have been recorded; these consist of low voltage of

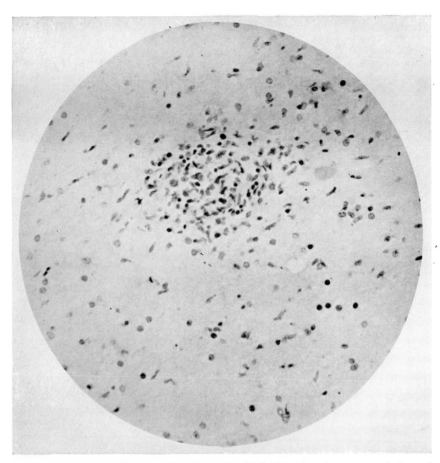

FIG. 44. Section of brain of patient who died of typhus fever on 13th day of disease showing a typical typhus nodule in the medulla oblongata; note proliferative character of the lesion. × 275. (Dr. W. B. MacAllister and the U.S.A. Typhus Commission; photograph by Dr. R. M. Allen.)

combining power of the blood is either normal or reduced; serum pH is normal in most instances. Likewise, values for plasma volume are within the accepted normal range. The slight reduction in whole blood volume encountered toward the end of the disease in some patients is attributed to a reduction in red cell volume alone (Phillips, Yeomans and Tierney, 1948). Roentgenograms of the chest frequently reveal a diffuse mottling of various areas in the QRS complexes, low or inverted T waves, and less often, depression of the S-T segment. (References dealing with laboratory findings in typhus: Otto and Munter, 1930; Woodward and Bland, 1944; Yeomans et al., 1945; Tierney and Yeomans, 1946; Yeomans, 1947, 1948.)

PATHOLOGIC PICTURE

There are no gross findings characteristic of typhus fever at necropsy except the skin lesions. Bronchopneumonia, myocardial changes and petechial hemorrhages in the subcutaneous tissues and brain are the principal features which may be observed. Rarely, symmetrical gangrene of the extremities and thrombosis of a large blood vessel may be present. The microscopic pathology of typhus is quite characteristic. Rickettsiae multiply inside endothelial cells lining small blood vessels. Affected cells become swollen and proliferation occurs as shown by numerous mitotic figures. Thrombosis results from injury caused by rickettsial growth. Accumulation of polymorphonuclear leukocytes, macrophages and lymphoid cells around such lesions in capillaries, arterioles or venules gives rise to distinctive histologic appearance sometimes referred to as Fraenkel's nodules (Fig. 44). Early stages in the development of these lesions have been studied by skin biopsies (Wolbach, Todd and Palfrey, 1922). Rickettsiae can be demonstrated by careful technic in some of the endothelial cells. Vascular lesions are most numerous in the skin, central nervous system and myocardium, but are scattered widely throughout different organs of the body. Necrotic areas of the skin appear to be associated with thrombosis of capillaries, small arteries, and veins beginning in the corium. Symmetrical gangrene of the extremities may be due to nerve lesions instead of thrombosis of large vessels. Lesions in the respiratory tract are similar to those in terminal bronchopneumonic processes in various diseases and are not distinctive of typhus. (References which describe the pathology of typhus: Ceelen, 1919; Wolbach, Todd and Palfrey, 1922; Wolbach, 1948.)

Experimental Infection;
Host Range

Classic epidemic typhus is a disease which occurs as a natural infection of man, the human body louse, *Pediculus humanus corporis,* and the human head louse, *Pediculus humanus capitis.* The role of the human body louse in the transmission of typhus, although previously suspected (Otto, 1909), was first demonstrated experimentally by Nicolle, Comte and Conseil (1909). Their observations were promptly confirmed (Ricketts and Wilder, 1910a; Anderson and Goldberger, 1912). The human body louse spends its entire existence in the clothes of man. Eggs are laid in the seams of the undergarments. After about eight days, the eggs hatch and the nymphs in the course of two weeks go through three moults to become adults. The insects crawl about on the clothes, leaving the garments only to take a blood meal from their host. Lice cannot fly or jump but they have been observed to crawl for several yards. Each louse takes four to six blood meals a day from its host under natural conditions. Human blood constitutes their only food. *R. prowazeki* is present in the blood of patients suffering from typhus during the febrile period of the disease. The body louse becomes infected by imbibing a blood meal containing rickettsiae, which then enter cells lining the intestinal tract of the louse. All stages of lice, whether newly hatched lymphs or fully developed adults, are susceptible to infection with *R. prowazeki.* After a few days the rickettsiae have multiplied so profusely that the cells containing them are swollen and may burst. The organisms may then be passed in the feces of the louse or may enter uninvolved cells lining the intestinal tract. Ordinarily, rickettsiae appear in the feces of a typhus-infected louse about three to five days after the first infective meal. The louse usually succumbs to the infection after seven to ten days, but it is important to note that 24 days may elapse before all cells of the mid-intestine become full of rickettsiae.

Lice have been extensively used in typhus research. For this purpose a colony of normal stock lice is maintained by feeding on healthy human subjects twice daily. The lice are confined in a small capsule covered with bolting silk which is strapped to the leg or arm. Sometimes it is more convenient to store the capsule in an incubator between feedings. If the temperature is lower than 30° C., or higher than 32° C., rickettsiae may fail to develop; at temperatures above 37° C. the louse colony fares poorly. An ingenious technic was developed for the experimental infection of lice by means of a glass capillary inserted into the insect's rectum (Weigl, 1920). Lice thus infected develop typhus which is similar in every respect to the infection acquired by feeding. Although lice ordinarily do not thrive if nourished on other species than man, it has been possible to infect and to nourish them on rabbits, thereby permitting a wider range of experiments with these insects (Snyder and Wheeler, 1945). Quantitative studies with lice have been facilitated by the development of a technic for feeding the insects through a membrane of chick skin (Fuller, Murray and Snyder, 1949).

The presence of rickettsiae in the feces of lice or in the intestinal tract of a louse may be demonstrated by means of smear preparations or fixed tissue sections (Wolbach, Todd and Palfrey, 1922). Since nonpathogenic rickettsiae may be encountered in the intestinal tract of normal lice, the demonstration of rickettsialike organisms in smears of louse feces or intestines is not sufficient evidence upon which to base a diagnosis of typhus infection. *Rickettsiae prowazeki* are present only in the intestinal lining cells and the feces of infected lice; they have not been demonstrated in other tissues, such as the salivary glands; they are not passed from generation to generation of lice in the egg.

The course of typhus infection in the human head louse is identical to that in the body louse (Goldberger and Anderson, 1912), but the latter is far more important in transmission of epidemic typhus. (References: Wolbach, Todd and Palfrey, 1922; da Rocha-Lima, 1930; Buxton, 1939.)

Monkeys, guinea pigs, rats and other rodents, developing chick embryos, and certain arthropods are susceptible to experimental infection with classic epidemic typhus. Monkeys inoculated with *R. prowazeki* undergo a febrile illness of a few days' duration from which they survive as a rule (Nicolle, 1909; Anderson and Goldberger, 1912). A skin eruption has been described in typhus-infected monkeys, but more often this is absent. The animals suffer loss of appetite and become apathetic, but otherwise exhibit no evidence of illness. In typhus research, the inoculation of monkeys is neither satisfactory nor practicable.

Typhus was transmitted to guinea pigs by Nicolle, Conseil and Conor (1911), who observed that the animals responded to inoculation by developing a fever of several days' duration. Typhus is established in guinea pigs by the intraabdominal inoculation of blood taken from a typhus patient during the febrile period. If the specimen is obtained in the first week of illness, whole blood may be used. After the seventh or eighth day it is advisable to allow the specimen to clot; after centrifugation the serum is separated and stored for use in serologic tests; the clot is then ground with an equal volume of a sterile diluent, such as saline solution, skimmed milk or nutrient broth. After allowing gross particles to settle out, the suspension of ground clot is inoculated into two male guinea pigs, each weighing about 500 grams; each animal is given four to five cubic centimeters. Female pigs may be employed successfully, but, for reasons to be mentioned in the section on murine typhus, male guinea pigs are preferred. Removal of the serum from the clot serves to increase the chance of successful detection of rickettsiae by eliminating antibodies which are present in the patient's blood serum after the seventh day of illness. In some instances, the pigs may be sick during the first 18 to 24 hours after the inoculation, probably as a consequence of the large volume of blood which is required for successful isolation of rickettsiae. A small percentage of animals may succumb at this stage. Usually, however, the animals remain entirely well after the inoculation and the detection of the rickettsial infection depends solely on the temperature curve. The normal morning temperature of a guinea pig varies between 38° and 39.5° C.; values above 40.0° C. are indicative of fever. Ordinarily, guinea pigs which are inoculated with a patient's blood have a somewhat prolonged incubation

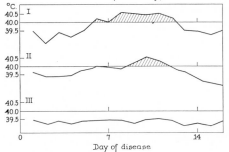

Temperatures of Guinea Pigs
Inoculated with Classical Epidemic Typhus-Breinl Strain

CHART 31. Temperature curves of guinea pigs infected with classic typhus fever. (I) Usual curve found in about 90 per cent of guinea pigs. (II) Atypical curve found in about 5 per cent of guinea pigs. (III) No febrile response found in about 5 per cent of guinea pigs.

period before their temperature exceeds 40.0° C.; 12 to 24 days may elapse before the rise occurs. When suspensions of brain or spleen of such animals are removed on the third or fourth day of fever for subinoculation to fresh guinea pigs by the intraabdominal route, the incubation period is shortened to seven to nine days and remains at this interval in successive transfers made in this manner.

To accomplish a transfer, a febrile guinea pig is lightly anesthetized with ether and bled out from the heart; the brain is removed and ground to a 10 per cent suspension in a suitable diluent. One or two cc. of the suspension are used for the intraabdominal inoculation of each guinea pig in the next passage. Spleen may be employed successfully instead of brain if taken on the second or third day of fever. The only evidence of infection with *R. prowazeki* to be observed grossly at the time

of sacrifice of the guinea pig is a fibrinous exudate over the surface of the spleen; this is a constant finding on first passage as well as in subsequent transfers. Direct smears made by scraping a few cells from the surface of the spleen just beneath this exudate, when stained appropriately, may contain a few large serosal cells in which rickettsiae are found. It is extremely difficult to find cells containing rickettsiae in smears of spleen or tunica vaginalis in guinea pigs infected with classic epidemic strains unless the search is made on the first or second day of the febrile reaction. The fever may last for only two or three days, more commonly about a week, rarely longer than ten days. Guinea pigs survive typhus infection without sequelae unless the infecting dose is a massive one, e.g., large volume of infected yolk sac containing billions of rickettsiae per cubic centimeter; in such circumstances the incubation period lasts only a few hours, and, in addition to fever, the animal may show enlargement of the scrotum and adhesions between the testes and the scrotal sac. This "tunica reaction" or "scrotal swelling" was first observed by Neill (1917) and further studied by Mooser (1928); the phenomenon is sometimes called the Neill-Mooser reaction. Although it may be observed in pigs infected with classic epidemic typhus, particularly if numerous rickettsiae are present in the inoculum, the reaction is more common in murine typhus.

Guinea pigs do not develop a skin eruption as a consequence of typhus infection, but microscopic examination of the brain taken in the period from the third or fourth day of fever up to a few days after the end of the fever shows the presence of many vascular lesions similar to those found in the brains of man and monkeys. A serious disadvantage to the use of guinea pigs for the laboratory study of classic epidemic typhus is the fact that the only evidence of infection is obtained by taking the rectal temperatures daily for several weeks (Chart 31, curves I and II). Unfortunately, fever is not a constant feature of typhus infection in guinea pigs. Approximately 5 per cent of guinea pigs inoculated with fully virulent material fail to exhibit a febrile response (Chart 31, curve III).

The cotton rat (*Sigmodon hispidus his-*

sist several fatal challenge doses. The minimal number of typhus rickettsiae detectable in cotton rats is approximately the same as that required for detection in human body lice (Fuller, Snyder and Murray, 1952); by contrast several times as many are usu-

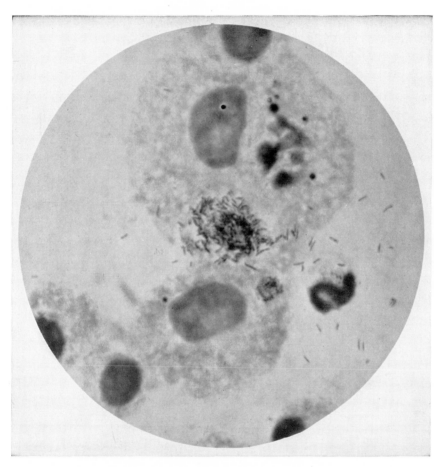

Fig. 45. Microphotograph showing typhus rickettsiae inside and outside of cells. Macchiavello's stain. × 2000. (Photograph by Dr. R. M. Allen.)

pidus) has been very useful in recent quantitative studies with typhus rickettsiae (Snyder and Anderson, 1942; Anderson, 1944; Murray and Snyder, 1951). This species succumbs to infection following intracardial inoculation of 10^7 to 10^8 living typhus rickettsiae. It develops a definite immunity by 21 days after intraabdominal inoculation of very small numbers of rickettsiae; complement-fixation tests become strongly positive, and the animals then re-

ally required to produce fever in guinea pigs (Murray, Pauls and Snyder, 1952).

The white rat is not susceptible to infection with classic epidemic typhus in the usual sense; it undergoes only an inapparent infection. An attempt to maintain a strain by serial passage in white rats usually is unsuccessful, a phenomenon of value in differentiating murine from classic epidemic typhus.

The white mouse undergoes only an inapparent infection when inoculated by the intraabdominal route with most strains of classic epidemic typhus if the inoculum contains relatively few *R. prowazeki*. It is possible, however, to maintain a strain for several passages in mice by intraabdominal inoculation of brain suspensions. Intranasal inoculation of rich suspensions of *R. prowazeki* is followed by pulmonary consolidation and death; strains have been

hispidus hispidus (Snyder and Anderson, 1942); the South African gerbil, *Tatera brantsi* (Gear and Davis, 1942) and Egyptian gerbilles, *Gerbillus gerbillus* and *Gerbillus pyramidum* (Snyder, Zarafonetis and Liu, 1945). Giroud (1938) studied skin lesions produced in rabbits by living as well as killed rickettsiae. It should be emphasized that the attempt to recover typhus rickettsiae from a patient is a research prob-

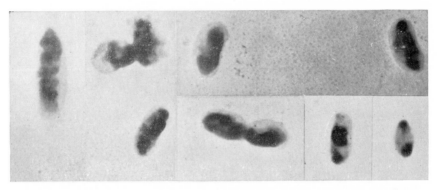

FIG. 46. Electron micrographs, rickettsiae of epidemic typhus. Original magnification × 8000, enlarged twice for reproduction. (Plotz, H., Smadel, J. E., Anderson, T. F., and Chambers, L. A., 1943, Morphological structure of rickettsiae. Journal of Experimental Medicine, *77*, 358.)

maintained in mice indefinitely by passage in this manner (Durand and Giroud, 1940). Exposure of white mice to large doses of x-ray increases their susceptibility, and small numbers of rickettsiae given by the intraabdominal route then produce a fatal infection within several days (Liu, Snyder and Enders, 1941). Intravenous or intraabdominal inoculation of concentrated suspensions of living, fully virulent rickettsiae into normal white mice is followed in a few hours by death of the animals as a consequence of a "toxic" reaction (Gildemeister and Haagen, 1940). The white rat also succumbs to the toxic property of epidemic typhus rickettsiae a few hours following intravenous inoculation of concentrated suspensions of the micro-organisms (Neva and Snyder, 1952).

Various other species have been employed in laboratory experiments with typhus, notably the cotton rat, *Sigmodon*

lem not to be undertaken for ordinary diagnostic purposes.

ETIOLOGY

As a consequence of conflicting evidence bearing on the etiology of typhus (Plotz, Olitsky and Baehr, 1915) which followed the initial publications of Ricketts and Wilder (1910b) and von Prowazek (1914), there was a period of some uncertainty as to the specific etiologic agent. Da Rocha-Lima's studies of typhus (1916) clearly implicated the etiologic role of the microorganisms which he named; similar findings were obtained in the carefully controlled experiments of Wolbach, Todd and Palfrey (1922) which eliminated all doubts as to the causative relationship of *Rickettsia prowazeki* to epidemic typhus.

R. prowazeki exhibits remarkable variation in its size and shape (Fig. 45). In smear preparations, rickettsiae appear as minute coccoid or rod-shaped organisms, frequently occurring in pairs, sometimes in long chains, and have a diameter of approximately 0.3μ. The organisms often have a bipolar appearance in stained preparations and when visualized by phase contrast microscopy (Ris and Fox, 1949). Studies with the electron microscope (Fig. 46) reveal that rickettsiae "would appear to have a limiting membrane which surrounds a substance that seems to be protoplasmic in nature; numbers of dense granules are embedded in the inner protoplasm" (Plotz et al., 1943). It is difficult to stain *R. prowazeki* by Gram's method. The method described by Macchiavello (1937) is the most satisfactory stain for rickettsiae.

Directions for Macchiavello's stain: Solutions: (A) 0.25 per cent basic fuchsin in distilled water; (B) freshly prepared 0.25 to 0.5 per cent citric acid; (C) 1 per cent methylene blue in distilled water. Smears are fixed lightly in heat, stained for three to five minutes with freshly filtered fuchsin; the fuchsin is poured off the slide which is then quickly dipped in the freshly prepared citric acid solution; it is removed immediately and placed in a dish containing running tap water. The final step is the flooding of the slide with methylene blue which is poured off after a few seconds. The slide is then washed briefly in running tap water, and dried with a piece of filter paper. Rickettsiae are stained a bright pink or red against a bluish background.

R. prowazeki is relatively labile and easily killed by the common antiseptics such as formalin, phenol, merthiolate, etc. Temperatures above 56° C. for 30 minutes result in its death. Viability may be retained in blood specimens at icebox temperature (+2° to +4° C.) for one or more days, but the organisms die in a few hours at room temperature or at 37° C. *R. prowazeki* in louse feces remains viable for several months if the temperature and humidity are low (Starzyk, 1936). Tap water, distilled water, and ordinary physiologic saline have a deleterious effect on its viability; sterile skimmed milk (Topping, 1940) or "sucrose PG" (Bovarnick, Miller and Snyder, 1950) are the most satisfactory media for preserving viability of rickettsiae

in suspensions. They have remained alive in tissues stored in glycerol under some circumstances (Pinkerton, 1942). The most satisfactory method of preserving rickettsiae is the quick freezing in an alcohol-dry-ice mixture in a sealed glass ampule with subsequent storage in a dry-ice cabinet (—76° C.); in this state rickettsiae retain their viability for at least six years (Snyder, 1951). Rapid thawing is important, however, since slow return from the temperature of —76° C. to room temperature results in great loss of viability. Furthermore, even brief periods of storage at temperatures between —5° and —20° C. after quick freezing in an alcohol-dry-ice bath likewise may result in loss of viability (Topping, 1947). Desiccation from the frozen state is satisfactory for storage of strains under appropriate circumstances (Topping, 1940).

Difficulty in obtaining large quantities of pure suspensions of typhus rickettsiae has impeded adequate chemical analyses. Fragmentary evidence indicates the presence of carbohydrate-protein complexes, nucleic acid, and lipids (Castaneda, 1934; Cohen and Chargaff, 1944; Cohen, 1950; Ris and Fox, 1949). When care is taken to preserve the viability of typhus rickettsiae during purification procedures, it is possible to demonstrate that these micro-organisms have independent respiratory activity (Bovarnick and Snyder, 1949; Wisseman et al., 1951); the presence of a transaminase in rickettsiae has also been demonstrated (Bovarnick and Miller, 1950).

Many attempts have been made to cultivate *R. prowazeki* in cell-free media without success. Cultivation in various types of tissue culture has been accomplished (Wolbach and Schlesinger, 1923; Nigg and Landsteiner, 1930; Kligler and Aschner, 1934; Zinsser, Wei and FitzPatrick, 1938). Castaneda (1939) showed that an abundance of rickettsiae could be obtained by the intranasal inoculation of rodents with murine typhus; his observations were extended to the classic louse-borne strains by French workers (Durand and Giroud, 1940). The yolk-sac membrane of developing chick embryos was shown by Cox (1938; 1941; 1948) to be an excellent medium for the cultivation of *R. prowazeki* and several other species of rickettsiae. In general, this technic is the most widely used at the present time. Material containing rickettsiae is inoculated directly into the yolk sac of a six or seven day old embryonated hen's egg. After several days' incubation at 34° to 36° C., the yolk-sac membrane is removed for examination or for subsequent inoculation into other chick embryos. Such infected yolk-sac membranes may contain more than 10^9 viable rickettsiae per cc. Successful isolation of *R. prowazeki* from the blood or bone marrow of patients has been accomplished by direct inoculation of blood or ground clot into developing chick embryos. Rickettsiae may be few or absent in stained smears of the yolk-sac preparation in the first few transfers, but become very abundant in subsequent passages. An important characteristic of *R. prowazeki* is its location only in the cytoplasm of cells, never within nuclei. This feature distinguishes the typhus group from the spotted fever group, members of which do invade nuclei (Pinkerton, 1936).

Infection with *R. prowazeki* evokes serologic responses in man and lower animals; specific antibodies can be demonstrated by fixation of complement, agglutination of rickettsiae, precipitin reactions, opsonic tests, and neutralization or protection tests. There is also a very important serologic test called the Weil-Felix reaction, the agglutination of Proteus OX 19 by sera of typhus patients. Weil and Felix (1916) obtained from the urine of a typhus patient a proteus strain which was agglutinated not only by the serum of the original patient but also by the sera of other typhus patients. Further study of various strains of proteus revealed that the one now called OX 19 is the most suitable for diagnosis of typhus. This phenomenon has been the subject of much experimentation and numerous hypotheses have been advanced in its explanation. Although no etiologic relationship has been detected between strains of this bacterium and typhus fever, Castaneda (1934) demonstrated a carbohydrate antigen common to Proteus OX 19 and to *R. prowazeki*. Although the Weil-Felix reaction occurs in more than 90 per cent of patients suffering from proven louse-borne typhus, the sera of typhus-infected guinea pigs and some other animals fail to develop agglutinins for Proteus OX 19.

Studies by Craigie and associates (1946), Fulton and Begg (1946), and Topping et al. (1945), demonstrated the existence of two components in *R. prowazeki*, a heat-labile component which is specific for *R. prowazeki* and a heat-stable component which is common to both *R. prowazeki* and *R. mooseri*. By repeated washing in a high-speed centrifuge (Plotz et al., 1948), the common antigen can be reduced to a low concentration, resulting in a considerable increase in specificity of some rickettsial suspensions.

Living typhus rickettsiae are toxic for white mice (Gildemeister and Haagen, 1940) and white rats (Neva and Snyder, 1952). They also cause, *in vitro*, the lysis of red blood cells of several species (Clarke and Fox, 1948; Bovarnick, Miller and Snyder, 1952). Both of these properties can be neutralized by sera of man and lower animals convalescent from typhus. Further studies by Topping and associates (1945), Hamilton (1945), and Craigie and associates (1946) indicate that the toxic factors of murine and epidemic rickettsiae are immunologically distinct. Toxicity is intimately associated with living rickettsiae; manipulations which reduce the numbers of living rickettsiae likewise reduce the toxicity of the suspensions. There is no evidence that a true exotoxin is concerned in this phenomenon.

DIAGNOSIS

Before the appearance of the characteristic rash, and on clinical grounds alone, it is impossible to assert with accuracy that a patient is suffering from typhus. The clinical picture of the early stage of several acute infectious diseases closely resembles that of epidemic typhus. Those which are likely to be confused with it are murine typhus, smallpox, relapsing fever, malaria, typhoid fever, meningococcic meningitis, measles and yellow fever. The appearance and evolution of the typhus rash serve to distinguish it from eruptions which are features of certain other acute infectious diseases. In differentiation of typhus from Rocky Mountain spotted fever it is helpful to recall that the rash in the latter disease ordinarily appears first on the exposed extremities and then extends to the trunk, frequently involving the face, palms, and soles as well. The clinical diagnosis of epidemic typhus is particularly difficult in children or in persons who have previously received antityphus vaccine. In such instances, the rash may be of very short duration or absent, the symptoms much less severe, and the duration of the fever as short as three to five days.

Agglutinins for Proteus OX 19 appear in the sera of most typhus patients between the fifth and eighth days of illness. In a high proportion of cases, the titer rises to 1/160 or higher, often attaining values greater than 1/1,000 at the peak of the response which usually occurs in the third week of illness or in the first two weeks of convalescence. The Weil-Felix titer subsides to levels below 1/160 a few weeks after the end of the disease. In exceptional cases, repeated examination of a patient's serum throughout the disease and early convalescence may reveal no rise in Weil-Felix titer, or the patient may succumb without a rise in titer being observed at any time. An infection caused by *Proteus vulgaris* gives rise to agglutinins against Proteus OX 19. In rare instances, a person may be encountered whose serum agglutinates Proteus OX 19, although he is not currently suffering from typhus fever; if this is the case,

the titer remains static, not exhibiting the rise and fall which is characteristic of the response to epidemic typhus. Felix (1944) has reviewed the data on the Weil-Felix test at length and concludes that a rise in titer from a low level (0 or 1/20) to more than double the original value is of diagnostic significance even though the highest titer is less than 1/160. Other writers stress the importance of the rise to values greater than 1/160 before diagnostic significance is attained. The test can be performed with living or killed Proteus OX 19 organisms, but care must be taken to use cultures which are in the "0" form. Slide Weil-Felix tests have been developed by Holt-Harris and Grubbs (1922), Castaneda and Silva (1938), and Brumpt (1943), which can be performed in three to five minutes at the bedside. Different strains of proteus are used for diagnosis of other rickettsial diseases, principally OX 2 and OX K. The sera of typhus patients may show a slight rise in agglutinins for OX 2, but very rarely any for OX K. (Reviews of literature: Felix, 1944; Zarafonetis, 1948; Wertman, 1948.)

Early experiments with antigens derived from infected lice indicated the presence of complement-fixing antibodies in the sera of typhus patients (Jacobsthal, 1917; Epstein, 1922). Castaneda (1936b) prepared suspensions of rickettsiae from the peritoneal washings of x-rayed rats and demonstrated complement-fixing antibodies in human sera and in the sera of convalescent guinea pigs. Cox's development (1938) of the yolk-sac technic for the cultivation of rickettsiae made it possible to prepare large amounts of antigen for serologic tests. Plotz et al. (1948) and Scoville et al. (1948) found that suspensions of rickettsiae derived from yolk sac after repeated washing gave specific antigens suitable for differentiation of antibodies of classic epidemic typhus from those of murine typhus in the sera of man and lower animals. Complement-fixing antibodies may be detected in the sera of patients as early as the seventh or the eighth day of illness; they increase in titer, reaching a peak by the twelfth to the sixteenth day after onset. Subsequently, the titer usually falls slowly over a period of months to low values which may persist for years. Occasionally, titers may fall to zero a few weeks after the end of the disease. It may be difficult or impossible to differentiate epidemic typhus from murine typhus by complement-fixation tests on the sera of persons who have previously been vaccinated with killed rickettsial vaccines (Plotz and Wertman, 1945; Zarafonetis et al., 1946; Smadel, 1948).

Specific agglutination of rickettsiae by sera of typhus patients was demonstrated by Otto and Dietrich (1917) and Zinsser and Castaneda (1932). The phenomenon was studied in greater detail (van Rooyen and Bearcroft, 1943; Stuart-Harris, Rettie and Oliver, 1943) when rich rickettsial suspensions were obtained by the technics of Cox (1938) and Craigie (1945). In general, the remarks made for the time of appearance of complement-fixing antibodies apply to the antibodies which agglutinate rickettsiae. Castaneda (1945) has developed a slide technic for the specific agglutination of suspensions of rickettsiae at the bedside. (Review of subject: Smadel, 1948.)

Tests for the presence of opsonins, precipitins, and neutralizing antibodies are valuable in the study of typhus, but are practicable only for laboratories in which extensive work with rickettsial diseases is in progress. Precipitins: Lim and Kurotchkin (1929); Topping and associates (1945). Opsonins: Epstein (1922); Castaneda (1936a). Neutralization and protection tests: Gildemeister and Haagen (1940); Giroud (1938); Clavero and Perez Gallardo (1943); Anderson (1944); Topping and associates (1945); van den Ende and associates (1946).

Serologic technics are the methods of choice in the diagnosis of louse-borne typhus, since attempts to recover *R. prowazeki* by inoculation of animals, eggs or insects involve procedures which require special laboratory facilities as well as skill in interpretation of results. Thus, in order to establish definitely that *R. prowazeki* has been isolated from a patient, it is necessary to demonstrate the development of specific antibodies, the absence of cultivable bacteria, the existence of reciprocal cross immunity with known typhus strains, and the occurrence of specific pathologic lesions with typical intracellular rickettsiae.

TREATMENT

All persons who handle typhus cases should be immunized. To prevent lice from gaining access to their clothing, they should protect themselves carefully during the delousing of patients by the use of rubber gloves and surgical gowns. On admission to a hospital, a patient should be bathed with soap and water or one per cent solution of lysol, and his clothes should be promptly disinfected, preferably by heat. A patient and his hospital garments should be carefully dusted with 10 per cent DDT delousing powder on admission to the wards and once a week thereafter until discharge. In order to disinfect and delouse a patient, it was formerly required that his head and axillary and pubic regions be shaved; this is no longer necessary. After the disinfestation procedures are completed, ordinary precautions are adequate.

Skillful and diligent nursing is of great importance. Constant supervision is necessary to prevent a delirious patient from doing himself bodily harm. Stuporous patients or those in coma should be moved frequently from side to side to prevent bed sores. A rise of body temperature to 40.5° C. or above should be treated promptly by cold sponges. Oral hygiene is very important in the prevention of parotitis. Fluids should be administered at frequent intervals in adequate quantity to produce at least 1,500 cubic centimeters of urine daily. A liquid or semisolid diet high in caloric content and in vitamins is desirable. Paraldehyde and chloral hydrate are valuable in the control of active delirium or restlessness, and are preferable to morphine for this purpose. Barbiturates should be avoided since some typhus patients appear to react unfavorably to them (Yeomans, 1947). Codeine may be required for the relief of headache. Digitalis and other drugs which act principally on the heart are rarely indicated. Oxygen by face mask or tent appears to make patients more comfortable when cyanosis is present, but it is doubtful whether oxygen administration has done more than prolong life for a few hours in patients with deep cyanosis. The typhus-immune sera of man and several animal species have been administered to typhus patients (Zinsser, 1940; Wolman, 1944; Durand and Balozet, 1944; Leon, 1944; Yeomans, Snyder and Gilliam, 1945; Stevens, 1945; Snyder, 1948). A beneficial effect may be observed if potent immune serum is administered very early in the disease, but such sera are expensive and not generally available.

The three antibiotics, aureomycin, chloramphenicol and terramycin, are highly effective in the treatment of experimental typhus infections (Wong and Cox, 1948; Smadel and Jackson, 1947; Snyder et al., 1950). Although relatively few patients with primary epidemic louse-borne typhus have been treated with these antibiotics, their efficacy in patients with scrub typhus and Rocky Mountain spotted fever gives assurance that they will be effective against epidemic typhus as well. A clinician must choose the one that he prefers on the basis of his own experience, since aureomycin, chloramphenicol and terramycin are of about equal value in clinical trials. These antibiotics are usually given by mouth, although preparations suitable for intravenous use are available. The initial or loading dose is given in the course of 2 to 4 hours and depends on the body weight of the patient, from 2 to 3 grams being used for a subject weighing 70 kilograms. The continuing dose thereafter is 1 to 2 grams per 24-hour period, divided into 4 doses. See Chapter 36 and Chapter 37 for references and more detailed instructions regarding the use of antibiotics. Response to the antibiotics is observed within 24 to 48 hours. Progress of the clinical course is usually arrested at whatever stage the illness had attained when treatment was begun. The temperature returns to normal, and concomitantly there is rapid subjective improvement in a patient's condition. Regardless of which antibiotic is used, it should be administered for 1 to 3 days after the temperature becomes normal, to reduce the incidence of recurrent bouts of fever which may occur if therapy is withdrawn prematurely.

Penicillin (Greiff and Pinkerton, 1948) and streptomycin (Morgan, Stevens and Snyder, 1947; Smadel, Jackson and Gauld, 1947) have a slight effect on experimental rickettsial infections, but their use in man is not indicated. If aureomycin, chloramphenicol, or terramycin is not available, para-aminobenzoic acid may be of value (references and details given by Snyder et al., 1947).

Sulfonamides may have a deleterious effect on typhus and are contraindicated (Snyder, 1948).

EPIDEMIOLOGY

Classic epidemic typhus fever occurs principally in Korea, Japan, China, Indo-China, Serbia, Russia, Central Europe, North Africa, Egypt, Ethiopia, South Africa, Mexico, Guatemala, Colombia, Peru, Bolivia and Chile. The disease is more common in cold climates. Epidemics ordinarily reach their peak in late winter and taper off in the spring. Typhus thrives under conditions of human misery which predispose to an increase in louse infestation, such as crowding of people, lack of fuel, inadequate facilities for bathing, and weather so cold that the same garments are worn continuously day and night for months at a time. Persons of all ages are susceptible to typhus. In children under 15 years of age, the disease is mild; probably it occurs much more frequently in young children than has been reported. As age increases, the case-fatality

TABLE 21. TYPHUS FEVER IN NAPLES, DECEMBER 1943 TO FEBRUARY 1944
(Van den Ende and associates, 1946, p. 35)

YEARS	MALES		FEMALES		TOTAL		MORTALITY PERCENTAGE
	CASES	DEATHS	CASES	DEATHS	CASES	DEATHS	
Under 3	20	1	18	0	38	1	2.6
3-11	133	2	91	1	224	3	1.3
12-20	221	9	166	10	387	19	4.9
21-29	105	11	108	10	213	21	9.8
30-38	111	14	127	18	238	32	13.4
39-47	59	29	116	28	175	57	32.5
48-56	43	18	56	19	99	37	36.3
57-65	10	7	27	15	37	22	59.4
66-74	2	2	8	3	10	5	50.0
75 and over	1	1	1	1	2	2	100.0
Gross	705	94	718	105	1,423	199	13.9

TABLE 22. TYPHUS FEVER, CAIRO, EGYPT, JANUARY 1943 TO AUGUST 1944
(Ecke and associates, 1945, p. 451)

AGES	MALES			FEMALES		
	CASES	DEATHS	MORTALITY PERCENTAGE	CASES	DEATHS	MORTALITY PERCENTAGE
16-20	1247	120	9.6	689	60	8.7
21-25	1363	208	15.2	586	61	10.4
26-30	988	252	25.5	540	74	13.7
31-35	598	184	30.8	377	71	18.8
36-40	422	142	33.6	232	59	25.4
41-48	264	124	47.0	135	44	32.6

rate rises sharply, as shown in Tables 21 and 22. In certain epidemics the case-fatality rate has been greater in males than in females in the age groups from 20 to 50 (Ecke and associates, 1945). There is considerable variation in the severity of typhus in different epidemics. Overall case-fatality rates for various epidemics range from less than 10 to more than 40 per cent. Very little is known of the relative resistance of different races of people to the disease, and the effect of nutrition on resistance to the disease is not well understood. An attack of epidemic typhus confers immunity which persists for many years. Second attacks are discussed in the section on Brill's disease. A person who has recovered from epidemic typhus is immune to murine typhus, and vice versa.

R. prowazeki occurs in the blood of patients during the febrile period; the human body louse becomes infected by sucking blood from them. Lice tend to leave a febrile patient in favor of persons with normal temperature. They quickly abandon a corpse and seek a new host. Whenever a louse bites, it makes a small puncture in the skin and defecates at the same time. Since the louse bite is irritating, the bitten person usually scratches and may thus rub the feces of the louse into the injured skin. Probably this is the usual way in which typhus infection is passed from man to man. It is also possible to become infected by crushing an infected louse on the skin, by rubbing infected louse feces into the eyes or by having dried infected louse feces gain access to the conjunctivae or to the mucous membranes of the respiratory tract. Once deloused and bathed, typhus patients are not capable of transmitting the infection to other persons by contact; *R. prowazeki* does not occur in saliva, sputum, urine or feces of patients unless blood is also present. With the exception of man (see Brill's disease), no other reservoirs of classic epidemic typhus are known.

CONTROL MEASURES

The official recommendations of the American Public Health Association (1950, pp. 146-148) should be followed by physicians who are faced with outbreaks of epidemic typhus. "The most important measure for the rapid control of typhus, where the reporting has been good and the number of cases small, is the application of insecticides with residual effect to all contacts. Where the infection is known to be widespread, the systematic application of residual insecticide to all persons in the community is indicated." Immunization of persons in contact with cases is recommended; exposed susceptible persons, if louse infested, should be dusted with residual insecticide; quarantine is then unnecessary. The nearest World Health Organization Regional Epidemiological Information Station should be notified at once of the existence of a typhus epidemic. The disinfection of patients and their clothes is described above under Treatment.

These recommendations may be amplified in regard to immunization and louse control. Both of these procedures are applicable to an individual as well as to a community. Vaccines developed for protection against an attack of classic epidemic typhus are of two sorts. In one, living murine rickettsiae, treated with certain agents in an effort to attenuate the organisms, are employed (Laigret and Durand, 1939; Blanc and Baltazard, 1941). These living vaccines have been used on a very large scale for immunization of natives in French North Africa (reviewed by Biraud, 1943), but their use is not without danger, since they cause attacks of murine typhus: deaths have been recorded (Palacios, Chavez and Avendano, 1935; Sadusk and Kuhlenbeck, 1946). The preferred type of anti-

TABLE 23. EFFECTS OF COX-TYPE VACCINE ON EPIDEMIC TYPHUS, CAIRO, EGYPT, 1943 AND 1944

	NUMBER OF PATIENTS*	AVERAGE AGE	AVERAGE DURATION OF FEVER	NUMBER OF DEATHS
		years	days	
No vaccine ..	47	26	18	9
Vaccinated† .	20	32	11.6	0

* Figures refer to male Egyptian patients, ages 18-48, studied in U.S.A. Typhus Commission ward in the Cairo Fever Hospital.

† Vaccinated: One or more doses of Cox vaccine, 1 cc. each, more than 20 days before onset of illness. Average amount of vaccine this group, 2.5 cc. Average interval between last dose and onset, 2½ months.

typhus vaccine contains killed *R. prowazeki* which cannot cause typhus. Adequate quantities of rickettsiae for such vaccines may be obtained from the intestines of human lice (da Rocha-Lima, 1918; Weigl, 1930), from rodent lungs (Castaneda, 1939; Durand and Giroud, 1940), from tissue cultures (Zinsser, Wei and FitzPatrick, 1938), and from the yolk-sac membrane of developing chick embryos (Cox, 1938, 1941, 1948; Craigie, 1945; Topping et al., 1945). The latter, known as the Cox-type vaccine, was produced on a tremendous scale during World War II, and was administered to several million troops who were sent to areas where they might be exposed to epidemic typhus. Civilian populations in certain of the danger zones were also given the vaccine (Table 23). Cox-type vaccine probably reduces the incidence of the disease in a group of exposed persons, but there are no data with satisfactory controls on this point. It has been definitely established, however, that it reduces the mortality from typhus practically to zero. The course of the disease in persons immunized with this vaccine is milder and shorter than is that in unvaccinated persons; furthermore, the incidence of serious complications is sharply reduced. (References: Ding, 1943; Ecke and associates, 1945; Gilliam, 1946.)

In immunized American troops in World War II there were only 64 patients with mild epidemic typhus, all of whom recovered (Sadusk, 1947). The official recommendations for the Cox-type vaccine are two subcutaneous doses of 1 cc. each, separated by an interval of from 10 to 14 days, followed by a booster dose of 1 cc. at the beginning and in the middle of the typhus season (Sadusk, 1947). Before receiving yolk-sac vaccine, persons should be asked if they are sensitive to egg proteins. If so, the use of the vaccine should be undertaken only with caution, since severe reactions may occur. Complement-fixing antibodies may persist for several years after a course of Cox-type typhus vaccine; furthermore, a booster dose of 1 cc. induces a rapid serologic response in persons immunized several years before, even though they may not have had demonstrable antibodies at the time the booster dose was given (Murray, Ofstrock and Snyder, 1952).

The efficacy of delousing in controlling epidemics was shown in North Africa in 1912 (Otto and Munter, 1930) and in Serbia in 1915 (Strong et al., 1920). At that time and until very recently, in order to be deloused it was necessary for infested persons to remove all clothes, which were then subjected to heat while they bathed. When large groups were involved, this process was very cumbersome, expensive and time consuming.

The disadvantages of delousing by heat were eliminated in 1943, when various antilouse powders were developed and methods devised (Wheeler, 1943; Soper and associates, 1945) whereby large numbers of people could be treated without removing their garments. The powders were shown to be effective when blown into the hair, up the sleeves, down the neck, and around the waist into trousers. The now famous insecticide, DDT, dichloro-diphenyl-trichloroethane, (Mooser, 1942; Bishopp, 1945; Knipling, 1948) proved to be nearly ideal. DDT has been synthesized by a German student in 1874, but its usefulness was not appreciated until Swiss workers demonstrated its insecticidal properties (Wiesmann, quoted from Bishopp, 1945; Müller, quoted from Mooser, 1946). The most satisfactory property of DDT is the persistence of its lethal effect on lice for more than two weeks after being dusted into the garments, or for more than four weeks after impregnation from an emulsion. Reinfestation of dusted persons was reduced to a negligible degree by this persisting effect of DDT. Recent reports suggest that lice in Korea are resistant to DDT. Other residual-effect insecticides such as gamma benzene hexachloride are available for louse control when DDT may be ineffective.

The final improvement in delousing technic was the development of a power duster, a device consisting of an air compressor which operates ten dust guns simultaneously; the technic has been described by Greeley (1948).

BRILL'S DISEASE
(RECRUDESCENT TYPHUS)
(Synonym: Sporadic typhus)

History

Brill's disease is a recrudescence of epidemic louse-borne typhus fever in relatively mild form years after the primary attack. In 1898, Brill noted the occurrence in New York City of a disease resembling typhus fever. Cases continued to appear sporadically in that city (Brill, 1910) and elsewhere (Lee, 1912). No association with human body lice could be established. Anderson and Goldberger (1912) showed that Brill's disease was a form of typhus by transmitting the infection to monkeys and by demonstrating reciprocal cross immunity with classic typhus. As first described, the illness seemed to appear chiefly among Jewish immigrants to the United States from various parts of eastern Europe. However, in the period preceding the recognition of murine flea-borne typhus, all sporadic cases of typhus in the United States were customarily referred to as Brill's disease; this fact resulted in much confusion (see section on murine flea-borne typhus).

Zinsser (1934), after scrutinizing the records of 538 cases of Brill's disease, advanced his hypothesis that Brill's diesase is a recrudescence of epidemic typhus in persons who suffered an attack of the classic disease many years previously while residing in areas where epidemics of typhus were occurring. Zinsser postulated the persistence of the typhus rickettsiae during the latent interval somewhere in the tissues of the human subject. Zinsser's hypothesis has been verified in large part by recent studies.

CLINICAL PICTURE

The factors which precipitate Brill's disease are not known; consequently, there are no data on the incubation period. Clinical features are those of epidemic louse-borne typhus with the following exceptions: (1) Brill's disease is shorter in duration (7 to 12 days); (2) the temperature curve is more irregular with a tendency for the occurrence of wide swings; (3) the rash may be absent in many cases; (4) complications are much less frequent, except in persons of advanced age; and (5) the age-specific case-fatality rate is lower.

PATHOLOGIC PICTURE

Although the histopathology of Brill's disease has not been studied extensively, the lesions which have been observed do not differ in any important respect from those found in the primary epidemic form of typhus fever.

EXPERIMENTAL INFECTION; HOST RANGE

The rickettsiae isolated from patients with Brill's disease are indistinguishable from classic epidemic strains as regards experimental infection and host range (Murray and Snyder, 1951).

ETIOLOGY

Extensive comparisons of seven strains of Brill's disease rickettsiae with standard epidemic and murine strains have established that Brill's disease is caused by *R. prowazeki,* not *R. mooseri* (references cited by Murray and Snyder, 1951). It is thus erroneous to refer to Brill's disease as endemic or murine typhus, or to use the term Brill's disease to describe an illness transmitted to man by rat fleas (see section on murine typhus).

DIAGNOSIS

A diagnosis of Brill's disease should be considered when a patient who has lived in a typhus zone develops a fever, a severe intractable headache and possibly a macular or maculopapular rash. The diagnosis can be confirmed by the demonstration in serial serum specimens of a rising titer of antibodies which fix complement in the presence of epidemic typhus antigen or agglutinate suspensions of washed epidemic typhus rickettsiae. There are two important differences between the serologic features of Brill's disease and primary epidemic louse-borne typhus. The first difference is that in Brill's disease the rise in specific antibodies begins early, on the fourth to the sixth day after the onset of illness; the peak response is usually attained by the tenth day (Murray et al., 1951). In the primary attack of epidemic typhus, on the other hand, the specific antibody rise begins later, about the eighth to the twelfth day with maximum titers being reached from the twelfth to the sixteenth day after onset (Plotz et al., 1948). The second important serologic difference is that the Weil-Felix reaction (agglutination of Proteus OX 19) usually is negative in Brill's disease (Murray et al., 1950; Murray et al., 1951).

At least 30 per cent of persons who formerly lived in an epidemic typhus area can be expected to have residual antityphus complement-fixing and neutralizing antibodies, even though 40 to 50 years may have elapsed since their last possible exposure to typhus (Murray et al., 1952). Thus, a definite rise in titer of more than fourfold in the complement-fixation test with epidemic typhus antigen must be demonstrated in association with a particular illness in such persons in order to establish a diagnosis of Brill's disease by serologic procedures.

Antibodies which fix complement in the presence of murine typhus antigen may also develop during Brill's disease. The maximum titers are, however, regularly lower than those with epidemic antigen when the highly specific washed rickettsial suspensions are used as test antigens (Murray et al., 1950).

TREATMENT

Aureomycin, chloramphenicol, or terramycin can be expected to exert a beneficial effect on Brill's disease, although the evaluation of such therapy is more difficult because of the relatively short and mild course of the untreated disease.

EPIDEMIOLOGY

Brill's disease has been recognized in persons who migrated to several countries in which epidemic louse-borne typhus is not present, namely, the United States (Brill, 1910; Zinsser, 1934; Morgan et al., 1948; and Murray et al., 1950), Switzerland (Mooser and Loeffler, 1946), England (Hawksley and Stokes, 1950), France (Giroud et al., 1950; Worms, 1950) and Portugal (Soares, 1950). The illness is by no means restricted to that portion of a population which has migrated away from a typhus zone. In a very brief interval in the summer of 1950 Murray and his associates identified 26 cases of Brill's disease in a relatively small part of Yugoslavia, an area which had been swept over by louse-borne typhus in 1944-45 (Murray et al., 1951). These cases were about equally distributed between males and females; the age range was 9 to 56 years; there were no secondary cases; there was no association with human body lice; nearly all of the patients gave a clear history of a previous attack of typhus which occurred during the louse-borne epidemics of 1944-45. Only one of the cases was sufficiently like classic typhus to appear in the official case reports. These

observations indicate several features of epidemiologic importance:

(1) Brill's disease can be expected to occur in the native population of typhus zones as well as in persons who migrate to nontyphus zones; (2) the disease definitely is not restricted to any one race, sex or age group; (3) the incidence of Brill's disease may be considerably greater than formerly suspected; (4) many of the hundreds of thousands of displaced persons who recently have settled in nontyphus zones are possible future victims of Brill's disease because they suffered a primary attack of louse-borne typhus in their former residences or in the notorious concentration camps (Snyder, 1947); (5) Brill's disease probably will not be recognized unless physicians are alert to the mild course, the frequent absence of a rash, and the negative Weil-Felix reaction.

No clues have been obtained as to factors which precipitate the recrudescence of typhus. It is believed that after a person recovers from primary louse-borne typhus the rickettsiae remain viable somewhere in his tissues. The balance between the immune mechanism and the parasite is disturbed somehow, and a recrudescence occurs. The early serologic response in Brill's disease and its milder course strongly suggest that partial immunity is still present.

The significance of Brill's disease lies in the fact that it explains the appearance of new epidemics of classic typhus. Zinsser (1934) offered this suggestion, predicting that human body lice might become infected if they fed upon patients with Brill's disease. This has now been conclusively demonstrated; 7 patients studied in the United States were infectious for lice which were allowed to feed on them at some time before the eighth day of the illness (Murray et al., 1950). The typhus rickettsiae in these lice were fully virulent, indistinguishable from the classic strains (Murray and Snyder, 1951). Thus, under disturbed conditions in a community which permit the development of louse infestation, patients with Brill's disease may be the foci from which an epidemic of louse-borne typhus fever may spread to susceptible persons in the population.

Control Measures

There are no control measures which are known to be effective in reducing the incidence of Brill's disease. If such cases occur in the presence of louse infestation, the situation should be regarded potentially as the beginning of an epidemic, and those measures described for the control of classic epidemic louse-borne typhus should be applied.

MURINE TYPHUS (FLEA-BORNE)

(Synonyms: Endemic typhus, urban or shop typhus of Malaya, flea typhus, rat typhus)

Introduction

Murine typhus is a relatively mild, acute febrile illness of 9 to 15 days' duration, characterized by headache and macular rash. It is a natural infection of rats and mice transmitted sporadically to man by the rat flea, *Xenopsylla cheopis*. The etiologic agent is *Rickettsia mooseri* (Monteiro, 1931). The case-fatality rate for all ages is approximately 2 per cent.

History

Murine typhus probably has occurred since ancient times, but only in recent years has it been differentiated from classic epidemic louse-borne typhus. Although sporadic cases of typhus in Europe had been referred to occasionally (McCrae, 1907), such reports received little notice. In the United States, sporadic cases of typhus were noted by Brill (1910), Lee (1912), and Paullin (1913). Hone (1922) described several isolated cases in Australia, and Wheatland (1926) called attention to the occurrence of a noncontagious typhuslike fever among the farm population in Queensland, at a time when a plague of mice afflicted the region. Sinclair and Maxcy (1925) and

later Maxcy (1926; 1929) investigated cases of "endemic" typhus in southeastern United States. On epidemiologic grounds, Maxcy (1929) postulated that a reservoir of the disease other than man exists and mentioned that rats and mice might serve as such a reservoir. He also mentioned that fleas, mites or ticks might be the vectors. The epidemiologic evidence for postulating a separate variety of typhus was strengthened by observations of differences in the pathologic features (Wolbach and Todd, 1920) and in the characteristics of strains isolated from the sporadic cases of typhus in Mexico. Neill (1917) observed that male guinea pigs inoculated with typhus strains obtained from Mexico exhibited enlargement of the scrotal sac and adhesions of the testes. Mooser (1928) reported that certain strains of typhus rickettsiae isolated from patients in Mexico not only caused the tunica reaction in male guinea pigs, but also multiplied profusely in the serosal cells over the testes. The tunica reaction of guinea pigs has been referred to as the "Neill-Mooser reaction" and the cells packed with rickettsiae as "Mooser cells." The final steps proving the existence of a second variety of typhus were made by Dyer, Rumreich and Badger (1931) who isolated rickettsiae from rat fleas in Baltimore, and by Mooser, Castaneda and Zinsser (1931a) who found the typhus agent in brains of rats trapped in Mexico City. The disease was then named murine typhus to indicate its presence as a natural infection of rats (Mooser, 1932). It was promptly sought for and found in most parts of the world (Biraud and Deutschman, 1936). Biologic differences between typhus strains isolated from rats or fleas and those isolated from patients suffering from classic louse-borne epidemic typhus were demonstrated by Zinsser and his colleagues (references cited by Zinsser, 1940; Mooser, 1945). The two varieties of typhus were further characterized by application of serologic technics (references cited by Smadel, 1948) and by cross-vaccination experiments (Topping et al., 1945; Craigie et al., 1946; Murray and Snyder, 1951).

CLINICAL PICTURE

Murine typhus in man is similar to classic louse-borne typhus. In the absence of epidemiologic and laboratory data, it is impossible on the basis of clinical findings alone to determine whether a patient is suffering from murine typhus instead of classic typhus. However, murine typhus is relatively mild with a negligible mortality except in persons more than 50 years old. The onset is likely to be more gradual than that of classic typhus, the symptoms less severe, the rash shorter in duration, and the skin lesions less numerous. The central nervous system, the myocardium, and the kidneys are less severely involved. Complications, e.g., parotitis, necrosis of the skin, gangrene of the extremities, otitis media, furunculosis, azotemia and bronchopneumonia, occur infrequently. The temperature curve usually shows wider fluctuations than that of classic typhus. The febrile period is terminated by rapid lysis after 9 to 14 days. Recovery is prompt without sequelae. Laboratory data are similar to those described for classic typhus, except that abnormal findings tend to be slight or absent in murine typhus. Clinical features are described in detail by Maxcy (1926), Miller and Beeson (1946), and Woodward (1948).

PATHOLOGIC PICTURE

The pathology of murine typhus in man probably is similar to that of classic epidemic typhus. However, there is a paucity of data on this point, since very few postmortems have been reported in cases of proven murine typhus.

EXPERIMENTAL INFECTION; HOST RANGE

Murine typhus occurs as a natural infection of rats and mice. It is transmitted from rat to rat either by the rat louse, *Polyplax spinulosus* (Mooser, Castaneda and Zinsser, 1931b), or by the rat flea, *Xenopsylla cheopis* (Dyer, Rumreich and Badger, 1931). Transmission from rat to man is attributed to *X. cheopis*. The infection in man is an accidental occurrence, unconcerned in the maintenance of the infection in nature. Some observers (Zinsser, 1937) regard the present evidence sufficient to establish the fact that murine typhus may be spread from man to man in epidemic form by the human body louse (Mooser, 1945). Many species in addition to those mentioned are susceptible to murine typhus: monkeys, donkeys, cats, squirrels, deer mice, voles, gerbilles, cotton rats, guinea pigs, developing chick embryos, cat fleas, tropical rat mites, etc.; see articles by Wolbach (1940) and Philip (1948).

The rat flea, *X. cheopis*, becomes infected by feeding on a rat which is in the acute phase of an infection. The rickettsiae multiply in the cells of the flea without causing damage to the host. Once infected, the flea continues to discharge rickettsiae in its feces for the duration of its life. Other species of fleas, notably *Pulex irritans*, are susceptible, but their reaction to typhus infection has not been thoroughly studied. When human body lice are experimentally infected with murine typhus, the resulting disease is similar in all respects to the infections caused by classic epidemic strains (Mooser, 1945). Whether lice acquire murine typhus under natural conditions is open to question; experimental passage of two strains of murine typhus serially in human body lice for several transfers was not accompanied by any change in characteristics toward classic epidemic strains (Murray and Snyder, 1951).

Murine typhus can be established in guinea pigs by intraabdominal inoculation of the blood of a patient by the method described for classic typhus. The infection, once established in serial passage in these animals, has an incubation period of from three to seven days. The temperature curve often exhibits fluctuations but tends to stay at or above 40° C. for several days. The fever is usually accompanied by enlargement of the scrotal sac of male guinea pigs, reddening of the skin of the scrotum, and adhesions between testes and tunica vaginalis. This "tunica reaction" is quite distinct from the more severe "scrotal reaction" caused by spotted fever. In the latter, necrosis of the scrotal skin often occurs. When an animal is sacrificed on the first or second day of the tunica reaction, two phenomena are observed at necropsy: the spleen is covered by a thin coat of fibrin which may cause the spleen to adhere to the abdominal wall, and the testes may show adhesions and a few small subserosal hemorrhages. Smear preparations from the surface of the testes, peritoneum, or spleen contain numerous rickettsiae, intracellular and extracellular in location. Transfer to other guinea pigs is accomplished by removing the spleen, grinding it in a mortar with sterile sand or alundum to a 10 per cent suspension in a suitable diluent; after gross particles are removed by light centrifugation, the supernatant suspension in 1 or 2 cc. amounts is inoculated intraabdominally into fresh normal male guinea pigs. An alternate method of transfer is the use of a suspension obtained by shaking the testes in a flask with glass beads and 20 to 30 cc. of a suitable diluent. The materials prepared in this manner on the first or second day of the tunica reaction contain at least 10^4 viable rickettsiae per cc. It is a common observation that during the hot summer months, murine typhus tends to lose its distinguishing features in guinea pigs, but in the cold months the fever and tunica reaction reappear. Great reliance was formerly placed on the tunica reaction of guinea pigs as a means of differentiating between the classic epidemic and the murine varieties. More extensive experience has shown that occasionally classic strains may produce the tunica reaction, and, conversely, that a murine strain may fail to cause it. Specific serologic tests and cross-vaccination experiments now provide such reliable and rapid differentiation between epidemic and murine strains that the tunica reaction of guinea pigs is no longer relied

upon to distinguish one variety from the other.

Murine typhus may be maintained indefinitely by passage in white rats, whereas classic strains die out after a few passages. Murine rickettsiae usually multiply profusely in the cells of the peritoneum and may cause fever and scrotal swelling, but the animals recover as a rule. An important feature of the murine infection in rats is the persistence of viable rickettsiae in the brain for several months (Philip, 1948). Large doses of *R. mooseri* may produce death of white mice within a few hours as a consequence of their toxic properties (Gildemeister and Haagen, 1940). Slightly smaller doses cause extensive peritonitis with death of the animals in three to eight days. Enormous numbers of rickettsiae are found in the peritoneal exudate of moribund mice. Inocula containing relatively few *R. mooseri* render mice immune within three weeks to toxic and infective doses of the organism. Rats and mice, as well as sheep, dogs and rabbits, may be infected by the intranasal route and succumb in a few days with extensive pneumonitis. This procedure has been utilized for vaccine production. Irradiation of white rats and cotton rats with deep x-rays greatly increase the yield of murine typhus rickettsiae in these animals.

Etiology

The causative agent of murine typhus has been named *Rickettsia mooseri* (Monteiro, 1931) in honor of Mooser, and is similar to *R. prowazeki* as regards size, shape, staining properties, and resistance to chemical and physical agents, but exhibits less pleomorphism. Antigenic composition has been described in the section on etiology under classic typhus. *R. mooseri* has been cultivated in the yolk-sac membrane of developing chick embryos with considerable success (Cox, 1938).

Diagnosis

Classic epidemic typhus and murine typhus cannot be distinguished solely on clinical grounds in individual cases. Since murine typhus may exist in the same regions with Rocky Mountain spotted fever (United States, Mexico, South America, probably India), it may be emphasized that the rash of typhus appears on the body first, then spreads to the extremities, whereas in spotted fever the reverse is true. The rash of the latter disease has a greater tendency to be papular and to become petechial or hemorrhagic. Isolation of *R. mooseri* can be accomplished by inoculation of white rats or guinea pigs with the blood of a patient. Comments in the section on epidemic typhus in regard to use of ground clot apply equally well to murine typhus. Direct isolation of murine typhus strains by inoculation of human blood into developing chick embryos, although entirely feasible, has not been reported. The Weil-Felix reaction occurs in murine as well as in classic typhus. The complement-fixation test, the agglutination of rickettsiae, and the neutralization of toxic properties have been discussed in the section on classic typhus. There are no important differences between the two types of typhus in regard to the time of appearance, peak of occurrence, or persistence of the various antibodies. Sera of animals and man in convalescence from attacks caused by proven murine typhus strains usually have higher titers against homologous than against heterologous antigens. Sera of patients who contract murine typhus after having received killed vaccine of the epidemic type may show no difference in titer when tested against the two antigens (Plotz and Wertman, 1945; Zarafonetis et al., 1946).

TREATMENT

Treatment of murine typhus differs in no important respect from that described for classic epidemic typhus. The mildness of the disease and its slower onset tend to delay its clinical recognition until the optimum period for administration of antibiotics has passed.

TABLE 24. MURINE TYPHUS IN THE UNITED STATES

YEAR	CASES*	DEATHS†
1931	332	22
1936	1,732	112
1941	2,787	135
1945	5,193	214
1949	983	**
1950	686	**

* Cases have been reported from more than three fourths of the states. In the entire United States, from 1931 through 1946, approximately 42,000 cases were reported.
† Figures taken from Supplements to Public Health Reports, U. S. Pub. Health Service.
** Figures not yet available.

EPIDEMIOLOGY

Murine typhus is world-wide in distribution. In the United States, the reported cases from 1931 to 1945 (Table 24) indicate an increase in prevalence which seems to be of greater magnitude than can be accounted for on the basis of improved diagnosis. In the years 1948 to 1951, however, a sharp decline occurred in the reported cases of murine typhus in the United States. Maximum incidence occurs in the summer and fall months.

Persons of all ages are susceptible. Although there appear to be fewer cases in negroes than in white people, this may be attributable in part to difficulty in recognizing the rash in dark-skinned individuals. Persons of both sexes are equally susceptible to the illness. The most important factor influencing the occurrence of murine typhus in human beings is residence or occupation in areas where rats abound. Although the disease often involves only one member of a household, it may appear in several occupants of a dwelling. The usual manner in which the infection is transmitted to man is as follows: at the time an infected flea sucks blood, it deposits feces which may be scratched into the wound made by the bite. There are other possible modes of infection, for example, infected flea feces may gain access to the conjunctivae or mucous membranes of the respiratory tract; experiments with volunteers have shown that murine typhus can be contracted by the ingestion of viable *R. mooseri* (Pollard et al., 1946); it is possible that cases may be caused by eating food recently contaminated by the urine of infected rats. A patient suffering from murine typhus cannot transmit the infection to other persons by contact; *R. mooseri* does not occur in the sputum, feces or urine unless gross blood is also present. An attack of the disease results in immunity which persists for many years.

As knowledge of the differences between classic epidemic typhus and murine typhus has accumulated, it has become evident that both types are present in Mexico, and that classic epidemic strains are frequently isolated in that country from patients (Varela and Zozaya, 1945). Moreover, complement-fixation tests on sera of residents of Mexico indicate the preponderance of the classic infection in that region (Silva-Goytia, 1944). The term "Mexican typhus", therefore, is ambiguous and should be avoided.

The relationship of murine to classic epidemic typhus has been the subject of much speculation. One theory postulates that murine typhus is the more ancient disease as shown by the fact that the two principal hosts of *R. mooseri*, the rat and the rat flea, undergo no harmful effects from their intimate association with it. By contrast, *R. prowazeki* causes a serious illness in man and a fatal infection in the louse. These facts have been taken as evidence that, from the evolutionary viewpoint, the association of man and human lice with typhus rickettsiae is relatively recent.

Control Measures

The official recommendations of the American Public Health Association (1950, pp. 148-149) are as follows:

A. Preventive measures:
1. Application of appropriate insecticide powders or similar agents to rat runs, burrows and harborages.

B. The infected individual, contacts and environment:
1. Recognition of the disease and reporting.
2. Isolation: None.
3. Terminal disinfection: None.
4. Quarantine: None.
5. Immunization: A vaccine similar to that described under epidemic typhus is commercially available and presumably equally effective. It may be administered to groups exposed by occupation or residence to an unusual risk.
6. Investigation of source of infection: Rodents about the place of occupation or home of the patient.
7. Rodent and flea control: In and about the premises where the patient was infected.

C. Epidemic measures: Not applicable.

D. International measures: Not applicable.

Measures for protection of individuals against murine typhus, such as the wearing of flea-proof garments, are impracticable. Vaccines containing killed *R. mooseri* afford protection in laboratory tests, but it is debatable whether vaccination of man is advisable as a control measure, except for persons who are frequently exposed to the infection. More data are needed in regard to the efficacy of murine vaccine for human use. It should be emphasized that, although an attack of epidemic typhus protects against murine typhus and vice versa, vaccines made from dead rickettsiae satisfactorily protect only against homologous strains. To achieve protection against murine typhus, vaccines should be made with *R. mooseri*, not *R. prowazeki*. Considerable progress in the control of murine typhus on a community-wide basis has been made in three directions: (1) rat proofing of buildings; (2) reducing flea populations through the use of DDT on rat runs; and (3) poisoning of rats with alpha naphthyl thiourea, warfarin (Hayes and Gaines, 1950) and other rodenticides. The use of DDT in order to kill potentially infected fleas before their hosts are poisoned should precede rat-poisoning campaigns. Otherwise there may be a temporary increase in cases of murine typhus (Davis, 1947; Bradley and Wiley, 1948).

REFERENCES

American Public Health Association, 1950, The Control of Communicable Diseases, ed. 7, New York, Am. Pub. Health Assn.

Anderson, C. R., 1944a, Survival of *Rickettsia prowazeki* in different diluents. J. Bact., *47*, 519-522.

Anderson, C. R., 1944b, Experimental typhus infection in the eastern cotton rat (*Sigmodon hispidus hispidus*). J. Exp. Med., *80*, 341-356.

Anderson, J. F., and Goldberger, J., 1912, Collected Studies on Typhus. Hygienic Lab. Bull., No. 86, Washington, D. C.

Bayne-Jones, S., 1948, Epidemic typhus in North Africa, Italy and Jugoslavia. Symposium on Rickettsial Diseases, Dec. 1946, Boston, American Association for the Advancement of Science.

Beeuwkes, H., 1926, American Medical and Sanitary Relief in the Russian Famine, 1921-1923. New York, American Relief Administration Bulletin, Series 2, No. 45.

Biraud, Y., 1943, The present menace of typhus fever in Europe and the means of combating it. Bull. Health Organization, League of Nations, *10*, 1-64.

Biraud, Y., and Deutschman, S., 1936, Typhus and typhus-like rickettsia infections. Geneva, Epidemiological Reports, League of Nations, *181; 183.*

Bishopp, F. C., 1945, The medical and public health importance of the insecticide DDT. Bull. New York Acad. Med., *21*, 561-580.

Blanc, G., and Baltazard, M., 1941, Vaccination contre le typhus exanthématique par virus vivant de typhus murin. Arch. Inst. Pasteur du Maroc, *2*, 445-486.

Bovarnick, M. R., Miller, J. C., and Snyder, J. C., 1950, The influence of certain salts, amino acids, sugars, and proteins on the stability of rickettsiae. J. Bact., *59*, 509-522.

Bovarnick, M. R., and Snyder, J. C., 1949, Respiration of typhus rickettsiae. J. Exp. Med., *89*, 561-565.

Bovarnick, M. R., and Miller, J. C., 1950, Oxidation and transamination of glutamate by typhus rickettsiae. J. Biol. Chem., *184*, 661-676.

Bovarnick, M. R., Miller, J. C. and Snyder, J. C., 1952. Manuscript in preparation.

Bradley, G., and Wiley, J. S., 1948, The control of murine typhus in the United States. Symposium on Rickettsial Diseases, Dec. 1946, Boston, American Association for the Advancement of Science

Brill, N. E., 1910, An acute infectious disease of unknown origin. A clinical study based on 221 cases. Am. J. Med. Sci., *139*, 484-502.

Brumpt, L., 1943, L'hémoagglutination rapide appliquée au dépistage du typhus exanthématique. Bull. Soc. path. exotique, *36*, 175-187.

Buxton, P. A., 1939, The Louse. London, Arnold.

Castaneda, M. R., 1934, The antigenic relationship between proteus X-19 and typhus rickettsia. II. A study of the common antigenic factor. J. Exp. Med., *60*, 119-125.

Castaneda, M. R., 1936a, Studies on the mechanism of immunity in typhus fever. III. Demonstration of opsonins for *Rickettsia prowazeki* in typhus-immune serum. J. Immunol., *31*, 227-236.

Castaneda, M. R., 1936b, Studies on the mechanism of immunity in typhus fever. Complement-fixation in typhus fever. J. Immunol., *31*, 285-91.

Castaneda, M. R., 1939, Experimental pneumonia produced by typhus rickettsiae. Am. J. Path., *15*, 467-475.

Castaneda, M. R., 1945, Differentiation of typhus strains by slide-agglutinative tests. J. Immunol., *50*, 179-183.

Castaneda, M. R., and Silva, R., 1938, Prueba rápida para el diagnóstico del tifo exantemático a la cabecera del enfermo. Medicina, Revista Mexicana, *18*, 581-585.

Ceelen, W., 1919, Die pathologische Anatomie des Fleckfiebers. Ergeb. der allg. Path. und path. Anat., *19*, 307-350.

Clarke, D. H., and Fox, J. P., 1948, The phenomenon of *in vitro* hemolysis produced by the rickettsiae of typhus fever, with a note on the mechanism of rickettsial toxicity in mice. J. Exp. Med., *88*, 25-41.

Clavero, G., and Perez Gallardo, F., 1943, Técnicas de laboratorio en el tifus exantemático, Madrid, Prensa española.

Cohen, S. S., 1950, Studies on commercial typhus vaccines. IV. The chemical composition of the antigens of commerical typhus vaccine. J. Immunol., *65*, 475-483.

Cohen, S. S., and Chargaff, E., 1944, Studies on the composition of *Rickettsia prowazeki*. J. Biol. Chem., *154*, 691-704.

Cox, H. R., 1938, Use of yolk sac of developing chick embryo as medium for growing rickettsiae of Rocky Mountain spotted fever and typhus groups. Pub. Health Rep., *53*, 2241-2247.

Cox, H. R., 1941, Cultivation of rickettsiae of the Rocky Mountain spotted fever, typhus, and Q fever groups in the embryonic tissues of developing chicks. Science, *94*, 399-403.

Cox, H. R., 1948, Method for the preparation and standardization of rickettsial vaccines. Symposium on Rickettsial Diseases, Dec. 1946, Boston, American Association for the Advancement of Science.

Craigie, J., 1945, Application and control of ethyl-ether-water interface effects to the separation of rickettsiae from yolk sac suspensions. Canad. J. Res., E, *23*, 104-114.

Craigie, J., Watson, D. W., Clark, E. M., and Malcomson, M. E., 1946, The serological relationships of the rickettsiae of epidemic and murine typhus. Canad. J. Res., E, *24*, 84-103.

Davis, D. E., 1947, The use of DDT to control murine typhus fever in San Antonio, Texas. Pub. Health Rep., *62*, 449-463.

Ding, E., 1943, Über die Schutzwirkung verschiedener Fleckfieberimpfstoffe beim Menschen und den Fleckfieberverlauf nach Schutzimpfung. Ztschr. f. Hyg. u. Infektkr., *124*, 670-682.

Durand, P., and Balozet, L., 1944, Serothérapie du typhus épidémique par sérum de cheval hyperimmunisé. Congrès médical interallié, Fed. Soc. des sci. med. de l'Afrique du Nord, Algiers, fév. 1944, p. 14.

Durand, P., and Giroud, P., 1940, Essais de vaccination contre le typhus historique au moyen de rickettsias tuées par le formol (souches pulmonaires). Compt. rend. Acad. sci., *210*, 493-496.

Dyer, R. E., Rumreich, A., and Badger, L. F., 1931, Typhus fever. A virus of the typhus type derived from fleas collected from wild rats. Pub. Health Rep., *46*, 334-338.

Ecke, R. S., Gilliam, A. G., Snyder, J. C., Yeomans, A., Zarafonetis, C. J., and Murray, E. S., 1945, The effect of Cox-type vaccine on louse-borne typhus fever. Am. J. Trop. Med., *25*, 447-462.

van den Ende, M., Stuart-Harris, C. H., Fulton, F., Niven, J. S. F., Andrewes, C. H., Begg, A. M., Elford, W. J., White, M. H. G., Hawley, W. L., Mills, K. C., Hamilton, F., and Thomas, C. C., 1946, Chemotherapeutic and other studies of typhus. Series Medical Research Council Special Report, no. 255, London, His Majesty's Stationery Office.

Epstein, H., 1922, Beiträge zur Kenntnis der *Rickettsia prowazeki*. Zentralbl. f. Bakt., *87*, 553-556.

Felix, A., 1944, Technique and interpretation of the Weil-Felix test in typhus fever. Trans. Roy. Soc. Trop. Med. and Hyg., *37*, 321-341.

Fracastorius, H., 1546, De Contagione et Contagiosis Morbis et Eorum Curatione, Libri III. [Translated by W. C. Wright, New York, Putnam, 1930.]

Fuller, H. S., Snyder, J. C., and Murray, E. S., 1952, Quantitative comparison of the susceptibility of cotton rats and human body lice to experimental infection with epidemic typhus rickettsiae. Manuscript in preparation.

Fuller, H. S., Murray, E. S., and Snyder, J. C., 1949, Studies of human body lice, *Pediculus humanus corporis*. I. A method for feeding through a membrane and experimental infection with *Rickettsia prowazeki*, *R. mooseri*, and *Borrelia novyi*. Public Health Rep., *64*, 1287-1292.

Fulton, F., and Begg, A. M., 1946, Chemotherapeutic and other studies of typhus. V. The antigenic structure of typhus rickettsiae. Medical Research Council, Special Report Series No. 255, pp. 163-191, London, His Majesty's Stationery Office.

Gear, J., and Davis, D. H. S., 1942, The susceptibility of the South African gerbils (Genus Tatera) to rickettsial diseases and their use in the preparation of anti-typhus vaccine. Trans. Roy. Soc. Trop. Med. and Hyg., *36*, 1-7.

Gerhard, W. W., 1837, On the typhus fever which occurred at Philadelphia in the spring and summer of 1836; etc. Am. J. Med. Sci., *19*, 289-322.

Gildemeister, E., and Haagen, E., 1940, Fleckfieberstudien. I. Mitteilung: Nachweis eines Toxins in Rickettsien—Eikulturen (*Rickettsiae mooseri*). Deutsche med. Wchnschr., *66*, 878-880.

Gilliam, A. G., 1946, Efficacy of Cox-type vaccine in the prevention of naturally acquired louse-borne typhus fever. Am. J. Hyg., *44*, 401-410.

Giroud, P., 1938, Essai de mise en évidence des anticorps du typhus exanthématique par un test cutané. Compt. rend Soc. biol., *127*, 397-399.

Giroud, P., Boyer, J., and Vargues, R., 1950, A propos de quelques cas de typhus exanthématique survenus chez des sujets non parasités. Presse med., *58*, 334-336.

Goldberger, J., and Anderson, J. F., 1912, The transmission of typhus fever, with especial reference to transmission by the head louse (*Pediculus capitis*). Pub. Health Rep., *27*, 297-307.

Greeley, D., 1948, Methods of application of DDT. Symposium on Rickettsial Diseases, Dec. 1946, Boston, American Association for the Advancement of Science.

Greiff, D., and Pinkerton, H., 1948, The rickettsiostatic action of crystalline penicillin factions in embryonate eggs. Proc. Soc. Exp. Biol. and Med., *68*, 228-232.

Hamilton, H. L., 1945, Specificity of the toxic factors associated with the epidemic and the murine strains of typhus rickettsiae. Am. J. Trop. Med., *25*, 391-395.

Hawksley, J. C., and Stokes, E. J., 1950, A case of Brill's disease in London. Lancet, *2*, 97-99.

Hayes, W. J., and Gaines, T. B., 1950, Control of Norway rats with residual rodenticide warfarin. Public Health Rep., *65*, 1537-1555.

Hirsch, A., 1883, Handbook of Geographical and Historical Pathology. [Translated by Creighton, London, New Sydenham Society, Vol. 1.]

Holt-Harris, J. E., and Grubbs, S. B., 1922, Weil-Felix test for typhus fever. Pub. Health Rep., *37*, 1675-1680.

Hone, F. S., 1922, A series of cases closely resembling typhus fever. Med. J. Australia, *1*, 1-13.

Hunter, W., 1919, The Serbian epidemics of typhus and relapsing fever in 1915. Proc. Roy. Soc. Med., (Sect. Epidemiol.), *13*, 29-158.

Jacobsthal, E., 1917, Zur Komplementbindungsreaktion zwischen Fleckfieberläuseextrakt und Fleckfieberserum. Berlin. klin. Wchnschr., *54*, 1028.

Kligler, I. J., and Aschner, M., 1934, Immunization of animals with formolized tissue cultures of rickettsia from European and Mediterranean typhus. Brit. J. Exp. Path., *15*, 337-346.

Knipling, E. F., 1948, Insecticides, especially DDT. Symposium on Rickettsial Diseases, Dec. 1946, Boston, American Association for the Advancement of Science.

Laigret, J., and Durand, P., 1939, La vaccination contre le typhus exanthématique. Nouvelle technique de préparation du vaccin: emploi des cerveaux de souris. Bull. Acad. méd., *122*, 84-89.

Lee, R. I., 1913, Typhus fever (Brill's disease) at the Massachusetts General Hospital in ten years (Oct. 1, 1902, to Oct. 1, 1912). Boston Med. and Surg. J., *168*, 122-127.

León, A. P., 1944, Suero anti-tifo de conejos convalecientes en el tratamiento del tifo exantematico. Rev. Inst. salub. y enferm. trop., *5*, 117-128.

Lim, C. E., and Kurotchkin, T. J., 1929, A precipitin test for typhus fever with specific substance of *Bacillus proteus X 19*. Nat. Med. J. China, *15*, 6-10.

Liu, P. Y., Snyder, J. C., and Enders, J. F., 1941, Fatal infection of irradiated white mice with European typhus by the intra-abdominal route. J. Exp. Med., *73*, 669-679.

Macchiavello, A., 1937, Estudios sobre tifus exantematico. III. Un nuevo método para tenir Rickettsia. Revista chilena de hig. y med. prev., *1*, 101-106.

McCrae, T., 1907. Typhus fever, *in* Osler, Modern Medicine. Philadelphia, Lea, Vol. 2, p. 232.

Maxcy, K. F., 1926, Clinical observations on endemic typhus (Brill's disease) in the United States. Pub. Health Rep., *41*, 1213-1220.

Maxcy, K. F., 1929, Typhus fever in the United States. Pub. Health Rep., *44*, 1735-1742.

Miller, E. S., and Beeson, P. B., 1946, Murine typhus fever. Medicine, *25*, 1-15.

Monteiro, J. L., 1931, Estudos sobre o typho exantematico de Sao Paulo. Memorias do Instituto Butantan, *6*, 1-135.

Mooser, H., 1928, Experiments relating to the pathology and the etiology of Mexican typhus (tabardillo). J. Infect. Dis., *43*, 241-272.

Mooser, H., 1932, Essai sur l'histoire naturelle du typhus exanthématique. Arch. Inst. Pasteur de Tunis, *21*, 1-19.

Mooser, H., 1942, Le typhus exanthématique. Cours de méd. et chir. de guerre, Genève, sept., Q. G. du l er corps d'armée. [Quoted from Mooser, 1946.]

Mooser, H., 1945, Die Beziehungen des murinen Fleckfiebers zum klassichen Fleckfieber. Acta Tropica, Supplementum 4, Basel, Reinhardt.

Mooser, H., 1946, Twenty years of research in typhus fever. Schweiz. med. Wchnschr., *76*, 877-882.

Mooser, H., Castaneda, M. R., and Zinsser, H., 1931a. Rats as carriers of Mexican typhus fever. J. Am. Med. Assn., *97*, 231-232.

Mooser, H., Castaneda, M. R., and Zinsser, H., 1931b, The transmission of Mexican typhus from rat to rat by *Polyplax spinulosus*. J. Exp. Med., *54*, 567-575.

Mooser, H., and Loeffler, W., 1946, Ein Fall Sogenannter Brillscher Krankheit in Zurich. Schweiz. med. Wchnschr., *76*, 150-153.

Morgan, H. R., Stevens, D. A., and Snyder, J. C., 1947, Effect of streptomycin on growth of rickettsiae in eggs. Proc. Soc. Exp. Biol. and Med., *64*, 342-345.

Morgan, H. R., Neva, F. A., Fahey, R. J., and Finland, M., 1948, Report of two serologically proved cases of typhus fever in Irish-born residents of Boston. New Eng. J. Med., *238*, 871-873.

Murchison, C., 1884, A Treatise on the Continued Fevers of Great Britain, ed. 3. London, Longmans, Green.

Murray, E. S., 1945, Report to the Director, U. S. A. Typhus Commission. War Department, Washington, D. C.

Murray, E. S., Baehr, G., Shwartzman, G., Mandelbaum, R. A., Rosenthal, N., Doane, J. C., Weiss, L. B., Cohen, S., and Snyder, J. C., 1950, Brill's disease. I. Clinical and laboratory diagnosis. J. Am. Med. Assoc., *142*, 1059-1066.

Murray, E. S., Cohen, S., Jampol, J., Ofstrock, A., and Snyder, J. C., 1952, Epidemic typhus antibodies in human subjects in Boston, Mass. New Eng. J. Med., *246*, 355-59.

Murray, E. S., Ofstrock, A., and Snyder, J. C., 1952, Antibody response of human subjects to epidemic typhus vaccine three to eight years after previous immunization. J. Immunol., *68*, 207-18.

Murray, E. S., Pauls, E. P., and Snyder, J. C., 1952,

Relative susceptibilities of chick embryos, cotton rats, and guinea pigs to epidemic typhus rickettsiae. Manuscript in preparation.

Murray, E. S., Pšorn, T., Djakovic, P., Sielski, S., Broz, V., Ljupša, F., Gaon, J., Pavlevic, R., and Snyder, J. C., 1951, Brill's Disease. IV. Study of 26 cases in Yugoslavia. Am. J. Pub. Health, *41*, 1359-1369.

Murray, E. S., and Snyder, J. C., 1951, Brill's disease. II. Etiology. Am. J. Hyg., *53*, 22-32.

Neill, M. H., 1917, Experimental typhus fever in guinea pigs. A description of a scrotal lesion in guinea pigs infected with Mexican typhus. Pub. Health Rep., *32*, 1105-1108.

Neva, F. A., and Snyder, J. C., 1952, Susceptibility of the white rat to the acute lethal toxin of typhus rickettsiae with a note on pathologic changes. J. Inf. Dis., in press.

Nicolle, C., 1909, Reproduction expérimentale du typhus exanthématique chez le singe. Compt. rend. Acad. sci., *149*, 157-160.

Nicolle, C., Comte, C., and Conseil, E., 1909, Transmission expérimentale du typhus exanthématique par le pou du corps. Compt. rend. Acad. sci., *149*, 486-489.

Nicolle, C., Conseil, E., and Conor, A., 1911, Le typhus expérimental du cobaye. Compt. rend. Acad. sci., *152*, 1632-1634.

Nigg, C., and Landsteiner, K., 1930, Growth of rickettsia of typhus fever (Mexican type) in the presence of living tissue. Proc. Soc. Exp. Biol. and Med., *28*, 3-5.

Otto, R., 1909, Die Bedeutung der Insekten und anderen Ungeziefers bei der Verbreitung von Kriegsseuchen. 16. Intern. med. Kongr., Budapest, Sect. 20, 119-143.

Otto, R., and Dietrich, A., 1917, Beiträge zur "Rickettsien"—Frage. Deut. med. Wchnschr., *43*, 577-580.

Otto, R., and Munter, H., 1930, Fleckfieber, *in* Kolle, Kraus, and Uhlenhuth, Handbuch der pathogenen. Mikroorganismen, ed. 3., Jena, Fischer, Vol. 8, pp. 1107-1262.

Palacios, R., Chavez, F., and Avendano, O., 1935, Aislamiento de virus murino de individuos inoculados con vacun Blanc. Rev. Inst. bact. de Chile, *4*, 49-52.

Paullin, J. E., 1913, Typhus fever with a report of cases. Southern Med. J., *6*, 36-43.

Philip, C. B., 1948, The reservoirs of infection in rickettsial diseases. Symposium on Rickettsial Diseases, Dec. 1946, Boston, American Association for the Advancement of Science.

Phillips, R. A., Yeomans, A., and Tierney, N. A., 1948, Clinical studies of the Cairo Unit of the United States of America Typhus Commission, to be published.

Pinkerton, H., 1936, Criteria for the accurate classification of the rickettsial diseases (Rickettsioses) and of their etiological agents. Parasitol., *28*, 172-189.

Pinkerton, H., 1942, The pathogenic rickettsiae with particular reference to their nature, biologic properties, and classification. Bact. Reviews, *6*, 37-78.

Plotz, H., 1943, Complement fixation in rickettsial diseases. Science, *97*, 20-21.

Plotz, H., Bennett, B. L., Wertman, K., Snyder, M. J.,

and Gauld, R., 1948, Serological pattern in typhus fever. I. Epidemic. Am. J. Hyg., *47*, 150-165.

Plotz, H., Olitsky, P. K., and Baehr, G., 1915, The etiology of typhus exanthematicus. J. Infect. Dis., *17*, 1-68.

Plotz, H., Smadel, J. E., Anderson, T. F., and Chambers, L. A., 1943, Morphological structure of rickettsiae. J. Exp. Med., *77*, 355-358.

Plotz, H., and Wertman, K., 1945, Modification of serological response to infection with murine typhus by previous immunization with epidemic typhus vaccine. Proc. Soc. Exp. Biol. and Med., *59*, 248-251.

Pollard, M., Wilson, D. J., Livesay, H. R., and Woodland, J. C., 1946, The oral transmission of murine typhus strains in humans. Texas Rep. Biol. and Med., *4*, 446-451.

Prinzing, F., 1916, Epidemics Resulting from Wars. Oxford, Clarendon Press.

von Prowazek, S., 1914, Ätiologische Untersuchungen über den Flecktyphus in Serbien 1913 und Hamburg 1914. Beitr. z. Klin. der Infektionskr., *4*, 5-31.

Ricketts, H. T., and Wilder, R. M., 1910a, The transmission of the typhus fever of Mexico (tabardillo) by means of the louse (*Pediculus vestamenti*). J. Am. Med. Assn., *54*, 1304-1307.

Ricketts, H. T., and Wilder, R. M., 1910b, The etiology of the typhus fever (tabardillo) of Mexico City. A further preliminary report. J. Am. Med. Assn., *54*, 1373-1375.

Ris, H., and Fox, J. P., 1949, The cytology of rickettsiae. J. Exp. Med., *89*, 681-686.

da Rocha-Lima, H., 1916, Zur Aetiologie des Fleckfiebers. Kriegspathol. Tagung, April 26, 1916; pp. 45-50, Beiheft zu Band *27*, Zentralbl. f. allg. Path. u. path. Anat.

da Rocha-Lima, H., 1918, Schutzimpfungsversuche gegen Fleckfieber. Münch. med. Wchnschr., *65*, 1454-1456.

da Rocha-Lima, H., 1930, Rickettsien, *in* Kolle, Kraus, and Uhlenhuth, Handbuch der pathogenen Mikroorganism, ed. 3. Jena, Fischer, Vol. 8, pp. 1347-1368.

van Rooyen, C. E., and Bearcroft, W. G. C., 1943, Typhus rickettsial agglutination tests in the Middle East forces and Egypt. Edinburgh Med. J., *50*, 257-272.

Sadusk, J. F., Jr., 1947, Typhus fever in the United States Army following immunization. Incidence, severity of the disease, modification of the clinical course and serologic diagnosis. J. Am. Med. Assn., *133*, 1192-1199.

Sadusk, J. F., Jr., and Kuhlenbeck H., 1946, Dangers associated with the use of living "attenuated" typhus vaccine. Am. J. Pub. Health, *36*, 1027-1030.

Scoville, A. B., 1948, Epidemic typhus in Japan and Korea. Symposium on Rickettsial Diseases, Dec. 1946, Boston, American Association for the Advancement of Science.

Scoville, A. B., Jr., Bennett, B. L., Wertman, K., and Gauld, R., 1948, The serological pattern in typhus fever. II. Murine. Am. J. Hyg., *47*, 166-176.

Silva-Goytia, R., 1944, Fijación de complemento con sueros de enfermos de tifo exantemático. Rev. del Inst. de salub. y enferm. trop., *5*, 241-245.

Sinclair, C. G., and Maxcy, K. F., 1925, Mild typhus (Brill's disease) in the lower Rio Grande Valley. Pub. Health Rep., *40*, 241-248.

Smadel, J. E., 1948, The complement-fixation and agglutination reaction in rickettsial diseases. Symposium on Rickettsial Diseases, Dec. 1946, Boston, American Association for the Advancement of Science.

Smadel, J. E., and Jackson, E. B., 1947, Chloromycetin, an antibiotic with chemotherapeutic activity in experimental rickettsial and viral infections. Science, *106*, 418-419.

Smadel, J. E., Jackson, E. B., and Gauld, R., 1947, Factors influencing growth of rickettsiae. I. Rickettsiostatic effect of streptomycin in experimental infections. J. Immunol., *57*, 273-284.

Snyder, J. C., 1947, Typhus fever in the second World War. California Med., *66*, 3-10.

Snyder, J. C., 1951, Unpublished observations.

Snyder, J. C., 1948, The treatment of the rickettsial diseases of man. Symposium on Rickettsial Diseases, Dec. 1946, Boston, American Association for the Advancement of Science.

Snyder, J. C., and Anderson, C. R., 1942, The susceptibility of the eastern cotton rat, *Sigmodon hispidus hispidus,* to European typhus. Science, *95*, 23.

Snyder, J. C., Fagan, R., Wells, E. B., Wick, H. C., and Miller, J. C., 1950, Experimental studies on the antirickettsial properties of terramycin. Ann. N. Y. Acad. Sci., *53*, 362-374.

Snyder, J. C., and Wheeler, C. M., 1945, The experimental infection of the human body louse, *Pediculus humanus corporis,* with murine and epidemic louse-borne typhus strains. J. Exp. Med., *82*, 1-20.

Snyder, J. C., Yeomans, A., Clement, D. H., Murray, E. S., Zarafonetis, C. J. D., and Tierney, A., 1947, Further observations on the treatment of typhus fever with para-aminobenzoic acid. Ann. Int. Med., *27*, 1-27.

Snyder, J. C., Zarafonetis, C. J. D., and Liu, W. T., 1945, The susceptibility of the rodents, *Gerbillus gerbillus,* and *Gerbillus pyramidum,* to experimental typhus infection. Proc. Soc. Exp. Biol. and Med., *59*, 110-112.

Soares, J. A., 1950, Doenca do Brill. A Proposito de Tres Casos de Recrudescencia de Tifo Exantematico Historico Observados em Braga. Bol. Inst. Sup. d. Hyg. Duot. Ric. Jor., *V*, 1-18.

Soper, F. L., Davis, W. A., Markham, F. S., Riehl, L. A., and Buck, P., 1945, Louse powder studies in North Africa (1943). Arch. Inst. Pasteur d'Algerie, *23*, 183-223.

Starzyk, J., 1936, Vitalité, toxicité et pouvoir d'immunisation de *Rickettsia prowazeki* conservées hors de l'organisme du pou, en milieu liquide et en milieu sec. Compt. rend. Soc. biol., *123*, 1221-1225.

Stevens, R. S., 1945, Louse-borne typhus fever: trial of serum treatment. Lancet, *1*, 106-109.

Strong, R. P., Shattuck, G. C., Sellards, A. W., Zinsser, H., and Hopkins, J. G., 1920, Typhus Fever with Particular Reference to the Serbian Epidemic. Cambridge, Harvard University Press.

Stuart-Harris, C. H., Rettie, G. K. C., and Oliver,

J. O., 1943, Rickettsial agglutination studies in typhus fever. Lancet, 2, 537-538.

Tierney, N. A., and Yeomans, A., 1946, Metabolic studies in louse-borne typhus. Observations on serum electrolyte pattern, serum protein partition, and nitrogen balance. J. Clin. Investig., 25, 822-837.

Topping, N. H., 1940, The preservation of the infectious agents of some of the rickettsioses. Pub. Health Reports, 55, 545-547.

Topping, N. H., 1947, Personal communication.

Topping, N. H., Bengtson, I. A., Henderson, R. G., Shepard, C. C., and Shear, M. J., 1945, Studies of typhus fever. National Institute of Health Bull. No. 183, U. S. Govt. Printing Office, Washington, D. C.

Varela, G., and Zozaya, J., 1945, Distribución en México de las cepas de tifo exantematico hasta ahora estudias. Rev. Inst. salub. y enferm. trop., 6, 11-14.

Villalba, J., 1803, Epidemiologia española, etc. Madrid, F. Villalpando. [Quoted from Zinsser, H., 1935, pp. 242-243.]

Weigl, R., 1920, Untersuchungen und Experimente an Fleckfieberläusen. Die Technik der Rikettsia-Forschung. Beitr. z. Klin. der Infektionskr., 8, 353-376.

Weigl, R., 1930, Die Methoden der aktiven Fleck-fieber-Immunisierung. Bull. Internat. Acad. Polonaise sci. et lettres (Cl. Med), July, 1930, 25-62.

Weil, E., and Felix, A., 1916, Zur serologischen Diagnose des Fleckfiebers. Wien. klin. Wchnschr., 29, 33-35.

Wertman, K., 1948, The Weil-Felix reaction. Symposium on Rickettsial Diseases, Dec. 1946, Boston, American Association for the Advancement of Science.

Wheatland, F. T., 1926, A fever resembling a mild form of typhus fever. Med. J. Australia, 1, 261-266.

Wheeler, C. M., 1943, Report to the Typhus Conference, London, Nov. 1943. Files of the National Research Council, Washington, D. C.

Wisseman, C. L., Jr., Hahn, F. E., Jackson, E. B., and Smadel, J. E., 1951, Metabolic studies of rickettsiae: pathway of glutamate oxidation in suspensions of Rickettsia mooseri. Fed. Proc., 10, 424.

Wolbach, S. B., 1940, The rickettsial diseases. A general survey, in Virus and Rickettsial Diseases. Cambridge, Harvard University Press, pp. 789-816.

Wolbach, S. B., 1948, The pathology of typhus fever. Symposium on Rickettsial Diseases, Dec. 1946, Boston, American Association for the Advancement of Science.

Wolbach, S. B., and Todd, J. L., 1920, Note sur l'étiologie et l'anatomie pathologique du typhus exanthématique au Mexique. Ann. Inst. Pasteur, 34, 153-158.

Wolbach, S. B., and Schlesinger, M. J., 1923, The cultivation of the micro-organisms of Rocky Mountain spotted fever (Dermacentroxenus rickettsi) and of typhus (Rickettsia prowazeki) in tissue plasma cultures. J. Med. Research, 44, 231-256.

Wolbach, S. B., Todd, J. L., and Palfrey, F. W., 1922, The Etiology and Pathology of Typhus. Cambridge, Harvard University Press.

Wolman, M., 1944, Treatment of typhus with anti-typhus horse serum. Lancet, 2, 210-212.

Wong, S. C., and Cox, H. R., 1948, Action of aureomycin against experimental rickettsial and viral infections. Ann. N. Y. Acad. Sci., 51, 290-305.

Woodward, T. E., 1948, Clinical course of murine typhus. Symposium on Rickettsial Diseases, Dec. 1946, Boston, American Association for the Advancement of Science.

Woodward, T. E., and Bland, E. F., 1944, Clinical observations in typhus fever with special reference to the cardiovascular system. J. Am. Med. Assn., 126, 287-293.

Worms, R., 1950, Le problème du typhus sporadique. Semaine des hôpitaux de Paris, 26, 1-13.

Yeomans, A., 1947, Typhus fever, in Oxford Medicine. New York, Oxford University Press, Vol. 5, pp. 439-466 (23).

Yeomans, A., 1948, The symptomatology, clinical course and management of louseborne typhus fever. Symposium on Rickettsial Diseases, Dec. 1946, Boston, American Association for the Advancement of Science.

Yeomans, A., Snyder, J. C., Murray, E. S., Ecke, R. S., and Zarafonetis, C. J. D., 1945, Azotemia in typhus fever. Ann. Int. Med., 23, 711-753.

Yeomans, A., Snyder, J. C., and Gilliam, A. G., 1945, The effects of concentrated hyperimmune rabbit serum in louse-borne typhus. J. Am. Med. Assn., 129, 19-24.

Zarafonetis, C. J. D., 1948, The serological reactions in the rickettsial diseases of man, general considerations. Symposium on Rickettsial Diseases, Dec. 1946, Boston, American Association for the Advancement of Science.

Zarafonetis, C. J. D., Ecke, R. S., Yeomans, A., Murray, E. S., and Snyder, J. C., 1946, Serologic studies in typhus-vaccinated individuals. III. Weil-Felix and complement-fixation findings in epidemic typhus fever occurring in the vaccinated. J. Immunol., 53, 15-30.

Zinsser, H., 1934, Varieties of typhus virus and the epidemiology of the American form of European typhus fever (Brill's disease). Am. J. Hyg., 20, 513-532.

Zinsser, H., 1935, Rats, Lice, and History. Boston, Little, Brown and Co.

Zinsser, H., 1937, The rickettsia diseases. Varieties, epidemiology, and geographical distribution. Am. J. Hyg., 25, 430-463.

Zinsser, H., 1940, Epidemiology and immunity in the rickettsial diseases, in Virus and Rickettsial Diseases, Harvard School of Public Health. Cambridge, Harvard University Press, pp. 872-907.

Zinsser, H., and Castaneda, M. R., 1932, Studies on typhus fever. IX. On the serum reactions of Mexican and European typhus rickettsia. J. Exp. Med., 56, 455-467.

Zinsser, H., Wei, H., and FitzPatrick, F., 1938, Further studies of agar-slant tissue cultures of typhus rickettsiae. Proc. Soc. Exp. Biol. and Med., 38, 285-288.

HERALD R. COX, sc.d.

Lederle Laboratories Division, American Cyanamid Company

36

The Spotted-Fever Group

The spotted-fever group includes, in addition to Rocky Mountain spotted fever of the United States, other tick-borne or mite-borne diseases such as boutonneuse fever of the Mediterranean regions in Europe and North Africa, tick-borne typhus (tick typhus or tick-bite fever) of all parts of Africa including Ethiopia, Kenya, Nigeria and the Union of South Africa, Brazilian spotted fever (which includes the São Paulo and Minas Gerais typhus fevers), Tobia fever of Colombia, Choix or pinta fever of Mexico, North Queensland tick typhus, rickettsialpox, maculatum disease and probably some of the tick-borne rickettsioses of India and Russia.

ROCKY MOUNTAIN SPOTTED FEVER

(Synonyms: Mountain fever, typho-malaria fever, Bull fever, black fever, blue disease, spotted fever)

Introduction

Rocky Mountain spotted fever is an acute, endemic, infectious febrile disease. The causative agent is *Rickettsia rickettsii* (Bengtson, 1946), (*Dermacentroxenus rickettsi*, Wolbach, 1919; *Rickettsia rickettsi*, Brumpt, 1927; *Rickettsia brasiliensis*, Monteiro, 1931; *Rickettsia typhi*, do Amaral and Monteiro, 1932). The only known means of natural transmission to lower animals or to man is through the medium of infected ticks.

History

Rocky Mountain spotted fever was first recognized in the Rocky Mountain region of the United States. The first account in the literature (Maxey, 1899) described the disease as "an acute, endemic, non-contagious but probably infectious, febrile disease, characterized clinically by a continuous moderately high fever, severe arthritic and muscular pains, and a profuse petechial or purpural eruption in the skin, appearing first on the ankles, wrists and forehead, but rapidly spreading to all parts of the body." Wilson and Chowning (1902) made an investigation of the disease and claimed an erythrocytic parasite, *Piroplasma hominis*, to be the causative agent. They suggested that the disease was transmitted by the bite of the wood tick *Dermacentor andersoni*. The first transmission of the disease to guinea pigs and monkeys by inoculation with infected human blood was achieved by Howard Taylor Ricketts in 1906 (1906a).

In the same year Ricketts (1906b) and King (1906) independently showed that the disease was transmitted by the wood tick,[*] and in the following year Ricketts (1907a)

---

[*] Ricketts (1907b) reported that the first experiments performed with the purpose of showing a possible relationship of the wood tick to spotted fever were done on human subjects but were not formally reported by the authors. Thus, Doctors McCalla and Brereton of Boise, Idaho, infected two individuals in series by the bite of a tick which they had removed from one of their patients. These experiments were unknown to Ricketts (1906b) and King (1906) at the time they conducted their experiments, although the studies of McCalla and Brereton antedated theirs by more than a year.

demonstrated the occurrence of naturally infected ticks in the Bitter Root Valley of Montana. These data, together with epidemiologic findings, were conclusive evidence of the part the wood tick plays in causing human infection. Later, Ricketts (1907c) showed that the infectious agent

multiplication of the rickettsiae in tick tissue.

CLINICAL PICTURE

In many of its general aspects, Rocky Mountain spotted fever resembles typhus, the chief differential points being the dura-

Typical Rocky Mountain Spotted Fever

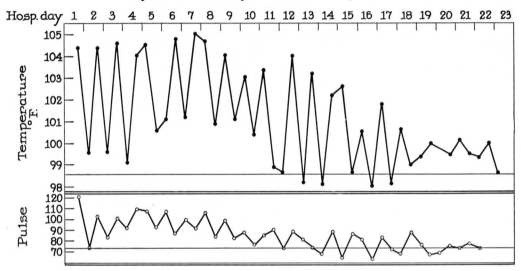

CHART 32. Temperature and pulse-rate curves of a typical case of Rocky Mountain spotted fever before the introduction of treatment by para-aminobenzoic acid and serum. (Dr. R. R. Parker, Rocky Mountain Spotted Fever Laboratory, U. S. Public Health Service, Hamilton, Montana.)

acquired by either of the immature stages was carried through to adult ticks and that from at least a certain proportion of infected females the infection was transmitted through eggs to their progeny. In 1909, Ricketts described the micro-organism of the disease in smears prepared from the blood of man, monkey and guinea pig and from tissues of the tick. In 1910, Ricketts and Wilder showed by cross-immunity experiments that Rocky Mountain spotted fever and typhus fever are separate and distinct diseases. In 1919, Wolbach published the results of his careful etiologic and pathologic studies and named the etiologic agent *Dermacentroxenus rickettsi*. Wolbach differentiated between this organism and nonpathogenic organisms in ticks, and was the first to demonstrate the intranuclear

tion of fever and the time of appearance and location of the rash. Attacks range from mild ambulatory and abortive forms to rapidly terminating fatal infections. The fatality rate varies in different regions.

The following description is based on the appearance of the disease as it occurs in nonvaccinated adults. In vaccinated persons and young children, attacks are frequently mild and atypical. The incubation period ranges from 2 to 12 days but averages 6 or 7 days. The actual onset, like that of typhus, may be preceded by a few days of ill-defined symptoms—listlessness, loss of appetite and headache. Onset is commonly abrupt with chills, profound prostration and a rapidly rising fever that continues to mount into the second week. Myalgia and arthralgia are marked and in the more

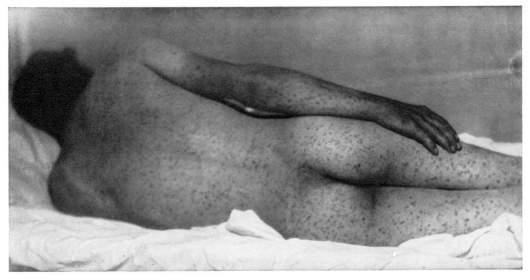

FIG. 47. Typical rash on a patient suffering from Rocky Mountain spotted fever. (Dr. R. R. Parker, Rocky Mountain Spotted Fever Laboratory, U. S. Public Health Service, Hamilton, Montana.)

severe forms epistaxis may occur early. Remissions of 1 to 3 degrees (F.) are observed in morning temperatures. The fever terminates by rapid lysis, usually at about the end of the third week, although mild cases may become afebrile before the end of the second week. Chart 32 shows temperature and pulse-rate curves of a typical case of Rocky Mountain spotted fever.

A distinctive rash usually appears on the third or fourth day which resembles the slight mottling seen in early measles. This fades shortly to be followed by typical, rose-red, maculopapular lesions characterized by first appearing on the ankles and wrists and rapidly spreading to the legs, arms and chest. The palms and soles and at times even the face and scalp become involved. The abdomen is the last and least affected. Early in the course of the disease, the spots are less pronounced during morning remissions of fever but become progressively more distinct each day until they are definitely petechial in all but the mildest types of infection (Fig. 47). In severe cases the spots are confluent, deep red or purplish in color and often necrotic. In convalescence the rash is brownish, and branny desquama-

tion occurs over the more heavily involved areas.

There are no significant hematologic changes. The white cell count usually does not exceed 15,000 per c.mm. but may go as high as 30,000. Nervous manifestations are common and include headache, restlessness, insomnia, confusion, coma, convulsions, hyperactive and pathologic reflexes, cranial-nerve palsies, paraplegia and hemiplegia. Although these neurologic changes may persist for weeks or occasionally months after onset of illness, they usually are transitory and subside without leaving clinically detectable residua. However, there is evidence that occasional patients may show permanent severe neurologic sequelae resulting in death (Berlin and Thomas, 1948). In fulminating cases, coma usually precedes death, which commonly occurs around the end of the second week of illness. Convalescence is slow even in the mild cases and complete recovery, particularly from severe infection, may require several months and sometimes even a year or longer. Disturbances of sight, hearing and mental acuity are not uncommon, and various symptoms associated with vascular damage may be observed. It is generally considered that persons having recovered from spotted fever are more or less permanently immune.

PATHOLOGIC PICTURE

The distinctive gross features are those related to the distribution and character of the lesions of blood vessels in the skin and subcutaneous tissues. Extensive hemorrhages in the scrotal tissues, often with necrosis, and similar lesions of the testes and their appendages are the most characteristic gross findings in man. The spleen is always enlarged, several times the normal size, and is firm. Microscopic examination reveals that lesions are practically limited to the peripheral blood vessels, including those of the external genitalia. In the beginning, a proliferative lesion is apparent in the vascular endothelium; polymorphonuclear leukocytes may or may not play a part, depending upon the degree of intensity of the reaction before thrombosis occurs. Following thrombosis, polymorphonuclear leukocytes are necessarily present. The degenerative changes found in the endothelial cells and in the smooth-muscle cells of the media result from a direct injury caused by the rickettsiae. The general reaction to the infection is shown by endothelial cell accumulation in the blood vessels of the lung, liver, spleen and lymph nodes. Lillie has reported (1941) that the pathologic picture of spotted fever in the Rocky Mountain area and in the eastern United States is essentially the same.

According to Wolbach (1919), one feature of spotted fever, which cannot be too strongly emphasized, is that it may be duplicated exactly in experimental animals. The histologic character of individual lesions in the brain of infected guinea pigs does not differ appreciably from that found in typhus, but in spotted fever a higher proportion of the focal lesions are found in the pons, medulla, midbrain and cerebellum. Guinea pigs sacrificed for examination at the height of infection show edema and hemorrhages in the skin and subcu-

taneous tissues of the scrotum. Blood vessels of the skin are finely injected, but generalized hemorrhages do not occur: hemorrhage and necrosis of the skin occur only in the scrotum, paws and ears. Inguinal and axillary lymph nodes are swollen and reddened. The spleen is from three to five times larger than normal and is dark red and firm; occasionally there is a very thin, translucent layer of fibrin upon its surface. The most striking changes are found in the testes and adnexa. The former are swollen and markedly injected, usually with minute hemorrhages in the tunica at both poles. The polar fat is discolored and shows small hemorrhages. The cremasteric muscles and parietal tunicae are deep red, often hemorrhagic, and both are adherent to each other and to the testes. Small hemorrhages are practically constant in the epididymis. Late in the course of the disease, the testes become adherent to the scrotum, and the subcutaneous tissues surrounding the anus and scrotum are thickened and hemorrhagic. The central nervous system may be injected, but shows no gross lesions.

EXPERIMENTAL INFECTION; HOST RANGE

Man is an incidental victim to spotted fever and is in no way responsible for the maintenance of the infection in nature, which is due largely to ticks and the wild rodents on which they feed. Animals serving as hosts to *D. andersoni,* and believed responsible for maintaining the infection in nature, are the tree squirrel, ground squirrel, snowshoe rabbit, jack rabbit, cottontail rabbit, chipmunk, pack rat, wood rat, meadow mouse, deer mouse, weasel and marmot. It may be significant, as pointed out recently by Jellison (1945), that in the United States a close geographic relationship exists between spotted fever and one species of cottontail rabbit, *Sylvilagus nuttalli*. Thus far no naturally infected animal has been found in the United States, although it seems quite likely that Hassler, Sizemore and Robinson (Parker, Kohls and Steinhaus, 1943) isolated the infectious agent from a pocket gopher, but the strain was lost before it could be identified with certainty. Most of the natural hosts show only inapparent infections with no diagnostic gross lesions or distinctive febrile reactions and seldom die. In Brazil, the opossum (*Didelphus paraguayensis* and *D. aurita* in São Paulo and *D. marsupialis* in Minas Gerais) has been found naturally infected (Travassos, 1948). There is also evidence showing that the dog is naturally infected. Travassos (see p. 418, 1948) inoculated guinea pigs with blood from an apparently normal dog that lived in a spotted-fever endemic area and found that the guinea pigs were immune subsequently to a spotted-fever challenge. Experimentally, the dog and the opossum *(D. aurita)* develop inapparent infections with the São Paulo strain, and viable rickettsiae persist in these hosts for long periods of time. Six serial passages of the São Paulo strain through opossums *(D. aurita)* resulted in a loss of virulence of the agent. The Brazilian cavy *(Cavia aperea)*, the wild rabbit *(Sylvilagus minensis)* and the capybara *(Hydrochoerus capybara)* react to Brazilian strains of spotted fever; the cavy is the most susceptible (Travassos, 1948).

Most large domestic animals are insusceptible. However, Badger (1933) found dogs and sheep mildly susceptible to experimental infection. Older dogs showed no clinical manifestations although rickettsiae were recovered from their blood on the fourth, sixth and eighth days after inoculation. A grown dog, reared in an endemic spotted-fever area, was apparently immune. A puppy reacted with fever and respiratory symptoms, and rickettsiae were recovered from its blood on the fourth day. Infected *D. andersoni* were fed on two puppies which, after incubation periods of five and six days, respectively, developed signs of illness, and rickettsiae were recovered from the blood of each. Rickettsiae were recovered from the blood of a young sheep on the fourth, sixth, eighth and tenth days after inoculation. Magalhães and Rocha (1942) not only found

dogs susceptible to experimental infection with Brazilian spotted fever but also found them naturally infected. Miller (1950) was unable to induce obvious disease in 6 foxes and 2 raccoons by inoculating them with the highly virulent Bitter Root strain of spotted-fever rickettsiae; the animals, however, produced complement-fixing antibodies. Dogs, foxes and raccoons, on which

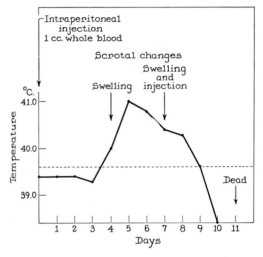

CHART 33. Temperature curve of a guinea pig infected with the Bitter Root strain of Rocky Mountain spotted fever.

D. variabilis nymphs and adults were found under natural conditions on Long Island, N. Y., showed complement-fixing antibodies in high titer for spotted fever.

Of the common laboratory animals, the guinea pig is the most suitable for experimental purposes. After inoculation of blood from human patients the temperature usually does not rise until three or more days have passed, and generally a few passages in guinea pigs are required before the incubation period becomes fixed at two or three days (Chart 33). The febrile period lasts from 5 to 14 days. Death, which usually occurs with well established strains on the sixth to eighth day of fever, is preceded by a sudden drop in temperature to subnormal (Chart 33). If a guinea pig recovers, its temperature begins to drop at the end of seven or eight days, and gradually reaches normal within three to six days. The first sign of the disease in male guinea pigs is swelling and reddening of the scrotal skin on the third or fourth day of fever (Chart 33). At this time an animal shows signs of discomfort, loss of appetite and roughening of the coat. The scrotal reaction may develop into a necrotic condition, followed by sloughing and subsequent healing with scar formation. Necrosis and sloughing of the foot pads and ears also occur frequently. Rabbits rarely die of the disease, although they develop fever and may show ear and scrotal reactions similar to those seen in guinea pigs. Rabbits develop antibodies detectable by the Weil-Felix reaction. The course of the disease in monkeys may be very rapid with early death occurring with very virulent strains. Monkeys frequently develop a rash on the face, over the lower back and on the thighs. Swelling and redness of the scrotum is common. Necrosis of the ears also occurs. Monkeys, like rabbits, develop antibodies detectable by the Weil-Felix reaction. White rats are moderately susceptible. White mice are relatively insusceptible.

ETIOLOGY

According to Wolbach (1919), the distribution and morphology of *R. rickettsii* are identical in the tissues of man, monkey, rabbit and guinea pig. In tissue sections, the rickettsia is a minute organism, frequently occurring in pairs and often surrounded by a very narrow but definite clear zone, or halo, as if encapsulated. Often the distal ends of the pairs are tapered, so that they resemble minute pneumococci. The rickettsiae average about 1 μ in length and from 0.2 to 0.3 μ in width. They are best stained by special methods; with Giemsa stain the rickettsiae take a purplish tinge, with the Castaneda method they take a light blue appearance, whereas with the Macchiavello method they stain red. Figure 48 shows rickettsiae in a stained smear. Like other rickettsiae, *R. rickettsii* is gram-

negative. All attempts to cultivate *R. rickettsii* on artificial media have been unsuccessful, but they do grow readily in tissue cultures and in the chorio-allantois and yolk sac of the developing chick embryo. The striking feature of *R. rickettsii* in plasma tissue cultures is its apparent preference for the cell nuclei where they grow in compact clusters (Pinkerton and Hass. 1932); often the entire nucleus becomes distended with organisms. There is a definite peripheral condensation of the nuclear chromatin, similar to that seen in association with the intranuclear inclusions of certain virus diseases. According to Pinkerton (1942, p. 62), the "multiplication of parasites within the nuclei of their host cells is a very unusual occurrence. Excluding 'virus bodies' like those of herpes, the only definite micro-organisms other than *R. rickettsii* which exhibit this phenomenon, are relatively large protozoa, such as *Karyophagus salamandrae*, which is a parasite of the salamander." The unique intranuclear localization of *R. Rickettsii* was used by Pinkerton (1936) in the classification of atypical strains which gave ambiguous cross-immunity reactions. Spotted-fever rickettsiae do not pass Berkefeld V, N or W candles, or Seitz filter pads. They are killed in a few minutes by exposure to moist heat at 50° C. or to chemical agents, and in a few hours by desiccation at room temperature. Red and white blood cells from infected guinea-pig blood retain their infectivity even after repeated washings. At room temperature guinea-pig blood retains its infectivity for only about a week, but in a cold room it remains infectious for about two weeks. Infected guinea-pig brain and spleen suspended in glycerol stored in sealed containers at −7° C., or in a dry-ice box, remain infectious for periods ranging up to a year.

DIAGNOSIS

In spite of the commonly expressed opinion that spotted fever is an easily recognized infection, errors in diagnosis may be made even by those familiar with the disease. Often it is not possible to diagnose clinically the very mild infections or the fulminating types. Furthermore, in areas where both spotted fever and murine (endemic) typhus are prevalent, an additional difficulty is encountered because of their clinical similarity.

testicular washings taken from an infected pig on the second or third day of fever. By establishing the disease in guinea pigs, it is possible to apply cross-immunity tests with known strains of spotted-fever rickettsiae or other infectious agents.

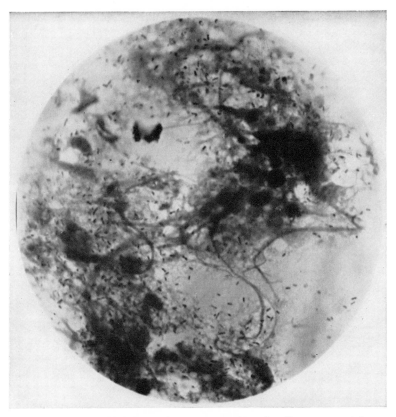

FIG. 48. Photograph of stained preparation of yolk-sac material from infected chick embryo. × 1,245.

The laboratory tests ordinarily used for diagnosis are the infection test, the Weil-Felix reaction, the protection or virus-neutralization test and the complement-fixation test. In the infection test male guinea pigs are inoculated intraperitoneally with blood from a suspected patient. Clotted blood, plasma, serum, or preferably whole citrated blood, may be used. Once the disease is established, it may be maintained by inoculating normal guinea pigs intraperitoneally with blood, splenic tissue or

The Weil-Felix reaction, that is testing a patient's serum for agglutinins against Proteus OX-19, aids in limiting the probable diagnosis to the rickettsial group of diseases, but it is of no aid in differentiating spotted fever from typhus. In testing for the Weil-Felix reaction, it is desirable that at least two blood samples be used; one taken as soon as spotted fever is suspected, the other between the twelfth and fifteenth day after onset. The first sample is seldom diagnostic and is valuable chiefly as a reference point in determining whether there is a subsequent rise in titer. A titer of less than 1:320 cannot be considered definitely diagnostic. In the majority of sera the titers for OX-19 agglutinins are highest, but occasionally, particularly with sera from patients in certain areas of Wyoming (Parker, 1938), those for OX-2 agglutinins are highest. The Proteus agglutinins usually appear toward the end of the second week of the disease, but occasionally they do not appear until early convalescence; in some patients none is produced.

According to Parker (1938), the protection or virus-neutralization test is nearly always of diagnostic value. As performed in his laboratory, "duplicate mixtures are prepared, each containing 0.5 cc. of serum and 0.1 cc., 0.25 cc. and 0.5 cc. of serum virus, respectively." The mixtures are held at room temperature for 30 minutes and then injected intraperitoneally into guinea pigs. Control animals receive the same amount of infectious serum mixed with normal serum. The most consistent results are obtained with blood samples taken in convalescence, although some sera taken during lysis show definite neutralizing capacity. The neutralization test is of greater value than the agglutination reaction in testing blood specimens from relatively mild cases and may give even better results than the infection test.

The complement-fixation test is an additional laboratory aid and has a distinct advantage over the Weil-Felix reaction in that it is highly specific and may be used to differentiate spotted fever from epidemic typhus, murine typhus, Q fever, scrub typhus and boutonneuse fever. Satisfactory antigens may be prepared from rickettsiae cultivated by the agar-tissue culture method of Zinsser, FitzPatrick and Wei (1939), or by the yolk-sac method of Cox (1938). Spotted-fever and boutonneuse-fever rickettsiae contain soluble antigens which give cross-fixation respectively with boutonneuse-fever or spotted-fever antisera. However, the soluble antigens may be removed by subjecting the rickettsiae to repeated washings and the resulting washed rickett-siae provide highly specific antigens (Plotz, Reagan and Wertman, 1944). Van der Scheer, Bohnel and Cox (1947) have prepared purified soluble antigens from spotted-fever rickettsiae which are highly specific and give little or no fixation with syphilitic human sera. Schubert, Stanford and Tiffany (1951) compared five procedures commonly used in the performance of the complement-fixation test. They found that the modified Kolmer test used by van der Scheer, Bohnel and Cox (1947) possesses the advantages of being specific, sensitive, and already essentially familiar to workers in many public health laboratories.

The Weil-Felix reaction and the protection test are of no value in testing for long-past infections. The agglutinin titer for Proteus strains falls rapidly after recovery is complete, and it is unusual for a patient's serum to show neutralizing capacity a year after illness. On the other hand, complement-fixing antibodies usually appear during the second week of illness and persist for at least six to eight years. Shepard and Topping (1946) carried out complement-fixation tests using spotted-fever antigen and dog sera collected from various parts of the country and obtained high titers with sera procured from dogs in known spotted-fever areas.

TREATMENT

In the early days, the only treatment for spotted fever was symptomatic. Metaphen, sulfanilimide, sulfapyridine and penicillin, have been tried with no clean-cut evidence of benefit. The sulfonamide compounds are not only useless, but in all probability harmful. Sulfonamide-treated guinea pigs died sooner than did the untreated controls (Topping, 1939). Numerous reports in the literature describe attempts to produce a satisfactory immune serum for treatment. The most promising work along these lines is that of Topping (1943), who used hyperimmune sera prepared in rabbits by injecting them with living rickettsiae derived from infected ticks or yolk sacs. The results obtained in a few patients indicate that serum treatment reduces the case-fatality rate if it is administered before the third day of rash. Another promising line of attack has been the work of Harrell, Venning and Wolff (1944) who showed that a very severe form of peripheral circulatory collapse develops in spotted fever and that the "toxic" condition is strikingly similar to early "shock" associated with functional capillary damage produced by burns, bacterial toxins or other substances. Because of the widespread vascular lesions, plus starvation, there is a tremendous loss of circulating body fluids and protein, with lowering of the blood chlorides, elevation of the nonprotein nitrogen of the blood and actual or potential development of circulatory collapse. They believe that intravenous therapy is not harmful but, on the contrary, definitely indicated provided it is properly chosen. It should include plasma and whole blood in adequate quantities, in addition to glucose, salts, vitamins and amino acids, and should be controlled by careful laboratory studies.

Para-aminobenzoic acid (PABA) has been found useful in the treatment of spotted fever; this procedure is based on the original work of Snyder, Maier and Anderson (1942) who showed that in white mice its oral administration reduced the mortality from experimental murine typhus. PABA has been reported to give favorable results in spotted-fever infected guinea pigs (Anigstein and Bader, 1945) in chick embryos (Hamilton, 1945) and in human beings (Rose, Duane and Fischel, 1945; Ravenel, 1947). However, it is now a matter of record that the problem of treatment of spotted fever as well as of all other rickettsial diseases has essentially been solved, for there are now available three antibiotics, namely, aureomycin, chloramphenicol and terramycin, which have been proved of great value not only in the laboratory but by repeated clinical trials. Each of these antibiotics has been found to be far superior to para-aminobenzoic acid. Results of ex-

tensive laboratory studies with aureomycin have been reported by Wong and Cox (1948) and Anigstein, Whitney and Beninson (1948); reports on the use of chloramphenicol have been made by Smadel and Jackson (1947) and Smadel, Jackson and Cruise (1949); Snyder and his associates (1950), Smadel, Jackson and Ley (1950) and Rose (1950) have reported their findings on the efficacy of terramycin. Clinical tests carried out by numerous competent observers have fully substantiated the laboratory results. Good reviews have been published by Finland et al. (1949), Rose and Kneeland (1949) and Smadel (1949, 1951). It is now well recognized that all of the above named antibiotics are rickettsiostatic in their action and not rickettsiocidal. The antibiotics suppress the growth of rickettsiae and permit time for the protective mechanism of the host to function; thus, final recovery of a host in all cases depends on the development of specific immunity, in which state the host may continue to harbor living micro-organisms for considerable periods of time. All three antibiotics are extremely efficacious in the treatment of spotted fever and all other rickettsial diseases. The matter of drug dosage for any of the rickettsioses including spotted fever is essentially the same and relatively simple. The administration of 2.0 to 3.0 grams orally each day until the patient's temperature has been normal for 24 to 48 hours is a good general rule to follow. Smadel (1951) recommends an initial loading dose of 3.0 grams when chloramphenicol is used. It is not necessary to use such a loading dose for aureomycin or terramycin. In the case of aureomycin, it is recommended that the daily amount of drug given orally be approximately 100 mg. per 10 pounds body weight; the total amount should be divided and given at 2- to 4-hour intervals. It is best to administer each dose of antibiotic with a glassful (240 ml.) of a bland drink, preferably milk, or one ounce of milk (30 ml.) to each 30 mg. of antibiotic. Spotted-fever patients usually become afebrile within 48 to 72 hours after initiation of therapy so that it can be discontinued after 4 or 5 days. There is practically no evidence of the development of drug resistance or drug fastness to these antibiotics. In case therapy should be discontinued too soon and a recrudescence of the disease should occur, another course of antibiotic therapy may be given with fully satisfactory results; in such instances also, therapy should be continued until the patient has shown a normal temperature for 24 to 48 hours.

EPIDEMIOLOGY

Until 1930, spotted fever was thought to be confined to the northwest mountainous sections of the United States, although a case had been reported in Indiana in 1925. At present, the disease has been reported from 44 states, the exceptions being Connecticut, Maine, Rhode Island and Vermont. Michigan, the latest state to report cases of spotted fever, had one case in 1949 and two in 1950 (Dauer, 1951). It has also been recognized in Canada (British Columbia, Alberta, and Saskatchewan) and in parts of western and central Mexico. In South America, it is known to exist in Brazil (States of São Paulo, Rio de Janeiro and Minas Gerais), in Colombia (Cundinamarca and Santander del Sur), and possibly in Venezuela. In Brazil, the disease has been called exanthematic typhus of São Paulo or Minas Gerais typhus, whereas in Colombia it was originally designated as Tobia fever. In the United States, an average of about 480 cases are reported yearly (1939-1946); in Brazil, 663 cases were reported for the period 1929-1942 (Bol. Oficina sanitaria panamericana, 1944); in Canada, only 12 cases were recorded between 1919 and 1939 (Gibbons, 1942).

In the western United States, most cases are reported in April and May, the season of prevalence of *D. andersoni*. In sections of higher altitudes, such as Wyoming and Colorado, the danger period may extend into the summer. Occasional cases have been reported during the late summer, fall and even winter months. In the eastern United States, most cases occur during the summer, the season of greatest activity of *D. variabilis*. In the West, most cases occur in adult males since they, through vocational pursuits, are more exposed to tick bites. Persons living in livestock-range areas, and particularly those handling sheep, are in greatest danger. Other groups affected include forest-service personnel, highway-construction workers, railroad-section hands, prospectors, miners, trappers, hunters, fishermen, campers and tourists. In the West, only a relatively small percentage of the cases occurs in city dwellers, due, no doubt, to the fact that *D. andersoni* is generally found in areas removed from habitation and ordinarily does not infest domestic animals. On the other hand, in the East a high percentage of infections is among children and women. This may be due in part to the fact that the vector in the East, *D. variabilis*, infests the dog, a household pet.

The virulence of the infection varies with the locality and is correlated in any selected area with the maximum level of virulence of the strain of rickettsia in the local tick population. In the Bitter Root Valley of Montana, the death rate for nonvaccinated adults averages about 80 per cent, and for children about 37.5 per cent. A high case-fatality rate also prevails in other parts of western Montana, in certain areas of Wyoming and Oregon, in all affected portions of northern Idaho, and along the extreme eastern edge of Washington. In other areas of the West, the case-fatality rate varies with a minimum of at least 10 per cent (Parker, 1938). On the average, however, spotted fever in the East is just about as fatal as it is in the West. In comparing data for a 10-year period (1930-1939 inclusive) Topping (1941) reported that the crude-fatality rate for Idaho and Montana was 28.1 per cent, while for Maryland and Virginia it was 18.4 per cent. Little difference was found in the fatality rates when the two areas were compared on basis of age.

In the western states, one-half of the cases (50.2 per cent) occurred in persons aged 40 years or over, while in the eastern states this was practically reversed with the largest number (46.8 per cent) occurring in persons under 15 years of age. As already indicated, in the East the incidence among females (39.4 per cent) was considerably higher than in the West (16.5 per cent).

Extensive bionomic studies have been confined almost exclusively to *D. andersoni,* but the following short outline of the distribution of known vectors and of those shown experimentally to be capable of transmitting spotted fever will serve to indicate the wide dispersal of such species and the threat they represent to man (Steinhaus, 1946; Philip, 1939; Parker, Philip and Jellison, 1933; Spencer and Parker, 1923; Davis, 1939, 1943a, 1943b; Patiño-Camargo, 1941; Parker, 1938; Parker, Kohls and Steinhaus, 1943). Ticks found infected in nature are: in the United States—*Dermacentor andersoni, D. variabilis, Amblyomma americanum, Haemaphysalis leporis-palustris, Ixodes dentatus, Rhipicephalus sanguineus;* in Brazil— *Amblyomma cajennense, A. striatum, A. ovale, A. brasiliensis, A. cooperi* and *Ixodes loricatus* (also *Cimex rotundatus, C. lectularius*); in Colombia—*A. cajennense;* in Mexico—*R. sanguineus, A. cajennense;* in Canada—*D. andersoni.* Ticks shown experimentally capable of transmission are: in United States—*A. cajennense, A. striatum, D. occidentalis, D. parumapertus marginatus, D. albipictus, Ornithodoros parkeri, O. hermsi, O. nicollei, O. turicata, O. rudis;* in Brazil—*A. cajennense, A. striatum, A. brasiliensis, A. cooperi, Rhipicephalus sanguineus* and *Ixodes loricatus;* in Colombia —*Otocentor nitens, Ornithodoros rudis, O. parkeri, O. turicata, D. andersoni.*

D. andersoni is found throughout the Rocky Mountain region and adjacent areas. Rickettsiae may be found in all stages, including the egg, and survive to the adult stage; they may be transmitted during copulation, and infected females pass them to their progeny. So far as is known, the only way in which the rickettsiae survive the winter is in infected nymphs and adult ticks. Developmental forms feed on a great variety of rodents and certain small carnivores, many of which are susceptible to spotted fever. Adult ticks mainly infest large wild and domestic animals but are also found on jack rabbits and porcupines. Ticks are active during spring and early summer, but at higher altitudes their activity may occur at later periods of the year. The life cycle is normally completed in two years. Adult ticks bite man readily, and occasionally nymphs have been found attached on children.

D. variabilis is found in the Great Plains region extending eastward to the Atlantic coast and occurs sporadically in California and south-central Oregon. To the south it reaches into Mexico. In Canada it occurs eastward from southern Manitoba and has been reported in Labrador. Developmental forms feed on rodents, but certain species of mice are apparently more favored. Adults occur in abundance on dogs although they also feed on deer, cattle and other large domestic and wild animals. Nymphs engorge over a period of months and have been found feeding even during the winter. Adult ticks appear in late spring and remain active longer during the summer than does *D. andersoni.* The importance of this tick lies in its close contact with human habitation; the adult tick bites man readily.

H. leporis-palustris occurs throughout the United States extending northward to central Alaska and the southern end of Hudson Bay and southward into South America. Its importance to spotted fever does not depend on its direct connection with man whom it does not attack, but upon the fact that by feeding on rabbits it supplies a possible source of rickettsiae for the immature forms of *D. andersoni* and *D. variabilis* feeding simultaneously on the same host-rabbit. In the northern United States it is prevalent from early spring to early fall but in the South its period of activity is considerably extended. Under favorable conditions its life cycle is completed in one year. *H. leporis-palustris* consistently carries an extremely mild strain of spotted-fever rickettsia with which in laboratory animals only inapparent, immunizing infections are produced. The possibility of dissemination of infected rabbit ticks by birds should also be given consideration, since certain ground birds and meadow larks are not uncommon hosts of this tick.

R. sanguineus, while most prevalent in the Gulf Coast states, has been found in Massachusetts, Ohio and Minnesota. It has been found naturally infected in the United States (Anigstein and Bader, 1943) and in Mexico (Bustamente, Varela and Ortiz-Mariotte, 1946). In Europe this species commonly attacks man, but in the United States there are few records of any forms having been found on hosts other than dogs.

Among the other species of ticks listed, *A. americanum, A. cajennense,* and *D. occidentalis* are of importance because they are parasites of man. *A. americanum* is prevalent in the southern states around the Gulf Coast, occurs in southeastern and south-central parts of the United States and has been reported in Labrador and in South America as far down as Argentina. It feeds on a variety of wild and domestic animals, on certain species of birds, and developmental forms may also parasitize man. *A. cajennense* is found in southern Texas and Florida and is abundant in Mexico, Central America and parts of South America. It is a natural carrier of spotted fever in Brazil and Colombia. Recently Bustamente and Varela (1946) reported that it had been found naturally infected in the State of Veracruz, Mexico. It attaches to a wide variety of mammals, including man, as well as to some carnivores and certain wild and domestic fowl. Its limited distribution in the United States is fortunate, since it is in all stages a vicious parasite of man. *D. occidentalis,* although limited in distribution, is nonetheless important because it could convey spotted

fever to man, and, in addition, will hybridize with *D. andersoni* (Cooley, 1938). It infests most domestic animals, deer and rabbits, and the developmental forms probably feed on rodents. *D. parumapertus* has thus far been found almost exclusively on rabbits but occasionally has been collected on deer, coyote and man. Its chief importance, having been shown to be a capable experimental carrier, would be its conveyance of spotted fever to rabbits on which developmental forms of known vectors of the disease were feeding. *D. parumapertus* is found mainly in southwestern areas of the United States which thus far are of minor importance in the epidemiology of spotted fever, but in the northern regions its distribution overlaps that of *D. andersoni* and in the West and Northwest both that of *D. occidentalis* and of *D. variabilis.*

In 1923, Spencer and Parker reported that it was unwise to rely upon feeding or inoculation alone as an index of the presence of spotted-fever rickettsiae in unfed adult ticks. However, inoculation was apparently the most reliable technic for testing ticks that had been fed recently. When infected, unfed ticks were inoculated into guinea pigs, no frank infection resulted, but many of the animals subsequently were found to be immune to spotted fever. The transition of the virus from a nonvirulent immunizing phase to a virulent, infection-producing phase brought about by the ingestion of fresh blood was called "reactivation." As Spencer and Parker (1923) pointed out, "it is not known whether this transition is due to multiplication of the virus, to development of a possible distinct stage in its life cycle, to renewal of virulence following a period of attenuation, or perhaps to some other unrecognized condition initiated by the ingestion of fresh mammalian blood." The "reactivation" phenomenon explains why ticks do not infect unless they have been attached and have fed for several hours. Ricketts (1907a) observed an immunizing phase of rickettsiae in tick eggs. Spotted fever was produced by the injection of from 5 to 80 eggs recently laid by infected female tick. However, with eggs that had been dried for four months, immunity instead of fever developed. Spencer and Parker (1923) likewise produced immunity in guinea pigs by injecting into them comparatively fresh eggs from an infected rabbit tick *H. leporis-palustris*.

Spencer and Parker (1930) showed that tick rickettsiae would produce infection of guinea pigs through the unabraded skin and uninjured conjunctival sacs, and suggested that infection in man in this way is a distinct possibility and doubtless occurs occasionally. Infection in such a manner could occur if an infected tick is crushed between the fingers when handpicking ticks from horses, cattle, dogs or other domestic animals, or when handling tick-infested small animals (rabbits, ground squirrels, etc.) that had been trapped or shot. Fresh tick feces are also infectious, but the rickettsiae in feces are much less virulent than in tick tissue and apparently will not infect through unabraded skin. However, both tick tissue and tick feces can produce infection through an abrasion. Dried tick feces rapidly lose their infectiousness so that infection via the respiratory tract by dry air-borne feces, such as happens with louse feces in epidemic typhus, is not likely.

Control Measures

Control of the spotted-fever vectors has not proved feasible. There are two ways of preventing infection: first, personal care; second, vaccination.

Under personal care are included avoidance of tick-infested areas, the wearing of suitable clothing so as to minimize the possibility of tick bites, and the early removal of ticks that become attached to the body. Known infested areas should be avoided as far as possible during the tick season; however, this is not possible for many persons living in affected areas. Furthermore, any area in which a tick vector is present is potentially dangerous and the areas in

which the disease is known to exist are constantly expanding. It is important to wear proper apparel (high boots, leggings or socks worn outside the trouser legs) so that ticks will find it more difficult to become attached. If one spends much time in tick-infested country, some ticks will reach the body in spite of all precautions, and the body and clothing should be examined frequently for ticks. Ticks seldom attach at once, and since they rarely transfer infection until they have fed for several hours, examinations made twice daily are generally sufficient. It is best to remove attached ticks immediately either with small forceps or with a piece of paper held between the fingers. The hands should be thoroughly washed with soap and water after handling ticks. There is little danger of leaving the mouth parts of the tick in the wound. The wound itself should be treated as any other abrasion. There is nothing characteristic which will distinguish the bite of an infected tick from that of a noninfected one. The arthropod repellents, dibutyl-phthalate and dimethyl-phthalate, have been suggested as being useful for impregnation of clothing to prevent attachment of ticks (Joint OIHP/WHO Study-Group on African Rickettsioses, 1950).

A vaccine made from the tissues of infected ticks (*D. andersoni*) is prepared and distributed by the Rocky Mountain Laboratory, United States Public Health Service, Hamilton, Montana. A similar type of spotted-fever vaccine made from infected *A. cajennense* is prepared at the Butantan Institute, São Paulo, Brazil. A second type of vaccine is prepared from rickettsiae grown in the yolk-sac tissue of fertile hens' eggs (Cox, 1941). This vaccine is prepared at both the above named institutions, as well as at the Central Laboratory of the Department of Health, Nicteroi, State of Rio de Janeiro, Brazil, and by various commercial manufacturers of biologics in the United States. Evidence from animal experiments, and from use in human beings, indicates that the yolk-sac and tick vaccines are of comparable value in their immunizing capacity. It is recommended that these vaccines be given either subcutaneously or intramuscularly in three injections of 1 cc. each, or in two injections of 2 cc. each, at five to seven day intervals. They should be administered in the spring or early summer before the advent of the tick season and should be repeated each year, since the maximum degree of protection conferred is retained for less than a year. The vaccines have definite protective value. The degree and duration of immunity vary with the individual vaccinated and with the virulence of regional strains of spotted fever. The vaccine usually affords full protection against relatively mild strains, but is apparently less effective against more virulent ones. Most children are fully protected against even the highly fatal types of spotted fever, whereas adults are fully protected only occasionally. However, in the latter the degree of protection is sufficient to modify the severity of the disease and to ensure recovery in practically all cases. It is questionable whether the vaccine is of value after infection has been acquired; it is of no value in treatment after onset of signs of illness. Cox (1941) reported on the development of an avirulent strain of spotted-fever rickettsiae derived from *D. variabilis* by continued passage in the yolk sac and suggested that it might prove of value for immunization of human beings.

BOUTONNEUSE FEVER (FIÈVRE BOUTONNEUSE)

(SYNONYMS: *Fièvre escharonodulaire, exanthème typhoide estival, dothiendermie aiguë, exanthème infectieux épidémique,* exanthematous fever, eruptive fever, Marseilles fever, fever of Conor and Bruch)

INTRODUCTION

Boutonneuse fever is a tick-borne, acute, febrile disease characterized by an almost constant appearance of maculopapular eruption on palms and soles, and a *tâche noire* (black spot) usually at the site of the tick bite.

HISTORY

Conor and Bruch (1910) first described the disease as a clinical entity, and the name they proposed for it has been retained although it is not descriptive of the rash. After their publication of what was then believed to be an endemic disease of Tunis, analogous cases were reported from various regions of the Mediterranean basin. Olmer first postulated that the infection was transmitted by the bite of dog ticks (*Rhipicephalus sanguineus*) which was later confirmed by other investigators.

CLINICAL PICTURE

The incubation period generally is from five to seven days, although occasionally it may be as long as 18 days. The onset is usually sudden with a chill, followed by a rise in temperature, often above 104° F. The febrile period lasts from 8 to 14 days with defervescence taking place by rapid lysis. Associated symptoms are a violent and persistent headache, a feeling of lassitude, and pains in various joints and muscles. The tongue is coated; there is slight constipation, seldom diarrhea. Prostration is usually not a prominent feature. Frequently at the time of onset a small ulcer, from about 2 to 5 mm. in diameter, showing a black necrotic center surrounded by a dark reddish area of variable dimensions, appears at the site of the tick bite and may persist until the temperature falls. The *tâches noires* may be found on any part of the body, usually on those covered by clothing and invariably are accompanied by enlargement of the regional lymph nodes. Three or four days after the initial chill, a maculopapular eruption develops, spreading rapidly over the whole body involving the palms, soles and face. The rash on the abdomen may be less pronounced than elsewhere. Small round red spots which persist only a few days may be found on the soft palate. The macules, which at first disappear on pressure, are small, clearly outlined and separated by healthy skin. They soon become papular, are occasionally hemorrhagic, and may persist for some time after defervescence. The eruption disappears without leaving residual traces and there is no desquamation. The general condition of a patient is usually good, although insomnia is common throughout the febrile period. The spleen is not enlarged. Stupor, delirium and meningeal symptoms are usually absent. The case-fatality rate is less ᵗhan 3 per cent.

PATHOLOGIC PICTURE

Because of its low mortality, the pathologic picture of boutonneuse fever in man has not been studied. In guinea pigs it duplicates, in all essential details, the pathology of spotted fever (Hass and Pinkerton, 1936). There is practically no mortality in inoculated guinea pigs, but if the animals are sacrificed at the height of the febrile period (the second or third day of fever) the spleen may be found two or three times larger than normal; the testes are injected, and the tunicae are adherent to the scrotal sac.

EXPERIMENTAL INFECTION; HOST RANGE

Durand (1932) produced the disease experimentally in 13 human beings; in three by inoculation of triturated infected ticks, in seven by inoculation of blood from naturally infected patients, in two by inoculation of brain suspensions from animals inoculated with blood from naturally infected patients, and in one by inoculation of a *tâche noire* taken at biopsy. Blanc and Caminopétros (1932) showed that the disease could be reproduced experimentally in human beings by subcutaneous inoculation or by application of macerated infected tick tissue to slightly traumatized conjunctivae. Dogs play an important indirect role but they do not act as a reservoir of the

rickettsiae. Blanc and Caminopétros (1932) were unsuccessful in their attempts to infect dogs either with the blood of patients in the stage of full eruption or with proved infected ticks. Thus far, no host except man has been found infected in nature. Blanc and Caminopétros (1932) have shown that white mice may have inapparent infections, and that the Macedonian spermophile (*Citellus citellus*) is highly susceptible but because of its limited habitat could not be considered as a "universal" reservoir of the rickettsiae. On the other hand, they reported rabbits, sheep, pigs, pigeons and guinea pigs to be resistant to the disease. Durand and Laigret (1932) extended the studies to wild rodents of France and Africa which, because of their association with human habitations, could be considered as potential hosts of the vector. *Mus barbarus, Jaculus jaculus,* and *Meriones shawi,* found frequently around Tunis, were fully resistant to infection. With the white rat (*Mus rattus*) they obtained two inapparent infections, and from the gerbille (*Gerbillus campestris*) they succeeded in passing the infection to man by inoculating a mixture of blood and brain tissue from an infected animal. Blanc and Caminopétros (1932) suggested that a vertebrate host is not essential for maintenance of the rickettsiae and that ticks can maintain the cycle not only because they remain infectious after hibernation but also because they transmit the infection through eggs. While the monkey is susceptible, the guinea pig is probably the most useful animal for experimental purposes. When inoculated intraperitoneally there is an incubation period of from three to six days, followed by a rise of temperature to 104° or 105° F. for four or six days, after which the temperature gradually returns to normal. Marked scrotal swelling, with the tunicae adherent to the scrotal sac, develops but no sloughing results. Few, if any, of the animals die. Transfer of the infection is most readily accomplished by injecting guinea pigs intraperitoneally with testicular and tunica washings.

ETIOLOGY

The causative agent, *Rickettsia conorii,* is named after A. Conor, who, together with A. Bruch, in 1910 published the first clinical description of boutonneuse fever cases occurring in Tunis, North Africa. *R. conorii* is morphologically and tinctorially similar to *R. rickettsii.* Present evidence, based principally on the work of Mason and Alexander (1939a) and Gear and his coworkers (Gear and Bevan, 1936; Gear and Douthwaite, 1938; Gear, 1938; Gear and deMeillon, 1939; Gear, 1950), strongly indicates that *R. conorii* is the etiologic agent of all the tick-borne rickettsial fevers of Africa, including boutonneuse fever, Kenya typhus, Nigerian typhus and South African tick-bite fever. Ticks, in which the etiologic agent *R. conorii* is hereditary, form the reservoir of infection. The rickettsiae live for more than 18 months in infected ticks without producing apparent deleterious effects in their hosts (Brumpt, 1932). Hass and Pinkerton (1936) found them in nearly all tissues of infected ticks, particularly in the cells of the gut, hypoderm and ovaries where they appear to occur more abundantly shortly after feeding. The cell nucleus is frequently infected, but rickettsiae are found more often in the cytoplasm. The rickettsiae have not been cultivated on artificial media, but they grow readily in plasma-clot, agar-slant or Maitland-type tissue cultures and in the yolk sac of the developing chick embryo. Intranuclear rickettsiae are readily found in plasma-clot and agar-slant tissue cultures. Blanc and Caminopétros (1932) reported that *R. conorii* pass L_2 Chamberland candles and claimed that the virulence of infected human blood is lost after 12 days' storage in an icebox. Guinea pigs recovered from Rocky Mountain spotted fever are solidly immune to boutonneuse fever, and vice versa. However, spotted-fever vaccine made from infected *D. andersoni,* which affords complete protection against Rocky Mountain spotted fever in guinea pigs, gives no protection against boutonneuse fever (Davis and Parker, 1934; Hass and Pinkerton, 1936). An attack of boutonneuse fever confers an immunity of at least two months' duration.

DIAGNOSIS

A positive Weil-Felix reaction occurs late in the course of the disease, rarely being present before the tenth day. Apparently, a variety of agglutination reactions may be obtained, such as agglutination only of Proteus OX-2, a higher titer with OX-2 than with OX-19, equal titers with OX-2 and OX-19, or higher titers with OX-K than with either OX-2 or OX-19 (Joint OIHP/WHO Study-Group on African Rickettsioses, 1950). Agglutination of rickettsiae and complement-fixation reactions are much more specific and sensitive than is the Weil-Felix test. With purified, washed rickettsial antigens prepared from infected yolk sacs, Plotz, Reagan and Wertman (1944) have shown that boutonneuse fever may be differentiated from spotted fever by the complement-fixation reaction.

TREATMENT

Both aureomycin and chloramphenicol have been found to be highly efficacious in treating the disease, and undoubtedly terramycin will be found to give equally satisfactory results. The treatment schedule for spotted fever is recommended.

EPIDEMIOLOGY

Following the description of cases in Tunis in 1910, the disease was reported in France (the Avignon region), Tripoli, Italy, Greece (also Crete) and Roumania (Blanc and Caminopétros, 1932). The disease is widespread throughout various parts of Africa, such as Morocco, Algeria, Tunisia, Tripolitania, Cyrenaica and Egypt in North Africa; Senegal, French Guinea, Gold Coast, Nigeria, Togoland, Cameroons and French Equatorial Africa in West and Equatorial Africa; the Belgian Congo, Angola, Mozambique, Nyasaland and the Union of South Africa in South Africa; and the Anglo-Egyptian Sudan, Eritrea, Ethiopia, Kenya, Uganda and Tanganyika in Central and Eastern Africa. In addition to the dog tick, *R. sanguineus,* which was early recognized as a principal vector, other ticks such as *Rhipicephalus simus, R. appendiculatus, Haemaphysalus leachi, Hyalomma aegyptium,* and *Amblyomma hebraeum* have been shown to be natural vectors. Gear (1950) has shown that all species of ticks found in the Union of South Africa can be experimentally infected.

CONTROL MEASURES

No vaccine is available at present. The preventive measures are those recommended for spotted fever; avoidance as far as possible of tick-infested areas and use of all precautions to prevent tick bite. Since dogs are infested with *R. sanguineus,* it is advisable to free them of ticks frequently.

SOUTH AFRICAN TICK-BITE FEVER

INTRODUCTION

Tick-bite fever is a typhuslike disease characterized by a local lesion at the site of the tick bite and regional lymphadenopathy. A rash may or may not occur.

HISTORY

The name tick-bite fever was given by Nuttall (1911) to a disease described independently by McNaught (1911) and Sant' Anna (1911). Comparative studies carried out by Pijper (1936) and Pijper and Dau (1934) on spotted fever, boutonneuse fever and tick-bite fever led to the conclusion (Pijper, 1936) that "tick-bite fever must be regarded as a rickettsiosis *sui generis* and that it deserves a place by itself in the group." However, the studies of Mason and Alexander (1939a) and Gear and his coworkers (Gear and Bevan, 1936; Gear and Douthwaite, 1938; Gear, 1938; Gear and DeMeillon, 1939; and Gear, 1950) showed that there was cross immunity between tick-bite fever and boutonneuse fever of North Africa. Present evidence indicates that the various tick-borne rickettsioses of Africa, such as boutonneuse fever, Kenya typhus, Nigerian typhus and South African tick-bite fever, should be grouped together under the general terminology of tick-borne typhus, of which *R. conorii* is the causative agent (Joint OIHP/WHO Study-Group on African Rickettsioses, 1950).

CLINICAL PICTURE

The pathognomonic sign is at the site of the tick bite (Pijper and Crocker, 1938), and is a raised red area of skin varying in size from that of a "sixpence" to that of a "half crown" with a typical necrotic black center, which is always accompanied by swelling of the regional lymph glands. The lesion itself is painless and may be found on any part of the body, whereas the lymph glands are always painful and tender. The incubation period is about one week. In many cases the local lesion and the sore lymph glands are the only manifestations of the disease. In mild cases there may be fever and headache for three or four days, but not severe enough to cause the patient to go to bed. The immunizing effect of these light infections is complete as a rule and seems to be as good as that produced by the fully developed disease. In severe cases there is excruciating headache, often accompanied by photophobia, stiffness of the neck, delirium and sleeplessness. The average duration of a severe attack is 10 or 12 days. In the severe form, a rash appears on the fifth or sixth day of illness. It may be papular or macular, bright red or brownish, diffuse or discrete and may appear on the soles and palms; often only a few discrete papules are found on the arms, abdomen and chest. The prognosis is usually good. The disease, however, is not always mild, since Gear (1938) has described grave forms with complications or death in aged or physically deficient persons; two patients had femoral thrombosis, one developed retinal hemorrhages, and two died.

PATHOLOGIC PICTURE

Nothing is known of the pathologic picture of tick-bite fever in man. In guinea pigs the mortality is low, especially when large animals are used. Testicular swelling of varying degrees occurs in some animals. Hemorrhages in the testicles occasionally occur and frequently the testicles and spleen are covered with a whitish exudate. Focal lesions often containing rickettsiae are found in the brain.

EXPERIMENTAL INFECTION; HOST RANGE

The reservoir host has not been determined. Unlike boutonneuse fever, which it resembles in symptomatology, tick-bite fever is not necessarily related to dogs, for infection is transmitted by ticks which are veld dwellers and not found on domestic animals (Gear, 1938). However, Alexander and Mason (1939) isolated a strain from a tick-infested dog that became ill. Tick-bite fever may be transmitted to guinea pigs by the intraperitoneal injection of patients' blood. Blood taken during the first five days of illness or from patients who later develop a rash is best for making isolations. Once a strain is established, its serial passage in guinea pigs may be maintained fairly readily by intraperitoneal inoculation of brain tissue obtained from an animal at the height of fever; the minimum infective dose is about 0.003 Gm. Brain tissue is preferable as infective inoculum, although other tissues and blood can be used. The incubation period is about five days, followed by from five to ten days of fever. White mice apparently are not susceptible.

ETIOLOGY

The etiologic agent is *R. conorii* (Joint OIHP/WHO Study-Group on African Rickettsioses, 1950); *Dermacentroxenus rickettsi*, var. *pijperi* (Mason and Alexander, 1939b). A few rickettsiae may be found in testicular exudate of infected guinea pigs. Occasionally they are found in smears from the spleen, but not in those made from the liver, adrenals, lungs, meninges or kidneys. In infected cells, rickettsiae may be intracytoplasmic and intranuclear. Like other rickettsiae, they are stained well by the Giemsa, Castaneda or Macchiavello method. Alexander and Mason (1939) reported that rickettsiae of tick-bite fever and boutonneuse fever multiply intranuclearly when grown on the chorio-allantoic membrane of the fertile hen's egg. Tick-bite fever rickettsiae also grow well in the yolk sac. All attempts to pass them through Berkefeld candles or Seitz pads have failed.

DIAGNOSIS

The clinical picture of tick-bite fever is very similar to that of boutonneuse fever. The Weil-Felix reaction is variable and as a rule of low titer and slow in appearing. With OX-2 and OX-19 strains of Proteus, the agglutination titers vary between 1:50 and 1:500. With the OX-K strain, titers of 1:100 to 1:150 are obtained. A titer of 1:50 is regarded as the lowest reliable figure (Joint OIHP/WHO Study-Group on African Rickettsioses, 1950). Agglutination of the rickettsiae and the complement-fixation reaction are more specific and more sensitive than is the Weil-Felix test. Suspensions of rickettsiae isolated from tick-bite fever patients are agglutinated by the sera of patients who have had Kenya or Nigerian tick-borne typhus. Mason and Alexander (1939) showed that there is cross immunity between South African tick-bite fever and North African boutonneuse fever.

TREATMENT

Aureomycin has been reported to be a specific treatment for tick-bite fever (Gear and Harington, 1949; Gear, Discussion, see Yeo, 1950; Hildrick-Smith, 1949). Following aureomycin therapy, normal temperatures were attained in 48 hours and there were no relapses. Aureomycin given at the time of the primary lesions will abort the febrile attack. In all probability terramycin and chloramphenicol will also be found effective.

EPIDEMIOLOGY

The disease is widespread throughout South Africa and Rhodesia and occurs in Mozambique and Lourenço Marques. In the more temperate highveld of South Africa, there is a definite seasonal incidence with most cases occurring in the summer months when ticks are numerous. In the lowveld where the temperature is more uniform, cases occur with equal frequency throughout the year. Thus far the disease has been reported only in Europeans, but since it usually assumes a mild form it is doubtful whether doctors would be called to treat natives (Gear, 1938). Gear and Douthwaite (1938) isolated a strain of rickettsia from an adult female *Haemaphysalis leachi* removed from a dog belonging to a tick-bite fever patient. Mason and Alexander (1939b) isolated another strain from *Amblyomma hebraeum* nymphs collected from a hare. The agent apparently has been isolated also from *Rhipicephalus appendiculatus* larvae, and *Boöphilus decoloratus* is thought to be a vector (Pijper and Crocker, 1938). Finlayson, Grobler and Smithers (1940) were able to infect guinea pigs, white rats and white mice with an emulsion of *Hyalomma aegyptium* taken from a cow and believe that this tick may transmit the disease. It has been shown experimentally that all species of ticks found in the Union of South Africa can be infected (Gear, 1950).

CONTROL MEASURES

No vaccine is available at present. The preventive measures are those recommended for spotted fever and boutonneuse fever.

RICKETTSIALPOX

INTRODUCTION

Rickettsialpox is a mild disease characterized by an initial lesion caused by the bite of an infected mite.

HISTORY

Rickettsialpox is the name given by Huebner, Stamps and Armstrong (1946) to a newly recognized disease first reported in New York City and described independently by Sussman (1946), Shankman (1946) and Greenberg, Pellitteri, Klein and Huebner (1947).

CLINICAL PICTURE

The disease is characterized by an abrupt onset of chills, fever, sweats and backache, followed three or four days later by a rash. About a week prior to the onset of fever, a firm, red papule appears at the site of a mite bite that develops into a deep seated vesicle which ultimately shrinks and dries to form a black eschar. The initial lesions, found chiefly on the covered parts of the body although they may occur on the neck, face, arms and dorsum of hands, persist approximately three or four weeks and in a fully developed state frequently resemble certain stages of a vaccinia vesicle. The regional lymph nodes usually become enlarged and are tender. Fever with morning remissions is often low grade at onset but usually rises rapidly to reach 103° or 104° F., and persists for about a week. The temperature gradually returns to normal. Chills or chilly sensations lasting for a day or so frequently precede the fever. Severe headache with frontal and retro-orbital pains occurs in practically all cases. Backache and general muscular soreness are common early in the course of the disease; lassitude is always present, and photophobia is not an infrequent symptom. Rash appears in all cases and is noticed most commonly at the onset of fever, or several days later. At first the lesions are maculopapular, discrete and erythematous, but after a day or so vesicles develop in the summit of the papules. They dry to form black crusts which ultimately fall off without producing scars. The rash may be scanty, moderate or abundant. There is no pattern in its distribution, and it may appear first on the arms, legs, abdomen, back, face or chest. It has not been observed on the palms or soles. The duration of rash varies from two to three days in mild cases to ten days in the most severe. Except for fever and rash, there are no unusual signs. An enlarged spleen occurs in a few cases; general lymphadenopathy is uncommon. Red blood cell counts and the amount of hemoglobin are normal. There is a moderate leukopenia with white cells varying between 2,400 and 7,500 per c. mm. The leukopenia usually lasts only during the acute illness and disappears about two weeks after onset of fever. Thus far all patients have recovered without sequelae.

PATHOLOGIC PICTURE

Since there have been no deaths, the pathologic picture in man is unknown. In mice, intraperitoneal inoculation results in definite signs of illness, but few deaths occur. Mice that die or that are sacrificed when moribund show a small amount of blood-tinged peritoneal fluid, enlarged lymph nodes, an enlarged, edematous liver and a dark, engorged spleen eight to ten times normal size. The respiratory and intestinal tracts show no gross changes. Guinea pigs inoculated intraperitoneally with tunica washings or infected yolk-sac tissue show redness and swelling of the scrotum with adherence of the testes to the tunica vaginalis which is thickened and markedly injected, moderately enlarged spleen and lymph nodes, occasional small areas of pneumonic consolidation, and indurated cutaneous and subcutaneous nodules at the site of inoculation.

EXPERIMENTAL INFECTION; HOST RANGE

Wild house mice (*Mus musculus*) trapped in nonendemic areas, guinea pigs, chick embryos and albino mice are susceptible. Mice inoculated intraperitoneally show ruffled fur as early as the sixth day after inoculation. The peak of the disease is reached between the ninth and thirteenth days, and deaths may occur at any time during this period. Both brain and spleen tissue may be used for transfer. Guinea pigs

inoculated intraperitoneally with tunica washings first show a scrotal reaction on about the fifth day. Onset of fever may occur from the fourth to the sixth day. A febrile period, marked by remission, lasts from three to five days. Guinea-pig blood is not so infectious as tunica washings and gives less consistent results on inoculation. Chick embryos are highly susceptible to infection and show large numbers of rickettsiae both in the yolk sac (Huebner, Stamps and Armstrong, 1946) and the amniotic sac. Infected yolk-sac tissue diluted 1:10 to 1:10,000 produces death of embryos in four to seven days. Guinea pigs inoculated intraperitoneally with 10 per cent yolk-sac suspensions show a short incubation period (1 or 2 days) followed by a sudden onset of high fever which is sustained without remissions for four or five days. The scrotal reaction is usually delayed until the fourth day. Attempts to produce the disease in monkeys even with massive doses of infected yolk-sac suspensions have failed.

ETIOLOGY

The etiologic agent has been classified with the rickettsiae, and the name *Rickettsia akari* (GREEK, mite) has been proposed (Huebner, Jellison and Pomerantz, 1946). The organism stains poorly with methylene blue and by Gram's method but stains well with Giemsa or by Macchiavello's method, and the red-staining diplobacillary and diplococcal forms closely resemble *R. prowazeki* and *R. mooseri*. Rickettsiae apparently are located within nuclei of infected yolk-sac cells—this property they have in common with organisms of spotted fever. Occasional rickettsiae are found in the peritoneum and tunica tissues of infected guinea pigs. During the early studies of Huebner and his associates, 2 strains were isolated from the blood of patients, 6 strains from pools of infected mites, *Allodermanyssus sanguineus* Hirst, which apparently is the principal vector, and 1 strain from a wild house mouse (*Mus musculus*) trapped on the premises where cases of rickettsialpox had occurred. The human, mite and mouse strains are apparently identical (Huebner, Jellison and Armstrong, 1947). Subsequent studies by the New York City Health Department, Rose (1949) and others have resulted in the isolation of many additional strains from human beings and have shown that Manhattan, Queens, Kings and the Bronx are the chief sites of human infection with rickettsialpox. Rickettsial pox is serologically related to Rocky Mountain spotted fever in that there is crossing in complement-fixation tests. Indeed, when the sera from some rickettsialpox patients are used, the complement-fixation test is more strongly positive with spotted-fever antigen than with rickettsialpox antigen, whereas the reverse has also been found true for the sera from some spotted-fever patients. In addition, minor cross reactions have been noted occasionally with murine typhus antigen (Rose, 1949). Guinea pigs recovered from rickettsialpox show partial although not complete protection against both spotted fever and boutonneuse fever (Rose, 1951, personal communication). Rickettsialpox is serologically related to other members of the spotted-fever group but not to epidemic typhus, scrub typhus, Q fever or Colorado tick fever.

DIAGNOSIS

Rickettsialpox shows many similarities to boutonneuse fever. However, certain differences have been observed. For instance, the rash in boutonneuse fever is papular or maculopapular and frequently involves the palms and soles. Monkeys are susceptible to boutonneuse fever, whereas they apparently are not susceptible to rickettsialpox. Furthermore, sera from boutonneuse-fever patients show a positive Weil-Felix reaction late in the course of the disease, whereas rickettsialpox patients apparently fail to produce agglutinins for Proteus strains. Rickettsialpox may be differentiated from Rocky Mountain spotted fever not only on clinical grounds but by the fact that sera

from patients with these diseases usually show a higher complement-fixation titer in the presence of homologous antigens. However, further studies are needed to elucidate the relationship of rickettsialpox to other members of the spotted-fever group.

TREATMENT

Aureomycin produces a prompt therapeutic response in rickettsialpox patients (Rose et al., 1950) and should be used when a clinical diagnosis of the disease has been made. Chloramphenicol and terramycin likewise appear to be of value.

EPIDEMIOLOGY

The disease was first recognized in the Borough of Queens, New York City (Shankman, 1946), but it is now believed that it occurred and was listed among febrile conditions of unknown etiology for a number of years previously. Thus far, at least 734 cases have been reported in New York City, all from the boroughs of Bronx, Manhattan, Kings and Queens. The borough of Richmond (Staten Island) has not reported any cases. Two cases have been reported in Boston (Franklin, Wasserman and Fuller, 1951). The recovery of many strains of *Rickettsia akari* from the tissues of *Allodermanyssus sanguineus*, an ectoparasite of house mice (*Mus musculus*), indicates that human beings acquire the infection through the bite of mites.

CONTROL MEASURES

No vaccine is yet available, although one probably could be made readily from infected chick-embryo tissues. Preventive measures should include the eradication of all rodents known to be actual or potential hosts for the mite vector, as well as carrying out those measures necessary for killing the mites themselves.

NORTH QUEENSLAND TICK TYPHUS

A rickettsial disease assumed to be transmitted by ticks was reported recently in Australia by Andrew, Bonnin and Williams

(1946); it was recognized in 12 patients and from 2 a rickettsial agent was isolated. The disease was designated North Queensland tick typhus (Funder and Jackson, 1946; Plotz, Smadel, Bennett, Reagan and Snyder, 1946). The chief complaints were malaise and headache. Fever was either continuous or intermittent and lasted from five to seven days. A rash, variable in character, occurred in 11 of the 12 cases. In general the disease was mild, and none of the patients became seriously ill. Sera from all the patients gave a positive Weil-Felix reaction with Proteus OX-2 and a negative one with OX-K. Sera from five failed to fix complement in the presence of epidemic typhus, murine typhus, boutonneuse fever, South African tick-bite fever and spotted-fever antigens. Mice and guinea pigs were reported susceptible (Andrew, Bonnin and Williams, 1946) with the latter showing fever and a scrotal reaction similar to that produced by murine typhus. Guinea pigs sacrificed at the height of disease showed inflammatory changes in the tunicae and testes and a moderately enlarged spleen. Rickettsiae, readily stained by Macchiavello's technic, were found in the cytoplasm but not in the nuclei of large endothelial cells of the tunica vaginalis. The rickettsiae were readily cultivated in the yolk sac of fertile hens' eggs and in agar-slant tissue cultures. In the latter numerous intranuclear rickettsiae were found (Funder and Jackson, 1946; Plotz, Smadel, Bennett, Reagan and Snyder, 1946), thus indicating a possible relationship of this rickettsia to other members of the spotted-fever group. Funder and Jackson (1946) reported that the sera of convalescent patients fixed complement in the presence of antigens prepared from yolk sacs infected with the North Queensland tick typhus agent, but Plotz and his colleagues (1946) failed in their efforts with the PHS (patient's name) strain of tick typhus isolated from the Australian patients. Plotz and his colleagues confirmed the findings of the Australian workers in that they found guinea

pigs recovered from the PHS tick typhus strain to have specific complement-fixing antibodies which reacted with antigens prepared from the homologous rickettsiae but not with antigens of epidemic typhus, murine typhus, spotted fever, boutonneuse fever, South African tick-bite fever and Q fever. Thus, the serologic data obtained by the above workers indicated no relationship between the PHS organism and those of the other diseases mentioned. Subsequent studies, however, carried out by Lackman and Parker (1948) on the same PHS (Phillips) strain of North Queensland tick typhus definitely showed that this strain belongs to the spotted-fever group of diseases. Complement-fixation tests carried out in the presence of soluble antigens or rickettsial suspensions of North Queensland tick typhus and guinea pig antisera prepared against various rickettsial strains showed relationship to but not identity with other members of the spotted-fever group, such as Rocky Mountain spotted fever, boutonneuse fever, tick-bite fever (South African strain), rickettsialpox and maculatum disease. No relationship was shown between North Queensland tick typhus, murine typhus and Q fever. Cross-immunity tests carried out in guinea pigs by Plotz and co-workers (1946) showed some cross-resistance between North Queensland tick typhus on the one hand and South African tick-bite fever and murine typhus on the other. The resistance induced against heterologous organisms was related to the period of time intervening between the initial infection and the subsequent challenge. For example, guinea pigs recovered from North Queensland tick typhus were completely resistant to challenge with the homologous agent after 50 days and after eight months, whereas guinea pigs similarly recovered from North Queensland tick typhus showed considerable resistance against South African tick-bite fever after 50 days, but practically none after eight months. Cross-immunity tests indicated no relationship between North Queensland tick typhus and various strains of scrub typhus (tsutsugamushi disease).

MACULATUM DISEASE

Strains of a rickettsia mildly pathogenic for laboratory animals were isolated from specimens of the Gulf Coast tick, *Amblyomma maculatum* collected from cattle near Cleveland, Texas, in 1937. The disease produced in guinea pigs and the cultural characteristics and immunologic relationships of the agent were first described by Parker, Kohls, Cox and Davis (1939). The name maculatum disease was given to the syndrome produced in guinea pigs. Additional isolations were made from *A. maculatum* collected in Georgia (Parker, 1940), Mississippi and Texas (Lackman, Parker and Gerloff, 1949). The infectious agent grows readily in the yolk sac of the developing chick embryo. The guinea pig is the laboratory animal of choice; intraperitoneal injection of testicular washings is used in making transfers. The disease in the guinea pig is characterized by a mild (never fatal) infection, a short febrile period and a swollen, pinkish scrotum—not infrequently there is only fever or a scrotal reaction. Monkeys, rabbits and white rats are mildly susceptible, while the Sawatch meadow mouse is quite susceptible (Parker, 1940). There is good reciprocal cross immunity in guinea pigs between maculatum infection and Rocky Mountain spotted fever, boutonneuse fever and Brazilian spotted-fever. Guinea pigs recovered from murine or louse-borne typhus are usually resistant to maculatum infection, but reverse cross immunity does not take place nor is there any relationship between maculatum disease and Q fever. Complement-fixation studies carried out by Lackman, Parker and Gerloff (1949) confirmed the fact that maculatum-disease rickettsiae belong to the spotted-fever group but are antigenically different from the rickettsiae of North Queensland tick typhus, South African tick-bite fever, Rocky Mountain spotted fever and rickettsial pox. On the basis of the clinical picture induced in the guinea pig, Parker (1940) stated that the infection is apparently more closely related to boutonneuse fever than to spotted fever. Guinea pigs vaccinated against spotted fever are not protected against maculatum disease. Thus far no human cases of maculatum disease have been reported.

TICK-BITE RICKETTSIOSES IN INDIA

In 1921, Megaw described a spotted-fever-like illness that probably resulted from a tick bite. The disease was characterized by a diffuse macular erythematous rash that covered the entire body, including palms and soles. The rash became brownish red and petechial within two days and faded on the twelfth day when the temperature returned to normal. Following Megaw's publication, many similar cases were reported. Heilig and Naidu (1941, 1942) published studies on typhus fever in Mysore in which the clinical aspects of the disease are suggestive of spotted fever in the United States. Recently, Topping, Heilig and Naidu (1943) reported the results of complement-fixation tests on three sera obtained from patients in Mysore which indicated that the causative agent was more closely related to spotted fever than to the typhus group. The exact relationship of the etiologic agent or agents found in India to other recognized rickettsial agents of the spotted-fever group should be studied further.

TICK-BITE RICKETTSIOSES IN RUSSIA

Recent reports from several Russian workers indicate that a tick-borne infection or infections, possibly related to the spotted-fever group, exists in Siberia. Korshunova (1943) reporting on "tick typhus" in central Siberia states that the infection probably occurs in ground squirrels and other rodents and is transmitted to man by *Dermacentor nuttalli* and perhaps by other ticks. A strain of the active agent isolated from a patient immunized experimental animals against boutonneuse fever. Krontovskaya and Shmatikov (1943) state that *Dermacentor nuttalli* was practically the only tick found in the "tick typhus" endemic area in the steppe district of central Siberia. They demonstrated ticks to be naturally infected. Bocharova (1943) reported on several foci of "tick typhus" in eastern Siberia. All patients gave a history of tick bite. Natural infection was demonstrated in *Eutamias asiaticus, Cricetulus furunculus, Microtus*

michnoi, Apodermus agrarius and *Rattus norvegicus,* as well as in tick larvae found on rodents and in adult ticks found on cows and dogs. Guinea pigs were infected by inoculation with tick eggs collected in central Siberia. Larvae and nymphs of *D. nuttalli, D. silvarum* and *Haemaphysalis concinna* infected guinea pigs by feeding on them. Shkorbatov (1944), referring to "tickborne typhus" in far eastern Siberia, stated that the vector appears to be *D. silvarum.* Patients' sera gave a Weil-Felix reaction with Proteus OX-19 most commonly. Rickettsiae were isolated from naturally infected ticks.

REFERENCES

Alexander, R. A., and Mason, J. H., 1939, Studies of the rickettsias of the typhus-Rocky-Mountain-spotted-fever group in South Africa. II. Morphology and cultivation. Onderstepoort J. Vet. Sci. Animal Ind., *13*, 25-39.

Amaral, A. do, and Monteiro, J. L., 1932, Ensaio classificacao das rickettsioses a luz dos nossos actuaes conhecimentos. Mem. Inst. Butantan, *7*, 343-376.

Andrew, R., Bonnin, J. M., and Williams, S., 1946, Tick typhus in North Queensland. Med. J. Australia, *2*, 253-258.

Anigstein, L., and Bader, M. N., 1943, Investigations on rickettsial diseases in Texas. I. Epidemiological role of ticks common to the Gulf Coast in relation to local spotted fever. Texas Repts. Biol. Med., *1*, 105-115.

Anigstein, L., and Bader, M. N., 1945, Para-aminobenzoic acid. Its effectiveness in spotted fever in guinea pigs. Science, *101*, 591-592.

Anigstein, L., Whitney, D. M., and Beninson, J., 1948, Aureomycin—a new antibiotic with antirickettsial properties: its effect on experimental spotted fever and epidemic typhus. Ann. N. Y. Acad. Sci., *51*, 306-317.

Badger, L. F., 1933, Rocky Mountain spotted fever: susceptibility of the dog and sheep to the virus. Pub. Health Rep., *48*, 791-795.

Bengtson, I. A., 1946, Family Rickettsiaceae. Bergey's Manual of Determinative Bacteriology, Sixth Edition, p. 1083. Williams and Wilkins Co., Baltimore, 1948.

Berlin, L., and Thomas, M. H., 1948, Neurologic sequelae of Rocky Mountain spotted fever. Univ. Michigan Hosp. Bull., *14*, 22-23.

Blanc, G., and Caminopétros, J., 1932, Études épidémiologiques et expérimentales sur la fièvre boutonneuse, faites à l'Institut Pasteur d'Athènes. Arch. Inst. Pasteur Tunis, *20*, 343-394.

Bocharova, T. V., 1943, On the epidemiology of tick spotted typhus. Zhur. Mikrob. Epid. Immunologii., nos. 1-2, 68-72. (In Russian.)

Boletin Oficina sanitaria panamericana, 1944, Las Rickettsiasis en la América Latina., *23*, 206-209.

Brumpt, E., 1927, Précis de parasitologie. 4th Edition. Masson et Cie., Paris, 1452 pp. (see p. 872).

Brumpt, E., 1932, Longévité du virus de la fièvre boutonneuse (*Rickettsia conori* n. sp.) chez la tique, *Rhipicephalus sanguineus*. Compt. rend. Soc. biol., *110*, 1199-1202.

Bustamente, M. E., and Varela, G., 1946, III. Estudios de fiebre manchada en Mexico. Hallazgo del *Amblyomma cajennense* naturalmente infectado en Veracruz. Rev. Inst. salub. enferm. trop., *7*, 75-78.

Bustamente, M. E., Varela, G., and Ortiz Mariotte, C., 1946, II. Estudios de fiebre manchada en Mexico. Fiebre manchada en la Laguna. Rev. Inst. salub. enferm. trop., *7*, 39-48.

Conor, A., and Bruch, A., 1910, Une fièvre éruptive observée en Tunisie. Bull. Soc. path. exotique, *3*, 492-496.

Cooley, R. A., 1938, The genera *Dermacentor* and *Otocentor* (Ixodidae) in the United States with studies in variation. Nat. Inst. Health Bull., *171*, 1-89.

Cox, H. R., 1938, Use of yolk sac of developing chick embryo as medium for growing rickettsiae of Rocky Mountain spotted fever and typhus groups. Pub. Health Rep., *53*, 2241-2247.

Cox, H. R., 1941, Cultivation of rickettsiae of the Rocky Mountain spotted fever, typhus and Q fever groups in the embryonic tissues of developing chicks. Science, *94*, 399-403.

Davis, G. E., 1939, The Rocky Mountain spotted fever rickettsia in the tick genus *Ornithodoros*. Proc. 6th Pacific Sci. Congr., *5*, 577-579.

Davis, G. E., 1943a, The tick *Ornithodoros rudis* as a host to the rickettsiae of the spotted fevers of Colombia, Brazil and the United States. Pub. Health Rep., *58*, 1016-1020.

Davis, G. E., 1943b, Experimental transmission of the rickettsiae of the spotted fevers of Brazil, Colombia and the United States by the Argasid tick

Ornithodoros nicollei. Pub. Health Rep., *58,* 1742-1744.

Davis, G. E., and Parker, R. R., 1934, Comparative experiments on spotted fever and boutonneuse fever (I). Pub. Health Rep., *49,* 423-428.

Dauer, C. C., 1951, Personal communication, National office of vital statistics, U. S. Public Health Service, Washington, D. C.

Durand, P., 1932, La réaction de Weil-Felix dans la fièvre boutonneuse. Arch. Inst. Pasteur Tunis, *20,* 395-421.

Durand, P., and Laigret, J., 1932, Sensibilité de certaines rongeurs au virus de la fièvre boutonneuse. Arch. Inst. Pasteur Tunis, *20,* 426-429.

Finland, M., Collins, H. S., Gocke, T. M., and Wells, E. B., 1949, Present status of aureomycin therapy. Ann. Int. Med., *31,* 39-52.

Finlayson, M. H., Grobler, J. M., and Smithers, R., 1940, Studies in South African rickettsiosis. South African J. Med. Sci., *5,* 41-45.

Franklin, J., Wasserman, E., and Fuller, H. S., 1951, Rickettsialpox in Boston. Report of a case. New England J. Med., *244,* 509-511.

Funder, J. F., and Jackson, A. V., 1946, North Queensland tick typhus: A comparative study of the rickettsia with that of murine typhus. Med. J. Australia, *2,* 258-263.

Gear, J. H. S., 1938, South African typhus. South African J. Med. Sci., *3,* 134-160.

Gear, J. H. S., 1950, Rickettsioses dans l'Union Sud-Africaine. OMS, doc. WHO/Typhus/5.

Gear, J. H. S., and Bevan, C., 1936, An outbreak of tick-bite fever. South African Med. J., *10,* 485-488.

Gear, J. H. S., and Douthwaite, M., 1938, The dog tick *Haemaphysalis leachi* as a vector of tick typhus. South African Med. J., *12,* 53-55.

Gear, J., and Harington, A. L., 1949, Tick-bite fever. Two cases treated with aureomycin (Lederle), a new antibiotic. South African Med. J., *23,* 507-508.

Gear, J., and de Meillon, B., 1939, The common dog tick *Haemaphysalis leachi* as a vector of tick typhus. South African Med. J., *13,* 815-816.

Gibbons, R. J., 1942, Rocky Mountain spotted fever in Canada. Proc. 6th Pacific Sci. Congr., *5,* 573-575.

Greenberg, M., Pellitteri, O., Klein, I. F., and Huebner, R. J., 1947, Rickettsialpox—a newly recognized rickettsial disease. II. Clinical observations. J. Am. Med. Assn., *133,* 901-906.

Hamilton, H. L., 1945, Effect of p-aminobenzoic acid on growth of rickettsiae and elementary bodies, with observations on mode of action. Proc. Soc. Exp. Biol. and Med., *59,* 220-226.

Harrell, G. T., Venning, W., and Wolff, W. A., 1944, The treatment of Rocky Mountain spotted fever, with particular reference to intravenous fluids. A new approach to basic supportive therapy. J. Am. Med. Assn., *126,* 929-934.

Hass, G. M., and Pinkerton, H., 1936, Spotted fever. II. Experimental study of fièvre boutonneuse. J. Exp. Med., *64,* 601-623.

Heilig, R., and Naidu, V. R., 1941, Endemic typhus in Mysore. Ind. Med. Gaz., *76,* 705-710.

Heilig, R., and Naidu, V. R., 1942, Further experiences on endemic typhus in Mysore. Ind. Med. Gaz., *77,* 338-342.

Hildick-Smith, G., 1949, Tick bite fever. Report of a case treated with aureomycin. South African Med. J., *23,* 702-703.

Huebner, R. J., Jellison, W. L., and Pomerantz, C., 1946, Rickettsialpox—a newly recognized rickettsial disease. IV. Isolation of a rickettsia apparently identical with the causative agent of rickettsialpox from *Allodermanyssus sanguineus,* a rodent mite. Pub. Health Rep., *61,* 1677-1682.

Huebner, R. J., Jellison, W. L., and Armstrong, C., 1947, Rickettsialpox—a newly recognized rickettsial disease. V. Recovery of *Rickettsia akari* from a house mouse (*Mus musculus*). Pub. Health Rep., *62,* 777-780.

Huebner, R. J., Stamps, P., and Armstrong, C., 1946, Rickettsialpox—a newly recognized rickettsial disease. I. Isolation of the etiological agent. Pub. Health Rep., *61,* 1605-1614.

Jellison, W. L., 1945, The geographical distribution of Rocky Mountain spotted fever and Nuttall's cottontail in the western United States. Pub. Health Rep., *60,* 958-961.

Joint OIHP/WHO Study-Group on African Rickettsioses. Report on the first session. World Health Organization Technical Report Series No. 23. World Health Organization, Geneva, Dec., 1950.

King, W. V., 1906, Experimental transmission of Rocky Mountain spotted fever by means of the tick. Preliminary report. Pub. Health Rep., *21,* 863-864.

Korshunova, O. S., 1943, Etiology of tick spotted typhus in Krasnoyarsk Province. Zhur. Mikrob., Epid., Immunologii, nos. 1-2, 59-64. (In Russian.)

Krontovskaya, M. K., and Shmatikov, M. D., 1943, On the epidemiology of the tick spotted typhus of central Siberia. Zhur. Mikrob., Epid., Immunologii, nos. 1-2, 65-68. (In Russian.)

Lackman, D. B., Parker, R. R., and Gerloff, R. K., 1949, Serological characteristics of a pathogenic rickettsia occurring in *Amblyomma maculatum.* Pub. Health. Rep., *64,* 1342-1349.

Lillie, R. D., 1941, Pathology of Rocky Mountain spotted fever. Nat. Inst. Health Bull., *177,* 1-59.

McNaught, J. G., 1911, Paratyphoid fevers in South Africa. J. Roy. Army Med. Corps, *16,* 505-514.

de Magalhães, O., and Rocha, A., 1942, Tifo exantemático do Brasil; papel do cão (*C. familiaris*) na constituição dos focos da moléstia. Brasil-Medico, *56,* 370-377.

Mason, J. H., and Alexander, R. A., 1939a, Studies of the rickettsias of the typhus-Rocky-Mountain-spotted-fever-group in South Africa. III. The disease in the experimental animal. Cross-immunity tests. Onderstepoort J. Vet. Sci. and Animal Ind., *13,* 41-65.

Mason, J. H., and Alexander, R. A., 1939b, Studies of the rickettsias of the typhus-Rocky-Mountain-spotted-fever-group in South Africa. IV. Discussion and classification. Onderstepoort J. Vet. Sci. and Animal Ind., *13,* 67-76.

Maxey, E. E., 1899, Some observations on the so-called spotted fever of Idaho. Med. Sentinel, Portland, Oregon, *7,* 433-438.

Megaw, J. W. D., 1921, A typhus-like fever in India, possibly transmitted by ticks. Indian Med. Gaz., *56*, 361-371.

Miller, J. K., 1950, Rocky Mountain spotted fever on Long Island. Ann. Int. Med., *33*, 1398-1406.

Monteiro, J. L., 1931, Estudos sobre o typho exanthematico de São Paulo. Mem. Inst. Butantan, *6*, 5-135.

Nuttall, G. H. F., 1911, On symptoms following tick-bites in man. Parasitology, *4*, 89-93.

Parker, R. R., 1938, Rocky Mountain spotted fever. J. Am. Med. Assn., *110*, 1185-1188; 1273-1278.

Parker, R. R., 1940, A pathogenic rickettsia from the gulf coast tick, *Amblyomma maculatum*. Proc. Third Int. Cong. for Microbiology. New York, International Association of Microbiologists, pp. 390-391.

Parker, R. R., Kohls, G. M., Cox, G. W., and Davis, G. E., 1939, Observations on an infectious agent from *Amblyomma maculatum*. Pub. Health Rep., *54*, 1482-1484.

Parker, R. R., Kohls, G. M., and Steinhaus, E. A., 1943, Rocky Mountain spotted fever: spontaneous infection in the tick *Amblyomma americanum*. Pub. Health Rep., *58*, 721-729.

Parker, R. R., Philip, C. B., and Jellison, W. L., 1933, Rocky Mountain spotted fever: potentialities of tick transmission in relation to geographical occurrence in the United States. Am. J. Trop. Med., *13*, 341-379.

Patiño-Camargo, L., 1941, Nuevas observaciones sobre un tercer foco de fiebre petequial (maculosa) en el hemisferio americano. Boletin Oficina sanitaria panamericana, *20*, 1112-1124.

Philip, C. B., 1939, Rocky Mountain spotted fever: known and potential tick vectors in the United States. Proc. 6th Pacific Sci. Congr., *5*, 581-584.

Pijper, A., 1936, Etude expérimentale comparée de la fièvre boutonneuse et de la tick-bite-fever. Arch. Inst. Pasteur de Tunis, *25*, 388-401.

Pijper, A., and Crocker, C. G., 1938, Rickettsioses of South Africa. South African Med. J., *12*, 613-630.

Pijper, A., and Dau, H., 1934, Die fleckfieberartigen Krankheiten des sudlichen Afrika, Zentralbl. f. Bakt. (Abt. 1), *133*, 7-22.

Pinkerton, H., 1936, Criteria for the accurate classification of the rickettsial diseases (rickettsioses) and of their etiological agents. Parasitology, *28*, 172-189.

Pinkerton, H., 1942, The pathogenic rickettsiae with particular reference to their nature, biologic properties, and classification. Bact. Rev., *6*, 37-78.

Pinkerton, H., and Hass, G. M., 1932, Spotted fever. I. Intranuclear rickettsiae in spotted fever studied in tissue culture. J. Exp. Med., *56*, 151-156.

Plotz, H., Reagan, R. L., and Wertman, K., 1944, Differentiation between fièvre boutonneuse and Rocky Mountain spotted fever by means of complement fixation. Proc. Soc. Exp. Biol. and Med., *55*, 173-176.

Plotz, H., Smadel, J. E., Bennett, B. L., Reagan, R. L., and Snyder, M. J., 1946, North Queensland tick typhus: Studies of the aetiological agent and its relation to other rickettsial diseases. Med. J. Australia, *2*, 263-268.

Ravenel, S. F., 1947, Para-aminobenzoic acid therapy of Rocky Mountain spotted fever. J. Am. Med. Assn., *133*, 989-994.

Ricketts, H. T., 1906a, The study of "Rocky Mountain Spotted Fever" (tick fever?) by means of animal inoculations. A preliminary communication. J. Am. Med. Assn., *47*, 33-36.

Ricketts, H. T., 1906b, The transmission of Rocky Mountain spotted fever by the bite of the wood tick (*Dermacentor occidentalis*). J. Am. Med. Assn., *47*, 358.

Ricketts, H. T., 1907a, The role of the wood tick (*Dermacentor occidentalis*) in Rocky Mountain spotted fever, and the susceptibility of local animals to this disease. A preliminary report. J. Am. Med. Assn., *49*, 24-27.

Ricketts, H. T., 1907b, Summary of investigations of the nature and means of transmission of Rocky Mountain spotted fever. From Trans. Chic. Path. Soc., 1907. Contributions to Medical Science by Howard Taylor Ricketts, 1870-1910. University of Chicago Press, 1911, pp. 333-342.

Ricketts, H. T., 1907c, Further experiments with the wood tick in relation to Rocky Mountain spotted fever. J. Am. Med. Assn., *49*, 1278-1281.

Ricketts, H. T., 1909, A micro-organism which apparently has a specific relationship to Rocky Mountain spotted fever. A preliminary report. J. Am. Med. Assn., *52*, 379-380.

Ricketts, H. T., and Wilder, R. M., 1910, The relation of typhus fever (tabardillo) to Rocky Mountain spotted fever. Arch. Int. Med., *5*, 361-370.

Rose, H. M., 1949, The clinical manifestations and laboratory diagnosis of rickettsial-pox. Ann. Int. Med., *31*, 871-883.

Rose, H. M., 1950, The experimental and clinical evaluation of terramycin against Rickettsia akari (rickettsialpox). Ann. N. Y. Acad. Sci., *53*, 385-394.

Rose, H. M., Duane, R. D., and Fischel, E. E., 1945, The treatment of spotted fever with para-aminobenzoic acid. J. Am. Med. Assn., *129*, 1160-1161.

Rose, H. M., and Kneeland, Y., Jr., 1949, Aureomycin in the treatment of infectious diseases. Am. Jour. Med., *7*, 532-541.

Rose, H. M., Kneeland, Y., Jr., and Gibson, Count Dillon, 1950, The treatment of rickettsialpox with aureomycin. Am. Jour. Med., *9*, 300-307.

Sant'Anna, J. F., 1911, On a disease in man following tick-bites and occurring in Lourenço Marques. Parasitology, *4*, 87-88.

Schubert, J. H., Stanford, S. M., and Tiffany, E. J., 1951, Comparative evaluation of several complement fixation techniques for laboratory diagnosis of the rickettsioses. J. Lab. and Clin. Med., *37*, 388-393.

Shankman, B., 1946, Report on an outbreak of endemic febrile illness, not yet identified, occurring in New York City. New York State J. Med., *46*, 2156-2159.

Shepard, C. C., and Topping, N. H., 1946, Rocky Mountain spotted fever. A study of complement fixation in the serum of certain dogs. J. Infect. Dis., *78*, 63-68.

Shkorbatov, V. I., 1944, On the results of work by the Epidemiological Section of DVIEM on tick borne typhus fever in Khabarovsk Province. Zhur. Mikrob., Epid. Immunologii, nos. 1-2, 43-46. (In Russian.)

Smadel, J. E., 1949, Chloramphenicol (chloromycetin) in the treatment of infectious diseases. Am. Jour. Med., 7, 671-685.

Smadel, J. E., 1951, Present status of antibiotic therapy in viral and rickettsial disease. Bull. N. Y. Acad. Med., 27, 221-231.

Smadel, J. E., and Jackson, E. B., 1947, Chloromycetin, an antibiotic with chemotherapeutic activity in experimental rickettsial and viral infections. Science, 106, 418-419.

Smadel, J. E., Jackson, E. B., and Cruise, A. B., 1949, Chloromycetin in experimental rickettsial infections. J. Immunol., 62, 49-65.

Smadel, J. E., Jackson, E. B., and Ley, H. L., Jr., 1950, Terramycin as a rickettsiostatic agent and its usefulness in patients with scrub typhus. Ann. N. Y. Acad. Sci., 53, 375-384.

Snyder, J. C., Fagan, R., Wells, E. B., Wick, H. C., and Miller, J. C., 1950, Experimental studies on the antirickettsial properties of terramycin. Ann. N. Y. Acad. Sci., 53, 362-374.

Snyder, J. C., Maier, J., and Anderson, C. R., 1942, Report to the Division of Medical Sciences, National Research Council, December 26.

Spencer, R. R., and Parker, R. R., 1923, Studies on Rocky Mountain spotted fever. Infectivity of fasting and recently fed ticks. Pub. Health Rep., 38, 333-339.

Spencer, R. R., and Parker, R. R., 1930, Studies on Rocky Mountain spotted fever. Infection by other means than tick bite. Hyg. Lab. Bull., 154, 60-63.

Steinhaus, E. A., 1946, Insect Microbiology. Ithaca, N. Y., Comstock Publishing Co.

Sussman, L. N., 1946, Kew Garden's spotted fever. New York Med., 2, no. 15, 27-28. (Each number paged separately.)

Topping, N. H., 1939, Experimental Rocky Mountain spotted fever and endemic typhus treated with prontosil or sulfapyridine. Pub. Health Rep., 54, 1143-1147.

Topping, N. H., 1941, Rocky Mountain spotted fever. A note on some aspects of its epidemiology. Pub. Health Rep., 56, 1699-1703.

Topping, N. H., 1943, Rocky Mountain spotted fever. Further experience in the therapeutic use of immune rabbit serum. Pub. Health Rep., 58, 757-775.

Topping, N. H., Heilig, R., and Naidu, V. R., 1943, A note on the rickettsioses in India. Pub. Health Rep., 58, 1208-1210.

Travassos, J., 1948, Studies on rickettsial diseases in Brazil. Proc. of the Fourth International Congresses on Tropical Medicine and Malaria, Vol. I. Department of State, U. S. Govt. Printing Office, Washington, D. C.

Van der Scheer, J., Bohnel, E., and Cox, H. R., 1947, Diagnostic antigens for epidemic typhus, murine typhus and Rocky Mountain spotted fever. J. Immunol., 56, 365-375.

Wilson, L. B., and Chowning, W. M., 1902, The so-called "spotted fever" of the Rocky Mountains. A preliminary report to the Montana State Board of Health. J. Am. Med. Assn., 39, 131-136.

Wolbach, S. B., 1919, Studies on Rocky Mountain spotted fever. J. Med. Res., 41, 1-197.

Wong, S. C., and Cox, H. R., 1948, Action of aureomycin against experimental rickettsial and viral infections. Ann. N. Y. Acad. Sci., 51, 290-305.

Yeo, R. M., 1950, Common tropical diseases encountered at the W.N.L.A. and their treatment, with special reference to some of the newer drugs. Proc. Transvaal Mine Med. Officers Assn., 29, 93-102.

Zinsser, H., FitzPatrick, F., and Wei, H., 1939, A study of rickettsiae grown on agar tissue cultures. J. Exp. Med., 69, 179-190.

JOSEPH E. SMADEL, M.D.

Army Medical Service Graduate School

37

Scrub Typhus

(SYNONYMS: Tsutsugamushi disease, mite-borne typhus, Japanese river fever, tropical typhus, rural typhus)

INTRODUCTION

Scrub typhus is an infectious disease caused by *Rickettsia tsutsugamushi* (also designated *Rickettsia orientalis*) and characterized by sudden onset, fever of about two weeks' duration and a cutaneous rash which appears on approximately the fifth day. The disease is transmitted by certain mites and an eschar usually develops at the site of attachment of the "chigger." Patients with scrub typhus generally develop agglutinins against the OX-K strain of proteus bacillus.

HISTORY

"Seldom has a disease emerged from comparative obscurity to notoriety so rapidly as has scrub typhus" (Megaw, 1945). Scrub typhus was first mentioned in Occidental literature in the last quarter of the nineteenth century. It had been described early in that century in Japan, and a disease that may have been identical was mentioned in Chinese writings of the sixteenth century. The disease in Japan has remained limited to a number of small, sharply defined areas in river valleys of the Akita, Yamagata and Niigata prefectures in the northwestern part of Honshu Island. A few hundred cases occur each year; 20 to 40 per cent of the patients die. Japanese investigators have studied the malady assiduously since the beginning of the present century and have become familiar with its clinical features, the mite vector, the etiologic agent and its host range and rodent reservoirs. Most of their reports were published in Japanese but even those which appeared in the western languages generally elicited little more than academic interest. However, investigators in the Malay States and the Dutch East Indies recognized the similarity of a disease encountered in their areas with tsutsugamushi disease in Japan, and, in addition, established the relationship between the rickettsial agents which they recovered and a Japanese strain of *R. tsutsugamushi*. Two contributions of major significance were made by the British and Dutch workers, namely, the observation that patients with scrub typhus developed agglutinins against the OX-K strain of *B. proteus* but not the OX-19 strain (Fletcher, Lesslar and Lewthwaite, 1929) and the finding that white mice were more suitable for laboratory studies on *R. tsutsugamushi* than rabbits, guinea pigs and monkeys which had been employed previously (Dinger, 1933). At the beginning of World War II, scrub typhus was known to occur in India, Indo-China, New Guinea and

Australia, in addition to the areas already mentioned. The excellent monograph of Blake and associates (1945) reviews in detail the history of scrub typhus.

During World War II, approximately 6,685 cases of scrub typhus were reported among U. S. Army personnel; this was in sharp contrast to the 64 cases of epidemic typhus which occurred during the same period (Sadusk, 1947). There were 284 deaths attributed to the former and none to the latter. The high attack rates in military personnel in certain areas are illustrated by the following experiences. In a regiment of Americans at Sansapor in the southwest Pacific, 403 men developed the disease between the sixth and the twentieth days after landing; moreover, the attack rate during the second week at Sansapor reached 900 cases per thousand troops per year. Similarly, 18 per cent of a British battalion contracted scrub typhus during two months in Burma in 1944 and 5 per cent of the total strength died of the disease; here the attack rate was 1,080 per thousand per year. The impact of scrub typhus on military operations in the Asiatic-Pacific Area (over 20,000 cases among Allied troops) resulted in extensive studies on all aspects of the disease by various groups in America and the British Commonwealth. By the end of the war, preventive measures involving control of the mite vector had been developed to the stage where the disease ceased to be of great military importance. Furthermore, a chemotherapeutic agent (para-aminobenzoic acid) was shown to be of definite value in the treatment of the malady.

CLINICAL PICTURE

Following an incubation period of from 6 to 21 days, generally 10 to 12, illness begins suddenly with fever, chilliness, severe headache, conjunctival injection and moderate generalized lymphadenopathy. The primary lesion or eschar is found in the majority of Caucasians but in few Asiatics.

It occurs at sites where skin surfaces meet or clothes bind, viz., axilla and waist. At the onset of fever the eschar is an indurated erythematous lesion about a centimeter in diameter surmounted by a multiloculated vesicle, but within a few days the vesicle ulcerates and later becomes covered by a black scab. The fever increases progressively during the first week of the disease, generally reaching 104° or 105° F. The pulse rate during this period is relatively slow, being 70 to 100. Between the fifth and eighth days the characteristic skin eruption appears on the trunk. This red, macular rash may extend to the arms and legs and at times becomes maculopapular in character. It usually persists for several days before fading; it may disappear at times within a few hours.

During the first week of fever, cough is commonly present. Physical and roentgenographic evidence of pneumonitis occurs frequently; Ahlm and Lipshutz (1944) observed the former in 67 per cent and the latter in 20 per cent of 70 patients.

The temperature remains elevated during the second week, and the pulse rate increases in the more severely affected patients. The rate may reach 120 or 140 and the systolic blood pressure may fall below 100. Conjunctival congestion and some deafness are commonly present. Headache may abate somewhat during the second week, but apathy of the patient continues. Certain individuals develop signs of involvement of the central nervous system, for example, delirium, stupor and muscular twitching. Others develop frank signs of pneumonia or circulatory failure. Toward the end of the second week or the beginning of the third, the temperature of those patients who are destined to recover falls by lysis over a period of several days. With the reduction in fever, the pulse rate and blood pressure return to normal, the eschar is practically healed, and the spleen is no longer palpable if it had been felt during the febrile period. Convalescence is generally protracted. Sequelae in the form of nervous or psychiatric difficulties were frequent among military patients; it is probable that the rigorous campaigns and intercurrent diseases which accompanied scrub typhus contributed materially to this high incidence. The possibility that myocarditis, which occurred in some of the patients, might proceed to permanent damage of the heart has been overemphasized.

Death, when it occurs, supervenes about the end of the second week and is attributable in about equal numbers of cases to secondary bacterial pneumonia, encephalitis or circulatory failure. The mortality varies from 1 to 60 per cent in different geographic areas and different populations. Since the introduction of specific antibiotic therapy in 1948, the picture has changed radically, and now the mortality approaches zero.

Second attacks of scrub typhus are not uncommon and may occur in exposed persons within a few years after the initial illness. Observations on naturally acquired disease have been augmented by studies on volunteers (Smadel, Ley et al., 1950). Antigenic differences in strains of *R. tsutsugamushi* play an important role in susceptibility to reinfection. Persons recovered from illness caused by one strain are resistant to this strain for a number of years, and to heterologous strains for some months. However, the majority of such persons are susceptible to infection with heterologous strains one to two years after recovery.

There is no specific blood picture in scrub typhus. The leukocyte count remains essentially within the normal range unless secondary bacterial infection occurs. Anemia is rarely observed. Plasma proteins may be lowered slightly during the febrile illness. If this occurs, the proportionately greater decrease in albumin content of the plasma may produce a reversal of the albumin-globulin ratio. Hypochloremia often develops late in the febrile stage as a result of inadequate salt intake and excessive sweating. Certain patients with hepatic impairment show a decrease in plasma fibrinogen and an elevated icteric index.

PATHOLOGIC PICTURE

Changes observed at necropsy are not striking. Usually the eschar is found, but no rash is seen. The body cavities contain a moderate amount of serofibrinous fluid. Congestion and cloudy swelling of the parenchymatous tissues are observed consistently. The lungs usually show evidence of hemorrhagic pneumonia with a superimposed, secondary bronchopneumonia. The spleen and lymph nodes are enlarged.

Microscopic examination brings out the fact that here, as in other rickettsial diseases, the vascular tree is primarily affected, showing a disseminated focal vasculitis and a perivasculitis of the smaller vessels consisting of accumulations of monocytes, plasma cells and lymphocytes. These lesions are less severe than in epidemic typhus; furthermore, the necrosis and inflammatory reaction of the vessel wall, so characteristic of spotted fever, if present, are limited to the eschar. Vascular changes with resultant lesions in adjacent parenchymatous tissue are most conspicuous in the heart, lung, brain, and kidney. Thus, an acute, non-suppurative myocarditis of focal and diffuse distribution and of varying intensity is characteristically present. Interstitial pneumonitis occurs in practically all fatal cases. The lesions in the brain may consist of a few vascular and perivascular reactions such as are found throughout the body. In certain instances, however, a true lymphocytic meningitis and an encephalitis with perivascular cuffing and formation of glial nodules occur. The spleen and lymph nodes display similar changes with infiltrations of cells of the mononuclear series in the pulp and sinuses, and necrosis of the follicles. The kidneys characteristically show focal interstitial lesions which occasionally are associated with damage to adjacent nephrons.

Allen and Spitz (1945) were inclined to attribute many of the pathologic lesions of scrub typhus to "hyperergic effects." Settle, Pinkerton and Corbett (1945) postulated that the peripheral circulatory collapse, to which death was ascribed in about one third of the cases, might depend not only on the diffuse myocarditis and rickettsial vasculitis but also on the effect of rickettsial toxin on the peripheral capillaries. It is of interest that a specific rickettsial toxin was subsequently demonstrated to be associated with *R. tsutsugamushi* (see Etiology).

EXPERIMENTAL INFECTION; HOST RANGE

The host range of *R. tsutsugamushi* is very broad; two species of mites, many species of rodents (see Epidemiology), and man are infected in nature while most of the common laboratory animals are susceptible. White mice are the animals of choice for most laboratory studies of *R. tsutsugamushi*. Seven or eight days after intraperitoneal inoculation of highly infectious material an animal appears sick; during the next few days the abdomen swells, subcutaneous edema of the abdominal wall may appear, dyspnea develops and death ensues. At necropsy, in addition to subcutaneous edema, lymphadenitis is apparent when the skin is reflected, the peritoneal cavity contains several cubic centimeters of serofibrinous exudate and the surfaces are injected, and the spleen is enlarged and usually is coated with flecks of fibrinous exudate. The pleural cavities generally contain serofibrinous fluid, and areas of hemorrhagic consolidation are found in the lungs. Rickettsiae can be found with more or less difficulty in impression smears of any of the involved tissues, but are most readily demonstrated in stained smears prepared from the surface of the spleen or the peritoneum. Blood, exudates, and all tissues are infectious. Suspensions of splenic tissue from mice infected with one of the typical laboratory strains of *R. tsutsugamushi* usually have a lethal titer of about 10^{-7} when inoculated into mice by the intraperitoneal route; the titer of the blood from such animals is about

10^{-5}. Mice become infected with scrub typhus following inoculation by the subcutaneous, intranasal, or intravenous route, but the resultant disease differs somewhat from that described above. The lethal titer of a suspension of rickettsiae may be 10^{-7} when tested intraperitoneally but only 10^{-2} on subcutaneous inoculation; nevertheless, a 10^{-5} dilution of the same suspension administered subcutaneously induces an inapparent infection which is followed by solid immunity to infection after the intraperitoneal injection of many lethal doses of the agent. Accordingly, the subcutaneous route is used when immune mice are desired. The intravenous or intranasal inoculation of mice with suspensions rich in organisms results in their death in four to six days with hemorrhagic lesions in their lungs; suspensions of such pulmonary tissue have titers of 10^{-8} to 10^{-9}. Strains of *R. tsutsugamushi* vary widely in their virulence for mice; with some the minimal lethal dose and the minimal infectious dose are identical when the intraperitoneal route is used, while with others the lethal dose may be 100 to 1,000 times greater than infectious doses; finally, certain of the strains are rarely lethal for mice under any condition. Such variations in virulence have been noted among recently isolated strains and have been observed to develop in strains maintained in the laboratory.

R. tsutsugamushi grows well in the yolk-sac tissue of embryonated eggs and in agar tissue cultures; the former method of cultivation is employed extensively. Five- or six-day-old embryos are inoculated into the yolk sac with highly infectious material and then incubated at 35° C. Death occurs in six to ten days without pathognomonic lesions. Rickettsiae are most numerous in the yolk-sac tissue which has an infectious titer of 10^{-8} to 10^{-9}, and are readily demonstrable in stained smears. Infected yolk-sac tissue serves as seed inoculum, as a source of the toxin of scrub typhus, and as starting material for the preparation of rickettsial complement-fixing antigens, but has been

FIG. 49. Electron micrograph of *R. tsutsugamushi,* chromium shadowed. × 23,000.

of practically no value for the preparation of vaccines. Agar tissue cultures of *R. tsutsugamushi* have infective titers of the same order of magnitude as yolk-sac tissues.

Cotton rats infected by the intranasal route and white rats injected intravenously with highly infectious inocula die in four to six days and yield lung tissue with infective titers of 10^{-8} to 10^{-9}. Studies on the experimental disease in monkeys, rabbits and guinea pigs provided information of historic importance, but these animals are not employed extensively at present; in the monograph of Blake et al. (1945) these studies are reviewed, as well as early work on growth of the agent in tissue culture and the experimental disease in hamsters. Several species of gerbilles, rodents native to Africa, are susceptible to infection with *R. tsutsugamushi* and have proved useful in certain types of studies (Murray, Zarafonetis and Snyder, 1945; Mackie et al., 1946).

ETIOLOGY

The etiologic agent of scrub typhus has the general properties of rickettsiae. It is an obligate, intracellular, parasitic microorganism which is perhaps less pleomorphic than most of the other rickettsiae which affect man. The organisms are usually seen as small diplococcuslike structures or short rods, with bipolar dark staining bodies, which have a length of from 0.3 to 0.5 μ

and a width of from 0.2 to 0.4 μ. The rickettsiae appear as purple structures in the cytoplasm of mononuclear cells when viewed in impression smears of infected tissues stained by Giemsa's method. The Macchiavello technic, which has proved so satisfactory for staining other rickettsial agents, is not widely used for *R. tsutsugamushi.* The difficulty with this method is dependent upon the ease with which the rickettsiae of scrub typhus are decolorized after staining with fuchsin; as a result, in the final preparation, the rickettsiae and cellular material take the methylene blue color and the usual contrast of red organism and blue background is lacking. Many workers have described contrast stains for use on this agent, but the writer prefers a modified Macchiavello stain. The morphologic structure of *R. tsutsugamushi* as revealed by electron microscopy is similar to that of other rickettsiae; the organisms have a limiting membrane enclosing protoplasmic material in which are dispersed dense granules. The electron micrograph illustrated in Figure 49 was prepared by S. S. Breese and A. C. Ley of the Army Medical Service Graduate School from washed *R. tsutsugamushi* obtained by differential centrifugation from infected yolk-sac tissue.

Taxonomy of the agent of scrub typhus continues in a confused state. Opinion has vacillated between the designation *R. orientalis,* proposed by Nagayo and co-workers (1930), and *R. tsutsugamushi,* proposed by Ogata (1931). At the present time, the term *R. tsutsugamushi* appears to be the choice of the majority of workers in the field.

The rickettsia of scrub typhus is relatively labile but remains viable for long periods of time when stored at −70° C. Lyophilization under carefully controlled conditions is relatively satisfactory. Although appreciable loss in infectivity accompanies drying, the residual activity, usually titering 10^{-4}, remains unchanged for months (Jackson and Smadel, 1951). Transportation of a newly isolated strain from the field to a central laboratory is accomplished best by shipment of inoculated mice. The organism of scrub typhus undergoes lysis rather rapidly even in formalinized suspensions of infected tissue; because of this the methods which are used in preparing washed suspensions of other rickettsiae do not give satisfactory results with *R. tsutsugamushi.* Ten per cent suspensions of infected tissues freed of large particles by light centrifugation are rendered noninfectious within a few hours by the addition of 0.1 per cent U. S. P. formaldehyde solution.

Specific complement-fixing antigens of scrub typhus have been prepared from several types of infected material, namely, yolk-sac tissue, mouse lung, white rat lung, and cotton rat lung. As indicated in a preceding paragraph, the organism of scrub typhus readily undergoes lysis, and this characteristic interferes with the preparation and use of purified suspensions of rickettsiae. Bengtson's early method (1945) for making scrub typhus antigens from yolk sacs was similar to that used for other rickettsial antigens, namely, ether extraction of an aqueous suspension. Methods, in which ether extraction of undiluted ground infected yolk-sac tissue is used, have provided more uniform scrub typhus antigens; the author prefers the procedure of Topping and Shepard (1946), although the method of Wolfe et al. (1946) has given satisfactory results. Smadel, Rights and Jackson (1946a) pointed out that the complement-fixing antigen of scrub typhus demonstrable in their preparations of mouse and rat lung and in the sera of moribund animals possessed certain characteristics of a soluble antigen. The cleanest of the scrub typhus antigens were those prepared by Fulton and Joyner (1945). These consisted of washed suspensions of rickettsiae obtained from lungs of infected cotton rats; the crude tissue suspensions were processed shortly after harvesting before disintegration of rickettsiae occurred. The complement-fixation technic has been used for the diagnosis of scrub typhus in patients, but the observations of

Bengtson (1945) indicate that differences in strains are so great that antigens prepared from several strains must be used in testing each human serum. Good agglutination tests with *R. tsutsugamushi* await the preparation of satisfactory antigens. Because of difficulties encountered in the use of specific rickettsial materials, the nonspecific Weil-Felix reaction, in which the OX-K strain of the proteus bacillus is employed, continues to be the most useful serologic test for the diagnosis of the disease in man.

In scrub typhus, as in other viral and rickettsial diseases, convalescent animals and patients develop specific neutralizing antibodies. Moreover, sera from rabbits hyperimmunized with infectious material contain immune substances which protect mice inoculated with mixtures of the sera and the homologous strain (Topping, 1945). The neutralization technic has proved useful in studies on the antigenic variations in different strains of *R. tsutsugamushi* (Bell, Bennett and Whitman, 1946; Bennett, Smadel and Gauld, 1947). When a comparison was made of materials from ten strains of *R. tsutsugamushi,* which had been recovered from man, mites and rodents from widely scattered areas of the Orient and South Pacific, it was found that potent antisera against two of the strains offered no protection against infection with any of the heterologous strains. On the other hand, potent antisera against two other strains provided some protection against practically all of the heterologous organisms. Tests with materials from the other strains indicated that these agents occupied an intermediate position between the organisms with very broad and very narrow specificity.

A toxin is associated with the organism of scrub typhus (Smadel, Jackson, Bennett and Rights, 1946); its properties are similar to those of other rickettsial toxins (see Chapter 3). Only embryonated eggs infected with the Gilliam strain of *R. tsutsugamushi* have provided a toxic material capable of killing mice within a few hours. Antitoxin against this substance is highly specific;

not only is it unrelated to the antitoxins of epidemic and murine typhus but it is not found in sera of animals convalescent from infection with a number of different strains of *R. tsutsugamushi,* even though such sera contain neutralizing or complement-fixing antibodies against homologous organisms.

Serologic and immunologic relationships among different strains of *R. tsutsugamushi* require further investigation. It may be noted that animals which recover from infection with any of the organisms now classified as *R. tsutsugamushi* are resistant to infection with any other strain. Nevertheless, the accumulated information obtained in studies made by means of complement-fixation, neutralization, antitoxin and vaccination tests indicate that certain of the strains are as distinct from each other as are *R. prowazeki* and *R. mooseri.*

When results of intensive work in Australia (Lewthwaite et al., 1946), England and the United States indicated that a potent vaccine against scrub typhus could not be prepared readily from highly infectious yolk-sac material, other sources for vaccine were sought. During the summer of 1944 materials capable of immunizing mice against several thousand minimal lethal doses of *R. tsutsugamushi* were obtained in three laboratories (Fulton and Joyner, 1945; Plotz, Bennett and Reagan, 1946; Smadel, Rights and Jackson, 1946b). The British vaccine, consisting of a formalinized suspension of infected cotton rat lungs, was produced on a large scale prior to the cessation of hostilities (Buckland et al., 1945) and a portion of it was used for immunization of soldiers in the field; the information thus obtained was inadequate for estimating its value (Card and Walker, 1947). The American vaccines were prepared from agar tissue cultures and from lung and splenic tissues of infected white rats. Difficulties associated with the protection of human beings by vaccination are greatly multiplied by the antigenic differences which are now known to exist among strains of *R. tsutsugamushi.* Thus, vaccines, pre-

pared from infected tissues of white rats against four strains, induced resistance to homologous organisms. Furthermore, all four induced appreciable immunity against several of the seven heterologous strains which were used for challenge. However, none of the vaccines immunized mice against one of the standard strains of *R. tsutsugamushi* (Rights, Smadel and Jackson, 1947). Two field trials with American formalinized scrub typhus vaccines gave clear-cut negative results. In one test, vaccine prepared from a relatively broadly antigenic strain was employed for the immunization of approximately 1,000 Japanese farmers exposed to infection in their work; the number of cases which subsequently developed in the test group was essentially the same as that observed in the control group of similar size which received an unrelated vaccine (Berge, Gauld and Kitaoka, 1949). The other test was made with Malayan volunteers who were exposed by sitting in the grass in a hyperendemic area after inoculation with a bivalent vaccine containing a strain of rickettsia which had been recovered from infected mites collected from the exposure-area used for challenge (Smadel, Bailey and Diercks, 1950). Such failures led the Army research group to abandon studies on inactive scrub typhus vaccines and to turn to chemoprophylaxis of exposed persons and to the use of live vaccine combined with chemoprophylaxis to suppress clinical disease without interfering with the development of immunity. These last procedures, which were reasonably successful, are discussed in the section on Control Measures.

Chemotherapeutic studies on *R. tsutsugamushi* have been closely connected with those on other rickettsiae. The steps which led to the great success in treatment of these infections have been reviewed elsewhere (Snyder, 1948; Smadel, 1949). Suffice it to say that the first significant development in the therapeutic conquest of scrub typhus began with the demonstration of Snyder, Maier and Anderson (1942) that para-aminobenzoic acid possessed antirickettsial activity in mice infected with *R. typhi*. This was followed in 1947 by the observation that chloramphenicol was highly effective in treating mice with experimental scrub typhus (Smadel and Jackson, 1947). The therapeutic value of the antibiotics chloramphenicol, aureomycin and terramycin in patients with this disease is elaborated on in the section on Treatment. Jackson (1951), who reviewed current experimental work and added her own comparative studies, concluded: "The general order of rickettsiostatic activity of eight substances as judged on a gravimetric basis in embryonated eggs infected with one of a number of *Rickettsiae* is as follows: terramycin, aureomycin, chloramphenicol, PABA, nitroacridine, penicillin B, subtilin and streptomycin. . . . Subtilin is more effective against *R. tsutsugamushi* than against *R. typhi* or *R. rickettsii*, while the reverse order is true for PABA." It must be emphasized that none of the clinically useful drugs is rickettsiocidal in the concentrations attained in a patient's blood; each is active because of its rickettsiostatic properties.

DIAGNOSIS

A history of exposure in an area where scrub typhus is endemic and the finding of the primary lesion (eschar) are of great assistance in the early diagnosis of the disease. Other signs and symptoms of the malady, such as headache, conjunctival injection, fever, relative bradycardia and absence of leukocytosis are common to many diseases, for example, the other rickettsial infections, dengue, malaria, infectious hepatitis, typhoid fever, and others. The appearance of the skin eruption at about the end of the first week of fever is of some diagnostic assistance.

The Weil-Felix test is of great value in the diagnosis of scrub typhus. Agglutinins for the OX-K strain of *B. proteus* generally appear in a patient's serum by the end of the second week, but none develops against the OX-19 strain. The agglutinins reach a maximum titer by the end of the third week and then decline rapidly, often disappearing by the fifth or sixth week. It is highly important that serial specimens of serum be obtained to demonstrate the appearance and rise in titer of OX-K agglutinins. While a titer of 1/160 obtained with a single convalescent serum is generally regarded as significant, the result of one Weil-Felix test is of even less value in scrub typhus than in epidemic or murine typhus. In the latter diseases, OX-19 agglutinins usually reach higher levels than do OX-K antibodies in scrub typhus. Indeed, in a fair number of instances patients with scrub typhus fail to develop OX-K titers of 1/160, although serial examinations may show a diagnostic rise in the agglutinins. Rare individuals with proved scrub typhus fail to develop OX-K agglutinins. The Weil-Felix reaction, while valuable in typhus fevers and spotted fever, is not specific; relapsing fever (leptospirosis) may evoke an OX-K response similar to that displayed in scrub typhus (Zarafonetis et al., 1946).

A specific diagnosis of scrub typhus may be made by recovering the causal rickettsia from the blood of a patient during the febrile period or from tissues obtained at necropsy. A suspension of ground blood clot or of tissue is injected intraperitoneally into white mice. Infected mice may die 10 to 18 days after inoculation and show serofibrinous peritonitis and enlarged spleens. Microscopic examination of impression smears made from the surface of the spleen or the parietal peritoneum, fixed in methyl alcohol and stained by Giemsa's method, reveal the presence of minute intracellular and extracellular diplococcal organisms which have a purple color. The experimental disease is maintained by passage of bacteriologically sterile peritoneal fluid, blood, or suspensions of spleen, liver or lung. Final identification of the rickettsial agent is made by cross-immunity tests performed in mice. Not all strains of *R. tsutsugamushi* are lethal for mice when first recovered from patients. Therefore, in some

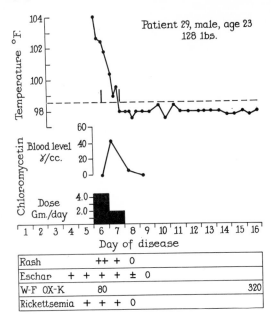

Patient 29, male, age 23
128 lbs.

Rash	++ + 0
Eschar	+ + + + ± 0
W-F OX-K	80 ... 320
Rickettsemia	+ + + 0

CHART 34. Response of scrub typhus Patient 29 to chloramphenicol. (Smadel, et al., 1949, Chloramphenicol [Chloromycetin] in the treatment of tsutsugamushi disease [scrub typhus]. J. Clin. Investigation, *28*, 1202.)

instances examination and passage of materials from sick or apparently healthy animals may be necessary to establish the strain.

Specific serologic tests, in which rickettsial materials are employed, have not been developed sufficiently for use as standard diagnostic procedures.

TREATMENT

Chloramphenicol, aureomycin and terramycin are specific therapeutic agents for scrub typhus. Patients are rendered afebrile and almost asymptomatic in a day or two after institution of therapy (Bailey et al., 1951). Chart 34 illustrates the prompt return of temperature to normal levels within 24 hours following administration of chloramphenicol to one of the patients in the first group studied (Smadel et al., 1949).

Each of the specific antibiotics may be given orally to adults according to a schedule consisting of a loading dose of 3 grams followed by 0.5 gram every 6 hours until

the temperature reaches normal. Usually 5 grams administered over a period of 24 hours are adequate, but in the more seriously ill patients treatment may be required for another day or two. There are no ordinary contraindications to the use of these highly effective drugs in this serious disease. The parenteral forms of these antibiotics are indicated in rare instances in which oral medication is impossible. In Table 25 are summarized the results of treatment of 151 Malayan patients with scrub typhus which may be compared with those obtained in 19 patients with the disease who did not receive the benefits of specific therapy. The data for the table are compiled from the paper of Bailey et al. (1951) and other publications of the Army Scrub Typhus Research Unit.

The three antibiotics do not sterilize the tissues but elicit their effect by suppressing growth of the rickettsiae. Ultimate recovery depends on the development of immunity by the patient. The suppressive effect of the 24-hour regimens mentioned earlier lasts for about one week. Immunity begins to develop late in the second week of illness and gains the ascendency over the agent on about the fourteenth day. Hence, relapses

THERAPY	NUMBER OF PATIENTS	AVERAGE DURATION OF FEVER AFTER TREATMENT (hrs)	FATALITIES
CHLOR- AMPHENICOL	100	31	0
AUREOMYCIN	29	25	0
TERRAMYCIN	7	47	0
PABA	15	89	0
		DURATION OF DISEASE	
NONE	19	17 DAYS	1

TABLE 25. Scrub typhus patients treated with chloramphenicol, aureomycin, terramycin or para-aminobenzoic acid. (From Smadel, J. E., 1951, Present status of antibiotic therapy in viral and rickettsial disease. Bull, New York Acad. Med., *27*, 223.)

are practically never seen in patients in whom treatment is begun on the seventh day of disease or later. On the other hand, recrudescence of disease is noted in about half the patients started on the short course of therapy on the fourth to the sixth day of illness and in about three quarters of those given specific antibiotic on the second day after onset. Relapses respond promptly to another course of 3 to 5 grams of antibiotic. Moreover, they can be prevented, in those patients who might be expected to relapse, by administering a single 3-gram dose of antibiotic on the sixth day after termination of the original course of therapy (Smadel, Bailey and Diercks, 1950).

Severely ill patients who do not receive specific therapy until late in the disease may still require the general supportive measures and good nursing care which were so important prior to the introduction of the broad-spectrum antibiotics. Penicillin is of no value in uncomplicated scrub typhus, and sulfonamides are contraindicated. Patients whose disease has been terminated by therapy during the first week after onset enjoy a rapid convalescence and may return to sedentary occupations within 10 days to 2 weeks after becoming afebrile. Those with a more protracted illness should be permitted a longer convalescence.

EPIDEMIOLOGY

Scrub typhus is transmitted to man by the larvae of at least two species of mite, *Trombicula akamushi* and *T. deliensis* (Blake et al., 1945; Mackie et al., 1946; Audy and Harrison, 1951); the former has been indicted in Japan and New Guinea, the latter in New Guinea and Burma; both probably serve as vectors also in other areas. Only the six-legged larvae are parasitic on vertebrates. These small, 0.15 to 0.4 mm., red larvae attach themselves to the skin and obtain a feeding of lymph or tissue juice; at this time the mite may acquire infection from the host or vice versa. Infection in mites may be maintained by transovarial passage of the rickettsial agent, but the

natural cycle of the disease involves mites and a vertebrate host. This cycle as depicted diagrammatically by Philip (1947) is presented in Figure 50. Both species of mite mentioned above have been found infected in nature as have various rodents which

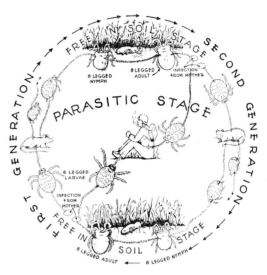

Fig. 50. Cycle of *R. tsutsugamushi* infection in nature, indicating transovarial transmission in mites, rodent hosts with incidental human host, and development of adult mite. (Philip, C. B., 1947, Observations on tsutsugamushi disease [mite-borne or scrub typhus] in northwest Honshu Island, Japan, in the fall of 1945. I. Epidemiological and ecological data. American Journal of Hygiene, *46*, 50.)

constitute the animal reservoir. In different areas voles, shrews, rats, field mice and other small animals make up this reservoir.

In Japan, the vector mites are prevalent during the summer months and the disease has a seasonal incidence. In the tropics there is an increased incidence during the rainy periods, but the occurrence of human disease is influenced especially by arrival of susceptible persons in an endemic area. Various types of terrain may serve as endemic areas; it is impossible to identify an infected area from its ecology. The common features of a focus are a suitable rodent population, adequate ground moisture favor-

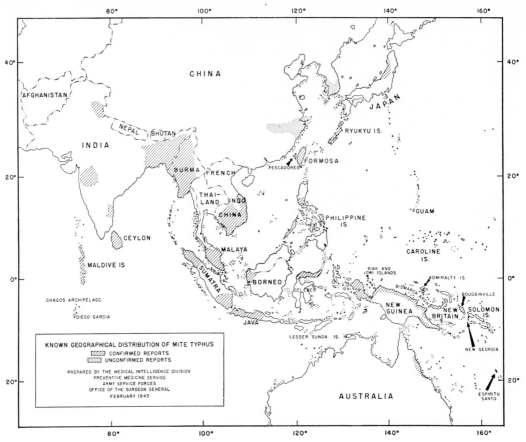

F<small>IG</small>. 51. Geographic distribution of scrub typhus. (Blake et al., 1945, Studies on tsutsugamushi disease [scrub typhus, mite-borne typhus] in New Guinea and adjacent islands: Epidemiology, clinical observations, and etiology in the Dobadura area. American Journal of Hygiene, *41*, 279.)

able to the specific mite vectors, and the occurrence of *R. tsutsugamushi* in hosts of the area. The exacting conditions necessary for a focus result in such a sharp perimeter that Audy and Harrison (1951) have called the areas "typhus islands." Thus, in the endemic areas in Japan infection may be contracted in an uncultivated area on the river side of an embankment but not 30 feet away in the tilled field inside the dike. The geographic distribution of scrub typhus is indicated in the map reproduced in Figure 51.

CONTROL MEASURES

The prevention of scrub typhus during military campaigns has been attained by the application of control measures aimed at the mite vector; these consist of the use of insecticides by the individual and of appropriate treatment of the terrain of endemic areas (War Department Technical Bulletin TB Med 31, Scrub Typhus, 1948). These procedures cannot be expected to provide such satisfactory results when used by civilians in peacetime because of their cost and the difficulties associated with their attainment. Measures for the individual are built around the use of miticidal chemicals, such as dimethyl phthalate, dibutyl phthalate, and benzyl benzoate which are applied to the clothing either by hand or by dipping. The Army antimite fluid used for impregnating clothing contains benzyl benzoate and dibutyl phthalate plus an emulsifier. Clothing is dipped into a properly diluted aqueous emulsion of this material, wrung out and allowed to dry. Under field conditions such treated clothing remains miticidal after prolonged soaking in fresh or salt water. The chemicals are slowly removed by laundering with soap and cold water; hence, clothing should be re-treated after three washings. Hot water dissolves the miticide and should not be used. The systematic use of such procedures undoubtedly reduces greatly the incidence of scrub typhus in exposed susceptible persons, but it is difficult to obtain statistically significant data on this point. However, Sir Neil Hamilton Fairley (1951) in speaking of the control program said that ". . . within one year of its introduction in New Guinea the rate had fallen in infected areas from 36 per 1,000 to approximately 1 per 1,000." The method employed for disinfecting a camp site is as follows. All vegetation is cut level with the ground and burned or hauled away. After thorough clearing, the ground usually dries sufficiently in two or three weeks to kill the mites. If the site is to be occupied before this time, the ground may be sprayed with a miticide, such as lindane or chlordane, which will render the area free of mites for several weeks. The prevention of scrub typhus, like that of malaria, can be accomplished by control of the insect vector; however, the cost and effort in each instance is so great that the measures cannot be employed except by an enlightened and wealthy society.

Chemoprophylaxis with chloramphenicol has been used successfully in suppressing scrub typhus in Malayan volunteers exposed in hyperinfected areas. Administration of 3-gram oral doses at weekly intervals controlled infection sufficiently to permit volunteers to remain ambulatory even though rickettsemia occurred from time to time. If the drug was continued for approximately a month after the infecting mite bite, the person remained well, but shorter periods of chemoprophylaxis were followed by clinical disease within a week after the last dose of drug (Smadel, Traub et al., 1950).

When noninfectious scrub typhus vaccines were found in field trials to be of no value (see section on Etiology), a combined procedure was studied which consisted of inoculation of volunteers with a vaccine containing living rickettsiae plus administration of chloramphenicol according to the chemoprophylactic schedule described above. The volunteers developed a primary lesion at the site of inoculation and, although ambulatory, had rickettsemia and subsequently displayed the antibody response of scrub typhus fever. Here, as in the chemoprophylactic field studies, withdrawal of the antibiotic before the third week was followed by clinical disease, but prolongation into the fourth week allowed time for immunity to develop, and breakthroughs did not occur (Smadel et al., 1951). This combined procedure is cumbersome and is not yet suitable for general use, but it is applicable under special circumstances.

There is no evidence of communicability of scrub typhus from man to man. Therefore, isolation of patients and quarantine measures are not indicated in this disease.

REFERENCES

Ahlm, C. E., and Lipshutz, J., 1944, Tsutsugamushi fever in the Southwest Pacific Theater. J. Am. Med. Assn., *124*, 1095-1100.

Allen, A. C., and Spitz, S., 1945, A comparative study of the pathology of scrub typhus (tsutsugamushi disease) and other rickettsial diseases. Am. J. Path., *21*, 603-681.

Audy, J. R., and Harrison, J. L., 1951, A review of investigations on mite typhus in Burma and Malaya, 1945-1950. Trans. Roy. Soc. Trop. Med. and Hyg., *44*, 371-404.

Bailey, C. A., Ley, H. L., Jr., Diercks, F. H., Lewthwaite, R., and Smadel, J. E., 1951, Treatment of scrub typhus: evaluation of chloramphenicol, aureomycin, terramycin and para-aminobenzoic acid. Antibiotics and Chemotherapy, *1*, 16-30.

Bell, E. J., Bennett, B. L., and Whitman, L., 1946, Antigenic differences between strains of scrub typhus as demonstrated by cross-neutralization tests. Proc. Soc. Exp. Biol. and Med., *62*, 134-137.

Bengtson, I. A., 1945, Apparent serological heterogeneity among strains of tsutsugamushi disease (scrub typhus). Pub. Health Rep., *60*, 1483-1488.

Bennett, B. L., Smadel, J. E., and Gauld, R. L., 1947, Differences in strains of *Rickettsia orientalis* as demonstrated by cross-neutralization tests (abstract). J. Bact., *54*, 93.

Berge, T. O., Gauld, R. L., and Kitaoka, M., 1949, A field trial of a vaccine prepared from the Volner strain of *Rickettsia tsutsugamushi*. Am. J. Hyg., *50*, 337-342.

Blake, F. G., Maxcy, K. F., Sadusk, J. F., Jr., Kohls, G. M., and Bell, E. J., 1945, Studies on tsutsugamushi disease (scrub typhus, mite-borne typhus) in New Guinea and adjacent islands: Epidemiology, clinical observations, and etiology in the Dobadura area. Am. J. Hyg., *41*, 243-373.

Buckland, F. E., Dudgeon, A., Edward, D. G., Henderson-Begg, A., MacCallum, F. O., Niven, J. S. F., Rowlands, I. W., van den Ende, M., Bargmann, H. E., Curtis, E. E., and Shepherd, M. A., 1945, Scrub-typhus vaccine: large-scale production. Lancet, *2*, 734-737.

Card, W. I., and Walker, J. M., 1947, Scrub-typhus vaccine: field trial in South-east Asia. Lancet, *1*, 481-483.

Dinger, J. E., 1933, Tropical ("scrub") typhus bij witte muizen. Geneesk. Tijdschr. v. Nederl.-Indië, *73*, 329-349.

Fairley, Sir Neil Hamilton, 1951, Discussion of report of Audy, J. R., and Harrison, J. L., 1951, Trans. Roy. Soc. Trop. Med. and Hyg., *44*, pp. 399.

Fletcher, W., Lesslar, J. E., and Lewthwaite, R., 1929, The aetiology of the tsutsugamushi disease and tropical typhus in the Federated Malay States. Part II. Trans. Roy. Soc. Trop. Med. and Hyg., *23*, 57-70.

Fulton, F., and Joyner, L., 1945, Cultivation of *Rickettsia tsutsugamushi* in lungs of rodents: preparation of a scrub-typhus vaccine. Lancet, *2*, 729-733.

Jackson, E. B., 1951, Comparative efficacy of several antibiotics on experimental rickettsial infections in embryonated eggs. Antibiotics and Chemotherapy, *1*, 231-241.

Jackson, E. B., and Smadel, J. E., 1951, Immunization against scrub typhus. II. Preparation of lyophilized living vaccine. Am. J. Hyg., *53*, 326-331.

Lewthwaite, R., O'Connor, J. L., and Williams, S. E., 1946, The tsutsugamushi disease; attempted preparation of a prophylactic vaccine from fertile hens' eggs experimentally infected with the virus. Med. J. Australia, *2*, 37-43.

Mackie, T. T., Davis, G. E., Fuller, H. S., Knapp, J. A., Steinacker, M. L., Stager, K. E., Traub, R., Jellison, W. L., Millspaugh, D. D., Austrian, R. C., Bell, E. J., Kohls, G. M., Wei, H., and Girsham, J. A. V., 1946, Observations on tsutsugamushi disease (scrub typhus) in Assam and Burma. Preliminary report. Am. J. Hyg., *43*, 195-218.

Megaw, J. W. D., 1945, Scrub typhus as a war disease. Brit. Med. J., *2*, 109-112.

Murray, E. S., Zarafonetis, C. J. D., and Snyder, J. C., 1945, Further report on effect of para-amino-benzoic acid in experimental tsutsugamushi disease (scrub typhus). Proc. Soc. Exp. Biol. and Med., *60*, 80-84.

Nagayo, M., Tamiya, T., Mitamura, T., and Sato, K., 1930, On the virus of tsutsugamushi disease and its demonstration by a new method. Japanese J. Exp. Med., *8*, 309-318.

Ogata, N., 1931, Aetiologie der Tsutsugamushikrankheit: *Rickettsia tsutsugamushi*. Zentralbl. f. Bakt. (*Abt. 1*), Orig., *122*, 249-253.

Philip, C. B., 1947, Observations on tsutsugamushi disease (mite-borne or scrub typhus) in northwest Honshu Island, Japan, in the fall of 1945. I. Epidemiological and ecological data. Am. J. Hyg., *46*, 45-59.

Plotz, H., Bennett, B. L., and Reagan, R. L., 1946, Preparation of an inactivated tissue culture scrub typhus vaccine. Proc. Soc. Exp. Biol. and Med., *61*, 313-317.

Rights, F. L., Smadel, J. E., and Jackson, E. B., 1947, Differences in strains of *Rickettsia orientalis* as demonstrated by cross-vaccination studies (abstract). J. Bact., *54*, 92-93.

Sadusk, J. F., Jr., 1947, Typhus fever in the United States Army following immunization. Incidence, severity of the disease, modification of the clinical course and serological diagnosis. J. Am. Med. Assn., *133*, 1192-1199.

Settle, E. B., Pinkerton, H., and Corbett, A. J., 1945, A pathologic study of tsutsugamushi disease (scrub typhus) with notes on clinico-pathologic correlation. J. Lab. and Clin. Med., *30*, 639-661.

Smadel, J. E., 1949, Evaluation of new drugs in the treatment of rickettsial diseases. Bull. Pan American Sanitary Bureau, *28*, 1-19.

Smadel, J. E., 1951, Present status of antibiotic therapy in viral and rickettsial disease. Bull. New York Acad. Med., *27*, 221-231.

Smadel, J. E., Bailey, C. A., and Diercks, F. H., 1950, Chloramphenicol (Chloromycetin) in the chemoprophylaxis of scrub typhus (tsutsugamushi disease). IV. Relapses of scrub typhus in treated volunteers and their prevention. Am. J. Hyg., *51*, 229-241.

Smadel, J. E., Jackson, E. B., Bennett, B. L., and Rights, F. L., 1946, A toxic substance associated with the Gilliam strain of *R. orientalis*. Proc. Soc. Exp. Biol. and Med., *62*, 138-140.

Smadel, J. E., and Jackson, E. B., 1947, Chloromycetin, an antibiotic with chemotherapeutic activity in experimental rickettsial and viral infections. Science, *106*, 418-419.

Smadel, J. E., Ley, H. L., Jr., Diercks, F. H., and Traub, R., 1950, Immunity in scrub typhus: resistance to induced reinfection. Arch. Path., *50*, 847-861.

Smadel, J. E., Ley, H. L., Jr., Diercks, F. H., Traub, R., Tipton, V. J., and Frick, L. P., 1951, Immunization against scrub typhus. I. Combined living vaccine and chemoprophylaxis in volunteers. Am. J. Hyg., *53*, 317-325.

Smadel, J. E., Rights, F. L., and Jackson, E. B., 1946a, Studies on scrub typhus. I. Soluble antigen in tissues and body fluids of infected mice and rats. J. Exp. Med., *83*, 133-146.

Smadel, J. E., Rights, F. L., and Jackson, E. B., 1946b. Studies on scrub typhus. II. Preparation of formalinized vaccines from tissues of infected mice and rats. Proc. Soc. Exp. Biol. and Med., *61,* 308-313.

Smadel, J. E., Traub, R., Frick, L. P., Diercks, F. H., and Bailey, C. A., 1950, Chloramphenicol (Chloromycetin) in the chemoprophylaxis of scrub typhus (tsutsugamushi disease). III. Suppression of overt disease by prophylactic regimens of four-week duration. Am. J. Hyg., *51,* 216-228.

Smadel, J. E., Woodward, T. E., Ley, H. L., Jr., and Lewthwaite, R., 1949, Chloramphenicol (Chloromycetin) in the treatment of tsutsugamushi disease (scrub typhus). J. Clin. Investig., *28,* 1196-1215.

Snyder, J. C., 1948, The treatment of rickettsial diseases of man *in* The Rickettsial Diseases of Man. Am. Assn. Advancement of Science, Washington, pp. 169-177.

Snyder, J. C., Maier, J., and Anderson, C. R., 1942, Report to the Division of Medical Sciences of the National Research Council, Washington, December 26.

Topping, N. H., 1945, Tsutsugamushi disease (scrub typhus). The effects of an immune rabbit serum in experimentally infected mice. Pub. Health Rep., *60,* 1215-1220.

Topping, N. H., and Shepard, C. C., 1946, The preparation of antigens from yolk sacs infected with rickettsiae. Pub. Health Rep., *61,* 701-707.

War Department Technical Bulletin TB Med No. 31, Scrub typhus fever (mite-borne typhus, tsutsugamushi disease), revised 1948.

Wolfe, D. M., Van der Scheer, J., Clancy, C. F., and Cox, H. R., 1946, A method for the preparation of complement-fixing antigens in a study of experimental tsutsugamushi disease (scrub typhus). J. Bact., *51,* 247-255.

Zarafonetis, C. J. D., Ingraham, H. S., and Berry, J. F., 1946, Weil-Felix and typhus complement-fixation tests in relapsing fever, with special reference to B. *proteus* OX-K agglutination. J. Immunol., *52,* 189-199.

JOSEPH E. SMADEL, M. D.

Army Medical Service Graduate School

38

Q Fever

INTRODUCTION

Q fever is an acute febrile illness caused by *Rickettsia burneti* and characterized by sudden onset, malaise, headache, anorexia and weakness; rickettsemia occurs during the febrile phase and interstitial pneumonitis generally develops. Q fever is distinguished from other rickettsial diseases of man by failure of patients to develop either a cutaneous rash or agglutinins against the proteus organisms used in the Weil-Felix test.

HISTORY

Q fever was first recognized as a human disease in 1935 in Queensland, Australia, and its etiologic agent was named by Australian workers (Derrick, 1937, 1939; Burnet and Freeman, 1937). At about the same time in the western United States a similar rickettsia was recovered from naturally infected ticks, *Dermacentor andersoni* (Davis and Cox, 1938), which was proved subsequently to be identical with *R. burneti* (Burnet and Freeman, 1939; Dyer, 1939). During the course of extensive laboratory studies carried out in Australia and this country on the new rickettsial agent, a number of infections developed among laboratory personnel, but for a few years recog-

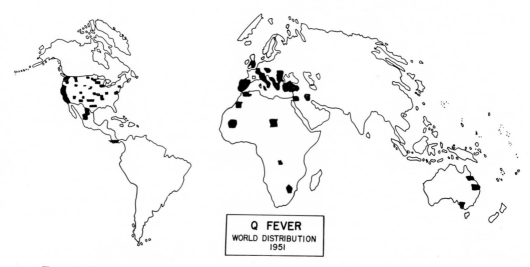

Fig. 52. World distribution of Q fever. Based on data regarding isolation of *R. burneti* from man, animals, and ticks, serologically confirmed cases of Q fever, and serologic surveys of indigenous human and animal populations. (Berge, T. O., and Lennette, E. H., 1952, World distribution of Q fever, human, animal and arthropod infection. To be published.)

nition of naturally occurring human infections was limited almost entirely to Australia. During 1944 and 1945 the disease was of military importance in the Mediterranean theater where more than 1,000 cases were recorded among Allied troops (Robbins, Gauld, and Warner, 1946; The Commission on Acute Respiratory Diseases, 1946a). An outbreak of Q fever had probably occurred the preceding winter in Athens, Greece, since the disease called "Balkan grippe" resembled Q fever, and Caminopétros recovered an agent, which was subsequently identified as *R. burneti,* from the blood of one of the patients (The Commission on Acute Respiratory Diseases, 1946c). There followed a veritable flood of reports on Q fever during the next few years. These indicate that outbreaks of Q fever in man, enzootic infections of the larger domesticated animals and the occurrence of naturally infected ticks are not uncommon in many parts of the world. Berge and Lennette (1952), whose review may be consulted for references to the original articles, prepared the map illustrated in Figure 52 which shows the world distribution of *R. burneti* and the disease Q fever.

CLINICAL PICTURE

The most thorough clinical studies of Q fever have been made on cases which occurred among laboratory workers (Hornibrook and Nelson, 1940; The Commission on Acute Respiratory Diseases, 1946b) and among military personnel who contracted the disease in the Mediterranean theater (Robbins and Ragan, 1946, Feinstein, Yesner and Marks, 1946). The following description is based mainly on the findings in the military patients who acquired the disease in Italy.

Following an incubation period of from 14 to 26 days, mean 19 days, the onset of the disease is generally sudden with headache, myalgia, feverishness, chilly sensations and loss of appetite. Symptoms referable to the upper respiratory or gastrointestinal tracts are not conspicuous. During the first few days physical signs generally are limited to fever, ranging from 101° to 104° F., and provide little help in arriving at a diagnosis. The febrile period lasts from one to ten or more days, but half the patients have fever of three to six days' duration. Temperature curves are of the swinging type. Symptoms noted at the onset continue while the temperature remains elevated; anorexia, often accompanied by nausea, is pronounced, and headache is severe. On about the fifth or sixth day, a mild dry cough develops in a majority of the cases, and many patients complain of pain in the chest. At this time careful physical examination of the chest often reveals the presence of a few crepitant rales and slight diminution in resonance. These signs are evanescent and rarely persist for more than a few days. They are generally found in the regions which show involvement on roentgenologic examination.

Evidence of pulmonary involvement demonstrated by roentgenogram is found in practically all patients; this includes even those who are so mildly ill that they would not ordinarily seek medical care. The roentgenographic changes are generally considered to be indistinguishable from those of primary atypical pneumonia. However, Feinstein, Yesner and Marks (1946) have described in minute detail the x-ray changes and think that the findings taken as a whole present certain distinctive characteristics. Suffice it to say, that during the first few days after onset, films of the chest appear normal. On about the third or fourth day, patchy areas of consolidation appear; these usually involve only a portion of one lobe and generally present a homogeneous, ground-glass appearance. Changes demonstrable by x-ray tend to persist beyond the termination of the febrile period (Chart 35) and in many instances roentgenograms still show evidence of pulmonary involvement at the time a patient is discharged from the hospital.

Salient features of the record of an individual who contracted his illness in the laboratory of the Commission on Acute Respiratory Diseases at Fort Bragg are given in Chart 35, and his roentgenograms are reproduced in Figure 53.

Complications rarely develop. As the temperature approaches normal, a patient's

R. burneti are discussed elsewhere in this chapter.

No discussion of the clinical disease would be complete without mentioning the observations of Blanc and his colleagues (Blanc et al., 1948) on *R. burneti* infections

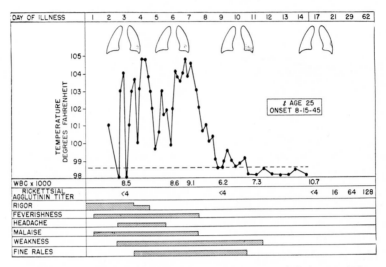

CHART 35. Chart of clinical findings in case of Q fever. (The Commission on Acute Respiratory Diseases, 1946, A laboratory outbreak of Q fever caused by the Balkan grippe strain of *Rickettsia burneti*. American Journal of Hygiene, *44,* 133.)

appetite returns and he has no sequelae except weakness which may persist for several weeks. The more severely affected patients may lose from 15 to 20 lbs. during the course of the illness but this is rapidly regained. Clark and his co-workers (1951b) emphasize the protracted nature of the disease in almost one fifth of their patients. Fever lasting for longer than 4 weeks occurred more often in persons over 40 years of age. Moreover, evidence of hepatic involvement, including clinical icterus, appeared in almost one third of the patients with protracted severe illness.

The usual clinical laboratory tests provide little diagnostic assistance. Total leukocyte and differential counts are essentially normal, but the erythrocyte sedimentation rate may be moderately elevated. Specific laboratory tests concerned with

induced in psychotic patients as part of their fever therapy. Intradermal inoculation of infectious material regularly resulted in a small local cutaneous lesion which lasted for about two weeks, but only 2 of the 10 persons developed fever and this was mild and of short duration. Intramuscular inoculation produced marked local swelling; fever of 104° F. began 48 hours after infection and persisted for several days, but no pulmonary involvement became evident, although rickettsemia occurred. Infected material administered by intranasal instillation or inhalation of aerosol produced typical Q fever with pulmonary lesions. Incidentally, not only the two subjects became infected as a result of the aerosol but also the two investigators performing the operation as well as two assistants who remained several yards distant. Persons with inapparent infection, viz., those who were inoculated intradermally, as well as those with overt disease resisted a second inoculation given several weeks later.

PATHOLOGIC PICTURE

The mortality from Q fever is usually low; none of the 1,000 military patients Histologic examination of sections from the consolidated area revealed a compact fibrinocellular exudate which filled alveoli, bronchioles and most bronchi. Lymphocytes, plasma cells and large mononuclear cells were most numerous in the exudate; erythrocytes were plentiful in some alveoli, but polymorphonuclear cells were scarce throughout the area. The bronchial epi-

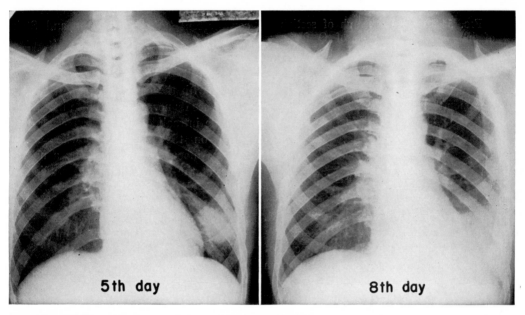

5th day

8th day

Fig. 53. Roentgenogram of chest of patient with Q fever, whose chart is shown in Chart 30. (The Commission on Acute Respiratory Diseases, 1946, A laboratory outbreak of Q fever caused by the Balkan grippe strain of *Rickettsia burneti*. American Journal of Hygiene, *44,* 133.)

succumbed. One death has been recorded in an elderly person who contracted a laboratory infection (Lillie, Perrin and Armstrong, 1941), two deaths occurred among the 55 patients with Q fever in Amarillo, Texas, in 1946 (Topping, Shepard and Irons, 1947) and one in an elderly man in England (Harman, 1949). The only detailed necropsy report is that of the laboratory worker. The essential findings at postmortem examination of this patient were limited to congestion and edema of the lungs associated with gray granular consolidation in one lobe, and acute splenic tumor.

thelium was generally desquamated. Alveolar epithelium was hyperplastic in certain areas and, generally, the interalveolar septa were thickened by accumulations of lymphocytes, plasma and large mononuclear cells and a variable number of fibroblasts. Capillaries in the septa contained little blood. Infiltrations of lymphocytes and plasma cells were encountered in peribronchial and perivascular tissues. Rickettsiae were not found on microscopic examination of any of the human material. Figure 54 illustrates the typical histopathologic lesion in the lung of this patient.

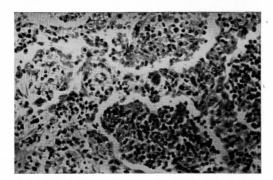

FIG. 54. Photomicrograph of section of lung from fatal case of Q fever. (Lillie, R. D., Perrin, T. L., and Armstrong, C., 1941, An institutional outbreak of pneumonitis. III. Histopathology in man and rhesus monkeys in the pneumonitis due to the virus of "Q" fever. Public Health Reports, *56*, facing page 152.)

EXPERIMENTAL INFECTION; HOST RANGE

The extremely broad host range of *R. burneti* includes numerous wild and domesticated animals, a number of species of ticks, and man. Sufficient work has been done with certain wild animals and cattle to indicate their susceptibility under experimental conditions. Mice, hamsters, guinea pigs and embryonated eggs, the last two being the most useful, have been employed in most of the investigative work in the laboratory. Infection in mice rarely results in death of the animals; therefore, confirmation of the disease depends upon pathologic examination which usually includes microscopic study of stained preparations of peritoneal exudate or splenic smears for the presence of rickettsiae. However, the agent multiplies freely, since infectious titers of 10^{-8} are obtained when mouse spleen is tested in guinea pigs. Guinea pigs regularly develop a febril illness, and certain strains, notably the Dyer "X" strain of American Q fever, regularly cause death even on inoculation of only a few infectious doses, i.e., 10^{-7} or $^{-8}$ dilution of guinea-pig spleen or 10^{-8} or $^{-9}$ dilution

of infected yolk-sac material. Other commonly employed strains, for example, the Henzerling strain from Italy, are lethal for guinea pigs only when highly concentrated material is used for inoculation; however, infection with such strains results following inoculation of dilutions of 10^{-7} or 10^{-8} of yolk-sac material. It is worthy of note that the urine of infected guinea pigs contains rickettsiae and that the organisms persist for a long time in the tissues and urine of convalescent animals (Parker and Steinhaus, 1943).

Gross pathologic lesions in guinea pigs are generally limited to enlargement of the spleen, with the organ increased to two to four times its normal size; when inoculation is made intraabdominally, some exudate is found on the peritoneum, while subcutaneous inoculation often elicits a nodular lesion at the site. Lillie (1942) studied the histopathology in guinea pigs and found small focal granulomatous lesions scattered throughout practically all organs and tissues, which consisted of vascular endotheliosis and of perivascular collections of cells of the lymphocytic series, monocytes and fibroblasts.

R. burneti grows well in tissue cultures and in embryonated eggs (Cox and Bell, 1939). The richest yields are generally obtained with the least labor from yolk-sac tissue of embryonated eggs inoculated in their yolk sacs when five or six days old. Death of the embryo occurs after incubation for four or five days at 35° C. Yolk-sac tissue from moribund embryos provides satisfactory starting material for the preparation of seed inocula, rickettsial antigens for diagnostic work, and vaccines.

ETIOLOGY

The etiologic agent of Q fever possesses the general properties of other members of the rickettsial group. *R. burneti* is an obligate, intracellular, parasitic microorganism. It is a small pleomorphic structure and may occur as a lanceolate rod 0.25μ by 0.5μ, as a bipolar rod 0.25μ by 1.0μ, or as a diplobacillus 0.25μ by 1.5μ. It takes a purple color when stained by Giemsa's method and red when stained by Macchiavello's technic. In some preparations the rickettsiae are so large that one suspects that the tissue has been contaminated by one of the common gram-negative bacteria. However, the same preparations also contain small particles, no larger than elementary bodies of vaccinia, which have tinctorial qualities similar to those of the rod-shaped structures. The small size of certain organisms in each suspension is indicated also by the ease with which the agent passes through Berkefeld N filters and the finding of some activity in filtrates from collodion membranes with an average pore diameter of 400 mμ (Bengtson, 1941a). It may be recalled that, because of its filterability, the American workers originally designated the organism as *Rickettsia diaporica* before it was found that the agent was identical with that previously named by the Australian workers (Cox, 1939). The morphologic structure of *R. burneti*, as revealed by electron microscopy, is similar to that of other rickettsiae and to certain bacteria (Plotz, Smadel, Anderson and Chambers, 1943). Thus, the electron micrographs show that the agent has a limiting membrane which encloses protoplasmic material in which are interspersed granules of dense material.

The rickettsia of Q fever is relatively resistant to desiccation. This, together with the fact that the feces of infected ticks and the excreta and secretions of infected domesticated animals contain viable organisms, is important in the transmission of the disease in the field (see Epidemiology). The agent remains viable for long periods of time when stored at −70° C. and after lyophilization. Furthermore, animal tissues suspended in 50 per cent glycerol and whole blood from guinea pigs have proved infectious after transportation for long distances without refrigeration. Preparations of *R. burneti* become noninfectious when stored for several days in a 0.2 per cent U. S. P.

formaldehyde solution or 0.4 per cent phenol; longer periods are required for inactivation of crude infectious yolk-sac materials containing cellular masses.

Suspensions of washed *R. burneti* provide specific antigens for use in diagnostic complement-fixation or agglutination tests. While such antigens may be prepared from several types of material, infected yolk sacs are the tissues of choice for this purpose. The method most commonly employed in recent years for processing such material is closely related to that used in preparing washed suspensions of *R. prowazeki*, which has been described in detail in Chapter 3. Certain groups of workers prefer the agglutination technic. Burnet and Freeman (1938) who originally used this method in Q fever made their antigen from infected spleens of mice. The Commission on Acute Respiratory Diseases (1946b, c) employed agglutinating suspensions derived from infected yolk sacs to obtain the serologic data given in Chart 35. It is of interest that the first of the satisfactory rickettsial complement-fixing antigens prepared from yolk-sac material was that of Q fever (Bengtson, 1941b). The complement-fixation technic is employed for the serologic diagnosis of Q fever at the Army Medical Service Graduate School. Not all strains of *R. burneti* are equally suitable for making complement-fixing antigens. Sera from guinea pigs which recover from infection with any of the strains develop two complement-fixing antibodies. One of these appears during the third week after inoculation and the other several weeks later; by the ninth week the titer of the second approaches the plateau attained earlier by the first antibody. While formalinized supensions of all the different strains of rickettsiae contain complement-fixing antigens which react with both antibodies, suspensions of certain strains are relatively deficient in the factor which combines with the first antibody to appear. Antigens prepared from the Henzerling strain isolated in Italy are suitable for diagnostic work since they contain both factors

in about equal amounts (Robbins, Rustigian, Snyder and Smadel, 1946). The in-
vitro serologic reactions obtained with Q
fever materials are highly specific; no cross
reactions are obtained with epidemic, murine, or scrub typhus, Rocky Mountain
spotted fever, North Queensland tick
typhus or with a number of nonrickettsial
materials. Neutralizing antibody capable of
protecting animals against infection occurs
in immune sera, but the neutralization test
is not widely employed since other diagnostic methods are simpler (Burnet and Freeman, 1939; Bengtson, 1941c).

Animals which recover from infection
with one strain of R. burneti are resistant
to reinfection with the same or other strains
(Dyer, Topping and Bengtson, 1940;
Topping, Shepard and Huebner, 1946).
However, it is occasionally possible to
break through the resistance of convalescent
guinea pigs when very highly infectious
challenge inocula are used, and under these
circumstances, a febrile reaction or even
death may result. Animals convalescent
from Q fever are not resistant to infection
with other members of the rickettsial group.
Noninfectious vaccines prepared from mice,
guinea pigs, or yolk-sac tissues rich in
rickettsiae are capable of immunizing animals against the disease (Bengtson, 1941c;
Smadel, Snyder and Robbins, 1948). The
latter type at least will also elicit the production of complement-fixing antibodies in
guinea pigs and man. Vaccinated animals
are not solidly immune. Although they are
completely resistant to a few minimal infectious doses (MID) of the homologous
or heterologous strain, inoculation of several
million MIDs is followed by a short non-
lethal febrile illness; death occurs in the
majority of control animals receiving the
more infectious challenge material.

Experimental infections of embryonated
eggs produced by R. burneti are interfered
with by aureomycin (Wong and Cox, 1948),
chloramphenicol (Smadel, Jackson and
Cruise, 1949) and terramycin (Smadel,
Jackson and Ley, 1950). The last group of
investigators pointed out that R. burneti is
as susceptible to small doses of terramycin
as are R. tsutsugamushi and R. rickettsii.
The doses of aureomycin and chloramphenicol essential for a significant therapeutic result are greater for the agent of Q
fever than for those of scrub typhus and
spotted fever.

DIAGNOSIS

The diagnosis of Q fever in man is established by the isolation of the etiologic agent
or the demonstration of the appearance
of specific antibodies against it in the serum
of a patient. The history, clinical findings
and the pathologic picture are insufficient,
either individually or collectively, to establish a diagnosis, but they should lead a
physician to suspect the disease and to obtain proper laboratory studies. During the
first few days of a patient's illness, prior to
the development of pulmonary lesions,
Q fever may resemble the early stage of
many acute febrile conditions such as influenza, meningitis, typhoid and paratyphoid,
brucellosis, sandfly fever, dengue, infectious
hepatitis, nonicteric leptospirosis, malaria,
as well as the other rickettsial diseases. With
the development of the pulmonary changes
of Q fever, differential diagnosis requires
consideration of bacterial pneumonia, primary atypical pneumonia, psittacosis and
other diseases capable of producing such
pulmonary changes (see Chapters 17 and
20); in certain geographic areas coccidiomycosis must be considered.

Isolation of R. burneti from the blood of
patients during the febrile phase, from
sputum, spinal fluid or urine, or from tissue
obtained at necropsy is accomplished without difficulty. Guinea pigs are commonly
employed for this purpose, but mice, hamsters, monkeys and embryonated eggs have
proved satisfactory. Identification of the
agent is made in the following manner.
Guinea pigs which develop a febrile response following an intraperitoneal inoculation of materials from a patient are
sacrificed and a suspension of their spleens

passed intraperitoneally into normal animals. During the early passages rickettsiae often cannot be found on microscopic examination of splenic smears stained by Giemsa's or Macchiavello's method. Identity of the agent is established by finding rickettsiae in stained smears of tissues of passage animals and by the results of cross-immunity tests performed in animals, or by the demonstration of specific complement-fixing antibodies in the sera of convalescent guinea pigs. Because of the great danger of infection of personnel, including not only those in immediate contact with the work but also those throughout the building, isolation of *R. burneti* should not be attempted except under unusual circumstances and then only in laboratories actively engaged in the study of Q fever.

Diagnosis of Q fever by serologic means is highly satisfactory and is recommended for general use. Under proper conditions either the agglutination or complement-fixation technic provides sufficiently accurate data so that neither false negative nor false positive diagnoses result to any appreciable extent. Methods involved in the preparation and use of Q fever antigens need not be discussed here since the principles are described in Chapter 3; for details of these technics, original communications should be consulted. In Q fever it is highly desirable, indeed almost essential, that early and late specimens of sera be tested for antibodies in order to demonstrate the appearance of antibodies during convalescence or their increase in titer. Although titers 1:8 in agglutination tests and 1:20 in complement-fixation tests are significant, one should hesitate to make a diagnosis of Q fever on the results obtained on a single specimen of convalescent serum unless the titers are considerably higher than these minimal levels.

Agglutinins rarely appear before the ninth day of illness and by the end of the second week only about one quarter of the patients give positive tests; however, toward the end of the fourth week, 90 per cent possess agglutinins (The Commission on Acute Respiratory Diseases, 1946c). Complement-fixing antibodies are detectable between the seventh and thirteenth day in practically all cases and rise steadily to a maximum titer usually in the range of 1:160, which is reached about the twenty-first day (Robbins, Rustigian, Snyder and Smadel, 1946). Specific complement-fixing antibodies persist in high titer for a number of months and may still be demonstrable in small but significant amounts several years after infection. In man as in lower animals, serologic reactions of Q fever are highly specific. No cross reactions occur with other members of the rickettsial group, with psittacosis, influenza, or miscellaneous bacteria; sera containing cold agglutinins do not react with Q fever antigens.

TREATMENT

Despite the indisputable evidence of the efficacy of terramycin, aureomycin and chloramphenicol in experimental Q fever infections in embryonated eggs, and the known clinical value of these antibiotics in other rickettsial diseases of man, it is difficult to evaluate their usefulness in patients with Q fever because of the variability of the untreated disease as regards severity and duration. Clark, Lennette and Meiklejohn (1951a) summarize their observations on 45 patients given aureomycin and 25 treated with penicillin in the following manner: "Treatment with aureomycin appeared to effect a significant reduction in the duration of fever, and the antibiotic is considered to be useful in the treatment of this disease. In some patients, however, response to aureomycin therapy appeared to be slight or negligible; no satisfactory explanation of these therapeutic failures was established."

Only a few patients with Q fever have received chloramphenicol (Harman, 1949; Zarafonetis and Bates, 1950) or terramycin (Bickel and Plattner, 1951) and all recovered. Penicillin, streptomycin and sulfonamides are of no value in this disease.

Until additional data become available, the suggested antibiotic therapy for adult patients with Q fever is 3 to 4 grams daily of terramycin or aureomycin administered orally. Treatment should be continued until several days after the patient becomes afebrile. If a relapse occurs, the initial course may be repeated.

EPIDEMIOLOGY

Human Q fever probably is most often contracted by inhalation of infected dusts from one or another source. Direct contact by handling infected tissues, excretions or secretions undoubtedly accounts for some cases. Moreover, the drinking of raw milk naturally contaminated with *R. burneti* probably plays a role in human disease. Much has been learned about the epidemiology of Q fever during the last few years, and this information has thrown new light on modes of transmission as well as strengthened certain hypotheses developed from the earlier observations made in Australia and Italy.

Q fever in Australia is apparently an enzootic disease of certain wild animals, especially bandicoots, and is transmitted in nature by ticks *(Haemaphysalis humerosa* and *Ixodes holocyclus)* (Derrick, 1944). These ticks are capable of infecting cattle which develop a mild illness. Furthermore, cattle ticks *(Boophilus annulatus microplus* and *Haemaphysalis bispinosa)* become infected by feeding on such cattle and their feces may contaminate the hides. Therefore, Australian workers believe that persons working in slaugther houses may contract the disease by direct contact with infected meat or by inhalation of infected dust from hides contaminated by tick feces. While the mode of transmission in the outbreaks among slaugther-house and stockyard workers in the United States has not been determined, it may be mentioned that two species of ticks *(D. andersoni* and *Amblyomma americanum)* found in several regions of the United States are naturally infected with the organism of Q fever (Davis and Cox, 1938; Parker and Kohls, 1943) and that infected *D. andersoni* ticks are capable of transmitting the disease to guinea pigs by feeding (Parker and Davis, 1938). Blanc and his colleagues (1949), as a result of their investigations of the natural history of Q fever in Morocco, regard *R. burneti* primarily as a parasite of ticks of the genus *Hyalomma* with transovarial transmission in these arthropods and with vertebrates in that area serving only an ancillary role in perpetuation of the organism.

The explosive character of certain of the outbreaks of Q fever among troops in Italy is well illustrated in Chart 36, which presents graphically the hospital admissions by days of 269 cases which occurred during a three-week period in an infantry battalion having a total strength of 900. The following discussion of the epidemiologic factors involved in the Italian outbreaks is quoted from Robbins, Gauld and Warner (1946).

Between 20 and 30 per cent of the strength of the units involved were attacked, but, in spite of this high attack rate, there appeared to be a distinct tendency for the epidemics to remain localized and to affect only the units occupying certain billets. This gave rise to the hypothesis that in Italy Q fever is what is known as a "place infection." Some of the outbreaks were explosive in character pointing to infection through a common source but in no instance has it been possible to incriminate food or water, and it seems unlikely that these were the source of any of the epidemics. The epidemiological evidence in most instances does not indicate person-to-person transfer, and this observation is borne out by the experience of the hospitals where the men were cared for. In spite of the absence of isolation precautions, there were no cross infections on any of the wards. The possibility of insect transmission must be considered, but the almost universal failure of the cases to report bites is unusual if this is the mode of transfer.

The majority of the epidemics was found to be associated with animal life, such as pigeons, rats, mice, and cattle, and there is a distinct possibility that some of these, or other lower animals not noted in the investigations, may serve as reservoirs of the infection. The association with dust, either accumulated in attics or on hay and straw, is quite striking. Such dust could be infected by contamination from excrement of any of the animals noted above or from their insect parasites. . . . The evidence presented that Mediterranean Q fever also occurs as a sporadic disease is highly significant, and suggests that a large proportion of the cases diagnosed as primary atypical pneumonia in Italy, at least, was due to the rickettsia of Q fever. . . . The finding of

infection, and, indeed, Bell, Beck and Huebner (1950) found that positive Q fever complement-fixation reactions were more frequent among drinkers of raw milk in the Los Angeles area than among their neighbors who did not. Nevertheless, epidemiologic studies on clinical cases of Q fever occuring in both Southern and Northern California failed to implicate clearly the drinking of raw milk (Bell et al., 1950;

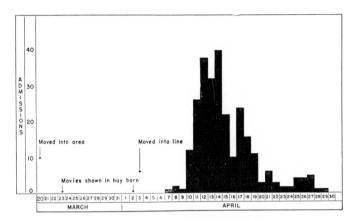

CHART 36. Incidence of Q fever in a battalion of 900 men stationed near Pagliana, Italy, during the spring of 1945. (Robbins, F. C., Gauld, R. L., and Warner, F. B., 1946, Q fever in the Mediterranean area: report of its occurrence in Allied troops. II. Epidemiology. American Journal of Hygiene, *44, 29.*)

complement-fixing antibodies in the blood sera of a large proportion of the adult civilian population of the town of Pagliana is evidence that the disease is endemic among civilians in the North Apennines.

Caminopétros (1948) found sheep and goats in Greece to be naturally infected and recovered *R. burneti* from the milk from such animals. Lennette, Clark and Dean (1949) made similar observations in Northern California. About the same time, Huebner and his associates (1948) demonstrated *R. burneti* in raw milk from infected diary cattle in Southern California, and shortly afterward infected raw milk was found in England (MacCallum, Marmion and Stoker, 1949). These findings pointed to contaminated milk as a source of human

Lennette and Clark, 1951) in the majority cases; a large proportion of the patients was exposed directly or indirectly to domestic livestock. *R. burneti* was then demonstrated (DeLay, Lennette, and DeOme, 1950; Lennette and Welsh, 1951) in the dust-laden air of dairy-cattle barns and of sheep and goat pens which harbored naturally infected animals. These investigators state: "The most plausible explanation for the occurrence of certain outbreaks of naturally acquired Q fever would appear to be that infection is related to air-borne dissemination of the rickettsia." Other examples of outbreaks which were in all likelihood caused by air-borne infection are those among laundry workers who handled soiled towels and overalls from a laboratory where

Q fever was under investigation (Oliphant et al., 1949), among workers in a plant which processed raw wool and goat hair (Sigel et al., 1950), and among workers in a machine shop who uncrated tools packed in straw (Wegmann, 1948).

CONTROL MEASURES

Satisfactory control of Q fever as regards both the individual and the group remains to be accomplished. It is difficult to see how any preventive measures other than immunization of the individual would prove of value in control of the disease which occurs among slaughter-house workers, dairymen, sheep and goat herders and other persons exposed to infected dusts. Since 1948, when it was shown that formalinized vaccine prepared from infected yolk-sac tissue elicited specific complement-fixing antibodies in human beings (Smadel, Snyder and Robbins, 1948), immunization of personnel has become an accepted practice in laboratories dealing with *R. burneti*. In the single report which has appeared on the efficacy of such a procedure, Meiklejohn and Lennette (1950) are justifiably cautious in interpreting their observation that no clinical cases occurred among 50 vaccinated workers in the Q fever laboratory although 6 of these persons apparently underwent an inapparent infection. The single case occurring among their large group actively engaged in studies on Q fever developed in a nonvaccinated serologist within a month after beginning work; she apparently became infected from a sample of blood submitted for complement-fixation tests. The author is unaware of any clinical case of Q fever which has occurred among properly vaccinated workers in Q fever laboratories which is in sharp contrast with the high infection rate in the unvaccinated. Neither controlled studies with volunteers nor field trials have been perfomed with the present Q fever vaccine, and, until data from such tests become available, it will be difficult to evaluate its usefulness.

Pasteurization or boiling of milk from cows, goats and sheep is indicated in areas when Q fever occurs. Pasteurization by the vat-holding method using the time-temperature combination required by California law may not be adequate to destroy *R. burneti* (Huebner et al., 1949; Marmion et al., 1951). The British workers point out that *R. burneti* is somewhat more heat resistant than is *Mycobacterium tuberculosis* and that heating at 161° F. offers less margin of safety in dealing with the former than with the latter.

Rather extensive hospital experience has indicated that danger of transmission of the disease by patients is so slight that quarantine and extensive isolation precautions are unwarranted; nevertheless, careful sterilization of the sputum and excreta is recommended. Precautions must be taken in the handling of bodies of patients dead of Q fever. Marmion and Stoker (1950) trace to such a source the infection of a nurse, two pathologists and an autopsy-room attendant. Moreover, the disposal of carcasses of dead experimental animals requires care, since an outbreak in a rendering plant was connected with the processing of discarded guinea pigs dead from experimental Q fever (Feldman, Silverman and Adair, 1950).

REFERENCES

Bell, J. A., Beck, M. D., and Huebner, R. J., 1950, Epidemiologic studies of Q fever in southern California. J. Am. Med. Assn., *142*, 868-872.

Bengtson, I. A., 1941a, Immunological relationships between the rickettsiae of Australia and American "Q" fever. Pub. Health Rep., *56*, 272-281.

Bengtson, I. A., 1941b, Complement fixation in "Q" fever. Proc. Soc. Exp. Biol. and Med., *46*, 665-668.

Bengtson, I. A., 1941c, Studies on active and passive immunity in "Q" fever infected and immunized guinea pigs. Pub. Health Rep., *56*, 327-345.

Berge, T. O., and Lennette, E. H., 1952, World distribution of Q fever, human, animal and arthropod infection. To be published.

Bickel, G., and Plattner, H., 1951, La terramycine en thérapeutique. Schweiz. med. Wchnschr., *81*, 1-4.

Blanc, G., Bruneau, J., Poitrot, R., and Delage, B., 1948, Quelques données sur la Q. fever (maladie de Derrick-Burnet) expérimentale. Bull. Acad. Nat. Med., *132*, 243-250.

Blanc, G., Martin, L.-A., and Bruneau, J., 1949, Q. fever expérimentale de quelques animaux domestiques. Ann. Inst. Pasteur, *77*, 99-107.

Burnet, F. M., and Freeman, M., 1937, Experimental studies on the virus of "Q" fever. Med. J. Australia, *2*, 299-305.

Burnet, F. M., and Freeman, M., 1938, The rickettsia of "Q" fever: further experimental studies. Med. J. Australia, *1*, 296-298.

Burnet, F. M., and Freeman, M., 1939, A comparative study of rickettsial strains from an infection of ticks in Montana (United States of America) and from "Q" fever. Med. J. Australia, *2*, 887-891.

Caminopétros, J., 1948, Q fever, a respiratory human epidemic disease in the Mediterranean area, determine a milk-borne infection from goats and sheep. Proc. 4th Internat. Congr. Trop. Med. and Malaria, *1*, 441-449.

Clark, W. H., Lennette, E. H., and Meiklejohn, G., 1951a, Q fever in California. III. Aureomycin in the therapy of Q fever. Arch. Int. Med., *87*, 204-217.

Clark, W. H., Lennette, E. H., Railsback, O. C., and Romer, M. S., 1951b, Q fever in California. VII. Clinical features in one hundred eighty cases. Arch. Int. Med., *88*, 155-167.

The Commission on Acute Respiratory Diseases, 1946a, Epidemics of Q fever among troops returning from Italy in the spring of 1945, II. Epidemiological studies. Am. J. Hyg., *44*, 88-102.

The Commission on Acute Respiratory Diseases, 1946b, A laboratory outbreak of Q fever caused by the Balkan grippe strain of *Rickettsia burneti*. Am. J. Hyg., *44*, 123-157.

The Commission on Acute Respiratory Diseases, 1946c, Identification and characteristics of the Balkan grippe strain of *Rickettsia burneti*. Am. J. Hyg., *44*, 110-122.

Cox, H. R., 1939, Studies of a filter-passing infectious agent isolated from ticks. V. Further attempts to cultivate in cell-free media. Suggested classification. Pub. Health Rep., *54*, 1822-1827.

Cox, H. R., and Bell, E. J., 1939, The Cultivation of *Rickettsia diaporica* in tissue culture and in the tissues of developing chick embryos. Pub. Health Rep., *54*, 2171-2178.

Davis, G. E., and Cox, H. R., 1938, A filter-passing infectious agent isolated from ticks. I. Isolation from *Dermacentor andersoni*, reactions in animals, and filtration experiments. Pub. Health Rep., *53*, 2259-2267.

DeLay, P. D., Lennette, E. H., and DeOme, K. B., 1950, Q fever in California. II. Recovery of *Coxiella burneti* from naturally-infected air-borne dust. J. Immunol., *65*, 211-220.

Derrick, E. H., 1937, "Q" fever, a new fever entity: clinical features, diagnosis and laboratory investigation. Med. J. Australia, *2*, 281-299.

Derrick, E. H., 1939, *Rickettsia burneti:* The cause of "Q" fever. Med. J. Australia, *1*, 14.

Derrick, E. H., 1944, The epidemiology of Q fever. J. Hyg., *43*, 357-361.

Dyer, R. E., 1939, Similarity of Australian "Q" fever and a disease caused by an infectious agent isolated from ticks in Montana. Pub. Health Rep., *54*, 1229-1237.

Dyer, R. E., Topping, N. H., and Bengtson, I. A., 1940, An institutional outbreak of pneumonitis. II. Isolation and identification of causative agent. Pub. Health Rep., *55*, 1945-1954.

Feinstein, M., Yesner, R., and Marks, J. L., 1946, Epidemics of Q fever among troops returning from Italy in the spring of 1945. I. Clinical aspects of the epidemic at Camp Patrick Henry, Virginia. Am. J. Hyg., *44*, 72-87.

Feldman, H. A., Silverman, A. C., and Adair, C. V., 1950, An epidemic of Q fever among employees of a rendering plant in Syracuse, New York. J. Clin. Investig., *29*, 812 (Abstr.).

Harman, J. B., 1949, Q fever in Great Britain. Clinical account of eight cases. Lancet, *2*, 1028-1030.

Hornibrook, J. W., and Nelson, K. R., 1940, An institutional outbreak of pneumonitis. I. Epidemiological and clinical studies. Pub. Health Rep., *55*, 1936-1944.

Huebner, R. J., Jellison, W. L., Beck, M. D., Parker, R. R., and Shepard, C. C., 1948, Q fever studies in southern California. I. Recovery of *Rickettsia burneti* from raw milk. Pub. Health Rep., *63*, 214-222.

Huebner, R. J., Jellison, W. L., Beck, M. D., and Wilcox, F. P., 1949, Q fever studies in southern California. III. Effects of pasteurization on survival of *Coxiella burneti* in naturally infected milk. Pub. Health Rep., *64*, 499-511.

Lennette, E. H., Clark, W. H., and Dean, B. H., 1949, Sheep and goats in the epidemiology of Q fever in northern California. Am. J. Trop. Med., *29*, 527-541.

Lennette, E. H., and Clark, W. H., 1951, Observations on the epidemiology of Q fever in northern California. J. Am. Med. Assn., *145*, 306-309.

Lennette, E. H., and Welsh, H. H., 1951, Q fever in California. X. Recovery of *Coxiella burneti* from the air of premises harboring infected goats. Am. J. Hyg., *54*, 44-49.

Lillie, R. D., 1942, Pathologic histology in guinea pigs following intraperitoneal inoculation with the virus of "Q" fever. Pub. Health Rep., *57*, 296-306.

Lillie, R. D., Perrin, T. L., and Armstrong, C., 1941, An institutional outbreak of pneumonitis. III. Histopathology in man and rhesus monkeys in the pneumonitis due to the virus of "Q" fever. Pub. Health Rep., *56*, 149-155.

MacCallum, F. O., Marmion, B. P., and Stoker, M. G. P., 1949, Q fever in Great Britain. Isolation of *Rickettsia burneti* from an indigenous case. Lancet, *2*, 1026-1027.

Marmion, B. P., and Stoker, M. G. P., 1950, Q fever in Great Britain. Epidemiology of an outbreak. Lancet, *2*, 611-616.

Marmion, B. P., MacCallum, F. O., Rowlands, A., and Thiel, C. C., 1951, The effect of pasteurization on milk containing *Rickettsia burneti*. Month. Bull. Min. Health, *10*, 119-128.

Meiklejohn, G., and Lennette, E. H., 1950, Q fever in California. I. Observations on vaccination of human beings. Am. J. Hyg., *52*, 54-64.

Oliphant, J. W., Gordon, D. A., Meis, A., and Parker, R. R., 1949, Q fever in laundry workers, presumably transmitted from contaminated clothing. Am. J. Hyg., *49*, 76-82.

Parker, R. R., and Davis, G. E., 1938, A filter-passing infectious agent isolated from ticks. II. Transmission by *Dermacentor andersoni*. Pub. Health Rep., *53*, 2267-2270.

Parker, R. R., and Kohls, G. M., 1943, American Q fever: the occurrence of *Rickettsia diaporica* in *Amblyomma americanum* in eastern Texas. Pub. Health Rep., *58*, 1510-1511.

Parker, R. R., and Steinhaus, E. A., 1943, American and Australian Q fevers: persistence of the infectious agents in guinea pig tissues after defervescence. Pub. Health Rep., *58*, 523-527.

Plotz, H., Smadel, J. E., Anderson, T. F., and Chambers, L. A., 1943, Morphological structure of rickettsiae, J. Exp. Med., *77*, 355-358.

Robbins, F. C., Gauld, R. L., and Warner, F. B., 1946, Q fever in the Mediterranean area: report of its occurrence in Allied troops. II. Epidemiology. Am. J. Hyg., *44*, 23-50.

Robbins, F. C., and Ragan, C. A., 1946, Q fever in the Mediterranean area: report of its occurrence in Allied troops. I. Clinical features of the disease. Am. J. Hyg., *44*, 6-22.

Robbins, F. C., Rustigian, R., Snyder, M. J., and Smadel, J. E., 1946, Q fever in the Mediterranean area: report of its occurrence in Allied troops. III. The etiological agent. Am. J. Hyg., *44*, 51-63.

Sigel, M. M., Scott, T. F. McN., and Henle, W., 1950, Q fever in a wool and hair processing plant. Am. J. Pub. Health., *40*, 524-532.

Smadel, J. E., Jackson, E. B., and Cruise, A. B., 1949, Chloromycetin in experimental rickettsial infections. J. Immunol., *62*, 49-65.

Smadel, J. E., Jackson, E. B., and Ley, H. L., Jr., 1950, Terramycin as a rickettsiostatic agent and its usefulness in patients with scrub typhus. Ann. New York Acad. Sci., *53*, 375-384.

Smadel, J. E., Snyder, M. J., and Robbins, F. C., 1948, Vaccination against Q fever. Am. J. Hyg., *47*, 71-81.

Topping, N. H., Shepard, C. C., and Huebner, R. J., 1946, Q fever: an immunological comparison of strains. Am. J. Hyg., *44*, 173-182.

Topping, N. H., Shepard, C. C., and Irons, J. V., 1947, Q fever in the United States. I. Epidemiologic studies of an outbreak among stock handlers and slaughterhouse workers. J. Am. Med. Assn., *133*, 813-815.

Wegmann, T., 1948, Ueber eine Q-fever (Queenslandfieber) — epidemie in Graubunden. Schweiz. med. Wchnschr., *78*, 529-531.

Wong, S. C., and Cox, H. R., 1948, Action of aureomycin against experimental rickettsial and viral infections. Ann. New York Acad. Sci., *51*, 290-305.

Zarafonetis, C. J. D., and Bates, R. C., 1950, Q fever: report of a case treated with chloromycetin. Ann. Int. Med., *32*, 982-987.

JOEL WARREN, ᴘʜ.ᴅ.

Army Medical Service Graduate School

39

Infections of Minor Importance

Diseases of minor importance will be discussed briefly in this chapter. Certain of them, e.g., trench fever and viral gastroenteritis, usually occur as epidemics. Others represent diseases of animals in which human infection is accidental. Still others, e.g., warts, are extremely common in man but rarely produce serious illness.

FOOT-AND-MOUTH DISEASE

(Synonyms: *Fièvre aphteuse, Maul-und Klauenseuche,* aphthous fever, epizootic aphthae, epizootic stomatitis)

Foot-and-mouth disease is a highly contagious infection of cloven-footed animals, especially of cattle, pigs, sheep, and goats, and is rarely transmitted to human beings who become infected by ingestion of virus-contaminated food, by handling the active agent, or through contact with affected animals. Since epizootics of the disease are rare in the United States, the malady in human beings in this country is uncommon. The disease, however, is now endemic in Mexico.

The disease in lower animals is characterized by fever, salivation and the appearance of large, coalescing vesicles in the mucous membranes of the mouth, tongue and lips, and in the skin of the hoofs, dew claws, interdigital areas, and udder. The disease in human beings manifests itself, after an incubation period of 2 to 18 days, by fever, salivation, vesicles in the mucous membranes of the mouth, pharynx, lips, and tongue and in the skin of the soles, palms, digits and interdigital areas. Within a few days, the vesicles rupture leaving ulcers with undermined, irregular edges. Eventually healing is complete without scar formation (Flaum, 1939). The histopathologic picture of experimentally induced lesions consists of hyperkeratosis, swollen and hyperplastic cells of the Malpighian layer which disintegrate to form loculated vesicles, intranuclear inclusions in cells near the vesicles, and infiltration of adjacent tissues with polymorphonuclear leukocytes. The disease can be transmitted experimentally to the guinea pig by cutaneous and subcutaneous inoculation of the foot pads. Rabbits, rats, mice, dogs and cats are irregularly susceptible, while fowl (except ducks), ferrets and horses are usually resistant. The resistance of the horse is of prime importance, for it serves to differentiate the virus of foot-and-mouth disease from that of equine vesicular stomatitis.

The diameter of the virus as determined by filtration through gradocol membranes is 10 to 12 millimicrons, while electron microscopy and ultracentrifugation indicate the average particle size to be larger, 20 to 30 millimicrons. The virus in tissues is fairly resistant to disinfectants; the most practicable virucidal agent is 0.5 to 2 per cent sodium hydroxide (Olitsky, Traum and Schoening, 1928). The active agent is stable in two pH zones, namely, 2.5-3.5 and 6.5-10.0. It can be grown in tissue cultures only when tissue from susceptible species is used. There are three immunologically distinct strains. During convalescence, human beings and lower animals produce antibodies specific for the particular strain inducing the infection.

Diagnosis is accomplished by the isolation and identification of the causal agent, and by serologic tests. There is no specific treatment. Since the virus is found in the blood, saliva, urine, feces, milk, and vesicular lesions of infected animals, such materials, as well as infected fodder, hair, bones, hides, meat, and dairy products, play an important role in the spread of infection. The boiling or pasteurizing of farm products under suspicion should be adequate for control of the disease in a human population. Ruthless slaughter of susceptible hosts is the most successful means of controlling epizootics; a less successful method consists of using hyperimmune serum and vaccines (Waldmann, 1938). A recently developed method for preparing large quantities of vaccine involves mass cultivation of the virus in explants of the tongue epithelium of cattle (Frenkel, 1950). Unfortunately, the best vaccines produce an immunity which lasts only 4 to 6 months and repeated vaccination is necessary.

NEWCASTLE DISEASE

(SYNONYMS: Avian pseudoplague, avian pneumoencephalitis)

Newcastle disease is an epizootic infection of fowl characterized by viremia and signs of involvement of the respiratory, gastro-intestinal and central nervous systems. The disease has been recognized as a distinct clinical and pathologic entity since the work of Doyle (1927) and has been encountered in continental Europe, England, Asia, Africa, and Australia. It was first recognized in the United States as pneumoencephalitis, in California (Beach, 1946); it is known to have reached the East coast by 1944. Beach (1944) showed that the viruses of Newcastle disease and pneumoencephalitis are immunologically identi-

cal. The present opinion is that pneumonic and nervous signs dominate the American type of infection, while respiratory and gastro-intestinal signs are the most obvious in the Old World type (Brandly et al., 1946a). The malady occasionally attacks human beings who handle infected fowl or work with the virus, manifesting itself chiefly as a superficial conjunctivitis; at least 5 proved (Burnet, 1943; Anderson, 1946; Jungherr, Luginbuhl and Kilham, 1949) and 17 suspected cases (Yatom, 1946) have been reported.

Newcastle disease in fowl usually has an incubation period of 4 to 11 days. Onset is sudden with drowsiness, rapid respiration and fever. Then, diarrhea sets in, brown fluid or saliva drools from the beak, a thick mucous discharge from the nose appears, and respiratory distress, cyanosis and petechiae of the wattles and comb occur. Opisthotonos, convulsions, ascending paresis, and abnormal movements have also been observed. Death ensues, usually on the sixth to eighth day; in the United States the mortality rate is comparatively low in adult birds. The disease in fowl produces multiple focal necroses in the viscera and hemorrhages, especially in the respiratory and alimentary tracts; at times an interstitial pneumonitis is observed. The CNS may show localized meningo-encephalitis characterized by areas of necrosis of the ground substance, neuronal necrosis and degeneration, and small hemorrhages.

The proved cases in man occurred in laboratory or poultry workers handling the virus, in whom the incubation period varied from a few hours to two days. The disease manifests itself as a unilateral superficial conjunctivitis without involvement of the cornea; or a syndrome, consisting of conjunctivitis, preauricular lymphadenitis, headache, malaise and chills, without significant rise in temperature, may occur. All reported patients have recovered completely within 1 or 2 weeks.

The natural disease is observed in chickens, turkeys, pheasants, guinea fowl, sparrows, crows, francolins and parrots; experimental infection has been achieved in chick embryos, ducks, geese, pigeons and several varieties of wild birds. Intracerebral inoculation of the virus into mice, hamsters, cotton rats and rhesus monkeys causes a meningo-encephalitis which becomes increasingly severe with repeated passage and adaptation to these hosts (Wenner, 1950). Large doses of virus given to mice intranasally produce consolidation of the lungs, but it is not possible to transfer the disease from mouse to mouse in this manner. Ferrets show no apparent malady after intranasal application of the active agent but do develop specific antibody. Guinea pigs, rabbits and pigs are resistant. Transmission of the disease can be effected by means of blood, brain, viscera, oral and nasal secretions, and feces. All routes of inoculation, except the intramuscular which may be followed by irregular results, can be employed successfully. The diameter of the virus as determined by filtration through gradocol membranes is 80 to 120 millimicrons, and 115 millimicrons (Bang, 1946) by electron micrography. The virus particle is filamentous (Bang, 1946) or spermlike (Cunha et al., 1947). According to the latter workers, it is difficult to estimate accurately the size of the active agent. They mention the following figures: width of head 70 millimicrons, length of head 180 millimicrons, and length of tail 500 millimicrons. It is said to be filterable through Berkefeld V, N and W candles, Chamberland L_3 and L_5 filters, and Seitz pads. It is inactivated at 60° C. for 30 minutes and at 55° C. for 45 minutes, by photodynamic action of methylene blue, by ultraviolet radiation, by 1 :5,000 dilution of formalin, and by N/50 sodium hydroxide in 1 hour but not by N/25 hydrochloric acid. Newcastle virus remains active at pH 4 for at least a week (Brandly et al., 1946b). The virus is preserved in 50 per cent glycerol, by being kept frozen at −70° C., and by lyophilization.

The virus multiplies readily in embryonated eggs, and allantoic fluid from infected embryos is capable of causing agglutination of fowl erythrocytes and also those of certain other species (Burnet, 1943). Infected allantoic fluid will also fix complement in the presence of immune serum. Hemagglutination caused by Newcastle disease virus is inhibited by serum containing antibodies against the active agent. The hemagglutination reaction has made possible the development of simple and rapid in-vitro technics by means of which the presence and the concentration of the virus as well as specific antibodies against it can be determined. This hemagglutination is in some respects analogous to that caused by certain other viruses, e.g., those of influenza and mumps (Burnet, 1945). Further details regarding the reaction are given in the chapter on Hemagglutination. Human erythrocytes treated with Newcastle disease virus are agglutinated by specific immune serum against this agent and also by serum of some patients with infectious mononucleosis (Burnet and Anderson, 1946; Florman, 1949). The recent demonstration that many persons convalescing from mumps develop antibodies to the Newcastle disease virus indicates some common antigenicity between these agents (Jungherr, Luginbuhl and Kilham, 1949). Neutralizing antibodies against Newcastle disease virus develop following infection with the agent in man and susceptible lower animals. They are produced also by animals which are resistant to infection following parenteral injection of the virus. Specific antibodies can be detected, and their titer can be determined by means of the hemagglutination-inhibition test, the virus-neutralization test in chick embryos, or the complement-fixation test.

The diagnosis of Newcastle disease in human beings is made by (1) a history of exposure to the virus or to fowl ill with the disease; (2) isolation of the virus from the conjunctival exudate and its identification by means of the hemagglutination-inhibition test; and (3) determination of the development of specific neutralizing antibody by tests on paired sera collected from patients during the acute and convalescent stages of the disease. Because of the presence in human serum of a heat-labile nonspecific neutralizing factor it is essential that suspect sera be inactivated at 56° C. for 30 minutes before being used in neutralization tests (Ginsberg and Horsfall, 1949; Howitt, 1950). There is no specific treatment available. Penicillin has no effect on the virus.

The few human cases reported point to the fact that exposure to the virus or to affected fowl is essential for infection. In fowl the disease is ordinarily conveyed by contact. A natural resistance develops with age, and passive immunity can be conferred upon a chick by way of the egg yolk of an immune dam (Brandly et al., 1946a). The prevention of the disease in man depends on protection from infection when exposed to the virus or affected fowl. The prevention of the disease in birds has been shown to be possible through the use of formolized or irradiated vaccines, or, if a stronger and more durable immunity is desired, by the employment of such vaccines, followed by a vaccine consisting of modified, active virus (Brandly et al., 1946c).

OVINE PUSTULAR DERMATITIS

(SYNONYMS: Contagious pustular dermatitis of sheep, contagious ecthyma, infectious labial dermatitis, "scabby mouth")

Ovine pustular dermatitis is a worldwide infectious disease of sheep and goats characterized by a vesicopustular eruption usually confined to the lips and adjacent tissues, but sometimes it attacks other nonwoolbearing parts of the body and causes serious systemic disturbances. It is a nosologic entity distinct from vaccinia, variola and sheep-pox. The mortality rate in sheep varies from 5 to 60 per cent. The virus was discovered in 1928, passes through Berkefeld V and Chamberland L₂ candles, and can be preserved in 50 per cent glycerol

and by desiccation. It has been adapted to guinea pigs, rabbits, dogs, calves, goats and macaque monkeys. A solid immunity can be achieved in sheep by vaccination with active virus.

The disease is transmissible to man in whom it appears as a mild exanthematous malady. Recently Carne et al (1946) reported the occurrence of the infection in 3 persons who were in close contact with affected lambs and from whom the virus was recovered and identified by animal passage and immunologic tests. The period of incubation was 3 to 6 days. The lesions were limited to the skin of the hands in which were noted papules that attained a diameter of 5 to 10 mm. within 14 days; local tenderness, lymphadenitis, headache, and malaise occurred. The papules exhibited central softening with serous exudate and disappeared within three or four weeks. The serous exudate applied to the scarified skin of lambs induced the typical ovine disease.

INFECTIOUS ANEMIA OF HORSES

(SYNONYMS: Swamp fever of horses, pernicious anemia of horses, equine "malaria")

Infectious anemia of horses may be acute or chronic and is characterized by viremia, fever, progressive anemia, edema, and emaciation. It is widely distributed over the world and is rarely transmitted to man. The acute disease in horses endures for 4 days to three weeks, while the chronic type may last for years, during which time the virus may be found in the blood. The disease in man manifests itself by fever, anemia, diarrhea, nephritic pain, and viremia. The blood of one person was infective for horses over a period of three years. The virus was discovered by Vallée and Carré (1904); its diameter as determined by filtration through gradocol membranes is 18 to 50 millimicrons; it is inactivated by heating to 60° C. for one hour. Equine animals are susceptible, while ordinary laboratory animals are resistant. Transmission can be effected by the parenteral injection of infectious material, by biting flies (*Stomoxys calcitrans*), or by virus coming in contact with abraded skin or mucous membranes (Stein et al., 1944). The idea, formerly held, that infection by ordinary contact or feeding is possible, has not been substantiated experimentally. It has, however, been demonstrated that infected mares may have virus in their milk and that suckling foals, although inapparently harboring the disease, may still be susceptible to experimental infection by a peripheral route. There is no specific treatment, and control measures consist of isolation or extermination of affected animals. It is important to note that all antisera made in equine animals for use in man or equine animals must be produced in a manner to eliminate the possibility of their containing the virus of infectious anemia in an active state.

WARTS: VERRUCAE

There are several types of wart (van Rooyen and Rhodes, 1940) which vary in appearance, location and preference of age. The types usually recognized are common warts, digitate warts, juvenile (plane) warts, filiform warts, genital warts and laryngeal papillomata. Common warts usually occur as discrete, oval, gray, dry growths on the hands. Juvenile warts are small, flat growths usually occurring in groups on the face. Digitate warts are growths broken into folds and are found on the face and scalp. Filiform warts are delicate threadlike growths on the eyelids and neck. Genital warts are small, gray, rough nodules which appear in the coronal sulcus of the penis or on the labia and around the vaginal orifice. During pregnancy they increase in size but become smaller after its termination. In the female, because of the moisture around the genital regions. warts may become large and secondarily infected with bacteria. Laryngeal papil-

lomata are flat or pedunculated and occur singly or in groups; they may recur after removal.

It has been definitely shown that an agent filterable through Berkefeld candles of all grades of porosity is responsible for warts. The virus survives a temperature of 50° C. for 30 minutes. Furthermore, most workers believe that a single etiologic agent is responsible for the different types of wart mentioned. Recent examination of extracts of certain papillomata of the skin by means of the electron microscope have revealed viruslike particles (Strauss, Bunting and Melnick, 1950). These particles tended to aggregate in rafts or masses with the appearance of crystals, and were usually associated with growths in which intranuclear inclusion bodies were also present. Practically all the experimental work has been done with human volunteers (Wile and Kingery, 1919; Kingery, 1921). Laryngeal papillomata are the only warts that have been transmitted to lower animals and this was accomplished by injecting the infectious material into the vaginal mucosa of bitches. Warts of dogs and cattle are not transmissible to man. The incubation period in the experimental disease has been as follows in reported experiments: 1, 6, 8, and 20 months, respectively.

If warts are made to bleed, new lesions may occur in neighboring parts of the skin. They are spread by direct or indirect contact in barber shops, bathing pools, chiropodists' offices, hairdressing establishments, and other places of similar character. The epithelium is the only tissue involved by some warts and shows a hyperkeratosis and many mitotic figures. In some warts the deeper tissues are involved and at times show an inflammatory reaction. As a rule, no specific inclusions have been found. Warts usually disappear spontaneously, and there is evidence that some immunity is present in a patient after recovery. Many kinds of treatment have been devised for warts, but none is specific.

TRENCH FEVER

(SYNONYMS: Wolhynian fever, His-Werner disease, shin fever, shank fever)

Trench fever (Swift, 1919-1920) was characterized by sudden onset, chilly sensations, headache, dizziness, postorbital pain, nystagmus, injection of conjunctivae, severe pains in legs and back, relapsing fever, tachycardia, large spleen, and several crops of erythematous macules or papules on the chest, abdomen and back. About one half of the patients had only one bout of fever, while the others had 3 to 8 relapses. The incubation period in most of the human volunteers ranged from 14 to 30 days. Most patients recovered in 5 or 6 weeks; others were sick for several months and in some instances for a year or two. White blood cell counts were not characteristic and varied from 4,000 to 27,000 per c.mm. The disease was never fatal and what is known concerning the pathologic picture was determined from biopsies of skin which showed inflammation around the small blood vessels without involvement of the walls of the vessels as is the case in typhus fever and Rocky Mountain spotted fever.

The disease was unknown until 1915, but during World War I it involved at least 1,000,000 men. With the exception of influenza, it caused the loss of more man-days in the armed forces than did any other sickness. It is believed to have come from Russia and is known to have occurred in England, France, Flanders, Salonica, Mesopotamia, Italy, Germany and Austria. In the years immediately following World War I the disease ceased to be recognized, but it reappeared in epidemic form on the eastern European front in World War II, particularly in Jugoslavia and the Ukraine.

Several commissions (Strong et al., 1918) were appointed to investigate trench fever and the combined results of the experimental work showed that none of the usual laboratory animals was susceptible to the disease. By use of human volunteers, it was shown that the etiologic agent was present in blood, sputum and urine. In 3 of 5 experiments the agent was passed with difficulty through Chamberland L filters. It resisted a temperature of 60° C. moist heat for 30 minutes, but was inactivated by a temperature of 70° C. moist heat for a similar length of time. The body louse, *Pediculus humanus,* var. *corporis,* was shown to be a vector; it became capable of transmitting the disease 5 to 10 days after having fed upon a patient. The etiologic agent was demonstrated in the lice and in their feces. Since the disease was transmitted by bites, it is obvious that the infectious agent was either in the saliva or in the material regurgitated during the process of biting. Human volunteers were also infected by bringing the causative agent in contact with abraded skin. Once a louse had been infected, it excreted the active agent for the remainder of its life which was not shortened as a result of the infection. The agent was not transmitted to larvae through eggs. Small bodies similar to rickettsiae were found in the guts of infected lice and in their feces, and were not present in the absence of infection. Many observations of this kind induced most investigators to place trench fever in the rickettsial group of diseases. The etiologic agent was picked up from patients by lice during the first few weeks of the disease. A patient who had completely recovered was no longer a source of danger. Some patients had a chronic infection, and in several instances lice became infected by biting such patients as late as the 300th and 443rd day after onset of illness. The immunity that developed was considered to endure for only a short time, viz., several months.

Mooser and his associates (Mooser, Leeman, Chao and Gubler, 1948; Mooser, Marti and Leeman, 1949) who investigated trench fever as it occurred in World War II, appear to have substantiated the rickettsial nature of the disease. They were able to isolate a strain of rickettsia, designated as *R. quintana,* by feeding lice on a trench fever patient in Jugoslavia. Although attempts to infect mice, rats, guinea pigs, hamsters or embryonated eggs with the agent were fruitless, lesions could be produced by the inoculation of infected lice intracutaneously or into the anterior optic chamber of rabbits. When louse feces containing *R. quintana* were rubbed into the scarified skin of human volunteers a disease identical with trench fever resulted. Mooser and his associates prepared an attenuated skin-test antigen from saline suspensions of desiccated infected intestinal tracts of lice. Intradermal inoculation of a nonimmune person with this material resulted in a vesicle at the site which developed into an escharlike scab and persisted for many weeks. The lesion was frequently accompanied by a rickettsemia and clinical trench fever. Persons recovered from trench fever developed only a transient papule.

Although as yet untried in trench fever, the present armamentarium of insecticides, e.g., DDT, for louse control, together with the effectiveness of several antibiotics in rickettsial diseases provide promising methods for control and treatment; thus, it appears unlikely that the disease will again appear as serious epidemics.

MOLLUSCUM CONTAGIOSUM

Molluscum contagiosum has been known as a clinical entity since 1817. The incubation period as determined by inoculation of human volunteers has been stated by three sets of investigators to be 50, 14 to 25, and 35 days, respectively. The disease is characterized by the formation of multiple discrete nodules, limited to the epidermal layer of the skin, with an average diameter of 2 millimeters. The lesions may appear on the face, arms, legs, buttocks, genitalia, or scalp; rarely in the mucous membranes of the mouth; and never on the soles and palms. The nodules are usually pearly white and painless, and at the top of each there is often an opening through which a small, white core can be seen. Some of the lesions may become secondarily infected with bac-

teria and break down. The disease is chronic and several months may be required for recovery.

Lesions involve circumscribed areas of the epidermis which become thickened by hyperplasia and hypertrophy of infected epithelial cells. In the germinal layer, hyperplasia is evidenced by an increase in mitotic figures. In cells above the germinal layer, definite pathologic changes in the nuclei and cytoplasm become obvious. As the surface of the epidermis is approached, these changes become more and more marked so that eventually each cell is many times larger than normal and the cytoplasm is filled with a large, hyaline, acidophilic, granular mass, known as the molluscum body, which pushes the nucleus to the edge of the cell. A fully developed lesion is usually loculated, and there is very little reaction in the corium unless a nodule is secondarily infected by bacteria.

The disease is not a serious one but is of particular interest because of discussions concerning the architecture and significance of the molluscum body which at one time was considered a protozoan parasite. According to Goodpasture and his associates (Goodpasture and King, 1927; Goodpasture and Woodruff, 1931), the molluscum body is surrounded by desiccated cytoplasmic protein which extends into the structure to form trabeculae. The covering and trabeculae can be digested away by trypsin; this procedure leaves a sticky, gelatinous mass, within which numerous elementary bodies, first described by Lipschütz (1907), are embedded. According to van Rooyen (1938; 1939), the molluscum body is not a mixture of cytoplasmic material and virus elementary bodies but constitutes a foreign entity in the cell resulting from the growth of an elementary body which passes through developmental stages finally to form a large structure surrounded by a membrane with an operculum at one pole and filled with elementary bodies. He believes that this structure has certain resemblances to the sporangium of a fungus, for example, *Rino-*

sporidium seeberi, which causes polyps in the nasal mucous membranes. Thin sections of molluscum contagiosum lesions have been studied by means of the electron microscope and histochemical technics (Rake and Blank, 1950; Banfield, Bunting, Strauss and Melnick, 1951). In the early infected cell, elementary bodies are scattered in a random fashion throughout the cytoplasm. These later become aggregated and surrounded by a large network of spongy matrix. In the larger inclusion bodies this matrix is divided into cavities in which are clustered numerous elementary bodies. Within the elementary bodies are still smaller particles, with diameters of 80 to 100 mμ, which may represent some simpler structural unit. Molluscum bodies have diameters ranging from 20 to 30 μ (Lipschütz, 1907), while an elementary body is brick-shaped and has average diameters of 200 x 300 mμ (Strauss et al., 1949). The latter stains well by Morosow's method (1926). Elementary bodies are said by various workers (van Rooyen and Rhodes, 1940) to pass through Chamberland L$_1$ and Berkefeld V filters. The virus retains its activity in 50 per cent glycerol for at least a month.

Man is the only known host; attempts to infect monkeys, apes, sheep, fowl, rabbits, guinea pigs, and mice have been unsuccessful. Molluscum contagiosum has a worldwide distribution, is particularly prevalent in certain areas, for example, Edinburgh; it is seen most frequently in children, but persons of all ages may be attacked; it is transmitted by personal contact or by fomites. There is no specific treatment. Some workers have stated that x-rays lead to rapid healing of the lesions; others have noted that healing takes place following bacterial invasion.

EPIDEMIC VIRAL GASTRO-ENTERITIS

(Synonyms: Acute infectious gastroenteritis, winter vomiting disease)

Epidemic viral gastro-enteritis is a wide-spread, nonseasonal communicable disease or family of diseases of man in which one of the causative agents has been shown to be a virus. The clinical and epidemiologic features of epidemic viral gastro-enteritis as it occurs in the United States and abroad have been well delineated (Cook and Marmion, 1947; Gordon, Ingraham and Korns, 1947; Reimann, Hodges and Price, 1945). Although its frequent appearance in public institutions and small communities has stimulated the majority of the reports, cases may occur sporadically or in small endemic foci. It affects persons of all ages with some or all of the following symptoms: anorexia, vomiting, gastric pain, diarrhea, fever, dizziness, generalized muscular aching, chills and malaise. The onset is usually very acute with vomiting and/or diarrhea. Thus, in an epidemic some individuals may have persistent vomiting without diarrhea, while others suffer an almost intractable fecal incontinence. The appearance of the vomitus or stools is not remarkable and may differ from one outbreak to another. Extremely high temperatures or respiratory signs are not usually observed. The disease is of short duration, rarely lasting longer than 2 or 3 days, and, like its onset, recovery is usually sudden. Fatalities are infrequent and are confined to aged and debilitated persons.

Since repeated bacteriologic studies of these outbreaks have been generally fruitless, a viral cause of this syndrome has long been postulated, and at least one causative virus has been isolated. Gordon and associates (1947, 1949) found that volunteers who ingested filtrates of stool from patients with epidemic gastro-enteritis developed the syndrome within a short time and that the illness could be serially transmitted in human beings. The agent failed to infect chick embryos. Human reinfection experiments indicated that while an attack conferred immunity this may be of very short duration.

A diagnosis of epidemic viral gastroenteritis is made on the basis of a clinical picture unlike that of bacterial gastroenteritis or dysentery, its infectiousness and rapid spread within a focus, and on negative bacteriologic findings. There is no specific therapy. Since it appears that entrance of the virus into the nose or the mouth results in infection, control measures involve strict attention to isolation and the general sanitary measures applicable to highly contagious diseases.

It is unknown whether or not epidemic viral gastro-enteritis is related to the more severe epidemic diarrhea of the newborn. It is noteworthy that in the latter disease adult infection is rare, the course is more severe, and fatal cases are not uncommon. Search for an enterotropic virus in such outbreaks has yielded two agents. Light and Hodes (1943) produced a transmissable, bloody, mucoid diarrhea in calves by the intranasal administration of stool filtrates from sick infants. Recovered calves could not be re-infected, nor were the stools of normal infants or calves able to produce the disease. [The latter fact may be of significance in differentiating this virus from that described by Baker (1943) as causing diarrhea in calves.] Buddingh and Dodd (1944) investigated the etiology of nonfatal sporadic stomatitis and diarrhea of infants. A filterable virus was detected in throat-washings and stools which was capable of causing an iritis and conjunctivitis in the eye of the rabbit. It does not appear to be herpes simplex virus on the basis of the nonkeratitic nature and short duration of the ocular lesions in rabbits, and the fact that the sera of convalescent patients neutralize the virus but fail to neutralize herpes virus. Buddingh and Dodd also present evidence that adults in close contact with the disease may become asymptomatic temporary carriers.

CAT-SCRATCH DISEASE

(SYNONYMS: Cat-scratch fever, benign lymphoreticulosis)

Cat-scratch disease is a nonfatal, systemic illness characterized by malaise, fever and lymphadenitis; it is caused by a virus closely related to the psittacosis-lymphogranuloma venereum group of active agents.

The syndrome was first described under the name *la maladie des griffes de chat* (Debre et al., 1950), but its occurrence without a history of contact with cats affords some justification for the term, benign lymphoreticulosis, first proposed by Mollaret and associates (1950).

Most patients have a history of a cat bite, scratch or merely of having been licked by a cat a few days prior to onset of illness. A cutaneous lesion resembling a small, pustular furuncle may represent the primary pathologic reaction. Regional lymph nodes draining the area soon become inflamed, swollen and usually painful; mild generalized lymphadenopathy and splenomegaly are also present. Malaise, chills and fever are common; and a macular rash over the extremities has been reported in several cases (Mollaret et al., 1950; Greer and Keefer, 1951). These symptoms persist from 4 to 20 days but invariably subside, usually after spontaneous drainage of the suppurating regional node. Fatal cases have not been reported.

Successful transmission of the agent to monkeys has been reported by Mollaret et al. (1951) following intradermal inoculations of suspensions of lymph nodes from patients with cat-scratch disease. Small nodules developed at the sites of inoculation, which, when excised and again passaged to monkeys, induced cutaneous nodules and generalized lymphadenopathy. Attempts to infect mice, guinea pigs, rabbits, dogs and ferrets have been fruitless. The histopathologic appearance of infected nodes in man or the monkey is that of an inflammatory reticular reaction without specific characters. Germinal follicles contain small abscesses which coalesce to form larger areas of necrosis. Spontaneous drainage is followed by rapid healing. Heat-inactivated suspensions of infected lymph nodes or heat-inactivated pus from a bubo have been employed as skin-test antigens (Mollaret et al., 1950; Greer and Keefer, 1951). When injected intradermally in persons convalescent from cat-scratch disease, the antigen induced a delayed (tuberculin-type) erythematous reaction within 24 hours. Normal controls failed to react.

There is considerable evidence that the agent of cat-scratch disease belongs to the psittacosis-lymphogranuloma venereum group of viruses. Stained sections of infected human and monkey lymph node contain large numbers of intracellular and extra-cellular granules identical in appearance with the elementary bodies of psittacosis. Although the Frei test is usually negative, the sera of persons convalescent from cat-scratch disease will fix complement in the presence of the psittacosis-lymphogranu-loma group antigen; this reaction may be useful in diagnosis. A relationship between the viruses of cat-scratch disease and feline pneumonitis (Baker, 1944) has been sug-gested and merits further investigation.

All patients so far reported have recovered spontaneously. Aureomycin and terramycin have been described as chemotherapeutically active in accelerating recovery (Mollaret et al., 1950).

GENERALIZED SALIVARY-GLAND VIRUS INFECTION

(Synonyms: Inclusion disease, cytomeg-alic inclusion disease, submaxillary gland virus)

Generalized salivary-gland virus infection is caused by an agent or family of agents of low virulence, and in many instances no clinical disease is observed in infected hosts. It was first described nearly 50 years ago, and the presence of intranuclear and cyto-plasmic inclusions in the cells of many organs, especially the salivary glands, is pathognomonic.

Strains of the virus are species-specific. In the case of rodents, experimental inocu-lation usually fails to produce apparent dis-ease. This seems to be due to widespread inapparent infection and resulting immun-ity, for intraperitoneal inoculation of sali-vary-gland virus into young mice causes a generalized disease in which there is severe visceral necrosis resulting in death in from

4 to 7 days (McCordock and Smith, 1936). Fatal infection in young guinea pigs has been produced by intracerebral inoculation or intrafetal injection of the virus (Mark-ham and Hudson, 1936).

The cytologic picture presents greatly en-larged cells, usually in epithelial tissues, whose nuclei contain large basophilic inclu-sions surrounded by a clear halo. The cyto-plasm may contain several small basophilic satellite bodies arranged around the periph-ery of the cell. In experimentally infected guinea pigs, inclusion bodies are only found in mesodermal tissues. Excellent colored photographs of salivary-gland virus inclu-sions appear in an article by Cappell and McFarlane (1947).

Experimental transmission of salivary-gland virus disease has been obtained only in mice and guinea pigs. However, patho-logic evidence of the infection has been found in rats, hamsters, moles, monkeys and human beings. Although no virus has been demonstrated in human infection, the pathologic lesions and inclusions are iden-tical with those encountered in rodents. In addition to the salivary glands, inclusions have been found most commonly in the lungs, liver, pancreas, kidneys, endocrine glands and occasionally the brain. Approxi-mately 100 instances of the infection have been reported in man, mostly in children under 2 years of age (Smith and Vellios, 1950). In young infants, the disease appears as a generalized blood dyscrasia associated with hepatomegaly and hepatic damage. It is generally fatal at this age. When infec-tion occurs in older children, the clinical picture varies, depending upon the organs involved and, according to Smith and Vellios (1950), it is frequently secondary to an-other disease.

The murine virus is destroyed by heating at 60° C. for 30 minutes, while the hamster strain is killed at 56° C. for 30 minutes (Kuttner and Wang, 1934). They can be preserved in 50 per cent glycerol in saline solution.

Diagnosis of human salivary-gland virus

infection can be made only by finding characteristic intranuclear inclusions within the tissues, and this can be done only after death. Additional experimental investigation of this relatively obscure family of viruses is indicated.

There is no known therapy for salivary-gland virus infection.

ENCEPHALOMYOCARDITIS

(SYNONYMS: Columbia-SK disease, MM-virus infection, Mengo encephalomyelitis)

INTRODUCTION

Members of this group of viruses were discovered in widely separated areas and in certain instances were regarded as different agents. However, they are now known to be immunologically indistinguishable and comprise a family of closely related viruses. While all are highly infectious for certain rodents, which probably serve as reservoirs, proved human infections are infrequent.

HISTORY

The first of the agents to be recognized was isolated by Jungeblut and Sanders (1940) from cotton rats which were being used for the passage of the Yale-SK strain of poliomyelitis virus. It differed antigenically and in its pathogenicity from the Yale-SK virus, and was designated as Columbia-SK virus. Shortly thereafter, a similar agent, MM, was isolated from hamster brain inoculated with material from human spinal cord and medulla taken from a patient who had died of an undiagnosed paralytic disease (Jungeblut and Dalldorf, 1943). Because both agents were discovered under circumstances where material, either known to be or suspected of being infected with poliomyelitis virus, was being passaged through rodents, considerable confusion surrounded the relationship of the agents to poliomyelitis virus. Indeed, for a time it was thought that they represented murine variants of the latter. Subsequent study has failed to provide adequate evidence of any antigenic relationship between the agents of this group and poliomyelitis.

The encephalomyocarditis (EMC) and Mengo encephalomyelitis viruses were isolated from captive monkeys in Florida (Helwig and Schmidt, 1945) and in Uganda (Dick, Haddow, Best and Smithburn, 1948), respectively. Subsequently, strains of Mengo virus were obtained from mosquitoes (*Taeniorrhynchus fuscopennatus*) and a wild mongoose caught in the vicinity of the monkey compound at Entebbe, Uganda. Human infections with the EMC and the Mengo strains have occurred, and in all instances close proximity to rodents has been noted. A mild febrile disease of man, called three-day fever, appeared in epidemic form among U. S. troops quartered in Manila in 1945-46. Neutralizing antibodies to the EMC and MM strains were demonstrated in the sera taken from many of these patients during convalescence (Smadel and Warren, 1947). Human infection with the Mengo virus occurred in a laboratory worker intimately engaged in its study at Entebbe (Dick et al., 1948).

CLINICAL PICTURE

In the cases occurring in the Philippines, onset of the disease was sudden with severe headache and a moderately high fever, reaching 104° F. in some instances. The fever lasted for 2 or 3 days and was often accompanied by pharyngitis, stiff neck, positive Kernig's sign and hyperactive deep reflexes. An occasional patient was comatose on admission to the hospital. The only notable laboratory finding was pleocytosis of from 50 to 500 cells, principally lymphocytes, in the spinal fluid. All patients recovered promptly and usually were discharged from the hospital in 4 or 5 days. There were no known sequelae, and no signs of cardiac disease were observed. On the basis of these findings, a clinical differentiation of encephalomyocarditis from aseptic meningitis, nonparalytic poliomyelitis and the denguelike fevers was not possible.

The single known human infection with

the Mengo strain was a meningo-encephalitis characterized by an elevated temperature lasting 4 days accompanied by severe headache, nuchal rigidity, photophobia, vomiting and short episodes of delirium (Dick et al., 1948). The patient recovered rapidly, the only sequelae being a transient unilateral nerve deafness. Mengo virus was isolated from the blood on the first and the second days of illness by animal inoculation, and neutralizing antibodies were demonstrated in the patient's serum following recovery.

PATHOLOGIC PICTURE

Nothing is known of the pathologic picture in human beings, because no deaths have been reported among the patients with this virus infection.

EXPERIMENTAL INFECTION; HOST RANGE

Although all strains of the encephalomyocarditis group can multiply in most laboratory animals, the clinical response varies with the host. Mice and hamsters of all ages die following inoculation, by any of the usual routes, with a $10^{-7.0}$ dilution of a suspension of brain tissue from moribund mice, hamsters or cotton rats. Within 72 or 96 hours, such an inoculation produces clinical signs consisting of ruffled fur, lethargy and flaccid paralysis, which are invariably followed by prostration and death. When greater concentrations of virus are given intracerebrally, death occurs as early as 18 hours after inoculation; animals receiving this amount of virus show no paralysis but die with signs of an acute encephalitis. Mice can occasionally be infected with virus-contaminated drinking water. Guinea pigs and rabbits experience an infection characterized by fever for the first 4 or 5 days after inoculation. Paralysis, occasionally fatal, occurs in 10 to 50 per cent of infected guinea pigs; all animals develop infection as evidenced by the appearance of neutralizing antibody. The disease is not fatal in rabbits. The albino rat undergoes only an inapparent infection following a massive inoculation, although considerable virus may persist in the central nervous system for several weeks. The response of rhesus monkeys to viruses of the EMC group is variable, ranging from an acute febrile course followed by death within the first week to a mild infection characterized by a short fever and subsequent appearance of serum antibodies. Paralysis in monkeys is not infrequent, but the animals usually recover. The viruses can be propagated in chick embryos causing death in 72 to 96 hours without pathognomonic lesions. Viremia occurs during some portion of the febrile period in infected animals of all species mentioned above. Virus usually persists for several days, and blood specimens when titered in mice are infectious in dilutions of $10^{-3.0}$ to $10^{-4.0}$.

Lesions in experimentally infected animals are found in the entire central nervous system and in striated and cardiac muscles. This is a common feature of the agents of the EMC group, hence their generally accepted designation. The extent of the pathologic changes is related to the portal of inoculation and duration of disease. If the virus is inoculated directly into a muscle, e.g., the gastrocnemius, there is a rapidly progressing necrosis of the muscle fibers accompanied by edema and inflammatory reaction (Rustigian and Pappenheimer, 1949). Cardiac lesions require longer to develop, and, in animals dying after a number of days, these appear grossly as pale yellow plaques 0.5 to 2.0 mm. in diameter. Microscopically, the extent of a lesion ranges from involvement of a single muscle fiber to an acute interstitial myocarditis affecting a large area of the heart. The pathologic process appears to begin with a mild perivascular monocytic infiltration and with swelling and loss of striations of muscle fibers which progress to complete necrosis. Cellular infiltrations are usually extensive, lymphocytes and histiocytes predominating (Schmidt, 1947). Focal granulomatous lesions containing multinucleated giant cells have also been observed occasionally in the hearts of monkeys and mice. The viruses of the EMC group are also highly neurotropic with the severity of lesions varying with the duration of the disease. Thus, in animals which survive only 1 or 2 days lesions in the CNS are minimal. When, however, the incubation period is prolonged to 4 or 5 days by giving a small dose of virus by a peripheral route, the usual lesions of encephalitis are encountered, which consist of congestion of the capillaries and infiltration of lymphocytes and mononuclear cells into the subarachnoid space, perivascular spaces and cerebral parenchyma. However, neither the meningitis nor the cuffing is intense. The most striking and characteristic change consists of sharply demarcated focal areas of necrosis scattered throughout the central nervous system, most common in the cerebellum where they usually involve the granular and Purkinje cells layers.

Etiology

The Columbia-SK, MM, EMC and Mengo encephalomyelitis agents are small viruses, readily passing through Berkefeld and Seitz filters and through gradocol membranes with average pore-diameters of 30 mμ; thus, according to results with gradocol membranes, they have diameters of 8 to 15 millimicrons. However, direct visualization by electron microscopy or determination of the sedimentation constants of highly purified preparations indicates a particle size of 25 to 29 mμ (Col.-SK, Jungeblut and Bourdillion, 1943; EMC, Weil, Warren, Breese and Russ, 1951). They are quite stable when stored at —70° C. and can also be preserved in 50 per cent glycerol or 0.05 molar glycine. They are inactivated by a temperature of 60° C. for 30 minutes and usually lose their infectivity following lyophilization. Specific antibodies which cross-react equally with all strains appear in the sera of convalescent animals and man. In the rhesus monkey and in man antibodies may be present late in the first week or early in the second. Tests for neutralizing antibodies are performed in mice by means

of intracerebral or intraperitoneal inoculation of serum-virus mixtures. Complement-fixing antibodies have been found in the sera of immune hamsters, guinea pigs and rats (Warren, Smadel and Russ, 1949); studies of other hosts have not been reported. Ability of members of the EMC group to agglutinate sheep erythrocytes was first reported by Hallauer (1949, 1951) and later by Olitsky and Yager (1949) and Gard and Heller (1951). Agglutination occurs at 4° C. and virus is eluted from the cells above 20° C. Agglutination is inhibited by specific immune serum. The Columbia-SK, MM, EMC and Mengo strains of virus are indistinguishable by cross-protection, neutralization, complement-fixation and hemagglutination-inhibition technics. Differences in pathogenicity between the strains do not provide adequate criteria for their differentiation, as variations in strain pathogenicity for a given host or route of inoculation are readily produced by repeated adaptive passages (Warren and Russ, 1947-1951).

Diagnosis

The diagnosis of encephalomyocarditis in man rests on the isolation and the identification of the virus and the demonstration of the development during convalescence of specific antibodies. The symptoms and signs of the disease are not sufficiently diagnostic to permit its differentiation from a number of short febrile illnesses. There is no evidence that the virus causes cardiac disease in man.

Treatment

Treatment is symptomatic.

Epidemiology

Primary isolation of strains of the EMC group have been reported from the cotton rat (Col.-SK; Jungeblut and Sanders, 1940), hamster (MM; Jungeblut and Dalldorf, 1943), mongoose (Mengo; Dick et al., 1948), rhesus monkey (Mengo; Dick et al., 1948), chimpanzee (EMC; Helwig and Schmidt, 1945), and several species of *Taeniorrhynchus* mosquitoes (Mengo; Dick et al., 1948; Horgan, 1951). There is considerable evidence that rodents, in particular wild rats, constitute a reservoir for this group of viruses. The albino rat, when infected in the laboratory, undergoes an inapparent infection and a considerable amount of virus persists for several weeks in the central nervous system and circulation (Warren and Russ, 1947-1951). Further evidence that rats in nature may harbor viruses of the EMC group is the finding of neutralizing antibodies in a significant proportion of *Rattus norvegicus* and *R. alexandrinus* collected in certain areas of the United States and Canada (Warren, Russ and Jeffries, 1949), and

R. kyjabius and *R. coucha* trapped in Uganda (Horgan, 1951). Tests for antibodies in other small animals in the same areas have been uniformly negative. The finding of neutralizing antibodies against the viruses in the serum of healthy human beings is an infrequent occurrence (Warren, Smadel and Russ, 1949; Horgan, 1951; Gard and Heller, 1951). An occasional serum from patients with a febrile disease accompanied by neurologic signs may neutralize the EMC viruses (Warren, Smadel and Russ, 1949; Jungeblut, 1950) but the meaning of the findings remains to be established.

CONTROL MEASURES

No control measures are known.

REFERENCES

FOOT-AND-MOUTH DISEASE

Flaum, A., 1939, Foot-and-mouth disease in man. Acta. Path. et Microbiol. Scand., *16*, 197-213.

Frenkel, H. S., 1950, Research on foot-and-mouth disease. II. The cultivation of the virus in explantions of tongue epithelium of bovine animals. Am. J. Vet. Res., *11*, 371-373.

Olitsky, P. K., Traum, J., and Schoening, H. W., 1928, Report of the Foot-and-Mouth-Disease Commission of the United States Department of Agriculture. U. S. Dept. Agric. Technical Bull., No. *76*, 1-172 (p. 93).

Waldmann, O., 1938, Riemser Maul-und Klauenseuche (M. K. I.) Vakzine. Deutch. Tierärztl. Wchschr., *46*, 569.

NEWCASTLE DISEASE

Anderson, S. G., 1946, A note on two laboratory infections with the virus of Newcastle disease of fowls. Med. J. Australia, *1*, 371.

Bang, F. B., 1946, Filamentous forms of Newcastle virus. Proc. Soc. Exp. Biol. and Med., *63*, 5-7.

Beach, J. R., 1944, The neutralization *in vitro* of avian pneumoencephalitis virus by Newcastle disease immune serum. Science, *100*, 361-362.

Beach, J. R., 1946, Avian pneumoencephalitis—past and present. Nulaid News, *23*, 26-29.

Brandly, C. A., Moses, H. E., Jungheer, E. L., and Jones, E. E., 1946a, Epizoötiology of Newcastle disease of poultry. Am. J. Vet Res., *7*, 243-249.

Brandly, C. A., Moses, H. E., Jungherr, E. L., and Jones, E. E., 1946b, Isolation and identification of Newcastle disease virus. Am. J. Vet. Res., *7*, 289-306.

Brandly, C. A., Moses, H. E., Jones, E. E., and

Jungherr, E. L., 1946c, Immunization of chickens against Newcastle disease. Am. J. Vet. Res., *7*, 307-332.

Burnet, F. M., 1943, Human infection with the virus of Newcastle disease of fowls. Med. J. Australia, *2*, 313-314.

Burnet, F. M., 1945, Haemagglutination by mumps virus: relationship to Newcastle disease and influenza viruses. Australian J. Sci., *8*, 81-83.

Burnet, F. M., and Anderson, S. G., 1946, Modification of human red cells by virus action. II. Agglutination of modified human red cells by sera from cases of infectious mononucleosis. Brit. J. Exp Path., *27*, 236-244.

Cunha, R., Weil, M. L., Beard, D., Taylor, A. R.. Sharp, D. G., and Beard, J. W., 1947, Purification and characters of the Newcastle disease virus (California strain). J. Immunol., *55*, 69-89.

Doyle, T. M., 1927, A hitherto unrecorded disease of fowls due to a filter-passing virus. J. Comp. Path and Therap., *40*, 144-169.

Florman, A. L., 1949, The agglutination of human erythrocytes modified by treatment with Newcastle disease and influenza virus. J. Bact., *57*, 31-38.

Ginsberg, H. S., and Horsfall, F. L., Jr., 1949, A labile component of normal serum which combines with various viruses. Neutralization of infectivity and inhibition of haemagglutination by the component. J. Exp. Med., *90*, 475-495.

Howitt, B. F., 1950, A nonspecific heat-labile factor in the serum neutralization test for Newcastle disease virus. J. Immunol., *64*, 73-84.

Jungherr, E., Luginbuhl, R. E., and Kilham, L., 1949, Serological relationships of mumps and Newcastle disease virus. Science, *110*, 333-334.

Wenner, H. A., Monley, A., and Todd, R. N., 1950,

Studies on Newcastle disease virus encephalitis in rhesus monkeys. J. Immunol., *64*, 305-321.

Yatom, J., 1946, Conjunctivitis caused by virus of Newcastle disease. In Foreign Letters. J. Am. Med Assn., *132*, 169.

OVINE PUSTULAR DERMATITIS

Carne, H. R., Wickham, N., Whitten, W. K., and Lockley, R. P., 1946, Infection of man by the virus of contagious pustular dermatitis of sheep. Australian J. Sci., *9*, 73-74.

INFECTIOUS ANEMIA OF HORSES

Stein, C. D., Osteen, O. L., Mott, L. O., and Shahan, M. S., 1944, Experimental transmission of equine infectious anemia by contact and body secretions and excretions. Vet. Med., *39*, 46-52.

Vallée and Carré, 1904, Sur la nature infectieuse de l'anémie du cheval. Compt. rend. Acad. sci., *139*, 331-333.

WARTS: VERRUCAE

Kingery, L. B., 1921, The etiology of common warts. Their production in the second generation. J. Am. Med. Assn., *76*, 440-442.

Rake, G., and Blank, H., 1950, The relationship of host and virus in molluscum contagiosum. J. Investig. Dermatol., *15*, 81-94.

van Rooyen, C. E., and Rhodes, A. J., 1940, Warts (verrucae) *in* Virus Diseases of Man. London, Milford, pp. 131-135.

Strauss, M. J., Bunting, H., and Melnick, J. L., 1950, Virus-like particles and inclusion bodies in skin papillomas. J. Investig. Dermatol., *15*, 433-443.

Strauss, M. J., Shaw, E. W., Bunting, H., and Melnick, J. L., 1949, "Crystalline" virus-like particles from skin papillomas characterized by intranuclear inclusion bodies. Proc. Soc. Exper. Biol. Med., *72*, 46-50.

Wile, U. J., and Kingery, L. B., 1919, The etiology of common warts. Preliminary report of an experimental study. J. Am. Med. Assn., *73*, 970-973.

TRENCH FEVER

Mooser, H., Leeman, A., Chao, S. H., and Gubler, H. V., 1948, Beobachtungen an Fünftagfieber. Schweiz. Zeit. f. allg. Path. u. Bakt., *11*, 513-522.

Mooser, H., Marti, C., and Leeman, A., 1949, Beobachtungen an Fünftagfieber; Hautläsionen nach kutaner und intrakutaner Inoculation mit Rickettsia quintana. Schweiz. Zeit. f. allg. Path. u. Bakt., *12*, 476-483.

Strong, R. P., Swift, H. F., Opie, E. L., MacNeal, W. J., Baetjer, W., Pappenheimer, A. M., Peacock, A. D., and Rapport, D., 1918, Trench Fever, Report of Commission, Medical Research Committee, American Red Cross. London, Oxford University Press.

Swift, H. F., 1919-1920, Trench fever. The Harvey Lectures, Series XV, 58-86, Philadelphia, Lippincott.

MOLLUSCUM CONTAGIOSUM

Banfield, W. G., Bunting, H., Strauss, M. J., and Melnick, J. L., 1951, Electronmicrographs of thin sections of molluscum contagiosum. Proc. Soc. Exp. Biol. and Med., *77*, 843-847.

Goodpasture, E. W., and King, H., 1927, A cytologic study of molluscum contagiosum. Am. J. Path., *3*, 385-394.

Goodpasture, E. W., and Woodruff, C. E., 1931, A comparison of the inclusion bodies of fowl-pox and molluscum contagiosum. Am. J. Path., *7*, 1-8.

Lipschütz, B., 1907, Zur Kenntnis des Molluscum contagiosum. Wien. klin. Wchnschr., *20*, 253-254.

Morosow, M. A., 1926, Die Färbung der Paschenschen Körperchen durch Versilberung. Zentralbl. f. Bakt., Abt. 1, Orig., *100*, 385-387.

van Rooyen, C. E., 1938, The micromanipulation and microdissection of the molluscum contagiosum inclusion body. J. Path. and Bact., *46*, 425-436.

van Rooyen, C. E., 1939, The chemical composition of the molluscum contagiosum inclusion body. J. Path. and Bact., *49*, 345-349.

van Rooyen, C. E., and Rhodes, A. J., 1940, Molluscum contagiosum, *in* Virus Diseases of Man, London, Milford, pp. 121-130.

EPIDEMIC VIRAL GASTRO-ENTERITIS

Baker, J. A., 1943, A filterable virus causing enteritis and pneumonia in calves. J. Exp. Med., *78*, 435-446.

Buddingh, G. J., and Dodd, K., 1944, Stomatitis and diarrhea of infants caused by a hitherto unrecognized virus. J. Pediat., *25*, 105-113.

Cook, G. T., and Marmion, B. P., 1947, Gastroenteritis of unknown aetiology. Brit. Med. J., *2*, 446-450.

Gordon, I., Ingraham, H. S., Korns, R. F., and Trussel, R. E., 1949, Gastro-enteritis in man due to a filtrable agent. N. Y. State J. Med., *49*, 1918-20.

Light, J. S., and Hodes, H. L., 1943, Studies on epidemic diarrhea of the newborn: Isolation of a filterable agent causing diarrhea in calves. Am. J. Pub. Health, *33*, 1451-1454.

Reimann, H. A., Hodges, J. H., and Price, A. H., 1945, Epidemic diarrhea, nausea and vomiting of unknown cause. J. Am. Med. Assn., *127*, 1-6.

CAT-SCRATCH DISEASE

Baker, J. A., 1944, A virus causing pneumonia in cats and producing elementary bodies. J. Exp. Med., *79*, 159-172.

Debré, R., Lamy, M., Jammet, M.-L., Costil, L., and Mozziconacci, P., 1950, La maladie des griffes de chat. Bull. mem. soc. med. hôp. Paris, *66*, 76-79.

Greer, W. E. R., and Keefer, C. S., 1951, Cat-scratch fever. A disease entity. New England J. Med., *244*, 545-548.

Mollaret, P., Reilly, J., Bastin, R., and Tournier, P., 1950, Documentation nouvelle sur l'adénopathie régionale subaiguë et spontanément curable décrite en 1950. La lymphoréticulose bénigne d'inoculation. Presse med., *58*, 1353-1355.

Mollaret, P., Reilly, J., Bastin, R., and Tournier, P.,

1951, La découverte du virus de la lymphoréticulose bénigne d'inoculation. Presse med., *59,* 681-682; 701-704.

GENERALIZED SALIVARY-GLAND VIRUS INFECTION

Cappell, D. F., and McFarlane, M. N., 1947, Inclusion bodies (protozoon-like cells) in the organs of infants. J. Path. Bact., *59,* 385-398.

Kuttner, A. G., and Wang, S. H., 1934, The problem of the significance of the inclusion bodies found in the salivary glands of infants, and the occurrence of inclusion bodies in the submaxillary gland of hamsters, white mice, and wild rats (Peiping). J. Exp. Med., *60,* 773-792.

Markham, F. S., and Hudson, N. P., 1936, Susceptibility of the guinea pig fetus to the submaxillary gland virus of guinea pigs. Am. J. Path., *12,* 175-182.

McCordock, H. A., and Smith, M. G., 1936, The visceral lesions produced in mice by the salivary gland virus of mice. J. Exp. Med., *63,* 303-310.

Smith, M. G., and Vellios, F., 1950, Inclusion disease or generalized salivary gland virus infection. Arch. Path., *50,* 862-884.

ENCEPHALOMYOCARDITIS

Dick, G. W. A., Haddow, A. J., Best, A. M., and Smithburn, K. C., 1948, Mengo encephalomyelitis. A hitherto unknown virus affecting man. Lancet, *2,* 286-289.

Dick, G. W. A., 1949, The relationship of Mengo encephalomyelitis, encephalomyocarditis, Columbia-SK and M.M. viruses. J. Immunol., *62,* 375-386.

Gard, S., and Heller, L., 1951, Hemagglutination by Col-MM-virus. Proc. Soc. Exp. Biol. Med., *76,* 68-73.

Hallauer, C., 1949, Agglutination von Hammelerythrocyten durch murine Poliomyelitisvirusstämme. Proc. 4th Int. Cong. Microbiol, 1947. Copenhagen, pp. 257.

Hallauer, C., 1951, Die Haemagglutination muriner Poliomyelitisvirusstämme. Arch. f. d. ges. Virusforsch., *4,* 224-248.

Helwig, F. C., and Schmidt, E. C. H., 1945, A filterpassing agent producing interstitial myocarditis in

anthropoid apes and small animals. Science, *102,* 31-33.

Horgan, E. S., 1951, Virus research institute, annual report, 1950. East Africa High Commission, Nairobi.

Jungeblut, C. W., 1950, Neutralization of Columbia-SK and Yale-SK virus by polio-convalescent and normal human sera. Arch. Pediat., *67,* 519-530.

Jungeblut, C. W., and Bourdillion, J., 1943, Electron micrography of murine poliomyelitis virus preparations. J. Am. Med. Assn., *123,* 399-402.

Jungeblut, C. W., and Dalldorf, G., 1943, Epidemiological and experimental observations on the possible significance of rodents in a surburban epidemic of poliomyelitis. Am. J. Pub. Health, *33,* 169-172.

Jungeblut, C. W., and Sanders, M., 1940, Studies of a murine strain of poliomyelitis virus in cotton rats and white mice. J. Exp. Med., *72,* 407-436.

Olitsky, P. K., and Yager, R. H., 1949, Hemagglutination by Columbia-SK, Columbia MM, Mengo encephalomyelitis and encephalomyocarditis viruses: experiments with other viruses. Proc. Soc. Exp. Biol. Med., *71,* 719-724.

Rustigian, R., and Pappenheimer, A. M., 1949, Myositis in mice following intramuscular injection of viruses of the mouse encephalomyelitis group and of certain other neurotropic viruses. J. Exp. Med., *89,* 69-92.

Schmidt, E. C. H., 1948, Virus myocarditis. Pathologic and experimental studies. Am. J. Path., *24,* 97-118.

Smadel, J. E., and Warren, J., 1947, The virus of encephalomyocarditis and its apparent causation of disease in man. J. Clin. Investig., *26,* 1197.

Warren, J., and Russ, S. B., 1947-1951, unpublished experiments.

Warren, J., Russ, S. B., and Jeffries, H., 1949, Neutralizing antibody against viruses of the encephalomyocarditis group in the sera of wild rats. Proc. Soc. Exp. Biol. Med., *71,* 376-387.

Warren, J., Smadel, J. E., and Russ, S. B., 1949, The family relationship of encephalomyocarditis, Columbia-SK, M.M., and Mengo encephalomyelitis viruses. J. Immunol., *62,* 387-398.

Weil, M. L., Warren, J., Breese, S. S., and Russ, S. B., 1951, Separation of encephalomyocarditis from tissue components by means of protamine precipitation and enzymic digestion. J. Bact., *63,* 99-105.

Bibliographic Index

461, 463, 467, 468, 473, 476, 478, 480, 481, 483, 484, 489, 501, 509, 511, 672, 679

Rake, H., 461

Ramberg, E. G., 71

Rammelkamp, C. H., Jr., 381, 391

Randall, R., 27, 69, 241, 264

Ransohoff, N. S., 318, 335

Ransom, S. E., 347, 356

Rao, R. S., 568, 576

Rappaport, E. M., 361, 376

Rapport, D., 679

Rasmussen, A. F., 232, 266, 335

Rasmussen-Ejde, R. K., 446, 463

Ravaut, P., 462

Ravenel, S. F., 619, 636

Rawlins, T. E., 43, 71

Raynaud, M., 432, 438

Read, M. R., 368, 376

Reagan, R. L., 92, 98, 131, 140, 447, 456, 464, 616, 626, 632, 636, 644, 650

Records, E., 291, 298

Reed, L. J., 152, 298, 541, 550

Reed, W., 18, 69, 532, 533, 538, 539, 550

Rees, D. M., 262

Reeves, W. C., 214, 225, 226, 228, 231, 234, 237, 253, 262, 264

Rehaag, H., 297

Reilley, W. A., 318, 335

Reilly, J., 679

Reimann, H. A., 383, 391, 672, 679

Reinhold, J. G., 376

Reinie, L., 462

Relova, 133

Remlinger, P., 268, 278, 286, 287, 298

Rendtorff, R. C., 335

Repaci, G., 515, 520

Rexer, W. F., 375

Reymann, F., 457, 463

Reyn, A., 457, 463

Reynolds, F. H. K., 556, 557, 568

Rhazes, 478

Rhian, M., 334, 347, 357

Rhoads, C. P., 446, 463

Rhodes, A. J., 169, 171, 326, 335, 336, 341, 355, 357, 420, 428-430, 435, 438, 669, 672, 679

Ricci, N. I., 537, 539, 550

Rice, E. C., 340, 357, 467, 473, 476

Rice, E. P., 308, 335

Rice, L., 556, 567

Rich, A. R., 376

Rich, W. H., 150, 160

Richards, A. G., Jr., 50, 69

Richards, P., 468, 477

Richards, R. L., 318, 335

Richardson, L., 427, 437

Richardson, S., 357

Richmond, A. E., 569, 577

Rickard, E. R., 91, 97, 159, 160, 396, 404, 406, 408-412, 542, 550

Ricketts, H. T., 578, 586, 590, 609, 611, 612, 622, 636

Ridenour, G. M., 335

Riehl, L. A., 609

Rietschel, P., 481, 483

Rights, F. L., 96, 98, 99, 643, 644, 650, 651

Riordan, J. T., 131, 139, 264, 335

Rios, F. A., 241, 242, 263

Ris, H., 591, 609

Rischel, E. E., 619, 636

Ritchie, F. S., 357

Ritchies, R. C., 171, 335

Rivers, T. M., 1, 3, 7, 9, 14, 17, 18, 67, 69, 91, 98, 128, 131, 132, 136, 137, 139, 140, 214, 219, 221, 223, 231, 237, 242, 244, 247, 256-258, 261, 263, 264, 289, 298, 427, 429, 430, 432-435, 437-439, 441, 443, 446, 447, 450, 463, 503, 508, 509, 512, 522, 553, 555

Robbins, F. C., 88, 89, 98, 126, 127, 131, 134, 140, 148, 149, 160, 317, 332, 335, 336, 517, 521, 653, 658, 660, 662, 664

Roberts, E. C., 83, 98

Robinow, C. F., 136, 139, 418, 436

Robinson, 614

Robinson, F., 314, 336

Robinson, L. K., 348, 357

Robinson, R. C. V., 449, 458, 463

Roca-Garcia, M., 253, 264, 440, 463, 538, 549, 550

Rocha, A., 627, 635

da Rocha-Lima, H., 534, 550, 578, 587, 590, 597, 609

Rockefeller Foundation, The, 251, 253, 278, 293

Roesel, C. E., 199, 212, 213

Rogers, A. M., 500, 501

Rogers, L., 566, 567

Roholm, K., 361, 376

Roizin, L., 256, 257, 264

Romer, M. S., 663

Rommelaere, G., 143

Rook, A. F., 569, 575, 577

Rose, H. M., 114, 125, 127, 140, 391, 619, 631, 636

Rosenau, M. J., 286, 298

Rosenberg, D., 318, 336

Rosenberg, E. B., 164, 169, 170

Rosenberg, P., 520, 521

Rosenthal, N., 373, 376, 608

Ross, A. F., 58, 59, 62, 69, 70

Ross, S., 340, 357

Rost, G., 451, 463

Rotman, R., 198, 203, 206, 212

Roubakine, A., 441, 463

Roubtzova, V. P., 576

Rountree, P. M., 110, 441, 460

Rous, P., 110, 125

Roux, E., 268, 269, 298

Rovelstad, R. A., 375

Rowe, A. P., Jr., 331

Rowlands, A., 663

Rowlands, I. W., 650

Rowlands, R. A., 461

Roy, T. E., 336

Rubarth, S., 363, 376

Rubenstein, A. D., 330, 333, 336

Ruchman, I., 265, 493-495, 498, 501, 504, 505

Rudd, G. V., 443, 448, 463

Ruedemann, R., Jr., 377

Ruge, H., 370, 377

Rumreich, A., 601, 602, 607

Ruska, E., 66, 70

Ruska, H., 66, 70, 191, 213

Russ, S. B., 99, 215, 266, 677, 678, 680

Russ, V. K., 575, 576

Russell, P. B., 439

Russell, W. R., 303, 336

Rustigian, R., 658, 659, 664, 676, 680

Ryan, A. J., 318, 332

Sabin, A. B., 85, 98, 102, 108, 155, 160, 165, 172, 222, 224, 226-232, 234, 239, 241, 246, 250-252, 259-265, 307, 309, 326, 329, 336, 376, 452, 463, 498, 501, 554-576

Sacco, 432

Saddington, 110

Sadusk, J. F., Jr., 156, 159, 597, 598, 609, 638, 650

Saenz, A. C., 235, 237, 262, 264, 557, 567

Said, A., 460

St. John, E., 446, 463

St. John, J. H., 556, 557, 568

Salaman, M. H., 432, 434, 435, 437, 438

Salk, J. E., 61, 70, 101, 108, 159, 160, 399, 405, 409, 411, 412

Salm-Reifferscheidt, 268

Samper, B. A., 97

Sanders, M., 126, 128, 132, 135, 140, 464, 503, 505, 675, 677, 680

Sandler, F., 330

Sanford, K. K., 134, 140

Sant'Anna, J. F., 627, 636

Sarnoff, S. J., 336

Sartwell, P. E., 143, 160

Sather, G., 262

Saum, A. M., 35, 69

Sautter, V., 449, 461, 525

Savran, J., 518, 521

Sawyer, W. A., 537, 540, 547, 550

Sborov, V. M., 366, 377

Scadding, J. G., 394, 412

Schabel, F. M., Jr., 223, 228, 265, 328, 332, 336

Schachman, H. K., 38-40, 42, 70

Schalm, L., 449, 463

Schamberg, I. L., 449, 458, 463

Schaub, I. G., 391

Schaughnessy, H. J., 440, 441, 464

Subject Index

697